Hoover's Handbook of

World
Business
2017

HOOVERS™

A D&B COMPANY

Austin, Texas

Hoover's Handbook of World Business 2017 is intended to provide readers with accurate and authoritative information about the enterprises covered in it. Hoover's researched all companies and organizations profiled, and in many cases contacted them directly so that companies represented could provide information. The information contained herein is as accurate as we could reasonably make it. In many cases we have relied on third-party material that we believe to be trustworthy, but were unable to independently verify. We do not warrant that the book is absolutely accurate or without error. Readers should not rely on any information contained herein in instances where such reliance might cause financial loss. The publisher, the editors, and their data suppliers specifically disclaim all warranties, including the implied warranties of merchantability and fitness for a specific purpose. This book is sold with the understanding that neither the publisher, the editors, nor any content contributors are engaged in providing investment, financial, accounting, legal, or other professional advice.

The financial data (Historical Financials sections) in this book are from a variety of sources. Mergent Inc., provided selected data for the Historical Financials sections of publicly traded companies. For private companies and for historical information on public companies prior to their becoming public, we obtained information directly from the companies or from trade sources deemed to be reliable. Hoover's, Inc., is solely responsible for the presentation of all data.

Many of the names of products and services mentioned in this book are the trademarks or service marks of the companies manufacturing or selling them and are subject to protection under US law. Space has not permitted us to indicate which names are subject to such protection, and readers are advised to consult with the owners of such marks regarding their use. Hoover's is a trademark of Hoover's, Inc.

10 9 8 7 6 5 4 3 2 1

Publishers Cataloging-in-Publication Data

Hoover's Handbook of World Business 2016

    Includes indexes.

    ISBN 978-1-68200-312-1

    ISSN 1055-7199

    1. Business enterprises — Directories. 2. Corporations — Directories.

HF3010 338.7

U.S. AND WORLD BOOK SALES

Mergent Inc.

580 Kingsley Park Drive
Fort Mill, SC
29715
Phone: 800-342-5647
e-mail: orders@mergent.com
Web: www.mergentbusinesspress.com

Mergent Inc.

CEO: Jonathan Worrall

Executive Managing Director: John Pedernales

Executive Vice President of Sales: Fred Jenkins

Managing Director of Relationship Management: Chris Henry

Managing Director of Print Products: Thomas Wecera

MERGENT CUSTOMER SERVICE

Support and Fulfillment Manager: Melanie Horvat

ABOUT MERGENT, INC.

Mergent, Inc. is a leading provider of business and financial data on global publicly listed companies. Based in the U.S, the company maintains a strong global presence, with offices in New York, Charlotte, San Diego, London, Tokyo and Melbourne.

Founded in 1900, Mergent operates one of the longest continuously collected databases of: descriptive and fundamental information on domestic and international companies; pricing and terms and conditions data on fixed income and equity securities; and corporate action data.

In addition, Mergent's Indxis subsidiary develops and licenses equity and fixed income investment products based on its proprietary investment methodologies. Our licensed products have over $9 billion in assets under management and are offered by major investment management firms. The Indxis calculation platform is the chosen technology for some of the world's largest index companies. Its index calculation and pricing distribution protocols are used to administer index rules and distribute real-time pricing data.

Abbreviations

AB – Aktiebolag (Swedish)*

ADR – American Depositary Receipts

AG – Aktiengesellschaft (German)*

AFL-CIO – American Federation of Labor and Congress of Industrial Organizations

AMEX – American Stock Exchange

A/S – Aktieselskab (Danish)*

ASA – Allmenne Aksjeselskaper (Norwegian)*

ATM – asynchronous transfer mode; automated teller machine

CAD/CAM – computer-aided design/computer-aided manufacturing

CASE – computer-aided software engineering

CD-ROM – compact disc – read-only memory

CEO – chief executive officer

CFO – chief financial officer

CMOS – complementary metal-oxide semiconductor

COMECON – Council for Mutual Economic Assistance

COO – chief operating officer

DAT – digital audio tape

DOD – Department of Defense

DOE – Department of Energy

DOT – Department of Transportation

DRAM – dynamic random-access memory

DVD – digital versatile disc/digital video disc

EC – European Community

EPA – Environmental Protection Agency

EPS – earnings per share

EU – European Union

EVP – executive vice president

FCC – Federal Communications Commission

FDA – Food and Drug Administration

FDIC – Federal Deposit Insurance Corporation

FTC – Federal Trade Commission

GATT – General Agreement on Tariffs and Trade

GmbH – Gesellschaft mit beschränkter Haftung (German)*

GNP – gross national product

HDTV – high-definition television

HMO – health maintenance organization

HR – human resources

HTML – hypertext markup language

ICC – Interstate Commerce Commission

IMF – International Monetary Fund

IPO – initial public offering

IRS – Internal Revenue Service

KGaA – Kommanditgesellschaft auf Aktien (German)*

LAN – local-area network

LBO – leveraged buyout

LNG – liquefied natural gas

LP – limited partnership

Ltd. – Limited

MFN – Most Favored Nation

MITI – Ministry of International Trade and Industry (Japan)

NAFTA – North American Free Trade Agreement

Nasdaq – National Association of Securities Dealers Automated Quotations

NATO – North Atlantic Treaty Organization

NV – Naamlose Vennootschap (Dutch)*

NYSE – New York Stock Exchange

OAO – open joint stock company (Russian)

OAS – Organization of American States

OECD – Organization for Economic Cooperation and Development

OEM – original equipment manufacturer

OOO – limited liability company (Russian)

OPEC – Organization of Petroleum Exporting Countries

OS – operating system

OTC – over-the-counter

P/E – price-to-earnings ratio

PLC – public limited company (UK)*

RAM – random-access memory

R&D – research and development

RISC – reduced instruction set computer

ROA – return on assets

ROI – return on investment

SA – Société Anonyme (French)*; Sociedad(e) Anónima (Spanish and Portuguese)*

SA de CV – Sociedad Anónima de Capital Variable (Spanish)*

SEC – Securities and Exchange Commission

SEVP – senior executive vice president

SIC – Standard Industrial Classification

SpA – Società per Azioni (Italian)*

SPARC – scalable processor architecture

SVP – senior vice president

VAR – value-added reseller

VAT – value-added tax

VC – venture capitalist

VP – vice president

WAN – wide-area network

WWW – World Wide Web

ZAO – closed joint stock company (Russian)

---

* These abbreviations are used in companies' names to convey that the companies are limited liability enterprises; the meanings are usually the equivalent of *corporation* or *incorporated*.

Contents

List of Lists

HOOVER'S RANKINGS

Companies Profiled

Companies Profiled (continued)

Companies Profiled (continued)

About Hoover's Handbook of World Business 2017

This edition of *Hoover's Handbook of World Business* is focused on its mission of providing you with premier coverage of the global business scene. Featuring 500 of the world's most influential companies based outside of the United States, this book is one of the most complete sources of in-depth information on large, non-US-based business enterprises available anywhere.

Hoover's Handbook of World Business is one of our four-title series of handbooks that covers, literally, the world of business. The series is available as an indexed set, and also includes *Hoover's Handbook of American Business*, *Hoover's Handbook of Private Companies*, and *Hoover's Handbook of Emerging Companies*. This series brings you information on the biggest, fastest-growing, and most influential enterprises in the world.

HOOVER'S ONLINE FOR BUSINESS NEEDS

In addition to Hoover's widely used MasterList and Handbooks series, comprehensive coverage of more than 40,000 business enterprises is available in electronic format on our Web site at www.hoovers.com. Our goal is to provide our customers the fastest path to business with insight and actionable information about companies, industries, and key decision makers, along with the powerful tools to find and connect to the right people to get business done. Hoover's has partnered with other prestigious business information and service providers to bring you all the right business information, services, and links in one place.

We welcome the recognition we have received as the premier provider of high-quality company information — online, electronically, and in print — and continue to look for ways to make our products more available and more useful to you.

We believe that anyone who buys from, sells to, invests in, lends to, competes with, interviews with, or works for a company should know all there is to know about that enterprise. Taken together, this book and the other Hoover's products and resources represent the most complete source of basic corporate information readily available to the general public.

HOW TO USE THIS BOOK

This book has four sections:

1. "Using Hoover's Handbooks" describes the contents of our profiles and explains the ways in which we gather and compile our data.

2. "A List-Lover's Compendium" contains lists of the largest, fastest-growing, and most valuable companies of global importance.

3. The company profiles section makes up the largest and most important part of the book — 500 profiles of major business enterprises, arranged alphabetically.

4. Three indexes complete the book. The first sorts companies by industry groups, the second by headquarters location. The third index is a list of all the executives found in the Executives section of each company profile.

Using Hoover's Handbooks

SELECTION OF THE COMPANIES PROFILED

The 500 profiles in this book include a variety of international enterprises, ranging from some of the largest publicly traded companies in the world — Daimler AG, for example — to Malaysia's largest and oldest conglomerate, Sime Darby Berhad. It also includes many private businesses, such as Bertelsmann AG and LEGO, as well as a selection of government-owned entities, such as Mexico's Petróleos Mexicanos. The companies selected represent a cross-section of the largest, most influential, and most interesting companies based outside the United States.

In selecting these companies, we followed several basic criteria. We started with the global giants, including Toyota and Royal Dutch Shell, and then looked at companies with substantial activity in the US, such as Vivendi and Diageo. We also included companies that dominate their industries (e.g., AB Electrolux, the world's #1 producer of household appliances), as well as representative companies from around the world (an Indian conglomerate, Tata; two firms from Finland, Nokia and Stora Enso Oyj; and two companies from Russia, OAO Gazprom and OAO LUKOIL). Companies that weren't necessarily global powerhouses but that had a high profile with consumers (e.g., IKEA) or had interesting stories (Virgin Group) were included. Finally, because of their truly global reach, we added the Big Four accounting firms (even though they are headquartered or co-headquartered in the US).

ORGANIZATION

The profiles are presented in alphabetical order. You will find the commonly used name of the enterprise at the beginning of the profile; the full, legal name is found in the Locations section. For some companies, primarily Japanese, the commonly translated English name differs from the actual legal name of the company, so both are provided. (The legal name of Nippon Steel Corporation is Shin Nippon Seitetsu Kabushiki Kaisha.) If a company name starts with a person's first name (e.g., George Weston Limited), it is alphabetized under the first name. We've also tried to alphabetize companies where you would expect to find them — for example, Deutsche Lufthansa is in the L's and Grupo Televisa can be found under T.

The annual financial information contained in the profiles is current through fiscal year-ends occurring as late as June 2016. We have included certain nonfinancial developments, such as officer changes, through September 2016.

OVERVIEW

In the first section of the profile, we have tried to give a thumbnail description of the company and what it does. The description will usually include information on the company's strategy, reputation, and ownership. We recommend that you read this section first.

HISTORY

This extended section, which is present for most companies, reflects our belief that every enterprise is the sum of its history and that you have to know where you came from in order to know where you are going. While some companies have limited historical awareness, we think the vast majority of the enterprises in this book have colorful backgrounds. We have tried to focus on the people who made the enterprises what they are today. We have found these histories to be full of twists and ironies; they make fascinating reading.

EXECUTIVES

Here we list the names of the people who run the company, insofar as space allows. We have shown age and pay information where available, although most non-US companies are not required to report the level of detail revealed in the US.

Although companies are free to structure their management titles any way they please, most modern corporations follow standard practices. The ultimate power in any corporation lies with the shareholders, who elect a board of directors, usually including officers or "insiders," as well as individuals from outside the company. The chief officer, the person on whose desk the buck stops, is usually called the chief executive officer (CEO) in the US. In other countries, practices vary widely. In the UK, traditionally, the Managing Director performs the functions of the CEO without the title, although the use of the term

CEO is on the rise there. In Germany it is customary to have two boards of directors: a managing board populated by the top executives of the company and a higher-level supervisory board consisting of outsiders.

As corporate management has become more complex, it is common for the CEO to have a "right-hand person" who oversees the day-to-day operations of the company, allowing the CEO plenty of time to focus on strategy and long-term issues. This right-hand person is usually designated the chief operating officer (COO) and is often the president of the company. In other cases one person is both chairman and president.

We have tried to list each company's most important officers, including the chief financial officer (CFO) and the chief legal officer. For companies with US operations, we have included the names of the US CEO, CFO, and top human resources executive, where available.

The people named in the Executives section are indexed at the back of the book.

The Executives section also includes the name of the company's auditing (accounting) firm, where available.

LOCATIONS

Here we include the company's full legal name and its headquarters, street address, telephone and fax numbers, and Web site, as available. We also list the same information for the US office for each company, if one exists. Telephone numbers of foreign offices are shown using the standardized conventions of international dialing. The back of the book includes an index of companies by headquarters location.

In some cases we have also included information on the geographic distribution of the company's business, including sales and profit data. Note that these profit numbers, like those in the Products/Operations section below, are usually operating or pretax profits rather than net profits. Operating profits are generally those before financing costs (interest income and payments) and before taxes, which are considered costs attributable to the whole company rather than to one division or part of the world. For this reason the net income figures (in the Historical Financials section) are usually much lower, since they are after interest and taxes. Pretax profits are after interest but before taxes.

PRODUCTS/OPERATIONS

This section lists as many of the company's products, services, brand names, divisions, subsidiaries, and joint ventures as we could fit. We have tried to include all its major lines and all familiar brand names. The nature of this section varies by company and the amount of information available. If the company publishes sales and profit information by type of business, we have included it (in US dollars).

COMPETITORS

In this section we have listed enterprises that compete with the profiled company. This feature is included as a quick way to locate similar companies and compare them. Because of the difficulty in identifying companies that only compete in foreign markets, the list of competitors is still weighted to large international companies with a strong US presence.

HISTORICAL FINANCIALS

Here we have tried to present as much data about each enterprise's financial performance as we could compile in the allocated space. Financial data for all companies is presented in US dollars, using the appropriate exchange rate at fiscal year-end.

While the information presented varies somewhat from industry to industry, it is less complete in the case of private companies that do not release data (although we have always tried to provide annual sales and employment). The following information is generally present.

A five-year table, with relevant annualized compound growth rates, covers:

- Sales — fiscal year sales (year-end assets for most financial companies)
- Net income — fiscal year net income (before accounting changes)
- Net profit margin — fiscal year net income as a percent of sales (as a percent of assets for most financial firms)
- Employees — fiscal year-end or average number of employees
- Stock price — the fiscal year close
- P/E — high and low price/earnings ratio
- Earnings per share — fiscal year earnings per share (EPS)
- Dividends per share — fiscal year dividends per share

The information on the number of employees is intended to aid the reader interested in knowing whether a company has a long-term trend of increasing or decreasing employment. As far as we know, we are the only company that publishes this information in print format.

The numbers on the left in each row of the Historical Financials section give the month and the year in which the company's fiscal year actually ends. Thus, a company with a September 30, 2015, year-end is shown as 9/15.

In addition, we have provided in graph form a stock price history for companies that trade on the major US exchanges. The graphs, covering up to five years, show the range of trading between the high and the low price, as well as the closing price for each fiscal year. For public companies that trade on the OTC or Pink Sheets or that do not trade on US exchanges, we graph net income. Generally, for private companies, we have graphed net income, or, if that is unavailable, sales.

Key year-end statistics in this section generally show the financial strength of the enterprise, including:

- Debt ratio (long-term debt as a percent of shareholders' equity)
- Return on equity (net income divided by the average of beginning and ending common shareholders' equity)
- Cash and cash equivalents
- Current ratio (ratio of current assets to current liabilities)
- Total long-term debt (including capital lease obligations)
- Number of shares of common stock outstanding
- Dividend yield (fiscal year dividends per share divided by the fiscal year-end closing stock price)
- Dividend payout (fiscal year dividends divided by fiscal year EPS)
- Market value at fiscal year-end (fiscal year-end closing stock price multiplied by fiscal year-end number of shares outstanding)
- Fiscal year sales for financial institutions.

Per share data has been adjusted for stock splits. The data for public companies with sponsored American Depositary Receipts has been provided to us by Morningstar, Inc. Other public company information was compiled by Hoover's, which takes full responsibility for the content of this section.

In the case of private companies that do not publicly disclose financial information, we usually did not have access to such standardized data. We have gathered estimates of sales and other statistics from numerous sources.

Hoover's Handbook of

World Business

A List-Lover's Compendium

The 100 Largest Companies by Sales in Hoover's Handbook of World Business 2017

Rank	Company	Sales ($ mil)	Rank	Company	Sales ($ mil)	Rank	Company	Sales ($ mil)
1	China Petroleum & Chemical C	$310,858	35	Mangalore Refinery And Petroch	$92,602	69	Metro AG	$66,394
2	Cementos Bio-Bio S.A. (Chile)	$296,138	36	China Railway Construction C	$92,468	70	Marubeni Corp.	$65,009
3	Royal Dutch Shell Plc	$272,156	37	China Railway Group Ltd	$92,376	71	Deutsche Post RG	$64,514
4	Oil and Natural Gas Corp. Lt	$266,779	38	HSBC Holdings Plc	$91,617	72	Deutsche Post AG	$64,514
5	PetroChina Co Ltd	$265,674	39	Nestle SA	$89,702	73	AUDI AG	$63,632
6	Toyota Motor Corp	$252,929	40	Hitachi, Ltd.	$89,355	74	ArcelorMittal SA	$63,578
7	Volkswagen A.G. (Germany, Fe	$232,320	41	Siemens AG (Germany)	$88,908	75	People's Insurance Company (	$63,515
8	BP plc	$225,316	42	Carrefour S.A.	$85,892	76	China Communications Constru	$62,147
9	Samsung Electronics Co Ltd	$170,545	43	Credit Agricole SA	$84,290	77	Nippon Life Insurance Co.	$61,795
10	Glencore PLC	$170,497	44	Banco Santander SA	$83,591	78	Mitsubishi Corp	$61,672
11	Daimler AG	$162,801	45	Enel SpA	$82,408	79	Prudential Plc	$61,564
12	Industrial and Commercial Ba	$162,175	46	PJSC Gazprom	$82,294	80	Reliance Industries	$61,404
13	JCR Pharmaceuticals Co Ltd	$155,288	47	Electricite de France	$81,697	81	Dai-ichi Life Holdings Inc	$60,770
14	Total SA	$143,421	48	SoftBank Group Corp	$81,512	82	Zurich Insurance Group Ltd	$60,568
15	China Construction Bank Corp	$143,167	49	China Life Insurance Co Ltd	$78,439	83	Peugeot SA	$59,554
16	Hon Hai Precision Industry C	$136,401	50	Hyundai Motor Co., Ltd.	$78,160	84	Vodafone Group Plc	$58,978
17	Honda Motor Co., Ltd.	$130,023	51	PJSC Lukoil	$77,852	85	Unilever N.V.	$58,024
18	Agricultural Bank of China	$129,100	52	JX Holdings, Inc.	$77,810	86	Unilever Plc (United Kingdom	$58,024
19	E.ON SE	$127,119	53	Bosch (Robert) GmbH (Germany	$76,906	87	ING Groep NV	$56,269
20	AXA S.A.	$121,508	54	BASF SE	$76,734	88	PTT Public Co Ltd.	$56,256
21	Fiat Chrysler Automobiles NV	$120,461	55	Engie SA	$76,633	89	Bank of Communications Co.,	$55,233
22	Bank of China Ltd	$118,738	56	Tesco PLC	$75,950	90	Statoil ASA	$54,782
23	BNP Paribas (France)	$111,240	57	Deutsche Telekom AG	$75,404	91	Tokyo Electric Power Company	$54,053
24	Allianz SE	$109,571	58	ENI S.p.A.	$75,096	92	Seven & i Holdings Co. Ltd.	$53,519
25	Nissan Motor Co., Ltd.	$108,547	59	Toyota Tsusho Corp	$72,756	93	Toshiba Corp	$52,569
26	Societe Generale	$106,254	60	Indian Oil Corporation	$72,543	94	Fonciere Euris SA	$51,947
27	SAIC Motor Corp Ltd	$103,233	61	Aeon Co. Ltd. (Japan)	$72,384	95	Finatis SA	$51,947
28	China Mobile Limited	$102,907	62	Sony Corp	$72,181	96	America Movil SAB de CV	$51,473
29	Nippon Telegraph & Telephone	$102,772	63	CITIC Ltd	$71,938	97	Telefonica SA	$51,431
30	Ping An Insurance (Group) Co	$100,503	64	Airbus Group SE	$70,200	98	Rallye S.A. Neuilly-Sur-Sein	$51,010
31	Bayer Motoren WK	$100,398	65	Rosneft Oil Co OJSC (Moscow)	$69,740	99	China Telecom Corp Ltd	$50,997
32	Bayerische Motoren Werke AG	$100,398	66	Munich Re Group	$68,237	100	Roche Holding Ltd	$50,753
33	Assicurazioni Generali S.p.A	$98,290	67	Panasonic Corp	$67,266			
34	Petroleo Brasileiro S.A.	$97,314	68	Noble Group Ltd	$66,712			

SOURCE: MERGENT INC., DATABASE, OCTOBER 2016

The 100 Most Profitable Companies in
Hoover's Handbook of World Business 2017

Rank	Company	Net Income ($ mil)
1	Industrial and Commercial Ba	$42,671
2	China Construction Bank Corp	$35,129
3	Oil and Natural Gas Corp. Lt	$29,313
4	Agricultural Bank of China	$27,805
5	Bank of China Ltd	$26,306
6	Cementos Bio-Bio S.A. (Chile)	$21,141
7	Toyota Motor Corp	$20,594
8	China Mobile Limited	$16,712
9	JCR Pharmaceuticals Co Ltd	$15,935
10	Samsung Electronics Co Ltd	$15,889
11	HSBC Holdings Plc	$13,522
12	GlaxoSmithKline Plc	$12,481
13	Korea Electric Power Corp KE	$11,295
14	Alibaba Group Holding Ltd	$11,065
15	PJSC Gazprom	$10,658
16	Surgutneftegas OAO	$10,313
17	Bank of Communications Co.,	$10,244
18	Taiwan Semiconductor Manufac	$9,216
19	Daimler AG	$9,176
20	Nestle SA	$9,129
21	Roche Holding Ltd	$8,925
22	China Merchants Bank Co Ltd	$8,884
23	Ping An Insurance (Group) Co	$8,346
24	Anheuser Busch InBev SA/NV	$8,273
25	Royal Bank of Canada (Montre	$7,777
26	Industrial Bank Co., Ltd.	$7,731
27	Sumitomo Mitsui Financial Gr	$7,515
28	Norges Bank (Norway)	$7,499
29	BNP Paribas (France)	$7,291
30	Allianz SE	$7,206
31	Mitsubishi UFJ Financial Gro	$7,145
32	China Minsheng Banking Corp	$7,100
33	Bayer Motoren WK	$6,937
34	Bayerische Motoren Werke AG	$6,937
35	Commonwealth Bank of Austral	$6,865
36	Novartis AG Basel	$6,712
37	Nippon Telegraph & Telephone	$6,570
38	Itau Unibanco Holding S.A.	$6,499
39	Banco Santander SA	$6,498
40	Toronto Dominion Bank	$6,488
41	British American Tobacco Plc	$6,358
42	China Citic Bank Corp Ltd	$6,337
43	UBS Group AG	$6,246
44	Alecta pensionsforsakring, om	$6,196
45	AXA S.A.	$6,118
46	Siemens AG (Germany)	$6,084
47	Westpac Banking Corp	$5,672
48	Bidvest Group Ltd	$5,481
49	PetroChina Co Ltd	$5,469
50	Hyundai Motor Co., Ltd.	$5,454
51	CITIC Ltd	$5,394
52	Novo-Nordisk A/S	$5,386
53	ING Groep NV	$5,365
54	Unilever N.V.	$5,347
55	Unilever Plc (United Kingdom	$5,347
56	China Life Insurance Co Ltd	$5,343
57	Bank Nova Scotia Halifax	$5,223
58	Baidu, Inc.	$5,183
59	Total SA	$5,087
60	Saudi Basic Industries Corp -	$4,999
61	China Petroleum & Chemical C	$4,995
62	NTT DoCoMo Inc	$4,883
63	Rosneft Oil Co OJSC (Moscow)	$4,807
64	Sanofi	$4,669
65	Swiss Re Ltd.	$4,665
66	Nissan Motor Co., Ltd.	$4,665
67	European Investment Bank	$4,659
68	Dalian Wanda Commercial Prop	$4,615
69	SAIC Motor Corp Ltd	$4,588
70	AUDI AG	$4,579
71	Banco Bradesco S.A.	$4,578
72	China Everbright Bank Co Ltd	$4,547
73	SK C&C Co Ltd	$4,544
74	Fortum OYJ	$4,507
75	Bayer AG	$4,477
76	Hon Hai Precision Industry C	$4,469
77	Tencent Holdings Ltd.	$4,435
78	KDDI Corp	$4,403
79	Societe Generale	$4,358
80	Australia & New Zealand Bank	$4,349
81	BASF SE	$4,343
82	Telstra Corp., Ltd.	$4,300
83	China Overseas Land & Invest	$4,298
84	SoftBank Group Corp	$4,222
85	Sun Hung Kai Properties Ltd	$4,210
86	ANZ National Bank Ltd	$4,151
87	Accenture plc	$4,112
88	Japan Tobacco Inc.	$4,035
89	Nordea Bank AB	$3,989
90	PJSC Lukoil	$3,942
91	Allergan PLC	$3,915
92	LVMH Moet Hennessy Louis Vui	$3,892
93	Fuji Heavy Industries Ltd	$3,888
94	LyondellBasell Industries NV	$3,836
95	Credit Agricole SA	$3,830
96	Prudential Plc	$3,822
97	Reliance Industries	$3,768
98	Brookfield Property Partners	$3,766
99	National Grid plc	$3,730
100	BT Group Plc	$3,725

SOURCE: MERENT INC., DATABASE, OCTOBER 2016

The 100 Largest Employers in
Hoover's Handbook of World Business 2017

Rank	Company	Employees
1	Hon Hai Precision Industry C	830,174
2	China Eastern Airlines Corp.	710,330
3	Randstad Holding N.V.	627,150
4	G4S Plc	611,366
5	Volkswagen A.G. (Germany, Fe	610,076
6	Compass Group PLC (United Ki	527,180
7	PetroChina Co Ltd	521,566
8	Agricultural Bank of China	514,370
9	ISS A/S (Denmark)	504,816
10	Deutsche Post RG	497,745
11	Deutsche Post AG	497,745
12	Tesco PLC	482,152
13	Industrial and Commercial Ba	466,346
14	PJSC Gazprom	462,400
15	Jardine Matheson Holdings Ltd	440,000
16	China Mobile Limited	438,645
17	Sodexo	425,594
18	Pou Chen Corp	415,296
19	Yue Yuen Industrial (Holding	411,000
20	Accenture plc	384,000
21	Carrefour S.A.	380,920
22	Hitachi, Ltd.	380,355
23	Bosch (Robert) GmbH (Germany	374,778
24	China Construction Bank Corp	369,183
25	China Petroleum & Chemical C	351,019
26	Siemens AG (Germany)	351,000
27	Toyota Motor Corp	348,877
28	Nestle SA	335,000
29	Sberbank Russia	330,700
30	Fonciere Euris SA	330,433
31	Finatis SA	330,433
32	Rallye S.A. Neuilly-Sur-Sein	330,433
33	Securitas AB	327,800
34	Casino Guichard Perrachon S.	325,820
35	Deutscher Sparkassen-und Giro	324,200
36	Bank of China Ltd	310,042
37	Deutsche Bahn AG	297,202
38	China Telecom Corp Ltd	291,526
39	China Railway Group Ltd	291,149
40	Sumitomo Electric Industries	279,989
41	Ping An Insurance (Group) Co	275,011
42	China Unicom (Hong Kong) Ltd	268,887
43	HSBC Holdings Plc	264,000
44	Rosneft Oil Co OJSC (Moscow)	261,500
45	China Railway Construction C	254,366
46	Jardine Cycle & Carriage Ltd	250,000
47	Daimler AG	248,015
48	Reserve Bank Of New Zealand	247,000
49	Fomento Economico Mexicano,	246,158
50	Nippon Telegraph & Telephone	241,450
51	Koninklijke Ahold Delhaize N	236,000
52	Fiat Chrysler Automobiles NV	234,621
53	Metro AG	233,962
54	Wal-Mart de Mexico S.A.B. de	231,996
55	JBS S.A.	230,000
56	Deutsche Telekom AG	225,243
57	Fresenius SE & Co KGaA	222,305
58	Wesfarmers Ltd.	220,000
59	State Bank of India	213,238
60	ArcelorMittal SA	209,404
61	Johnson Controls Internation	209,000
62	Honda Motor Co., Ltd.	208,399
63	Continental AG (Germany, Fed	207,899
64	Woolworths Ltd.	205,000
65	ACS Actividades de Construcc	200,516
66	Flex Ltd	200,000
67	BYD Co Ltd	200,000
68	Yamato Holdings Co., Ltd.	196,582
69	Societe Nationale des Chemins	196,152
70	Loblaw Companies Ltd	196,000
71	America Movil SAB de CV	195,475
72	Infosys Ltd.	194,044
73	People's Insurance Company (	193,687
74	Canon, Inc.	189,571
75	Banco Santander SA	189,464
76	BNP Paribas (France)	189,077
77	Teleperformance SA	188,426
78	Toshiba Corp	187,809
79	CRRC Corp Ltd	186,963
80	Vinci SA	185,452
81	Denso Corp. (Japan)	182,229
82	Schneider Electric SE	181,362
83	Cap Gemini SA	180,639
84	Dairy Farm International Hold	180,000
85	Nissan Motor Co., Ltd.	174,043
86	Veolia Environnement	173,959
87	Fujitsu Ltd.	173,722
88	Unilever N.V.	171,000
89	Unilever Plc (United Kingdom	168,921
90	Compagnie de Saint-Gobain	168,114
91	PICC Property and Casualty C	167,709
92	J.Sainsbury PLC	162,700
93	Prosegur Compania De Segurid	161,822
94	Electricite de France	159,112
95	Royal Mail Plc	156,535
96	ThyssenKrupp AG	156,487
97	Glencore PLC	156,468
98	Atento SA	155,832
99	Engie SA	154,935
100	Industria De Diseno Textil I	152,854

SOURCE: MERGENT, INC., DATABASE, OCTOBER 2016

Hoover's Handbook of

World Business

The Companies

77 Bank, Ltd. (The) (Japan)

Unlike 77 Sunset Strip 77 Bank's name doesn't denote its address but its order in the history of Japanese banking. 77 Bank was founded in 1878 as the 77th national bank in Japan. Operating more than 140 branches in the northern area of Japan's largest island Honshu 77 Bank provides the usual banking services of savings and lending as well some other operations such as temporary employment property appraisal and credit-document custody. 77 Bank also provides financial-related services that include leasing credit investigation computer-based contract services and a credit card.

EXECUTIVES

President, TERUHIKO UJIIE
Chairman, Iwao Muramatsu
Auditors: Deloitte Touche Tohmatsu LLC

LOCATIONS

HQ: 77 Bank, Ltd. (The) (Japan)
3-3-20 Chuo, Aoba-ku, Sendai, Miyagi 980-8777
Phone: (81) 22 267 1111
Web: www.77bank.co.jp

COMPETITORS

Fukuoka Financial
  Group
Gunma Bank

Ito-Yokado
Japan Post
Sumitomo Mitsui

HISTORICAL FINANCIALS

Company Type: Public

Income Statement — FYE: March 31

	ASSETS ($ mil.)	NET INCOME ($ mil.)	INCOME AS % OF ASSETS	EMPLOYEES
03/16	76,570	141	0.2%	4,420
03/15	71,582	142	0.2%	4,367
03/14	82,418	145	0.2%	3,002
03/13	87,798	132	0.2%	3,038
03/12	92,853	130	0.1%	3,128
Annual Growth	(4.7%)	2.0%	—	9.0%

2016 Year-End Financials

Return on assets: 0.1%
Return on equity: 3.5%
Long-term debt ($ mil.): —
No. of shares (mil.): 374
Sales ($ mil): 969

Dividends
  Yield: —
  Payout: —
  Market value ($ mil.): —

	STOCK PRICE ($) FY Close	P/E High/Low	PER SHARE ($) Earnings	Dividends	Book Value
03/16	0.00	— —	0.38	0.00	10.40
Annual Growth	—	— —	—	—	—

Aareal Bank AG

Aareal Bank is engaged internationally in a variety of property-related banking and financial services for the public and private sectors. The company's business is organized into two primary segments. Structured property financing (its most profitable business) specializes in financing large-scale retail hotel and logistics industry properties. The consulting/services segment offers IT products that help users manage residential and commercial properties. Aareal Bank operates in more than 30 countries in Europe North America and the Asia/Pacific region. In fiscal 2014 the financial institution boosted its core business by acquiring Germany's Corealcredit Bank AG for euro 342 million.

EXECUTIVES

Member Management Board, Thomas Ortmanns, $300,000 total compensation
Chairman Supervisory Board, Marija G. Korsch, age 68
Chairman Management Board, Hermann J. Merkens, age 50
Auditors: PricewaterhouseCoopers Aktiengesellschaft Wirtschaftprufungsgesellschaft

LOCATIONS

HQ: Aareal Bank AG
Paulinenstrasse 15, Wiesbaden D-65189
Phone: (49) 611 348 3009   **Fax:** (49) 611 348 2637
Web: www.aareal-bank.com

PRODUCTS/OPERATIONS

2015 Sales

	% of total
Interest income	90
Commission income	1
Other operating income	9
Total	**100**

COMPETITORS

AWD
BayernLB
Commerzbank
Deutsche Bank
HSBC

Landesbank Berlin
UBS
UniCredit Bank AG
Wstenrot &
  Wrttembergische

HISTORICAL FINANCIALS

Company Type: Public

Income Statement — FYE: December 31

	ASSETS ($ mil.)	NET INCOME ($ mil.)	INCOME AS % OF ASSETS	EMPLOYEES
12/15	56,582	386	0.7%	2,861
12/14	60,236	384	0.6%	2,548
12/13	59,173	161	0.3%	2,375
12/12	60,279	138	0.2%	2,289
12/11	54,084	147	0.3%	2,353
Annual Growth	1.1%	27.3%	—	5.0%

2015 Year-End Financials

Return on assets: 0.7%
Return on equity: 13.4%
Long-term debt ($ mil.): —
No. of shares (mil.): 59
Sales ($ mil): 1,329

Dividends
  Yield: —
  Payout: —
  Market value ($ mil.): 2,101

	STOCK PRICE ($) FY Close	P/E High/Low	PER SHARE ($) Earnings	Dividends	Book Value
12/15	35.10	7 6	6.16	0.00	50.99
12/14	41.00	8 7	5.92	0.00	50.38
12/13	37.40	20 11	2.68	0.00	50.78
12/12	21.08	14 9	2.31	0.00	46.44
12/11	17.50	16 7	2.73	0.00	41.62
Annual Growth	19.0%	— —	22.6%	—	5.2%

ABB Ltd

You could be forgiven for thinking that ABB is short for "A Bunch of Businesses" —though that bunch has evolved over some 130 years. ABB engineers power and automation technologies for a broad base of utility industrial and commercial customers. Its lines run from robots to light switches. Power products include transmission and distribution components as well as turnkey substation systems. Automation technologies are used to monitor and control equipment and processes in industrial plants and utilities. The company has established a presence in about 100 countries with its core businesses concentrated in power and automation markets.

Geographic Reach

ABB's operations extend to around 100 countries. A large portion of the company's production and development facilities reside in Canada China Finland Germany India Italy Norway Sweden Switzerland and the US.

Europe accounted for 36% of its total sales in 2012; the Americas and Asia each generated 27% while Africa and the Middle East brought in 10%.

Operations

ABB operates through five segments: Power Products Power Systems Discrete Automation and Motion Low Voltage Products and Process Automation. The Power Products and Power Systems segments are driven primarily by the capital expenditures of electrical utilities.

The Automation Products Process Automation and Low Voltage Products segments are impacted by the health of several industries including automotive consumer products metals and minerals paper and pulp and pharmaceuticals. A global presence and competitive cost base however have helped to buffer ABB's exposure to regional recessions and slow economies.

Major subsidiaries owned by ABB include ABB Inc. ABB Limited Baldor Electric Company Thomas & Betts Ventyx Tropos Networks ABB AG ABB Ltda. Power-One and ABB Contracting.

Sales and Marketing

ABB sells its products through direct sales and external channel partners like wholesalers distributors system integrators EPCs and OEMs.

Financial Performance

ABB generated $39.3 billion in revenues for 2012 a historic milestone for the company; this represented a 3% increase from the $37.8 billion it earned in 2011. The spike in revenues was mainly due to a solid order level as well as the favorable impact of its 2012 Thomas & Betts acquisition.

While ABB has enjoyed three straight years of revenue growth its profits slipped by 15% from $3.2 billion in 2011 to $2.7 billion in 2012 due to an increase in the cost of sales. This was the result of an unfavorable business mix coupled with higher prices involved with restructuring its segments.

Strategy

As the global economy moves away from the recession ABB has been making some milestone acquisitions to boost its product offerings operations and geographic reach. In mid-2013 it purchased Power-One a major provider of solar inverters technology used to convert the sun's energy into electricity. ABB made the $1 billion deal to boost its renewable energy business and expand its solar product portfolio.

In 2012 ABB bought Thomas & Betts (T&B) for about $3.9 billion. T&B sells electrical connectors HVAC equipment and transmission towers. The acquisition significantly added to ABB's North American presence giving it access to T&B's network of more than 6000 distributor locations and wholesalers throughout the continent. Shortly after that transaction was made ABB snapped up Tropos Networks a California firm that makes wireless technologies and products for distribution area communication networks. The acquisition broadened ABB's communications systems portfolio and enabled it to better cater to North American clients in the power transportation and mining sectors.

In 2011 ABB acquired the Trasfor Group which advanced its portfolio of specialty dry-type transformers used in drives railway rolling stock offshore wind power and other renewable energy applications. Months earlier ABB swallowed up Baldor Electric for $3.1 billion. Baldor Electric a US industrial motors business strengthened ABB's energy efficient offerings most notably in North America.

Other completed acquisitions that year include ABB's takeover of Mincom an Australia-based software and services company with clients ranging from mining companies (Rio Tinto and Anglo American) to big manufacturing companies (Boeing and Caterpillar). Not only did the deal bring an estimated $200 million in revenues but it also expanded ABB's software capabilities.

HISTORY

Asea Brown Boveri (ABB) was formed in 1988 when two giants ASEA AB of Sweden and BBC Brown Boveri of Switzerland combined their electrical engineering and equipment businesses. Percy Barnevik head of ASEA became CEO.

ASEA was born in Stockholm in 1883 when Ludwig Fredholm founded Electriska Aktiebolaget to manufacture an electric dynamo created by engineer Jonas Wenstrom. In 1890 the company merged with Wenstrom's brother's firm to form Allmanna Svenska Electriska Aktiebolaget (ASEA) a pioneer in industrial electrification. Early in the 1900s ASEA began its first railway electrification project. By the 1920s it was providing locomotives and other equipment to Sweden's national railway and by the next decade ASEA was one of Sweden's largest electric equipment manufacturers. In 1962 it bought 20% of appliance maker Electrolux. ASEA created the nuclear power venture ASEA-ATOM with the Swedish government in 1968 and bought full control in 1982.

BBC Brown Boveri was formed in 1891 as the Brown Boveri and Company partnership between Charles Brown and Walter Boveri in Baden Switzerland. It made power generation equipment and produced the first steam turbines in Europe in 1900. BBC entered Germany (1893) France (1894) and Italy (1903) and diversified into nuclear power equipment after WWII.

By 1988 BBC the bigger company had a West German network that ASEA the more profitable company coveted. Both had US joint ventures. In an unusual merger ASEA (which became ABB AB) and BBC (later ABB AG) continued as separate entities sharing equal ownership of ABB. Barnevik crafted a unique decentralized management structure under which national subsidiaries were closely linked to their local customers and labor forces. In six years ABB took over more than 150 companies worldwide.

An ABB-led consortium built one of the world's largest hydroelectric plants in Iran in 1992 and in 1995 ABB merged its transportation segment into Adtranz (a joint venture with Daimler-Benz) to form the world's #1 maker of trains.

Tragedy struck in 1996. Robert Donovan CEO of ABB's US subsidiary died in a plane crash along with Commerce Secretary Ron Brown and other executives on a trade mission. Donovan's death hastened the US unit's restructuring.

In 1997 Barnevik gave up the title of CEO remaining as chairman and was succeeded by Göran Lindahl an engineer who worked his way up the ranks at ASEA. (Barnevik remained chairman until 2001.) After 1997 profits dipped drastically Lindahl scrapped Barnevik's vaunted regional matrix structure in favor of one organized by product areas under a strong central management. Though the Asian financial crisis slowed orders ABB still pulled in large contracts including one to build the world's largest cracker plant in Texas in 1998.

In 1999 ABB acquired Elsag Bailey a Dutch maker of industrial control systems for about $1.5 billion and sold its 50% stake in Adtranz to DaimlerChrysler for about $472 million. ABB and France's ALSTOM combined their power generation businesses to form the world's largest power plant equipment maker. That year ABB AB and ABB AG were at last united under a single stock through holding company ABB Ltd.

ABB scaled back its power plant-related activities in 2000. The company sold its nuclear power business to BNFL for $485 million and its 50% stake in ABB Alstom Power to ALSTOM for $1.2 billion. (Areva acquired ALSTOM's transmission and distribution business in 2004.) In 2001 Lindahl resigned and Jürgen Centerman head of the company's automation business replaced him. Centerman promptly reorganized ABB's industrial operations into four segments based on customer type and two based on product type.

Also in 2001 ABB acquired French company Entrelec a supplier of industrial automation and control products. With economic slowdowns occurring in the company's key markets ABB announced plans in 2001 to cut 12000 jobs over 18 months. Later that year amid rising numbers of asbestos claims against US subsidiary Combustion Engineering ABB took a $470 million fourth-quarter charge to cover asbestos liabilities. The claims charged asbestos exposures stemming from products supplied before the mid-1970s by Combustion Engineering which ABB acquired in 1990.

In 2002 ABB found itself embroiled in controversy after revealing not only a record loss but also payments of large pensions to former chairman Barnevik and former chief executive Lindahl. The former executives agreed that year to return a part (about $82 million) of their pension payouts to ABB. That year the company which faced $4.4 billion in debts after industry slumps affected its sales of power systems and equipment industrial automation and controls sold part of its financial services unit to GE Commercial Finance for $2.3 billion.

The day after the company sold its structured finances unit ABB's chief executive Jürgen Centerman resigned and was replaced by the chairman Jürgen Dormann. That year ABB sold its metering business to Germany-based Ruhrgas for $244 million.

In 2003 as part of its settlement with asbestos plaintiffs ABB placed Combustion Engineering into bankruptcy. Later that same year the company announced that it would sell its Sirius International reinsurance business to the Bermuda-based White Mountains; the deal was completed in 2004 for about $425 million. ABB also sold its upstream oil gas and petrochemicals unit to Candover Partners 3i and J.P. Morgan Partners for $925 million in 2004. (To clear the way for the sale ABB also agreed to pay US regulators $16 million in fines to settle bribery cases at US-based ABB Vetco Gray and Scotland-based ABB Vetco UK. The subsidiaries —part of the petroleum business that was sold —allegedly paid off government officials in Angola Kazakhstan and Nigeria in order to win oil contracts between 1998 and 2003.)

Sulzer CEO Fred Kindle succeeded Dormann as ABB's CEO in 2005. (Dormann remained chairman until his retirement in 2007.) The company made a number of small dispositions in 2005 including its Japanese control valves business its foundry business and several cable and power line businesses.

ABB ended years of litigation —and a major corporate headache —when it reached a settlement on an asbestos liability case related to US subsidiary Combustion Engineering in 2006. As part of the settlement ABB committed more than $1.4 billion to pay settled claims.

After consolidating its remaining businesses into the two areas power technologies and automation technologies ABB restructured its operations into five divisions in 2006: Power Products Power Systems Automation Products Process Automation and Robotics. It took further steps to streamline operations and position itself for growth for example by moving its main robotics operation from Detroit to Shanghai.

In 2006 ABB voluntarily disclosed to the US Department of Justice and the SEC that the company made payments in the Middle East that might have violated anti-bribery laws. The following year ABB disclosed similar suspect payments at subsidiaries in Asia Europe and South America.

Kindle left ABB in 2008 due to what the company called "irreconcilable differences" concerning the leadership of the company; former GE Healthcare CEO Joe Hogan became CEO of ABB later that year.

In 2008 the company dug deeper into its investment purse spending $653 million to complete 12 deals. Most notably ABB purchased Kuhlman Electric a US-based transformer manufacturer from The Carlyle Group for $513 million including assumed debt. Kuhlman Electric was integrated into ABB's Power Products division in North America and deepens ABB's geographic footprint and product offerings in the industrial and electric utility sectors.

ABB's bunch of businesses has been peeled back too. Several divestitures were completed in 2008 and 2007; ABB exited its 50% interest in South Africa's ABB Powertech Transformers to Powertech owned by the Altron Group for $11 million. In 2007 ABB sold subsidiary ABB Lummus Global to Chicago Bridge & Iron Co. for some $870 million in cash as well as its Building Systems business in Germany and power plant interests in India and Morocco to Abu Dhabi National Oil. Power Lines businesses in Brazil and Mexico were also put on the sale block for $20 million.

ABB plowed in $209 million in 2009 adding eight new operations. Among them the company acquired the assets of Sinai Engineering a designer and provider of services for electrical generation and transmission systems planning as well as construction management. The transaction completed through its US ABB Inc. expanded ABB's presence in western Canada. On the other side of the world ABB picked up South Africa's Westingcorp (Pty) Ltd. The move ramped up ABB's line of power capacitors (machines that add to a system's power quality and energy efficiency) and opened the door to local and global electric utilities and mining markets.

ABB in mid-2010 acquired K-TEK a maker of level detection technology used in the oil and gas industry as well as water and other industries. Its instrumentation and sensing technologies which number more than 350000 installations enhanced ABB's slate of measurement products part of its Process Automation division. The deal garnered K-TEK's facilities in the US the Netherlands China India and South Africa.

ABB picked up US software provider Insert Key Solutions in late 2010. Its combination with the earlier acquisition of Ventyx (valued at approximately $1 billion) from Vista Equity Partners created a comprehensive portfolio of software for managing asset-intensive businesses engaged in the utility energy and communications industries. Ventyx and Insert Key Solutions joined ABB's network management business.

EXECUTIVES

President Region Americas and Head of Group Service Business Integration, Greg Scheu, age 55
President Region Asia Middle East and Africa (AMEA), Frank Duggan, age 57
President Region Europe and Chairman of Divisional Transformation Team, Bernhard Jucker, age 62, $919,999 total compensation
Mergers and Acquisitions and New Ventures, Eric Elzvik, age 56
CEO, Ulrich Spiesshofer, age 52, $730,004 total compensation
President Process Automation Division, Peter Terwiesch, age 50
CFO, Timo Ihamuotila, age 50
President Discrete Automation and Motion (DM) Division, Sami Atiya
President Power Grids Division, Claudio Facchin, age 51
President Electrification Products Division, Tarak Mehta, age 50
Managing Director ABB Finland, Pekka Tiitinen, age 50
Managing Director ABB India, Bazmi Husain
Vice Chairman, Jacob Wallenberg, age 60
Chairman, Peter R. Voser, age 58
Auditors: Ernst & Young AG

LOCATIONS

HQ: ABB Ltd
Affolternstrasse 44, Zurich CH-8050
Phone: (41) 43 317 7111   **Fax:** (41) 43 317 7992
Web: www.abb.com

2012 Sales

	$ mil.	% of total
Europe	14,073	36
Asia	10,750	27
Americas	10,699	27
Middle East & Africa	3,814	10
Total	**39,336**	**100**

PRODUCTS/OPERATIONS

2012 Sales

	$ mil.	% of total
Power Products	10,717	25
Discrete Automation & Motion	9,405	22
Process Automation	8,156	19
Power Systems	7,852	18
Low Voltage Products	6,638	16
Corporate & other	(3432)	-
Total	**39,336**	**100**

Selected Mergers and Acquisitions

FY2013
Power-One Inc. ($1 billion; Camarillo California; maker of solar inverters)
FY2012
Thomas & Betts Corporation ($3.9 billion; Memphis Tennessee; electrical connectors HVAC equipment and transmission towers)
Tropos Networks Inc. (Silicon Valley California; wireless technologies and products for distribution area communication networks)
FY2011
Trasfor Group (Switzerland; specialty dry-type transformers)
Baldor Electric ($3.1 billion; Fort Smith Arkansas; industrial motors)

Selected Products

Automation Products
Breakers
Control products
DIN-rail components
Drives
Enclosures
Generators
Instrumentation
Low-voltage switchgear
Motors
Power electronics systems
Switches
Wiring accessories
Electrical Products
Boxes and covers (Bowers Commander Steel City)
Cable ties (Catamount Ty-Fast Ty-Rap)
Connectors (Blackburn Color-Keyed)
Lighting (Carlon Red Dot Lumacell)
Wire management systems (Carlon T&B)
HVAC
Evaporative cooling and energy recovery equipment (International Energy Saver)
Heaters (EK Campbell Reznor)
Heating mechanical and refrigeration supplies (T&B)
Power Products
Circuit breakers for all current and voltage levels
High- and medium-voltage switchgear and apparatus
Power and distribution transformers
Sensors
Power Systems
Power plant automation and electrification solutions
Transmission and distribution systems
Process Automation
Automation products and solutions
Controls
Industry-specific application knowledge and services
Plant optimization
Robotics
Industrial robots
Industrial software products
Robot contollers and software
Steel Structures
Power connectors and accessories (Elastimold)
Steel poles (Meyer)
Transmission towers (Lehigh)

COMPETITORS

ALSTOM	KUKA
AREVA	Kawasaki Heavy
Bharat Heavy	Industries
Electricals	Larsen & Toubro
Cisco Systems	Legrand
Crompton Greaves	Metso
Danaher	Mitsubishi Heavy
Dᴇʀ	Industries
Eaton	Nokia
Emerson Electric	Rittal Corp.
Endress + Hauser	Rockwell Automation
Ericsson	SPX
FANUC	Schneider Electric
GE	Siemens AG
Hitachi	Toshiba
Honeywell	Voith
International	WEG Indstrias
Hyosung	Yaskawa Electric
Hyundai Corporation	Yokogawa Electric

HISTORICAL FINANCIALS

Company Type: Public

Income Statement

FYE: December 31

	REVENUE ($ mil.)	NET INCOME ($ mil.)	NET PROFIT MARGIN	EMPLOYEES
12/15	35,481	1,933	5.4%	135,800
12/14	39,830	2,594	6.5%	140,400
12/13	41,848	2,787	6.7%	147,700
12/12	39,336	2,704	6.9%	146,100
12/11	37,990	3,168	8.3%	133,600
Annual Growth	(1.7%)	(11.6%)	—	0.4%

2015 Year-End Financials

Debt ratio: 17.9%   No. of shares (mil.): —
Return on equity: 12.5%   Dividends
Cash ($ mil.): 6,198   Yield: 4.2%
Current ratio: 1.44   Payout: 85.8%
Long-term debt ($ mil.): 5,985   Market value ($ mil.): —

	STOCK PRICE ($) FY Close	P/E High/Low	PER SHARE ($) Earnings	Dividends	Book Value
12/15	17.73	27 20	0.87	0.75	6.61
12/14	21.15	24 18	1.13	0.77	7.20
12/13	26.56	22 17	1.21	0.70	8.14
12/12	20.79	19 13	1.18	0.69	7.36
12/11	18.83	20 12	1.38	0.67	6.89
Annual Growth	(1.5%)	— —	(10.9%)	2.7%	(1.0%)

Abbey National Treasury Services PLC (United Kingdom)

EXECUTIVES

Director, Jacques Ripoll
Auditors: Deloitte LLP

LOCATIONS

HQ: Abbey National Treasury Services PLC (United Kingdom)
2 Triton Square, Regent's Place, London NW1 3AN
Phone: (44) 870 607 6000

HISTORICAL FINANCIALS

Company Type: Public

Income Statement

FYE: December 31

	ASSETS ($ mil.)	NET INCOME ($ mil.)	INCOME AS % OF ASSETS	EMPLOYEES
12/15	161,334	394	0.2%	977
12/14	167,761	188	0.1%	862
12/13	345,929	271	0.1%	764
12/12	351,245	425	0.1%	717
12/11	340,444	531	0.2%	817
Annual Growth	(17.0%)	(7.2%)	—	4.6%

2015 Year-End Financials

Return on assets: 0.2%   Dividends
Return on equity: 7.5%   Yield: —
Long-term debt ($ mil.): —   Payout: —
No. of shares (mil.): —   Market value ($ mil.): —
Sales ($ mil): 2,757

Abu Dhabi Commercial Bank

LOCATIONS

HQ: Abu Dhabi Commercial Bank
Sheikh Zayed Bin Sultan Street, Plot C-33, Secotr E-11, P.O. Box 939, Abu Dhabi
Phone: (971) 2 696 2222
Web: www.adcb.com

HISTORICAL FINANCIALS

Company Type: Public

Income Statement

FYE: December 31

	ASSETS ($ mil.)	NET INCOME ($ mil.)	INCOME AS % OF ASSETS	EMPLOYEES
12/15	62,148	1,340	2.2%	0
12/14	55,548	1,102	2.0%	0
12/13	49,861	916	1.8%	0
12/12	49,218	744	1.5%	0
12/11	50,019	823	1.6%	0
Annual Growth	5.6%	12.9%	—	—

2015 Year-End Financials

Return on assets: 2.2%
Return on equity: 17.8%
Long-term debt ($ mil.): —
No. of shares (mil.): —
Sales ($ mil): 2,783

Dividends
Yield: —
Payout: —
Market value ($ mil.): —

Accenture plc

For Accenture the accent is on helping businesses improve their performance. The world's largest consulting firm Accenture offers a well-balanced portfolio of management consulting technology and business process outsourcing (BPO) services to some of the top companies and government organizations in the world. Corporate clients span a broad spectrum of industries —from retail to communications —and include more than three-quarters of the FORTUNE 500. Clients use Accenture's services to enter new markets increase revenue in existing markets improve operational performance and deliver new products to market. Accenture is domiciled in Dublin but headquartered in New York.

Geographic Reach

Accenture serves clients in more than 200 cities spanning 120 countries. The majority of its revenue is balanced between the Americas and Europe Middle East and Africa (EMEA). The US is its largest individual market generating about one-third of total revenue. The remainder is made in the Asia/Pacific region.

Operations

Accenture's business is divided into five operating groups: Communications Media & Technology; Financial Services; Health & Public Service; Products; and Resources. Although revenue generated by these operating groups is well dispersed Products is the company's largest segment serving mainly consumer-oriented industries including automotive consumer goods life sciences retail transportation and travel services.

Accenture has a global network of innovation centers in the US Australia China Japan Singapore India France and South Africa.

Financial Performance

As the global economy has improved and the demand for its consulting and outsourcing services has increased Accenture recognized a 9% spike in revenue ($27.4 billion to $29.7 billion) and a 12 % rise in profits ($2.3 billion to $2.6 billion) from 2011 to 2012.

The recent growth was attributed to double digit growth across all its five operating groups. Accenture has also benefited from its growth strategy that is focused on further differentiating its products and services in the marketplace and improving its competitiveness. It has also been helped from a positive increase in the local currency.

Strategy

Accenture's strategy is focused on deepening and differentiating its industry and technology capabilities from competitors. It is doing so in part by investing in analytics cloud computing insight-driven health interactive and digital marketing mobility and smart grid. Acquisitions joint ventures and alliances are key means through which Accenture enhances and adds to its offerings. One such partnership is a five-year research collaboration with MIT announced in early 2013 to develop advanced analytics specifically how to harness the challenges of big data and develop new approaches to improve the science of decision-making. In late 2012 Accenture and GE Aviation formed a joint venture company called Taleris to provide global airlines and cargo carriers with intelligent operations services to improve efficiency.

From a geographic standpoint the company is focusing expansion efforts on certain emerging markets in particular such as Brazil China India Mexico Russia South Africa South Korea Turkey and certain countries in Southeast Asia and the Middle East.

Mergers and Acquisitions

To help its clients more effectively measure and monitor the progress of their change programs Accenture in 2013 acquired ChangeTrack Research an Australia-based provider of analytics-based tools and services for change management usage. The acquisition complemented Accenture's suite of tools and capabilities to help its clients achieve the goals of their most significant organizational transformations.

Adding to its footprint in Asia/Pacific Accenture acquired in 2012 Singapore-based Newspage Pte Ltd a provider of distributor management and mobility software that helps consumer goods companies improve their operations sales performance and data visibility.

Earlier in 2012 the company expanded its operations through the purchase of Octagon Research Solutions a provider of clinical and regulatory information management solutions and software for the pharmaceutical industry. The deal gives Accenture a means to provide clinical and regulatory services to pharmaceutical companies.

HISTORY

Accenture traces its history back to the storied accounting firm of Arthur Andersen & Co. Founded by Northwestern University professor and accounting legend Arthur Andersen in 1913 the firm's expanding scope of operations led it into forensic accounting and advising clients on financial reporting processes forming the basis for a management consulting arm. Arthur Andersen led the firm until his death in 1947. His successor Leonard Spacek split off the consulting operations as a separate unit in 1954.

The consulting business grew quickly during the 1970s and 1980s thanks in part to an orgy of US corporate re-engineering. By 1988 consulting accounted for 40% of Andersen's sales. Chafing at sharing profits with the auditors (who faced growing price pressures and a rising tide of legal action due to the accounting irregularities of their clients) the consultants sought more power within the firm. The result was a 1989 restructuring that established Andersen Worldwide (later Andersen) as the parent of two independent units Arthur Andersen and Andersen Consulting (AC). The growing revenue imbalance between the operations remained unresolved however and a year later Arthur Andersen poured gas on the flames by establishing its own business consultancy.

Meanwhile AC continued to expand during the 1990s by forming practices focused on manufacturing finance and government. It addressed the shift from mainframes to PCs by forming alliances with technology heavyweights Hewlett-Packard Sun Microsystems and Microsoft. In 1996 AC teamed up with Internet service provider BBN (acquired by GTE in 1997) to form ServiceNet a joint venture to develop Internet commerce and other systems.

The Andersen family feud took a turn for the worse in 1997 with the retirement of CEO Lawrence Weinbach. A deadlocked vote for a new leader led the board to appoint accounting partner Robert Grafton as CEO angering the consulting partners. Later that year AC asked the International Chamber of Commerce to negotiate a breakup of Andersen Worldwide. George Shaheen to whom many attributed the heightened tensions between the units resigned as CEO of AC in 1999 and was replaced by Joe Forehand.

While the separation dispute dragged on the consulting business grew and diversified amid increasing consolidation in the industry. In 1999 the company moved into e-commerce venture funding with the formation of Andersen Consulting Ventures and in 2000 it inked partnership deals with Microsoft (Microsoft system implementation services) Sun Microsystems (for B2B Internet office supply sales) and BT (Internet-based human resources services).

That year an international arbitrator finally approved AC's separation from its parent ruling that the consultancy must change its name and pay Andersen Worldwide $1 billion (far less than the $15 billion demanded by the accounting partners). Renamed Accenture the company went public in 2001. While the new name (a made-up word) might have struck some as a marketing challenge having an identity distinct from that of its former parent proved to be a stroke of luck for Accenture. Andersen broke apart in 2002 after becoming embroiled in the accounting scandals of energy giant Enron.

In 2004 Accenture successfully bid on a $10 billion 10-year contract to create a system to identify visitors and immigrants coming into the country. Dubbed US-VISIT (United States Visitor and Immigrant Status Indicator Technology) the system was to be employed by the Department of Homeland Security to prevent terrorists from entering the US. However Accenture's bid nearly ran afoul of congressional critics who tried to pass spending amendments barring firms headquartered outside the US from winning security-related business.

Forehand stepped down as CEO of Accenture in 2004 and was replaced by company veteran William Green. Forehand remained chairman until he retired in 2006 when Green was named to that post as well.

Accenture acquired Capgemini's North American health practice in 2005 for $175 million in order to strengthen its offerings to hospitals and health care systems. In 2006 the firm expanded its outsourcing operations by buying NaviSys a leading provider of software for the life insurance industry along with key assets of Kansas-based accountant Savista.

In mid-2008 Accenture swallowed up ATAN an industrial and automation services provider based in Brazil that caters to the mining energy and utilities sectors. It also obtained SOPIA a Tokyo-based consulting firm specializing in Oracle systems integration. During that year Accenture added to its transportation and travel services operations (located within its Products Division) when it bought AddVal Technology. AddVal provided software and technology used for freight order management and the deal enhanced Accenture's ability to integrate and simplify its clients' freight management services capabilities.

In late 2009 Accenture looked to solidify its position in a vital market when it obtained the Symbian professional services unit of Nokia. The unit offers engineering and support services for the Symbian operating system one of the world's most widely used operating systems for smart phones. The acquired operations provided a broad range of embedded software services for mobile devices and were rebranded Accenture Embedded Mobility Services.

Accenture obtained RiskControl a consulting firm based in Brazil in early 2010. Also that year Accenture bought Beijing Genesis Interactive Technology Company an embedded software firm providing mobile software outsourcing services to companies in China. The acquisitions furthered Accenture's penetration into the cutting-edge smart phone support services market.

Focusing on beefing up its Financial Services segment in 2011 Accenture acquired Duck Creek Technologies a provider of software and tools catering to the insurance and health care sectors. At the time of the transaction Duck Creek served about 60 clients throughout North America and the UK.

At the beginning of 2011 Pierre Nanterme the former head of the company's financial services operations was promoted to become the company's newest CEO. Green remains with Accenture as chairman.

EXECUTIVES

Group Chief Executive Accenture Strategy, Mark A. Knickrehm, age 51

Group Chief Executive Financial Services, Richard A. Lumb, age 55, $972,812 total compensation

Chairman and CEO, Pierre Nanterme, age 57, $957,585 total compensation

CFO, David P. Rowland, age 55, $1,136,125 total compensation

Group Chief Executive Growth Markets, Gianfranco Casati, age 57, $967,329 total compensation

COO, Johan G. (Jo) Deblaere, age 54

Group Chief Executive Resources, Jean-Marc Ollagnier, age 55

Group Chief Executive Products, Alexander M. (Sander) van't Noordende, $1,136,125 total compensation

Group Chief Executive Communications Media and Technology, Robert E. (Bob) Sell

Group Chief Executive Health and Public Service, Daniel T. (Dan) London, age 51

Chief Technology and Innovation Officer, Paul Daugherty

Group Chief Executive Accenture Technology Delivery, Bhaskar Ghosh

Group Chief Executive Accenture Digital, Michael R. (Mike) Sutcliff

Group CEO North America, Julie Sweet, age 48, $1,136,125 total compensation

Group Chief Executive Accenture Operations, Debra A. Polishook

Auditors: KPMG LLP

LOCATIONS

HQ: Accenture plc
1 Grand Canal Square, Grand Canal Harbour, Dublin 2
Phone: (353) 1 646 2000
Web: www.accenture.com

2012 Sales

	% of total
Americas	45
Europe Middle East & Africa	40
Asia/Pacific	15
Total	**100**

PRODUCTS/OPERATIONS

2012 Sales

	% of total
Products	23
Communications media & tech	22
Financial services	22
Resources	18
Health & public service	15
Total	**100**

2012 Sales

	% of total
Consulting	56
Outsourcing	44
Total	**100**

Selected Mergers and Acquisitions

FY2013
ChangeTrack Research Pty Ltd (Sydney Australia; analytics-based tools and services)

FY2012
Octagon Research Solutions Inc. (clinical and regulatory information management services and software)

FY2011
Duck Creek Technologies (software and tools for insurance and health care)
CAS Computer Anwendungs- und Systemberatung (CRM and mobility software)

FY2010
Beijing Genesis Interactive Technology Co. (embedded software services)
Knowledge Rules (provider of business solutions utilizing BPM software)
Acceria (technology and consulting business services)
CadenceQuest (customer data and analytics)
Risk Control (risk management)

Selected Practice Areas

Communications and high technology
  Communications
  Electronics and high technology
  Media and entertainment
Products
  Automotive
  Consumer goods and services
  Health and life sciences
  Industrial equipment
  Retail
  Transportation and travel services
Financial services
  Banking
  Capital markets
  Insurance
Resources
  Chemicals
  Energy
  Natural resources
  Utilities
Government

Selected Services

Business consulting
  Customer relationship management
  Finance and performance management
  Human performance
  Strategy
  Supply chain management
Outsourcing
  Application outsourcing
  Business process outsourcing (BPO)
  Customer contact
  Finance and accounting
  Human resources

Learning
  Procurement
  Infrastructure outsourcing
Systems integration and technology
  Enterprise architecture
  Information management
  Infrastructure consulting
  Intellectual property
  Research and development

COMPETITORS

Bain & Company	Computer Sciences
Booz Allen	Corp.
Boston Consulting	Deloitte Consulting
Capgemini	HP Enterprise Services
Capgemini North	IBM
America	McKinsey & Company
Charteris	Unisys

HISTORICAL FINANCIALS

Company Type: Public

Income Statement

FYE: August 31

	REVENUE ($ mil.)	NET INCOME ($ mil.)	NET PROFIT MARGIN	EMPLOYEES
08/16	34,797	4,111	11.8%	384,000
08/15	32,914	3,053	9.3%	358,000
08/14	31,874	2,941	9.2%	305,000
08/13	30,394	3,281	10.8%	275,000
08/12	29,777	2,553	8.6%	257,000
Annual Growth	**4.0%**	**12.6%**	**—**	**10.6%**

2016 Year-End Financials

Debt ratio: 0.1%
Return on equity: 59.9%
Cash ($ mil.): 4,905
Current ratio: 1.35
Long-term debt ($ mil.): 24

No. of shares (mil.): 642
Dividends
  Yield: 1.9%
  Payout: 37.1%
Market value ($ mil.): 73,898

	STOCK PRICE ($) FY Close	P/E High/Low		PER SHARE ($) Earnings	Dividends	Book Value
08/16	115.00	18	14	6.45	2.20	11.76
08/15	94.27	22	16	4.76	2.04	9.44
08/14	81.06	18	15	4.52	1.86	8.73
08/13	72.25	16	12	4.93	1.62	7.44
08/12	61.60	17	13	3.84	1.35	6.13
Annual Growth	**16.9%**	**—**	**—**	**13.8%**	**13.0%**	**17.7%**

ACS Actividades de Construccion y Servicios, S.A.

Turning the rains (and the wind) on the plains of Spain into electricity provides the current for growth at ACS Actividades de Construccioon y Servicios one of Spain's largest construction and infrastructure groups. ACS Group operates in three primary business areas: construction environment and industrial services. The company's activities include civil engineering installation and maintenance for energy facilities transport services and highway management. ACS has grown by investing in such firms as former construction rival Dragados and Germany-based infrastructure giant HOCHTIEF. The group is active in more than 70 countries mainly in Europe and Latin America.

Operations

Of ACS' four business segments (construction environment industrial services and corporate) the construction unit is the largest. Bringing in nearly three-fourths of the group's revenues in 2014 the unit includes subsidiaries Dragados Hochtief and Iridium which are engaged in the construction of civil works and residential and commercial buildings the management of concession activities and mining and real estate ventures. Typical construction projects include roads railways parking garages sports facilities and hospitals. ACS focuses on public-private partnership arrangements for jobs such as public protection housing developments.

Industrial services (including installing and maintaining industrial infrastructure projects in the energy communications and control systems sectors) represented nearly 20% of sales in 2014. ACS has invested in the segment's growth including making investments in renewable energies. The group develops such projects as wind farms and solar energy plants as well as traditional power stations and toll systems.

Environment the smallest segment provides services ranging from road cleaning and waste collection to urban landscaping and (through Clece) building maintenance; it contributed some 7% of sales in 2014.

Geographic Reach

ACS is active in more than 70 countries; its largest markets are the US (accounting for nearly 40% of all sales) Australia Spain Mexico and Germany.

Financial Performance

Note: Growth rates may differ after conversion to US dollars.

After seeing years of growth revenue declined 35% to euro 34.8 billion in 2014 as sales in the construction and industrial services segments fell; this was partially offset by growth in the environment segment. Overall the construction business was sluggish in Spain and industrial services slowed down in that country as the company completed a number of projects. Elsewhere the sale of Hochtief's services business negatively impacted ACS in the rest of Europe while the devaluation of the Australian dollar affected results in the Asia/Pacific region. Activity in Africa also dipped slightly.

Net income has recovered after taking a major loss in fiscal 2012. In 2014 it rose 2% to euro 707 million largely due to a decline in fixed asset depreciation costs and other operating results. Cash flow from operations fell euro 262 million to euro 824 million due to changes in working capital.

Strategy

To maintain growth the group plans to continue expanding in key markets including North America Europe the Asia/Pacific region and Latin America. It is also intent on investing in infrastructure development projects.

HISTORY

Company Background

In war-torn Europe in 1942 the Spanish construction company Obras y Construcciones Industriales (Ocisa) was born. The company soon began a 50-year association with Spain's hydroelectric industry marked by the completion of the dam and reservoir project Presa de Bachimana in 1950. The company built nine more dam and reservoir projects in Spain (including Presa de la Llosa completed in 1997).

As the demand for public works projects decreased and competition increased Spanish constructors began working abroad especially in Latin America where Ocisa was contracted in 1975 to create an irrigation tunnel in Venezuela's Andes.

A six-year economic expansion measured by the success of Spain's "Big Seven" construction companies including #5 Ocisa reached its end in 1992 when the Spanish government the country's biggest builder was forced to cut spending on infrastructure. This triggered consolidation in Spain's construction industry including Ocisa's 1993 acquisition of Construcciones Padros in which Ocisa held a 25% stake. Adopting the new name OCP Construcciones it also absorbed the assets of its installation and assembly subsidiary Compania de la Distribucion de Electricidad (Grupo Cobra).

The slowdown in public works projects continued and companies sought additional pooling of resources and diversification of activities at home and abroad. In 1996 OCP bought a 40% stake in the state-owned construction firm Auxini increased to 100% a year later. Also in 1997 the OCP group led by its president Florentino Perez acquired Gines Navarro Construcciones controlled (79%) by the powerful investment group led by brothers Carlos and Juan March. The two companies combined to create Spain's third-largest construction group Actividades de Construcciones y Servicios or Grupo ACS.

EXECUTIVES

Chairman President and CEO, Florentino Perez Rodr guez, age 69

Chairman and CEO Industrial Services, Eugenio Llorente G mez

Chairman and CEO Turner Construction, Peter J. Davoren, age 61

Chairman and CEO Flatiron, John A. DiCiurcio, age 61

CEO Dragados, Ignacio Segura Suri ±ach

Corporate General Manager, Angel Manuel Garcia Altozano

Chairman and CEO Construction Environment & Logistics and Concesisons; Chairman and CEO Dragados, Marcelino Fern ndez Verdes

General Manager Urbaser, Jose Mar a L pez-Pi ±ol

CEO HOCHTIEF Solutions, Nikolaus Graf von Matuschka, age 53

CEO Iridium, Juan Santamaria Cases

Vice Chairman, Pablo Vallbona Vadell

Executive Vice Chairman, Antonio Garc a Ferrer, age 71

Auditors: DELOITTE, S.L.

LOCATIONS

HQ: ACS Actividades de Construccion y Servicios, S.A.
Avda. Pio XII, 102, Madrid 28036
Phone: (34) 91 343 9200   **Fax:** (34) 91 343 9456
Web: www.grupoacs.com

2013 Sales

	% of total
Asia Pacific	39
Americas	34
Spain	14
Rest of Europe	12
Africa	1
Total	**100**

PRODUCTS/OPERATIONS

2013 Sales

	% of total
Construction	77
Industrial Services	18
Environment	5
Total	**100**

Selected Subsidiaries

Concessions
  Concesiones Viarias Chile S.A. (infrastructures)
  Iridium Concesiones de Infraestructuras S.A.
Construction
  Acainsa S.A. (real estate development)
  Ave Lalin
  Consorcio Tecdra S.A.
  Constructora Norte Sur S.A. (48% Chile)
  Desaladora Barcelona (28%)
  Guadarrama Iv (33%)
  Inmobiliaria Alabega S.A. (real estate development)
  Isla Verde Ute (35%)
  Soterram. Basurto Ute Tecsa-Necso (50%)
  Terminal Aeropuerto (70%)
Environment
  Consenur S.A. (management and treatment of hospital waste)
  Empordanesa de Neteja S.A. (urban solid waste management and street cleaning)
  Mapide S.A. (interior cleaning)
  Publimedia Sistemas Publicitarios S.L. (advertising services)
  RetraOil S.L. (treatment of oils and marpoles)
  Servicios Generales de Jaén S.A. (75% water)
  Somasur S.A. (intermediary company Morocco)
  Urbaser de México S.A. (collection of urban solid waste and street cleaning)
  Urbaser Valencia C.A. (collection of urban solid waste and street cleaning)
  Ute Ecoparc V (20% USW treatment)
  Vertederos de Residuos S.A. (84% VERTRESA collection of urban solid waste and street cleaning)
Industrial Services
  ACS industrial Services LLC (energy production US)
  Actividades de Servicios e Instalaciones Cobra S.A. (auxiliary energy and communications distribution Guatemala)
  Andasol 1 S.A. (energy production)
  API Movilidad S.A. (road maintenance)
  BTOB Construccion Ventures S.L. (administrative management)
  Central Térmica de Mejillones S.A. (engineering supply and construction Chile)
  Cobra Ingeniería de Montajes S.A. (installations and assembly)
  Cobra Perú S.A. (auxiliary energy and communications distribution)
  Coinsal Instalaciones y Servicios S.A. de C.V. (installations and assembly El Salvador)
  Cymi Holding S.A. (securities holding company Brazil)
  Dragados Gulf Construction Ltd. (Saudi Arabia)
  Emurtel S.A. (50% electrical installations)
  Enq S.L. (electrical installations)
  Etra Catalu?a S.A. (electrical installations)
  Extresol-1 S.L. (energy production)
  Gerovitae La Guancha S.A. (senior social and health center operations)
  Humiclima Est S.A. (air conditioning)
  Incro S.A. (50% engineering)
  Infraest. Energéticas Medioambi. Extreme?as S.L. (services)
  Instalaciones y Servicios Codeven C.A. (air conditioning)
  Mantenimiento y Montajes Industriales S.A. (industrial maintenance and assemblies)
  Mexsemi S.A. de C.V. (99.7% assemblies Mexico)
  Opade Organizac. y Promoc de Actividades Deportivas S.A. (athletic activities organization and promotion)
  Parque Eólico Marmellar S.L. (70% energy production)
  Portumasa S.A. (manufacture and sale of electical equipment Portugal)
  Semi Maroc S.A. (99.7% assemblies)
  Serveis Catalans Serveica S.A. (electrical installations)
  SICE LLC. (design construction installation and maintenance of traffic and trade)
  Sistemas Radiantes F. Moyano S.A. (telecommunications)
  Tecnotel de Canarias S.A. (air conditioning)
  Ute C.T. Andasol 1 (80% fossil fuel plant)
  Venezolana de Limpiezas Indust. C.A. (83% VENELIN Venezuela)
Services
  Valdemingomez 2000 S.A. (34% Valdemingómez degasification)

COMPETITORS

Abengoa	Ferrovial
Acciona	Grupo San Jose
Aker Solutions	Hyundai Engineering
Andrade Gutierrez	and Construction
Balfour Beatty	Kellogg Brown & Root

Bechtel	UK
Bilfinger	OHL
Black & Veatch	Odebrecht
Brisa	Salini Impregilo
Cintra	Skanska
DP World	TECNOCOM
FCC Barcelona	VINCI

HISTORICAL FINANCIALS
Company Type: Public

Income Statement
FYE: December 31

	REVENUE ($ mil.)	NET INCOME ($ mil.)	NET PROFIT MARGIN	EMPLOYEES
12/15	38,506	790	2.1%	200,516
12/14	43,201	871	2.0%	217,908
12/13	53,626	965	1.8%	164,750
12/12	51,173	(2,539)	—	164,342
12/11	37,520	1,244	3.3%	164,923
Annual Growth	0.7%	(10.7%)	—	5.0%

2015 Year-End Financials
Debt ratio: 32.0%
Return on equity: 22.4%
Cash ($ mil.): 6,321
Current ratio: 1.11
Long-term debt ($ mil.): 7,809
No. of shares (mil.): 319
Dividends
Yield: —
Payout: —
Market value ($ mil.): 2,634

	STOCK PRICE ($) FY Close	P/E High/Low		PER SHARE ($) Earnings	Dividends	Book Value
12/15	8.25	—	—	2.52	0.00	11.67
12/14	8.25	4	3	2.72	0.00	11.35
Annual Growth	(0.0%)	—	—	(1.9%)	—	0.7%

Adecco Group AG

Any way you stack it Adecco is the world's largest employment agency serving some 100000 clients from more than 5500 offices worldwide. The company primarily provides temporary staffing services but Adecco also offers permanent employee placement project assistance outsourcing and other human resources-related services. Besides its core industrial and office staffing services Adecco maintains six professional lines: Engineering & Technical; Finance & Legal; Human Capital Solutions; Information Technology; Medical & Scientific; and Sales Marketing & Events. Adecco traces its roots to 1957 and has a history of growing through mergers and acquisitions.

EXECUTIVES
Regional Head North America, Robert P. (Bob) Crouch, age 48
Regional Head of Asia Pacific, Christophe Duchatellier, age 54
Regional Head of UK and Ireland, John L. Marshall
Regional Head of Italy Eastern Europe & MENA and India, Sergio Picarelli, age 50, $187,500 total compensation
CEO, Alain Dehaze, age 52, $150,745 total compensation
Regional Head Iberia and South America, Enrique Sanchez, age 50, $161,296 total compensation
CFO, Hans P. van Amstel
Regional Head of France, Christophe Catoir, age 44
Regional Head of Northern Europe, Mark De Smedt
Regional Head of Germany Austria and Switzerland (DACH), Franz-Josef Sch rmann, age 47

Vice Chairman, Thomas C. (Tom) O'Neill, age 71
Chairman, Rolf Dorig, age 59
Auditors: Ernst & Young Ltd.

LOCATIONS
HQ: Adecco Group AG
Saegereistrasse 10, Glattbrugg 8152
Phone: (41) 44 878 88 88   **Fax:** (41) 44 829 88 88
Web: www.adecco.com

2015 sales
	% of total
France	21
North America	21
UK & Ireland	10
Germany & Austria	8
Italy	6
Japan	5
Benelux	5
Lee Hecht Harrison	2
Other	22
Total	**100**

PRODUCTS/OPERATIONS

2015 Sales
	% of total
General Staffing	74
Professional Staffing	23
Solutions	3
Total	**100**

Selected Services
Career Transition
Outsourcing Talent Development and other services
Permanent Placement
Temporary Staffing

COMPETITORS
Insperity	Synergie
Kelly Services	Technical Aid
ManpowerGroup	Corporation
Randstad Holding	Volt Information
Robert Half	

HISTORICAL FINANCIALS
Company Type: Public

Income Statement
FYE: December 31

	REVENUE ($ mil.)	NET INCOME ($ mil.)	NET PROFIT MARGIN	EMPLOYEES
12/15	23,973	8	0.0%	32,000
12/14	24,310	775	3.2%	31,576
12/13	26,850	766	2.9%	31,329
12/12	27,067	496	1.8%	32,987
12/11	26,573	671	2.5%	32,826
Annual Growth	(2.5%)	(66.2%)	—	(0.6%)

2015 Year-End Financials
Debt ratio: 25.1%
Return on equity: 0.2%
Cash ($ mil.): 1,304
Current ratio: 1.31
Long-term debt ($ mil.): 1,995
No. of shares (mil.): 170
Dividends
Yield: 3.1%
Payout: —
Market value ($ mil.): 5,820

	STOCK PRICE ($) FY Close	P/E High/Low		PER SHARE ($) Earnings	Dividends	Book Value
12/15	34.17	874603		0.05	1.08	21.36
12/14	34.31	11	8	4.39	1.08	26.88
12/13	39.83	13	9	4.24	0.94	27.46
12/12	26.45	13	10	2.64	0.95	26.39
12/11	20.86	12	7	3.52	0.00	28.90
Annual Growth	13.1%	—	—	(64.7%)	—	(7.3%)

Adidas AG

From famous athletes to school kids adidas wants to help everyone get in the game. The company sells sports shoes apparel and equipment sporting its iconic three-stripe logo in 160 countries. The #3 sporting goods manufacturer (behind NIKE and Under Armour) focuses on football soccer basketball running and training gear and apparel as well as lifestyle goods including SLVR and Y-3 fashion brands. adidas' wholesale division gets adidas and Reebok products to retailers while the retail group runs its own 2445 Reebok and adidas shops. Other businesses include TaylorMade-adidas Golf and Reebok-CCM Hockey. Founder Adi Dassler brother of PUMA creator Rudi began making shoes in the early 1920s.

Geographic Reach

Germany's adidas rings up more than 40% of its sales in Europe. North America and Greater China contribute 20% and 12% of sales respectively. It also sells and distributes its shoes and apparel in Latin America and other markets in Asia. Key growth markets for the company include North America China Russia Latin America Japan and the UK.

Operations

Adidas produces more than 660 million products. Its brand shoes are the company's cash cow accounting for almost half of total sales. The Reebok brand and TaylorMade-adidas Golf each represent about 10%. While the company operates its own retail stores and sells shoes online wholesaling is the bigger business representing nearly two-thirds of total sales. The company supplies adidas and Reebok brand shoes to retailers.

The Retail segment comprises all business activities relating to the sale of adidas and Reebok products directly to end consumers through own retail and own e-commerce platforms.

TaylorMade-adidas Golf segment includes the four brands –TaylorMade adidas Golf Adams Golf and Ashworth. TaylorMade designs develops and distributes primarily golf clubs balls and accessories. Adidas Golf products include footwear apparel and accessories. Adams Golf designs and distributes golf clubs and a small range of accessories. Ashworth designs and distributes men's and women's golf-inspired apparel and footwear.

Reebok-CCM Hockey designs produces and distributes ice hockey equipment such as sticks skates and protection gear and apparel (mainly under the brand names Reebok Hockey and CCM).

Other brands include Y-3 and Porsche Design Sport by adidas as well as the business activities of the brand Five Ten in the outdoor action sports sector and the adidas NEO label.

Financial Performance

In 2014 adidas' net revenues increased by 11.4% due to the following : Wholesale revenues rose 6% driven by strong growth at adidas while Reebok revenues remained stable; Retail revenues increased 21% as a result of double-digit sales growth at both adidas and Reebok (concept stores factory outlets and concession corners were all up at double-digit rates); while eCommerce grew by 72% on a currency-neutral basis.

Offsetting these gains revenues of Other Businesses decreased 19% due to double-digit sales declines at TaylorMade-adidas Golf partially countered by sales growth at Reebok-CCM Hockey and other centrally managed brands. Net income plummeted by 45% in 2014 driven by higher cost of sales and currency conversion and depreciation and amortization increases which strongly outpaced higher revenues.

In 2014 cash from operating activities grew by 11% due to higher payables to affiliated companies.

Strategy

In 2010 adidas unveiled its strategic business plan –called "Route 2015" –outlining its strategies and objectives for the next five years. The plan set ambitious total group sales growth targets of 45% to 50% (on a currency-neutral basis). Aiming to grow its bottom line faster than its top line adidas hopes to grow annual earnings at a compound annual growth rate of 15% and reach an operating margin of 11% sustainably by 2015. (In 2014 its operating margin was 6.6%.) Three markets singled out for their growth potential are North America Greater China and Russia which are expected to contribute about 50% of the total group growth under the Route 2015 plan. In the US the company believes its brands have enormous opportunity to gain market share by focusing on improved distribution and launching more innovative products.

To fulfill its goal of growth in China adidas says it will add 2500 stores there by the end of 2015 putting upscale outlets in the large cities and teen-targeted casual NEO shops in smaller markets. Other moves include expanding e-commerce through a venture with China's biggest online retailer Taobao.com; sponsoring running competitions; and partnering with workout center chains. Growing its business in Asia in 2014 adidas expanded its own-retail activities in Beijing/China.

Going forward one of the company's strategies for success is to continue offering products with both mass and niche appeal allowing each of its brands to maintain a unique identity. Part of the innovation is a fashion and sport line of apparel from a deal with Giorgio Armani to go with adidas' SLVR and Y-3 lines. Another example is the mi line that combines technology and gear in customizable shoes digital coaches online support heart rate sensing apparel and mobile hardwear to connect it all.

In 2014 it extended its longterm partnership with FIFA (adidas dominates the soccer boot market) until 2030. In 2014 due to the continued weakness in the golf market negative economic developments in Russia/CIS as well as ongoing currency headwinds adidas postponed the delivery of its top- and bottom-line Route 2015 targets. As a result the Group has been undergoing a thorough review of its strategic priorities. To raise cash that year the company announced plans to sell its Rockport brand (which designs and distributes leather footwear for men and women) to a new entity formed by Berkshire Partners for $280 million.

HISTORY

Company Background

adidas grew out of an infamous rift between German brothers Adi and Rudi Dassler who created athletic shoe giants adidas and Puma. As WWI was winding down Adi scavenged for tires rucksacks and other refuse to create slippers gymnastics shoes and soccer cleats at home. His sister cut patterns out of canvas. By 1926 the shoes' success allowed the Dasslers to build a factory. At the 1928 Amsterdam Olympics German athletes first showcased Dassler shoes to the world. In 1936 American Jesse Owens sprinted to Olympic gold in Dassler's double-striped shoes.

Business boomed until the Nazis commandeered the Dassler factory to make boots for soldiers. Although both Rudi and Adi were reportedly members of the Nazi party only Rudi was called to service. Adi remained at home to run the factory. When Allied troops occupied the area Adi made friends with American soldiers –even creating shoes for a soldier who wore them at the 1946 Olympics. Rudi came home from an American prison camp and joined his brother; together they scavenged the war-torn landscape for tank materials and tents to make shoes.

Soon a dispute between the brothers split the business. Rumors circulated that Rudi resented that Adi had failed to use his American connections to help spring him from prison camp. Rudi set up his own factory facing Adi across the River Aurach. The brothers never spoke to each other again except in court. Rudi's company was named Puma and Adi's became adidas. Adi added a third stripe to the Dassler's trademark shoe while Rudi chose a cat's paw in motion. Thus began one of the most intense rivalries in Europe. The children of Puma and adidas employees attended separate elementary schools and the employees even distinguished themselves by drinking different beers.

With Adi's innovations throughout the late 1940s and 1950s (such as the replaceable-cleat soccer shoe) adidas came to dominate the world's athletic shoe market. In the late 1950s it capitalized on the booming US market overtaking the canvas sneakers made by P.F. Flyers and Stride Rite (Keds). The company also initiated the practice of putting logos on sports bags and clothing.

adidas continued to expand globally in the 1960s and 1970s to maintain its dominant position. However a flood of new competitors following the 1972 Munich Olympics and the death of Adi in 1978 signaled the end of an era. As NIKE and Reebok captured the North American market during the 1980s adidas made one of its biggest missteps –it turned down a sneaker endorsement offer from a young Michael Jordan in 1984.

French politician and entrepreneur Bernard Tapie bought the struggling company in 1989 but he stepped down in 1992 amid personal political and business scandals. The next year Robert Louis-Dreyfus became CEO. He shifted production to Asia pumped up the advertising budget and brought in former NIKE marketing geniuses to re-establish the company's identity.

adidas became adidas-Salomon in 1997 with its $1.4 billion purchase of Salomon a French maker of skis and other sporting goods. The company also opened its first high-profile store in Portland Oregon that year. In a 1998 reorganization Louis-Dreyfus sacked Jean-Francois Gautier as Salomon's president in the wake of disappointing sales particularly from TaylorMade Golf Salomon's golf subsidiary.

Amid a 10% slide in revenue several key executives decided to leave the company in 2000 including adidas America CEO Steve Wynne. Citing poor health Louis-Dreyfus soon followed (but remained as chairman); he was replaced by the new CEO of adidas America Ross McMullin who soon after was diagnosed with cancer. Later that year the company announced it would consolidate its apparel under the Heritage label to reinforce its position in the burgeoning casual wear market.

In 2001 Louis-Dreyfus retired as chairman and in March COO Herbert Hainer became chief executive. That year adidas-Salomon opened adidas Originals retail stores in Tokyo and Berlin; that was followed with a New York City store in 2002. Despite slumping sales in the US amid deep discounting by competitors adidas announced in 2003 that it would not offer discounts and still intended to capture 20% of the country's shoe market.

Britain's Barclays Bank PLC became adidas' largest shareholder in 2004 raising its stake to 5.4%. The company changed its name in 2006 to adidas AG.

In May 2008 adidas AG won a $305 million award from a federal jury in Oregon for trademark violation of its three-stripe design by Collective Brands the operator of the Payless and Stride Rite shoe-store chains.

In November 2011 adidas acquired outdoor specialist Five Ten a leading brand in the technical outdoor markets and outdoor action sports community for $25 million.

EXECUTIVES

President Adidas America, Mark King
Member Executive Board Finance, Robin J. Stalker, age 59
Global Operations, Glenn Bennett, age 54
CEO and Director, Kasper B. Rorsted, age 53
Global Brands, Eric Liedtke
CEO TaylorMade-adidas Golf, Ben Sharpe
Chairman, Igor Landau, age 72
Deputy Chairwoman, Sabine Bauer, age 53
Director, Willi Schwerdtle, age 63
Auditors: KPMG AG

LOCATIONS

HQ: Adidas AG
Adi-Dassler-Strasse 1, Herzogenaurach D-91074
Phone: (49) 91 32 84 0   **Fax:** (49) 91 32 84 2241
Web: www.adidas-group.com

2014 Sales

	% of total
Western Europe	28
North America	20
Other Asia markets	14
European Emerging Markets	13
Greater China	13
Latin America	12
Total	**100**

PRODUCTS/OPERATIONS

2014 Sales by Segment

	% of total
Wholesale	65
Retail	26
Other	9
Total	**100**

2014 Sales by Product

	% of total
Footwear	46
Apparel	43
Hardware	11
Total	**100**

2014 Sales by Brand

	% of total
adidas Sports Performance	66
adidas Origianls & Sport Style	24
Reebok	10
Total	**100**

COMPETITORS

ASICS	New Balance
Amer Sports	PUMA SE
Beam Suntory	PVH
Benetton	Quiksilver
Callaway Golf	Ralph Lauren
Columbia Sportswear	Rawlings Sporting
Converse	Goods
Cutter & Buck	Rollerblade
Deckers Outdoor	Rossignol
FUBU	Saucony
Fila Korea	Skechers U.S.A.
Fila USA	Trek Bicycle
Head N.V.	Under Armour
Huffy Corporation	VF Corporation
K-Swiss	Victoria's Secret
Mizuno	Stores
NIKE	

HISTORICAL FINANCIALS
Company Type: Public

Income Statement
FYE: December 31

	REVENUE ($ mil.)	NET INCOME ($ mil.)	NET PROFIT MARGIN	EMPLOYEES
12/15	18,424	690	3.7%	55,555
12/14	17,666	595	3.4%	53,731
12/13	19,951	1,083	5.4%	50,728
12/12	19,616	693	3.5%	46,824
12/11	17,259	867	5.0%	46,824
Annual Growth	1.6%	(5.6%)	—	4.4%

2015 Year-End Financials

Debt ratio: 14.9%	No. of shares (mil.): 200
Return on equity: 11.2%	Dividends
Cash ($ mil.): 1,486	Yield: 1.2%
Current ratio: 1.40	Payout: 17.1%
Long-term debt ($ mil.): 1,593	Market value ($ mil.): 9,712

	STOCK PRICE ($) FY Close	P/E High/Low		PER SHARE ($) Earnings	Dividends	Book Value
12/15	48.51	16	9	3.43	0.60	30.82
12/14	34.51	24	14	2.86	0.74	33.46
12/13	64.23	17	12	5.18	0.63	36.12
12/12	44.80	18	13	3.32	0.46	33.41
12/11	32.61	12	9	4.14	0.36	32.93
Annual Growth	10.4%	—	—	(4.6%)	13.7%	(1.6%)

Adient Plc

LOCATIONS
HQ: Adient Plc
25-28 North Wall Quay, IFSC, Dublin 1
Phone: (41) 4 220 8900
Web: www.adient.com

HISTORICAL FINANCIALS
Company Type: Public

Income Statement
FYE: September 30

	REVENUE ($ mil.)	NET INCOME ($ mil.)	NET PROFIT MARGIN	EMPLOYEES
09/16	16,837	(1,533)	—	75,000
09/15	20,071	475	2.4%	74,000
09/14	22,041	307	1.4%	0
09/13	20,470	187	0.9%	0
Annual Growth	(6.3%)	—	—	—

2016 Year-End Financials

Debt ratio: 27.3%	No. of shares (mil.): 93
Return on equity: (-31.0%)	Dividends
Cash ($ mil.): 2,139	Yield: —
Current ratio: 1.34	Payout: —
Long-term debt ($ mil.): 3,485	Market value ($ mil.): —

	STOCK PRICE ($) FY Close	P/E High/Low		PER SHARE ($) Earnings	Dividends	Book Value
09/16	0.00	—	—	(16.36)	0.00	44.93
Annual Growth	—	—	—	—	—	—

AEGON N.V.

Dutch life insurance giant AEGON has truly gone global. The company is using its expertise in acquisition (US rival Transamerica was its largest catch) and consolidation to build a transnational collection of financial service businesses serving 40 million customers worldwide. Its subsidiaries operate primarily in the US the Netherlands and the UK offering personal and commercial life insurance pensions and annuities and accident and supplemental health insurance as well as retirement and savings advice and management services. AEGON has insurance operations in 25 countries in the Americas Europe and Asia as well as banking operations in the Netherlands.

Operations

The group operates in five segments: Aegon Americas (which includes business units in the US Canada Brazil and Mexico); Aegon the Netherlands; Aegon UK; New Markets (Central and Eastern Europe Asia Spain France as well as variable annuity activities in Europe and asset management); and Holding (financing employee relations and other administrative expenses).

Asset management operations include equity and fixed-income and cover Aegon's insurance subsidiaries as well as third-party clients and insurance-linked products.

Geographic Reach

Aegon's primary operations are in the Netherlands the US and the UK. In Central and Eastern Europe it operates in the Czech Republic Hungary Poland Romania Slovakia Turkey and the Ukraine. The group also operates in Hong Kong Ireland and Spain. Through a distribution agreement with Santander Aegon sells its products in Portugal.

The group also has joint ventures in Brazil China France India Japan and Mexico.

Sales and Marketing

Marketing arm Aegon Direct Affinity Marketings operates in Australia Indonesia Japan Singapore and Thailand. The group sells in the UK through retail advisor channels workplace channels and direct channels. In the Netherlands Aegon offers non-life insurance products through its intermediary channel and through the direct Aegon Online channel and partnerships.

Financial Performance

After seeing a dip in 2011 the group's revenues climbed for two years. In 2014 revenues again slipped 4% to euro 46.3 billion as financial transactions declined; these declines were partially offset by an increase in investment fee and commission income. Following the decline in revenues net income fell 23% to euro 757 million.

Cash flow from operations rose to euro 4.1 billion (versus an outflow of euro 2 billion in 2013); this improvement was due to an increase in cash provided by sales of investments and derivatives.

Strategy

The company has established a strong growth pattern for existing and new international markets largely through strategic acquisitions. Aegon which derives about 60% of its revenues from life insurance premiums is focused on organic expansion in the high-growth regions of Asia Central and Eastern Europe and Latin America. To consolidate its market position in Spain Aegon in mid-2013 inked an exclusive 25-year strategic partnership with Santander. As part of the agreement AEGON acquired a 51% stake in the joint venture which consists of a life insurance company and a non-life insurance company. The venture distributes life and general insurance products through Santander's branch network while Aegon Spain provides back-office services.

Aegon's strategic priorities also include divesting or closing business that don't contribute to its long-term goals. It has divested units worth more than euro 3 billion since 2010 including its stake in France's La Mondiale Participations the UK's Guardian Assurance as well as its US reinsurance activities. It has placed its institutional markets division in run-off.

Other goals include improving customer service to increase client loyalty investing in new distribution channels and strengthening its brands. The group is also focused on growing its online presence and cutting operational costs.

HISTORY
Company Background

AEGON traces its roots to 1844 when former civil servant and funeral society agent J. Oosterhoff founded Algemeene Friesche a burial society for low-income workers. The next year a similar organization Groot-Noordhollandsche was founded. These companies later became insurers and expanded nationwide. Meanwhile Olveh a civil servants' aid group was founded in 1877. The three companies merged in 1968 to form mutual insurer AGO.

AEGON's other operations came from different traditions. Vennootschap Nederland was founded in 1858 as a tontine (essentially a death pool with the survivors taking the pot) by Count A. Langrand-Dumonceau an ex-French Foreign Legionnaire from Belgium. In 1913 the company merged with Eerste Nederlandsche whose accident and health division had been previously spun off as Nieuwe Eerste Nederlandsche.

A year after Vennootschap was founded C. F. W. Wiggers van Kerchem founded a similar scheme Nillmij in the Dutch East Indies. The government promoted Nillmij to colonial civil servants and military people and for a while the company enjoyed a monopoly in the colony. Nillmij's Indonesian operations were nationalized after independence in 1957 but its Dutch subsidiaries continued to operate. All insurers were hit by fast-growing postwar government social programs. As a result industry consolidation came early to the Netherlands. In 1969 Eerste Nederlandsche Nieuwe Eerste Nederlandsche and Nillmij merged to form Ennia.

AGO demutualized in 1978 and became AGO Holding N.V. which was owned by Vereniging AGO. Meanwhile the shrinking Dutch insurance market forced companies to look overseas. AGO moved into the US in 1979 by buying Life Investors; by 1982 half of its sales came from outside the Netherlands. Ennia meanwhile expanded in Europe (it entered Spain in 1980) and the US (buying Arkansas-based National Old Line Insurance in 1981).

AGO and Ennia merged in 1983 to form AEGON. Vereniging AGO became Vereniging AEGON and received a 49% stake in the combined entity. (This stake was later reduced.) The company made more purchases at home and abroad and spent much of the rest of the decade assimilating operations.

AEGON's US units accounted for about 40% of sales in the mid-1980s and the firm increased that figure with acquisitions. In 1986 it bought Baltimore-based Monumental Corp. (life and health insurance) and expanded the company's US penetration.

This left AEGON underrepresented in Europe as deregulation paved the way for economic union and social service cutbacks spurred opportunities in private financial planning in the region. So in the 1990s AEGON began buying European companies including Regency Life (UK 1991) and Allami Biztosito (Hungary 1992). It formed an alliance with Mexico's Grupo Financiero Banamex in 1994. This reduced its reliance on US sales. It continued buying specialty operations in the US particularly asset management lines.

In 1997 AEGON began to concentrate on life insurance and financial services and shed its other operations. It bought the insurance business of Providian (now part of Washington Mutual) and sold noncore lines such as auto coverage. The next year it sold FGH Bank (mortgages) to Germany's Bayerische Vereinsbank (now Bayerische Hypotheken und Vereinsbank) and in 1999 sold auto insurer Worldwide Insurance.

That year AEGON expanded further in the US with the $9.7 billion purchase of Transamerica and bought the life and pensions businesses of the UK's Guardian Royal Exchange. In 2000 the company sold Labouchere N.V. a Dutch banking subsidiary to Dexia. Also in 2000 AEGON acquired UK-based third-party administrator HS Administrative Services.

Following the Transamerica acquisition the company divested several assets to focus on life insurance and pensions. In 2003 and 2004 diverse parts of Transamerica Finance (including its real estate tax unit and trailer leasing business) were sold to various companies including First American GE Commercial Finance and a joint venture held by Goldman Sachs and Cerberus Capital Management.

EXECUTIVES

CEO AEGON Continental Europe, Marco Keim, age 55
CEO, Alexander R. (Alex) Wynaendts, age 57, $864,583 total compensation
CEO AmericasMember Management Board;, Mark W. Mullin, age 54
CEO AGEON Asset Management, Sarah A. C. Russell, age 54
CFO, Matthew J. Rider
CEO Aegon UK Member Management Board Aegis N.V., Adrian Grace, age 53
Chief Risk Officer, Allegra van H Ŋell-Patrizi, age 42
Global CTO, Mark Bloom, age 51
CEO AEGON the Netherlands, Maarten Edixhoven
Vice Chairman, Shemaya Levy, age 69
Chairman, Robert J. Routs, age 70
Auditors: PricewaterhouseCoopers Accountants N.V.

LOCATIONS

HQ: AEGON N.V.
 Aegonplein 50, P.O. Box 85, The Hague 2501 CB
Phone: (31) 70 3445458
Web: www.aegon.com

2014 Sales

	% of total
The Americas	42
UK	23
The Netherlands	24
Other regions	11
Total	**100**

PRODUCTS/OPERATIONS

2014 Revenue

	% of total
Life insurance	56
Investment income	27
Accident & health insurance	8
Fee and commission income	7
General insurance	2
Total	**100**

Selected Subsidiaries and Affiliates
The Americas
 AEGON USA LLC Cedar Rapids Iowa (US)
 Transamerica Advisors Life Insurance Company Little Rock Arkansas (US)
 Transamerica Advisors Life Insurance Company of New York New York New York (US)
 Transamerica Premier Life Insurance Company (formerly Monumental Life Insurance Company Cedar Rapids Iowa) (US)
 Stonebridge Casualty Insurance Company Columbus Ohio (US)
 Stonebridge Life Insurance Company Rutland Vermont (US)
 Transamerica Financial Life Insurance Company Inc. Purchase New York (US)
 Transamerica Life Insurance Company Cedar Rapids Iowa (US)
 Western Reserve Life Assurance Co. of Ohio Columbus Ohio (US)
 Transamerica Life Canada Toronto Ontario (Canada)
The Netherlands
 AEGON Bank NV Utrecht
 AEGON Levensverzekering NV The Hague
 AEGON Schadeverzekering NV The Hague
 OPTAS Pensioenen NV Rotterdam
The UK
 Scottish Equitable plc Edinburgh
 Origen Financial Services Ltd. London
 Positive Solutions (Financial Services) Ltd. Newcastle
Other regions
 AEGON Espa?a S.A. Madrid Spain (99.98%)
 AEGON Magyarország Általános Biztosító Zrt. Budapest Hungary
 AEGON Towarzystwo Ubezpieczeń na Życie Spółka Akcyjna. Warsaw Poland
 AEGON Asset Management Company Mumbai India (75%)

Selected Joint Ventures
AEGON Sony Life Insurance Cy (50%) life insurance Tokyo
AEGON-CNOOC Life Insurance Company Ltd (50%) life insurance Shanghai
AMVEST Vastgoed BV (50%) property management and development; Utrecht Netherlands
CAN Vida y Pensiones Sociedad Anónima de Seguros (50%) life insurance and pension; Pamplona Spain
Caixa Terrassa Vida y Pensiones Sociedad Anónima de Seguros (50%) life and accident insurance and pension; Terrassa Spain

COMPETITORS

AIG
AXA
Achmea
Allianz
Allstate
American General
Ameriprise
Aviva
Aviva Life Insurance India
BMO Financial Group
Canada Life
Delta Lloyd
Desjardins Financial Security
E-L Financial
FMR
Fidelity & Guaranty Life
Franklin Templeton
Generali Deutschland
ING
Industrial Alliance Insurance and Financial Servic
Jackson National Life
John Hancock Financial Services
Legal & General Group
Lincoln Financial Group
Lloyds Banking Group
Manulife Financial
MassMutual
MetLife
Munich Re Group
Mutual of Omaha
Nationwide
New York Life
Old Mutual
OppenheimerFunds
Power Corporation of Canada
Primerica
Principal Financial
Prudential
Prudential plc
Putnam
RBC Insurance
Rabobank Group
SNS REAAL
Standard Life
Sun Life
Swiss Life
Symetra
T. Rowe Price
The Hartford
The Vanguard Group
Western & Southern Financial
Zurich Insurance Group

HISTORICAL FINANCIALS
Company Type: Public

Income Statement

	ASSETS ($ mil.)	NET INCOME ($ mil.)	INCOME AS % OF ASSETS	FYE: December 31 EMPLOYEES
12/15	454,391	774	0.2%	31,530
12/14	515,941	918	0.2%	26,981
12/13	487,013	1,346	0.3%	26,891
12/12	482,493	2,017	0.4%	24,407
12/11	446,987	1,124	0.3%	25,288
Annual Growth	**0.4%**	**(8.9%)**	**—**	**5.7%**

2015 Year-End Financials

Return on assets: 0.1%	Dividends
Return on equity: 2.5%	Yield: 4.7%
Long-term debt ($ mil.): —	Payout: 88.8%
No. of shares (mil.): —	Market value ($ mil.): —
Sales ($ mil): 31,652	

	STOCK PRICE ($) FY Close	P/E High/Low		PER SHARE ($) Earnings	Dividends	Book Value
12/15	5.67	31	20	0.29	0.27	11.19
12/14	7.50	29	24	0.35	0.30	12.62
12/13	9.48	26	17	0.50	0.29	16.52
12/12	6.44	10	6	0.88	0.23	20.11
12/11	4.02	—	—	(0.08)	0.00	17.69
Annual Growth 9.0% (10.8%)		**—**	**—**	**—**	**—**	**—**

Aeon Co. Ltd. (Japan)

Japanese giant AEON CO. has enough retail ventures to last for eons. The holding company has about 180 subsidiaries and 25 affiliated companies. It runs the Aeon and Jusco chains of general merchandise stores and Japan's #1 supermarket chain with 1300 stores under the MaxValu and other banners as well as 3500-plus MINISTOP convenience stores. AEON also operates specialty chains including The Body Shop and Laura Ashley stores in Japan. It has a joint venture in Japan with Sports Authority and also operates HapYcom a leading drugstore chain in Japan. Other operations include shopping center development and financial services. Facing slow growth at home AEON is expanding in China and other Asian economies.

To that end AEON's China-based subsidiary and its MaxValu supermarket chain in 2012 formed a joint venture to operate supermarkets in China.

Sales across the vast AEON group inched up less than 1% in fiscal 2011 (ends February) vs. the previous year. Sales in Japan rose 4% while sales in the rest of Asia fell.

AEON has adopted a holding company structure in a bid to increase its responsiveness to changing (mostly negative) retail trends in Japan where it rings up about 95% of its total sales. A prolonged economic slump aging and shrinking population and weakness in the supermarket and department store sectors have the Japanese retailer looking abroad for future growth. Important Asian markets for AEON include China Hong Kong Malaysia South Korea and Thailand. The company beat a hasty retreat from North America with the sale of its majority stake in ladies apparel chain The Talbots in 2010 to better focus on its retail and financial service operations in Asia.

To grow in China AEON established a subsidiary in Shenzhen and greatly increased its investment there. At the end of fiscal 2011 (ends February) AEON had about 80 stores in China including specialty and general merchandise stores and supermarkets. Also AEON operates two mall-style shopping centers located in Beijing and in Huizhou northeast of Shenzhen. The malls are populated by specialty shops including AEON-owned banners such as Jusco and The Body Shop.

To adapt to changing demographics in its home country AEON is focusing on the "senior market" by developing products especially for seniors and developing senior-friendly floor plans and stores as well as services. The company's My Basket chain of more than 220 small-size urban supermarkets was developed specifically to serve Japan's aging and increasingly urban population. In early 2012 the retailer spun off its My Basket division into a wholly-owned subsidiary with the aim of tripling its store count in the Tokyo metro area by the end of fiscal 2013.

Among Japanese retailers AEON is one of the most proactive in preparing to defend its business from foreign competitors including the world's #1 retailer Wal-Mart and Britain's Tesco. To compete it has cut prices and distribution costs adopted western sales techniques and has acquired smaller retailers. The company is upgrading its computer systems to rival those of US giant Wal-Mart. Also AEON beat out Wal-Mart to buy eight hypermarkets in Japan operated by France's Carrefour which abandoned the Japanese market. In mid-2012 AEON agreed to acquired a 50% stake in Tesco Japan a subsidiary of UK's largest retailer Tesco plc for just 1 yen. Tesco Japan operates about 120 small Tesco and Tsurukame supermarkets in and around Tokyo. AEON is expected to acquire the remainder of Tesco Japan in the future.

EXECUTIVES

President, Motoya Okada, age 64
Group COO, Yoshiki Mori, age 66
VP; President AEON Mall, Soichi Okazaki
EVP, Shouhei Murai
EVP, Masaaki Toyoshima
VP IT Innovation, Hidenori Osano
CFO, Akinori Yamashita
EVP, Hiroshi Yokoo
Auditors: Deloitte Touche Tohmatsu LLC

LOCATIONS

HQ: Aeon Co. Ltd. (Japan)
1-5-1 Nakase, Mihama-ku, Chiba 261-8515
Phone: (81) 43 212 6042
Web: www.aeon.info

2015 Sales

	% of total
Japan	92
ASEAN	4
China	3
Other	1
Total	**100**

PRODUCTS/OPERATIONS

2015 Sales

	% of total
GMS	45
Supermarket DiscountStore and Small-sizedStore	29
SpecServices and Specialty Store	10
Financial Services	4
Shopping Center Development	3
ASEAN	3
China	2
Other	4
Adjustments	0
Total	**100**

Selected Store Names

Abilities Jusco (CDs DVDs and books)
Asbee (shoe stores)
Blue Grass (apparel for teenage girls)
Claire' s Nippon (women' s clothing)
Cox (family casual clothing)
HapYcom (drugstores)
Home Wide Corp. (home centers)
JUSCO (apparel food and household item superstores)
JUS-Photo (film developing)
Laura Ashley Japan (clothing and home furnishings)
Maxvalu (supermarkets)
Mega Sports (Sports Authority stores)
MINISTOP (convenience stores)
MYCAL Corporation (supermarkets)
My Basket (small-scale supermarkets)
Nustep (family footwear stores)
Petcity (pets & pet supplies)
Sports Authority (sporting goods)

COMPETITORS

A.S. Watson	Ito-Yokado
Carrefour	METRO AG
Costco Wholesale	Rakuten
Dairy Farm	Seiyu
International	Seven & i
Fast Retailing	Takashimaya
Heiwado	Tesco
Isetan Mitsukoshi	The Gap

HISTORICAL FINANCIALS

Company Type: Public

Income Statement

FYE: February 29

	REVENUE ($ mil.)	NET INCOME ($ mil.)	NET PROFIT MARGIN	EMPLOYEES
02/16	72,383	53	0.1%	135,058
02/15	59,323	352	0.6%	126,440
02/14	62,775	447	0.7%	109,523
02/13	61,696	810	1.3%	91,646
02/12	64,736	830	1.3%	81,483
Annual Growth	**2.8%**	**(49.7%)**	**—**	**13.5%**

2016 Year-End Financials

Debt ratio: 0.2%
Return on equity: 0.5%
Cash ($ mil.): 6,515
Current ratio: 0.98
Long-term debt ($ mil.): 12,533
No. of shares (mil.): 841
Dividends
Yield: —
Payout: —
Market value ($ mil.): 11,124

	STOCK PRICE ($) FY Close	P/E High/Low		Earnings	PER SHARE ($) Dividends	Book Value
02/16	13.22	—	—	0.06	0.00	19.14
02/15	10.67	—	—	0.42	0.00	18.23
02/14	12.14	—	—	0.49	0.25	19.55
02/13	11.27	—	—	0.95	0.43	19.86
02/12	12.66	—	—	0.95	0.26	20.72
Annual Growth	**1.1%**	**—**	**—**	**(49.4%)**	**—**	**(2.0%)**

Ageas NV

Auditors: KPMG Reviseurs d'Entreprises/Bedrijfsrevisren

LOCATIONS

HQ: Ageas NV
Rue du Marquis 1, Brussels 1000
Phone: (32) 2 557 57 11   **Fax:** (32) 2 557 57 50
Web: www.ageas.com

HISTORICAL FINANCIALS

Company Type: Public

Income Statement

FYE: December 31

	ASSETS ($ mil.)	NET INCOME ($ mil.)	INCOME AS % OF ASSETS	EMPLOYEES
12/15	113,807	838	0.7%	11,919
12/14	125,876	578	0.5%	12,204
12/13	131,802	784	0.6%	13,071
12/12	127,999	979	0.8%	13,335
12/11	117,189	(747)	—	12,557
Annual Growth	**(0.7%)**	**—**		**(1.3%)**

2015 Year-End Financials

Return on assets: 0.7%
Return on equity: 7.1%
Long-term debt ($ mil.): —
No. of shares (mil.): 212
Sales ($ mil): 14,940
Dividends
Yield: 2.8%
Payout: 32.7%
Market value ($ mil.): 9,845

	STOCK PRICE ($) FY Close	P/E High/Low		Earnings	PER SHARE ($) Dividends	Book Value
12/15	46.38	13	9	3.89	1.30	58.37
12/14	35.47	19	14	2.59	2.81	56.65
12/13	42.81	18	13	3.43	2.55	51.83
12/12	30.25	10	1	4.13	0.00	56.35
12/11	1.52	—	—	(2.97)	0.00	41.71
Annual Growth	**135.0%**	**—**	**—**			**8.8%**

Agricultural Bank of China

Agricultural Bank of China (ABC) provides a veritable alphabet soup of products and services to customers across China. Boasting assets of $2.6 trillion and more than 23600 branches across China the commercial bank is its home country's (and the world's) third-largest bank. Beyond providing retail and commercial banking and lending services to agricultural industrial commercial and transportation enterprises in rural areas the bank also offers credit cards treasury management investment banking fund management private banking and life insurance products and services. Founded in 1951 ABC also operates around 10 overseas branches in locations including Hong Kong and Singapore and representative offices in London and Tokyo.

Operations

ABC divides its banking operations into three segments: Corporate Banking (54% of total operating income in 2014) Retail Banking (36%) and treasury (9%). By the end of 2014 ABC had 3.45 million corporate banking customers (up from

2.81 million in 2011) and 456 million retail customers (up from 395 million in 2011). About 64% of its loan assets were corporate loans in 2014 while retail loans and overseas loans made up 30% and 5% of its loan portfolio respectively. ABC's net interest income made up about 82% of ABC's total operating income in 2014 while 15% came from net fee and commission income including bank card fees (4%) settlement and clearing fees (4%) agency commissions (4%) consultancy and advisory fees (2%) electronic banking service fees (1%) custody and fiduciary service fees (less than 1%) and various other miscellaneous income sources. Geographic Reach

Most of ABC's operating income in 2014 came from customers located in Western China (21%) the Yangtze River Delta (19%) and the Bohai Rim (16%). The bank's overseas operations brought in 2% of its operating income. Financial PerformanceNote: Growth rates may differ after conversion to US dollars. This analysis uses financials from the company's annual report. ABC's revenues and profits have been rising over the past several years mostly thanks to aggressive loan business growth (its loan assets grew 60% from 2009 through 2014) but also thanks to its expansion of fee-based business lines.

The he bank's revenue grew double digits to RMB$801.25 billion ($130.2 billion) mostly thanks to higher interest income as its loan assets grew by 9% to nearly RMB$8 trillion ($1.3 trillion); medium and long-term corporate loans and retail loan growth led most of the growth. The bank's loan yields also rose by eight basis points to 6.06% as it improved its mix of loan business also boosting interest income. Fee and commission income dipped by around 4% mostly as its consultancy and advisory fees (and other investment banking business) declined during the year. Higher revenue and a decrease in the bank's cost-to-income ratio drove ABC's net income up 8% to RMB$179.51 billion ($29.2 billion). The bank's operating cash levels also improved modestly to RMB$34.62 billion ($5.6 billion) with the higher cash earnings.

Strategy

ABC in late 2014 remained "committed to catering to the needs of Sannong and capitalizing on the synergy between the Urban and County areas across China." The company's business in urban areas has been growing and made up 62.2% of its operating income in 2014 up from 60% in 2013. The company also in 2014 continued to grow its higher-margin investment banking and private banking businesses. That year it established private banking departments in 30 branches and grew its private banking customer base of high net worth individuals to 57000 with some RMB$640 billion ($104 billion) in assets under custody.

Beyond China it also looked to continue its international expansions plans and provide a variety of services "to become an international first-class large-scale commercial bank."

Company Background ABC completed one of the world's largest initial public offerings in 2010 raising more than $22 billion. Prior to the listing ABC was the only non-listed bank among the big four state-owned commercial banks in China. (The others are Bank of China China Construction Bank and Industrial and Commercial Bank of China.) The money raised in the IPO was used to strengthen the bank's capital base.

EXECUTIVES

EVP, Cai Huaxiang, age 56
Executive Director and EVP, Lou Wenlong, age 58
EVP and Secretary Party Discipline Committee, Gong Chao
EVP, Wang Wei
EVP, Li Zhenjiang

Vice Chairman, Huan Zhao
Chairman, Zhou Mubing
Auditors: PricewaterhouseCoopers Zhong Tian LLP

LOCATIONS

HQ: Agricultural Bank of China
No. 69, Jianguomen Nei Avenue, Dongcheng District, Beijing 100005
Phone: (86) 10 85109619   Fax: (86) 10 85108557
Web: www.abchina.com

2011 Sales

	% of total
Yangtze River Delta	22
Western China	21
Bohai Rim	15
Head Office	13
Pearl River Delta	13
Central China	12
Northeastern China	3
Overseas & other	1
Total	**100**

PRODUCTS/OPERATIONS

2011 Sales

	% of total
Corporate banking	58
Retail banking	36
Treasury operations	6
Total	**100**

COMPETITORS

Bank of China
China Construction Bank
China Development Bank
China Merchants Bank
Hua Xia Bank
Industrial and Commercial Bank of China
Shenzhen Development Bank

HISTORICAL FINANCIALS

Company Type: Public

Income Statement

FYE: December 31

	ASSETS ($ mil.)	NET INCOME ($ mil.)	INCOME AS % OF ASSETS	EMPLOYEES
12/15	2,739,437	27,805	1.0%	514,370
12/14	2,573,832	28,915	1.1%	517,671
12/13	2,405,410	27,472	1.1%	513,750
12/12	2,124,449	23,273	1.1%	501,762
12/11	1,855,232	19,370	1.0%	490,121
Annual Growth	**10.2%**	**9.5%**	**—**	**1.2%**

2015 Year-End Financials

Return on assets: 1.0%	Dividends
Return on equity: 16.1%	Yield: 6.0%
Long-term debt ($ mil.): —	Payout: 698.4%
No. of shares (mil.): —	Market value ($ mil.): —
Sales ($ mil): 129,099	

	STOCK PRICE ($) FY Close	P/E High/Low	PER SHARE ($) Earnings	Dividends	Book Value
12/15	10.22	25 17	0.08	0.62	0.57
12/14	12.62	23 18	0.09	0.60	0.51
12/13	12.33	29 19	0.08	0.52	0.43
12/12	12.60	29 20	0.07	0.42	0.37
12/11	10.63	43 20	0.06	0.17	0.32
Annual Growth	**(1.0%)**	**— —**	**8.8%**	**37.3%**	**15.9%**

AIA Group Ltd.

What's decades old brand brand new named "American" but operates in Asia? American International Assurance —better known as AIA Group! The life insurance and wealth management company operates in 17 countries across Asia and the Pacific. It offers life insurance credit insurance employee benefits and pension services to its corporate clients. For individuals the company provides basic life insurance along with savings investment and retirement products. Founded in 1919 it was the original business that would later grow to become American International Group (AIG) and was a cornerstone of that company's Asia-based operations. However in 2010 AIG spun off the business through a public offering.

Operations

AIA's reportable segments are Hong Kong (including Macau) Thailand Singapore (including Brunei) Malaysia China Korea Other Markets and Group Corporate Centre. Except for the latter segment they all provide life accident and health insurance and distribute savings plans and related financial services. Through its extensive network of agents partners and employees across the region AIA serves more than 28 million individual policyholders and more than 16 million participating members of group insurance schemes.

Geographic Reach

The company has operations in 17 countries in the Asia/Pacific region with the notable exception of Japan. (AIG kept its Japanese holdings separate.) It owns branches and subsidiaries in Hong Kong Thailand Singapore Malaysia China Korea the Philippines Australia Indonesia Taiwan Vietnam New Zealand Macau Brunei Sri Lanka; it also owns a minority stake in an Indian joint venture and has a representative office in Myanmar.

Sales and Marketing

AIA markets its products through agents partners and employees throughout the region.

Financial Performance

In 2014 revenue increased 16% to $25.4 billion primarily on growth of new business. China and Hong Kong in particular performed well as did Malaysia Thailand and Singapore. Net income increased 22% to $3.4 billion that year driven by the higher revenue.

Cash flow from operations fell 30% to $744 million due to higher financial investments and an increase in taxes paid.

Strategy

While its roots are deep in China the company is looking to grow in markets with underdeveloped life insurance markets including India the Philippines and Vietnam. Its growth plans include selling its individual insurance products through banks. In 2013 it reached a bancassurance agreement with Citibank that encompasses 11 markets in the Asia/Pacific.

The company is also expanding the scope of its offerings to attract new customers. In 2014 AIA introduced a comprehensive critical illness product for families and a new disability income plan targeting the middle class.

EXECUTIVES

Executive Director and Group Chief Executive and President, Mark E. Tucker, age 58
Group CFO, Garth Jones
Regional Chief Executive, Gordon Watson
Regional Chief Executive, Ng Keng Hooi
Group COO, Simeon Preston
Group Chief Investment Officer, John Tai-Wo Chu
CEO AIA Singapore, Patrick Teow

Regional Chief Executive Malaysia Korea Sri Lanka India and Cambodia, William Lisle, age 51
Chairman, Edmund S.W. Tse, age 78
Auditors: PricewaterhouseCoopers

LOCATIONS

HQ: AIA Group Ltd.
35/F, AIA Central, No. 1 Connaught Road Central,
Phone: (852) 2832 1800   **Fax:** (852) 2834 1753
Web: www.aia.com

2014 Sales

	% of total
Hong Kong	24
Thailand	19
Singapore	16
Malaysia	11
China	10
Korea	9
Other markets	10
Group corporate	1
Total	**100**

PRODUCTS/OPERATIONS

2014 Sales

	% of total
Net premiums & fee income	67
Investment returns	32
Other operating revenue	1
Total	**100**

COMPETITORS

AXA Asia Pacific	Chubb Limited
Aviva	MetLife
Cathay Life Insurance	Ping An Insurance
China Insurance	Sun Life
China Life Insurance	
China Pacific	
Insurance	

HISTORICAL FINANCIALS

Company Type: Public

Income Statement

FYE: November 30

	ASSETS ($ mil.)	NET INCOME ($ mil.)	INCOME AS % OF ASSETS	EMPLOYEES
11/15	167,622	2,691	1.6%	20,000
11/14	166,919	3,450	2.1%	20,000
11/13	146,585	2,822	1.9%	26,000
11/12	134,439	3,019	2.2%	18,000
11/11	114,461	1,600	1.4%	20,000
Annual Growth	10.0%	13.9%	—	0.0%

2015 Year-End Financials

Return on assets: 1.6%
Return on equity: 8.9%
Long-term debt ($ mil.): —
No. of shares (mil.): —
Sales ($ mil): 23,274

Dividends
  Yield: 1.0%
  Payout: 109.2%
Market value ($ mil.): —

	STOCK PRICE ($) FY Close	P/E High/Low	Earnings	Dividends	Book Value
11/15	24.12	130 93	0.22	0.24	2.44
11/14	23.12	81 62	0.29	0.19	2.56
11/13	20.31	88 65	0.24	0.17	2.05
11/12	15.62	65 46	0.25	0.15	2.22
11/11	12.53	116 79	0.13	0.05	1.77
Annual Growth	17.8%	— —	14.1%	48.5%	8.4%

Air China Ltd

A leading people-mover in the country with the world's largest population Air China provides domestic and international passenger and cargo transportation. From hubs in Beijing Chengdu and Shanghai the carrier serves more than 150 destinations —mainly in China but also in more than 30 other countries —with a fleet of about 275 aircraft. Air China extends its offerings as a member of the Star Alliance a global marketing and code-sharing partnership led by United Airlines and Lufthansa. (Code-sharing allows airlines to sell tickets on one another's flights.) The Chinese government through China National Aviation Holding Company (CNAHC) controls Air China.

Besides its Star Alliance connections Air China maintains an alliance with Hong Kong-based Cathay Pacific Airways that includes joint operation of service between Beijing and Hong Kong. The carriers also are connected through cross-shareholdings; each owns about 18% of the other. In a move to solidify its presence in Hong Kong even further in mid-2009 Air China upped its stake in Cathay to about 30%.

Air China provides freight service through its majority stake in Air China Cargo. In mid-2010 Cathay Pacific and Air China agreed to create a cargo airline using Air China Cargo as the platform. The joint venture is being formed to take a chunk out of the 70% market share of China's international air cargo that is being handled by foreign carriers including Air France Lufthansa and Cargolux.

Air China also has interests in several other airlines including Air Macau and two mainland Chinese regional carriers Shandong Airlines and Shenzhen Airlines as well as stakes in companies that provide aircraft engineering and maintenance catering and ground handling services. In March 2010 Air China upped its stake in Shenzhen Airlines to 51% (from 25%). It had previously taken over management of the carrier late in 2009 after Shenzhen Airlines' major shareholder Li Zeyuan was arrested; his company Shenzhen Huirun Investments was liquidated.

Air China's a corporate aircraft branch provides services including aircraft management chartering consulting and ground handling services. Based on demand from business passengers forecasts predict that China will require as many as 1200 corporate aircraft in the next decade. Realizing the opportunity Air China (80% stake) and the Beijing government (20% stake) formed a joint venture in early 2011 to expand services to corporate aircraft.

Although Air China has been a public company since its IPO in 2004 it is still considered China's national flag carrier and as such the company provides air transportation to Chinese government leaders and other official delegations.

EXECUTIVES

President, Zhiyong Song
Chairman, Jianjiang Cai
Vice Chairman, Yinxiang Wang
Auditors: KPMG

LOCATIONS

HQ: Air China Ltd
5th Floor, CNAC House, 12 Tung Fai Road, Hong Kong International Airport,
Phone:
Web: www.airchina.com.cn

2014 Sales

	% of total
China	64
Europe	11
North America	9
Hong Kong Macao and Taiwan	6
Japan & Korea	5
Asia Pacific and Others	5
Total	**100**

PRODUCTS/OPERATIONS

2014 Sales

	% of total
Air traffic	96
Other	4
Total	**100**

COMPETITORS

Aeroflot	Delta Air Lines
American Airlines Group	Garuda Indonesia
British Airways	Hainan Airlines
China Airlines	Japan Airlines
China Eastern Airlines	Korean Air
China Southern Airlines	Qantas
	Singapore Airlines

HISTORICAL FINANCIALS

Company Type: Public

Income Statement

FYE: December 31

	REVENUE ($ mil.)	NET INCOME ($ mil.)	NET PROFIT MARGIN	EMPLOYEES
12/15	16,070	1,087	6.8%	77,374
12/14	16,335	615	3.8%	68,553
12/13	15,626	539	3.4%	64,854
12/12	15,289	743	4.9%	25,269
12/11	14,829	1,125	7.6%	24,474
Annual Growth	2.0%	(0.8%)	—	33.3%

2015 Year-End Financials

Debt ratio: 7.5%
Return on equity: 12.4%
Cash ($ mil.): 1,099
Current ratio: 0.40
Long-term debt ($ mil.): 13,363

No. of shares (mil.): —
Dividends
  Yield: 0.0%
  Payout: 144.4%
Market value ($ mil.): —

	STOCK PRICE ($) FY Close	P/E High/Low	Earnings	Dividends	Book Value
12/15	15.95	43 22	0.09	0.13	0.70
12/14	16.17	54 36	0.05	0.11	0.66
12/13	14.81	73 48	0.04	0.15	0.68
12/12	17.19	44 30	0.06	0.32	0.62
12/11	14.81	44 22	0.09	0.32	0.57
Annual Growth	1.9%	— —	(1.1%)	(20.4%)	5.5%

Air France-KLM

Air France and KLM represent years of French and Dutch airline tradition but Air France-KLM represents a first: a holding company made up of two national airlines. Together Air France-KLM is the second-largest airline in Europe after Deutsche Lufthansa and one of the largest in the world. Through its operating units the company serves more than 315 destinations in about 115 countries with a fleet of some 540 aircraft. Air France and KLM operate independently from hubs in Paris and Amsterdam but have coordinated their operations both as sister companies and as members of the SkyTeam alliance which also includes Alitalia Delta Air Lines and Korean Air Lines.

Geographic ReachThe Air France-KLM network is organized around its hubs at Paris-Charles de Gaulle and Amsterdam-Schiphol. With these two major hubs the company links Europe to the rest of the world spanning 316 destinations in 115 countries.

OperationsAir France-KLM offers passenger transportation cargo transportation and aircraft maintenance services and transported 87.4 million passengers and 1.3 million tons of cargo in 2015. It has a fleet of 546 aircraft in operation.

Financial Performance

The company's net sales decreased by euro 608 million from 2013 to 2014 due to decreased sales from its passenger and cargo businesses. The company also suffered net losses in 2013 and 2014 due to impairment charges and negative impacts from fuel hedges.

Strategy

Air France-KLM has identified three main growth areas: Asia where it plans to reinforce its existing partnerships and develop new ones with airlines which are similar to its own airlines in size; the European leisure market where it will accelerate Transavia's growth; and the maintenance market where it plans to continue to make acquisitions to supplement its organic growth.

EXECUTIVES

EVP Fleet Management; Managing Director and CFO KLM, Frederic Gagey, age 61
EVP Human Resources and Corporate Secretary, Jer´me Nanty, age 56
CEO Air France, Franck Terner, age 56
EVP Commercial Sales and Alliances, Patrick Alexandre, age 61
EVP Commercial Strategy, Pieter Bootsma, age 47
President and CEO KLM Royal Dutch Airlines, Pieter Elbers, age 46
EVP Strategy Passenger Business, Bram Gr¤ber, age 51
EVP Information Technology, Jean-Christophe Lalanne, age 52
Chairman and CEO Air France-KLM and Chairman Air France, Jean-Marc Janaillac, age 63
COO KLM, Rene de Groot, age 48
EVP Marketing Digital and Communication, Adeline Challon-Kemoun
Vice Chairman, Peter Hartman, age 67
Auditors: Deloitte et Associés

LOCATIONS

HQ: Air France-KLM
2, rue Robert Esnault-Pelterie, Paris 75007
Phone: (33) 1 41 56 78 00   **Fax:** (33) 1 41 56 56 00
Web: www.airfranceklm.com

2014 Sales

	% of total
Metropolitan France Benelux	31
Africa	22
Europe	14
America	11
North	10
Middle-EasternGulfIndia	5
West Indies Caribbean Guyana Indian Ocean South America	5
AsiaPacific	2
Total	**100**

PRODUCTS/OPERATIONS

2014 Sales

	% of total
Passenger	78
Cargo	11
Maintenance	5
Other	6
Total	**100**

COMPETITORS

Aer Lingus	Ryanair
Air Berlin	SAS
American Airlines Group	SNCF
	United Continental
Austrian Airlines	Virgin Atlantic
Brussels Airlines	Airways
IAG	easyJet
Lufthansa	

HISTORICAL FINANCIALS

Company Type: Public

Income Statement

FYE: December 31

	REVENUE ($ mil.)	NET INCOME ($ mil.)	NET PROFIT MARGIN	EMPLOYEES
12/15	28,387	128	0.5%	96,417
12/14	30,302	(240)	—	94,666
12/13	35,148	(2,515)	—	95,961
12/12	33,806	(1,571)	—	100,744
12/11	24,672	(571)	—	102,277
Annual Growth	**3.6%**	**—**	**—**	**(1.5%)**

2015 Year-End Financials

Debt ratio: 42.3%	No. of shares (mil.): 296
Return on equity: ***.***.*%	Dividends
Cash ($ mil.): 3,380	Yield: —
Current ratio: 0.63	Payout: —
Long-term debt ($ mil.): 7,689	Market value ($ mil.): 2,226

	STOCK PRICE ($) FY Close	P/E High/Low	PER SHARE ($) Earnings	Dividends	Book Value
12/15	7.52	27 18	0.37	0.00	0.83
12/14	9.47	— —	(0.81)	0.00	(2.76)
12/13	10.47	— —	(8.49)	0.00	10.43
12/12	9.67	— —	(5.31)	0.00	21.92
12/11	5.16	— —	(1.94)	0.00	26.52
Annual Growth (58.0%)	**9.9%**	**— —**	**—**	**—**	**—**

Airbus Group SE

Airbus Group (formerly European Aeronautic Defence and Space Company or EADS) is busy in the commercial and military aerospace and related markets. Considered Europe's largest supplier it rivals Boeing in the competitive skies. The company's largest segment is Airbus; its commercial division ranks among the top two makers of large commercial aircraft (seats 100-plus passengers) while its military division manufactures transport tankers and mission aircraft. Other segments include Airbus Helicopters (civil/military helicopters); and Airbus Defence and Space (satellites and launcher systems combat aircraft missile systems radar defense electronics and unmanned aerial systems).

Geographic Reach

Airbus Group operates in more than 170 locations worldwide.

Operations

Airbus Group has three operating Divisions: Airbus Airbus Defence and Space and Airbus Helicopters.Airbus is one of the world's leading aircraft manufacturers offering the most modern and efficient passenger aircraft on the more than 100-seat market. The Airbus commercial product line comprises aircraft that range in size from the 107-seat single-aisle A318 aircraft to the 525-seat A380 widebody aircraft.Airbus Helicopters (for-

merly Eurocopter) is a global leader in the civil and military rotorcraft market. Its product range includes light single-engine light twin-engine medium and medium-heavy rotorcraft which are adaptable to all kinds of mission types based on customer needs. With more than 3000 operators in more 150 countries Airbus Helicopters supports some 12000 in-service rotorcraft.

In 2014 the defense and space businesses of Airbus Military Astrium and Cassidian were combined into the new Airbus Defence and Space. This segment is Europe's number one defense and space enterprise and the world's second largest space business. Its core businesses are Space Military Aircraft Missiles and related systems and services.

Other businesses include turboprop manufacturer ATR aerostructure and aircraft seat business Sogerma.

Financial Performance

Airbus Group's revenues have risen consistently since 2010.

In 2014 net sales increased by 5% due to higher Airbus and Airbus Helicopters segment sales partially offset by decreased sales from Airbus Defence and Space.Airbus' revenues increased by 7% driven by the overall increase in deliveries to a more favorable delivery mix including 30 A380s (compared to only 25 in 2013); Airbus Helicopters sales increased thanks to government programs including the ramp-up in NH90 activity. By contrast Airbus Defence and Space's revenue decrease was driven by lower deliveries of military aircraft and fewer Ariane 5 launches.Airbus Group's net income has followed similar a trend that of its revenues.

In 2014 net income increased by 58% due to higher sales lower selling expenses and administrative expenses partially offset by increased research and development expenses. Selling and administrative expenses decreased by 6% in 2014. Research and development expenses increased by 9% reflecting R&D activities at Airbus. The main contribution to the expenses comes from the A350 XWB program. Net cash provided by the operating activities increased by 35%.

Strategy

Airbus Group is seeking to dominate the commercial aeronautics military aircraft and space markets by driving innovation globalization services and value-chain optimization. As part of this strategy in 2014 the company pooled its scattered defense activities into a new unit Airbus Defence and Space. In 2015 Airbus launched its global aerospace business accelerator where start-ups and Airbus “intrapreneurs” (internal entrepreneurs) can work together to speed up the transformation of their innovative ideas into valuable businesses.

That year ATR and TAP M&E signed a dual partnership. On one hand TAP M&E joined the network of centers recommended by ATR for the maintenance of the airframes of its aircraft; on the other hand the aircraft manufacturer has also chosen TAP M&E as first spare parts repair center in Brazil for support of its maintenance contracts offered to ATR operators.

In 2014 the joint venture Airbus Safran Launchers was created after the approval of the development and production of a new Ariane 6 launcher at the ESA Ministerial Conference.

The company has also sold a number of assets as part of its streamlining process and to pay down debt. In 2014 Airbus Defence and Space sold its Test & Services activities to a consortium consisting of ACE Management S.A. and IRDI S.A. for euro 31 million. That year it also sold its 26.8% share in Patria Oyj to the Finnish defence security and aviation services provider for euro 133 million. It also sold Dassault Aviation shares for euro 794 million.

Mergers and Acquisitions

In 2014 Airbus Operations S.L.U. Getafe (Spain) acquired a additional 58.49% shares in Alestis Aerospace S.L. La Rinconada (Spain) for euro 28 million including euro 6 million due to the separate recognition of settlements of preexisting relationships. That year Airbus Group acquired Salzburg München Bank AG from Raiffeisenverband Salzburg allowing the aeronautics and space group to establish a company bank in order to provide additional financing options. All parts of Airbus Group should benefit from the increased financing flexibility that this bank will provide.

HISTORY

Company Background

The growth of the European Aeronautic Defence and Space Company —EADS —is overshadowed by the long history of its components and by the obstacles overcome to cement the deal: The French and the Germans historically aren't overly fond of each other so how did it come to pass that Germany's DaimlerChrysler Aerospace AG (DASA) and France's Aerospatiale Matra put aside their differences to band together with Spain's Construcciones Aeronauticas SA (CASA)?

The US aerospace sector in the 1990s saw many companies consolidate scrambling to make their way in the post-Cold War era. Boeing the largest aerospace company in the world got that way by acquiring a number of operations including Rockwell International's aerospace and defense operations (1995) and most importantly McDonnell Douglas in a $16 billion deal (1997). In the same era defense giant Lockheed merged with Martin Marietta (1995) and acquired Loral (1997). These US companies had it relatively easy —they all paid taxes to Uncle Sam but acquisition deals in Europe were stymied by concerns over national security and privatization because much of Europe's defense industry was government-owned.

Spurred into action by their US rivals DASA and British Aerospace (now BAE SYSTEMS) —partners in Airbus —began merger talks in 1997. Fearful of being left out in the cold France's government-owned Aerospatiale —another Airbus partner —began talks to merge with Matra a French defense company controlled by Lagardère. Weeks after the Aerospatiale-Matra deal was announced in 1998 the chairman of DASA's parent company Jürgen Schrempp met with Lagardère's CEO Jean-Luc Lagardère and proposed a three-way deal. It never occurred and in 1999 the BAE SYSTEMS and DASA deal fell through as well.

Later that year Schrempp and Lagardère met again and laid the groundwork for a merger between DASA and Aerospatiale Matra. Less than three weeks after the Aerospatiale-Matra merger was completed Lagardère found itself pitching the DASA/Aerospatiale Matra merger idea to a stunned French government (which still held a 48% stake in Aerospatiale Matra). Marathon negotiations ensued. Late in the year Spain's Construcciones Aeronauticas SA (CASA) agreed to become part of EADS.

In 2000 EADS went public and Airbus announced that it would abandon its consortium structure in favor of incorporation. The next year EADS began pushing for a consolidation of army and naval equipment manufacturing among EU countries similar to the aerospace consolidation that created EADS. For Airbus the long-sought switch from consortium to corporation finally occurred in July 2001 when Airbus S.A.S. was incorporated.

EADS bought out BAE SYSTEMS' 25% share in their Astrium joint venture in 2003. In October 2004 EADS agreed to acquire US defense electronics maker Racal Instruments as part of its plan to increase defense sales in the US. Rumors surfaced the next month that EADS was discussing a merger deal with French defense company Thales.

In December 2004 EADS and BAE SYSTEMS gave Airbus the green-light to build the super-jumbo twin-deck A380 a plane that competes directly with Boeing's upcoming 787 Dreamliner. A few months later in early 2005 EADS was given preferred bidder status for the UK's Royal Air Force aerial refueling tanker contract. The program was valued at approximately $25 billion.

Claiming victory at last in 2006 Airbus beat Boeing on deliveries (434 vs. 398) but Boeing racked up a record 1004 plane orders while Airbus notched only 790. Moreover EADS' shares took a pounding in 2006 on Airbus' announcement that deliveries of the A380 would be delayed by six or seven months due to manufacturing glitches. A group of EADS shareholders cried foul and filed suit when it was revealed that co-CEO Noël Forgeard and five other EADS directors exercised stock options weeks before an internal investigation into the delays was launched. Two weeks later Forgeard fell on his sword and resigned. Louis Gallois former chairman of Societe Nationale des Chemins de Fer Français (SNCF) France's state railway company was named to replace him. The same fate befell Airbus boss Gustav Humbert who was replaced by Christian Streiff a former executive at French building materials concern Compagnie de Saint-Gobain.

The production logjams at Airbus also prompted some of the company's airline customers to seek compensation in lieu of taking their business elsewhere (Boeing). EADS forecast that the production delays at Airbus would be a $2.5 billion drain on profits over four years. In the wake of the additional delivery delays Airbus CEO Christian Streiff was sent packing after only three months on the job. EADS Co-CEO Louis Gallois was named as his replacement.

In 2006 Daimler announced plans to gradually reduce its stake in EADS from about 30% to half that amount. Later that year EADS acquired Sofrelog of France (a maker of maritime monitoring systems). Russian bank Vneshtorgbank (100% controlled by the Russian government) also purchased a 5% stake in EADS for about $1.17 billion. The stake did not entitle Vneshtorgbank to a board seat but the move was expected to strengthen cooperation between EADS and the re-emerging Russian aerospace industry.

After long negotiations EADS shifted in 2007 to a new management structure aimed at cutting down on the damaging political bickering between its German and French management and shareholder factions. Politicians like German Chancellor Angela Merkel and French President Nicolas Sarkozy touted the compromise as a success. Others namely labor forces were more skeptical —calling the latest management shake-up just another round of musical chairs that leaves the power struggles between Paris and Munich largely unresolved.

EADS continued to expand into emerging markets especially regions including Asia the Middle East and North and South America. Deliveries included the company's (long-delayed) A380 model launched with Singapore Airlines in late 2008. Adding to Airbus's standing the all-new A350-XWB (made for the most part of lighter-weight composite materials) sliced into about two-thirds of jet demand in the Middle East. It also forged alliances and won contracts in Brazil China Japan and North America.

Airbus launched a cost-cutting initiative in 2008 that slashed some 10000 jobs. Dubbed Power8 the plan marched out cost-saving measures that aimed to reduce development cycles by two years and boost overall productivity by 20%. Central to Power8 was the spinoff of some of Airbus's manufacturing facilities to new partners. Partner funding of planes like the A350-XWB (spurred by assurances of subcontract work) plus plant sales risked an ongoing row between Airbus and unions as well as factory owners —stakeholders who feared plant divestitures and more job cuts. That year EADS captured its first big US military contract when Airbus North America was given the opportunity to make US Army light utility helicopters.

The company was awarded a contract to replace outdated KC-135 refueling tankers in conjunction with Northrop Grumman for the US Air Force —an upset protested by rival bidder Boeing. Soon after the Government Accountability Office (GAO) announced its findings of flaws in the bidding process. EADS and Northrop Grumman dropped out of the bidding in early 2010 with EADS vowing not to submit a proposal unless it was assured that it had a fair chance to win. By late summer —after US president Obama assured French president Nicolas Sarkozy that the Pentagon tanker bidding process would be fair —EADS announced that it would consider once again to enter into the bidding war. The contract to build the US tanker valued at approximately $35 billion went to Boeing in early 2011.

In September 2012 EADS (now the Airbus Group) announced it was considering a merger with UK-based BAE Systems a global provider of sensors flight controls and aircraft. However the proposed $45 billion merger —which would have created the largest global aerospace and defense player on the planet both in total sales and market value —was called off weeks later after it failed to pass European governmental and regulatory hurdles.

Preparing to capitalize on demand Airbus Group hammered out its Vision 2020 goals under which it pursues the world's #1 position in air and space platforms systems and services. Services are targeted to achieve a 25% share of the business in less than 10 years. To this end Airbus Group has been scouting deals in the services sector. In August 2011 it agreed to purchase Vizada a global satellite-based mobile communication services provider from French private-equity Apax France. The whopping euro 673 million ($969 million) deal bolsters Airbus Group's subsidiary Astrium a top contractor of space-technology wares in Europe and furthers opportunities beyond Europe with maritime aerospace as well as land media and other commercial customers. Hard on its heels Airbus Group took over more than 98% of Canada-based Vector Aerospace for C$625 million (about $341 million). Vector joins Eurocopter as a stand-alone business adding a multi-platform aviation repair and overhaul business.

EXECUTIVES

EVP Space Systems; CEO Airbus Defence and Space France, Fran $is Auque, age 58

CEO, Thomas (Tom) Enders, age 55

CTO, Jean J. Botti, age 57

CEO Airbus Helicopters, Guillaume Faury, age 47

CFO Airbus Group and Airbus, Harald Wilhelm, age 48

EVP Military Aircraft Airbus Defence and Space, Domingo Urena-Raso, age 56

CEO Airbus, Fabrice Bregier, age 53

COO, Gunter Butschek, age 53

Chief Human Resources Officer Airbus Group and Airbus, Thierry Baril, age 49

CEO Airbus Defence and Space, Bernhard Gerwert, age 61
CEO Airbus Group North America, Allan McArtor, age 73
Vice Chairman, Josep Pique i Camps, age 61
Chairman, Denis Ranque, age 64
Auditors: KPMG Accountants N.V.

LOCATIONS

HQ: Airbus Group SE
Mendelweg 30, Leiden 2333 CS
Phone:
Web: www.airbus-group.com

2014 Sales

	% of total
Europe	33
Asia/Pacific	32
North America	16
Rest of the World	19
Total	**100**

PRODUCTS/OPERATIONS

2014 Sales

	% of total
Airbus	68
Airbus Defence and Space	21
Airbus Helicopters	11
Other HQ / Consolidation	0
Total	**100**

Selected Operations and Interests

Business aircraft (JV with Dassault Aviation 46%)
Commercial airplanes (Airbus)
  A320 (single-aisle aircraft)
  A330/A340
  A350 XWB (extra wide body)
Helicopters (Eurocopter SAS)
  EC135 (light twin engine)
  EC175 (multi-role)
  EC225 (Super Puma)
  EC725
  E225/ED725 (twin engine)
  NH90 (medium-weight multi-role)
  Tiger (medium-weight
Satellites (Astrium)
  Ariane 5 (heavy-lift satellite)
  Automated Transfer Vehicle (ATV)
  Eurostar 3000 (telecommunications satellite)
Security combat and missile systems (Cassidian)
  Cassidian Professional Mobile Radio (PMR)
  Eurofighter (aka "Typhoon")combat aircraft (JV with Dassault Aviation 46%)
  MBDA missile systems (JV with BAE systems and Finmeccanica)
  Radars
  Unmanned Aerial Systems (UAS; partnered with Northrop Grumman
Other businesses
  ATR (50- to 74-seat turboprop aircraft; JV with Alenia Aeronautica)
  EADS North America
  EADS UK

COMPETITORS

Aerojet Rocketdyne	Embraer
AgustaWestland	Lockheed Martin
BAE SYSTEMS	Northrop Grumman
BAE Systems Inc.	RUAG Holding
Boeing	Raytheon
Bombardier	Textron
E' Prime Aerospace	

HISTORICAL FINANCIALS
Company Type: Public

Income Statement
FYE: December 31

	REVENUE ($ mil.)	NET INCOME ($ mil.)	NET PROFIT MARGIN	EMPLOYEES
12/15	70,199	2,936	4.2%	136,574
12/14	73,796	2,847	3.9%	138,622
12/13	81,579	2,016	2.5%	144,061
12/12	74,443	1,618	2.2%	140,405
12/11	63,544	1,336	2.1%	140,405
Annual Growth	**2.5%**	**21.8%**	**—**	**(0.7%)**

2015 Year-End Financials

Debt ratio: 9.3%
Return on equity: 41.3%
Cash ($ mil.): 8,157
Current ratio: 0.96
Long-term debt ($ mil.): 6,900

No. of shares (mil.): 783
Dividends
  Yield: 1.5%
  Payout: 35.0%
Market value ($ mil.): 13,196

	STOCK PRICE ($) FY Close	P/E High/Low		PER SHARE ($) Earnings	Dividends	Book Value
12/15	16.84	5	3	3.73	0.25	8.29
12/14	12.34	6	4	3.63	0.20	10.94
12/13	19.15	37	9	2.53	0.83	19.43
12/12	39.71	28	21	1.98	0.59	16.69
12/11	31.40	26	18	1.64	0.28	14.05
Annual Growth	**(14.4%) (12.4%)**	**— —**		**22.7%**	**(3.0%)**	

Aisin Seiki Co Ltd

Nothing stops Aisin Seiki from making its line of brake systems and powertrain components for cars. Aisin's main automotive business offers automotive-related products such as transmissions brakes and engine and car navigation systems. Its Life and Amenity business offers items for more comfortable living with products that range from heating and cooling systems to toilets with jet sprays; well-care items include electric wheelchairs and reclining beds. The company has around 180 consolidated subsidiaries and companies worldwide. Separate business segments include Aisin AW Group Aisin Seiki Group Advics Group and Aisin Takaoka Group.

Operations

Aisin Seiki operates through nearly 180 subsidiaries that are spread throughout four main segments. Aisin AW Group is its largest segment (37% of total sales in 2015) and makes automatic transmissions and car navigation systems. Aisin Seiki Group (36%) sells its automotive parts as well as its life and energy products. Advics Group is responsible for making brake components (17%) while Aisin Takaoka Group (6%) manufacturers the cart-iron parts for engines and brakes.

Financial Performance

Aisin Seiki's revenues increased 5% from 2014 to 2015. The growth was due to increased sales from Aisin AW Group Aisin Seiki Group and Aisin Takaoka Group. The company's net income in 2015 declined mainly due to increased freight and packaging expenses coupled with a spike in selling general and administrative expenses.

Strategy

Aisin Seiki is looking to diversify its customer mix by expanding production overseas to achieve a 50% ratio in the years ahead. It established new subsidiaries in Indonesia in 2014 and began constructing a new facility in Brazil also that year.

Aisin Seiki continues to make automotive components and systems but it also focuses on increasing sales of main products such as transmissions car navigation systems and power sliding doors. The company's business segments have worked autonomously in the past; however Aisin Seiki is working to combine and link its individual businesses thus strengthening and maximizing the potential of the products and technologies that are cultivated by each company.

Company Background

Aisin Seiki traces its roots to 1943 when Tokai Hikoki was founded to produce airplane engines for the Japanese war effort. After the war the company switched to manufacturing sewing machines and auto parts. Aisin Seiki took its present name in 1965 after Tokai Hikoki merged with Shinkawa Kogyo.

EXECUTIVES

EVP, Toshikazu Nagura
EVP and Director, Fumio Fujimori
Managing Officer, Naofumi Fujie
EVP, Makoto Mitsuya
EVP, Toshiyuki Mizushima
Chairman, Kanshiro Toyoda, age 74
Auditors: PricewaterhouseCoopers Aarata

LOCATIONS

HQ: Aisin Seiki Co Ltd
2-1 Asahi-machi, Kariya, Aichi 448-8650
Phone: (81) 566 24 8265
Web: www.aisin.co.jp

PRODUCTS/OPERATIONS

2015 Sales

	% of total
Aisin AW Group	37
Aisin Seiki Group	36
Advics Group	17
Aisin Takaoka Group	6
Other	4
Total	**100**

Selected Products

Automotive
  Drivetrain products (transmission and clutch systems)
  Brake and chassis products (drum brakes master cylinders air suspension systems)
  Body products (door frames and locks sunroofs power seats)
  Engine products (water pumps pistons exhaust manifolds)
  Information and other products (navigation systems Intelligent Parking Assist)
  Aftermarket products
Energy System
  GHP
  Cogeneration system
  Cryopump
  Cryocooler
  Peltier modules
Life and Amenity
  Bed furniture and fabric (ASLEEP)
  Housing equipment
  House remodeling service (Livelan)
  Home-use sewing machine
  Embroidery machine
  Facility consulting service (CONTRACT)
  Business consulting service (TSS)
  Audio equipment

COMPETITORS

APM Automotive	Meritor
BorgWarner	Mitsubishi Electric
Calsonic Kansei	Modine Manufacturing
DENSO	Panasonic Corp
DURA Automotive	Robert Bosch
Dana	Sumitomo Electric
Delphi Automotive	Tenneco

Systems
Faurecia
Haldex
Hitachi America
Lear Corp
Magna International

Torotrak
Valeo
Visteon
ZF Friedrichshafen
ZF TRW Automotive

HISTORICAL FINANCIALS
Company Type: Public

Income Statement
FYE: March 31

	REVENUE ($ mil.)	NET INCOME ($ mil.)	NET PROFIT MARGIN	EMPLOYEES
03/16	28,880	863	3.0%	120,976
03/15	24,709	646	2.6%	115,303
03/14	27,341	872	3.2%	89,531
03/13	26,888	823	3.1%	83,378
03/12	28,089	676	2.4%	78,212
Annual Growth	0.7%	6.3%	—	11.5%

2016 Year-End Financials

Debt ratio: 0.1%
Return on equity: 8.5%
Cash ($ mil.): 2,752
Current ratio: 1.44
Long-term debt ($ mil.): 2,844

No. of shares (mil.): 283
Dividends
　Yield: 0.0%
　Payout: 29.0%
Market value ($ mil.): 10,618

	STOCK PRICE ($) FY Close	P/E High/Low		PER SHARE ($) Earnings	Dividends	Book Value
03/16	37.49	0	0	3.04	0.88	34.69
03/15	36.25	0	0	2.28	0.97	34.30
03/14	36.21	—	—	3.09	0.87	45.62
03/13	30.60	—	—	2.92	0.00	42.85
03/12	36.71	—	—	2.40	0.00	41.94
Annual Growth	0.5%	—	—	6.1%	—	(4.6%)

AKBANK

The vaults at Akbank have enough room for Turkish lira and the euro. The bank provides banking services in Turkey through nearly 1000 branches about 4300 ATMs and more than 360000 point-of-sale terminals. Internationally Akbank operates branches in Germany and in Malta; it also has subsidiary banks in the Netherlands and in Dubai. Akbank which is Turkey's second-largest publicly traded bank after Is Bankasi also provides private bank and international trade finance services. Subsidiaries provide non-banking financial capital-market and investment services. The Sabanci family and its companies control 55% of Akbank.

OperationsAkbank operates five main business segments: Retail Banking which serves consumers; the Corporate Banking Commercial Banking and SME Banking division which provides financial and banking services to large medium and small corporate and commercial customers; The Treasury Unit which trades a variety of treasury bond foreign currency and derivative trading securities on behalf the bank; Private Banking which provides banking and investment management services for affluent individuals; and International Banking which provides foreign currency financing foreign currency and TL clearances and money transfers through agent financial institutions.Akbank generated 81% of its total revenue from interest income on loans in 2014 while 16% of the bank's revenue came from fee and commission income. Its loan portfolio was comprised of corporate loans (32% of loan assets) SME loans (37%) and consumer loans (31%). Akbank's overseas subsidiaries include its German bank Akbank AG; Akbank Dubai Limited while its non-banking subsidiaries include AkInvestment AKAsset Management and Aklease. Geographic ReachAkbank boasts more than 990 branches across Turkey and has an additional branch in Malta. It also operates overseas through subsidiary banks in Frankfurt Germany and in Dubai UAE.

Sales and Marketing

Akbank serves a wide variety of industries including the energy infrastructure petrochemicals real estate telecommunications and transportation industries. Financial PerformanceNote: Growth rates may differ after conversion to US dollars.Akbank has struggled to sustain revenue or profit growth in recent years though its business has remained stable. The bank had a breakout year in 2014 however with revenue jumping by 22% to TL$18.1 billion (around $7.7 billion). Most of the rise was driven by strong interest income growth from both the Retail Banking and the Corporate Banking Commercial banking and SME Banking divisions as the bank successfully grew its consumer loans (excluding credit card loans) by nearly 12% its general purpose loans by 21% and its mortgage loans by nearly 4% during the year. Akbank's fee and commission income also grew by 12% during the year further padding its top line.

Higher revenue and foreign exchange gains in 2014 drove the bank's net income higher by 7% to TL$3.3 billion (roughly $1.4 billion). Akbank's operating cash however declined by 30% to TL$1.4 billion for the year as the bank collected less cash from deposits during the year.

Strategy

As the second-largest bank in Turkey Akbank reiterated in 2015 that it's mid to long-term growth plans include being the leader of the country's banking industry while also looking toward international growth in markets where its clients enjoy high business volumes. It's also been working to manage its costs effectively executing more than 60 effective cost management actions in 2014 alone for an estimated TL$26 million (about $11 million) in sustainable savings.

Domestically Akbank has been moving toward digital banking channels that are quickly taking the industry by storm allowing the bank to slow expensive branch-expansion plans and cut operating costs significantly while giving customers faster access to banking services. In 2014 the bank launched new versions of its Akbank Direkt platform for mobile and internet banking differentiating user experiences for its variety of customer groups. Its Direkt Business was introduced for micro business segment customers while its Akbank Direkt Plus was unveiled for higher-income clients. Meanwhile its Mobile Banking platform was updated with iBeacon technology which allowed customers to make card-free cash withdrawal transactions from ATMs; while its cash management e-Invoice system allowed bank customers to send and receive e-invoices to and from business partners and suppliers.

Toward gaining more international exposure in growing regions Akbank sometimes partners with prominent banks in based in other regions. In 2014 for example the bank secured a cooperation agreement with Barclays Africa Group to provide banking services for Turkish companies that do business or invest in sub-Saharan countries in Africa via Barclays Africa branches. The deal also included joint financing opportunities for Turkish companies looking to grow in Africa as well as cooperation in trade and letters of guarantee transactions between Turkey and African countries.

EXECUTIVES

EVP Treasury, Kerim Rota
EVP Information Technology, Turgut G ney
EVP Consumer Banking, A. Galip T ʒge
CEO and Board Member, Hakan Binbasgil
EVP International Banking, H lya Kefeli
EVP Payment Systems and Corporate Communication, Mehmet Sindel
EVP Commercial Banking, Kaan G r
EVP Credits, Ahmet Fuat Ayla
EVP Corporate Banking, Alper Hakan Y ksel
EVP Direct Banking, Orkun Oguz
EVP SME Banking, B lent Oguz
EVP and CFO, K.Atil zus
EVP Private Banking, Saltik Galatali
EVP Operation, zlen Sanibelli
EVP Human Resources and Strategy, Burcu Civelek Y ce
Vice Chairman, Hayri Culhaci
Chairman, Suzan Sabanci Din ǝr
Auditors: Guney Bagimsiz Denetim ve Serbest Muhasebeci Mali Musavirlik A.S.

LOCATIONS

HQ: AKBANK
Sabanci Center 4, Istanbul, Levent 34330
Phone: (90) 212 385 55 55   **Fax:** (90) 212 319 52 52
Web: www.akbank.com

PRODUCTS/OPERATIONS

2014 Sales

	% of total
Interest income	81
Fee and commission received	16
Dividend income	-
Other operating income	3
Total	**100**

Selected Businesses

AKAssetmanagement
AKLease
AKInvestment
AKbank AG
Akbank Dubai Limited

COMPETITORS

Citi Turkey
Finansbank
GarantiBank
Isbank

Ko§
Trk Ekonomi Bankasi
Yapi Kredi

HISTORICAL FINANCIALS
Company Type: Public

Income Statement
FYE: December 31

	ASSETS ($ mil.)	NET INCOME ($ mil.)	INCOME AS % OF ASSETS	EMPLOYEES
12/15	85,759	1,149	1.3%	14,418
12/14	93,246	1,480	1.6%	16,543
12/13	90,778	1,509	1.7%	16,473
12/12	90,693	1,721	1.9%	16,515
12/11	73,777	1,370	1.9%	15,548
Annual Growth	3.8%	(4.3%)	—	(1.9%)

2015 Year-End Financials

Return on assets: 1.4%
Return on equity: 12.1%
Long-term debt ($ mil.): —
No. of shares (mil.): —
Sales ($ mil): 6,570

Dividends
　Yield: 1.6%
　Payout: 2,411.0%
Market value ($ mil.): —

	STOCK PRICE ($)	P/E		PER SHARE ($)		
	FY Close	High/Low	Earnings	Dividends	Book Value
12/15	4.61	779510	0.00	0.08	0.02
12/14	7.32	893557	0.00	0.08	0.03
12/13	6.25	1207720	0.00	0.12	0.03
12/12	10.05	1294762	0.00	0.09	0.03
12/11	6.28	1443905	0.00	0.11	0.02
Annual Growth	(7.4%)	— —		(4.4%)	(8.7%)	0.3%

Akzo Nobel N.V. (Netherlands)

Akzo Nobel may be the world's largest paint manufacturer but it does more than just paint a pretty picture. The company is also among the world's largest chemical manufacturers and salt producers. Akzo Nobel divides its business into three main lines: Decorative Paints which produces consumer and commercial paints and primarily serves Europe and North America; Performance Coatings which manufactures marine and protective coatings packaging coatings automotive finishes and industrial coatings; and Specialty Chemicals which makes pulp and performance chemicals functional chemicals (flame retardants crop nutrients) industrial chemicals (salt and chlor-alkalis) surfactants and specialty starches.

Operations

Akzo Nobel's Specialty Chemicals segment holds a number of leading positions for various chemicals such as ethyline amines salt specialties and organic peroxides produced by its functional chemicals unit. Its industrial chemicals unit also is a leading producer of caustic lye and chlorine in Europe as well as salt. Surface Chemistry produced surfactants synthetic polymers and bio-polymers. The segment's products are used to make a number of everyday items including cosmetics detergents disinfectants ice cream plastics and soaps. The segment accounts for around 40% of total revenue.

Akzo Nobel has established a global leadership position in Decorative Paints enjoying economies of scale while expanding its global footprint. In the US it has introduced its products in Wal-mart and relaunched the Glidden brand for its Home Depot sales. In Canada it markets through major retailer RONA. It has strengthened its presence in the high-growth markets of Asia Latin America and Eastern Europe. In China it has penetrated mass markets and in India it is gaining momentum with an investment in its flagship Dulux brand. The segment accounts for around 34% of total revenue.

The company's Performance Coatings segment is represented in most markets of the industry including general industrial coatings for metals and plastic; and protective coatings for oil and gas airports and stadia power generation mining and minerals and water and wastewater markets. The segment holds market leadership positions in marine coatings protective coatings and yacht coatings and it also supplies coatings for commercial vehicles and aircraft. Its powder coatings unit provides electrostatically applied coatings that are sprayed and then cured by applying heat. And its wood finishes and adhesives are used for furniture flooring cabinets windows and doors. The segment accounts for around 27% of revenue.

Geographic Reach

The Netherlands-based Akzo Nobel operates in more than 80 countries but most of its holdings are in Western Europe North America and the Asia/Pacific. It is expanding in emerging markets within Latin America and Eastern Europe.

Europe as a whole brings in around 43% of revenue with Germany and the UK the biggest two European markets at around 7% each. North America provides some 17% of revenue and China 12%.

Sales and Marketing

The company's customer base include a swathe of the biggest companies out there: Airbus Boeing IKEA Philips Samsung Shell Volkswagen Whirlpool Bayer Dow GE Huntsman Monsanto Stora Enso and Unilever. It has thousands of distributors across the world and large retail outlets including B&Q Leroy Merlin and OBI.

Financial Performance

Sales of euro 14.9 billion in 2015 represented a 4% rise on prior year a reversal of recent trends of slight negative growth. Sales growth came from increases in Specialty Chemicals and Decorative Paints. Much of the 2% increase in Specialty Chemicals however was due to favorable currency effects; overall volumes were flat. Growth of 3% in Decorative Paints came from higher revenue in Asia more than compensating for flat growth in Europe and a fall in Latin America.

Net income climbed 79% to euro 979 million from euro 546 million in 2015 due mostly to an increase in operating income.

Cash flow from operating activities rose 40% to euro 1.1 billion.

Strategy

The company's strategy is to invest in its brands distribution system and people with a focus on expansion in mid-tier markets. Akzo Nobel is concentrating on growth in regions such as Asia Eastern Europe and Latin America as demand begins to decline in mature markets such as Western Europe and North America (though those two regions still account for about half of Akzo Nobel's business). In addition to growing in strong emerging markets the company seeks strategic bolt-on acquisitions and continues to make significant investments.

In 2016 Akzo-Nobel strengthened its position in the North American hydrogen peroxide market after it acquired OCI Peroxygen's shares in joint venture EkO Peroxide. In the same year the company acquired BASF's industrial coatings business for euro 475 million to strengthen its position in the coatings market which processes coiled metal sheets into facades fridges and window blinds.

Promoting its global brand in 2015 Akzo Nobel extended its official supplier partnership with McLaren Racing.

Innovations in 2014 included the launch of a new barrier coating which made it possible to create the world's first fully compostable and recyclable paper cup for cold drinks. Its Decorative Paints business launched the Visualizer app enabling users to see in real time what a room will look like in a wide range of different colors.

The company also has also sold non-core assets to pay down debt. In 2015 Akzo Nobel sold its Paper Chemicals portfolio for euro 153 million. In the same year the company announced plans to sell Zeta Fraction biofunctional technology to Ashland in order to focus on its core technology platforms of specialty surfactants and polymers.

Mergers and Acquisitions

In 2016 Azko Nobel bought German chemicals producer BASF's industrial coatings business (which makes products for use in wind farms and in other areas) for about $499 million.

HISTORY

Company Background

The Akzo side of Akzo Nobel traces its roots to two companies —German rayon and coatings maker Vereinigte Glanzstoff-Fabriken (founded 1899) and Dutch rayon maker Nederlandsche Kunstzijdebariek (founded 1911 and known as NK or Enka). In 1928 NK built a plant near Asheville North Carolina in what later became the town of Enka. The two companies merged in 1929 to create Algemene Kunstzijde-Unie (AKU).

In 1967 two Dutch companies merged to form Koninklijke Zout-Organon (KZO). Two years later KZO bought US-based International Salt and merged with AKU to form Akzo. In the 1980s Akzo focused on building its chemicals coatings and pharmaceuticals businesses. Akzo sold its paper and pulp business to Nobel in 1993. A few months later the company reclaimed that business when it bought Nobel.

Best remembered for the prizes that bear his name (which were first awarded in 1901 through a bequest in his will) Alfred Nobel invented the blasting cap in 1863 making it possible to control the detonation of nitroglycerin. He then persuaded Stockholm merchant J. W. Smitt to help him finance Nitroglycerin Ltd. to make and sell the volatile fluid (1864). Nobel's quest to improve nitroglycerin led to his invention of dynamite in 1867.

After Nobel's death in 1896 Nitroglycerin Ltd. remained an explosives maker and in 1965 it changed its name to Nitro Nobel. In 1978 Swedish industrialist Marcus Wallenberg bought Nitro Nobel for his KemaNord chemical group known afterward as KemaNobel. Within six years industrialist Erik Penser controlled both KemaNobel and armaments maker Bofors and he merged them in 1984 as Nobel Industries.

Risky investments led Penser to ruin in 1991. His holdings including Nobel were taken over by a government-owned bank and conveyed into Securum a state-owned holding company (which still owns 18% of Akzo Nobel). In 1992 Nobel spun off its consumer-goods segment.

Akzo bought Nobel in 1994. Although the company had good financial results in 1995 it faced pressure from rising costs for raw materials and a difficult foreign-exchange environment. Akzo announced major closings and layoffs —it sold its polyethylene packaging resin business and moved some clothing-grade rayon operations to Poland.

The merger between Akzo and Nobel was legally completed in 1996. That year the company introduced Puregon a fertility drug and Remeron touted as a replacement for Prozac in the US and other countries. In 1997 Akzo Nobel put most of its worst-performing segment fibers into a joint venture with Turkish conglomerate Sabanci. It also sold its North American salt unit to Cargill.

Akzo Nobel acquired Courtaulds (coatings sealants and fibers) in 1998 and changed the firm's name to Akzo Nobel UK. AkzoNobel also bought BASF deco the European decorative-coatings business of BASF Coatings. Akzo Nobel combined its fiber business with AkzoNobel UK to form a new division Acordis. AkzoNobel then sold Acordis to investment firm CVC Capital Partners in 1999 for $859 million (AkzoNobel retains a minority share). That year AkzoNobel bought Hoechst's animal-health unit Hoechst Roussel Vet for $712 million. In 2000 the company bought Dexter Corporation's aircraft coatings business.

In 2001 Akzo Nobel sold its medical diagnostics division to French drugmaker bioMerieux-Pierre Fabre. Later that year the company picked up the vehicle refinishes business of MAC Specialty Coatings of the US. It also agreed to sell its printing inks business to a private equity firm.

CEO Cees van Lede retired in mid-2003 succeeded by Hans Wijers who immediately set about restructuring cutting costs and erasing debt. By year's end more than 3300 jobs were cut and AkzoNobel had sold off three big chemical units: catalysts (to Albemarle for about $750 million) coating resins and phosphorous chemicals (to Ripplewood Holdings for another $270 million).

The fruits of those sell-offs came with 2005 acquisitions in Germany France and Switzerland. The last purchase of Swiss Lack made Akzo Nobel the largest paint company in Switzerland as well. The following year the company made a bigger buy that of Canadian coatings maker Sico for $285 million.

Also in 2006 Akzo Nobel decided to pare down its operations further with the sale of its inks and adhesive resins business to Hexion Specialty Chemicals. The business was concentrated in Europe but had strong international operations as well. The deal brought the company about $100 million.

Early in 2006 Akzo announced plans to split off its pharmaceuticals segment Organon. It originally planned to float a minority share early in 2007 and then fully separate the new company by 2009. In a surprise move however Schering-Plough came in and bought the unit for $14.4 billion.

In what turned out to be a major turning point for the company Akzo Nobel approached UK coatings and chemicals maker ICI with a $14 billion takeover offer in late 2007. ICI's board rejected the price tag as insufficient. Akzo Nobel countered twice and ended up agreeing to a deal worth $16 billion. As part of the deal Henkel bought the adhesives and electronic materials businesses of ICI subsidiary National Starch and Chemical. The buy of ICI built up Akzo's coatings business even further. The acquired businesses have great strength in retail decorative paints and in North America both areas in which Akzo Nobel's coatings business had been lacking.

Another business acquired in the deal was Akzo Nobel's new Chemicals Pakistan division which was composed of the company's majority holdings in two publicly traded companies. Those subsidiaries made soda ash polyester fibers and pure terephthalic acid (PTA). In 2009 though the company sold its 75% stake in the subsidiary that makes PTA to Korean manufacturer KP Chemical.

Akzo Nobel subsidiary National Starch acquired Penford Australia's specialty grain wet milling and manufacturing facility in 2009 expanding National Starch's reach into the Asia/Pacific region. However in 2010 Corn Products International (renamed Ingredion) acquired National Starch for $2.7 billion.

In 2010 Akzo Nobel acquired the powder coatings business of Dow Chemical Company. The deal brought technological know-how and significant synergy potential to Akzo Nobel's Powder Coatings line and enhanced the company's position in the US.

As part of its three-year performance improvement program launched in late 2011 Azko Nobel restructured business lines such as its European and North American decorative paints and its performance coatings' wood finishes and adhesives. The company has managed to raise prices enough in 2012 to offset most of the raw material price increases. Although the costs of titanium dioxide continue to rise Akzo Nobel has been successful in passing on most of its raw material cost increases.

In early 2012 the company completed its acquisition of Boxing Oleochemicals a leading Chinese surfactants producer. Boxing makes nitrile amines and derivatives used for industrial and consumer applications ranging from asphalt additives to fabric softeners. The buy enhances Azko Nobel's position in specialty surfactants and broadens its reach in Asia. Boxing's operations will be integrated into the company's Surface Chemistry unit.

In early 2012 the company also moved to strengthen its packaging coatings operations by trying to acquire the part of Italy's Packaging Coatings Metlac Group it doesn't own (it holds a 49% stake). However the UK's office of Fair Trading put the brakes on the deal because of competition concerns and referred the case to the UK's Competition Commission. Both Metlac and Akzo Nobel supply metal packaging coatings used in food and beverage cans.

In 2012 Akzon Nobel split its ICI Pakistan subsidiary into two new companies: AkzoNobel Pakistan Limited (comprising the paints and specialty chemicals business) and ICI Pakistan Limited (comprising all other businesses of ICI Pakistan). In the process AkzoNobel maintains 76% control of the paints business while seeking a buyer for ICI Pakistan.

To expand its industrial coatings business Akzo Nobel acquired Germany-based Schramm Holding in 2011. Akzo Nobel believes the acquisition makes it the global leader for specialty plastic coatings for the lucrative market serving mobile devices laptops TVs and auto interiors. Also in 2011 Akzo Nobel opened a new coatings plant in India.

That year the company's Decorative Paints unit expanded with the company's entry into a partnership in China with Quangxi CAVA Titanium Industry Co. to ensure a supply of titanium dioxide. It also invested euro 110 million ($135 million) in 2011 in a replacement manufacturing plant in the North East of England.

To raise cash to pay down debt in 2012 AkzoNobel divested its North American Decorative Paints business to PPG Industries for $1.05 billion.

EXECUTIVES

CEO and Chairman, Ton B chner, age 50
Managing Director and Head Specialty Chemicals, Werner Fuhrmann
Managing Director and Head Decorative Paints, Ruud Joosten
Managing Director and Head Performance Coatings, Conrad Keijzer
CFO, Ma dys Castella
Chairman, Antony Burgmans, age 69
Deputy Chairman, Uwe-Ernst Bufe, age 72
Auditors: KPMG Accountants N.V.

LOCATIONS

HQ: Akzo Nobel N.V. (Netherlands)
Christian Neefestraat 2, P.O. Box 75730, Amsterdam 1070 AS
Phone: (31) 20 502 7555   **Fax:** (31) 20 502 7666
Web: www.akzonobel.com

2015 sales

	% of total
The Netherlands	5
Germany	7
Sweden	3
UK	7
Other European countries	21
US and Canada	17
Latin American countries	10
China	12
Other Asian countries	13
Other regions	5
Total	**100**

PRODUCTS/OPERATIONS

2015 sales

	% of total
Performance Coatings	27
Specialty Chemicals	40
Decorative Paints	34
Corporate and other (1)	
Total	**100**

Selected Products

Specialty chemicals
  Base chemicals
  Functional chemicals
  Polymer chemicals
  Pulp and paper chemicals
  Surfactants
Decorative paints
Performance coatings
  Car refinishes
  Industrial finishes
  Marine and protective coatings
  Powder coatings

COMPETITORS

Alfa SA	Ferro
Asahi Kasei	Formosa Plastics
BASF SE	H.B. Fuller
Compass Minerals	Orica
DuPont	PPG Industries
Eastman Chemical	Sherwin-Williams
Evonik Degussa	Valspar

HISTORICAL FINANCIALS

Company Type: Public

Income Statement

FYE: December 31

	REVENUE ($ mil.)	NET INCOME ($ mil.)	NET PROFIT MARGIN	EMPLOYEES
12/15	16,184	1,066	6.6%	45,600
12/14	17,376	663	3.8%	47,200
12/13	20,086	996	5.0%	50,200
12/12	20,284	(2,858)	—	52,200
12/11	20,303	616	3.0%	56,400
Annual Growth	(5.5%)	14.7%	—	(5.2%)

2015 Year-End Financials

Debt ratio: 17.6%	No. of shares (mil.): 248
Return on equity: 15.9%	Dividends
Cash ($ mil.): 1,486	Yield: 1.9%
Current ratio: 1.24	Payout: 10.3%
Long-term debt ($ mil.): 2,353	Market value ($ mil.): 5,531

	STOCK PRICE ($) FY Close	P/E High/Low		PER SHARE ($) Earnings	Dividends	Book Value
12/15	22.22	7	5	4.27	0.44	28.37
12/14	22.80	11	9	2.70	0.53	28.60
12/13	25.87	9	7	4.10	0.63	31.74
12/12	22.50	—	—	(12.05)	0.50	38.00
12/11	48.30	34	19	2.61	0.49	50.77
Annual Growth (13.5%)	(17.6%)	—	—	13.1%	(2.8%)	

Alecta pensionsforsakring, omsesidigt (Sweden)

EXECUTIVES

Ekonomichef, Katarina Thorslund
Auditors: Ernst & Young AB

LOCATIONS

HQ: Alecta pensionsforsakring, omsesidigt (Sweden)
Regeringsgatan 107, Stockholm SE-103 73
Phone: (46) 20 441 60 00   **Fax:** (46) 8 441 60 90
Web: www.alecta.se

HISTORICAL FINANCIALS
Company Type: Public

Income Statement
FYE: December 31

	ASSETS ($ mil.)	NET INCOME ($ mil.)	INCOME AS % OF ASSETS	EMPLOYEES
12/15	88,972	6,195	7.0%	392
12/14	90,621	2,356	2.6%	406
12/13	95,447	13,525	14.2%	424
12/12	85,837	10,446	12.2%	426
12/11	72,503	(13,343)	—	445
Annual Growth	5.3%	—	—	(3.1%)

2015 Year-End Financials

Return on assets: 7.2%
Return on equity: 18.7%
Long-term debt ($ mil.): —
No. of shares (mil.): —
Sales ($ mil): 8,699

Dividends
Yield: —
Payout: —
Market value ($ mil.): —

Alfresa Holdings Corp Tokyo

Alfresa Holdings primarily serves as a pharmaceutical wholesaler in the Japanese market. The company encompasses Alfresa Corp. which oversees the wholesale side of the business and Alfresa Pharma which takes care of development manufacturing and marketing of prescription pharmaceuticals and medical devices. The wholesale division which accounts for 99% of the company's revenues deals not only in prescription drugs but also OTC pharmaceuticals diagnostic reagents medical equipment health foods and beauty supplies. Customers include hospitals medical centers drugstores and pharmacies throughout Japan. Founded in 2003 Alfresa operates about 10 distribution centers and two manufacturing plants.

Operations

Alfresa's three operating segments are Ethical Pharmaceutical Wholesaling Self-Medication Products Wholesaling (general pharmaceuticals) and Manufacturing.

Financial Performance

Alfresa decreased revenues by 3% to some ¥2421 billion in fiscal 2015 (ended March) due to declines across all operating segments. In the ethical pharmaceuticals wholesaling business drug prices declined by an average of nearly 3% under new medical fee revisions made in 2014. Net income fell 10% to ¥22.9 billion due to an absence of settlement earnings received that year as well as corporate restructuring expenses.

Strategy

Alfresa is focused on growing its network of wholesaling businesses as well as on expanding the operations of its manufacturing division. Growth measures include organic build-up of its nationwide marketing network as well as expanding its services in the self-medication wholesale market.

In 2015 Alfresa merged subsidiaries Seiwa Sangyo and Tokiwa Yakuhin to form TS Alfresa Corporation. The unit provides ethical pharmaceuticals and devices from a wide range of manufacturers; it is focused on improving its own operating efficiencies and strengthening its marketing activities.

In manufacturing subsidiary Alfresa Fine Chemical Corporation is increasingly focused on making active pharmaceutical ingredients (APIs) for ethical pharmaceuticals; it is also working to release new products in point-of-care testing and other fields. In addition to launching new products it intends to increase market share for growth.

Mergers and Acquisitions

Alfresa expanded its business during 2015 through the acquisition of 51% of Nihon Apoch a pharmacy business serving Saitama Prefecture.

Company Background

Another example of merger and acquisition activity in the Japanese drug industry Alfresa was created in 2003 from the combination of wholesalers Azwell and Fukujin.

EXECUTIVES

VP Executive Officer and Director, Shozo Hasebe
SVP Director and Executive Officer, Taizo Kubo
Deputy President and Director, Yasuo Takita
President and Representative Director, Denroku Ishiguro, age 65
Deputy President and Director, Hidetomi Takahashi
SVP Director and Executive Officer, Shunichi Miyake
Deputy President and Director, Hiroyuki Kanome
Deputy President and Director, Tsuneo Shinohara
Auditors: KPMG AZSA LLC

LOCATIONS

HQ: Alfresa Holdings Corp Tokyo
1-1-3 Otemachi, Chiyoda-ku, Tokyo 100-0004
Phone: (81) 3 5219 5100   **Fax:** (81) 3 5219 5103
Web: www.alfresa.com

COMPETITORS

Astellas	Sumitomo Dainippon
Daiichi Sankyo	Pharma
Medipal	Suzuken
Shionogi & Co.	Takeda Pharmaceutical
Sumitomo Chemical	Toho Pharmaceutical

HISTORICAL FINANCIALS
Company Type: Public

Income Statement
FYE: March 31

	REVENUE ($ mil.)	NET INCOME ($ mil.)	NET PROFIT MARGIN	EMPLOYEES
03/16	22,949	3	0.0%	14,556
03/15	20,185	0	0.0%	14,020
03/14	24,263	247	1.0%	10,936
03/13	25,374	220	0.9%	10,939
03/12	28,443	80	0.3%	10,713
Annual Growth	(5.2%)	(54.0%)	—	8.0%

2016 Year-End Financials

Debt ratio: 0.0%
Return on equity: 0.1%
Cash ($ mil.): 1,052
Current ratio: 1.16
Long-term debt ($ mil.): 41

No. of shares (mil.): 216
Dividends
Yield: —
Payout: —
Market value ($ mil.): —

Alibaba Group Holding Ltd

Auditors: PricewaterhouseCoopers

LOCATIONS

HQ: Alibaba Group Holding Ltd
26/F Tower One, Times Square, 1 Matheson Street, Causeway Bay,
Phone: (852) 2215 5100   **Fax:** (852) 2215 5200
Web: www.alibabagroup.com

HISTORICAL FINANCIALS
Company Type: Public

Income Statement
FYE: March 31

	REVENUE ($ mil.)	NET INCOME ($ mil.)	NET PROFIT MARGIN	EMPLOYEES
03/16	15,660	11,064	70.7%	36,446
03/15	12,288	3,912	31.8%	34,985
03/14	8,443	3,749	44.4%	22,072
03/13	5,553	1,372	24.7%	20,674
03/12	3,179	671	21.1%	21,930
Annual Growth	49.0%	101.5%	—	13.5%

2016 Year-End Financials

Debt ratio: 2.4%
Return on equity: 39.2%
Cash ($ mil.): 16,539
Current ratio: 2.58
Long-term debt ($ mil.): 8,278

No. of shares (mil.): —
Dividends
Yield: —
Payout: —
Market value ($ mil.): —

	STOCK PRICE ($) FY Close	P/E High/Low		PER SHARE ($) Earnings	Dividends	Book Value
03/16	79.03	3	2	4.32	0.00	13.60
03/15	83.24	11	8	1.56	0.00	9.44
Annual Growth	(5.1%)	—	—	28.9%	—	9.6%

Alimentation Couche-Tard Inc

Alimentation Couche-Tard sells fuel for you and your car on both sides of the US-Canada border. It's the second-largest convenience store operator in North America and the leader in Canada with some 6000 outlets: Couche-Tard in Quebec; Mac's in central and western Canada; and more than 4600-plus Circle K shops in more than 40 US states and a dozen countries. (It bought the Circle K chain in the US from ConocoPhillips in 2003.) Most of its sales are rung up in the US. Alimentation Couche-Tard French for "food for those who go to bed late" sells gas at more than three-quarters of its stores. The fast-growing chain is known for expanding at home and abroad through splashy acquisitions.

Operations

In Couche-Tard's global operations Statoil Couche-Tard Mac's and Circle K are its key brands. Fuel makes up a majority of sales in every geographic region but merchandise helps even out fuel volatility and delivers generally better profit margins.

Geographic Reach

Couche-Tard operates and licenses a total of about 13100 global locations with more than 6000 convenience stores in North America. The company divides the US market into nine geographic business units with the largest retail presence in the Great Lakes region and Arizona. Its European operations include about 2260 stores concentrated in Scandinavia and the Baltics with a growing presence in Poland. In Asia it licenses the Circle K brand to operators of more than 4600 stores in a dozen mostly Asian countries.

Financial Performance

Sales at Couche-Tard's convenience stores in fiscal 2014 (ends April) climbed to $38 billion an increase of 7% over the prior year due to higher sales driven by recovering economic conditions and new store acquisitions. Net earnings rose about 42% from $573 million to $812 million due to higher revenue and some non-recurring costs in 2013 that made 2014's books look good by comparison. Without the one-time events net earnings still would have grown 23% due to contributions from acquisitions higher fuel margins in Europe and Canada and growth in same-store merchandise sales. Cash from operations rose 23% from $1161 to $1429 based on the higher net earnings one-off events in 2013 and a better exchange rate for foreign currency.

Strategy

Acquisitions are a big part of Couche-Tard's growth strategy.

In 2016 it agreed to buy 279 retail stations from Imperial Oil in Ontario and Quebec for $1.7 billion.

Its purchase of The Pantry Inc. is one of the latest is the latest in a long chain of acquisitions that includes the 2012 purchase of Statoil its largest ever and the purchase of Circle K nearly a decade ago. The Circle K acquisition established the Canadian firm as a major player in the US market while Statoil moved it into Europe. The fragmented US convenience store market and trend by major oil companies to cast off their retail operations has afforded Couche-Tard (and rival 7-Eleven) ample opportunity to acquire small independently-operated chains and occasionally a big fish. With about 70% of its sales (even more in the US) coming from gas Couche-Tard is vulnerable to fluctuations in motor fuel prices. To protect itself from such volatility the retailer is focused on developing its in-store merchandise sales (especially fresh foods) which return higher margins and are less volatile.

Mergers and Acquisitions

In 2016 the company agreed to acquire US-based CST Brands in a $3.7 billion deal.

Overall in fiscal 2014 the company acquired about 166 stores and built only 25. The big news came at the end of the calendar year with Couche-Tard said it would pay $860 million for The Pantry Inc. with more than 1500 Kangaroo Express stores in 13 US states; locations are concentrated in the southeast part of the country.

The $2.6-billion purchase of Statoil Fuel & Retail ASA with about 2300 locations in northern Europe mainly in Scandinavia closed in June 2012. Statoil is a Norway-based road transport fuel retailer and operates a network of retail stores across Scandinavia Poland the Baltic States and Russia. Statoil owns and operates a dozen key terminals as well as 38 depots in eight countries and a fleet of about 400 road tankers.

EXECUTIVES

CEO, Brian P. Hannasch, $286,000 total compensation
CFO, Claude Tessier
Group President European Operations, Jacob Schram
Group President Global Fuels and Operations North-East, Jean Bernier
EVP Scandinavia, Hans-Olav H idahl
EVP Central and Eastern Europe, J rn Madsen
Chairman, Alain Bouchard
Auditors: PricewaterhouseCoopers LLP

LOCATIONS

HQ: Alimentation Couche-Tard Inc
4204 Boulevard Industriel, Laval, Quebec H7L 0E3
Phone: 450 662-3272   **Fax:** 450 662-6633
Web: www.couche-tard.com

2016 Sales

	$ mil.	% of total
US	23,245	68
Europe	7,107	21
canada	3,791	11
Total	**34,144**	**100**

PRODUCTS/OPERATIONS

2016 Sales

	$ mil.	% of total
Road Transportation Fuel	23,306	68
Merchandise and Services	10,071	21
Other	766	11
Total	**34,144**	**100**

Selected Proprietary Brands

Beverages
  Froster (frozen)
  Sloche (flavored)
  Sunshine Joe (coffee)
Sandwiches
  Handfull
  La Maisonné

COMPETITORS

7-Eleven	Publix
Casey' s General Stores	QuikTrip
Chevron	Racetrac Petroleum
Cumberland Farms	Royal Dutch Shell
Exxon Mobil	Sheetz
Gate Petroleum	Shell Oil
Kroger	Sobeys
Kum & Go	The Pantry
Loblaw	TravelCenters of
Marathon Oil	America
Pilot Flying J	

HISTORICAL FINANCIALS

Company Type: Public

Income Statement

FYE: April 24

	REVENUE ($ mil.)	NET INCOME ($ mil.)	NET PROFIT MARGIN	EMPLOYEES
04/16	34,144	1,193	3.5%	0
04/15	34,529	932	2.7%	0
04/14	37,956	811	2.1%	78,000
04/13	35,543	572	1.6%	78,500
04/12	22,997	457	2.0%	60,000
Annual Growth	**10.4%**	**27.1%**	—	—

2016 Year-End Financials

Debt ratio: 23.2%
Return on equity: 26.7%
Cash ($ mil.): 599
Current ratio: 1.08
Long-term debt ($ mil.): 2,828

No. of shares (mil.): 567
Dividends
Yield: 0.0%
Payout: 8.8%
Market value ($ mil.): 24,406

	STOCK PRICE ($) FY Close	P/E High/Low	PER SHARE ($) Earnings	Dividends	Book Value
04/16	43.00	23 18	2.10	0.19	8.89
04/15	39.79	25 16	1.64	0.15	6.86
04/14	27.35	59 19	1.43	0.11	7.00
04/13	58.57	57 37	1.02	0.10	5.72
04/12	42.55	50 31	0.83	0.09	4.05
Annual Growth	**0.3%**	—	**26.1%**	**19.1%**	**21.7%**

Allergan PLC

Specialty pharmaceutical maker Allergan (formerly Actavis) isn't content with leading a generic life. Although formerly #3 in the global generics market behind Teva Pharmaceutical and Sandoz Allergan has reinvented itself as a branded growth pharmaceutical. In 2016 the company sold its portfolio of more than 1000 generic products to Teva for $40.5 billion. Allergan is now focused on expanding the number of branded drugs in its portfolio. These drugs are principally geared at urology and women's health. In 2016 Allergan and US-based Pfizer called off their planned $160 billion merger citing tax reasons.

Operations

The firm changed its name from Actavis to Allergan three months after acquiring Botox-maker Allergan in 2015.

In 2014 after acquiring Forest Laboratories then-named Actavis reorganized its business structure. Its new North American Brands segment was given responsibility for patent-protected and off-patent products sold in North America. The North American Generics and International segment sold and marketed off-patent products in North America and all products including over-the-counter products in international markets; it also included the third-party business Medis a provider of pharmaceutical development services that outlicenses more than 200 products to customers in more than 100 countries.

The company's former Anda Distribution division —accounting for about 15% of revenues in 2014 —focused on distributing generic brand and OTC products from more than 350 drug manufacturers to pharmacies hospitals doctors' offices and other health care providers. Distribution was handled by subsidiary Anda Inc. and its divisions which stocked more than 12000 products. In 2016 after selling its generics business to Teva Pharmaceutical Allergan sold Anda to Teva for $500 million.

The Actavis + Allergan Brand portfolio includes franchises in the dermatology and aesthetics central nervous system eye care women's health and urology gastrointestinal and Cystic Fibrosis cardiovascular and infectious disease therapeutic areas.

Geographic Reach

As a combined entity Allergan's global generics business holds leadership positions in North America Europe and Asia/Pacific. It holds top 10 positions in more than 30 markets including the US Canada the UK Russia and Australia. Among other strong growth regions are South America South Africa and Southeast Asia. Allergan's branded drugs business is a leader in urology and women's health in the US and is expanding into Canada Latin America and markets outside of the Americas.

Allergan has global and US headquarters in Parsippany New Jersey and international headquarters in Dublin Ireland. It maintains about 25 manufacturing facilities and 15 R&D centers. The US contributed about 50% of the company's sales in 2014 down from about 90% in 2011 due to international acquisitions completed in recent years.

Sales and Marketing

The group sells to customers via wholesalers retailers and independent distributors as well as directly to pharmacies grocery stores hospitals clinics and government agencies. Its largest customers in 2014 were Amerisource Bergen (28% of revenues) McKesson (21%) and Cardinal Health (13%).

The Anda Distribution segment distributes to independent pharmacies alternate care providers and pharmacy chains; it also sells some products to physicians' offices.

Financial PerformanceThe company took the #3 market spot in generics (and the Actavis name) after Watson Pharmaceuticals acquired privately held Swiss-based Actavis Group in 2012. Even before the Actavis/Watson merger the company saw consistent revenue growth over the past decade from new products acquisitions and strategic alliances. The company reported a 51% increase in revenues to $13.1 billion in 2013 primarily due to 335% growth in its North American Brands segment. Those operations grew largely as a result of the Forest Laboratories and Warner Chilcott acquisitions. The other segments also saw growth: Anda

Distribution rose 51% (due to higher earnings in the US related to higher volume and sales prices) and North American Generics and International rose 5%.

Although revenue has been rising year over year net income has been on the decline since 2012. The company's net loss increased by 117% to $1.6 billion in 2014 due to higher operating expenses including expenses related to the Forest Laboratories purchase.

Cash flow from operations rose 88% that year to $2.2 billion due to numerous factors including a change in accounts payable and accrued expenses.

Strategy

Allergan's strategy is centered on its desire to buy and develop branded drugs that provide higher profit margins. In addition to internal development of new products Allergan is seeking opportunities to acquire license or partner on additional products to keep its business healthy and diverse. Growth in certain overseas markets is looking particularly attractive especially in emerging markets such as Russia.

The company has a strong commitment to R&D on which it plans to spend some $1.7 billion in 2015 as it works to develop new products across all platforms. In 2015 it received US FDA approval for Saphris (youth bipolar disorder) Liletta (long-term birth control) Avycaz (abdominal infections and urinary tract infections) and Namzaric (dementia). It also received approval in Europe to market Xydalba for the treatment of acute bacterial skin and skin structure infections. The company also launched a generic version of Fougera's corticosteroid Temovate.

The firm has also shed some operations mostly units acquired as part of its acquisition streak. In 2015 it sold the respiratory business that it gained through the Forest Laboratories purchase to AstraZeneca for some $600 million. In a similar move it plans to sell certain of Forest's manufacturing plants and contract manufacturing agreements to private equity firm TPG. It sold a Lincolnton manufacturing facility to G&W NC Laboratories for $21.5 million in 2014.

In a major restructuring Allergan sold its generics business to Teva Pharmaceuticals for $40.5 billion in 2016. It is also selling its Anda Distribution unit to Teva for $500 million.

In 2014 the firm opened a regional office in Singapore; that location became the company's headquarters for its Asia/Pacific and Africa regions.

Mergers and Acquisitions

While the dust was barely settled from the 2012 Watson/Actavis Group transaction Actavis struck another large deal to acquire pharma company Warner Chilcott for some $5 billion in 2013 (quelling rumors that it might be acquired itself by a larger drugmaker). The purchase of Warner Chilcott expanded its specialty pharmaceutical products and gave it a better competitive edge in the niche drug markets of women's health and urology. It also expanded the company's operations into the new niche fields of gastroenterology and dermatology. An added benefit of the deal lied in Actavis' move to Ireland (where Warner Chilcott was based) following the deal; the headquarters move lowered Actavis' tax rate.

In 2016 Allergan and Pfizer called off their plans to merge; the failed $160 billion merger would have moved Pfizer's tax base from the US to Allergan's home in Ireland; it would also have created the world's largest drug maker surpassing Johnson & Johnson. In the light of new US regulations designed to prevent such tax inversion deals the companies ultimately called off the deal.

The company has been no stranger to large deals. In 2014 it purchased drug maker Forest Laboratories for about $28 billion. The move created a global drug powerhouse with branded and generic medications and a strong development pipeline expected to generate revenues of around $15 billion. The following year Actavis acquired Allergan (maker of Botox and other aesthetic products) in a $66 billion deal. With that transaction the company became a top 10 global pharmaceutical firm with revenues expected to top $23 billion in 2015. The firm also plans to buy Auden Mckenzie maker of more than 650 generic medications and some 85 products under development in a deal which will make Allergan the largest supplier of generics in the UK.

Other completed deals include the 2014 purchases of Durata Therapeutics ($724.5 million) Furiex Pharmaceuticals ($1.2 billion) and Silom Medical Company ($103 million). The company also purchased Tretin-X a product formerly marketed by Onset Dermatologics from Valeant Pharmarceuticals for $70 million.

In 2016 in the wake of the failed Pfizer merger Allergan went on a shopping spree. It agreed to buy eye care company ForSight VISION5 for an upfront payment of $95 million plus potential milestone payments. ForSight is developing a peri-ocular ring to deliver drugs and reduce pressure in glaucoma patients. It also bought Vitae Pharmaceuticals which has a dermatology product pipeline including treatments for psoriasis and atopic dermatitis for $639 million. In an even larger deal it acquired clinical-stage biopharmaceutical Tobira Therapeutics which is developing treatments for liver diseases including non-alcoholic steatohepatitis (NASH); that deal valued at up to $1.7 billion added Tobira's Cenic riviroc and Evogliptin development programs. Allergan also acquired Akama Therapeutics which also has a NASH development program for $50 million and Chase Pharmaceuticals to expand its CNS and Alzheimer's research capabilities for $125 million.

Also that year the company acquired gene therapy company RetroSense Therapeutics for $60 million upfront plus additional milestone payments related to RetroSense's RST-001 development program. The deal boosted Allergan's eye care pipeline; RST-001 is a novel gene therapy that is being studied for the potential treatment of Retinitis Pigmentosa.

With no signs of slowing down Allergan in early 2017 bought LifeCell for $2.9 billion. LifeCell specializes in making soft tissue material for surgical procedures including breast reconstruction. The company is now buying Zeltiq Aesthetics which makes cooling technology used for body fat reduction for $2.5 billion.

HISTORY

Company Background

As a youth Watson Pharmaceuticals founder Allen Chao worked at his parents' Taiwan drug factory. After earning a PhD in pharmacology in the US and working at G.

D. Searle for 10 years Chao co-founded Watson in 1984 with $4 million raised from family and friends. Watson (an anglicized version of "Hwa's son" –based on his mother's name) introduced its first generic drug a furosemide tablet (a diuretic) in 1985. The company went public in 1993.

At first Watson focused on products that posed manufacturing challenges or had limited markets. In the mid-1990s it diversified into drug development in cooperation with other firms such as Rhône-Poulenc (now part of Sanofi-Aventis). It bought competitors (Circa Pharmaceuticals 1995) and invested in drug research companies. In 1996 the company launched its first proprietary drug Microzide an antihypertensive. Watson acquired Royce Laboratories (generic drugs) and Oclassen Pharmaceuticals (dermatology products)

and boosted its sales force substantially in 1997. It also acquired rights to several products including Dilacor XR.

In 1998 Watson bought drug-delivery systems maker TheraTech (taking immediate steps to regain control of its transdermal hormone-replacement system) and Rugby Group the US generic drug unit of Hoechst (now part of Sanofi). The 1999 launch of the company's Nicotine Polacrilax (an off-patent version of the nicotine gum made by SmithKline Beecham now GlaxoSmithKline) was hampered by SmithKline's claim that accompanying instructional materials breached its copyrights (the courts ruled in favor of Watson in 2000). To boost its research activities in 2000 the firm bought Makoff R&D Laboratories and Schein Pharmaceutical. Three years later it bought Amarin Corp.'s Swedish R&D subsidiary.

EXECUTIVES

EVP Chief Legal Officer and Corporate Secretary, A. Robert D. Bailey, age 52

President and CEO, Brenton L. (Brent) Saunders, age 46, $1,000,000 total compensation

COO, Robert A. (Bob) Stewart, age 48, $715,000 total compensation

Chief Commercial Officer, William (Bill) Meury, age 47, $594,231 total compensation

CFO, Maria Teresa (Tessa) Hilado, age 51, $594,231 total compensation

EVP and Chief Human Resources Officer, Karen Ling, age 52

Chairman, Paul M. Bisaro, age 56

Auditors: PricewaterhouseCoopers LLP

LOCATIONS

HQ: Allergan PLC
Clonshaugh Business and Technology Park, Coolock, Docklands 07054
Phone: (353) 862 261 7000
Web: www.allergan.com

PRODUCTS/OPERATIONS

2014 Sales

	$ mil.	% of total
North American Generics & International	6,747	52
North American Brands	4,631	35
Anda Distribution	1,683	13
Total	**13,062**	**100**

Selected Acquisitions

COMPETITORS

Abbott Labs	Johnson & Johnson
Allergan Limited	McKesson
AmerisourceBergen	Medicis Pharmaceutical
Bayer HealthCare	Merck
Pharmaceuticals	Mylan
Boehringer Ingelheim	Novartis
Corporation	Par Pharmaceutical
Bristol-Myers Squibb	Companies
Cardinal Health	Pfizer
Cephalon	Purdue Pharma
Dr. Reddy' s	Sanofi
Endo	Shire
Genzyme	Teva
GlaxoSmithKline	Valeant
Hospira	Pharmaceuticals

HISTORICAL FINANCIALS

Company Type: Public

Income Statement

FYE: December 31

	REVENUE ($ mil.)	NET INCOME ($ mil.)	NET PROFIT MARGIN	EMPLOYEES
12/15	15,071	3,915	26.0%	31,200
12/14	13,062	(1,630)	—	21,900
12/13	8,677	(750)	—	19,200
12/12	5,914	97	1.6%	17,700
12/11	4,584	260	5.7%	6,686
Annual Growth	34.7%	96.8%	—	47.0%

2015 Year-End Financials

Debt ratio: 31.5%	No. of shares (mil.): 394
Return on equity: 7.4%	Dividends
Cash ($ mil.): 1,096	Yield: —
Current ratio: 1.03	Payout: —
Long-term debt ($ mil.): 40,293	Market value ($ mil.): 123,281

	STOCK PRICE ($) FY Close	P/E High/Low		PER SHARE ($) Earnings	Dividends	Book Value
12/15	312.50	34	25	10.01	0.00	194.15
12/14	257.41	—	—	(7.42)	0.00	114.42
12/13	168.00	—	—	(5.27)	0.00	54.72
12/12	86.00	118	73	0.76	0.00	30.02
12/11	60.34	34	24	2.06	0.00	28.02
Annual Growth	50.9%	—	—	48.5%	—	62.2%

Allianz SE

One of the world's biggest insurers Allianz SE offers a range of insurance products and services —including life health and property/casualty coverage for individuals and businesses —through more than 1000 subsidiaries ventures and affiliates operating all over the globe (Allianz SE and its subsidiaries are collectively known as the Allianz Group). The company serves some 85 million customers in such key markets as France Germany Italy and the US. In addition to selling insurance Allianz provides retail and institutional asset management services through Allianz Global Investors private equity investment through Allianz Capital Partners and banking services through Allianz Bank.

Operations

On the insurance front Allianz gets more than half of its revenues from its life and health division which operates under the Allianz brand and serves individual and group accounts. The property/casualty operations account for 40% of revenues. Allianz offers specialty property/casualty and marine insurance under the Allianz Global Corporate and Specialty brand. The unit has offices in more than a dozen locations and is one of the world's largest providers of marine insurance.

Though it has restructured to focus on core insurance and asset management offerings Allianz still has banking operations in Germany and other global regions.

Its two primary investment management businesses PIMCO and AllianzGI operate under the Allianz Asset Management segment. The group has some euro 1801 billion total assets under management making it one of the largest active asset managers in the world. Some two-thirds of third-party assets are from institutional investors while the rest are from retail investors. Core markets include France Germany Italy the UK the US and the Asia/Pacific region.

Geographic Reach

Allianz operates in more than 70 countries with most of its operations in Europe. It also operates in the Asia/Pacific region and the Americas.

Sales and Marketing

Allianz markets its products through independent agents and brokers dedicated agents bank representatives and direct marketing channels. It has about 150000 sales force associates 1200 distribution partners and about 2000 agencies in its worldwide network.

Financials

Allianz reported a 2% increase in revenues to some euro 103.2 billion in 2014 due to a 4% increase in property/casualty premiums and 19% growth in life and health statutory premiums (largely driven by its fixed-index annuity business in the US). A rise in sales of unit-linked and savings products in Italy as well as increased single-premium sales in Germany also contributed to the improvement. However these rises were partially offset by lower asset management performance fees which declined after a very strong year in 2013. Banking operations remained flat.

Net income rose 4% to euro 6.6 billion in 2014 primarily as a result of the higher revenue as well as a decline in income tax provisions. Cash flow from operations increased 39% to euro 32.2 billion largely as a result of higher unearned premiums and reserves in the life and health segment.

Strategy

Allianz is focused on achieving sustainable growth in its property/casualty life and health and asset management operations. It also seeks to achieve operational synergies among its businesses through shared technology investments capital allocations and best practice sharing. The company's investment strategy is conservative with the goal of providing stable returns.

While the US and Europe are Allianz's largest markets the company is pursuing growth in emerging markets as well. It has established significant operations in select Asian countries and it is expanding its presence in Central and Eastern Europe and the Asia/Pacific region. Targeted markets include China India and Russia.

The group has been restructuring its North American business. In 2014 it absorbed the commercial lines of Fireman's Fund Insurance Company into its Allianz Global Corporate & Specialty industrial insurer; it plans to launch new financial lines including directors and officers coverage professional indemnity and errors and omissions insurance. The following year Allianz sold its Fireman's Fund Personal Insurance division to Chubb Limited for $365 million marking the end of the Fireman's Fund brand name.

Mergers and Acquisitions

Boosting its share of the Italian market Allianz acquired certain distribution activities (comprising a network of 725 agencies) of UnipolSai Assicurazioni's property/casualty business in 2014. It also purchased the property/casualty in-force portfolio managed by the acquired agencies.

The group also purchased the property/casualty business of Australia's Territory Insurance Office in late 2014; it additionally gained servicing responsibilities for the Government Motors Accidents Compensation program.

Ownership

Allianz is part of a web of interlocking German corporate ownership. It holds a stake in reinsurance giant Munich Re which in turn has a small stake in Allianz. Munich Re is also the company's principal external reinsurer though Allianz itself reinsures a significant amount of its insurance companies' risk. Allianz also serves as a reinsurer for third parties.

HISTORY

Company Background

Carl Thieme founded Allianz in Germany in 1890. That year the company took part in the creation of the Calamity Association of Accident Insurance Companies a consortium of German Austrian Swiss and Russian firms to insure international commerce.

By 1898 Thieme had established offices in the UK Switzerland and the Netherlands. His successor Paul von der Nahmer expanded Allianz into the Balkans France Italy Scandinavia and the US. After a hiatus during WWI Allianz returned to foreign markets.

In WWII Allianz insured Auschwitz Dachau and other death camps. Company documents show Allianz wasn't worried about risk at the SS troop-guarded camps. After the German defeat the victors seized Allianz's foreign holdings except for a stake in Spain's Plus Ultra. In the 1950s Allianz repurchased confiscated holdings in Italian and Austrian companies.

Allianz saturated the German market and began a full-scale international drive in the late 1950s and 1960s. It became Europe's largest insurer through a series of acquisitions beginning in 1973. Allianz formed Los Angeles-based Allianz Insurance in 1977.

In 1981 Allianz launched a takeover (which turned hostile) of the UK's Eagle Star insurance company. After a 1983 bidding joust with Britain's B.A.T Industries (now part of Zurich Financial Services) Allianz withdrew.

The firm consoled itself by shopping. In 1984 it won control of Riunione Adriatica di Sicurtà (Ras) Italy's second-largest insurance company. Two years later the firm bought Cornhill (now Allianz Insurance plc) on its third try. As the Iron Curtain crumbled Allianz in 1989 acquired 49% of Hungaria Biztosito. Its drang nach Osten continued the next year after national reunification when it gained control of Deutsche Versicherungs AG East Germany's insurance monopoly. Allianz that year became the first German insurer licensed in Japan; it also bought the US's Fireman's Fund Insurance.

Natural disasters led to large claims and set the company back in 1992 the first time in 20 years it lost money from its German operations. Allianz restructured operations that year; profits surged in 1993 mostly from international business.

Allianz expanded in Mexico in 1995 forming a life and health insurance joint venture with Grupo Financiero BanCrecer (now owned by Grupo Financiero Banorte). The company set up an asset management arm in Hong Kong in 1996 with an eye to further Asian expansion getting a license in China the next year. In 1997 after Holocaust survivors sued Allianz and other insurers for failing to pay on life policies after WWII Allianz agreed to participate in a repayment fund.

In 1998 Allianz bought control of Assurances Generales de France; it was the white knight that prevented Assicurazioni Generali from taking the company. In 1999 Allianz said it would restructure some of its insurance operations including spinning off its marine and aviation lines to better compete in the multinational market. That year US subsidiary Allianz Life bought Life USA Holding. In 2000 Allianz bought 70% of PIMCO Advisors Holdings to strengthen its asset management operations. That year the company continued its push into Asia buying a 12% stake in Hana Bank of South Korea and planning to boost its ownership of Malaysia British Assurance Life. Also in 2000 Allianz acquired Dutch insurer Zwolsche Algemeene.

Allianz remained acquisitive in 2001 buying US investment manager Nicholas-Applegate and taking a majority stake in ROSNO one of Russia's largest insurers. Also that year it bought a nearly 96% stake in German banking giant Dresdner and acquired the remainder the following year.

Allianz paid out claims of some $1.3 billion relating to the terrorist attacks on the World Trade Center. The company set up a terrorism insurance unit offering coverage primarily for companies within the European Union.

EXECUTIVES

CEO Allianz Worldwide Care, Ida Luka-Lognone, age 54

Member Management Board and Chairman and CEO, Oliver B☐te, age 51, $700,000 total compensation

Management Board Member and COO, Christof Mascher, age 56, $216,000 total compensation

Management Board Member and CFO, Dieter Wemmer, age 60

Management Board Member Investments, Maximilian Zimmerer, age 58

CEO Allianz Global Corporate and Specialty SE (AGCS), Axel Theis, age 59

CEO TIO, Daryl Madden

Chief Market Manager, Paul Kernaghan

Vice Chairman, Wulf H. Bernotat, age 68

Auditors: KPMG AG Wirtschaftsprufungsgesellschaft

LOCATIONS

HQ: Allianz SE
Koeniginstrasse 28, Munich D-80802
Phone: (49) 89 38 00 0   **Fax:** (49) 89 38 00 3425
Web: www.allianz.com

PRODUCTS/OPERATIONS

2014 Sales

	% of total
Life & health insurance	55
Property/casualty insurance	40
Asset management	5
Corporate & other	.
Total	**100**

Selected Operations and Brands
Allianz
Allianz Global Corporate and Specialty
Allianz Global Investors
Allianz Worldwide Care
Euler Hermes
PIMCO

COMPETITORS

AEGON	Munich Re Group
AXA	New York Life
Allstate	Nippon Life Insurance
Aviva	Old Mutual
Berkshire Hathaway	Prudential
CNP Assurances	Prudential plc
Citigroup	RSA Insurance
ERGO	State Farm
Generali	Swiss Re
Generali Deutschland	Talanx
Groupama	The Hartford
ING	Victoria Versicherung
Legal & General Group	Zurich Insurance Group
MetLife	ageas SA/NV

HISTORICAL FINANCIALS
Company Type: Public

Income Statement
FYE: December 31

	ASSETS ($ mil.)	NET INCOME ($ mil.)	INCOME AS % OF ASSETS	EMPLOYEES
12/15	924,676	7,206	0.8%	142,459
12/14	979,438	7,561	0.8%	147,425
12/13	979,588	8,254	0.8%	147,627
12/12	915,544	6,813	0.7%	144,094
12/11	829,713	3,291	0.4%	141,938
Annual Growth	**2.7%**	**21.6%**	**—**	**0.1%**

2015 Year-End Financials
Return on assets: 0.8%
Return on equity: 10.6%
Long-term debt ($ mil.): —
No. of shares (mil.): 454
Sales ($ mil): 109,571

Dividends
Yield: 3.2%
Payout: —
Market value ($ mil.): 8,014

	STOCK PRICE ($) FY Close	P/E High/Low		PER SHARE ($) Earnings	Dividends	Book Value
12/15	17.62	1	1	15.85	0.57	151.22
12/14	16.57	1	1	16.58	0.54	162.55
12/13	18.13	1	1	17.97	0.44	151.97
12/12	13.82	1	1	14.95	0.43	155.76
12/11	9.47	3	1	7.09	0.00	128.40
Annual Growth	**16.8%**	**—**	**—**	**22.3%**	**—**	**4.2%**

Allied Irish Banks Plc

Allied Irish Banks (AIB) one of Ireland's largest banks and private employers is looking beyond the Emerald Isle for its proverbial pot o' gold. The company offers retail and commercial accounts and loans life insurance financing leasing pension and trust services through a network of 200 branches 74 EBS Limited offices 10 business centers and 755 ATMs. The company's capital markets division offers commercial treasury services corporate finance and investment banking services. In the US AIB specializes in financial services for the not-for-profit sector.

Operations

Over the years AIB has reorganized into a more simplified structure in which its divisions were integrated and its AIB and First Trust operations were more closely aligned. To attract additional customers the bank also introduced mobile banking services to its offerings.

HISTORY

Allied Irish Banks was formed in 1966 by the "trinity" of Provincial Bank (founded 1825) The Royal Bank (founded 1836) and Munster and Leinster (founded 1885 but with origins back to the late 1600s). Both AIB and its then-larger rival Bank of Ireland had to consolidate in order to compete with North American banks entering Ireland. From its start AIB sought to expand overseas and by 1968 it had an alliance with Canada's Toronto-Dominion Bank.

In the 1970s AIB expanded its branch network to England and Scotland. The 1980s saw AIB boost its presence in the US market (it had already debuted AIB branches) with the acquisition of First Maryland Bancorp.

The Irish Parliament's Finance Act of 1986 instituted a withholding tax known as the Deposit Interest Retention Tax (DIRT) for Irish residents.

Consequently (with a wink and a nod) AIB and other banks let customers create bogus non-resident accounts to avoid paying DIRT. An investigation indicated that at one point AIB's branch in Tralee had 14700 non-resident accounts on its rolls –more than half the local population. After tax authorities began probing many of the accounts in question were reclassified as "resident" and customers had to pay the taxes on them. In 1991 AIB was reprimanded but neither the bank nor its customers have paid the remaining $100 million tax bill.

Tom Mulcahy who integrated AIB's treasury investment and international banking activities became chief executive in 1994. Mulcahy a respected leader envisioned AIB as an international Ireland-based bank.

In 1995 AIB bought UK-based investment fund manager John Govett from London Pacific Group (now Berkeley Technology Limited). Mulcahy moved AIB the same year into Eastern Europe with a stake in Poland-based Wielkopolski Bank Kredytowy (or WBK).

AIB was busy in 1999. It gained a toehold in Asia by entering a cross-marketing agreement with Singapore's Keppet TatLee bank a survivor of the region's financial crisis. Liberalized Singapore banking laws allowed AIB the right to buy one-quarter of the bank by 2001. AIB also bought an 80% stake of Bank Zachodni in Poland in 1999.

That year AIB merged First Maryland Bancorp and its other US holdings into the renamed Allfirst Financial a sizable mid-Atlantic states bank.

To consolidate its power in Eastern Europe in 2001 AIB merged its Polish banks (Wielkopolski Bank Kredytowy and Bank Zachodni) into Bank Zachodni WBK. That year Mulcahy retired but was appointed by the Irish government to take over as chairman of troubled airline Aer Lingus.

AIB lost nearly $700 million from 1996 to 2002 apparently from bogus foreign exchange transactions made by rogue trader John Rusnak who pleaded guilty to bank fraud.

In 2003 AIB sold troubled Maryland-based bank Allfirst Financial to M&T Bank Corporation. As part of the deal AIB assumed ownership of more than 20% of M&T becoming the company's largest shareholder. Under AIB's direction Allfirst had grown into a major regional player with about 250 branches in Maryland Pennsylvania Virginia and Washington DC.

In the midst of the global financial crisis the Irish government injected euro 2 billion ($2.8 billion) into AIB in exchange for a 25% share in voting rights in 2008. Ireland also provided capital for Bank of Ireland and Irish Bank Resolution Corporation to help stabilize the plunging Irish financial system. AIB also sought capital from the private sector.

EXECUTIVES

Director Personal Business and Corporate Banking, Bernard Byrne, age 47
CFO and Director, Mark G. Bourke, age 49
CEO, David Duffy, age 54
COO, Stephen White
Chairman, Richard A. Pym, age 67
CFO and Director, Mark G. Bourke, age 49
Deputy Chairman, Michael Somers, age 74
Auditors: Deloitte

LOCATIONS

HQ: Allied Irish Banks Plc
Bankcentre, P.O. Box 452, Ballsbridge, Dublin 4
Phone: (353) 1 660 0311   **Fax:** 212 515-6710
Web: www.aibgroup.com

PRODUCTS/OPERATIONS

2013 Sales

	% of total
Interest and similar income	86
Fee and commission income	11
Others	3
Total	**100**

COMPETITORS

Bank Millennium	HSBC
Bank of America	Irish Bank Resolution
Bank of Ireland	Lloyds Banking Group
Barclays	Royal Bank of Scotland
Citigroup	Ulster Bank

HISTORICAL FINANCIALS

Company Type: Public

Income Statement

FYE: December 31

	ASSETS ($ mil.)	NET INCOME ($ mil.)	INCOME AS % OF ASSETS	EMPLOYEES
12/15	112,321	1,503	1.3%	10,204
12/14	130,612	1,112	0.9%	11,047
12/13	162,088	(2,198)	—	12,648
12/12	161,482	(4,806)	—	14,708
12/11	176,751	(2,990)	—	16,716
Annual Growth	(10.7%)	—	—	(11.6%)

2015 Year-End Financials

Return on assets: 1.3%
Return on equity: 11.6%
Long-term debt ($ mil.): —
No. of shares (mil.): —
Sales ($ mil): 4,060
Dividends
  Yield: —
  Payout: —
Market value ($ mil.): —

	STOCK PRICE ($) FY Close	P/E High/Low		PER SHARE ($) Earnings	Dividends	Book Value
12/15	8.00	19	0	0.47	0.00	4.87
12/14	0.09	0	0	0.61	0.00	6.72
12/13	0.15	—	—	(1.03)	0.00	6.93
12/12	0.06	—	—	(2.31)	0.00	7.16
12/11	0.07	—	—	(2.91)	0.00	9.11
Annual Growth 227.0% (14.5%)		—	—	—	—	—

Aluminum Corp of China Ltd.

Auditors: Ernst & Young Hua Ming LLP

LOCATIONS

HQ: Aluminum Corp of China Ltd.
  No. 62, North Xizhimen Street, Haidian District,
  Beijing 100082
Phone: (86) 10 8229 8560   **Fax:** (86) 10 8229 8158
Web: www.chalco.com.cn

HISTORICAL FINANCIALS

Company Type: Public

Income Statement

FYE: December 31

	REVENUE ($ mil.)	NET INCOME ($ mil.)	NET PROFIT MARGIN	EMPLOYEES
12/15	19,007	31	0.2%	70,368
12/14	22,843	(2,612)	—	75,749
12/13	27,987	161	0.6%	90,207
12/12	23,977	(1,320)	—	97,990
12/11	23,175	37	0.2%	101,259
Annual Growth	(4.8%)	(4.3%)	—	(8.7%)

2015 Year-End Financials

Debt ratio: 8.8%
Return on equity: 0.6%
Cash ($ mil.): 3,195
Current ratio: 0.79
Long-term debt ($ mil.): 8,272
No. of shares (mil.): —
Dividends
  Yield: —
  Payout: —
Market value ($ mil.): —

	STOCK PRICE ($) FY Close	P/E High/Low	PER SHARE ($) Earnings	Dividends	Book Value
12/15	8.24	1660703	0.00	0.00	0.40
12/14	11.52	— —	(0.19)	0.00	0.34
12/13	8.70	195107	0.01	0.00	0.54
12/12	11.91	— —	(0.10)	0.00	0.52
12/11	10.80	1348521	0.00	0.04	0.61
Annual Growth	(6.5%)	— —(16.6%)	—	(9.9%)	

America Movil SAB de CV

America Movil offers wireless phone service from the Rio Grande to Tierra del Fuego. The company is Latin America's top mobile carrier with more than 285 million subscribers in 25 countries. In Mexico the company enjoys a 70% market share with nearly 74 million subscribers to its Telcel and Telmex brands which operate retail stores. Its second largest market is Brazil which serves about 69 million subscribers through Claro. America Movil also provides fixed-line service in Central America and the Caribbean with more than 6 million lines. TracFone Wireless is America Movil's US presence. Billionaire Carlos Slim Helu owns most of America Movil.

Operations

Not surprisingly mobile is the big money maker for America Movil providing more than half of its revenue. Mobile voice services account for 27% of the total with 26% coming from mobile data services. Fixed voice and data services generate about 24% of revenue.

Geographic Reach

Considering its nearly worldwide reach America Movil could be called Mundo Movil. The company has operations in throughout the western hemisphere (not including Canada) as well as Eastern Europe. About a third of revenue comes from Mexico with Brazil and the US as other significant countries accounting for 19% and 12% of revenue respectively.

Sales and Marketing

America Movil reaches customers through a network of retailers and service centers for retail customers and a dedicated sales force for corporate customers.

The company counts more than 200000 points of sale and some 2500 customer service centers.

Financial Performance

America Movil's revenue increased 5% in 2015 boosted by its wireless data and fixed data operations. Customers downloading media and content surfing the web and streaming videos pushed wireless data revenue 21% higher. Residential broadband use led to an 8% rise in fixed data revenue. Revenue from voice wireless and fixed dropped in 2015 from 2014.

Negative foreign exchange transactions pushed the company to a net loss for 2015 compared to a profit in 2014. Cash flow from operations also fell in 2015 from 2014.

Strategy

America Movil focuses on expanding its 4G LTE services. In 2015 it spun off Telesites which operate its cellular towers in Mexico. It also adds new markets through acquisitions.

Mergers and Acquisitions

In 2016 the company bought two wireless operators in Peru Olo del Peru S.A.C. and TVS Wireless S.A.C.

In 2015 America Movil acquired an additional 35% of Hitss Solutions a provider of IT services. The deal raised America Movil's stake in Hitss to about 69%.

HISTORY

The company was formed in 2000 as a result of a spinoff from Telmex which was at the time Mexico's largest local and long-distance phone service provider. In late 2006 America Movil acquired majority owner America Telecom in a move to streamline the structure of the company and to free up assets for share buybacks or dividends.

The company expanded its presence in the Caribbean region in 2007 with the acquisition of Puerto Rico Telephone from Verizon Communications and a handful of other shareholders for nearly $2 billion. The next year it bought Jamaican wireless service provider Oceanic Digital Jamaica and became licenced to provide wireless services in Panama.

Also in 2008 the company rebranded its operations in Argentina Paraguay and Uruguay to its Claro brand which America Movil now uses for all of its operations in Central America and the Caribbean. That year it bought Estesa Holding a cable TV and data services provider in Nicaragua for $48 million. The acquisition of Estesa boosted America Movil's cable television and broadband offerings and gave the company greater access to the Nicaraguan market.

EXECUTIVES

CEO Telmex, Hector Slim Seade, age 53
CFO, Carlos Jose Garc a Moreno Elizondo
CEO Peru, Humberto Ch ˇvez L pez
CEO Central America, Juan Antonio Aguilar
CEO Dominican Republic, Oscar Pe ±a Chac n
CEO Argentina Uruguay and Paraguay, Julio Carlos Porras
CEO and Director, Daniel Hajj Aboumrad, age 50
CEO Panama, Oscar Borda
CEO Puerto Rico, Enrique Ortiz de Montellano Rangel
CEO Telekom Austria, Alejandro Plater, age 49
Executive Director Fixed Line Operations, Oscar Von Hauske Sol s
Executive Director Mobile Operations, ngel Alija Guerrero
COO Telcel, Patricia Raquel Hevia Coto
CEO Columbia, Carlos Hern n Zenteno de los Santos
CEO Ecuador, Alfredo Escobar San Lucas
CEO Corporate Market Unit Brazil, Jose Formoso Mart nez

CEO Residential Market Unit Brazil, Daniel
Feldmann Barros
President Brazil, Jose Ant´nio Guaraldi Felix
CEO Chile, Mauricio Escobedo V´zquez
CFO and Acting CEO United States, Gustavo
Blanco Villanueva
Chairman, Carlos Slim Domit, age 49
Vice Chairman, Patrick Slim Domit, age 47
Auditors: Mancera, S.C. (member of Ernst & Young
Global)

LOCATIONS

HQ: America Movil SAB de CV
Lago Zurich 245, Plaza Carso/Edificio Telcel, Colonia
Ampliacion Granada, Mexico, D.F. 11529
Phone: (52) 55 2581 4449   **Fax:** (52) 55 2581 4422
Web: www.americamovil.com

2015 Sales

	% of total
Mexico wireless	22
Brazil	19
US	12
Mexico fixed	11
Southern cone	8
Europe	8
Colombia	7
Andean region	6
Central America	4
Caribbean	3
Total	**100**

PRODUCTS/OPERATIONS

2015 Sales

	% of total
Mobile voice services	27
Mobile data voice services	26
Sales of equipment accessories and computer	13
Fixed voice services	12
Fixed data services	12
Paid television	7
Other services	3
Total	**100**

Selected Operations

América Móvil Peru (8.3 million subscribers)
AM Wireless Uruguay (800000 subscribers)
AMX Argentina (17 million subscribers)
AMX Paraguay (500000 subscribers)
Claro Chile (3.6 million subscribers)
Claro Panama (100000 subscribers)
Codetel (Dominican Republic 4.8 million subscribers)
Comcel (Colombia 27.7 million subscribers)
Conecel (Ecuador 9.4 million subscribers)
CTE (El Salvador 800000 subscribers)
ENITEL (Nicaragua 2.2 million subscribers)
Oceanic (Jamaica 400000 subscribers)
Sercom Honduras (1.4 million subscribers)
TELPRI (Puerto Rico 1.6 million subscribers)
TracFone (US 14.4 million subscribers)
Telgua (Guatemala 1.2 million subscribers)

COMPETITORS

AT&T	Sprint Communications
Alfa SA	TIM Participa§µes
Axtel	Tele Norte Leste
Brasil Telecom	Telecom Argentina
Cable & Wireless	Telefnica
Communications	Telefnica de
Iusacell	Argentina
Millicom	Telef-´nica Brasil
NII Holdings	Telemig Celular
Portugal Telecom	Vivo Participa§µes

HISTORICAL FINANCIALS
Company Type: Public

Income Statement
FYE: December 31

	REVENUE ($ mil.)	NET INCOME ($ mil.)	NET PROFIT MARGIN	EMPLOYEES
12/15	51,473	2,017	3.9%	195,475
12/14	57,713	3,139	5.4%	191,156
12/13	60,030	5,698	9.5%	173,174
12/12	59,648	7,037	11.8%	158,719
12/11	47,627	5,931	12.5%	158,694
Annual Growth	**2.0%**	**(23.6%)**	**—**	**5.3%**

2015 Year-End Financials

Debt ratio: 3.0%	No. of shares (mil.): —
Return on equity: 23.6%	Dividends
Cash ($ mil.): 2,599	Yield: 4.7%
Current ratio: 0.83	Payout: 2,139.8%
Long-term debt ($ mil.): 32,443	Market value ($ mil.): —

	STOCK PRICE ($) FY Close	P/E High/Low		PER SHARE ($) Earnings	Dividends	Book Value
12/15	14.06	38	27	0.03	0.67	0.07
12/14	22.18	35	25	0.05	0.36	0.18
12/13	23.37	24	17	0.08	0.34	0.22
12/12	23.14	24	19	0.09	0.30	0.31
12/11	22.60	49	18	0.08	0.26	0.27
Annual Growth	**(11.2%) (28.9%)**	—	—	**(20.6%)**	**27.2%**	

AMP Ltd.

AMP is on top —down under. The company is
one of Australia's largest insurance and investment management groups. Through its AMP Financial Services (AFS) division more than 2000
representatives sell the company's financial offerings which include life home vehicle travel and
business insurance as well as retirement products
financial planning and advice superannuation
products (professionally managed retirement investment funds) and banking. AMP Capital Investors provides investment management to AFS
and to other individual and institutional investors.
AMP Limited also provides retail financial services
under the Hillcross and Arrive Wealth Management brands.

HISTORY

AMP was conceived in Sydney in 1848 by W. S.
Walsh (a clergyman) Thomas Mort (a businessman) and Thomas Holt (a wool trader) who con-
vened with two others to discuss forming a mutual
life insurance company in Australia. (Many of the
UK's and US's largest mutuals were also founded
about this time.) The next year Australian Mutual
Provident Society was born; it opened for business
with a staff of two: secretary William Perry and a
small boy. In its first year the company sold only
42 policies. Luckily no one died in the first three
years of operations and the company was able to
build up some reserves. The company grew slowly
over the next decade appointing just two agents —
in Auckland New Zealand and Hobart Australia.
Sales took off with the 1860 appointment of the
company's first full-time agent Benjamin Short
who had the novel idea of actively recruiting customers and actually selling policies. The company
opened an office in New Zealand in 1871; it opened
a branch in the UK in 1908.

In the next few decades the company helped
build the Australian economy through investment
of its reserves. It funded industry and infrastructure including farming communities as part of the
South Australian Land Development Scheme. The
company grew free of foreign competition protected by regulations severely restricting the activities of foreign companies in the banking and financial industries in Australia. In 1958 the
company formed AMP Fire and General Insurance
(changed to AMP General in 1990).

In 1988 AMP moved abroad with the acquisition
of London Life Assurance. The following year it
made history with its acquisition of funds management group Pearl Assurance then the largest
takeover of a British financial firm by a foreign
company.

The company founded AMP Asset Management
in 1991 to manage its overseas assets. In 1995 the
company expanded its international presence
through a joint venture with the financial services
arm of UK-based Virgin Group. The company also
began offering mortgage and banking products in
Australia through a new unit Priority One.

After a careful inquiry in 1996 AMP's board
recommended demutualization; policyholders approved in 1997 and the conversion was completed
the next year with the company taking the name
AMP Limited. Trading got off to a rocky start however as the company imposed an unusual pricing
mechanism by which the official initial stock price
was linked to pricing activity over the first five days
of trading. This was done to protect individual policyholders from typical opening-day stock gyra-
tions but institutional investors were unable to
value their investments for several days (a technical breach of accounting rules).

AMP bought Citibank's New Zealand retail
banking business and UK fund manager Henderson in 1998. The next year AMP battled to buy
general insurer GIO Australia Holdings picking up
57% after resistance to its original low-ball offer;
it also bought UK mutual insurer National Provident Institution (NPI).

The company streamlined all of its investment-
management operations into a single unit in 1999
and expanded Asian operations with offices in Beijing and Tokyo. In 2000 the problems arising from
the GIO takeover resulted in a board shakeup;
chairman Ian Burgess resigned.

Local rival Suncorp-Metway bought AMP's domestic general insurance unit in 2001 and
Churchill Insurance (a subsidiary of Credit Suisse)
acquired its similar operations in the UK that year.

AMP split off its UK-based operations as HHG
at the end of 2003 (retaining a 10% share). HHG
eventually changed its name to Henderson Group
plc in 2005. AMP sold its shares in Henderson later
that year.

EXECUTIVES

**Director Product Manufacturing AMP Financial
Services,** Craig Meller, age 53
CEO AMP Capital, Adam Tindall
Group Executive Operations, Wendy Thorpe
CFO, Gordon Lefevre
CIO, Craig Ryman
Group Executive Advice and New Zealand, Jack
Regan
Group Executive Wealth Solutions and Customer,
Paul Sainsbury
Group Executive AMP Bank, Sally Bruce
Group Executive Insurance, Megan Beer
Chief Risk Officer, Saskia Goedhart
Chairman, Catherine Brenner, age 46
Auditors: Ernst & Young

LOCATIONS

HQ: AMP Ltd.
33 Alfred Street, Sydney, New South Wales 2000
Phone: (61) 2 9257 5000   **Fax:** (61) 2 9257 7178
Web: www.amp.com.au

PRODUCTS/OPERATIONS

2015 Sales

	% of total
Investment gains	61
Fee revenue	21
Life insurance premiums & related revenue	17
Other	1
Total	**100**

Selected Services

Business Banking
Insurance Products
Investment Products
Loans
Personal Banking
Retirement Products
Superannuation

COMPETITORS

AXA Asia Pacific	National Australia
Australia and New	Bank
Zealand Banking	QBE
Aviva	RSA Insurance
Commonwealth Bank of	St. Andrew' s Australia
Australia	Suncorp-Metway
Macquarie Group	ageas SA/NV

HISTORICAL FINANCIALS

Company Type: Public

Income Statement

FYE: December 31

	ASSETS ($ mil.)	NET INCOME ($ mil.)	INCOME AS % OF ASSETS	EMPLOYEES
12/15	102,159	710	0.7%	5,400
12/14	110,678	725	0.7%	5,400
12/13	119,111	600	0.5%	5,700
12/12	123,395	731	0.6%	5,829
12/11	112,176	699	0.6%	6,000
Annual Growth	(2.3%)	0.4%	—	(2.6%)

2015 Year-End Financials

Return on assets: 0.7%
Return on equity: 11.6%
Long-term debt ($ mil.): —
No. of shares (mil.): —
Sales ($ mil) 10,273

Dividends
Yield: 0.0%
Payout: 302.2%
Market value ($ mil.): —

	STOCK PRICE ($) FY Close	P/E High/Low		Earnings	Dividends	Book Value
12/15	16.93	60	47	0.24	0.73	2.13
12/14	17.77	65	45	0.25	0.71	2.31
12/13	15.82	89	64	0.20	0.24	2.47
Annual Growth	3.4%	—	—	4.3%	32.0%	(3.6%)

ANA Holdings Inc

ANA Holdings is the parent of All Nippon Airways one of Japan's leading carriers along with Japan Airlines. With a fleet of more than 240 aircraft ANA flies to some 130 domestic destinations and 40 international ones. It extends its network through code-sharing with members of the Star Alliance an airline marketing partnership that in-

cludes such carriers as United Continental's United Airlines and Continental and Lufthansa. (Code-sharing enables airlines to sell tickets on one another's flights.) Besides passenger service ANA's air transportation operations include cargo and mail hauling and aircraft maintenance and ground support. The company also sells travel packages and operates hotels.

Operations

ANA's reportable segments are Air Transportation (73% of net sales) Airline Related (11%) Travel Services (8%) and Trade and Retail (6%).

Air Transportation conducts domestic and International passenger operations cargo and mail operations and other transportation services. Airline Related offers airport passenger and ground handling services and maintenance services.

Travel Services specializes in the development and sales of travel plans and also conducts planning and sales of branded travel packages using air transportation. Trade and Retail mainly imports and exports goods related to air transportation and is involved in in-store and non-store retailing.

Financial Performance

ANA's revenues climbed 9% from 2013 to 2014 primarily due to growth across the majority of its segments. Air Transportation increased due to additional revenue from its international routes in which the scale of its network grew.ANA was also helped in 2014 by a spike in Airlines Related revenue due to a surge in airport ground support services such as passenger check-in and baggage handling services commissioned by foreign airlines.

The company's net income skyrocketed over 100% from 2013 to 2014 due to decreased retirement benefit expenses increased equity in earnings of non-consolidated subsidiaries and the absence of the depreciation of idle assets.

Strategy

To keep growing ANA plans to introduce a total of 23 aircraft with an expansion of international operations mainly on Narita Airport (serving the Greater Tokyo area) and initiatives to match capacity and demand on domestic routes by using smaller sized aircraft.

Company Background

Two domestic Japanese air carriers that started in 1952 —Nippon Helicopter and Aeroplane Transport and Far East Airlines —consolidated operations in 1957 as All Nippon Airways (ANA).

EXECUTIVES

SVP Marketing and Products, Osamu Shinobe
SEVP Government and Industrial Affairs Strategic Planning-Asia Pacific Airport and Facilities Planning, Shigeyuki Takemura
EVP; Chairman CSR Promotion Committee Public Relations Executive Secretariat Legal and Insurance General Administration and CSR Promotion, Yoshinori Maruyama
EVP Finance Accounting and Investor Relations, Kiyoshi Tonomoto
EVP, Yuji Hirako
Chairman, Shinichiro Ito
Auditors: Ernst & Young ShinNihon LLC

LOCATIONS

HQ: ANA Holdings Inc
1-5-2 Higashi-Shimbashi, Minato-ku, Tokyo 105-7140
Phone: (81) 3 6735 1001   **Fax:** (81) 3 6735 1005
Web: www.anahd.co.jp

2014 Sales

	% of total
Japan	86
Overseas	14
Total	**100**

PRODUCTS/OPERATIONS

2014 Sales

	% of total
Air transportation	73
Airline related	11
Travel services	8
Trade and Retail	6
Other businesses	2
Total	**100**

COMPETITORS

Accor	Delta Air Lines
Air France-KLM	EVA Air
American Airlines	East Japan Railway
Group	Hyatt
American Express	Japan Airlines
British Airways	Kintetsu
Carlson Wagonlit	Korean Air
Cathay Pacific	Qantas
Central Japan Railway	Singapore Airlines
China Airlines	Virgin Atlantic
China Eastern Airlines	Airways
China Southern	West Japan Railway
Airlines	

HISTORICAL FINANCIALS

Company Type: Public

Income Statement

FYE: March 31

	REVENUE ($ mil.)	NET INCOME ($ mil.)	NET PROFIT MARGIN	EMPLOYEES
03/16	15,950	696	4.4%	40,040
03/15	14,281	327	2.3%	38,650
03/14	15,510	182	1.2%	33,719
03/13	15,767	458	2.9%	32,634
03/12	17,207	343	2.0%	32,884
Annual Growth	(1.9%)	19.3%	—	5.0%

2016 Year-End Financials

Debt ratio: 0.2%
Return on equity: 9.8%
Cash ($ mil.): 492
Current ratio: 1.08
Long-term debt ($ mil.): 5,282

No. of shares (mil.): —
Dividends
Yield: 1.1%
Payout: —
Market value ($ mil.): —

	STOCK PRICE ($) FY Close	P/E High/Low		Earnings	Dividends	Book Value
03/16	5.71	0	0	0.20	0.07	2.00
03/15	5.47	1	0	0.09	0.05	1.89
03/14	4.27	—	—	0.05	0.00	2.07
03/13	4.20	—	—	0.14	0.00	2.34
03/12	5.95	—	—	0.14	0.00	2.68
Annual Growth	(1.0%)	—	—	9.8%	—	(7.1%)

Anglo American Plc (United Kingdom)

Anglo American's name might be a little misleading —it has never been American. The UK-based company owns significant stakes in global producers of platinum (75% of Anglo Platinum) and diamonds (85% of De Beers S.A.). In addition Anglo American has interests in ferrous and base metals and industrial minerals. It ranks among the world's largest iron ore producers and is also a leading copper producer. Anglo is one of the world's largest coal miners and exporters of metallurgical coal a key raw material in steel production. It also produces thermal coal used to generate electricity. The founding Oppenheimer family no longer controls Anglo American.

Anglo American has been growing by strategic investments in long-life low-cost assets. It also has been increasing its organic growth by delivering projects ahead of or on schedule. For the past five years the company has been slimming down its operations setting strict targets and investing in strategic growth opportunities. It does not look to investments on the basis of short-term drivers but makes its decisions based on long-term investments that will be sound for the next decade or beyond. The company tries to look beyond current market volatility while making its investments.

It 2009 Anglo decided to continue investing in four major projects: Kolomela iron ore mine in South Africa Barro Alto (nickel) and Minas-Rio (iron ore) mines in Brazil and Los Bronces copper mine in Chile. By 2011 all but the Minas-Rio iron ore project had started production on or ahead of schedule. A discovery of caves at the Minas-Rio iron ore project caused a delay in the work schedule because of a need for specialized assessment.

In 2011 Anglo delivered a strong performance which was boosted by higher prices. The company achieved a record group operating profit that year of $11.1 billion up 14% from the prior year and driven in part by solid performances by its Kumba Iron Ore Metallurgical Coal and Thermal Coal divisions. However the company's net income dipped slightly from that in 2010 when the company posted larger gains on divestments.

Anglo also made acquisitions in 2011 that significantly increased its growth. Perhaps its most historic purchase in recent years was its agreement in late 2011 to acquire the Oppenheimer family's 40% stake in giant diamond company De Beers for $5.1 billion. The interest of the Oppenheimers —who had been in the diamond industry for more than a century—increased Anglo American's 45% stake to 85%. The government of Botswana holds the remaining 15%.

In addition to giving it majority control of the mining company Anglo American believes the acquisition will provide it with De Beers' expertise in administrative functions such as financial management supply chain and technical operations. The acquisition comes after a new 10-year sales agreement with the mining company's partner the government of Botswana. De Beers and Russia's AL-ROSA account for about half of the world's diamond production.

The company also stirred up controversy in 2011 by selling nearly 25% of its stake in Anglo American Sur copper mining subsidiary in Chile to Japan's Mitsubishi Corporation for $5.4 billion. The deal angered Chilean mining and government officials because Codelco Chile's state-owned resources company and the world's largest copper company wanted to exercise its option to buy a 49% stake in the company. Chile acted quickly to obtain a court injunction to block Anglo from selling any more of its shares of Anglo American Sur.

Although in 2012 a Chilean court rejected a bid by Codelco to have 49% of the dividends from Anglo American Sur frozen and held in escrow the dispute may drag on for years.

Anglo American and Lafarge SA agreed in 2011 to form a joint venture valued at $2.8 billion to combine their cement aggregates ready-mixed concrete asphalt and contracting businesses in the UK (Tarmac UK and Lafarge UK). The joint operations are expected to save a total of about $96 million a year through increased efficiency and improved logistics. The venture is designed to take advantage of an anticipated economic recovery. The UK's Competition Commission however ruled in 2012 that both Anglo and Lafarge would have to divest several operations including Lafarge's Hope cement plant in northern England —one of the largest in the UK.

The company also significantly expanded its metallurgical coal interests in 2011 with the acquisition of Peace River Coal Limited Partnership which holds exploration leases in British Columbia. Peace River Coal holds approximately 1 billion metric tons of high-quality coking coal.

In 2012 the company completed the final step of its $1.4 billion divestment of the Scaw Metals Group by selling Scaw South Africa an integrated steel maker to an investment consortium led by the Industrial Development Corporation of South Africa. The sale follows Anglo's disposal of Scaw's Moly-Cop and AltaSteel businesses to OneSteel (later renamed Arrium) in 2010.

HISTORY

In 1905 the Oppenheimers a German family with a major interest in the Premier Diamond Mining Company of South Africa began buying some of the region's richest gold-bearing land. The family formed Anglo American Corporation of South Africa in 1917 to raise money from J. P. Morgan and other US investors. The name was chosen to disguise the company's German background during WWI.

Under Ernest Oppenheimer the company bought diamond fields in German Southwest Africa (now Namibia) in 1920 breaking the De Beers hegemony in diamond production. Oppenheimer's 1928 negotiations with Hans Merensky the person credited with the discovery of South Africa's "platinum arc" led to Anglo American's interest in platinum.

The diamond monopoly resurfaced in 1929 when Anglo American won control of De Beers formed by Cecil Rhodes in 1888 with the help of England's powerful Rothschild family.

Anglo American and De Beers had become the largest gold producers in South Africa by the 1950s. They were also major world producers of coal uranium and copper. In the 1960s and 1970s Anglo American expanded through mergers and cross holdings in industrial and financial companies. It set up Luxembourg-based Minorco to own holdings outside South Africa and help the company avoid sanctions placed on firms doing business in the apartheid country.

Minorco sold its interest in Consolidated Gold Fields in 1989 and in 1990 it bought Freeport-Mc-MoRan Gold Company (US). In 1993 Minorco bought Anglo American's and De Beers' South American European and Australian operations as part of a swap that put all of Anglo American's non-African assets except diamonds in Minorco's hands. Some analysts claimed the company had moved the assets to protect them from possible nationalization by the new black-controlled South African government. The company spun off insurer African Life to a group of black investors in 1994.

Anglo American bought a stake in UK-based conglomerate Lonrho (now Lonmin) in 1996. In 1997 Anglo American made mining acquisitions in Zambia Colombia and Tanzania and began reorganizing its gold and diamond operations. In 1998 the company's First National and Southern Life financial units merged with Rand Merchant Bank's Momentum Life Assurers to form FirstRand. (Anglo American has divested most of its interest in FirstRand.)

The company moved to the UK in 1999 and began trading on the London Stock Exchange in an effort to reach international investors. When it was based in South Africa Anglo American was unable to send its money overseas (the result of boycotts connected to that country's apartheid policies) so it bulked up on South African interests. Anglo American has evolved such that it can depend on product and geographic diversity to weather global economic turmoil. South African operations now make up less than half of the company's total sales and its base metals and platinum units each account for about a quarter of sales.

In 2000 the company bought UK building materials company Tarmac plc and later sold Tarmac America to Greece-based Titan Cement for $636 million. That year De Beers paid $590 million for Anglovaal Mining's stake in De Beers' flagship Venetia diamond mine and $900 million for Royal Dutch Shell's Australian coal mining business. On the disposal side Anglo American sold its 68% stake in LTA and its 14% stake in Li & Fung a Hong Kong trading company. Harry Oppenheimer died that year at the age of 92.

In a surprising move in early 2001 Anglo American announced that it had formed a consortium with Central Holding (the Oppenheimer family) and Debswana Diamond to acquire De Beers. In February De Beers agreed to be acquired in a deal worth about $17.6 billion. The deal —giving Anglo American and Central Holding 45% each and Debswana a 10% stake —was completed in June 2001.

In 2002 Anglo American and Japan-based conglomerate Mitsui pooled their Australian coal resources; Anglo American owns 51% of the joint venture. The company also completed a $1.3 billion deal that year for Chilean copper assets (two mines and a smelter) formerly owned by Exxon Mobil. In 2003 the company eyed the red hot iron ore market when it acquired a controlling stake in South Africa-based iron producer Kumba Resources.

Anglo American sold its 20% stake in Gold Fields to Norilsk Nickel in 2004 and reduced its stake in AngloGold Ashanti to 42% from its former 51% in 2006 then to below 20% the following year and finally entirely in 2009. In divesting its gold interests Anglo American seemed to capitulate to demands from the investor community and the idea that the gold industry is sufficiently different from the rest of the mining industry as to necessitate separate management.

The company set up new units in 2009 along product and geographical lines. The new divisions consisted of platinum (South Africa) copper (Chile) nickel (Brazil) metallurgical coal (Australia) thermal coal (South Africa) Kumba Iron Ore (of which Anglo American owned 65% South Africa) and Iron Ore Brazil. The change capped off several years of reorganization and divestment.

In 2009 the board of Anglo American rejected an offer to merge with rival Xstrata (renamed Glencore in 2014). Although Xstrata called the bid a "merger of equals" based on similar capitalization sizes Anglo American's board was not convinced of the benefits of the $68 billion all stock deal. Although Anglo American used to have a majority stake in AngloGold Ashanti it divested its remaining shares in 2009.

In 2010 Anglo American through its subsidiary Anglo Zinc completed the divestment of its zinc assets to Vedanta Resources subsidiary Sterlite Industries in a $1.3 billion deal. That year the company also sold Tarmac's aggregates businesses in France Germany Poland and the Czech Republic as well as its French and Belgian concrete products operations for $483 million.

Nicky Oppenheimer grandson of the founder retired from the board in 2011.

EXECUTIVES

CEO Base Metals and Group Director Strategy and Business Development, Duncan Wanblad, age 49

CEO De Beers, Bruce Cleaver, age 51
Chief Executive, Mark Cutifani, age 57, $891,000
  total compensation
Group Director People and Organization, Didier
  Charreton, age 53
Deputy Chairman Anglo American South Africa,
  Norman B. Mbazima, age 58
CEO Platinum, Chris Griffith, age 51
Finance Director, Stephen Pearce, age 53
CEO Bulk Commodities, Seamus French, age 53
CEO Marketing, Peter Whitcutt, age 50
Group Director Technical and Sustainability, Tony
  OÅNeill, age 58
Chairman, John Parker, age 74
Auditors: Deloitte LLP

LOCATIONS

HQ: Anglo American Plc (United Kingdom)
  20 Carlton House Terrace, London SW1Y 5AN
Phone: (44) 20 7968 8888   **Fax:** (44) 20 7968 8500
Web: www.angloamerican.com

PRODUCTS/OPERATIONS

2015 sales

	% of total
Platinum	21
Coal	21
De Beers	20
Copper	16
Iron Ore and Manganese	15
Niobium and Phosphates	2
Nickel	1
Corporate and other	4
Total	**100**

Selected Subsidiaries

Platinum
  Anglo Platinum Corporation Limited (75% South
    Africa)
Base Metals
Anglo American Sur (75% copper mines Chile)
  Empresa Minera de Mantos Blancos SA (copper Chile)
  Minera Loma de Níquel CA (91% nickel
    Venezuela)
  Minera Quellaveco SA (80% copper Peru)
  Minera Sur Andes Limitada (copper Chile)
Coal
  Anglo Coal (South Africa)
  Anglo Coal (Callide) Pty Limited (Australia)
Ferrous Metals and Industries
  Kumba Resources Limited (65%; coal iron ore heavy
    minerals; South Africa)
Industrial Minerals
  Copebras Limitada (phosphate products Brazil)
Diamonds
  De Beers S.A. (45%)

COMPETITORS

BHP Billiton	Pe±oles
Freeport-McMoRan	Rio Tinto Limited
Glencore	Teck
Impala Platinum	Vale
Norilsk Nickel	Vedanta Resources

HISTORICAL FINANCIALS
Company Type: Public

Income Statement
FYE: December 31

	REVENUE ($ mil.)	NET INCOME ($ mil.)	NET PROFIT MARGIN	EMPLOYEES
12/15	20,455	(5,624)	—	91,000
12/14	27,073	(2,513)	—	95,000
12/13	29,342	(961)	—	98,000
12/12	28,680	(1,470)	—	106,000
12/11	30,580	6,169	20.2%	100,000
Annual Growth	**(9.6%)**	—	—	**(2.3%)**

Anheuser-Busch InBev SA/NV

Auditors: PwC Bedrijfsrevisoren Bcvba

LOCATIONS

HQ: Anheuser-Busch InBev SA/NV
  Brouwerijplein 1, Leuven 3000
Phone: (32) 16 27 6111   **Fax:** (32) 16 50 6111
Web: www.ab-inbev.com

HISTORICAL FINANCIALS
Company Type: Public

Income Statement
FYE: December 31

	REVENUE ($ mil.)	NET INCOME ($ mil.)	NET PROFIT MARGIN	EMPLOYEES
12/15	43,604	8,273	19.0%	152,321
12/14	47,063	9,216	19.6%	154,029
12/13	43,195	14,394	33.3%	154,587
12/12	39,758	7,243	18.2%	117,632
12/11	39,046	5,855	15.0%	116,278
Annual Growth	**2.8%**	**9.0%**	—	**7.0%**

2015 Year-End Financials

Debt ratio: 36.7%
Return on equity: 17.9%
Cash ($ mil.): 6,923
Current ratio: 0.64
Long-term debt ($ mil.): 43,541
No. of shares (mil.): 1,606
Dividends
  Yield: —
  Payout: —
Market value ($ mil.): 200,798

	STOCK PRICE ($) FY Close	P/E High/Low	PER SHARE ($) Earnings	Dividends	Book Value
12/15	125.00	26 21	4.96	0.00	26.23
12/14	112.32	21 17	5.54	0.00	31.09
12/13	106.46	12 9	8.72	0.00	31.36
12/12	87.41	20 13	4.45	0.00	25.68
12/11	60.99	17 14	3.63	0.00	23.46
Annual Growth	**19.7%**	— —	**8.1%**	—	**2.8%**

AntarChile S.A. (Chile)

AntarChile focuses on forestry fuel and fishing. As one of Chile's largest investment companies it buys shares of companies or properties that are linked to those industries. The holding company owns more than 60% of industrial conglomerate group Copec which is one of Chile's top distributors of petroleum and diesel fuel. Other holdings include investments in forestry and wood products groups Forestal Cholguan and Celulosa Arauco y Constitucion. AntarChile also is involved in the natural gas fishing forestry shipping and mining industries. Its forestry holdings produce cellulose and manufacture wood and wood panels. AntarChile is controlled by the powerful Angelini family of Chile.

EXECUTIVES

CEO, Jorge Andueza Fouque
Finance and Administration Manager, Patricio
  Tapia Costa
Vice Chairman, Jose Tom˜s Guzm˜n Dumas
Chairman, Roberto Angelini Rossi

LOCATIONS

HQ: AntarChile S.A. (Chile)
  Avenida El Golf 150, Piso 21, Santiago, Las Condes
Phone: (56) 2 461 7710   **Fax:** (56) 2 461 7717
Web: www.antarchile.cl

COMPETITORS

Endesa S.A.	Repsol
Enersis	Royal Dutch Shell
Falabella	Walmart Chile
International Paper	
Petrobras	
Distribuidora	

HISTORICAL FINANCIALS
Company Type: Public

Income Statement
FYE: December 31

	REVENUE ($ mil.)	NET INCOME ($ mil.)	NET PROFIT MARGIN	EMPLOYEES
12/15	18,160	316	1.7%	8
12/14	23,846	509	2.1%	8
12/13	24,345	458	1.9%	8
12/12	22,769	232	1.0%	8
12/11	21,131	567	2.7%	0
Annual Growth	**(3.7%)**	**(13.5%)**	—	—

2015 Year-End Financials

Debt ratio: 31.1%
Return on equity: 5.1%
Cash ($ mil.): 1,668
Current ratio: 2.58
Long-term debt ($ mil.): 5,909
No. of shares (mil.): 456
Dividends
  Yield: —
  Payout: —
Market value ($ mil.): —

ANZ National Bank Ltd

LOCATIONS

HQ: ANZ National Bank Ltd
  ANZ Centre Melbourne, Level 9, 833 Collins Street,
  Docklands, Melbourne, Victoria 3008
Phone: (61) 3 9273 5555   **Fax:** (61) 3 8542 5252
Web: www.nationalbank.co.nz

(Top-middle column, continued from Anglo American 2015 Year-End Financials)

2015 Year-End Financials

Debt ratio: 34.5%
Return on equity: (-26.1%)
Cash ($ mil.): 6,895
Current ratio: 2.36
Long-term debt ($ mil.): 16,318
No. of shares (mil.): 1,401
Dividends
  Yield: —
  Payout: —
Market value ($ mil.): 3,063

	STOCK PRICE ($) FY Close	P/E High/Low	PER SHARE ($) Earnings	Dividends	Book Value
12/15	2.19	— —	(4.36)	0.00	11.82
Annual Growth	—	— —	—	—	—

HISTORICAL FINANCIALS
Company Type: Public

Income Statement
FYE: September 30

	REVENUE ($ mil.)	NET INCOME ($ mil.)	NET PROFIT MARGIN	EMPLOYEES
09/16	23,058	4,150	18.0%	46,554
09/15	20,624	4,778	23.2%	50,152
09/12	26,432	4,714	17.8%	48,239
09/11	4,721	839	17.8%	0
09/10	4,531	611	13.5%	0
Annual Growth	31.1%	37.6%	—	—

2016 Year-End Financials
Debt ratio: —
Return on equity: 9.9%
Cash ($ mil.): 35,389
Current ratio: —
Long-term debt ($ mil.): —

No. of shares (mil.): —
Dividends
  Yield: —
  Payout: 84.5%
Market value ($ mil.): —

Aozora Bank, Ltd.

Aozora Bank hopes that the clouds have passed and blue skies are ahead. Aozora (which means blue sky in Japanese) was the second Japanese credit bank nationalized in the wake of Asia's financial crisis (after Shinsei Bank). Bad loans and Japan's "Big Bang" financial deregulation added to its troubles. Now a full-service commercial bank Aozora has some 20 branches in Japan and three offices overseas (New York Shanghai and Singapore). It provides a host of retail and business banking services as well as corporate banking services (loans and derivative products consulting and advisory) and specialty finance and financial markets offerings. Aozora is seeking to expand in Southeast Asia particularly Indonesia.

EXECUTIVES
President and Director, Shinsuke Baba
Deputy President and Director, Masaki Tanabe
Managing Executive Officer, Jorge A. Leon
Senior Managing Executive Officer Director Chief Risk Officer and Chief Credit Risk Officer, Takeo Saito
Managing Executive Officer, Clark D. Graninger
Managing Executive Officer, Katsuya Hosono
Managing Executive Officer, Kei Tanikawa
Managing Executive Officer, Yukio Sekizawa
Managing Executive Officer, Koji Yamakoshi
Managing Executive Officers, Hideaki Kuraishi
Chairman, Makoto Fukuda
Auditors: Deloitte Touche Tohmatsu LLC

LOCATIONS
HQ: Aozora Bank, Ltd.
  1-3-1 Kudan-Minami, Chiyoda-ku, Tokyo 102-8660
Phone: (81) 3 3263 1111
Web: www.aozorabank.co.jp

PRODUCTS/OPERATIONS

2013 Sales

	% of total
Interest income	
Loans and discounts	31
Dividends on securities	11
Others	2
Other ordinary income	19
Fees and commissions	10
Trading income	8

Others	19
Total	**100**

2013 Sales

	% of total
Lending	42
Securities investment	34
Derivatives	7
Others	17
Total	**100**

Selected affiliates
Aozora Asia Pacific Finance Limited
Aozora GMAC Investment Limited
Aozora Investment Inc.
Aozora Investments LLC
Aozora Regional Consulting Co. Ltd.
AZB CLO1 Limited
AZB CLO2 Limited
AZB CLO3 Limited
AZB CLO4 Limited
AZB Funding
AZB Funding 2
AZB Funding 3
AZB Funding 4 Limited

COMPETITORS

Mitsubishi UFJ Financial Group	Resona
Mizuho Financial	Shinsei Bank
Mizuho Trust & Banking Ltd	Sumitomo Mitsui
Norinchukin Bank	Sumitomo Mitsui Trust Holdings
	Tokyo Tomin Bank

HISTORICAL FINANCIALS
Company Type: Public

Income Statement
FYE: March 31

	ASSETS ($ mil.)	NET INCOME ($ mil.)	INCOME AS % OF ASSETS	EMPLOYEES
03/16	40,899	387	0.9%	2,124
03/15	41,044	364	0.9%	2,080
03/14	46,555	410	0.9%	1,655
03/13	53,316	431	0.8%	1,615
03/12	62,140	564	0.9%	1,604
Annual Growth	(9.9%)	(9.0%)	—	7.3%

2016 Year-End Financials
Return on assets: 0.9%
Return on equity: 8.9%
Long-term debt ($ mil.): —
No. of shares (mil.): 1,166
Sales ($ mil): 1,092

Dividends
  Yield: 0.0%
  Payout: 752.6%
Market value ($ mil.): 80,831

	STOCK PRICE ($) FY Close	P/E High/Low	Earnings	PER SHARE ($) Dividends	Book Value
03/16	69.30	2 2	0.31	2.30	3.09
03/15	75.35	2 1	0.23	3.10	4.05
03/14	58.20	— —	0.26	0.00	4.29
03/13	58.40	— —	0.24	0.00	4.88
Annual Growth	5.9% (10.8%)	— —	6.6%	—	

Arab National Bank

Arab National Bank offers banking services for primarily commercial but also growing retail segments of the Saudi Arabia market including Shariah (Islamic) services. Its 200-plus branches (51 are women-only) provide savings and checking accounts credit and debit cards loans and investment services. Its Corporate Banking Group segment serves mid-sized and large Saudi businesses while its treasury branch offers foreign exchange services international stock trading international bonds and margin trading accounts. Arab National Bank also owns and operates one branch located in the UK. Arab Bank owns a 40% stake in Arab National Bank which was formed in 1979.

EXECUTIVES
CEO, Bassam Al-Mubarak
Auditors: KPMG Al Fozan & Partners

LOCATIONS
HQ: Arab National Bank
  P.O. Box 56921, Riyadh 11564
Phone: (966) 1 402 9000   **Fax:** (966) 1 402 7747
Web: www.anb.com.sa

COMPETITORS

Ahli United Bank	NBK
Al Rajhi Banking	Saudi British Bank
Arab Banking Corp.	Standard Chartered
Dallah Albaraka Group	
Gulf International Bank	

HISTORICAL FINANCIALS
Company Type: Public

Income Statement
FYE: December 31

	ASSETS ($ mil.)	NET INCOME ($ mil.)	INCOME AS % OF ASSETS	EMPLOYEES
12/15	45,393	789	1.7%	4,846
12/14	43,883	766	1.7%	4,554
12/13	36,776	672	1.8%	4,586
12/12	36,432	632	1.7%	4,627
12/11	31,353	578	1.8%	4,225
Annual Growth	9.7%	8.1%	—	3.5%

2015 Year-End Financials
Return on assets: 1.7%
Return on equity: 13.9%
Long-term debt ($ mil.): —
No. of shares (mil.): 1,000
Sales ($ mil): 1,729

Dividends
  Yield: —
  Payout: —
Market value ($ mil.): —

ArcelorMittal SA

Few metal makers have the mettle of ArcelorMittal. The company is easily the largest steel-making entity in the world producing more than 90 million metric tons of crude steel annually about 6% of the world steel output. Operating in more than 60 countries ArcelorMittal manufactures the full range of steel products: slabs and coil coated steel and tinplate wire rod and rebar and billets and blooms as well as all manner of electrical steel products. It also has 15 mining operations and is one of the world's largest iron ore producers. In 2014 it produced 77 million metric tons of iron ore and 7.7 million metric tons of metallurgical coal. CEO and founder Lakshmi Mittal controls about 39% of ArcelorMittal.

Geographic Reach

The company has steel-making operations in 19 countries on four continents including 56 integrated and mini-mill steel-making facilities

ArcelorMittal operates through subsidiaries in Europe Africa Asia and the Americas (including ArcelorMittal Brasil). It's the largest producer of steel in North and South America and Africa the sixth-largest steel producer in the Commonwealth of Independent States region and has a growing presence in Asia including investments in China. It is also the largest steel producer in the European Union.

In addition many of ArcelorMittal's units have access to developing markets that are expected to experience significant future growth in steel consumption such as Central and Eastern Europe South America India Africa and Russia. Overall about 47% of its steel is produced in Europe 38% in the Americas and 15% in other countries such as Kazakhstan South Africa and Ukraine.

ArcelorMittal has steel-making operations in 19 countries on four continents including 56 integrated and mini-mill steel-making facilities.

Operations

In 2014 ArcelorMittal reorganized from six to five reportable segments: NAFTA; Europe; Brazil; ACIS (Africa and CIS); and Mining. NAFTA produces flat long and tubular products. Flat products include slabs hot-rolled coil cold-rolled coil coated steel products and plate. These products are sold primarily to customers in the following industries: distribution and processing; automotive; pipes and tubes; construction; packaging and appliances. In 2014 shipments from NAFTA totaled 23.1 million tons.

Brazil makes flat (slabs hot-rolled coil cold-rolled coil and coated steel) long and tubular products.

Europe produces flat long and tubular products. Flat products include hot-rolled coil cold-rolled coil coated products tinplate plate and slab. These products are sold primarily to customers in the automotive general industry and packaging industries. In 2014 shipments from Europe totaled 39.6 million tons. (Europe contributed about 47% of ArcelorMittal's revenues that year).ACIS manufactures flat long and tubular products at six flat and long production plants in three countries.

Mining provides the company's steel operations with high quality and low-cost iron ore and coal reserves and also sells limited amounts of mineral products to third parties. The company has mines in North and South America Europe the CIS and Africa.

Sales and MarketingArcelorMittal produces a wide variety of products across all steel-consuming industries including the automotive appliance engineering construction energy and machinery markets. The company sells its products in local markets and through a centralized marketing organization in more than 170 countries. Its strategy depends on maintaining its size and scale in the global steel market vertical integration of its operations producing a diverse portfolio of products and continuously improving its quality.

Financial Performance

The company's revenues have been declining in recent years.

In 2014 ArcelorMittal's net sales decreased by 0.2% due to the reduced revenues from Asia Africa and Europe. That year the company's net loss decreased by 62% due to lower cost of sales and net income attributable to non-controlling interests. Cost of sales was positively affected by a decrease in depreciation following a change in assessment of certain property plant and equipment and a decline in raw material prices. Net income attributable to non-controlling interests was $112 million in 2014 as compared with net loss attributable to non-controlling interests of $30 million in 2013. Net income attributable to non-controlling interests increased in 2014 primarily as a result of income attributable to non-controlling interests in Arcelor-Mittal Mines Canada and Belgo Bekaert Arames partially offset by losses generated in ArcelorMittal South Africa which were however significantly lower than in 2013.

In 2014 net cash provided by operating activities decreased by $426 million due to a change in inventories and trade accounts payable.

Strategy

ArcelorMittal's strategy is to leverage four distinctive attributes that will enable it to capture leading positions in the most attractive areas of the steel industry value chain from mining at one end to distribution and first-stage processing at the other. These are global scale and scope; unmatched technical capabilities; a diverse portfolio of steel and related businesses particularly mining; and financial capability.

In 2014 ArcelorMittal entered into an agreement to establish the joint venture in Turkey ArcelorMittal RZK Celik Servis Merkezi Sanayi ve Ticaret Anonim Sirketi (“AM RZK”).

To raise cash that year ArcelorMittal and Gerdau completed the sale of their respective 50% interests in Gallatin Steel Company a flat rolled mini-mill located in Gallatin County Kentucky to Nucor for $770 million.

In 2014 ArcelorMittal also sold its 78% stake in European port handling and logistics company ATIC Services for EUR 155.4 million; its interest in the Kuzbass coal mines in the Kemerovo region of Siberia Russia to Russia's National Fuel Company; and diluted its stake in Algeria's Tebessa mines in Ouenza and Boukhadra .

To focus on its core businesses and pay down debt in 2013 the company sold 15% of its ArcelorMittal Mines Canada subsidiary to Chinese and Korean steelmakers for $1.1 billion.

ArcelorMittal became a conglomerate through acquisitions and strategic partnerships. In 2013 it formed a joint venture with Nippon Steel & Sumitomo Metal to buy ThyssenKrupp Steel USA from ThyssenKrupp.

Mergers and Acquisitions

In 2014 the ArcelorMittal and Nippon Steel & Sumitomo Metal joint venture acquired ThyssenKrupp Steel USA and its steel processing plant in Calvert Alabama for $1.6 billion. The Calvert plant has a total capacity of 5.3 million tons including hot rolling cold rolling coating and finishing lines. The deal is expected to deliver $60 million in annual savings.

In 2013 ArcelorMittal also acquired control of the joint operation DJ Galvanizing a hot dip galvanizing line located in Canada through the acquisition of the 50% interest held by the other joint operator.

HISTORY

Company Background

ArcelorMittal is the product of decades of steel-making by India's Mittal family. In 1967 patriarch Mohan Mittal unsuccessfully tried to open a steel mill in Egypt. He and his four younger brothers then set up a steel company in India but squabbles pushed Mohan to chart his own course eventually giving rise to an empire that flourished under the Ispat name. Mohan's son Lakshmi began working part-time at the family steel mill while in school; he started full-time at 21 after graduating in 1971.

Mohan set up an operation in Indonesia in 1975 (Ispat Indo) and put Lakshmi in charge. The next year fueled by ambitions and held back by government regulations in India Lakshmi formed Ispat International in Jakarta Indonesia to focus on expansion through acquisitions. He spent the next decade strengthening the Indonesian operations and perfecting the minimill process using direct-reduced iron (DRI).

Ispat took advantage of the recessionary late 1980s and early 1990s by making a string of acquisitions. In 1988 it took over the management of Trinidad and Tobago's state steel companies (bought in 1994; renamed Caribbean Ispat).

In 1992 Ispat bought Mexico's third-largest (albeit bankrupt) steel and DRI producer. Two years later it acquired Canada's Sidbec-Dosco steelmaker. Also that year Lakshmi took exclusive control of international operations leaving his brothers Pramod and Vinod to control the Indian divisions.

The mid-1990s brought more acquisitions: In 1995 Ispat bought Germany's Hamburger Stahlwerks and a mill in Kazakhstan. The next year it purchased Ireland's only steelmaker Irish Steel. Lakshmi moved to London in 1996 and purchased a home on Bishops Avenue known as "millionaire's row." (Saudi Arabia's King Fahd was a neighbor.)

In 1997 the company bought the long-product (wire rod) division of Germany's Thyssen AG (renamed Ispat Stahlwerk Ruhrort and Ispat Walzdraht Hochfeld). It also completed a $776 million IPO.

Ispat acquired Chicago-based Inland Steel in 1998 (and renamed it Ispat Inland) including the steel-finishing operations of I/N Tek (60% Inland-owned joint venture with Nippon Steel) and I/N Kote (50% Inland-owned joint venture with NSC).

In 1999 Ispat formed a joint venture with Mexican steelmaker Grupo Imsa to make flat-rolled steel to sell throughout most of the Americas. It also paid $96 million for France-based Usinor's Unimetal Trefileurope and Societe Metallurgique de Revigny subsidiaries which specialize in carbon long products. That year Ispat Inland became the target of a US federal criminal grand jury investigation and a related civil lawsuit for allegedly defrauding the Louisiana Highway Department. (The case was settled for $30 million with the cost split between Ispat Inland and Contech Construction Products Inc. of Ohio.)

In 2000 the company responded to a downturn in the steel industry by starting a Web-based joint venture with Commerce One to connect buyers and sellers in the worldwide metals market. It also offered to buy VSZ Slovakia's #1 steelworks but was outbid by U.S. Steel.

After struggling with heavy debt high labor and energy costs new environmental regulations and EU steel quotas in 2001 Ispat closed down its subsidiary Irish Ispat which accounted for about 2% of the parent company's steel production.

In 2002 the company's 51%-owned pipe making subsidiary Productura Mexicana de Tuberia sold almost all of its production assets.

The present ArcelorMittal was forged in 2004 when Ispat International (of which the Mittal family owned 70%) purchased LNM Holdings (wholly owned by the Mittals) for $13 billion. In 2006 the former Mittal Steel agreed to buy rival Arcelor for about $34 billion to create ArcelorMittal.

Mittal Steel had established its hold on the world steel market through its 2005 purchase of the US-based International Steel Group (ISG) for $4.5 billion. The purchase made the company the largest steel producer (ahead of U.S. Steel and Nucor) in the US a market that had long been a targeted area for expansion for CEO Mittal. Once the deal closed the company combined ISG's operations with those of subsidiary Ispat Inland to form a single North American entity Mittal Steel USA (now ArcelorMittal USA).

Also in 2005 Mittal Steel acquired a 93% stake in Ukrainian state-run steel company KryvorizhStal with the winning $4.84 billion bid in an auction held by the Ukrainian government. The price was high but Mittal was anxious to gain a stronger foothold in the region –and to keep its rivals away from KryvorizhStal. (This fact incidentally went a long way to convincing Mittal it needed to combine with Arcelor; the competition for acquisitions was driving prices dramatically upward.)

The company also began to broaden its portfolio outside the steel industry dipping its toe into the energy business. In mid-2005 Mittal formed two joint ventures with India's government-controlled Oil & Natural Gas Corporation: one to buy stakes in foreign oil and gas projects the other involved in oil and gas trading and shipping. The ventures began to look for business in places like Indonesia Kazakhstan Angola and Trinidad and Tobago.

After consolidating his family's various steel interests in the early part of this decade Mittal began work on the steel industry as a whole and was soon the world's largest steel producer.

By 2006 Mittal Steel no longer was content to be merely the world's largest steel producer; it wanted to dominate the market. The company announced an offer to the shareholders of Arcelor then the industry's #2 player to buy that company and in the process create the world's first 100-million-ton steel producer. Arcelor and seemingly half the governments of Western Europe initially fought the attempt.

Mittal improved its proposed price however and Arcelor's board finally approved the offer when Mittal also made ownership/corporate governance concessions. The combined company is 43% owned by the Mittal family. After a few months of a transitional management team arrangement Lakshmi Mittal took over as CEO of the combined company toward the end of 2006.

In 2009 ArcelorMittal completed its acquisition of the laser-welding steel activities of Noble International a leader in the niche industry. It also acquired Mexican steel producer Sicarsta for nearly $1.5 billion an acquisition that combined with its Lazaro Cardenas created Mexico's largest steel company.

In 2011 the company spun off its stainless and specialty steels steel operations into Aperam which immediately became the world's sixth-largest stainless steel producer. ArcelorMittal made the decision in 2010 to spin off its stainless steel units in Europe and Brazil after determining that they were underperforming and would better thrive as a separate business.After spinning its wheels in an escalating bidding war in 2011 ArcelorMittal joined rival Nunavut Iron Ore in making a joint acquisition of Canada-based Baffinland Iron Mines for $594 million. Both companies sought access to Baffinland's Mary River Project an undeveloped deposit of iron ore on sparsely populated North Baffin Island located inside the Arctic Circle as a source of raw materials. The venture faces stiff challenges including building an infrastructure around the mine's formidable location and shipping the ore out to Europe and other production sites.

Also that year the company bought a 40% stake in G Steel Public Company greatly expanding its presence in Asia. G Steel produces about 2.5 million ton of steel annually at its two slab-rolling plants in Thailand. The deal was part of ArcelorMittal's strategy of establishing a presence in emerging markets with with the potential for future growth.

In 2012 ArcelorMittal expanded its presence in China by increasing its stake in a joint venture with Valin Group known as Valin ArcelorMittal Automotive (VAMA) from 33% to 49%. VAMA is trying to enhance its position in China as a supplier of high-strength steels and products for the automotive market. The joint venture scheduled to become operational in 2014 will increase its planned capacity from 1.2 million tons to 1.5 million tons.

That year it sold New Jersey-based Skyline Steel a North American steel foundation and piling products distributor and specialty steel plate and bar producer Astralloy to US-based Nucor for $605 million.

EXECUTIVES

CFO; CEO ArcelorMittal Europe, Aditya Mittal, age 40
CEO, Wim de Klerk
CEO ArcelorMittal USA, John L. Brett
CEO ArcelorMittal USA, Andy Harshaw
CEO South America Flat, Benjamin M. Baptista Filho
CEO AM/NS Calvert, Robrecht Himpe, age 58
VP Global Automotive and Commercial Coordination, Brian Aranha
CEO ArcelorMittal Mining, Simon Wandke
CEO ArcelorMittal Africa and CIS Algeria Kazakhstan South Africa and Ukraine, Davinder Chugh
CEO South America Long, Jefferson de Paula
Chairman, Lakshmi N. Mittal, age 65
Auditors: Deloitte Audit S.a.r.l.

LOCATIONS

HQ: ArcelorMittal SA
24-26, Boulevard dAvranches, Luxembourg L-1160
Phone: (352) 4792 2484   **Fax:** (352) 4792 89 3937
Web: www.arcelormittal.com

2014 Sales

	$ mil.	% of total
Europe	36,283	46
Americas	32,297	41
Asia & Africa	10,702	13
Total	**79,282**	**100**

PRODUCTS/OPERATIONS

Segments and Selected Products
Flat Carbon Europe
  Coated products
  Coil
  Cold-rolled
  Hot-rolled
  Plate
  Slab
  Tin plate
Flat Carbon Americas
  Coated products
  Steel
  Plate
  Coil
  Cold-rolled
  Hot-rolled
  Slabs
Long Carbon Americas & Europe
  Billets
  Blooms
  Rebar
  Sections
  Wire rod
Asia Africa & Comonwealth of Independent States
  Flat products
  Long products
  Pipes
  Tubes
ArcelorMittal Steel Solutions & Services (in-house trading and distribution arm)

COMPETITORS

AK Steel Holding Corporation
BHP Billiton
Baosteel
BlueScope Steel
China Steel
Essar Group
Evraz
Gerdau
JFE Holdings
Mechel OAO
Nippon Steel & Sumitomo Metal Corporation
Nucor
POSCO
Severstal
Shougang Corp.
Tata Steel
Tenaris
Ternium
ThyssenKrupp Steel
United States Steel

HISTORICAL FINANCIALS
Company Type: Public

Income Statement
FYE: December 31

	REVENUE ($ mil.)	NET INCOME ($ mil.)	NET PROFIT MARGIN	EMPLOYEES
12/15	63,578	(7,946)	—	209,404
12/14	79,282	(1,086)	—	222,327
12/13	79,440	(2,545)	—	232,353
12/12	84,213	(3,726)	—	273,811
12/11	93,973	2,263	2.4%	260,523
Annual Growth	**(9.3%)**	**—**	**—**	**(5.3%)**

2015 Year-End Financials
Debt ratio: 25.7%
Return on equity: (-23.5%)
Cash ($ mil.): 4,002
Current ratio: 1.24
Long-term debt ($ mil.): 17,478
No. of shares (mil.): 1,656
Dividends
  Yield: 4.0%
  Payout: —
Market value ($ mil.): 6,992

	STOCK PRICE ($) FY Close	P/E High/Low	PER SHARE ($) Earnings	Dividends	Book Value
12/15	4.22	— —	(4.43)	0.17	15.25
12/14	11.03	— —	(1.00)	0.17	25.44
12/13	17.84	— —	(1.46)	0.49	30.11
12/12	17.47	— —	(2.41)	0.64	33.39
12/11	18.19	26 10	1.19	0.64	36.60
Annual Growth (19.7%)	**(30.6%)**	**— —**	**—(28.1%)**		

Asahi Group Holdings Ltd.

Auditors: KPMG AZSA LLC

LOCATIONS

HQ: Asahi Group Holdings Ltd.
1-23-1 Azumabashi, Sumida-ku, Tokyo 130-8602
Phone: (81) 3 5608 5116
Web: www.asahigroup-holdings.com

HISTORICAL FINANCIALS
Company Type: Public

Income Statement
FYE: December 31

	REVENUE ($ mil.)	NET INCOME ($ mil.)	NET PROFIT MARGIN	EMPLOYEES
12/15	15,429	634	4.1%	22,194
12/14	14,964	579	3.9%	21,177
12/13	16,330	588	3.6%	18,001
12/12	18,333	663	3.6%	17,956
12/11	18,901	711	3.8%	16,759
Annual Growth	**(4.9%)**	**(2.8%)**	**—**	**7.3%**

2015 Year-End Financials
Debt ratio: 0.1%
Return on equity: 8.6%
Cash ($ mil.): 400
Current ratio: 0.84
Long-term debt ($ mil.): 1,472
No. of shares (mil.): 457
Dividends
  Yield: —
  Payout: —
Market value ($ mil.): —

Asahi Kasei Corp

Auditors: PricewaterhouseCoopers Aarata

LOCATIONS

HQ: Asahi Kasei Corp
  1-105 Kanda-Jinbocho, Chiyoda-ku, Tokyo 100-8101
Phone: (81) 3 3296 3024
Web: www.asahi-kasei.co.jp

HISTORICAL FINANCIALS

Company Type: Public

Income Statement   FYE: March 31

	REVENUE ($ mil.)	NET INCOME ($ mil.)	NET PROFIT MARGIN	EMPLOYEES
03/16	17,283	817	4.7%	32,821
03/15	16,556	880	5.3%	30,313
03/14	18,385	981	5.3%	29,127
03/13	17,712	570	3.2%	28,363
03/12	19,178	679	3.5%	25,409
Annual Growth	(2.6%)	4.7%	—	6.6%

2016 Year-End Financials

Debt ratio: 0.1%
Return on equity: 8.6%
Cash ($ mil.): 1,300
Current ratio: 1.18
Long-term debt ($ mil.): 1,203

No. of shares (mil.): 1,395
Dividends
  Yield: 2.4%
  Payout: —
Market value ($ mil.): 18,749

	STOCK PRICE ($) FY Close	P/E High/Low		PER SHARE ($) Earnings	Dividends	Book Value
03/16	13.44	0	0	0.58	0.32	6.65
03/15	19.13	0	0	0.63	0.35	6.46
03/14	13.56	—	—	0.70	0.28	6.43
03/13	13.47	—	—	0.41	0.00	6.27
03/12	12.41	—	—	0.49	0.00	6.28
Annual Growth	2.0%			4.7%	—	1.4%

Assicurazioni Generali S.p.A.

Italy's largest insurance company (and one of the largest in Europe) Assicurazioni Generali writes insurance for risks as varied as pensions and car insurance. Present in more than 60 countries Generali's core businesses are involved in both life and property/casualty insurance (including accident health motor fire marine/aviation and reinsurance). Generali is noted for being a leading insurer of satellite and space missions which it has been covering since 1964. In more earthbound realms the company targets individuals and small to midsized businesses and has been in business since 1831.

Operations

Generali operates through about 500 companies throughout the world. Life insurance makes up the lion's share of its business with products that include savings and protection policies health business and supplementary pension policies. More than 70% of its written premiums are generated through its life insurance segment. Its non-life segment centers on retail markets.

Generali also promotes its financial services operations including Banca Generali which offer such services as wealth management and bank insurance products.

Geographic Reach

The company primarily operates in Western Europe especially in Italy Austria Germany France Spain and Switzerland. It also does business in Central and Eastern Europe. Generali also operates in Asia (including China Hong Kong India Indonesia Japan the Philippines Singapore Thailand Malaysia and Vietnam) Central and South America and the Middle East; it has offices in India and China.

Sales and Marketing

Generali serves some 65 million customers around the world. It sells through channels including its own global network of agents as well as financial advisors and brokers. It also sells by telephone and online.

Financial Performance

Generali's earnings were negatively impacted in 2011 by broadspread economic instabilities in the eurozone but revenues have been climbing back since then. In 2014 revenues rose 5% to euro 88.3 billion thanks to premium growth in Italy that was driven by rising sales of alternative products and hybrid lines. Other markets performed well too including France Austria Asia and the Middle East. The banking segment also reported higher earnings that year.

However net income fell 13% to euro 1.7 billion as the company paid out more in claims and reported unrealized and impairment losses. Cash flow from operations rose 49% to euro 19.7 billion as Generali changed its mathematical provisions and other provisions in its life segment.

Strategy

Generali's strategy for growth is based entering new market segments and countries. With its place firmly cemented in Western Europe it is looking to expand its presence in Eastern Europe Latin America and Asia through joint ventures and acquisitions. To that end Generali has targeted the fast-growing life insurance market of Vietnam.

Other strategic initiatives include improving its overall operating efficiencies including centralizing its IT operations into a single data center; optimizing its distribution networks and the developing proprietary networks; delivering innovative products; and diversifying its distribution methods. To reach younger customers it is particularly vested in providing direct channels via mobile applications and the web. The company leads in direct-to-consumers telephone and online channels in Italy Germany and France where it offers both life and property/casualty products.

The group has been disposing of certain units to both raise capital and to focus on its core insurance businesses. It had a stated goal of raising euro 4 billion by 2015. To those ends Generali sold its BSI private banking division in 2014. It also sold Fata Assicurazioni Danni for euro 194.7 million and in 2013 it sold its US reinsurance business.

Mergers and Acquisitions

In 2014 Generali entered the Malaysian market when it acquired a 49% stake in property/casualty insurer Multi-Purpose Insurance a subsidiary of Multi-Purpose Capital Holdings for euro 81.4 million.

The following year the group acquired the 24% of Generali PPF Holding it didn't already own for euro 1.3 billion. The unit which operates in Central and Eastern Europe was renamed Generali CEE Holding.

HISTORY

Company Background

Assicurazioni Generali was founded as Assicurazioni Generali Austro-Italiche in 1831 by a group of merchants led by Giuseppe Morpurgo in the Austro-Hungarian port of Trieste. Formed to provide insurance to the city's bustling trade industry the company offered life marine fire flood and shipping coverage. That year Morpurgo established what he intended to be Generali's headquarters in Venice. (While the company maintained offices in both cities Trieste ultimately won out.)

By 1835 Generali had opened 25 offices in Central and Western Europe; it had also expelled Morpurgo. The firm moved into Africa and Asia in the 1880s. In 1900 Generali began selling injury and theft insurance. In 1907 Generali's Prague office provided the young experimental writer Franz Kafka his first job. (He found it disagreeable and quit after a few months.)

During WWI the firm's Venice office pledged allegiance to Italy while the office in Trieste (still part of Austria-Hungary) stayed loyal to the Hapsburgs. After the war Trieste was absorbed by the new Italian republic. Under Edgardo Morpurgo Generali expanded further in the 1920s managing 30 subsidiaries and operating in 17 countries. As fascist Italy aligned itself with Germany in the 1930s adoption of anti-Semitic laws caused Morpurgo and a number of other high-ranking Jewish employees to flee the country. In 1938 Generali moved its headquarters to Rome (but moved them back to Trieste after war's end).

The firm maintained steady business both before and during Nazi occupation in WWII; in 1945 however the Soviets seized all Italian properties in Eastern Europe including 14 Generali subsidiaries. In 1950 Generali invaded the US market offering shipping and fire insurance and reinsurance. Generali established a cooperative agreement with Aetna Life and Casualty (now Aetna Inc.) in 1966 further cementing its US connections.

In 1988 Generali tried to acquire French insurer Compagnie du Midi. Foreshadowing Generali's later dealings with Istituto Nazionale delle Assicurazioni (INA) Midi escaped Generali's grasp through a merger with AXA. As the Iron Curtain frayed in 1989 Generali formed AB Generali Budapest through a joint venture with a Hungarian insurer. In 1990 the firm opened an office in Tokyo through an agreement with Taisho Marine and Fire Insurance (which became Mitsui Marine & Fire Insurance and is now Mitsui Sumitomo Insurance). By 1993 Generali had become Italy's largest insurer.

In 1997 the firm was accused along with other major European insurers of not paying on policies of Holocaust victims. (It moved to settle claims in 1999.)

EXECUTIVES

Managing Director and Group CEO, Philippe Donnet, age 56
Group Compliance Officer, Maurizio Basso
CEO Generali CEE Holding B.V., Luciano Cirin , age 52
CEO Generali France, Eric Lombard
Group Chief Risk Officer, Sandro Panizza, age 58
CEO Generali Deutschland Holding and Country Manager Germany, Giovanni Liverani
Group Chief Information & Digital Officer, Bruce M. Hodges, age 49
Group Chief Insurance Officer, Valter Trevisani
Group Head of Corporate Finance, Luigi Lubelli
CEO Global Business Lines and International, Frederic de Courtois
Group Chief Investment Officer, Timothy (Tim) Ryan, age 48
CEO Generali Italia and Country Manager Italy, Marco Sesana, age 43
Vice Chairman, Francesco G. Caltagirone, age 73

Chairman, Gabriele Galateri di Genola, age 70
Vice Chairman, Clemente Rebecchini, age 52
Auditors: Reconta Ernst & Young S.p.A.

LOCATIONS

HQ: Assicurazioni Generali S.p.A.
Piazza Duca degli Abruzzi 2, P.O. Box 538, Trieste
34132
Phone: (39) 40 6711   **Fax:** (39) 40 671 600
Web: www.generali.com

2014 Written Premiums by Location

	% of total
Europe	
Italy	30
Germany	21
France	13
Austria	3
Spain	3
Switzerland	2
Other Europe	23
Other regions	5
Total	**100**

PRODUCTS/OPERATIONS

2014 Net Earned Premiums

	% of total
Life insurance	69
Non-life earned premium	31
Total	**100**

2014 Written Premiums

	% of total
Life insurance	71
Property and casualty	29
Total	**100**

Mergers Acquisitions and Divestitures

COMPETITORS

AIG	ING
AXA	Milano Assicurazioni
Achmea	Swiss Re
Allianz	Unipol
Allianz France	UnipolSai
Camfin	Zurich Insurance Group
ERGO	ageas SA/NV

HISTORICAL FINANCIALS

Company Type: Public

Income Statement   FYE: December 31

	ASSETS ($ mil.)	NET INCOME ($ mil.)	INCOME AS % OF ASSETS	EMPLOYEES
12/15	545,203	2,211	0.4%	76,191
12/14	609,354	2,029	0.3%	78,333
12/13	619,057	2,636	0.4%	77,185
12/12	582,241	118	0.0%	79,454
12/11	547,204	1,107	0.2%	81,997
Annual Growth	(0.1%)	18.9%	—	(1.8%)

2015 Year-End Financials

Return on assets: 0.4%	Dividends
Return on equity: 8.6%	Yield: 0.0%
Long-term debt ($ mil.): —	Payout: 14.6%
No. of shares (mil.): 1,556	Market value ($ mil.): 14,504
Sales ($ mil): 98,290	

	STOCK PRICE ($) FY Close	P/E High/Low		PER SHARE ($) Earnings	Dividends	Book Value
12/15	9.32	8	7	1.41	0.21	16.49
12/14	10.30	10	8	1.29	0.20	18.12
12/13	8.50	9	7	1.71	0.10	17.49
12/12	7.14	138	96	0.08	0.09	16.79
12/11	11.23	18	16	0.72	0.20	12.87
Annual Growth	(4.6%)	—	—	18.0%	1.2%	6.4%

Associated British Foods Plc

They say man cannot live on bread alone so foodstuffs producer Associated British Foods also sells clothes tea sugar and cereals. ABF's bread-baking operation is its oldest function but it makes the biggest chunk of its money from clothes -; the company owns low-cost high-street fashion chain Primark. ABF also makes and markets grocery products sugar ingredients and agricultural products. Its grocery lines include household staples Allinson Tip Top Karo syrup Argo corn starch Kingsmill bread Silver Spoon sugar and Twinings tea. In the US it owns Fleischmanns Yeast and ingredient and spice maker ACH. Other divisions churn out sugar specialty oils and animal feed. ABF's activities span nearly 48 countries worldwide.

Operations

ABF's business is divided up into Groceries Agriculture Sugar Ingredients and Retail. Several of the segments are customers of each other - for instance part of the Sugar division's output is sold under the Groceries segment as Silver Spoon. Groceries responsible for around 25% of sales manufactures products including hot beverages sugar oils and baked goods. The similarly sized Agriculture and Ingredients segments (around 10% of sales each) manufacture animal feed and bakery ingredients respectively. Food-related activities comprise 60% of total revenue.

However despite its focus on food ABF's largest segment by revenue is Retail. The segment owns low-cost high-street chain Primark which pulls in around 40% of total sales and has sites in the UK Republic of Ireland Spain Portugal Germany the Netherlands Belgium Austria and France and the US.

Geographic Reach

The company sells to more than 100 countries worldwide and has operations in 48 countries across Europe southern Africa the Americas Asia and Australia. The UK accounts for about 43% of sales the highest globally followed by Europe and Africa which together accounted for 32% of sales in 2015.

The first Primark store in the US opened in Boston in 2016 with 11 openings planned by year-end.

Sales and Marketing

The company's branded products are sold through supermarkets and other retail outlets and it also sells wholesale. To keep expenses down Primark neither has an online offering nor operates any significant marketing function. It relies on word-of-mouth for brand awareness.

Financial Performance

Note: Growth rates may differ after conversion to US Dollars.

Sales declined in 2015 by £143 million to £12.8 billion mostly due to a fall in global commodity prices and the subsequent impact on sugar earnings. However a rise in retail sales driven by strong and continued growth in Primark helped mitigate the decline.

Net income fell in 2015 for the first time since 2011 down a third to £524 million. This was mostly due to the fall in earnings related to low sugar prices but a £98 million non-cash charge to majority-owned Vivergo Fuel due to a decline in biofuel prices also contributed.

Cash flow from operating activities fell £273 million to £1.1 billion in line with the fall in revenue.

Strategy

ABF is vulnerable to sugar prices and the Sugar division's profits rise and fall in line with the commodity. To combat this volatility ABF has secured lower future sugar beet (i.e. input) costs and closed two unprofitable factories in China. The diversity of its operations also help mitigate price fluctuations with Primark key to this.

Indeed in recent years Primark has been the most successful segment by a distance and as a result is the focus of investment activities. ABF increased the low-cost chain's floor space by 9% or 1 million square feet mostly in Germany Belgium and the Netherlands. The first store in the US opened in 2015 hoped to be the first of many. The company also invested heavily in supply-side infrastructure and warehouse capacity particularly in the Czech Republic and the US.

The Grocery businesses are given leeway to operate independently. For instance Ryvita's growth strategy is to focus on growth in core markets while AB World Foods is looking to move into new markets and expand in developing ones.

Mergers and Acquisitions

In 2015 ABF acquired BP's 47% stake in Vivergo Fuels in which ABF already had a 47% stake taking the total to 94%. It hopes that the biofuels business will be better placed to focus on cane sugar for ethanol production in Brazil. The plant in the north of England produces about half of the UK's biofuel needs.

In 2014 the company acquired fast-growing Dorset Cereals a high-end muesli brand for the health conscious for £50 million expanding its presence in the specialty cereals market.

HISTORY

When Garfield Weston took over his father's company upon the elder Weston's death in 1924 George Weston Limited was one of Canada's largest bakeries. Ten years later taking advantage of the cheap prices afforded by a worldwide depression Garfield purchased a biscuit-making division from Scottish baker Mitchell & Muir and opened a factory in Edinburgh. He promptly purchased other UK bakeries and grouped them in 1935 as Allied Bakeries.

Allied went public that year with the Weston family controlling most of its shares. The company's early accomplishments included the introduction of sliced bread to the UK. By 1940 Allied had acquired more than 30 bakeries and had become Britain's largest baker by introducing inexpensive biscuits to the masses.

Garfield's son Garry joined Allied's board of directors in 1948. The following year the company acquired two Australian firms: Gold Crust Bakeries and Gartelle White. It also bought the Ryvita Company a maker of crispbread. Placed under Garry's control Ryvita eventually became a household name in the UK. Garry also helped the Burton's biscuit division launch the popular Wagon Wheels chocolate biscuits in 1951. Three years later he was sent to Australia to oversee the company's operations there.

To control the entire food-selling process Allied moved into retailing during the 1950s acquiring famous London department store Fortnum & Mason (later acquired by the Weston family). The company was renamed Associated British Foods (ABF) in 1960. During the 1960s ABF opened Primark clothing stores and bought the Fine Fare chain of supermarkets. By the time Garry returned to the UK to become CEO in 1966 his father had thrown together a number of businesses that made everything from flour to parrot food. To achieve a stronger focus Garry sold many of these.

Growth continued internally. In 1970 ABF opened the largest bakery in Western Europe in

Glasgow Scotland. Frozen foods were added in 1978 the year Garfield died. The company's Twinings Tea subsidiary opened its first North American factory in 1980. Two years later ABF formed AB Ingredients to make new ingredients and additives for baked goods. The company sold the Fine Fare chain to Dee Corp. (now Somerfield) in 1986 and the following year it formed AB Technology to develop high-tech improvements for food processing.

After nearly 25 years without a major acquisition in 1991 the company purchased British Sugar one of the UK's two sugar processors from Berisford a diversified holdings firm. In 1995 the company acquired AC Humko a manufacturer of specialty oils in the US from Kraft. The next year ABF sold its supermarkets in the Irish Republic and Northern Ireland to the UK's biggest supermarket chain Tesco. Peter Jackson was appointed CEO in 1999. That year the company acquired German baking ingredients producer Rohr Enzymes and bought several mills from Dalgety Feed.

In 2000 ABF sold its UK ice-cream business to Richmond Foods (now R&R Ice Cream). Deputy chairman Harry Bailey took over as chairman when Garry became ill. ABF sold Burtons Biscuits (Wagon Wheels) that year to investment firm HM Capital Partners (then called Hicks Muse Tate & Furst) for about $187 million and it bought several Procter & Gamble commercial shortening and oil brands. In 2001 ABF sold AB Coatings its food coatings business and Nelsons its jam and preserves business. Also that year the company agreed to buy the UK bakery ingredients business of the Kerry Group.

In 2002 ABF's subsidiary ACH Food Companies purchased 19 of Unilever's North American brands including Mazola corn oil Argo and Kingsford's corn starches Karo corn syrup and Henri's salad dressings. Also in 2002 ABF acquired the food and beverages business of Novartis with the exception of Puerto Rican and US assets. (Brands included Caotina Ovomaltine and Ovaltine.) Later in the year the company sold off its Allied Glass Containers business to management.

In 2003 ABF sold six UK flour mills to Archer Daniels Midland. In 2004 the company acquired Unilever's Mexican oils and fats brands including Inca Mazola and Capullo in a $110 million cash transaction. Later that year it acquired Irish feed ingredients companies Vistavet and Nutrition Services Ltd. ABF's subsidiary ACH Food Companies also acquired the global yeast herbs and spice businesses of Australian company Burns Philp. The acquisition included Burns Philp's Fleischmann's Yeast brand and herb and spice company Tone Brothers.

In 2004 chief executive Peter Jackson unexpectedly announced he was stepping down. A member of ABF's founding and controlling family George Weston was chosen to succeed Jackson. (The Weston family also controls Canadian food processor and supermarket operator George Weston Limited).

ABF's Allied Grain unit formed a joint venture with Banks Cargill Agriculture Frontier in 2005. Frontier's products include grains and oilseeds. The 2005 purchase of retailer Littlewoods' stores added to ABF's Primark retail department-store operations.

In 2006 AFB bought the ethnic foods business of Heinz subsidiary HP Foods; it also acquired a 51% stake in South Africa's largest sugar producer Illovo for $599 million in cash. The next year it acquired Indian food maker Patak's. Its meal-accompaniment products Blue Dragon and Westmill Foods add to ABF's other ethnic cuisine offerings. The acquisition included Patak's assets and brands in all countries with the exception of India.

Already a player in the breakfast-food sector both in the US and internationally in 2007 the company added to its branded food product offerings with the acquisition of Jordans a UK maker of breakfast cereals cereal bars muesli and oat porridge.

EXECUTIVES

Finance Director, John G. Bason, age 59, $493,000 total compensation
Chief Executive, George G. Weston, age 52, $715,000 total compensation
Chairman, Charles J. F. Sinclair, age 68
Auditors: Ernst & Young LLP

LOCATIONS

HQ: Associated British Foods Plc
Weston Centre, 10 Grosvenor Street, London W1K 4QY
Phone: (44) 20 7399 6500   **Fax:** (44) 20 7399 6580
Web: www.abf.co.uk

2015 Sales

	% of total
UK	42
Europe & Africa	32
Asia/Pacific	16
The Americas	10
Total	**100**

PRODUCTS/OPERATIONS

2015 Sales

	% of total
Retail	42
Grocery	25
Sugar	14
Ingredients	10
Agriculture	9
Total	**100**

Selected Products and Brands

Agriculture
  Animal feeds (AB Agri)
Grocery
  Bread baked goods and cereal
  Allinson breads
  Burgen breads
  Jordans cereals
  Kingsmill breads
  Ryvita rye crispbread
  Speedibake bakery products
  Sunblest bread snacks and rolls
  Tip Top bread and baked goods (Australia)
  Herbs and spices
  Durkee (US)
  Gravies
  Sauces
  Seasonings
  Soup bases
  Spices
  Spice Islands (US)
  Seasonings
  Spices
  Tone's spices (US)
  Hot beverages sugar and sweeteners
  Billington's cane sugars
  Jacksons of Picadilly teas
  Karo corn syrup
  Ovaltine
  Silver Spoon sugar (UK)
  La Tisaniere teas and infusions (France)
  Twinings teas
  Meat
  Don Deligoods (Australia)
  KRC (Australia)
  Vegetable oils
  Capullo canola oil (Mexico)
  Mazola corn oil (US)
  World foods
  Blue Dragon (Asian)
  Patak's (Indian)
  Other
  Askeys ice cream and dessert accompaniments

Baking Mad
  Baking advice
  Recipes
  Tips
  Crusha milkshake mix
Ingredients
  Specialty ingredients
  Enzymes
  Specialty proteins and lipids
  Yeast extracts
  Yeast and bakery ingredients
  Argo corn starch
Retail clothing
  Primark
  Accessories
  Childrenswear
  Footwear
  Homeware
  Hosiery
  Lingerie
  Menswear
  Womenswear
Sugar
  Beet sugar

COMPETITORS

ADM	Morrisons
ALDI	Nestle
ASDA	Nine West
Armani	Nordzucker
Bahlsen	NutraSweet
Bakkavor	Oscar Mayer Limited
Bill Blass	PVH
Burberry	Perry Ellis
Carrefour	International
Celestial Seasonings	Premier Foods
Chr. Hansen A/S	Pura Foods
Cosun	R.C. Bigelow
Cumberland Packing	Ralph Lauren
Danisco A/S	Renshawnapier
Donna Karan	Republic of Tea
Gap UK	St. John Knits
General Mills	Stash Tea
Greencore	Sucri̇̄ re de
Gucci	Pithiviers
Harrods	Sdzucker
Heinz	T.K. Maxx
Hwa Hong	Tata Global Beverages
Iconix Brand Group	Tate & Lyle
Imperial Sugar	Tereos
Ingredion	Tesco
J Sainsbury	Unilever
Kenneth Cole	Unilever UK Foods
Kerry Group	United Biscuits
Marks & Spencer	Waitrose
McCormick & Company	Wal-Mart
Merisant	Warburtons
Mondelez International	kate spade

HISTORICAL FINANCIALS

Company Type: Public

Income Statement

FYE: September 17

	REVENUE ($ mil.)	NET INCOME ($ mil.)	NET PROFIT MARGIN	EMPLOYEES
09/16	17,652	1,077	6.1%	129,916
09/15	19,737	820	4.2%	124,036
09/14	21,004	1,236	5.9%	118,209
09/13	21,057	934	4.4%	112,652
09/12	19,870	900	4.5%	106,243
Annual Growth	(2.9%)	4.6%	—	5.2%

2016 Year-End Financials

Debt ratio: 10.2%
Return on equity: 12.0%
Cash ($ mil.): 731
Current ratio: 1.41
Long-term debt ($ mil.): 843
No. of shares (mil.): 791
Dividends
  Yield: 0.0%
  Payout: 28.7%
Market value ($ mil.): 28,453

09/16	35.94	46 31	1.36	0.39	11.74
09/15	48.47	76 57	1.04	0.46	12.34
09/14	42.65	53 31	1.57	0.47	13.20
09/13	29.03	43 27	1.18	0.41	12.25
09/12	20.67	31 24	1.14	0.35	11.95
Annual Growth	14.8%	— —	4.5%	2.8%	(0.4%)

AstraZeneca Plc

AstraZeneca's products run the gamut from A (blood pressure drug Atacand) to Z (prostate and breast cancer drug Zoladex). One of the world's major pharmaceutical firms AstraZeneca specializes in drugs for cardiovascular metabolic neurological gastrointestinal respiratory oncology and infection therapy areas. The firm's biggest sellers include cholesterol reducer Crestor cardiovascular drug Brilinta acid reflux remedy Nexium and Symbicort for asthma. AstraZeneca also markets drugs that aim to treat high cholesterol diabetes pain viral diseases and various cancers. The company's products are sold in more than 100 countries.

Operations

In 2013 AstraZeneca sold its only non-pharma business Aptium Oncology which operates cancer treatment centers in the US. This came on the heels of selling its other noncore units Astra Tech (medical devices) and Dentsply Sirona (dental implant systems). The moves are part of the company's focus on streamlining its operations around core drug development and commercialization efforts in targeted therapeutic areas for the past few years as part of strategic restructuring efforts in the face of looming patent expirations and increasing generic competition.

Since 2010 the number of AstraZeneca's drugs with sales of more than $1 billion each dropped from 10 to seven: Crestor Atacand Nexium Seroquel IR Seroquel XR Zoladex and Symbicort. The firm has especially been feeling the effects of generic competition for some of its top sellers in the US (the company's largest market) where revenues were down due to patent losses and increased generic competition. Established markets Western Europe and Canada also saw double digit drops as Crestor lost patent protection in Canada and sales of Seroquel IR Nexium Arimidex and Meronem decreased.

AstraZeneca has had several successes in its R&D organization as it works to keep the bestsellers coming and sales of newer drugs such as Crestor and Symbicort have helped sustain overall revenues for the company. During 2014 it received a dozen approvals for new molecular entities or major life cycle management projects in major markets. With a pipeline of about 135 drugs in various development stages it also looks for acquisitions to boost its product development.

The company has been focusing efforts on respiratory inflammation and autoimmunity therapies where it has eight products in phase III or registration status. In 2015 it acquired rights to Almirall's respiratory business and it plans to buy Actavis' branded respiratory business in the US and Canada.

Geographic Reach

AstraZeneca has operations in Europe North America Central America South America the Middle East Africa and the Asia/Pacific region. It manufactures products in 16 countries.

Growth in China and other emerging markets (including Russia Africa India Indonesia Malaysia South Korea Vietnam Brazil Argentina and Chile) is key for AstraZeneca's as it sees sales dip in established markets due to patent expiration in its older medications.

The Americas accounted for about 50% of AstraZeneca's revenue in 2014. Sales in emerging markets were up 8% in 2013 and 12% in 2014 thanks to sales growth in China and Russia. China was really the bright spot with a 22% increase in sales on the strength of the company's cardio and respiratory drugs. As a result the firm is increasing investments in emerging markets; for instance it built a $200 million manufacturing plant to meet market needs in China.

Sales and Marketing

The company markets its products to physicians through sales and marketing teams who are active in more than 100 countries. It typically sells through local marketing companies which it owns as well as through distributors and local representative offices.

Financial Performance

AstraZeneca saw revenue declines in 2012 and 2013 as a result of patent losses. Despite these losses it has managed to stay one step ahead of the game through its balanced growth and cost-control efforts. In 2014 revenue increased by just over 1% to $26.1 billion; driving that growth were the successes of such products as Brilinta/Brilique its diabetes and respiratory franchises Farxiga/Forxiga and the Bydureon Pen (which was launched in the US). The company also grew in its emerging markets operations with China (its second-largest market) increasing 22% that year. Pricing pressures in the region put a bit of a damper on those increases though.

The US saw a 4% increase largely due to the firm's diabetes products as well as growth in the Symbicort and Brilinta lines. However this was offset by declines from sales of Nexium Seroquel IR and Synagis. European revenues also slipped in 2014 primarily as a result of dropping sales of Atacand and Seroquel XR both of which are contending with generics in the region.

Although revenue saw a modest rise in 2014 net income continued its downward trend that year falling 52% to $1.2 billion as a result of R&D expenses surrounding the company's late-stage pipeline. Other factors cutting into profits were selling general and administrative costs as AstraZeneca focuses on its growth platforms. Cash flow from operations fell 5% to $7.1 billion.

Strategy

After a number of strategic moves including workforce reductions exits from certain markets an overhaul of its IT organization and management changes AstraZeneca is on track to return to growth by 2017. The company introduced a sixth growth platform —oncology —adding to its focus on respiratory inflammation and autoimmunity; and cardiovascular and metabolic diseases.

The firm is making a concerted effort to strengthen its industry position ahead of patent expirations by overhauling its R&D organization including by building up its late-stage drug development pipeline through internal research and development acquisitions and collaborations. Through its MedImmune unit it is also building up its R&D programs for new biologic medicines which enjoy longer terms of patent protection. In 2014 its Lynparza was approved for ovarian cancer treatment in the US and Europe and its Movantik tablet (constipation) and Myalept (leptin deficiency) products were approved in the US. The company also launched Nexium Direct which delivers Nexium directly to the homes of eligible patients.

As the company faces losing exclusivity in the US for its cholesterol-lowering drug Crestor AstraZeneca is looking to boost its cardiovascular disease portfolio. It bought California-based biotech ZS Pharma for $2.7 billion in late 2015. That purchase adds ZS Pharma's ZS-9 candidate which is under review in the US for the treatment of hyperkalemia (high potassium levels in the blood).

At the same time AstraZeneca is streamlining the pipeline to concentrate on the most promising research areas by reducing the number of disease targets within its six core therapy areas (cardiovascular gastrointestinal infection neuroscience oncology and respiratory/inflammation). For example in late 2016 it sold its small-molecule antibiotics operations to Pfizer for $550 million plus milestone payments that could potentially bring the deal's value to $1.5 billion. It also agreed to sell cancer drug Caprelsa to Sanofi for up to $300 million. These efforts have resulted in the consolidation of some R&D facilities.

In emerging markets primarily China Russia and Brazil AstraZeneca has concentrated on delivering new products and investing in marketing and sales. In 2014 the company's facility in Taizhou China delivered its first product while its facility in Vorsino Russia is nearing regulatory validation.

Mergers and Acquisitions

Along with discovering its own new drugs and collaborating with its pharmaceutical cohorts AstraZeneca also expands its R&D pipeline through occasional acquisitions. In 2016 it took a majority (55%) stake in Acerta Pharma gaining access to that firm's acalabrutinib candidate for the treatment of B-cell cancers. In late 2015 it acquired biotech firm ZS Pharma adding that firm's ZS-9 candidate for the treatment of hyperkalemia. The company acquired Amylin buying out the partnership in early 2014. Also that year it acquired the rights to Almirall's respiratory franchise and inhalation device subsidiary. It bought out Bristol-Myers Squibb's share of the companies' diabetes alliance gaining ownership of the intellectual property and global rights for the development manufacturing and marketing of the related products which include Onglyza Kombiglyze XR Farxiga and Byetta.

In 2013 AstraZeneca focused expansion efforts on the cardiovascular market. It purchased AlphaCore a US-based private biotech firm; and purchased Omthera which is working to develop heart medicines based on omega-3 fatty acids for some $443 million.

HISTORY

Company Background

AstraZeneca forerunner Imperial Chemical Industries (ICI) was created from the 1926 merger of four British chemical companies —Nobel Industries; Brunner Mond and Company; United Alkali; and British Dyestuffs —in reaction to the German amalgamation that created I. G. Farben. ICI plunged into research recruiting chemists engineers and managers and forming alliances with universities. Between 1933 and 1935 at least 87 new products were created including polyethylene.

Fortunes declined as competition increased after WWII. In 1980 ICI posted losses and cut its dividend for the first time. In 1982 turnaround artist John Harvey-Jones shifted ICI from bulk chemicals to high-margin specialty chemicals such as pharmaceuticals and pesticides. That business became Zeneca which ICI spun off in 1993.

The takeover specter loomed large over the company during its first year. Zeneca had several drugs in its pipeline but it also had expiring patents on others making them fair game for competitors. Bankrolled by its agrochemical business Zeneca forged alliances with other pharmaceutical firms. In 1994 it entered a marketing alliance with Amersham International (now Amersham) to sell Metastron a nuclear-medicine cancer agent. The next year Zeneca formed a joint venture with Chinese companies Advanced Chemicals and Tianli to make textile-coating chemicals.

In 1995 Glaxo was forced to sell a migraine drug candidate to complete its merger with Wellcome. Zeneca's gamble in buying the then-unproven drug (Zomig) paid off when the product gained US FDA approval two years later.

By 1997 Zeneca completed its gradual acquisition of Salick Health Care formed to create more humane cancer treatment programs. The purchase followed a trend of large drug firms moving into managed care which raised concerns that centers might be pressured to use their parent companies' drugs but Zeneca maintained that Salick would remain independent except to the extent that it offered an opportunity to evaluate treatments.

In 1998 Zeneca got the FDA's OK to sell its brand of tamoxifen (Nolvadex) to women at high risk of contracting breast cancer. In 1999 it sued Eli Lilly to protect Nolvadex against Lilly's marketing claim that its osteoporosis treatment Evista reduced breast cancer risk a use for which it was not approved.

In 1999 Zeneca completed its purchase of Sweden's Astra to form AstraZeneca. That year the firm sold its specialty chemicals unit Zeneca Specialties to Cinven Group and Investcorp. With its agricultural business stagnated due to crippled markets in Asia and Europe AstraZeneca announced plans to merge the unit with the agrochemicals business of Novartis and spun it off as Syngenta.

EXECUTIVES

CEO, Pascal Soriot, age 55
EVP MedImmune, Bahija Jallal
EVP Global Portfolio and Product Strategy, Marc Dunoyer
EVP International, Mark Mallon
EVP IMED Biotech Unit, Menelas (Mene) Pangalos
EVP Europe, Ruud Dobber
EVP Global Product and Portfolio Strategy, Luke Miels
EVP Human Resources, Fiona Cicconi
EVP Operations and Information Technology, Pam Cheng
EVP Global Medicines Development and Chief Medical Officer, Sean Bohen
Chairman, Leif Johansson, age 65
Auditors: KPMG LLP

LOCATIONS

HQ: AstraZeneca Plc
2 Kingdom Street, London W2 6BD
Phone: (44) 20 7604 8000 **Fax:** (44) 20 7604 8151
Web: www.astrazeneca.com

2014 Sales

	$ mil.	% of total
Americas		
US	10,485	28
Canada & other Americas	4,094	10
Europe		
Continental Europe	10,520	28
UK	6,482	17
Asia Africa & Australia	6,397	17
Eliminations	(11883)	—
Total	**26,095**	**100**

PRODUCTS/OPERATIONS

2014 Sales

	$ mil.	% of total
Cardiovascular & Metabolic	9,802	38
Neuroscience Gastrointestinal Infection & other	8,203	31
Respiratory Inflammation & Autoimmunity	5,063	19
Oncology	3,027	12
Total	**26,095**	**100**

Selected ProductsCardiovascularAtacand (angiotensin II antagonist for hypertension and heart failure)Crestor (statin for cholesterol-lowering drug)Onglyza (type 2 diabetes)Plendil (calcium antagonist for hypertension and angina)Seloken/Toprol-XL (beta-bl

COMPETITORS

Abbott Labs	Memorial
Amgen	Sloan-Kettering
Aptium Oncology	Merck
Bayer AG	Novartis
Bristol-Myers Squibb	Pfizer
Eli Lilly	Roche Holding
Gilead Sciences	Sanofi
GlaxoSmithKline	Teva
Johnson & Johnson	US Oncology

HISTORICAL FINANCIALS

Company Type: Public

Income Statement

FYE: December 31

	REVENUE ($ mil.)	NET INCOME ($ mil.)	NET PROFIT MARGIN	EMPLOYEES
12/15	24,708	2,825	11.4%	61,500
12/14	26,095	1,233	4.7%	57,500
12/13	25,711	2,556	9.9%	51,500
12/12	27,973	6,297	22.5%	51,700
12/11	33,591	9,983	29.7%	57,200
Annual Growth	**(7.4%)**	**(27.1%)**	**—**	**1.8%**

2015 Year-End Financials

Debt ratio: 25.0%
Return on equity: 14.8%
Cash ($ mil.): 6,240
Current ratio: 1.08
Long-term debt ($ mil.): 14,137

No. of shares (mil.): 1,264
Dividends
  Yield: 4.0%
  Payout: 61.8%
Market value ($ mil.): 42,917

	STOCK PRICE ($) FY Close	P/E High/Low		PER SHARE ($) Earnings	Dividends	Book Value
12/15	33.95	33	14	2.23	1.38	14.63
12/14	70.38	83	60	0.98	1.40	15.54
12/13	59.37	29	22	2.04	1.40	18.47
12/12	47.27	10	8	4.98	1.43	19.04
12/11	46.29	7	6	7.30	1.35	17.99
Annual Growth	**(7.5%)**	**—**	**—**	**(25.7%)**	**0.6%**	**(5.0%)**

AUDI AG

Auditors: PricewaterhouseCoopers Aktiengesellschaft Wirtschaftpruefungsgesellschaft

LOCATIONS

HQ: AUDI AG
I/FF-12, P.O. Box 10 04 57, Ingolstadt 85045
Phone: (49) 841 89 0   **Fax:** (49) 841 89 325 24
Web: www.audi.com

HISTORICAL FINANCIALS

Company Type: Public

Income Statement

FYE: December 31

	REVENUE ($ mil.)	NET INCOME ($ mil.)	NET PROFIT MARGIN	EMPLOYEES
12/15	63,631	4,579	7.2%	84,435
12/14	65,378	5,308	8.1%	77,247
12/13	68,671	5,453	7.9%	71,781
12/12	64,282	5,646	8.8%	67,231
12/11	57,036	5,676	10.0%	62,806
Annual Growth	**2.8%**	**(5.2%)**	**—**	**7.7%**

2015 Year-End Financials

Debt ratio: 17.9%
Return on equity: 21.0%
Cash ($ mil.): 13,478
Current ratio: 1.43
Long-term debt ($ mil.): 1,816

No. of shares (mil.): 43
Dividends
  Yield: —
  Payout: —
Market value ($ mil.): —

Australia & New Zealand Banking Group Ltd

Auditors: KPMG

LOCATIONS

HQ: Australia & New Zealand Banking Group Ltd
ANZ Centre Melbourne, Level 9, 833 Collins Street, Docklands, Victoria 3008
Phone: (61) 3 9273 5555   **Fax:** (61) 3 8542 5252
Web: www.anz.com

HISTORICAL FINANCIALS

Company Type: Public

Income Statement

FYE: September 30

	ASSETS ($ mil.)	NET INCOME ($ mil.)	INCOME AS % OF ASSETS	EMPLOYEES
09/16	696,998	4,349	0.6%	46,554
09/15	625,438	5,266	0.8%	50,152
09/14	672,786	6,335	0.9%	50,328
09/13	654,877	5,842	0.9%	47,512
09/12	670,134	5,907	0.9%	45,900
Annual Growth	**1.0%**	**(7.4%)**	**—**	**0.4%**

2016 Year-End Financials

Return on assets: 0.6%
Return on equity: 9.9%
Long-term debt ($ mil.): —
No. of shares (mil.): —
Sales ($ mil): 26,958

Dividends
  Yield: 5.9%
  Payout: 91.8%
Market value ($ mil.): —

	STOCK PRICE ($) FY Close	P/E High/Low		PER SHARE ($) Earnings	Dividends	Book Value
09/16	21.25	11	9	1.44	1.26	15.10
09/15	19.05	10	7	1.81	0.83	13.92
09/14	27.07	11	9	2.24	1.57	15.63
09/13	28.59	13	9	2.09	1.47	15.56
09/12	25.69	12	9	2.15	1.45	15.90
Annual Growth	**(4.6%)**	**—**	**—**	**(9.5%)**	**(3.5%)**	**(1.3%)**

Aviva Plc (United Kingdom)

In the consolidating European insurance industry Aviva is a lively player. As the top insurance provider in the UK and a leading insurance firm worldwide Aviva offers both life and general insurance. Its long-term savings segment focuses on life insurance pensions unit trusts and other products while its general insurance segment includes the stuff which is called "non-life" or "property/casualty" elsewhere: home auto accident and fire coverage. Its Aviva Investors arm provides asset management globally. In the UK it also offers private medical insurance through employers. All of the company's businesses operate under the Aviva banner.

Operations

Aviva's long-term insurance segment includes life insurance pensions annuities bonds savings and other investment and protection products and accounts for about three-fourths of annual revenues. General insurance offerings include personal and commercial property/casualty coverage as well as health plans and account for nearly a quarter of sales.

Geographic Reach

Aviva operates in about 20 countries. In addition to the UK which accounts for about a third of sales primary markets include Canada France Ireland Italy and Spain. The company also has operations in emerging markets such as China India Poland Turkey and Singapore.

Sales and MarketingAviva distributes its products through many channels –including direct sales forces independent brokers partners and bank representatives –tailored to each market in which it operates. In the UK Aviva has exclusive distribution deals for the sale of protection products with such firms as Royal Bank of Scotland Barclays Santander and Tesco.

The company operates across four primary market sectors: life insurance and savings general insurance health insurance and fund management. It serves some 31 million customers around the globe.

Financial Performance

Revenue has fluctuated for Aviva in recent years due to economic conditions and restructuring measures. In 2014 the company achieved 18% revenue growth (to some £43.5 billion) due largely to higher investment income levels. Increased revenue was especially seen in core markets including France and Italy as well as certain emerging markets including Poland.

The company's net income fell 26% to £1.5 billion in 2014 due to higher unallocated divisible surplus expense primarily driven by France and Italy (which saw lower corporate and government bond yields during the year). After a couple of years of growth cash flow from operations took a huge dip. Aviva's net outflow of £544 million (versus an inflow of £5 billion in 2013) occurred for a number of reasons including lower premium income payments of claims and trades of operating assets including financial investments.

Strategy

Through restructuring measures in recent years Aviva has refocused on producing attractive financial returns in its narrowed business markets reducing capital volatility to build financial strength and improving revenue growth and profits.After taking a big hit due to investment losses tied to the global recession Aviva has downsized its opera-

tions in subsequent years to try to repair the damage including the sale of non-core international operations. To further focus on priority markets where it has a strong presence the company sold subsidiaries in Turkey Russia and Malaysia in 2013. The following year it divested holdings including Spain's CSG Aviva Corporaracion Caixa Galicia de Seguros y Reaseguros US equity manager River Road Asset Management and South Korean unit Woori Aviva Life Insurance.

To o further simplify its business the company has combined the operations of a number of businesses especially in Europe to simplify its product range and shorten the time to launch new products. For example in early 2016 it launched two new business products: Relevant Life Insurance the market's first such product offering optional critical illness coverage; and Business Life which provides life and critical illness coverage for business clients.

The company has also simplified its branding messages across its operations. Its global operations now operate as Aviva.

Mergers and Acquisitions

Building up its domestic market position in 2015 Aviva bought rival Friends Life for £5.6 billion sealing its presence at the top of the UK's life insurance market. To strengthen its presence on the other side of the pond Aviva Canada in 2016 acquired RBC General Insurance Company from Royal Bank of Canada's RBC Insurance subsidiary for £281 million. Canada is Aviva's second-largest general insurance market after the UK. (In a move that counters Aviva's single-brand strategy RBC General Insurance will continue to operate under the RBC brand.)

HISTORY

Company Background

When insurers hiked premiums after the 1861 Great Tooley Street Fire of London merchants formed Commercial Union Fire Insurance (CU). It opened offices throughout the UK and in foreign ports and soon added life (1862) and marine (1863) coverage.

Over the next 20 years CU's foreign business thrived. The firm had offices across the US by the 1880s. In the 1890s CU entered Australia India and Southeast Asia. Foreign business eventually accounted for some 75% of CU's sales.

CU went shopping in the 20th century adding accident insurer Palatine Insurance Co. of Manchester in 1900 and rescuing two companies ruined by San Francisco's 1906 earthquake and fire. CU recovered from the Depression with the help of a booming auto insurance market and spent most of the 1930s and WWII consolidating operations to cut costs.

Profits suffered in the 1950s as CU faced increased competition in the US. To boost sales it merged with both multi-line rival North British and Mercantile and life insurer Northern and Employers Assurance in the early 1960s. While US business continued to lag in the 1970s the company's European business grew.

From 1982 to 1996 CU cut its operations in the US entered new markets (Poland 1992; South Africa and Vietnam 1996) and sold its New Zealand subsidiaries (1995). As competition in the UK increased the company in 1997 reorganized and merged with General Accident in 1998.

General Accident & Employers Liability Assurance Association (GA) was formed in 1885 in Perth Scotland to sell workers' compensation insurance. Within a few years GA had branches in London and Scotland. It diversified into insurance for train accidents (1887) autos (1896) and fire (1899); in 1906 its name changed to General Accident Fire and Life Assurance.

GA expanded into Australia Europe and Africa at the turn of the century. After WWI the company's auto insurance grew along with car ownership. During the 1930s the company entered the US auto insurance market. WWII put a stop to GA's growth.

The company expanded after the war forming Pennsylvania General Fire Insurance Association (1963) and acquiring the UK's Yorkshire Insurance Co. (1967). By the 1980s about one-third of its sales came from the US.

After 1986 GA acquired some 500 real estate brokerage agencies to cross-sell its home and life insurance. To increase presence in Asia and the Pacific the company in 1988 acquired NZI Corp. a New Zealand banking and insurance company whose failing operations cost GA millions. At the same time new US government regulations and a series of damaging storms hammered the company.

In response GA cut costs posting a profit by 1993. As the industry consolidated the company bought nonstandard auto insurer Sabre (1995) life insurer Provident Mutual (1996) and General Insurance Group Ltd. in Canada (1997). Unable to compete on its own GA merged with CU to form CGU in 1998.

After the merger CGU added personal pension plans and entered alliances to sell insurance in Italy and India. Merger costs and exceptional losses for 1998 hit operating profits hard. In 1999 CGU upped its stake in French bank Societe Generale to about 7% to help it fend off a hostile takeover attempt by Banque Nationale de Paris (now BNP Paribas).

In 2000 CGU merged with rival Norwich Union to form CGNU and made plans to exit the Canadian life and the US general insurance businesses. In 2001 CGNU sold its US property/casualty operations to White Mountains Insurance.

In an attempt to strengthen its brand name the company changed its name to Aviva in 2002. Following the name change the company merged and rebranded many of its subsidiaries. Aviva also made changes to its Asian operations in 2004 selling its general insurance business in Asia to Mitsui Sumitomo Insurance.

Back home Aviva acquired UK-based automotive service company RAC in 2005 (sold to The Carlyle Group in 2011) to gain access to its auto insurance and loan businesses. To get to the meaty middle Aviva stripped off RAC's non-core businesses including its fleet services which it sold to VT Group in 2006. At around the same time the company also divested its 50% ownership in Lex Vehicle Leasing to HBOS (which later merged with Lloyds TSB to become Lloyds Banking Group).

As part of an effort to focus on the Aviva brand the company changed the long-time UK brand name of Norwich Union to Aviva UK in 2009.

EXECUTIVES

Group Chief Operations and IT Officer, Nick Amin, age 60

CEO Aviva Investors, Euan Munro, age 46

Group CEO, Mark A. Wilson, age 50

CEO International Insurance, Maurice Tulloch, age 47

CFO, Thomas D. (Tom) Stoddard

Group Chief Technologist and CIO, Monique Shivanandan, age 53

Chairman Aviva Asia and Global Chairman Aviva Digital, Chris Wei, age 49

CEO UK Insurance, Andy Briggs, age 50

Group Chief Risk Officer, Angela Darlington

Chairman, Adrian A. Montague, age 68

Auditors: PricewaterhouseCoopers LLP

LOCATIONS

HQ: Aviva Plc (United Kingdom)
St. Helen' s, 1 Undershaft, London EC3P 3DQ
Phone: (44) 20 7662 8934
Web: www.aviva.com

2014 Revenues

	% of total
UK & Ireland	41
France	27
Canada	11
Poland	2
Italy Spain & other	16
Asia	3
Total	**100**

PRODUCTS/OPERATIONS

2014 Net Earned Premium

	% of total
Long-term (life) insurance	59
General insurance & health	41
Fund management	-
Total	**100**

COMPETITORS

AEGON	Legal & General Group
AXA	Lloyds Banking Group
Ageas Insurance	Prudential plc
International	QBE
Allianz	RSA Insurance
Bank of Ireland	Royal Bank of Scotland
Canada Life	Standard Life
Generali	Zurich Insurance Group
ING	

HISTORICAL FINANCIALS

Company Type: Public

Income Statement

FYE: December 31

	ASSETS ($ mil.)	NET INCOME ($ mil.)	INCOME AS % OF ASSETS	EMPLOYEES
12/15	574,808	1,360	0.2%	29,639
12/14	446,013	2,449	0.5%	26,364
12/13	460,864	3,318	0.7%	27,718
12/12	508,848	(5,186)	—	33,122
12/11	482,575	347	0.1%	36,562
Annual Growth	**4.5%**	**40.7%**		**(5.1%)**

2015 Year-End Financials

Return on assets: 0.2%
Return on equity: 6.5%
Long-term debt ($ mil.): —
No. of shares (mil.): —
Sales ($ mil): 35,163

Dividends
Yield: 3.6%
Payout: 163.9%
Market value ($ mil.): —

	STOCK PRICE ($) FY Close	P/E High/Low	Earnings	PER SHARE ($) Dividends	Book Value
12/15	15.21	76 57	0.33	0.55	6.25
12/14	14.90	33 27	0.77	0.48	5.88
12/13	15.15	23 15	1.07	0.45	5.35
12/12	12.41	— —	(1.82)	0.82	5.35
12/11	9.25	259 146	0.09	0.80	7.35
Annual Growth	**13.2%**	**— —**	**39.2%**	**(9.0%)**	**(4.0%)**

AXA S.A.

Auditors: Mazars

LOCATIONS

HQ: AXA S.A.
25, avenue Matignon, Paris 75008
Phone: (33) 1 40 75 57 00
Web: www.axa.com

HISTORICAL FINANCIALS

Company Type: Public

Income Statement

FYE: December 31

	ASSETS ($ mil.)	NET INCOME ($ mil.)	INCOME AS % OF ASSETS	EMPLOYEES
12/15	966,206	6,118	0.6%	98,279
12/14	1,021,107	6,106	0.6%	96,279
12/13	1,042,385	6,170	0.6%	93,146
12/12	1,004,154	5,472	0.5%	94,364
12/11	944,329	5,592	0.6%	96,999
Annual Growth	**0.6%**	**2.3%**		**0.3%**

2015 Year-End Financials

Return on assets: 0.6%
Return on equity: 8.4%
Long-term debt ($ mil.): —
No. of shares (mil.): —
Sales ($ mil): 121,508

Dividends
Yield: 3.9%
Payout: 43.5%
Market value ($ mil.): —

	STOCK PRICE ($) FY Close	P/E High/Low	Earnings	PER SHARE ($) Dividends	Book Value
12/15	27.32	13 9	2.37	1.07	30.76
12/14	22.89	13 11	2.36	1.13	32.47
12/13	27.89	16 10	2.41	0.93	30.18
12/12	18.22	11 7	2.16	0.89	29.61
12/11	12.86	12 6	2.26	0.89	26.85
Annual Growth	**20.7%**	**— —**	**1.2%**	**4.5%**	**3.5%**

BAE Systems Plc

BAE Systems helped win the Battle of Britain in 1940 with its Spitfire and Mosquito fighters; today it is a leading military contractor and major foreign player in the US defense market. BAE's main operating groups —cyber security financial crime communications intelligence and digital transformation —provide products and services that include electro-optical sensors flight controls commercial and financial security ship repair and modernization and aircraft. BAE's fighter aircraft include the Hawk Tornado and the next-generation Eurofighter Typhoon. North America is BAE's biggest market (maintained by BAE Systems Inc.) with the US Department of Defense (DoD) its largest single customer.

Geographic Reach
The company is based in the UK and has 40 offices serving clients across the UK and Europe the Americas Asia Pacific and the Middle East. The US contributed 39% of its net sales in 2014.

Sales and MarketingBAE's largest customers are governments but it also sells to large prime contractors and commercial businesses. About 45% of its sales are services-related contracts that are typically longer term.

Financial Performance
BAE's revenues decreased from 2013 to 2014 due to volume reductions within its land and armaments business. The company was also affected by unfavorable foreign exchange translations.

Its profits increased by £576 million from 2013 to 2014 due to a decrease in taxation expenses and a decline in the impairment of intangible assets due to performance issues in the US commercial shipbuilding market.

Strategy
Amid sharp reductions in defense spending in both of the company's biggest markets the US and UK BAE Systems has launched a strategy that besides focusing on electronics and cyber and intelligence includes developing more export business to support its platforms segments and expanding its operations internationally.

In regards to the US market in late 2014 BAE for $233 million acquired Perimeter Internetworking Corp. which trades as SilverSky a commercial cyber service provider. SilverSky is a commercial cyber services and compliance provider headquartered in New York with operations in the US and the Philippines.

HISTORY

Company Background
Post-Wright brothers and pre-WWII a host of aviation companies sprang up to serve the British Empire —too many to survive after the war when the empire contracted. Parliament took steps in 1960 to save the industry by merging companies to form larger stronger entities —Hawker-Siddeley Aviation and British Aircraft Corporation (BAC).

Hawker-Siddeley made up of aircraft and missiles divisions was created by combining A.V. Roe Gloster Aircraft Hawker Aircraft Armstrong Whitworth and Folland Aircraft. It attained fame in the 1960s for developing the Harrier "jump jet."

BAC was formed from the merger of Bristol Aeroplane English Electric and Vicker-Armstrong. In 1962 it joined France's Aerospatiale to build the supersonic Concorde and became a partner in ventures to develop the Tornado and Jaguar fighters. The cost of these ventures plus the commercial failure of the Concorde was more than the company could bear. Realizing British aviation was again in trouble the British government nationalized BAC and Hawker-Siddeley in 1976 and merged them in 1977 with Scottish Aviation to form British Aerospace (BAe).

EXECUTIVES

Chairman BAE Systems India (Services) Private Limited, Deepak S. Parekh, age 70
COO, Charles Woodburn, age 44
CEO, Ian King, age 60, $850,000 total compensation
Group Managing Director International, Guy Griffiths
Group Finance Director, Peter Lynas
CEO Australia, Glynn Phillips
Chairman, Roger Carr
Auditors: KPMG LLP

LOCATIONS

HQ: BAE Systems Plc
6 Carlton Gardens, London SW1Y 5AD
Phone: (44) 1252 373232
Web: www.baesystems.com

2014 Sales

	% in total
US	39
UK	23
Saudi Arabia	20
Rest of Europe	10
Australia	4
Other	4
Total	**100**

PRODUCTS/OPERATIONS

Selected Products and Services
Air
Avionics

Combat aircraft
Commercial aircraft
Controls (flight and engine)
Jet trainers
Maintenance repair and upgrades
Missiles and counter measures
Reconnaissance aircraft
Unmanned aerial vehicle (UAV)
Homeland Security
Border and coastal surveillance
Information Technology
Intelligence Security & Resilience
Land
Artillery
Combat and tactical vehicles
Munitions
Radar
Unmanned systems
Sea
Amphibious and auxiliary ships
Naval guns
Submarines
Underwater systems
Warships
Systems Integration & Electronics
C4ISR (Command Control Communications
Computers Intelligence Surveillance Reconnaissance)
Communications
Electronic warfare & countermeasures
Imaging systems
Intelligence systems
Navigation systems
Sensor systems
Technology and Innovation
Through-Life Support

2014 Sales

	% of total
Platforms & services	
Platforms & services (UK)	41
Platforms & services (US)	20
Platforms & services (international)	17
Electronic systems	15
Cyber & intelligence	7
Total	**100**

COMPETITORS

Aerojet Rocketdyne	ITT Corp.
Airbus Group	L-3 Communications
Astronautics	Leonardo
Boeing	Lockheed Martin
Bombardier	Meggitt-USA
DRS Technologies	Navistar International
Fabbrica D' Armi Pietro	Northrop Grumman
Beretta	RUAG Holding
General Dynamics	Rockwell Collins
Honeywell	Sotera Defense
International	Thales
Horstman Defence	Ultra Electronics
Systems	United Technologies

HISTORICAL FINANCIALS

Company Type: Public

Income Statement

FYE: December 31

	REVENUE ($ mil.)	NET INCOME ($ mil.)	NET PROFIT MARGIN	EMPLOYEES
12/15	24,877	1,360	5.5%	75,000
12/14	24,086	1,155	4.8%	76,000
12/13	27,869	277	1.0%	78,000
12/12	26,789	1,721	6.4%	81,000
12/11	27,452	1,915	7.0%	87,000
Annual Growth	**(2.4%)**	**(8.2%)**	**—**	**(3.6%)**

2015 Year-End Financials

Debt ratio: 29.6%	No. of shares (mil.): —
Return on equity: 38.0%	Dividends
Cash ($ mil.): 3,759	Yield: 4.1%
Current ratio: 0.89	Payout: 279.0%
Long-term debt ($ mil.): 5,594	Market value ($ mil.): —

	STOCK PRICE ($) FY Close	P/E High/Low	PER SHARE ($) Earnings	Dividends	Book Value
12/15	29.46	114 87	0.43	1.21	1.40
12/14	29.16	129 104	0.36	1.29	0.91
12/13	29.29	596 419	0.09	1.20	1.74
12/12	22.28	72 53	0.53	1.15	1.84
12/11	17.66	61 41	0.57	1.06	2.02
Annual Growth	**13.6%**	**— —**	**(6.8%)**	**3.3%**	**(8.8%)**

Baloise Holding AG

Founded in 1863 as a fire insurance company Bâloise-Holding today is a general insurer that sells such standardized products as group and individual life policies and accident property and auto insurance to small firms and individuals. The company is one of the leading insurers in Switzerland operating primarily there and in Germany; together the countries account for about 70% of its sales. Through subsidiaries it also operates in other nearby countries including Belgium and Luxembourg. Bâloise also provides banking pension plans and other financial services through its Bâloise Bank SoBa. The company uses its own sales force as well as partner distributors and independent brokers to sell its wares.

Operations

Bâloise operates through four segments: Non-Life Life Banking (including asset management) and Other Activities. Its Non-Life segment offers accident and health coverage as well as liability motor property and marine products which are primarily targeted towards retail clients. Life provides individuals and companies with endowment policies term insurance investment-linked products and private placement life insurance. Bâloise's Banking segment includes subsidiaries Bâloise Bank SoBa in Switzerland and Deutscher Ring Bausparkasse in Germany while the group's Other Activities segment comprises investment companies real estate companies and financing firms.

Geographic Reach

Switzerland accounts for about half of Bâloise's revenues. The group also has operations in Germany (including the regional branches of Basler Sachversicherungs and Basler Lebensversicherungs in the Czech Republic and Slovakia). In Luxembourg the company operates Bâloise Life Liechtenstein.

Sales and Marketing

The company sells its products through its own sales department as well as partners and outside brokers. It serves individuals small to midsize firms and selected industrial enterprises.

Financial Performance

Revenue increased 3% to CHF 9.3 billion (approximately $10.4 billion) in 2014 as a result of growth in Switzerland Belgium and Luxembourg. Swiss division Basler Switzerland saw growth in its unit-linked life insurance business as did Bâloise's operations in Belgium which established new banking partnerships during the year. Business in Luxembourg rose primarily as a result of the acquisition of P&V Assurances which boosted its conventional life insurance lines. The group also benefited from an increase in realized gains on investments.

Net income rose 57% (percentages may differ upon conversion to US currency) to CHF 710.7 million thanks to the increased revenue as well as

the disposal of Bâloise's stake in Nationale Suisse and the sale of Basler Austria. Gains realized on equities and real estate also contributed to the rise in profits.

Cash flow from operations spiked more than 700% that year to CHF 609.7 million.

Strategy

Bâloise focuses on organic growth and market penetration to expand in its core geographic areas. The company also exits certain markets it feels are underperforming. In 2014 it sold its Croatian and Serbian subsidiaries to UNIQA Group for euro 75 million withdrawing from southeastern Europe. It also sold Basler Versicherungs-Aktiengesellschaft in Austria and National Suisse.

Mergers and Acquisitions

In Luxembourg Bâloise acquired P&V Assurances in 2014.

HISTORY

Company Background

In 1863 15 business leaders in Basel Switzerland formed the Bâloise Fire Insurance Company. This was followed in 1864 by the formation of the Baloise transportation and life insurance companies.

Bâloise-Holding was created in 1962 as a holding company for the previously independent insurance entities. In 1971 it merged all of its non-life companies into the Baloise Insurance Group.

Under its then-new chairman and president Rolf Schäuble Bâloise-Holding began in 1993 to reorganize its operations as it implemented a new corporate strategy. Key components of the strategy included a focus on the company's core European markets and a pattern of discarding less-profitable businesses. In 1998 Bâloise-Holding sold off its US operations.

Strengthening its position as a full-fledged financial services company in 2000 Bâloise acquired Swiss bank Solothurner (now Bâloise Bank SoBa).

The same year it purchased Belgian bank HBK-Spaarbank Belgian insurer Amazon Insurance N.V. and Swiss regional bank Solothurner Bank SoBa.

EXECUTIVES

Head Asset Management, Martin Wenk, age 59
CFO, German Egloff, age 58
Head Corporate Center, Thomas Sieber
CEO Basler Germany, Jan De Meulder
CEO Basler Switzerland, Michael Mueller
Group CEO, Gert De Winter
Auditors: PricewaterhouseCoopers Ltd.

LOCATIONS

HQ: Baloise Holding AG
Aeschengraben 21, Basel CH-4002
Phone: (41) 58 285 89 42   **Fax:** (41) 58 285 70 70
Web: www.baloise.com

2014 Sales

	% of total
Switzerland	48
Germany	18
Belgium	17
Luxembourg	16
Other	1
Total	**100**

PRODUCTS/OPERATIONS

2014 Sales

	% of total
Non-life insurance	47
Life	53
Total	**100**

Selected Subsidiaries

Austria
Basler Versicherungen (insurance and pension products for private and business clients)
Belgium
Mercator Verzekeringen (personal and property insurance for individuals and small to mid-sized businesses)
Germany
Basler Versicherungen (personal and property insurance for individuals small and mid-sized enterprises and selected industrial clients)
Deutscher Ring (insurance and pension products for individuals)
Luxembourg
Bâloise Assurances (life personal and property insurance for private and business clients)
Switzerland
Bâloise Bank SoBa (banking products and services)
Basler Versicherungen (insurance and pension products for individuals and small to mid-sized enterprises)

COMPETITORS

AEGON	Helvetia Group
AIG	ING
AXA	Itasa
AXA Versicherungen	Munich Re Group
Achmea	Prudential plc
Allianz	Swiss Life
Hannover Re	Zurich Insurance Group

HISTORICAL FINANCIALS

Company Type: Public

Income Statement
FYE: December 31

	ASSETS ($ mil.)	NET INCOME ($ mil.)	INCOME AS % OF ASSETS	EMPLOYEES
12/15	79,331	1,030	1.3%	7,387
12/14	80,209	1,438	1.8%	7,617
12/13	84,952	1,019	1.2%	8,613
12/12	80,208	958	1.2%	8,795
12/11	73,412	129	0.2%	9,141
Annual Growth	2.0%	67.9%	—	(5.2%)

2015 Year-End Financials

Return on assets: 1.2%
Return on equity: 18.2%
Long-term debt ($ mil.): —
No. of shares (mil.): 46
Sales ($ mil): 8,878

Dividends
Yield: 0.0%
Payout: 2.7%
Market value ($ mil.): 591

	STOCK PRICE ($) FY Close	P/E High/Low		PER SHARE ($) Earnings	Dividends	Book Value
12/15	12.70	1	1	10.72	0.29	117.44
12/14	13.05	1	1	14.79	0.28	124.69
12/13	12.42	1	1	10.53	0.29	116.02
12/12	7.89	1	1	9.91	0.29	112.25
12/11	9.71	8	6	1.37	0.28	87.76
Annual Growth	6.9%	—	—	67.2%	1.6%	7.6%

Banca Popolare dell'Emilia

Banca Popolare dell'Emilia Romagna's popularity expands beyond its home region of Emilia Romagna as it operates more than 1270 branches across 18 Italian regions through its local banking subsidiaries. The banking cooperative known as BPER Banca provides individuals and businesses with a variety of services including deposit banking lending and bancassurance (life insurance). Other BPER subsidiaries and affiliates offer such products and services as corporate and investment banking private banking and wealth management asset management life insurance factoring and leasing. Originally founded in 1867 BPER Banca now boasts $85 billion in assets and is Italy's sixth-largest bank by assets deposits and loans.

OperationsBPER Banca operates through five main subsidiary banks: Banca Popolare dell'Emilia Romagna s.c. which brought in more than 75% of the group's income in 2014; Bper (Europe) International; Banca di Sassari; Banca di Sardegna; and Cassa di Risparmio di Bra.

Broadly speaking net interest income (mostly from loans) made up more than 58% of BPER Banca's operating income in 2014. Another 31% of the group's operating income came from net commission income half of which came from commissions on loans and guarantees and the other half split between credit cards collections and payments; indirect deposits and insurance policies; and trading in currency/financial instruments. About 8% of the group's operating income came from net trading income.About 58% of BPER Banca's loan portfolio was tied to corporate loans in 2014 while about 41% was tied to retail and private banking customers.

Geographic Reach

The group's branches are located across Italy in the Lombardy and Triveneto Emilia West Emilia Centre Tuscan-Emilian Romagna Lazio Adriatica Campania and Southern Italy territories. Less than 1% of its operating income came from its operations outside of Italy in 2014.

Strategy

Unlike many of its banking competitors which get most of their business from retail customers BPER Banca gets the majority of its business from corporate clients. Indeed some 53% of the group's loan assets were tied to corporate loans in 2014 while another 5% of loans were extended to "large corporate" customers. With deeper pockets a corporate client base could offer the bank more existing business growth potential than with a less-affluent retail customer base.

BPER Banca has been working to boost its capitalization levels and reduce its bad loan debt in recent years. The group was one of nine Italian banks that failed the European Central Bank's capital stress test in late 2014. Meanwhile the group reported that its doubtful loan levels (which consisted of non-performing watch-list restructured and past-due loans) reached 14.9% of its total loan levels at the end of 2014. By comparison healthy banks around the world generally have a non-performing loan to total loan ratio of 5% or less. BPER Banca has since improved its capital levels above the minimum regulation thresholds but it could be unprepared to face a future financial crisis or deeper recession should it fail to keep its capital levels up.

EXECUTIVES

President Titolare, LUIGI ODORICI
Vice Presidente, ALBERTO MARRI
Vice Presidente, GIOSUE' BOLDRINI
Amministratore Delegato, ALESSANDRO VANDELLI
Consigliere, GUIDO LEONI
Consigliere, ETTORE CASELLI
Consigliere, PIETRO FERRARI
Consigliere, VALERIA VENTURELLI
Consigliere, COSTANZO JANNOTTI PECCI
Consigliere, ELISABETTA GUALANDRI

LOCATIONS

HQ: Banca Popolare dell' Emilia
Via San Carlo 8/20, Modena 41100
Phone: (39) 059 2021111   **Fax:** (39) 059 2022033
Web: www.bper.it

Selected Regions

Italy
Abruzzo
Basilicata
Calabria
Campania
Emilia Romagna
Lazio
Liguria
Lombardia
Marche
Molise
Puglia
Sardegna
Sicilia
Toscana
Trentiono Alto Adige
Umbria
Veneto
Abroad
China
Ireland
Luxembourg

COMPETITORS

Antonveneta	Banca di Legnano
BNL bc	Banco Popolare
Banca Carige	Banco di Desio
Banca Popolare Di Spoleto	CREDEM
Banca Popolare dell' Etruria	Intesa Sanpaolo
Banca Popolare di Milano	Monte dei Paschi di Siena
	UniCredit

HISTORICAL FINANCIALS

Company Type: Public

Income Statement
FYE: December 31

	ASSETS ($ mil.)	NET INCOME ($ mil.)	INCOME AS % OF ASSETS	EMPLOYEES
12/15	66,726	240	0.4%	11,447
12/14	73,723	17	0.0%	11,593
12/13	85,024	9	0.0%	11,718
12/12	81,241	(14)	—	11,834
12/11	78,238	277	0.4%	11,965
Annual Growth	(3.9%)	(3.5%)	—	(1.1%)

2015 Year-End Financials

Return on assets: 0.3%
Return on equity: 4.4%
Long-term debt ($ mil.): —
No. of shares (mil.): 480
Sales ($ mil): 3,022

Dividends
Yield: —
Payout: —
Market value ($ mil.): —

Banco Bilbao Vizcaya Argentaria SA (BBVA)

Auditors: DELOITTE, S.L.

LOCATIONS

HQ: Banco Bilbao Vizcaya Argentaria SA (BBVA)
Calle Azul 4, Madrid 28050
Phone: (34) 91 537 7000   **Fax:** (34) 91 537 6766
Web: www.bbva.com

HISTORICAL FINANCIALS

Company Type: Public

Income Statement

FYE: December 31

	ASSETS ($ mil.)	NET INCOME ($ mil.)	INCOME AS % OF ASSETS	EMPLOYEES
12/15	816,993	2,877	0.4%	137,968
12/14	768,128	3,182	0.4%	108,770
12/13	802,051	3,067	0.4%	112,589
12/12	840,632	2,209	0.3%	113,924
12/11	773,080	3,885	0.5%	109,694
Annual Growth	1.4%	(7.2%)	—	5.9%

2015 Year-End Financials

Return on assets: 0.3%
Return on equity: 5.4%
Long-term debt ($ mil.): —
No. of shares (mil.): —
Sales ($ mil) 40,692

Dividends
Yield: 5.5%
Payout: 72.8%
Market value ($ mil.): —

	STOCK PRICE ($) FY Close	P/E High/Low		PER SHARE ($) Earnings	Dividends	Book Value
12/15	7.33	27	19	0.42	0.41	8.14
12/14	9.39	27	21	0.53	0.54	9.74
12/13	12.39	32	22	0.54	0.55	10.12
12/12	9.42	30	18	0.42	0.53	10.05
12/11	8.57	19	11	0.83	0.57	10.16
Annual Growth	(3.8%)	—	—	(15.4%)	(7.9%)	(5.4%)

Banco BPI SA (Portugal)

Banco BPI is well aware of the color of Portuguese money. The bank is engaged in a wide range of investment banking and commercial banking activities. Investment services offered by the bank include corporate finance equities treasury and bonds asset management private banking and venture capital. Commercial offerings includes banking for individuals companies and institutions and the usual array of lending leasing and mortgaging and credit services. Banco BPI serves about 1.5 million customers through more than 600 branches across Portugal as well as more than 30 investment centers and other operations. Spain's CaixaBank bought a further 39% of BPI in 2017 taking its ownership to 84.5% in a deal worth $689.6 million.

In 2009 the Portugese government made an offer to buy Companhia de Seguro de Creditos or Cosec a provider of credit and bond insurance services. Banco BPI joinly owns Cosec with France's Euler Hermes.

EXECUTIVES

President Board of Directors, Artur Silva
Board of Directors Vice President, Fernando Ulrich
Membro du Conselho de Administra § Ło, Tom˜s Jervell
Membro du Conselho de Administra § Ło, Luis Pi

Membro du Conselho de Administra § Ło, Carla Bambulo
Membro du Conselho de Administra § Ło, Alfredo Almeida
Membro du Conselho de Administra § Ło, Ant˜nio Xavier
Membro du Conselho de Administra § Ło, Ant˜nio Silva
Membro du Conselho de Administra § Ło, Armando Pinho
Membro du Conselho de Administra § Ło, Carlos Silva
Membro du Conselho de Administra § Ło, Ign˜cio Villar
Auditors: Deloitte & Associados, SROC S.A.

LOCATIONS

HQ: Bánco BPI SA (Portugal)
Rua Tenente Valadim 284, 3 piso, Porto 4100-476
Phone: (351) 22 607 3337   **Fax:** (351) 22 607 4738
Web: www.bpi.pt

COMPETITORS

Banco Comercial Portugus
Caixa Geral de Depsitos

Espirito Santo Investment Bank
Esprito Santo

HISTORICAL FINANCIALS

Company Type: Public

Income Statement

FYE: December 31

	ASSETS ($ mil.)	NET INCOME ($ mil.)	INCOME AS % OF ASSETS	EMPLOYEES
12/15	44,301	257	0.6%	8,634
12/14	51,815	(198)	—	8,638
12/13	58,786	92	0.2%	8,864
12/12	58,738	328	0.6%	8,964
12/11	55,561	(368)	—	9,292
Annual Growth	(5.5%)	—	—	(1.8%)

2015 Year-End Financials

Return on assets: 0.5%
Return on equity: 10.4%
Long-term debt ($ mil.): —
No. of shares (mil.): 1,450
Sales ($ mil): 1,934

Dividends
Yield: —
Payout: —
Market value ($ mil.): 4,382

	STOCK PRICE ($) FY Close	P/E High/Low		PER SHARE ($) Earnings	Dividends	Book Value
12/15	3.02	18	18	0.18	0.00	1.81
12/14	2.62	—	—	(0.14)	0.00	1.78
12/13	3.28	70	67	0.07	0.00	1.91
Annual Growth	(4.0%)	—	—	27.8%	—	(1.4%)

Banco Bradesco S.A.

Auditors: KPMG Auditores Independentes

LOCATIONS

HQ: Banco Bradesco S.A.
Cidade de Deus S/N, Predio Vermelho - 3o andar, Sao Paulo, Osasco 06029-900
Phone: (55) 11 3684 3702   **Fax:** (55) 11 3684 3213
Web: www.bradesco.com.br

HISTORICAL FINANCIALS

Company Type: Public

Income Statement

FYE: December 31

	ASSETS ($ mil.)	NET INCOME ($ mil.)	INCOME AS % OF ASSETS	EMPLOYEES
12/15	259,228	4,578	1.8%	0
12/14	350,149	5,763	1.6%	95,520
12/13	354,881	5,247	1.5%	100,489
12/12	391,868	5,522	1.4%	103,385
12/11	387,177	5,875	1.5%	104,684
Annual Growth	(9.5%)	(6.0%)	—	—

2015 Year-End Financials

Return on assets: 1.8%
Return on equity: 20.9%
Long-term debt ($ mil.): —
No. of shares (mil.): —
Sales ($ mil) 35,217

Dividends
Yield: 7.0%
Payout: 32.0%
Market value ($ mil.): —

	STOCK PRICE ($) FY Close	P/E High/Low		PER SHARE ($) Earnings	Dividends	Book Value
12/15	4.81	3	2	0.79	0.31	4.14
12/14	13.37	6	4	0.99	0.35	5.58
12/13	12.53	8	5	0.90	0.26	5.49
12/12	17.37	9	7	0.95	0.32	6.28
12/11	16.68	10	7	1.01	0.39	5.72
Annual Growth	(26.7%)	—	—	(6.1%)	(5.7%)	(7.7%)

Banco BTG Pactual S.A.

Auditors: Ernst & Young Auditores Independentes S.S.

LOCATIONS

HQ: Banco BTG Pactual S.A.
Av. Brigadeiro Faria Lima, 3477, Sao Paulo
Phone: (55) 11 3383 2159   **Fax:** (55) 11 3383 2001
Web: www.btgpactual.com

HISTORICAL FINANCIALS

Company Type: Public

Income Statement

FYE: December 31

	ASSETS ($ mil.)	NET INCOME ($ mil.)	INCOME AS % OF ASSETS	EMPLOYEES
12/15	61,353	186	0.3%	0
12/14	59,350	796	1.3%	0
12/13	51,176	1,048	2.0%	0
12/12	60,857	1,043	1.7%	0
12/11	44,178	715	1.6%	0
Annual Growth	8.6%	(28.6%)	—	—

2015 Year-End Financials

Return on assets: 0.3%
Return on equity: 4.2%
Long-term debt ($ mil.): —
No. of shares (mil.): 1,424
Sales ($ mil): 4,172

Dividends
Yield: —
Payout: —
Market value ($ mil.): —

Banco Comercial Portugues SA

Auditors: KPMG & Associados - Sociedade de Revisores Oficiais de Contas, S.A.

LOCATIONS

HQ: Banco Comercial Portugues SA
Praca D. Joao I, 28, Porto 4000-295
Phone: (351) 21 321 1081   **Fax:** (351) 21 321 1079
Web: www.millenniumbcp.pt

HISTORICAL FINANCIALS

Company Type: Public

Income Statement

FYE: December 31

	ASSETS ($ mil.)	NET INCOME ($ mil.)	INCOME AS % OF ASSETS	EMPLOYEES
12/15	81,565	256	0.3%	17,252
12/14	92,817	(275)	—	17,939
12/13	112,902	(1,019)	—	18,873
12/12	118,287	(1,606)	—	21,297
12/11	120,914	(1,097)	—	21,470
Annual Growth	(9.4%)	—	—	(5.3%)

2015 Year-End Financials

Return on assets: 0.3%
Return on equity: 5.3%
Long-term debt ($ mil.): —
No. of shares (mil.): —
Sales ($ mil): 3,831

Dividends
  Yield: —
  Payout: —
  Market value ($ mil.): —

	STOCK PRICE ($) FY Close	P/E High/Low	PER SHARE ($) Earnings	Dividends	Book Value
12/15	6.82	137	113	0.01	0.00	0.09
12/14	9.19	—	—	(0.01)	9.38	0.09
12/13	1.00	—	—	(0.06)	0.00	0.18
Annual Growth	161.2% (17.2%)	—	—	—	—	—

Banco de Chile

Banco de Chile proffers a place for pesos. Chile's second-largest bank after Banco Santander Chile it has some 300 branches and 1400 ATMs in its home country as well as operations in Argentina Brazil China Mexico and the US. In addition to corporate and retail banking the company offers (through subsidiaries) mutual funds brokerage insurance financial planning factoring and other services. The Luksic family through such entities as Quiñenco and Sociedad Matriz Banco de Chile controls a majority of the bank. In 2008 Citigroup bought a 10% stake in the bank (with an option to acquire more) from Quiñenco and merged its Chilean operations into Banco de Chile.

In 2010 Citigroup upped its interest in the bank to more than 40% as part of its option to acquire up to half of the company.

Banco de Chile was founded in 1893.

EXECUTIVES

2do. Vicepresidente, Francisco Aristeguieta Silva
1er. Vicepresidente, Andronico Luksic Craig

Presidente Junta Directiva, Pablo Granifo Lavin
Auditors: Ernst & Young Ltda.

LOCATIONS

HQ: Banco de Chile
Paseo Ahumada 251, Santiago
Phone: (56) 2 637 1111   **Fax:** (56) 2 653 5156
Web: www.bancochile.cl

COMPETITORS

BBVA Chile
BBVA Provida
Banco Santander Chile

Banco de Credito e
Inversiones
CORPBANCA

HISTORICAL FINANCIALS

Company Type: Public

Income Statement

FYE: December 31

	ASSETS ($ mil.)	NET INCOME ($ mil.)	INCOME AS % OF ASSETS	EMPLOYEES
12/15	43,826	860	2.0%	14,973
12/14	45,540	983	2.2%	14,803
12/13	49,227	1,046	2.1%	14,723
12/12	48,274	994	2.1%	14,581
12/11	41,809	824	2.0%	14,129
Annual Growth	1.2%	1.1%	—	1.5%

2015 Year-End Financials

Return on assets: 2.0%
Return on equity: 20.0%
Long-term debt ($ mil.): —
No. of shares (mil.): —
Sales ($ mil): 3,145

Dividends
  Yield: 4.4%
  Payout: 26,791.3%
  Market value ($ mil.): —

	STOCK PRICE ($) FY Close	P/E High/Low	PER SHARE ($) Earnings	Dividends	Book Value
12/15	59.41	10	9	0.01	2.58	0.05
12/14	68.94	12	10	0.01	2.83	0.05
12/13	87.80	16	14	0.01	3.31	0.05
12/12	96.50	19	15	0.01	2.80	0.05
12/11	81.75	18	13	0.01	2.49	0.04
Annual Growth	(7.7%)	—	—	(0.8%)	0.9%	6.0%

Banco De Sabadell SA

Banco de Sabadell (also known as BancoSabadell) is one of the top banking groups in Spain offering corporate commercial and private banking through more than 2400 branches mostly in Spain as well as in France Morocco the UK and the US. The company operates under five banking brands: SabadellAtlantico and SabadellHerrero for business banking; SabadellSolbank which specializes in providing banking services for tourists and the tourism industry; ActivoBank for online banking; and SabadellUrquijo for private banking. BancoSabadell also offers insurance products through bancassurance along with asset management and securities brokerage services.

OperationsBancoSabadell operates four main business segments: Commercial Banking; Corporate Banking and Global Businesses; Markets and Private Banking; and Asset Management.

The Commercial Banking division generates more than 80% of BancoSabadell's total revenue and provides traditional banking products and services to large and medium-sized businesses SMEs retailers and sole proprietors mostly under its SabadellAtlantico brand in Spain as well as

---

under a number of regional brand names. The division also operates bancassurance which provides insurance products. Corporate Banking and Global Businesses (10% of overall revenue) provides corporate banking structured and corporate finance development capital consumer finance and national trade services serving mostly large corporations and financial institutions in Spain and overseas. The Markets and Private Banking segment (4% of overall revenue) provides savings and investment management services including securities market trading wealth management and custody services. The division comprises the group's SabadellUrquijo Private Banking business; Investment Products and Research unit; Treasury and Capital Markets unit; and Securities Trading and Custody Services unit.

The Asset Management division (3% of overall revenue) manages real estate as well as non-performing assets through real estate asset manager Solvia. Solvia boasts a retail sales unit and sales teams that specializes in consolidating portfolio assets for sale to institutional buyers. It also liquidates assets with special or unusual features.

The bank's foreign country affiliates include BS America (in Florida); and BancSabadell d'Andorra (in the Principality of Andorra) in which Banco Sabadell holds a nearly 51% controlling stake.

Geographic Reach

Most of the bank's 2400-plus branches are located in Spain though it also has branches in France Morocco the UK and the US (in Miami Florida). Additionally it has representative offices in Algeri Brazil China Dominican Republic India Mexico Poland Singapore Turkey Venezuela United Arab Emirates and the US.

Financial Performance

Note: Growth rates may differ after conversion to US dollars.

BancoSabadell's revenues and profits have been trending higher over the past few years thanks to growing fee income from the sale of managed investment products coupled with declining loan loss provisions as the bank has worked to de-risk its loan portfolio by selling off non-performing assets.

The bank's net interest income jumped by 25% to euro 2.26 billion ($2.74 billion) in 2014 as the bank paid less in interest expense on deposits while net fee income and net trading income also grew by double-digits due to higher sales of managed investment products and services and higher capital gains respectively. Higher revenue in 2014 also pushed BancoSabadell's profit higher by a whopping 154% to euro 371.68 million ($451.77 million) for the year.

Strategy

Banco Sabadell reiterated in 2015 its strategy toward improving profitability domestically which included three main priorities: to grow its existing domestic business by cross-selling its wide variety of services to existing customers and by leveraging its large scale to boost profit margins; continue to de-risk its loan portfolio and strengthen its balance sheet; and increase overall productivity across its operations without sacrificing service quality. These initiatives the company insists will help support future plans to expand internationally.As part of its global expansion plans the bank announced in late 2015 that it would begin operations in Mexico for the first time and begin to introduce its business banking services before launching its banking services for individuals. Earlier during the year the bank acquired TSB Bank expanding its reach significantly in the UK market.

Toward its long-term balance sheet transformation strategy which spanned from 2014 through 2016 Banco Sabadell regularly sells its non-performing loan assets to de-risk its loan portfolio. To this end in 2014 for example the company sold a fully-provisioned loan portfolio (worth euro 554 million or roughly $673 million) to international investor Aiqon Capital reducing the bank's exposure to non-strategic assets.

The company is not opposed to selling off underperforming parts of its business either to free up resources. In mid-2014 it sold its unpaid debt management and collection business to Lindorff Spain for a capital gain amounting to euro 162 million (about $197 million). Mergers and Acquisitions—In April 2014 the group purchased Britain-based TSB Banking Group plc from Lloyds Banking Group for £1.7 billion ($2.5 billion) as part of its global expansion plans. The deal meant that 22% of Sabadell's assets would be located outside of Spain compared with just 5% at present. In 2014 Banco Sabadell purchased JGB Bank from GNB Holdings for some $49.6 million. Following the acquisition JGB Bank was folded into Sabadell United Bank (SUB) the group's Florida-based subsidiary. In 2013 the bank purchased Lloyds Banking Group España from Lloyds TSB Bank Plc which included 28 branches and euro 1.71 million in assets as well as Spanish subsidiaries Lloyds Bank International S.A.U. and Lloyds Investment España.

Company Background

Previously BancoSabadell acquired Miami-based Mellon United National Bank (which it rebranded Sabadell United Bank) and its 15 branches from The Bank of New York Mellon in 2010. The following year it acquired the assets and branches of the failed Lydian Private Bank further adding to its operations in the region. In 2007 the company acquired TransAtlantic Bank and BBVA's private banking business also both based in Miami.

Closer to home BancoSabadell acquired smaller rival Banco Guipuzcoano in 2010. The following year it acquired savings bank Caja de Ahorros del Mediterraneo (CAM) which had been seized by the government for a symbolic euro 1. That deal brought some 5 million additional customers to the bank increased its assets by around 75% and upped its branch numbers by more than 900. CAM is now SabadellCAM.

EXECUTIVES

Managing Director, Jaime Guardiola Romojaro
General Manager, Tomas Varela Muina
General Manager, Miguel Montes Guell
Director-General Manager, Jose Luis Negro Rodriguez
Chairman, Jose Oliu Creus
Auditors: PricewaterhouseCoopers Auditores, S.L.

LOCATIONS

HQ: Banco De Sabadell SA
Plaza de Sant Roc, 20, Barcelona, Sabadell 08201
Phone: (34) 93 902 323 555 **Fax:** (34) 93 935 916 062
Web: www.bancsabadell.com

PRODUCTS/OPERATIONS

2013 Sales

	% of total
Net interest income	44
Income from trading and exchange differences	38
Fee and Commission income	18
Total	**100**

2014 Sales

%	
Commercial Banking	83
Corporate Banking	10
Sabadell Urquijo Banking	2
Investment Managment	2
Real Estate Asset Management	3
Total	**100**

COMPETITORS

BBVA	Banco Popular Espa±ol
Banco Pastor	Grupo Santander

HISTORICAL FINANCIALS

Company Type: Public

Income Statement

FYE: December 31

	ASSETS ($ mil.)	NET INCOME ($ mil.)	INCOME AS % OF ASSETS	EMPLOYEES
12/15	227,239	4	0.0%	21,879
12/14	198,547	6	0.0%	17,760
12/13	225,015	28	0.0%	16,427
12/12	212,927	18	0.0%	14,291
12/11	129,910	5	0.0%	10,675
Annual Growth	**15.0%**	**(5.2%)**	**—**	**19.7%**

2015 Year-End Financials

Return on assets: 0.0%
Return on equity: 0.0%
Long-term debt ($ mil.): —
No. of shares (mil.): —
Sales ($ mil): 8,530

Dividends
Yield: 0.0%
Payout: 293.6%
Market value ($ mil.): —

	STOCK PRICE ($) FY Close	P/E High/Low	PER SHARE ($) Earnings	Dividends	Book Value
12/15	3.35	58 25	0.15	0.43	2.45
12/14	5.39	82 57	0.11	0.02	3.24
12/13	5.03	150 57	0.09	0.33	3.41
12/12	5.77	265146	0.04	0.69	3.76
12/11	8.68	54 46	0.18	0.18	5.19
Annual Growth(21.2%) (17.1%)			**— —**	**(5.6%)**	**23.9%**

Banco Popular Espanol SA

Business services nec nsk
Auditors: PricewaterhouseCoopers Auditores, S.L.

LOCATIONS

HQ: Banco Popular Espanol SA
Velazquez 34, Madrid 28001
Phone: (34) 91 520 70 00 **Fax:** (34) 91 577 92 08
Web: www.bancopopular.es

HISTORICAL FINANCIALS

Company Type: Public

Income Statement

FYE: December 31

	ASSETS ($ mil.)	NET INCOME ($ mil.)	INCOME AS % OF ASSETS	EMPLOYEES
12/15	172,803	114	0.1%	15,079
12/14	196,251	401	0.2%	15,321
12/13	203,552	447	0.2%	16,027
12/12	207,748	(3,243)	—	16,501
12/11	169,346	620	0.4%	14,062
Annual Growth	**0.5%**	**(34.4%)**	**—**	**1.8%**

2015 Year-End Financials

Return on assets: 0.0%
Return on equity: 0.8%
Long-term debt ($ mil.): —
No. of shares (mil.): 2,100
Sales ($ mil): 5,278

Dividends
Yield: 0.0%
Payout: 111.2%
Market value ($ mil.): 28,203

	STOCK PRICE ($) FY Close	P/E High/Low	PER SHARE ($) Earnings	Dividends	Book Value
12/15	13.43	422266	0.05	0.06	6.48
12/14	21.31	157134	0.19	0.00	7.16
Annual Growth(37.0%)		**—**	**—(26.9%)**	**—**	**(2.5%)**

Banco Santander Brasil SA

If you're looking for a place to park a "brazillion" dollars Banco Santander (Brasil) is there. The bank part of Spain's Banco Santander provides financial services through 3566 branches primarily in Brazil's south and southeast with a major presence in the states of São Paulo and Rio Grande do Sul. Santander Brasil also offers wholesale banking to large corporations. Additional services include asset management private banking and insurance. In 2013 it launched a new category of specialized financial services (61 Santander Select branches with 400 relationship managers). The company accounts for about a quarter of its parent's revenues. Banco Santander owns more than 80% of Santander Brasil.

Company Background

The parent company listed approximately 15% of its shares of its Brazilian unit on the New York Stock Exchange in a 2009 IPO. It turned out to be the world's largest IPO that year raising some R$13 billion ($8 billion). The proceeds from the offering have been used to drive growth by funding new branches and lending. It is also growing its insurance and credit card businesses; the company recently began offering its Santander-Ferrari credit card.

In late 2010 Santander rebranded its Brazilian brands —Banco Real and Santander Brasil —under the same name and platform. (It completed similar restructuring efforts in the UK and Mexico.) The parent company has high hopes for its Latin American operations especially in the high-growth markets of Brazil and Mexico. As such Santander is committed to investing in those units as it solidifies its position as a leading global bank. Santander Brasil is the result of the 2006 merger of Banco Santander banks Banco Santander Brasil Banco Santander Meridional and Banco do Estado de São Paulo. The company added to its Brazilian bank empire when it acquired Banco Real in 2008. At the time Banco Real was the fourth largest non government-owned Brazilian bank. The acquisition boosted Santander Brasil into the top three of banks in Brazil (along with Banco Bradesco and Itau Unibanco)Brazil is a promising region of the world for banking. The country was a resilient market during the economic downturn. Employment levels rose and a new middle class emerged. As the Brazilian economy expands Santander Brasil expects lending and overall demand for banking services to grow.

EXECUTIVES

VP Executive Officer, Juan Sebasti ̈n Moreno Blanco, age 52
SVP Executive Officer, Conrado Engel, age 59
SVP Executive Officer, Jose de Paiva Ferreira, age 57

VP Executive Officer, Angel Santodomingo Martell, age 51
Vice Chairman, Jes s Maria Zabalza Lotina, age 58
VP Executive Officer, Antonio Pardo de Santayana Montes, age 45
VP Executive Officer, Carlos Alberto L pez Gal ˜n, age 54
VP Executive Officer, Carlos Rey de Vicente, age 42
VP Executive Officer, Ign ˜cio Dominguez-Adame Bozzano, age 48
VP Executive Officer, Jo o Guilherme de Andrade S Consiglio, age 48
VP Executive Officer, Manoel Marcos Madureira, age 65
VP Executive Officer, Oscar Rodrigues Herrero, age 45
Chairman, Celso Clemente Giacometti, age 73
Auditors: Deloitte Touche Tohmatsu

LOCATIONS

HQ: Banco Santander Brasil SA
Avenida Presidente Juscelino Kubitschek, 2235 and 2041 Bloco A, Sao Paulo 04543-011
Phone: (55) 11 3174 8589   Fax: (55) 11 3174 6751
Web: www.santander.com.br

PRODUCTS/OPERATIONS

2013 Sales

	% of total
Interest and similar income	82
Fee and commission income	17
Gains on financial transactons	1
Total	100

COMPETITORS

Banco Bradesco	Credicorp
Banco do Brasil	Ita-Unibanco
Caixa Econ mica Federal	

HISTORICAL FINANCIALS

Company Type: Public

Income Statement

FYE: December 31

	REVENUE ($ mil.)	NET INCOME ($ mil.)	NET PROFIT MARGIN	EMPLOYEES
12/15	18,384	2,470	13.4%	0
12/14	26,207	2,118	8.1%	49,309
12/13	25,823	2,422	9.4%	49,621
12/12	30,184	2,664	8.8%	53,992
12/11	32,163	4,154	12.9%	54,602
Annual Growth	(13.0%)	(12.2%)	—	—

2015 Year-End Financials

Debt ratio: —	No. of shares (mil.): —
Return on equity: 12.4%	Dividends
Cash ($ mil.): 22,507	Yield: 6.9%
Current ratio: —	Payout: 77.5%
Long-term debt ($ mil.): —	Market value ($ mil.): —

	STOCK PRICE ($) FY Close	P/E High/Low		PER SHARE ($) Earnings	Dividends	Book Value
12/15	3.89	4	2	0.31	0.27	2.66
12/14	5.02	9	6	0.27	0.87	4.26
12/13	6.10	469382		0.01	0.21	4.77
12/12	7.28	0	0	351.60	0.30	5.50
12/11	8.14	0	0	547.05	0.41	5.78
Annual Growth	(16.9%) (17.6%)	—	—	(84.5%)	(9.8%)	

Banco Santander Chile

A majority-owned indirect subsidiary of Spanish financial services giant Grupo Santander Banco Santander Chile is the largest bank in its home country. From more than 460 branches throughout Chile (including about 100 Banafe bank locations catering to middle-income clients) the bank offers consumer banking residential mortgage financing credit cards auto loans and investment management services for approximately 2.3 million customers. The bank also has about 40 payment centers operating as Santander SuperCaja. Corporate banking services include commercial lending and leasing trade financing financial advisory services and cash management.

The bank is looking to attract more small and medium sized business customers which only make up about 15% of its client base. About 40% of Banco Santander Chile's customers are individuals –a segment that also has the opportunity for growth. Only one in four working people in Chile has a checking account and about 50% of the population has no relationship with a bank.

Banco Santander Chile also offers mutual fund management insurance and securities brokerage services. The company sold its Santiago Express consumer finance business to Chilean chain store Almacenes Paris in 2004.
Auditors: Deloitte Auditores y Consultores Ltda.

LOCATIONS

HQ: Banco Santander Chile
Bandera 140, 20th Floor, Santiago
Phone: (11) 562 320 2000
Web: www.santander.cl

COMPETITORS

BBVA Chile	Banco de Credito e
BBVA Provida	Inversiones
Banco de Chile	Scotiabank

HISTORICAL FINANCIALS

Company Type: Public

Income Statement

FYE: December 31

	ASSETS ($ mil.)	NET INCOME ($ mil.)	INCOME AS % OF ASSETS	EMPLOYEES
12/15	48,878	632	1.3%	11,723
12/14	51,143	940	1.8%	11,478
12/13	51,602	841	1.6%	11,516
12/12	51,524	741	1.4%	11,713
12/11	47,440	772	1.6%	11,566
Annual Growth	0.7%	(4.9%)	—	0.3%

2015 Year-End Financials

Return on assets: 1.3%	Dividends
Return on equity: 16.5%	Yield: 5.1%
Long-term debt ($ mil.): —	Payout: 23,359.0%
No. of shares (mil.): —	Market value ($ mil.): —
Sales ($ mil): 3,166	

	STOCK PRICE ($) FY Close	P/E High/Low		PER SHARE ($) Earnings	Dividends	Book Value
12/15	17.64	8	7	0.00	0.90	0.02
12/14	19.72	8	6	0.00	0.77	0.02
12/13	23.57	12	9	0.00	0.81	0.02
12/12	28.49	47	14	0.00	0.89	0.02
12/11	75.70	41	30	0.00	0.77	0.02
Annual Growth	(30.5%)	—	—	(4.9%)	4.1%	(0.3%)

Banco Santander SA

Though it started as only a contender in the running of the banks in Spain Banco Santander has since expanded to become one of the largest banks in the world. Beyond Spain it offers retail banking and consumer finance in Portugal the UK and other parts of Europe as well as the US. Subsidiaries such as Banco Santander Chile Banco Santander (Brasil) Santander Rio in Argentina and Grupo Financiero Santander make it a top banking group in Latin America (almost 40% of the group's attributable profit). Other units offer asset management private banking corporate and investment banking and insurance. All told the company has some 117 million customers and 12950 locations in more than 40 countries.
Operations
The global banking concern has operations in retail banking and consumer finance commercial and wholesale banking private banking asset management and insurance.
Geographic Reach
The bank operates in Europe Latin America and the US.
Financial Performance
Despite a tough global regulatory environment Santander saw its revenues (gross income) grow by almost 2% in 2014 and its attributable profit rise by 39.3% largely thanks to improvement in commercial activities customer growth and cost containment.
Strategy
Over the years Santander has expanded to become more geographically diverse –a key strategy for the company as it looks to reduce risk. The bank's strategy revolves around making acquisitions and boosting deposits in growth nations; it generates more than half of its profits in emerging markets. Santander has taken advantage of the economic downturn to snap up businesses and asset portfolios from struggling companies at bargain prices.

One target market for growth is Latin America where profits have been growing; the company hopes to further strengthen its presence in the region and in a number of European countries as well. In addition to Latin America and Europe Banco Santander is making its move in the US. The company's American holdings include northeastern regional bank Santander Holdings USA (formerly Sovereign Bancorp).

The Botin family has led Grupo Santander since its founding in 1857. Under the leadership of Ana Botin (chairman since 2014) Santander aims to boost its "loyal" global retail customer base (only 12.1 million in 2014) to 17 million by 2017 while complying with growing regulatory demands to lower risk and increase banking transparency.

HISTORY

Company Background
In 1857 a group of Basque businessmen had formed Banco Santander to finance Latin American trade. The emergence of Cantabria as a leading province after WWI helped the bank expand first regionally and then nationally.

The Botin family has been closely identified with the bank for decades. Emilio Botin served first as a board member and then for a few years as chairman before his death in 1923. The post was held by his son Emilio Botin-Sanz de Sautuola from 1950 to 1986 when his son Emilio Botin Sanz de Sautuola y Garcia de los Rios (known as Don Emilio) took over.

Spanish banks were spared the worst of the Great Depression (thanks to their isolation and the country's shunning the gold standard) but Spain's civil war was draining. In the early 1940s Santander expanded into Madrid and other major Spanish cities and merged with a few rivals. In the 1950s and 1960s as interest rates were controlled and mergers halted banks competed by building branch networks and investing overseas particularly in Latin America. In 1965 Santander joined with Bank of America to form Bankinter (it divested most of its stake by the mid-1990s).

Tight economic controls were relaxed in the 1970s after Franco's death. Despite global recession Santander continued to invest in Latin America through the mid-1980s.

In the late 1980s Santander prepared to compete in a deregulated Spain and Europe forming alliances with Royal Bank of Scotland Kemper (now part of Zurich Financial Services) and Metropolitan Life Insurance. In 1989 the bank jump-started competition by introducing Spain's first high-interest account.

Santander focused on home in the 1990s. Spurned by Banco Hispano Americano (BHA) Santander acquired a 60% stake in the ailing Banco Español de Credito (Banesto) which became wholly owned in 1998. The bank took a hit when Latin America plunged into an economic crisis that year. With profit margins falling the bank merged with BCH in 1999.

BCH was formed by the 1991 merger of Banco Central and BHA. BHA had been established in 1900 by investors in Latin America; Central had been founded in 1919. The mixed banks offered both commercial and investment banking; they funded industrialization and investment in Latin America and became two of Spain's largest banks before the civil war.

After the war BHA sold its Latin American assets when the currency dried up while Central used mergers and acquisitions to expand across Spain. Isolated from WWII by Franco the two banks used their dual strategies to fund overseas investment and domestic-branch growth.

After Franco's death the banks faced increased competition at home and abroad. Central bought BHA in 1991 to remain competitive as Spain entered the European Economic Community (now the EU) in 1992.

Following the merger BCH trimmed 20% of its branches fired some 10000 employees and sold unprofitable holdings. Focused on Latin America the bank took small stakes in small banks. Losing its edge BCH merged with Santander in 1999.

In 2000 the newly merged BSCH focused on expanding in Europe and Latin America. Among its European moves was its alliance with Societe Generale to buy investment-fund management firms particularly in the US. In Latin America the bank bought Brazil's Banco Meridional Banco do Estado de São Paulo (Banespa) and Grupo Financiero Serfin Mexico's #3 bank. Critics questioned the $5 billion price tag BSCH paid for Banespa charging that the formerly state-run bank was overvalued in 2001. Executive in-fighting saw ex-Santander chairman Emilio Botin triumph over ex-BCH chairman Jose Maria Amusategui for control of BSCH's helm. Soon after the bank started doing business as simply Santander Central Hispano. The following year the bank sold off its shares of Germany's Commerzbank and France's Societe Generale.

In one of Europe's largest cross-border bank mergers ever Santander paid more than euro 12 billion ($15 billion) for British bank Abbey National in 2004. It solidified its UK operations through the approximately euro 1.25 billion ($2.6 billion) purchase of Alliance & Leicester. Abbey

then acquired the retail deposit business of Bradford & Bingley after it was nationalized in 2008.

Another acquisition helped Santander grow in South America. In 2007 the company along with Royal Bank of Scotland and Fortis acquired the Netherlands-based ABN AMRO (the international retail banking giant with more than 4350 branches) for around euro 71 billion ($87 billion). As part of the bid Banco Santander took ABN AMRO's Brazilian operations doubling its market share in Brazil. Also a part of the ABN AMRO deal Santander became the largest non-government-owned bank in Uruguay.

In 2009 the Venezuelan government took over Banco Santander subsidiary Banco de Venezuela the third-largest bank in the country. The government paid some euro 755 million ($1 billion) to nationalize the bank.

Also that year Santander acquired the approximately three-quarters of Sovereign it didn't already own. Santander then purchased a more than euro 3 billion ($4 billion) US car loan portfolio and a loan servicing platform from HSBC.

In 2010 Santander took full control of its Mexico unit by acquiring Bank of America's 25% stake in Grupo Financiero Santander for euro 2 billion ($2.5 billion) as well as the rest of Puerto Rican unit Santander BanCorp it didn't already own. It then acquired GE Capital's $2 billion consumer mortgage business in Mexico for $162 million plus the assumption of debt. The company has also been opening new branches in the region. While the financial downturn and the European sovereign debt crisis has been rough for Spain and Portugal Mexico holds promise for growth. Hoping to cash in on some of that growth Banco Santander spun off nearly 25% of Grupo Financiero Santander in a public offering worth more than $4 billion.

Banco Santander also made a big move into Eastern Europe. In 2011 it paid euro 4 billion (nearly $6 billion) for Poland's Bank Zachodni. The acquisition may signal more acquisitions for Santander in neighboring Eastern European countries.

In 2010 Santander bought a euro 2.5 billion ($3 billion) auto loan portfolio from Citigroup.

Banco Santander also operates Santander UK the result of the 2010 merger of Abbey National Bradford & Bingley and the former Alliance & Leicester (all of which were acquired by Santander). Santander's acquisitions in the UK helped bump up profits from the region in 2009 and 2010 but in 2011 profits slipped as a result of remediation charges related to mis-sold payment protection insurance.

EXECUTIVES

CEO Banco Santander USA, Scott E. Powell, age 53
CEO, Jose Antonio Alvarez
CFO, Jose Garcia Cantera
Head Technology and Operations, Andreu Plaza Lopez
President Brazil, Sergio Rial
First Vice Chairman, Bruce N. Carnegie-Brown, age 57
Vice Chairman, Rodrigo Echenique Gorillo
Chairman, Ana P. Bot n, age 56
Auditors: DELOITTE, S.L.

LOCATIONS

HQ: Banco Santander SA
Avenida de Cantabria s/n, Madrid, Boadilla del Monte 28660
Phone: (34) 91 289 0000
Web: www.santander.com

COMPETITORS

BBVA	Citigroup
Banco Comercial Portugus	Deutsche Bank
	Esprito Santo
Banco Popular Espa±ol	HSBC
Banco do Brasil	JPMorgan Chase
Bank of America	

HISTORICAL FINANCIALS

Company Type: Public

Income Statement

FYE: December 31

	ASSETS ($ mil.)	NET INCOME ($ mil.)	INCOME AS % OF ASSETS	EMPLOYEES
12/15	1,459,825	6,498	0.4%	189,464
12/14	1,539,188	7,069	0.5%	183,938
12/13	1,535,938	6,016	0.4%	186,373
12/12	1,673,432	2,906	0.2%	188,779
12/11	1,618,788	6,921	0.4%	187,233
Annual Growth	(2.6%)	(1.6%)	—	0.3%

2015 Year-End Financials

Return on assets: 0.4%
Return on equity: 7.0%
Long-term debt ($ mil.): —
No. of shares (mil.): —
Sales ($ mil): 83,591
Dividends
Yield: 7.0%
Payout: 99.2%
Market value ($ mil.): —

	STOCK PRICE ($) FY Close	P/E High/Low	PER SHARE ($) Earnings	Dividends	Book Value
12/15	4.87	19 12	0.44	0.34	6.64
12/14	8.33	20 16	0.58	0.62	7.80
12/13	9.07	23 17	0.55	0.63	8.57
12/12	8.17	37 23	0.29	0.64	9.53
12/11	7.52	20 11	0.78	0.79	11.09
Annual Growth (12.0%)	(10.3%)	—	— (13.4%)	(18.6%)	

BanColombia, S.A.

Bancolombia has a wealth of services for wealthy and average Colombians alike. Serving more than 6.4 million customers Bancolombia is the #1 bank in Colombia with more than 700 branches and some 2300 ATMs throughout the country. Its Banagricola division has another 100 branches located in El Salvador. The bank provides traditional commercial and retail banking services including deposit accounts loans and mortgages credit and debit cards and cash management. It also offers asset management insurance investment banking and brokerage services. In addition to its core Colombia and El Salvador operations the bank is also present in the US Panama and Peru. Bancolombia traces its roots back to 1945.
Auditors: PricewaterhouseCoopers Ltda.

LOCATIONS

HQ: BanColombia, S.A.
Carrera 48 # 26-85, Avenida Los Industriales, Medellin
Phone: (57) 4 404 1837   **Fax:** (57) 4 404 5146
Web: www.grupobancolombia.com

PRODUCTS/OPERATIONS

2013 Sales

	% of total
Interest income	
Loans	65
Financial leases	9

Investment sercurities		5
Fees and other service income		
Credit and debit card fees		7
Commissions from banking services		4
Collections and payment fees		3
Trust activities		2
Checking fees		1
Others		4
Total		**100**

Selected Subsidiaries

Banca de Inversion Bancolombia S.A. (investment banking)
Bancolombia (Panamá) S.A.
Bancolombia Puerto Rico
Factoring Bancolombia S.A. (99.97%)
Fiduciaria Bancolombia S.A. (trust services 98.8%)
Inversiones Financieras Banco Agricola S.A. (investments 98.4%)
Leasing Bancolombia S.A.
Patrimonio Autonomo CV Sufinanciamiento (loan management)
Valores Bancolombia S.A. (securities brokerage)

COMPETITORS

BBVA	Bicsa Panama
Banco Latinoamericano de Comercio Exterior	Citigroup
	Credicorp
Banco de Credito e Inversiones	

HISTORICAL FINANCIALS

Company Type: Public

Income Statement

FYE: December 31

	ASSETS ($ mil.)	NET INCOME ($ mil.)	INCOME AS % OF ASSETS	EMPLOYEES
12/15	60,892	794	1.3%	34,390
12/14	62,581	998	1.6%	30,158
12/13	67,799	785	1.2%	28,759
12/12	55,180	959	1.7%	24,820
12/11	44,098	858	1.9%	24,126
Annual Growth	8.4%	(1.9%)	—	9.3%

2015 Year-End Financials

Return on assets: 1.4%
Return on equity: 13.9%
Long-term debt ($ mil.): —
No. of shares (mil.): 509
Sales ($ mil): 4,936

Dividends
Yield: 4.4%
Payout: 124.4%
Market value ($ mil.): 13,635

	STOCK PRICE ($) FY Close	P/E High/Low		PER SHARE ($) Earnings	Dividends	Book Value
12/15	26.75	0	0	0.85	1.20	11.94
12/14	47.88	0	0	1.08	1.58	13.84
12/13	49.02	—	—	(0.00)	1.61	12.25
12/12	66.58	—	—	(0.00)	1.59	12.74
12/11	59.56	—	—	(0.00)	0.00	9.03
Annual Growth	(18.1%)	—	—	—	—	7.2%

Bangkok Bank Public Co., Ltd. (Thailand)

Bangkok Bank wants to protect the baht you've got. One of the largest commercial banks in Thailand Bangkok Bank provides a variety of banking services to individual and commercial clients including checking and savings accounts loans Internet banking and treasury and investment banking services. It operates about 1200 branches serving 16 million customers throughout Thailand about a dozen other Southeast Asian countries the UK and the US. The bank was founded in 1944 in response to the difficulty Thai businessmen encountered in receiving credit facilities from foreign banks; it has since had a hand in developing its homeland's industry and agriculture.

EXECUTIVES

President, Chartsiri Sophonpanich
Chairman of the Board, Chatri Sophonpanich
Auditors: Deloitte Touche Tohmatsu Jaiyos Audit Co., Ltd.

LOCATIONS

HQ: Bangkok Bank Public Co., Ltd. (Thailand)
333 Silom Road, Bangkok 10500
Phone: (66) 0 2231 4333
Web: www.bangkokbank.com

COMPETITORS

Bank of Ayudhya	Siam Commercial
CIMB Group	Standard Chartered
DBS Group Holdings	TMB Bank
KASIKORNBANK	Thanachart Capital
Krung Thai	United Overseas Bank

HISTORICAL FINANCIALS

Company Type: Public

Income Statement

FYE: December 31

	ASSETS ($ mil.)	NET INCOME ($ mil.)	INCOME AS % OF ASSETS	EMPLOYEES
12/15	78,707	948	1.2%	0
12/14	83,937	1,104	1.3%	26,132
12/13	79,311	1,096	1.4%	24,096
12/12	79,046	1,079	1.4%	22,934
12/11	66,949	868	1.3%	21,503
Annual Growth	4.1%	2.2%	—	—

2015 Year-End Financials

Return on assets: 1.2%
Return on equity: 9.9%
Long-term debt ($ mil.): —
No. of shares (mil.): 1,908
Sales ($ mil): 4,358

Dividends
Yield: 0.0%
Payout: —
Market value ($ mil.): 43,483

	STOCK PRICE ($) FY Close	P/E High/Low		PER SHARE ($) Earnings	Dividends	Book Value
12/15	22.78	2	1	0.50	0.71	5.26
12/14	30.00	2	1	0.58	0.80	5.15
12/13	27.80	2	1	0.57	0.89	4.74
12/12	34.50	3	2	0.57	0.27	4.68
Annual Growth	(12.9%)	—	—	(3.2%)	27.7%	3.0%

Bank Audi S.A.L

Auditors: BDO, Semaan, Gholam & Co.

LOCATIONS

HQ: Bank Audi S.A.L
Banque Audi Plaza, Bab Idriss, Beirut 2021 8102
Phone: (961) 1 994000 **Fax:** (961) 1 990555
Web: www.bankaudigroup.com

HISTORICAL FINANCIALS

Company Type: Public

Income Statement

FYE: December 31

	ASSETS ($ mil.)	NET INCOME ($ mil.)	INCOME AS % OF ASSETS	EMPLOYEES
12/15	42,253	389	0.9%	6,891
12/14	41,836	339	0.8%	6,408
12/13	36,311	302	0.8%	5,894
12/12	31,343	375	1.2%	5,070
12/11	28,736	361	1.3%	5,051
Annual Growth	10.1%	1.9%	—	8.1%

2015 Year-End Financials

Return on assets: 0.9%
Return on equity: 11.9%
Long-term debt ($ mil.): —
No. of shares (mil.): 283
Sales ($ mil): 3,004

Dividends
Yield: —
Payout: —
Market value ($ mil.): —

	STOCK PRICE ($) FY Close	P/E High/Low		PER SHARE ($) Earnings	Dividends	Book Value
12/15	0.00	—	—	0.92	0.00	11.45
12/14	0.00	—	—	0.86	0.00	11.63
Annual Growth	—	—	—	1.8%	—	(0.4%)

Bank Hapoalim B.M. (Israel)

The largest bank in Israel Bank Hapoalim caters to individual commercial and corporate clients at home and abroad. Within Israel the Bank Hapoalim Group has more than 270 full-service branches and business centers. Another 30 express branches are in the works. Overseas it has about 45 branches correspondent offices and financial subsidiaries in Asia Australia Europe Latin America and North America; its international focus is on private banking and the corporate sector. Bank Hapoalim provides investment banking services including the underwriting of and investment in companies; it also provides trust services to individuals and businesses.

Bank Hapoalim was founded in 1921. Shari Arison Israel's wealthiest person is the controlling shareholder.

The bank has undergone major shakeups in its leadership since Arison took control of the bank in 2007. Dan Dankner also came on board as chairman that year. In March 2009 Zvi Ziv resigned as CEO after clashing with Dankner; deputy CEO Zion Keinan was picked to replace him. Bank of Israel (the nation's central bank) then wrangled with Arison over Hapoalim's performance and leadership threatening to remove Dankner if significant changes weren't made. Dankner seemed to get the message and resigned in 2009. Yair Seroussi replaced him.

The company planned to acquire control of Ukraine bank OJSC Ukraininan Innovation Bank (Ukrinbank) but was blocked by Bank of Israel. As a result Bank Hapoalim has suspended its planned growth in Eastern Europe. However it is examining opportunities in other regions to add to such investments as Bank Pozitif in Turkey and DKB in Kazakhstan. Other international businesses include Hapoalim Switzerland The PAM Group and Bank Hapoalim (Cayman). Hapoalim Securities U.S.A.

offers securities trading for customers in Israel and abroad.
Auditors: Somekh Chaikin (a member of KPMG)

LOCATIONS

HQ: Bank Hapoalim B.M. (Israel)
50 Rothschild Blvd., Tel-Aviv 66883
Phone: (972) 3 567 3333   **Fax:** (972) 3 560 7028
Web: www.bankhapoalim.com

COMPETITORS

Bank Leumi le-Israel	Israel Discount Bank
First International	Mizrahi Tefahot
Bank of Israel	UBS

HISTORICAL FINANCIALS

Company Type: Public

Income Statement

FYE: December 31

	ASSETS ($ mil.)	NET INCOME ($ mil.)	INCOME AS % OF ASSETS	EMPLOYEES
12/15	110,354	787	0.7%	11,804
12/14	104,943	705	0.7%	12,405
12/13	109,581	743	0.7%	12,891
12/12	100,980	682	0.7%	27,113
12/11	93,300	718	0.8%	13,408
Annual Growth	4.3%	2.3%	—	(3.1%)

2015 Year-End Financials

Return on assets: 0.7%
Return on equity: 9.5%
Long-term debt ($ mil.): —
No. of shares (mil.): 1,329
Sales ($ mil): 4,175

Dividends
Yield: 1.4%
Payout: —
Market value ($ mil.): 34,232

	STOCK PRICE ($) FY Close	P/E High/Low		PER SHARE ($) Earnings	Dividends	Book Value
12/15	25.75	6	5	1.18	0.36	6.35
12/14	23.55	7	6	1.06	0.31	6.10
12/13	28.04	7	6	1.12	0.20	6.34
12/12	21.82	6	4	1.03	0.00	5.44
12/11	16.05	12	7	0.54	0.20	4.71
Annual Growth	12.5%	—	—	21.9%	16.8%	7.8%

Bank Leumi Le-Israel B.M.

Bank Leumi le-Israel looms large as one of Israel's largest financial institutions. The company whose name translates as National Bank of Israel offers retail banking (for consumers and small businesses) commercial banking (middle-market businesses) corporate banking (large companies) and private banking (wealthy clients) through deposits mortgages and other loans credit cards trust services and investments. It has about 235 branches in Israel and more than 80 locations (including branches agencies and representative offices) in some 20 countries including the US. Subsidiary Leumi Partners provides corporate investment banking services and makes direct investments in nonbanking businesses.

Other subsidiaries include The Arab Israel Bank Leumi Mortgage Bank and retail and private banking units in the UK Switzerland Luxembourg and Romania. In 2011 Bank Leumi bought Geneva-based private bank Banque Safdie from the Safdie family. It plans to merge the firm with Bank Leumi Switzerland. In a restructuring move that will cut

costs Bank Leumi plans to absorb Leumi Mortgage Bank in 2012. The company will then provide mortgage services through a newly created mortgage division.

After the Israeli parliament passed a number of capital market reform laws in 2005 Bank Leumi was compelled to sell its mutual fund and investment portfolio management operations. It has since focused on providing investment and pension counseling to its clients.

The Israeli government owns more than 10% of Bank Leumi but has been selling off its stake in the company and intends to eventually divest its entire holding.

HISTORY

At the beginning of the 20th century a group of prominent Jewish men led by Austrian Zionist Theodor Herzl founded the Jewish Colonial Trust (which would later become known as Otzar Hitsyashvut Hayehudim or OHH). An advocate of the Jewish settlement of Palestine the trust recognized the need for a financial institution to promote colonization in the region which was then part of the Ottoman Empire. In 1902 it established the Anglo-Palestine Company the forerunner of Bank Leumi le-Israel. A year later the London-based company opened its first Palestinian office in Jaffa (now Tel Aviv).

As WWI began the company had half a dozen branches. The outbreak of hostilities between Great Britain and the Ottoman Empire forced the London-based bank to close its offices but it continued to operate from the Spanish Consulate in Jerusalem. By the mid-1920s the company was known as the Anglo-Palestine Bank and was playing a significant role in the development of local agriculture.

During the following decade Palestine saw an influx of refugees from Nazism in Europe. The bank assisted in transferring assets to Palestine and anchored the area's economy through WWII. When Israel gained independence in 1948 the Anglo-Palestine Bank became the nation's fiscal agency and printed monetary notes for the new government. It began to focus its efforts on international operations and in 1950 opened its first US office in New York City. But even though it was the national bank of the newly formed Israeli state the bank was still based in London. In 1951 a company named leumi Le'Israel was founded in Tel Aviv and assumed control of the bank which took the name Bank Leumi le-Israel (National Bank of Israel) in 1954. Also that year the government formed the Bank of Israel and Bank Leumi resumed its commercial banking activities.

Bank Leumi maintained its status as Israel's leading bank until the 1980s when triple-digit inflation hit the country. The bottom fell out in 1983 when investors pulled out of the stock market fearing devaluation of the shekel. As they had done for several years Bank Leumi and Israel's other major banking groups reacted by taking out massive loans to buy their own stock and shield against losses in share price. The artificially inflated bank stocks crashed and thousands of individual investors lost their savings. The Israeli government intervened paying some $7 billion to bail out the banks. Though the state now held most of Bank Leumi's stock the OHH maintained voting rights.

In 1986 following a government inquiry into the stock scandal chairman Ernst Japhet and the company's board were forced to resign prompting more contention. On their way out Japhet and his officers received millions of dollars in severance pay and monthly pensions. The ramifications of what became known as "Leumigate" resulted in the company's next two chairmen also being ousted over the next two years. Rival Bank Hapoalim

wrested the mantle of Israel's #1 bank from Bank Leumi in 1987.

The government sold off 10% of its interest in the firm to a unit of Deutsche Bank in 1993 and in 1995 mandated that banks sell their nonfinancial holdings. That year Galia Maor became CEO as the first woman head of an Israeli bank and Eitan Raff became chairman (he announced his retirement in 2010).

Controversy continued however. In 1997 Bank Leumi sold a majority stake in Migdal Insurance to Assicurazioni Generali which amplified questions regarding the buyer's handling of life insurance policies of Jewish Holocaust victims. The inquiry spread to Bank Leumi which released information about dormant accounts the next year but nonetheless faced government scrutiny and lawsuits from descendants of Holocaust victims.

In 2006 an Israeli law established a company to collect restitution for property deemed abandoned by Holocaust victims who had made bank deposits and bought real estate and bank shares in Israel in anticipation of the establishment of a Jewish homeland in Palestine. After years of wrangling The Company for Restitution of Holocaust Victims Assets in mid-2009 filed suit against Bank Leumi considered to be the holder of the most Jewish Holocaust assets; the lawsuit asked for NIS 300 million ($75 million) in restitution for more than 3500 victims. Denying any financial culpability the bank later that year offered NIS 20 million ($5 million). In 2010 it agreed to arbitration.

LOCATIONS

HQ: Bank Leumi Le-Israel B.M.
34 Yehuda Halevi Street, Tel-Aviv 65546
Phone: (972) 3 514 8111   **Fax:** (972) 3 566 1872
Web: www.bankleumi.com

COMPETITORS

Bank Hapoalim	HSBC
Bank of America	Israel Discount Bank
Citigroup	Mizrahi Tefahot
First International	Standard Chartered
Bank of Israel	UniCredit

HISTORICAL FINANCIALS

Company Type: Public

Income Statement

FYE: December 31

	ASSETS ($ mil.)	NET INCOME ($ mil.)	INCOME AS % OF ASSETS	EMPLOYEES
12/15	106,484	724	0.7%	12,528
12/14	101,942	386	0.4%	12,690
12/13	107,885	561	0.5%	13,004
12/12	100,919	249	0.2%	13,407
12/11	95,697	494	0.5%	13,633
Annual Growth	2.7%	10.0%	—	(2.1%)

2015 Year-End Financials

Return on assets: 0.7%
Return on equity: 9.9%
Long-term debt ($ mil.): —
No. of shares (mil.): 1,473
Sales ($ mil): 3,855

Dividends
Yield: —
Payout: —
Market value ($ mil.): 5,306

	STOCK PRICE ($) FY Close	P/E High/Low		PER SHARE ($) Earnings	Dividends	Book Value
12/15	3.60	2	2	0.49	0.00	4.99
12/14	3.39	4	3	0.26	0.00	4.91
12/13	3.90	3	3	0.38	0.00	5.17
12/12	3.45	6	4	0.17	0.00	4.54
12/11	3.05	4	2	0.33	0.00	4.15
Annual Growth	4.3%	—	—	10.0%	—	4.7%

Bank of Canada (Ottawa)

Whether you say "bank" or "banque" the Bank of Canada is the country's central bank. It is responsible for setting monetary policy (by setting interest rates) issuing and safeguarding currency from counterfeiting managing the Canadian banking system and managing funds for the government and other clients. The Bank of Canada works through six regional offices including one in New York City. A governor senior deputy governor 12 outside directors and the Deputy Minister of Finance oversee the bank which averages a $1.8 billion profit annually. The funds are contributed to the government.

Operations

The Bank of Canada has eight set dates throughout the year when it announces whether or not it will adjust interest rates. Bank directors are appointed by the Minister of Finance for a three-year term. Appointees are subject to approval by Canada's Cabinet the Governor in Council.

Geographic Reach

The company is headquartered in Ontario Canada and has regional offices in Halifax (Atlantic Provinces) Montreal (Quebec) Toronto (Ontario) Calgary (Prairies Nunavut and the Northwest Territories) and Vancouver (British Columbia and the Yukon). The company also has an office in New York.

Financial PerformanceThe bank's revenues decreased 3% from 2014 to 2015 due to lower interest earned on investments. The decline in interest revenue was fueled by lower yields on newly acquired bonds compared with yields on investments that have matured. Net income however increased 4% from 2014 to 2015 due to lower interest expenses on deposits premises costs and bank note research production and processing expenses.

Company Background

The Bank of Canada was formed in 1934 as a private entity; it became part of the government four years later.

EXECUTIVES

Board Member, Stephen S. Poloz

LOCATIONS

HQ: Bank of Canada (Ottawa)
234 Laurier Avenue West, Ottawa, Ontario K1A 0G9
Phone: 613 782-8111   **Fax:** 613 782-7713
Web: www.bankofcanada.ca

HISTORICAL FINANCIALS

Company Type: Public

Income Statement

	ASSETS ($ mil.)	NET INCOME ($ mil.)	INCOME AS % OF ASSETS	EMPLOYEES
12/15	72,824	846	1.2%	1,600
12/14	81,270	973	1.2%	0
12/13	85,867	946	1.1%	1,252
12/12	78,231	1,105	1.4%	1,239
12/11	62,981	1,229	2.0%	1,228
Annual Growth	3.7%	(8.9%)	—	6.8%

2015 Year-End Financials

Return on assets: 1.2%
Return on equity: 248.1%
Long-term debt ($ mil.): —
No. of shares (mil.): 0
Sales ($ mil): 1,270

Dividends
  Yield: —
  Payout: —
  Market value ($ mil.): —

Bank of China Ltd

Auditors: Ernst & Young Hua Ming LLP

LOCATIONS

HQ: Bank of China Ltd
No. 1 Fuxingmen Nei Dajie, Beijing 100818
Phone: (86) 10 6659 6688   **Fax:** (86) 10 6601 6871
Web: www.boc.cn

HISTORICAL FINANCIALS

Company Type: Public

Income Statement   FYE: December 31

	ASSETS ($ mil.)	NET INCOME ($ mil.)	INCOME AS % OF ASSETS	EMPLOYEES
12/15	2,589,189	26,305	1.0%	310,042
12/14	2,457,375	27,325	1.1%	308,128
12/13	2,291,797	25,919	1.1%	305,675
12/12	2,034,025	22,365	1.1%	302,016
12/11	1,879,458	19,728	1.0%	289,951
Annual Growth	8.3%	7.5%	—	1.7%

2015 Year-End Financials

Return on assets: 1.0%
Return on equity: 13.9%
Long-term debt ($ mil.): —
No. of shares (mil.): —
Sales ($ mil): 118,737

Dividends
  Yield: 5.8%
  Payout: 719.4%
  Market value ($ mil.): —

	STOCK PRICE ($) FY Close	P/E High/Low	PER SHARE ($) Earnings	Dividends	Book Value
12/15	11.09	31 18	0.09	0.65	0.68
12/14	14.03	23 16	0.09	0.67	0.64
12/13	11.56	23 17	0.09	0.59	0.55
12/12	11.36	23 18	0.08	0.50	0.47
12/11	9.15	34 17	0.07	0.47	0.41
Annual Growth	4.9%	— —	6.0%	8.5%	13.5%

Bank of Communications Co., Ltd.

Auditors: PricewaterhouseCoopers Zhong Tian LLP

LOCATIONS

HQ: Bank of Communications Co., Ltd.
No. 188, Yin Cheng Zhong Road, Pudong New District, Shanghai 200120
Phone: (86) 21 58766688   **Fax:** (86) 21 58798398
Web: www.bankcomm.com

HISTORICAL FINANCIALS

Company Type: Public

Income Statement   FYE: December 31

	ASSETS ($ mil.)	NET INCOME ($ mil.)	INCOME AS % OF ASSETS	EMPLOYEES
12/15	1,101,750	10,243	0.9%	91,468
12/14	1,009,978	10,610	1.1%	93,658
12/13	984,645	10,290	1.0%	99,919
12/12	845,872	9,363	1.1%	96,259
12/11	732,584	8,060	1.1%	90,149
Annual Growth	10.7%	6.2%	—	0.4%

2015 Year-End Financials

Return on assets: 0.9%
Return on equity: 13.2%
Long-term debt ($ mil.): —
No. of shares (mil.): —
Sales ($ mil): 55,233

Dividends
  Yield: 0.0%
  Payout: 650.6%
  Market value ($ mil.): —

	STOCK PRICE ($) FY Close	P/E High/Low	PER SHARE ($) Earnings	Dividends	Book Value
12/15	18.00	29 18	0.14	0.90	1.11
12/14	23.55	26 17	0.14	0.90	1.02
12/13	19.15	26 21	0.14	0.85	0.93
12/12	17.99	22 20	0.14	0.34	0.82
12/11	19.15	35 24	0.13	0.02	0.70
Annual Growth	(1.5%)	— —	1.6%	149.9%	12.3%

Bank of East Asia Ltd.

Bank of East Asia provides retail and commercial banking services in Hong Kong and mainland China. Its offerings include deposit accounts consumer loans mortgages business loans credit cards private banking and investment management. Bank of East Asia has some 130 locations in Hong Kong and more than 60 in mainland China; internationally it has about 30 offices in the British Virgin Islands Malaysia Singapore the UK and Vietnam. The bank's subsidiaries include online securities and futures brokerage provider East Asia Securities Blue Cross (Asia-Pacific) Insurance and Tricor which performs outsourced business services.

Like many of its peers Bank of East Asia is seeking new revenue lines by branching into related industries. In 2009 it arranged to buy a minority stake in fund house Golden Eagle Asset Management allowing it to enter China's growing fund market. Bank of East Asia also launched a trust business in that country.

With an increased focus on Hong Kong and China the bank is also streamlining elsewhere. It sold a majority stake of its Canadian network (a half-dozen branches) to Industrial and Commercial Bank of China (ICBC) in 2010 and arranged to sell its US operations to that company the following year.

EXECUTIVES

Chairman and CEO, David K. P. Li, age 78
Chief Investment Officer, Samson K. C. Li, age 56
Deputy Chief Executive, Adrian David M. K. Li, age 43
Deputy Chief Executive, Brian David M. B. Li, age 42
COO, Tong Hon-shing, age 57
Deputy Chairman, Allan C. Y. Wong, age 65
Deputy Chairman, Arthur K. C. Li, age 71
Auditors: KPMG

LOCATIONS

HQ: Bank of East Asia Ltd.
  10 Des Voeux Road Central,
Phone: (852) 3608 3608   **Fax:** (852) 3608 6000
Web: www.hkbea.com

PRODUCTS/OPERATIONS

2014 Sales

	% of total
Interest income	83
Non-interest income	17
Total	**100**

COMPETITORS

Bank of China (Hong Kong)	Dah Sing Banking
Bank of Communications	Dah Sing Financial Holdings Limited
CITIC International Financial	Hang Seng Bank
China Development Bank	Public Financial Holdings
China Minsheng Banking	Shanghai Pudong Development Bank
Chong Hing Bank	

HISTORICAL FINANCIALS

Company Type: Public

Income Statement   FYE: December 31

	ASSETS ($ mil.)	NET INCOME ($ mil.)	INCOME AS % OF ASSETS	EMPLOYEES
12/15	100,808	712	0.7%	13,653
12/14	102,626	858	0.8%	13,103
12/13	97,236	852	0.9%	12,698
12/12	89,285	781	0.9%	12,441
12/11	78,707	561	0.7%	12,238
Annual Growth	6.4%	6.2%	—	2.8%

2015 Year-End Financials

Return on assets: 0.7%
Return on equity: 7.3%
Long-term debt ($ mil.): —
No. of shares (mil.): —
Sales ($ mil): 4,013

Dividends
  Yield: 3.3%
  Payout: 47.8%
Market value ($ mil.): —

	STOCK PRICE ($) FY Close	P/E High/Low		PER SHARE ($) Earnings	Dividends	Book Value
12/15	3.63	2	2	0.25	0.12	4.03
12/14	3.95	2	1	0.35	0.13	3.78
12/13	4.14	2	1	0.36	0.12	3.59
12/12	3.86	2	1	0.35	0.11	3.31
12/11	3.70	2	1	0.25	0.11	2.95
Annual Growth	(0.5%)	—	—	(0.1%)	1.9%	8.1%

Bank of Ireland (Ireland)

EXECUTIVES

Director, MICHAEL SWEENEY
Auditors: PricewaterhouseCoopers

LOCATIONS

HQ: Bank of Ireland (Ireland)
  40 Mespil Road, Dublin 4
Phone:
Web: www.bankofireland.com

HISTORICAL FINANCIALS

Company Type: Public

Income Statement   FYE: December 31

	ASSETS ($ mil.)	NET INCOME ($ mil.)	INCOME AS % OF ASSETS	EMPLOYEES
12/15	142,643	1,023	0.7%	11,145
12/14	157,772	955	0.6%	11,086
12/13	181,917	(670)	—	11,255
12/12	195,263	(2,404)	—	12,016
12/11	200,329	58	0.0%	13,671
Annual Growth	(8.1%)	104.8%	—	(5.0%)

2015 Year-End Financials

Return on assets: 0.7%
Return on equity: 10.5%
Long-term debt ($ mil.): —
No. of shares (mil.): —
Sales ($ mil): 6,504

Dividends
  Yield: —
  Payout: —
Market value ($ mil.): —

Bank of Kyoto Ltd (Japan)

For financial services in Kyoto proper protocol might involve a visit to The Bank of Kyoto. The regional bank serves Kyoto and neighboring prefectures through some 165 branch offices. The bank serves businesses particularly small and medium-sized local companies as well as individual consumers. In addition to traditional deposit banking and lending The Bank of Kyoto and its subsidiaries offer credit cards leasing stock brokerage and business consulting services. The bank has worked to expand its operations beyond its home base and has opened branches to the north in the Kinki Region. Founded in 1941 the bank has about $81 billion in assets and ranks as Kyoto Prefecture's largest retail bank.

Geographic Reach
The Bank of Kyoto operates 110 branches in Kyoto Prefecture 28 in Osaka Prefecture a dozen in Shiga eight in Hyogo and seven branches in Nara.

Strategy
The Bank of Kyoto is aggressively opening branches to expand its reach beyond Kyoto Prefecture. Since opening its first branch at Kusatsu in Shiga Prefecture in 2000 the bank has opened branches in five neighboring prefectures (Kyoto Osaka Shiga Nara and Hyogo).

EXECUTIVES

President, NOBUHIRO DOI
Auditors: Deloitte Touche Tohmatsu LLC

LOCATIONS

HQ: Bank of Kyoto Ltd (Japan)
  700 Yakushimae-cho, Karasuma-dori Matsubara-Agaru, Shimogyo-ku, Kyoto 600-8652
Phone: (81) 75 361 2211   **Fax:** (81) 75 343 1276
Web: www.kyotobank.co.jp

COMPETITORS

Mitsubishi UFJ Financial Group	Resona
Mizuho Financial	Sumitomo Mitsui

HISTORICAL FINANCIALS

Company Type: Public

Income Statement   FYE: March 31

	ASSETS ($ mil.)	NET INCOME ($ mil.)	INCOME AS % OF ASSETS	EMPLOYEES
03/16	72,614	189	0.3%	4,052
03/15	68,806	177	0.3%	4,029
03/14	76,476	162	0.2%	3,566
03/13	81,057	186	0.2%	3,570
03/12	89,714	189	0.2%	3,545
Annual Growth	(5.1%)	0.0%	—	3.4%

2016 Year-End Financials

Return on assets: 0.2%
Return on equity: 3.1%
Long-term debt ($ mil.): —
No. of shares (mil.): 377
Sales ($ mil): 994

Dividends
  Yield: —
  Payout: —
Market value ($ mil.): —

	STOCK PRICE ($) FY Close	P/E High/Low		PER SHARE ($) Earnings	Dividends	Book Value
03/16	0.00	—	—	0.50	0.00	15.20
Annual Growth	—	—	—	—	—	—

Bank of Montreal

Auditors: KPMG LLP

LOCATIONS

HQ: Bank of Montreal
  129 rue Saint-Jacques, Montreal, Quebec H2Y 1L6
Phone: 416 867-6785   **Fax:** 416 867-6793
Web: www.bmo.com

HISTORICAL FINANCIALS

Company Type: Public

Income Statement   FYE: October 31

	ASSETS ($ mil.)	NET INCOME ($ mil.)	INCOME AS % OF ASSETS	EMPLOYEES
10/16	514,211	3,454	0.7%	45,000
10/15	487,793	3,320	0.7%	47,000
10/14	526,078	3,822	0.7%	47,000
10/13	513,702	3,999	0.8%	45,500
10/12	526,880	4,126	0.8%	46,000
Annual Growth	(0.6%)	(4.3%)	—	(0.5%)

2016 Year-End Financials

Return on assets: 0.6%
Return on equity: 11.2%
Long-term debt ($ mil.): —
No. of shares (mil.): 645
Sales ($ mil): 19,222

Dividends
  Yield: 5.3%
  Payout: 49.1%
Market value ($ mil.): 41,070

	STOCK PRICE ($) FY Close	P/E High/Low		PER SHARE ($) Earnings	Dividends	Book Value
10/16	63.60	9	8	5.17	2.56	48.97
10/15	58.09	10	8	4.99	2.46	46.62
10/14	72.60	12	9	5.73	2.79	47.25
10/13	69.70	11	9	5.99	2.88	45.14
10/12	59.12	10	9	6.17	2.83	44.16
Annual Growth	1.8%	—	—	(4.3%)	(2.5%)	2.6%

Bank of Nova Scotia Halifax

The last place to look for The Bank of Nova Scotia's headquarters is in Nova Scotia. Although the company (aka Scotiabank) was founded in that province in 1832 it moved to Toronto in 1900. One of Canada's Big Five banks (along with Royal Bank of Canada TD Bank Bank of Montreal and CIBC) Scotiabank provides retail corporate and investment banking services around the world. In addition to about 1000 domestic branches Scotiabank has approximately 1700 offices in more than 50 other countries mainly in the Caribbean and Central and South America. Services include deposit accounts loans insurance brokerage asset management mutual funds and trust services.

While its domestic competitors have been expanding in the US Scotiabank has been focused mainly on making inroads in the Caribbean Latin America and Asia. The bank plans growth in Mexico the Caribbean and South America in addition to its home market. As it looks outward for growth Scotiabank has benefitted from a strong Canadian dollar bolstered by the nation's natural resources sector. The company reported record net income for fiscal 2010.

In 2012 the company rebranded its Scotia Capital Scotia Waterous and ScotiaMocotta investment banking units as Scotiabank in an effort to solidify its brand. The firms became part of Scotiabank's Global Banking and Markets division which offers such services as securities underwriting and mergers and acquisitions advice to corporate clients.

Later that year Scotiabank acquired US-based Howard Weil a boutique investment bank focused on the energy sector. The company built its investment banking practice in South America through the 2010 acquisitions of Dresdner Bank Brazil from Germany's Commerzbank and Royal Bank of Scotland's wholesale banking operations in Colombia.

Domestically Scotiabank wants to be the dominant money manager. As part of its strategy it announced a consolidated wealth management arm in 2009: Scotia Asset Management which includes ScotiaFunds ScotiaMcLeod and Scotia Cassels Investment Counsel. The year before Scotiabank acquired a large minority stake of fund manager CI Financial from Sun Life Financial. In a similar move the company acquired Dundee Corporation's stake in DundeeWealth for some $2.3 billion in 2011. The acquisition gave Scotiabank control of another one of Canada's largest wealth managers.

In 2012 Scotiabank agreed to buy ING Bank of Canada from Dutch group ING for C$3.1 billion. ING Bank of Canada operating as ING Direct primarily serves its clients via the Internet and has marketed itself as an alternative to big banks. Scotiabank plans to continue to run ING Direct as a standalone bank. (ING Groep has been selling off parts of its business as it tries to gain capital strength.)

The company also expanded its wealth management segment with the 2010 acquisition of the money management operations of BNP Paribas in the Bahamas the Cayman Islands and Panama and an agreement to purchase The WaterStreet Group which caters to ultra-high-net-worth clients. Scotiabank is also growing its wealth management business by offering new investment products.

Increasing its focus on insurance as well Scotiabank in 2009 rebranded its ScotiaLife Financial business which offers credit travel life and health coverage. It has also built up its online brokerage capabilities acquiring TradeFreedom Securities in 2007 and E*TRADE Canada from E*TRADE in 2008. Other areas of focus for Scotiabank include mobile banking and global foreign exchange.

Beyond Canada the company owns interests in banks in Chile (Scotiabank Chile formerly Banco del Desarrollo) Mexico (Scotiabank Inverlat) and Central America (Scotiabank El Salvador and Groupo BNS de Costa Rica). In 2010 Scotiabank bought Royal Bank of Scotland's Chilean business and its wholesale banking operations in Colombia making it the only Canadian-owned institution with a presence in the latter country. More expansion in the Caribbean was achieved when Scotiabank acquired R&G Financial's troubled R-G Premier Bank of Puerto Rico. The transaction which was assisted by the FDIC added nearly 30 branches to Scotiabank's network on the island.

Scotiabank expanded in Peru one of South America's fastest-growing economies with its 2006 acquisition of some 80% of Banco Wiese Sudameris (now Scotiabank Peru) from Italian banking group Banca Intesa (now Intesa Sanpaolo) which held on to the rest. It also holds an interest in Peru-based pension-fund manager AFP ProFuturo. Scotiabank entered Uruguay for the first time in 2010 by buying controlling stakes in private bank Nuevo Banco Comercial and consumer lender Pronto. Further expanding in Latin America during 2011 the company acquired wholesale bank Dresdner Bank Brasil (now Scotiabank Brasil) and a majority stake in Colombia-based retail bank Banco Colpatria. In 2012 it announced plans to buy a majority of Colfondos a Colombian pension fund firm with more than $9 billion in assets under management.

Building its position in the Asia-Pacific region Scotiabank in 2009 increased its stake in Thailand's Thanachart Bank to 49% the Thai limit for foreign ownership. The next year Thanachart acquired Siam City Bank making it Thailand's fifth-largest bank. Scotiabank also upped its stake in China's Xi'an City Commercial Bank to almost 15% and arranged to acquire nearly 20% of the state-run Chinese institution Bank of Guangzhou.

EXECUTIVES

EVP and Co-Head Information Technology Enterprise Technology, Michael Zerbs
EVP and General Counsel, Deborah M. Alexander
President and CEO, Brian J. Porter, $450,000 total compensation
Group Head Global Banking and Markets, Dieter W. Jentsch
Group Head and CFO, Sean McGuckin
Chief Risk Officer, Stephen P. Hart
EVP and Chief Administrative Officer International Banking, Marianne Hasold-Schilter
EVP Canadian Banking, James McPhedran
EVP and Chief Credit Officer, Terry Fryett
Group Head Canadian Banking, James O'Sullivan
Group Head International Banking and Digital Transformation, Ignacio (Nacho) Deschamps
EVP and Chief Marketing Officer, John Doig
EVP Retail Payments Deposits and Unsecured Lending, Mike Henry
EVP and Co-Head Information Technology Business Systems, Kyle McNamara
EVP Operations, Dan Rees
EVP Canadian Commercial Banking, Gillian Riley
EVP Digital Banking, Shawn Rose
EVP Retail Distribution Canadian Banking, Maria Theofilaktidis
Auditors: KPMG LLP

LOCATIONS

HQ: Bank of Nova Scotia Halifax
1709 Hollis Street, Halifax, Nova Scotia B3J 1W1
Phone: 416 866-6161   **Fax:** 416 866-7767
Web: www.scotiabank.com

PRODUCTS/OPERATIONS

2015 Sales

	% of total
Interest	
Loans	61
Securities	3
Other	1
Noninterest	
Banking	11
Wealth management	10
Others	14
Total	**100**

Selected Canadian Subsidiaries

BNS Capital Trust
BNS Investment Inc.
  Montreal Trust Company of Canada
  Scotia Merchant Capital Corporation
Dundee Bank of Canada
Maple Trust Company
National Trustco Inc.
  The Bank of Nova Scotia Trust Company
  National Trust Company
RoyNat Inc.
Scotia Capital Inc.
  1548489 Ontario Limited
  Scotia iTrade Corp.
Scotia Asset Management L.P.
Scotia Capital Inc.
Scotia Dealer Advantage Inc.
Scotia Insurance Agency Inc.
Scotia Life Insurance Company
Scotia Mortgage Corporation
Scotia Securities Inc.
Scotiabank Capital Trust
Scotiabank Subordinated Notes Trust.
Scotiabank Tier 1 Trust

Selected International Subsidiaries

The Bank of Nova Scotia Berhad (Malaysia)
The Bank of Nova Scotia International Limited (Bahamas)
  The Bank of Nova Scotia Asia Limited (Singapore)
  The Bank of Nova Scotia Trust Company (Bahamas) Ltd.
  Scotiabank & Trust (Cayman) Ltd. (Cayman Islands)
BNS (Colombia) Holdings Limited
Grupo BNS de Costa Rica S.A.
Scotia Insurance (Barbados) Limited
Scotiabank (Bahamas) Limited
Scotiabank (British Virgin Islands) Limited
Scotiabank Caribbean Treasury Limited (Bahamas)
Scotiabank (Hong Kong) Limited
Scotiabank (Ireland) Limited
Scotia Group Jamaica Limited (72%)
  The Bank of Nova Scotia Jamaica Limited
  Scotia DBG Investments Limited (77% Jamaica)
Grupo Financiero Scotiabank Inverlat S.A. de C.V. (97% Mexico)
Nova Scotia Inversiones Limitada (Chile)
  Scotiabank Chile S.A.
Scotia Capital (USA) Inc.
Scotia Holdings (US) Inc.
  The Bank of Nova Scotia Trust Company of New York
  Scotiabanc Inc. (US)
Scotia International Limited (Bahamas)
  Scotiabank Anguilla Limited
Scotiabank de Puerto Rico
Scotiabank El Salvador S.A.
Scotiabank Europe plc (UK)
Scotiabank Peru S.A.A.
Scotiabank Trinidad and Tobago Limited

COMPETITORS

BMO Financial Group	HSBC Bank Canada
Banamex	JPMorgan Chase
Banco Santander Chile	National Bank of
Bank of America	Canada
Bicsa Panama	RBC Financial Group

CIBC
Citigroup

TD Bank

HISTORICAL FINANCIALS
Company Type: Public

Income Statement
FYE: October 31

	ASSETS ($ mil.)	NET INCOME ($ mil.)	INCOME AS % OF ASSETS	EMPLOYEES
10/16	669,932	5,222	0.8%	88,901
10/15	650,889	5,241	0.8%	89,000
10/14	720,015	6,180	0.9%	86,932
10/13	711,122	5,932	0.8%	83,000
10/12	669,863	6,039	0.9%	81,497
Annual Growth	0.0%	(3.6%)	—	2.2%

2016 Year-End Financials

Return on assets: 0.8%	Dividends
Return on equity: 12.8%	Yield: 5.3%
Long-term debt ($ mil.): —	Payout: 70.3%
No. of shares (mil.): 1,207	Market value ($ mil.): 64,936
Sales ($ mil): 25,612	

	STOCK PRICE ($) FY Close	P/E High/Low		PER SHARE ($) Earnings	Dividends	Book Value
10/16	53.76	9	7	4.31	2.17	34.81
10/15	46.98	9	7	4.31	2.07	32.86
10/14	61.30	12	9	5.06	2.35	35.19
10/13	60.77	12	10	4.92	2.34	35.32
10/12	54.38	11	9	5.23	2.18	33.56
Annual Growth	(0.3%)	—	—	(4.7%)	(0.1%)	0.9%

Bank Otkritie Financial Corp Open Joint Stock Co

EXECUTIVES
Chairman, Ruben Abelovich Aganbegyan
Auditors: ZAO Deloitte & Touche CIS

LOCATIONS
HQ: Bank Otkritie Financial Corp Open Joint Stock Co
3/1, Verkhnyaya Radishchevskaya St., Moscow 109240
Phone: (7) 495 424 96 46   **Fax:** (7) 495 797 32 50
Web: www.nomos-bank.com

HISTORICAL FINANCIALS
Company Type: Public

Income Statement
FYE: December 31

	ASSETS ($ mil.)	NET INCOME ($ mil.)	INCOME AS % OF ASSETS	EMPLOYEES
12/15	45,548	173	0.4%	15,705
12/14	44,102	120	0.3%	16,904
12/13	41,960	453	1.1%	17,890
12/12	29,562	413	1.4%	10,999
12/11	20,512	309	1.5%	10,429
Annual Growth	22.1%	(13.4%)	—	10.8%

2015 Year-End Financials

Return on assets: 0.4%	Dividends
Return on equity: 8.1%	Yield: —
Long-term debt ($ mil.): —	Payout: —
No. of shares (mil.): 150	Market value ($ mil.): —
Sales ($ mil): 4,010	

Bank Polska Kasa Opieki SA

Bank Polska Kasa Opieki better known as Bank Pekao (from its initials P.K.O.) offers retail corporate and investment banking services primarily in Poland. It also provides leasing and asset management services. Branches can also be found in France and the Ukraine. In addition to traditional deposit products Bank Pekao offers loans leasing and factoring services custodial services currency exchange and foreign trade facilitation. Originally founded as a state-owned bank to provide banking services to Polish emigrants Bank Pekao is now controlled by Italian bank UniCredit which holds approximately 53% of its shares.

EXECUTIVES
Prezes Zarzadu, Luigi Lovaglio
Czlonek rady nadzorczej, Jerzy Marek Woznicki
Czlonek rady nadzorczej, Wioletta Rosolowska
Czlonek rady nadzorczej, Leszek Jerzy Pawlowicz
Auditors: Deloitte Polska Sp. z o.o.

LOCATIONS
HQ: Bank Polska Kasa Opieki SA
53/57 Grzybowska Street, Warsaw 00-950
Phone: (48) 22 656 00 00   **Fax:** (48) 22 656 00 04
Web: www.pekao.com.pl

COMPETITORS

AIB	Nordea Bank
Bank BPH	PKO Bank Polski SA
Bank Millennium	Provident Financial
Citi Handlowy	

HISTORICAL FINANCIALS
Company Type: Public

Income Statement
FYE: December 31

	ASSETS ($ mil.)	NET INCOME ($ mil.)	INCOME AS % OF ASSETS	EMPLOYEES
12/15	43,122	585	1.4%	18,327
12/14	47,604	770	1.6%	18,765
12/13	52,578	923	1.8%	18,916
12/12	48,793	955	2.0%	19,816
12/11	42,541	841	2.0%	20,256
Annual Growth	0.3%	(8.7%)	—	(2.5%)

2015 Year-End Financials

Return on assets: 1.3%	Dividends
Return on equity: 9.6%	Yield: —
Long-term debt ($ mil.): —	Payout: 87.1%
No. of shares (mil.): 262	Market value ($ mil.): 15,420
Sales ($ mil): 2,209	

	STOCK PRICE ($) FY Close	P/E High/Low		PER SHARE ($) Earnings	Dividends	Book Value
12/15	58.75	—	—	2.23	1.94	22.79
12/14	58.75	—	—	2.94	2.28	25.99
12/13	58.75	—	—	3.52	2.10	29.60
12/12	58.75	—	—	3.64	1.44	28.78
12/11	58.75	5	4	3.21	1.68	23.53
Annual Growth	(0.0%)	—	—	(8.7%)	3.8%	(0.8%)

Bank Sinopac

LOCATIONS
HQ: Bank Sinopac
No. 36, Nanking East Road, Sec. 3, Taipei 104
Phone: (886) 2 2506 3333
Web: www.banksinopac.com.tw

HISTORICAL FINANCIALS
Company Type: Public

Income Statement
FYE: December 31

	ASSETS ($ mil.)	NET INCOME ($ mil.)	INCOME AS % OF ASSETS	EMPLOYEES
12/15	43,850	279	0.6%	0
12/14	44,705	358	0.8%	0
12/13	45,505	322	0.7%	0
12/12	43,635	283	0.6%	5,277
12/11	40,103	81	0.2%	5,338
Annual Growth	2.3%	36.1%	—	—

2015 Year-End Financials

Return on assets: 0.6%	Dividends
Return on equity: 8.7%	Yield: —
Long-term debt ($ mil.): —	Payout: —
No. of shares (mil.): —	Market value ($ mil.): —
Sales ($ mil): 1,113	

Bankia S A

Auditors: Ernst & Young, S.L.

LOCATIONS
HQ: Bankia S A
Paseo de la Castellana 189, Madrid 28046
Phone: (34) 91 787 7575   **Fax:** (34) 91 791 1600
Web: www.bankia.com

HISTORICAL FINANCIALS
Company Type: Public

Income Statement
FYE: December 31

	ASSETS ($ mil.)	NET INCOME ($ mil.)	INCOME AS % OF ASSETS	EMPLOYEES
12/15	225,433	1,132	0.5%	13,571
12/14	284,001	908	0.3%	14,413
12/13	346,210	704	0.2%	15,560
12/12	372,099	(25,117)	—	20,358
12/11	391,717	(3,852)	—	21,382
Annual Growth	(12.9%)	—	—	(10.7%)

2015 Year-End Financials

Return on assets: 0.4%
Return on equity: 8.2%
Long-term debt ($ mil.): —
No. of shares (mil.): —
Sales ($ mil): 5,591

Dividends
  Yield: —
  Payout: —
  Market value ($ mil.): —

	STOCK PRICE ($) FY Close	P/E High/Low	PER SHARE ($) Earnings	Dividends	Book Value
12/15	1.13	17 12	0.10	0.00	1.19
12/14	1.45	28 20	0.09	0.00	1.32
12/13	1.73	242 3	0.10	0.00	1.39
12/12	0.94	— —	(13.37)	0.00	(3.97)
Annual Growth	6.3%	— —	—	—	—

Bankinter, S.A.

Founded in 1965 as a joint venture between what is now Grupo Santander and Bank of America Bankinter is among the top six banks in Spain. The company offers a variety of consumer and business banking services through about 360 branch locations agents telephone services mobile banking and the Internet. A pioneer in Internet stock trading Bankinter conducts more than half of its transactions online. It serves corporations individuals and small enterprises. Bankinter provides mutual and pension funds mortgages leasing and securities brokerage focusing on convenient low-cost delivery and customer service. Investment firm Cartival S.A. owns about 23% of Bankinter. Although Bankinter has about 360 branches in Spain more than half of its transactions are conducted on the Internet. The bank has pioneered technologies to make its online services more accessible including making Web pages compatible with software used by the visually impaired.

The bank is making a strong push to court the small and medium enterprise (SME) segment of the market. In recent years Bankinter launched dozens of new service centers catering to SMEs. The bank also continues to open other private banking and business management branches in fast-growing towns throughout the country.

Bankinter announced in 2009 it will buy the 50% of auto insurer Linea Directa Aseguradora it already does not own from Royal Bank of Scotland. The proposed shift follows a change in control at Royal Bank which was taken over by the government in 2008.

France's Credit Agricole owns about 20% of Bankinter. Through investment firm Cartival former Bankinter chairman Jaime Botin controls more than 15% of the bank's stock. The Botin family leads Grupo Santander which includes Spain's largest bank.

HISTORY

In 1962 Franco tried to end mixed banks in Spain with a decree that prevented banks from taking part in both commercial and investment operations. The banks circumvented this through cosmetic compliance spending the next decade nominally spinning off operations. In 1965 Banco Santander (now Grupo Santander) and Bank of America created Banco Intercontinental Espanol (Bankinter) in Madrid to specialize in industrial banking.

From 1970 to 1985 Bankinter evolved into a retail bank; it introduced credit cards personal loans and other services and offered financing to larger corporations. Bankinter was not consumed by the great branch race that defined banking-industry competition in Franco-era Spain; the bank had only 150 branches by 1985.

The bank became independent as both Bank of America (in 1987) and Santander (1994) reduced their stock holdings. Bankinter began diversifying its operations opening branches and gaining more clients. Bankinter's successful 1987 introduction of a high-interest special deposit account was dulled when other banks followed suit slowing growth. The bank took its current name in 1990 and in 1991 introduced some of Spain's first mutual funds. Within a recession-hammered economy Bankinter worked to cut costs through the introduction of telephone banking (1992) and other innovative conveniences.

Attracted by the low-cost liquidity of private banking Bankinter entered that segment in 1995. It took a step in the allfinanz direction that year creating an auto and home insurance alliance with Royal Bank of Scotland subsidiary Direct Line; the UK bank already had insurance ventures with Bankinter sibling Santander. Two years later Bankinter began BKNet Spain's first online stock-trading service.

In 1998 the bank opened a Mexican office to explore the possibility of transferring its high-tech operations into that country. As the financial industry's global consolidation continued the bank in 1999 said it was seeking a foreign ally possibly one that could help expand Bankinter's online technology.

The bank found willing partners later that year inking deals to form an Internet bank in Spain with a joint venture of US Web portal Lycos (now part of Terra Networks) and German media giant Bertelsmann as well as another Internet bank with Portugal's Banco Espirito Santo.

Although Bankinter recorded 2004 as a particularly profitable year with income up nearly 25% it also suffered the death of a deputy manager Jose Garcia in the March 11 terrorist attacks against Madrid.

In 2007 the bank sold 50% of its life insurance division to Spanish insurer Mapfre. The sale boosted Bankinter's capital.

In 2008 Credit Agricole increased its ownership in the bank to about 20%. It became the bank's largest shareholder edging out former chairman Jaime Botin.

EXECUTIVES

CEO, Mar a D. Dancausa Trevi ±o
Chairman, Pedro Guerrero Guerrero, age 64
Auditors: Deloitte, S.L. (member of Deloitte & Touche Tohmatsu)

LOCATIONS

HQ: Bankinter, S.A.
  Paseo de la Castellana, 29, Madrid 28046
Phone: (34) 91 339 75 00   **Fax:** (34) 91 339 83 23
Web: www.bankinter.es

PRODUCTS/OPERATIONS

2014 Sales

	% of total
Interest and similar income	54
Fee and commission income	14
Other revenues	32
Total	**100**

Selected Subsidiaries
Aircraft S.A.
Bankinter Consultoria Asesoramiento y Atencion Telefonica S.A.
Bankinter Gestion de Seguros S.A.
Bankinter International B.V. (Netherlands)
Bankinter Seguros de Vida S.A.
Gesbankinter S.A.
Hispamarket S.A.
Intergestora S.A.
Intergestora Nuevas Tecnologias S.C.R. S.A.
Intermobiliaria S.A.

COMPETITORS

AEGON
BBVA
Banco Espa±ol de Credito
Banco Popular Espa±ol

Banco de Sabadell
Deutsche Bank
Esprito Santo
Grupo Santander
La Caixa

HISTORICAL FINANCIALS
Company Type: Public

Income Statement

FYE: December 31

	ASSETS ($ mil.)	NET INCOME ($ mil.)	INCOME AS % OF ASSETS	EMPLOYEES
12/15	63,892	409	0.6%	4,205
12/14	69,688	335	0.5%	3,953
12/13	75,907	296	0.4%	3,820
12/12	76,665	164	0.2%	3,853
12/11	76,949	234	0.3%	3,904
Annual Growth	(4.5%)	15.0%	—	1.9%

2015 Year-End Financials

Return on assets: 0.6%
Return on equity: 10.1%
Long-term debt ($ mil.): —
No. of shares (mil.): 898
Sales ($ mil): 2,735

Dividends
  Yield: 0.0%
  Payout: 43.8%
  Market value ($ mil.): 6,202

	STOCK PRICE ($) FY Close	P/E High/Low	PER SHARE ($) Earnings	Dividends	Book Value
12/15	6.90	19 15	0.46	0.20	4.60
12/14	7.87	29 19	0.38	0.11	4.93
12/13	6.50	34 12	0.37	0.08	5.23
12/12	4.35	30 12	0.30	0.14	7.55
12/11	6.01	19 12	0.45	0.12	8.37
Annual Growth	3.5% (13.9%)	— —	0.3%	13.3%	

Banque Cantonale Vaudoise

Banque Cantonale Vaudoise (BCV) provides a variety of financial services primarily to customers in the canton of Vaud in southwestern Switzerland. With about 70 retail locations it offers commercial corporate and private banking services as well as wealth management and securities brokerage. The bank is dedicated to the canton's development and in fact does business with some two-thirds of Vaud's small and midsized enterprises. The Vaud government owns more than half of BCV which was originally founded in 1845.

EXECUTIVES

ManagingDirector, Pascal Kiener
Chairman Of The Board, Olivier Steimer
Vice Chairman Of The Board, Paul Andre Sanglard
Board Member, George Clemons
Board Member, Ingrid Deltenre
Board Member, Reto Donatsch
Board Member, Peter Ochsner
Board Member, Luc Recordon
Auditors: PricewaterhouseCoopers Ltd

LOCATIONS

HQ: Banque Cantonale Vaudoise
Place Saint-Francois 14, P.O. Box 300, Lausanne 1001
Phone: (41) 21 212 10 10 **Fax:** (41) 21 212 12 22
Web: www.bcv.ch

COMPETITORS

Bank Sarasin	Swiss Post
Credit Suisse	UBS
HSBC Private Bank	
Merrill Lynch Bank	
(Suisse)	

HISTORICAL FINANCIALS

Company Type: Public

Income Statement   FYE: December 31

	ASSETS ($ mil.)	NET INCOME ($ mil.)	INCOME AS % OF ASSETS	EMPLOYEES
12/15	43,719	338	0.8%	1,947
12/14	42,527	299	0.7%	1,946
12/13	45,400	314	0.7%	1,987
12/12	43,416	339	0.8%	1,931
12/11	40,288	321	0.8%	2,042
Annual Growth	2.1%	1.3%	—	(1.2%)

2015 Year-End Financials

Return on assets: 0.7%
Return on equity: 9.9%
Long-term debt ($ mil.): —
No. of shares (mil.): 8
Sales ($ mil): 1,274

Dividends
Yield: —
Payout: —
Market value ($ mil.): —

Banque Federative du Credit Mutuel (France)

EXECUTIVES

President Directeur General, Etienne PFLIMLIN
Auditors: ERNST & YOUNG et Autres

LOCATIONS

HQ: Banque Federative du Credit Mutuel (France)
34 rue du Wacken, B.P. 412, Strasbourg, Cedex 67000
Phone: (33) 3 88 14 88 14 **Fax:** (33) 3 88 14 67 00
Web: www.bfcm.creditmutuel.fr

HISTORICAL FINANCIALS

Company Type: Public

Income Statement   FYE: December 31

	REVENUE ($ mil.)	NET INCOME ($ mil.)	NET PROFIT MARGIN	EMPLOYEES
12/15	33,083	1,679	5.1%	42,825
12/14	37,780	1,682	4.5%	42,366
12/13	40,123	1,667	4.2%	39,686
12/12	39,298	1,225	3.1%	40,258
12/11	34,870	1,056	3.0%	40,223
Annual Growth	(1.3%)	12.3%	—	1.6%

2015 Year-End Financials

Debt ratio: —
Return on equity: 7.6%
Cash ($ mil.): 10,732
Current ratio: —
Long-term debt ($ mil.): —

No. of shares (mil.): 33
Dividends
Yield: —
Payout: —
Market value ($ mil.): —

Banque Nationale de Belgique (National Bank of Belgium)

No prizes for guessing the role of the Nationale Bank van Belgi «. NBB is indeed the national central bank for Belgium and a member of the European System of Central Banks (ESCB). Founded in 1850 the institution performs a variety of functions aimed at maintaining stability and liquidity for Belgium's banks and financial markets including arranging fund transfers between banks overseeing settlement activities for securities markets and issuing banknotes and coins. The bank's chief executive known as its governor is appointed by the Belgian monarch. NBB is also known by its names in French (Banque nationale de Belgique) English (National Bank of Belgium) and German (Belgische Nationalbank).

The bank carries out various other functions within Belgium's financial system. As the nation's lender of last resort NBB is also able to provide emergency funds when times of exceptional financial crisis. It did as much in 2008 with the cross-national bailout of Fortis. NBB has also printed currency notes (and distributed coins struck by Belgium's Royal Mint) since 1851.

EXECUTIVES

Manager Director, Fran $ise Masai
Manager Director, Norbert De Baetselier
Manager Director, peter Praet
Manager Director, Marcia De Wachter
Manager Director, Jean Hilgers
Auditors: Ernst & Young Réviseurs d'Entreprises sccrl/?Ernst &

LOCATIONS

HQ: Banque Nationale de Belgique (National Bank of Belgium)
Boulevard de Berlaimont 14, Brussels BE-1000
Phone: (32) 2 221 21 11 **Fax:** (32) 2 221 31 00
Web: www.nbb.be

COMPETITORS

Bank of England	Federal Reserve
Deutsche Bundesbank	Swiss National Bank

HISTORICAL FINANCIALS

Company Type: Public

Income Statement   FYE: December 31

	ASSETS ($ mil.)	NET INCOME ($ mil.)	INCOME AS % OF ASSETS	EMPLOYEES
12/15	96,903	599	0.6%	2,219
12/14	91,800	826	0.9%	2,265
12/13	107,110	1,303	1.2%	2,301
12/12	144,660	1,762	1.2%	2,103
12/11	165,193	1,162	0.7%	2,101
Annual Growth	(12.5%)	(15.3%)	—	1.4%

	STOCK PRICE ($) FY Close	P/E High/Low	PER SHARE ($) Earnings	Dividends	Book Value
12/15	0.00	— —	(0.00)	0.00	15,703
12/14	4,588.76	— —	(0.00)	0.00	16,908
12/13	3,857.70	— —	(0.00)	0.00	19,257
12/12	2,975.00	— —	(0.00)	0.00	18,613
Annual Growth	—	— —	—	—	(4.2%)

Baoshan Iron & Steel Co Ltd

Auditors: Deloitte Touche Tohmatsu Certified Public Accountants Limited

LOCATIONS

HQ: Baoshan Iron & Steel Co Ltd
Baosteel Command Center, No. 885, Fujin Road, Baoshan District, Shanghai 201900
Phone: (86) 21 26647000 **Fax:** (86) 21 26646999
Web: www.baosteel.com/plc/

HISTORICAL FINANCIALS

Company Type: Public

Income Statement   FYE: December 31

	REVENUE ($ mil.)	NET INCOME ($ mil.)	NET PROFIT MARGIN	EMPLOYEES
12/15	25,270	155	0.6%	0
12/14	30,257	933	3.1%	0
12/13	31,389	961	3.1%	0
12/12	30,719	1,666	5.4%	32,598
12/11	35,405	1,169	3.3%	41,919
Annual Growth	(8.1%)	(39.6%)		

2015 Year-End Financials

Debt ratio: 2.9%
Return on equity: 0.8%
Cash ($ mil.): 1,203
Current ratio: 0.76
Long-term debt ($ mil.): 2,749

No. of shares (mil.): —
Dividends
Yield: —
Payout: —
Market value ($ mil.): —

Barclays Bank Plc

Barclays Bank is the flagship subsidiary of global financial group Barclays PLC. The bank is primarily active in the UK where it has some 1700 branches but also has significant retail and commercial operations in Europe Africa (it owns more than half of South African bank Absa Group) the Middle East and the US. Barclays Bank offers standard retail services such as deposit accounts and lending including Woolwich-brand mortgages. The bank also provides commercial money transfer services insurance products the Barclaycard line of credit cards and financial advisory services. Barclays Bank traces its roots to the late 17th century.

Barclays Bank has been building up its portfolio of global credit card accounts especially as other financial groups sell off noncore units during the economic recovery. In 2010 the company acquired the Italian credit card accounts of Citigroup in a deal that included some 197000 card accounts and approximately euro 234 million ($320 million) worth of assets. It previously bought Goldfish the struggling UK credit card unit of Discover Financial Services for some £46 million ($70 million). In 2011 Barclays acquired Egg UK's credit card portfolio which added more than 1 million accounts; it has agreed to buy more Citibank card accounts.

The bank has also been offloading some of its own holdings as part of an overall corporate restructuring. In 2010 Barclays sold its US subprime loan servicing business HomEq Servicing to Ocwen Financial. It also announced plans to abandon retail banking in certain international markets and instead focus on wholesale and commercial banking. In 2011 it shuttered its Indonesian retail unit Bank Akita which it had acquired only two years before. The company also sold its Russian retail and commercial operations to a group of investors citing difficulties competing in the market. Barclays will instead focus on its investment banking activities in the region.

In 2010 Barclays acquired Standard Life Bank from Standard Life for £226 million ($369 million). The deal added Standard Life's savings and mortgage books to the Barclays fold. Also as part of the deal Barclays and Standard Life entered into a partnership whereby Barclays markets pension products to its clients.

Despite challenges in the economy especially in regards to Europe's debt problems Barclays Bank's revenues grew 8% in 2011. Its Africa business performed relatively strongly with credit impairments improving as did Barclaycard thanks to the portfolio acquisitions which delivered profits. That year the bank closed nearly 150 European branches (largely located in Spain) the costs of which contributed to a 5% decline in net income.

EXECUTIVES

Group Finance Director, Tushar Morzaria
Group Chief Executive, James E. (Jes) Stanley
Group COO, Paul Compton
Chairman, John McFarlane, age 69
Deputy Chairman, Gerry Grimstone
Auditors: PricewaterhouseCoopers LLP

LOCATIONS

HQ: Barclays Bank Plc
1 Churchill Place, London E14 5HP
Phone: (44) 20 7116 1000
Web: www.barclays.com

2014 Sales

	% of total
UK	48
Americas	22
Africa & Middle East	16
Europe	11
Asia	3
Total	**100**

PRODUCTS/OPERATIONS

2014 Sales

	% of total
Barclays Core	
Personal and corporate banking	35
Investment banking	29
Barclaycard	17
Africa Banking	14
Head office	1
Barclays Non-Core	4
Total	**100**

2014 Sales

	% of total
Interest	53
Fees & commissions	30
Net trading income	10
Net investment income	4
Net insurance premiums & other	3
Total	**100**

COMPETITORS

Citibank	Lloyds Banking Group
Credit Suisse	Nationwide Building
Deutsche Bank	Society
HSBC	Royal Bank of Scotland
ING	Standard Chartered

HISTORICAL FINANCIALS

Company Type: Public

Income Statement

FYE: December 31

	ASSETS ($ mil.)	NET INCOME ($ mil.)	INCOME AS % OF ASSETS	EMPLOYEES
12/15	1,660,856	1,350	0.1%	129,400
12/14	2,120,950	824	0.0%	132,300
12/13	2,169,572	1,591	0.1%	139,600
12/12	2,402,885	(1,165)	—	139,200
12/11	2,415,227	5,586	0.2%	141,100
Annual Growth	**(8.9%)**	**(29.9%)**	**—**	**(2.1%)**

2015 Year-End Financials

Return on assets: 0.0%
Return on equity: 1.4%
Long-term debt ($ mil.): —
No. of shares (mil.): —
Sales ($ mil): 47,140
Dividends
 Yield: —
 Payout: —
Market value ($ mil.): —

	STOCK PRICE ($) FY Close	P/E High/Low	PER SHARE ($) Earnings	Dividends	Book Value
12/15	20.10	— —	(0.00)	0.00	40.55
12/14	31.51	— —	(0.00)	0.00	42.51
12/13	42.55	— —	(0.00)	0.00	43.04
12/12	31.81	— —	(0.00)	0.00	41.31
12/11	35.53	— —	(0.00)	0.00	40.95
Annual Growth	**(13.3%)**	**— —**	**— —**	**—**	**(0.2%)**

Barclays PLC

Raising the bar for global finance Barclays owns one of Europe's largest banks a top market-making investment bank the top UK credit card and an international wealth management firm. Its flagship Barclays Bank has some 1500 branches in the UK as well as operations throughout Europe Africa the Middle East and the Americas. In addition to holding one of the world's largest investment banks the company's Barclaycard arm has more than 20 million credit cards and provides consumer lending and payment processing services primarily in Europe. Altogether Barclays serves more than 48 million customers in more than 50 countries.

OperationsBarclays PLC and Barclays Bank PLC operate two segments (as of 2016): Barclays UK which is made up of its retail banking consumer credit cards wealth and corporate banking businesses serving 22 million retail customers and 1 million business banking customers in the UK; and Barclays Corporate & International which consists of its corporate banking franchise its investment bank its credit cards business in the US (Barclaycard US) and abroad its international wealth management services and its merchant payment services offered through its corporate banking and Barclaycard business.

Before 2016 the group operated four segments. The Personal and Corporate Banking (PCB) busi-

ness generated 37% of Barclays' revenue in 2015 and consisted of its personal banking corporate banking and wealth and investment management businesses. Barclays' Investment Bank division (33% of revenue) offered financial advisory capital raising financing and risk management services to corporations and institutions as well as governments around the world. It also had a markets business within the segment which provided investment and risk management services as well as a research arm that provides economic and market research to its clients. The company's credit card and consumer-lending payments service provider business Barclaycard (which includes US division Barclays Bank Delaware) brought in 16% of revenue. Barclays announced in early 2016 its plans to sell its 62% stake in its recently struggling Africa Banking division (which includes the South African bank Absa) over the next two to three years. The division made up nearly 15% of the firm's total revenue in 2015 and includes the retail cards wealth corporate and investment banking operations in Africa. Geographic ReachBarclays serves some 48 million customers in more than 50 countries. About 48% of its revenue was generated in the UK during 2015 while another 25% came from the Americas. The rest of its revenue came from business in Africa and the Middle East (15% of revenue) and the rest of Europe (9%).

Sales and MarketingBarclays targets its marketing toward individuals small and medium businesses and corporate and institutional clients. The company spent £536 million ($794.5 million) on marketing in 2015 down from £558 million ($866.7 million) and £583 million ($961.3 million) in 2014 and 2013 respectively.

Financial Performance

Note: Growth rates may differ after conversion to US dollars. This analysis uses financials from the company's annual report. Barclays' revenue has trended downward in recent years due to shrinking interest margins in the low-interest environment lower fee and commission income and lower trading income. The company's total income (after regular operating expenses) grew less than 1% to £25.987 billion (about $ billion) with mixed results. Its net interest income grew 4% mostly on margin and volume growth in its Barclaycard division as well as margin and volume growth in its Africa Banking and PCB segments respectively. Net investment income was down nearly 10% on lower gains due to unfavorable market conditions while net fee and commission income was down 3% after the company sold its US Wealth and Spanish retail businesses and because its Investment Bank generated less in equity underwriting fees. The bank's statutory after-tax profit fell for a third year dropping 26% to £623 million ($923.5 million) in 2015 mostly as it set aside more loan provisions for UK customers and incurred more losses on the sale of its Spanish Portuguese and Italian businesses. Barclays operating cash levels spiked to £16.13 billion ($23.9 billion) for the year (operations used £10.44 billion in 2014) thanks to favorable changes in working capital mostly related to a net decrease in loans and advances a net decrease in reverse purchase agreements and similarly secured lending and a net decrease in trading assets.

Strategy

Enduring years of declining revenues in recent years following the last market crash Barclays has also been selling many of its non-core businesses cutting costs through branch closures and workforce reductions and restructuring its credit market exposures. In 2016 the bank looked to sell its African banking business after selling its Portuguese banking and insurance businesses to

Bankinter SA with the sale expected to save £72 million annually in costs. During 2015 working on a major restructuring and shrinking some of its struggling European divisions Barclays sold Italian retail banking network of 89 branches to CheBanca! as well as its Spanish retail and corporate banking operations to CaixaBank . That year the firm also sold its Barclays Risk Analytics and Index Solutions Ltd. business to Bloomberg LP for £520 million.

Barclays has been moving toward digital banking channels that are quickly taking the industry by storm allowing the bank to cut its expensive branch network and slash operating costs significantly while giving customers faster access to banking services. Indeed the bank has reduced its branch count from 1560 branches in 2013 to just 1362 at the end of 2015. Also toward its digitized foray in mid 2015 the bank rolled out its "Community Banking" service which allows its employees to offer branch-only services (including money transfers account changes or account opening services) through an iPad tablet from anywhere in a community with an online connection. Meanwhile its Barclaycard division continues to focus on next-generation payment technology in the UK South Africa and in the US helping its customers adopt new digital platforms to pay using "tap and go" cards contactless stickers and smart phones.

Company Background

Legal troubles have caused headwinds for Barclays's bottom line in recent years. In mid-2012 the company admitted to manipulating the London Interbank Offered Rate (LIBOR) a benchmark for daily global short-term interest rates. The bank repeatedly manipulated the LIBOR in order to make its funding position look stronger than it actually was; the rigging also helped the bank make money on credit derivatives. Chairman Martin Agius and CEO Bob Diamond both resigned as a result of the developments and the company paid US and UK regulators some £290 million ($453 million) in settlement fines. Shortly after the LIBOR scandal the UK's Serious Fraud Office launched an inquiry into payments Barclays made to sovereign investor Qatar Holding in 2008. That same year investment fund Qatar Investment Authority became the bank's largest shareholder with a 5% stake. Investigations for both the bid-rigging and bribery allegations continue.

HISTORY

Company BackgroundBarclays first spread its wings in 1736 when James Barclay united his family's goldsmithing and banking businesses. As other family members joined the London enterprise it became known as Barclays Bevan & Tritton (1782).

Banking first became regulated in the 19th century. To ward off takeovers 20 banks combined with Barclays in 1896. The new firm Barclay & Co. began preying on other banks. Within 20 years it bought 17 including the Colonial Bank chartered in 1836 to serve the West Indies and British Guiana (now Guyana). The company renamed Barclays Bank Ltd. in 1917 weathered the Depression as the UK's #2 bank.

Barclays began expanding again after WWII and by the late 1950s it had become the UK's top bank. It had a computer network by 1959 and in 1966 it introduced the Barclaycard in conjunction with Bank of America's BankAmericard (now Visa).

In 1968 the UK's Monopolies Commission barred Barclays' merger with two other big London banks but had no objections to a two-way merger so Barclays bought competitor Martins.

Barclays moved into the US consumer finance market in 1980 when it bought American Credit

138 former Beneficial Finance offices and Bankers Trust's branch network.

During the 1980s London banks faced competition from invading overseas banks local building societies and other financial firms. Banking reform in 1984 led to formation of a holding company for Barclays Bank PLC.

To prepare for British financial deregulation in 1986 Barclays formed Barclays de Zoete Wedd (BZW) by merging its merchant bank with two other London financial firms. Faced with sagging profits Barclays sold its California bank in 1988 and its US consumer finance business in 1989.

In 1990 Barclays bought private German bank Merck Finck & Co. and Paris bank L'Europeenne de Banque. The company countered 1992's bad-loan-induced losses by accelerating a cost-cutting program begun in 1989. To appease stockholders chairman and CEO Andrew Buxton (a descendant of one of the bank's founding families) gave up his CEO title hiring Martin Taylor (previously CEO of textile firm Courtaulds) for the post.

The company sold its Australian retail banking business in 1994 then began trimming other operations including French corporate banking and US mortgage operations. However it bought the Wells Fargo Nikko Investment Company to boost Asian operations.

Barclays' piecemeal sale of BZW signaled its failure to become a global investment banking powerhouse. In 1997 it sold BZW's European investment banking business to Credit Suisse First Boston retaining the fixed-income and foreign exchange business. (Credit Suisse bought Barclays' Asian investment banking operations in 1998.)

Losses in Russia and a $250 million bailout of US hedge fund Long-Term Capital Management hit Barclays Capital in 1998. Taylor resigned that year in part because of his radical plans for the bank. Sir Peter Middleton stepped in as acting CEO; Barclays later tapped Canadian banker Matthew Barrett for the post. (Middleton also became chairman upon Buxton's retirement.)

Barclays in 1999 started a move toward online banking at the expense of traditional branches. The company announced free lifetime Internet access for new bank customers.

In 2000 the bank ruffled feathers when it announced the closure of about 170 mostly rural UK branches. Also in 2000 the company sold its Dial auto leasing unit to ABN AMRO and bought Woolwich plc. The following year Barclay's closed its own life insurance division opting instead to sell the life insurance and pension products of London-based Legal & General Group.

In 2004 chief executive Barrett was named Barclays' chairman succeeding Peter Middleton who became chairman of Centre for Effective Dispute Resolution (CEDR) and later chancellor of the University of Sheffield.

After exiting the South African market in 1987 over apartheid concerns Barclays returned in a big way in 2005 buying a majority stake (about 57%) in the Absa Group one of the country's largest retail banks. The deal also represented the largest-ever direct foreign investment there. The next year Barclays sold its South African businesses including corporate international retail and commercial operations to Absa.

The company entered the US credit card market when it bought Juniper Financial (now Barclays Bank Delaware) from Canadian Imperial Bank of Commerce (CIBC) in 2004. In a previous hook-up with CIBC Barclays merged its Caribbean banking business with CIBC's to create an 85-branch regional bank FirstCaribbean International Bank with each company owning 44%; Barclays sold its stake to CIBC in 2006.

In 2005 the bank sold its vendor finance businesses in the UK and Germany to CIT Group. Bar-

clays said that the sale will allow it to focus on its commercial leasing business.

The bank moved to assimilate its Woolwich acquisition in 2006 when it closed 200 branches and consolidated Woolwich branches into existing Barclays locations. It retained the Woolwich mortgage brand but switched account holders to Barclays accounts.

The company and HSBC formed a joint venture that manages their cash handling operations in the UK. Named Vaultex the joint venture acquired Loomis Cash Management in 2007.

Marcus Agius succeeded the retiring Matthew Barrett as chairman in 2007.

Although the company withdrew its bid for Dutch banking giant ABN AMRO (narrowly escaping that troubled deal) in 2008 it bought Russian bank Expobank from Petropavlovsk Finance. Expobank was one of the largest ATM networks in Russia and part of the booming consumer banking industry there. Also that year Barclays sold noncore business Barclays Life and its portfolio of some 760000 life and pension policies to Swiss Re for £753 million ($1.5 billion).

The group chose not to participate in the UK's bank bailouts as the global financial crisis intensified in late 2008 but pursued its own capital-raising plan. Through the deal sovereign investment fund Qatar Investment Authority became the bank's largest shareholder with a 5% stake.

In 2009 it shut down US-based subprime mortgage lender EquiFirst which it had purchased from Regions Financial before it fell victim to the mortgage bust.

Later that year it sold a majority of Barclays Global Investors to American money manager BlackRock for £9.5 billion ($15 billion). In exchange it gained a 20% stake in the new BlackRock with some $3 trillion under management for institutional clients around the world. The deal provided the bank with much-needed cash and cleared the way for a commercial partnership with BlackRock.

Another major transaction was the £1 billion ($1.8 billion) acquisition of Lehman Brothers' North American operations a deal which made Barclays Capital one of the world's largest investment banks.

EXECUTIVES

Group CEO and Director, James E. (Jes) Staley, age 59

Group Finance Director, Tushar Morzaria

Group COO, Paul Compton

Group Chief Risk Officer, C.S. Venkatakrishnan

Executive Chairman, John McFarlane, age 69

Deputy Chairman, Gerry Grimstone

Auditors: PricewaterhouseCoopers LLP

LOCATIONS

HQ: Barclays PLC
1 Churchill Place, London E14 5HP
Phone: (44) 20 7116 1000
Web: www.barclays.com

2015 Sales

	% of total
UK	48
Americas	25
Africa & Middle East	15
Europe	9
Asia	3
Total	**100**

PRODUCTS/OPERATIONS

2015 Sales

	% of total
Interest income	53

Fee and Commission income	30
Net trading income	11
Net investment income	4
Net premiums from insurance contracts	2
Total	**100**

2015 Sales

	% of total
Barclays Core	
Personal and corporate banking	37
Investment banking	33
Barclaycard	16
Africa Banking	14
Total	**100**

COMPETITORS

AXA UK	Lloyds Banking Group
Bank of New York Mellon	Mitsubishi UFJ Financial Group
CIBC	Mizuho Financial
Citigroup	RBC Financial Group
Deutsche Bank	Royal Bank of Scotland
Grupo Santander	Standard Chartered
HSBC	The Vanguard Group
Invesco	UBS
JPMorgan Chase	

HISTORICAL FINANCIALS

Company Type: Public

Income Statement

FYE: December 31

	ASSETS ($ mil.)	NET INCOME ($ mil.)	INCOME AS % OF ASSETS	EMPLOYEES
12/15	1,659,796	(72)	—	129,400
12/14	2,119,722	118	0.0%	132,300
12/13	2,168,625	892	0.0%	140,300
12/12	2,402,198	(1,677)	—	143,700
12/11	2,415,420	4,645	0.2%	141,100
Annual Growth	**(9.0%)**	—		**(2.1%)**

2015 Year-End Financials

Return on assets: (-0.0%)	Dividends
Return on equity: (-0.0%)	Yield: 2.9%
Long-term debt ($ mil.): —	Payout: —
No. of shares (mil.): —	Market value ($ mil.): —
Sales ($ mil): 47,130	

	STOCK PRICE ($) FY Close	P/E High/Low	PER SHARE ($) Earnings	Dividends	Book Value
12/15	12.96	— —	(0.03)	0.38	5.27
12/14	15.01	— —	(0.01)	0.42	5.64
12/13	18.13	572435	0.06	0.40	5.68
12/12	17.32	— —	(0.14)	0.38	7.06
12/11	10.99	83 34	0.37	0.34	7.04
Annual Growth	**4.2%**	— —		**3.2%**	**(7.0%)**

BASF SE

BASF is the world's largest chemical company ahead of Dow and DuPont and serves upwards of 300000 customers worldwide from major global players to small businesses. It has more than 330 production sites and operates through five business segments: Chemicals (solvents plasticizers and electronic chemicals) Performance Products (including dispersions and pigments vitamins and food additives and products for the paper and oil and gas industries) Oil and Gas (exploration and production) Functional Materials and Solutions (catalysts industrial coatings battery materials) and Agricultural Solutions (fungicides herbicides insecticides).

Operations

No one segment dominates BASF's sales mix but Functional Materials is the largest at around a quarter of total sales. Performance Products Chemicals and Oil & Gas comprise around 20% each with Agricultural Solutions and Other making up the remainder.

Geographical Reach

BASF has enormous global reach: it has companies in more than 80 countries worldwide and supplies products to business partners in nearly every corner of the globe. Europe makes up just over half of total revenue with North America and the Asia-Pacific region at around 20% each.

The company operates more than 340 production sites across the globe including six Verbund sites - highly efficient production plants key to BASF's resource-efficiency philosophy - which reuse outputs (heat chemical by-products) to achieve lower energy consumption and higher chemical yields. There are two in Europe (Ludwigshafen Germany and Antwerp Belgium) two in the US (Geismar and Freeport) and two in Asia (Nanjing China and Kuantan Malaysia - site in Nanjing is currently being expanded).

Sales and Marketing

BASF sells to companies ranging from global enterprises to small businesses and half of business units are geared to specific industries. In the chemicals business marketing is partly carried out by e-commerce.

Financial Performance

Note: Growth rates may differ after conversion to US Dollars.

BASF is highly exposed to the ongoing global economic turbulence particularly given its dealings in oil and other commodities and 2015 proved a tough year for the company; forecasts for 2016 predict similarly gloomy outlook.

Total sales hit a five-year low in 2015 of euro 70 billion a 5% decline on prior year. The Chemicals division bore a big chunk of the losses falling 14% to euro 14.6 billion amid an increase in customer caution caused by the oil price slump. The significant drop in the price of raw materials was also a factor pushing retail prices down. A similar fall in the Oil & Gas segment was the result of the asset-swap with Gazprom - contributions from the natural gas trading and storage business ended as of Q4 2015.

Positive currency effects helped grow revenue in Functional Materials and Performance Products by 5% and 1% to euro 18.5 billion and euro 15.6 billion respectively. Higher sales prices helped Agricultural Solutions to revenue 7% higher than 2014 at euro 5.8 billion.

Net income fell from euro 5.1 billion to euro 4.0 billion in 2015 a 23% fall - this was the company's poorest performance since the start of the decade. Positively a reduction in inventories in 2015 among other factors led to an increase in cash flow from operations which hit a new high of euro 9.4 billion.

Strategy

BASF uses what it calls Verbund strategy throughout its facilities to reduce emissions and increase efficiency - plants are both customers and suppliers of each other. While the company still gets more than half its sales from Europe it continues to expand overseas particularly in Asia. It has long seen the potential in Asia and has put the region as a focus for growth and R&D and to this end an agricultural research centre was opened in Pune India in May 2015. For its GM products BASF focuses on markets in the Americas and Asia.

Difficult trading conditions have necessitated an adaptation period. In Q4 2015 BASF divested its gas trading and storage business to Russian gas giant Gazprom. The division which contributed euro 10 billion to sales in the first three quarters of 2015 was victim of the historic slump in oil prices seen in the year. Parts of BASF's pharmaceutical ingredients and services business were sold to Switzerland's Siegfried Holdings AG and BASF's white expandable polystyrene business in North and South America was sold to Alpek a Mexican company.

It is also undertaking cost-cutting measures including scaling-back capital expenditure and the sale of its pharmaceutical ingredients business; the sale of its industrial coatings business is being prepared and will likely be sold to Akzo Nobel for around euro 470 million.

Product and production innovation remains a cornerstone of long-term strategy and 2015 saw numerous promising developments in each operating segment. To name just three BASF improved the production process for Isononanol a plasticizer precursor product; its Acronal® EDGE 4750 paint product acts as both a primer and top-coat at once; and in the Plant Science space it launched Cultivance® a two-in-one GM soybean and corresponding herbicide. The company has about 3000 projects in its research pipeline.

Mergers and Acquisitions

In 2017 BASF bought Switzerland-based Rolic AG a specialist in light management for advanced LCD/OLED displays.

In 2016 the company acquired Albemarle's global surface treatment business Chemetall for about $3.2 billion.

In 2015 BASF acquired a number of businesses spending about euro 227 million. In a busy February it acquired Taiwan Sheen Soon Co. Ltd a manufacturer of precursors for adhesives; Seashell Technology LLC was acquired for its silver nanowires technology; and BASF acquired a 66% share in TODA KOGYO CORP for its cathode materials for lithium-ion batteries patents and production capabilities in Japan.

Later in the year it acquired the marketing and selling rights for the polyurethane business from Polioles based in Mexico and concluded the acquisition of technologies and patents for the production of high-molecular-weight polyisobutene from Lanxess Aktiengesellschaft.

HISTORY

Company Background

Originally named Badische Anilin & Soda-Fabrik BASF AG was founded in Mannheim Germany by jeweler Frederick Englehorn in 1861. Unable to find enough land for expansion in Mannheim BASF moved to nearby Ludwigshafen in 1865. The company was a pioneer in coal tar dyes and it developed a synthetic indigo in 1897. Its synthetic dyes rapidly replaced more expensive organic dyes.

BASF scientist Fritz Haber synthesized ammonia in 1909 giving BASF access to the market for nitrogenous fertilizer (1913). Haber received a Nobel Prize in 1918 but was later charged with war crimes for his work with poison gases. Managed by Carl Bosch another Nobel Prize winner BASF joined the I.G. Farben cartel with Bayer Hoechst and others in 1925 to create a German chemical colossus. Within the cartel BASF developed polystyrene PVC and magnetic tape. Part of the Nazi war machine I.G. Farben made synthetic rubber and used labor from the Auschwitz concentration camp during WWII.

After the war I.G. Farben was dismantled. BASF regained its independence in 1952 and rebuilt its war-ravaged factories. Strong postwar domestic demand for basic chemicals aided its recovery and in 1958 BASF launched a US joint venture with

Dow Chemical. (BASF bought out Dow's half in 1978.) The company moved into petrochemicals and became a leading manufacturer of plastic and synthetic fiber.

In the US the company purchased Wyandotte Chemicals (1969) Chemetron (1979) and Inmont (1985) among others. To expand its natural gas business in Europe in 1991 the company signed deals with Russia's Gazprom and France's Elf Aquitaine. BASF bought Mobil's polystyrene-resin business and gained almost 10% of the US market.

BASF bought Imperial Chemical's polypropylene business in 1994 and became Europe's second-largest producer of the plastic. The next year the company paid $1.4 billion for the pharmaceutical arm of UK retailer Boots.

In 1997 BASF formed a joint venture with PetroFina (now TOTAL); in 2001 the venture opened the world's largest liquid steam cracker in Port Arthur Texas.

BASF made seven major acquisitions in 1998 including the complexing business of Ciba Specialty Chemicals. It also made six divestitures which included its European buildings-paints operations sold to Nobel N.V.

In 1999 the US fined the company $225 million for its part in a worldwide vitamin price-fixing cartel (in 2001 the European Commission fined it another $260 million bringing the total expected cost of fines out-of-court settlements and legal expenses to about $800 million). BASF also faced a class-action suit as a result of the scheme. That year the company moved into oil and gas exploration in Russia through a partnership agreement with Russia's Gazprom. BASF also merged its textile operations into Bayer and Hoechst's DyStar joint venture forming a $1 billion company that is a world-leading dye maker.

BASF completed its acquisition of Rohm and Haas' industrial coatings business in 2000 and bought the Cyanamid division (herbicides fungicides and pesticides) of American Home Products (now Wyeth). That year BASF expanded its superabsorbents business by paying $656 million for US-based Amcol International's Chemdal International unit.

Rather than attempt to compete in the rapidly consolidating pharmaceutical industry in 2001 BASF sold its midsized Knoll Pharmaceutical unit to Abbott Laboratories for about $6.9 billion. It also announced that it was closing 10 plants and cutting about 4000 jobs (4% of its workforce).

BASF sold its fibers unit in 2003 to focus on core chemical operations which it added to throughout the next few years. For example it bought a portion of Bayer's agchem businesses for $1.3 billion when European antitrust regulators mandated the Bayer divestment following its acquisition of Aventis CropScience. BASF also acquired Honeywell Specialty Materials' engineering plastics business in exchange for its fibers division. BASF's acquisition later that year of MSA's Callery Chemical Division strengthened BASF's line of inorganics which it planned to focus on providing to the pharmaceutical industry. Other acquisitions included Ticona's nylon 66 business and Sunoco's plasticizers unit.

That year also brought chairman Jürgen Hambrecht's announcement that the company would push forward with a restructuring of its North American business. The focus of the plan was to save more than $250 million over the next three years. Included among the steps were job cuts of approximately 1000 and the relocation of its North American headquarters (though remaining in New Jersey) in late 2004. (The move to smaller facilities was enabled by the sale of Knoll Pharmaceuticals in 2001 which reduced operations at the home base.)

BASF sold Basell its petrochemical JV with Shell in 2005. The two companies had announced in 2004 that they planned to exit the polyolefins business with the sale of Basell. The deal was finalized late the next year. Investment group Access Industries came in with the winning bid of about $5.7 billion. That company's name was changed to LyondellBasell after its 2007 acquisition of Lyondell Chemical Company.

The company opened two Verbund sites in Asia —one in Nanjing China and the other in Kuantan Malaysia. The Chinese site delivered its first product in early 2005 and began operating fully in the middle of that year. It's the centerpiece and primary operation of BASF-YPC a joint venture with Sinopec that was formed in 2000. BASF's goal is to achieve 70% of its sales in the region from local production by 2015; that figure hovered at about 60% in 2008.

The company also legally changed its name from BASF Aktiengesellschaft to BASF SE in 2008. The move made formal BASF's transition to a European company as opposed to one organized in Germany.

In 2009 BASF spent about $4 billion to acquire Swiss chemicals giant Ciba. Following a review phase of Ciba's operations and their fit within the structure of BASF the company began integrating Ciba into its performance products segment; this entailed the sale or closure of almost half of Ciba's 55 manufacturing facilities and the loss of about 3700 of its employees. As part of that strategy BASF SE sold the Regulatory and Safety Testing businesses of Ciba's Expert Services unit to London-based Intertek Group in 2010.

Also in 2010 BASF acquired specialty chemicals company Cognis GmbH in a $3.8 billion deal. Cognis gave BASF a boost in entering several high-margin business lines such as personal care and cosmetics.

EXECUTIVES

Member Executive Board and CFO, Hans-Ulrich Engel, age 58, $555 total compensation
President Logistics and Information Services, Kurt W. Bock, age 59, $1,200 total compensation
Member Executive Board and Head of Construction Chemicals Crop Protection and Bioscience Research and Region Europe, Harald Schwager, age 57
Division Head Dispersions and Pigments Care Chemicals Nutrition and Health Paper Chemicals Performance Chemicals; Member Executive Board, Michael Heinz, age 52
Member Executive Board and Head of Engineering and Maintenance Environment Health and Safety European Site and Verbund Management Human Resources Industrial Relations Director and Site Director Ludwigshafen, Margret Suckale, age 60
Vice Chairman of the Board of Executive Directors and CTO, Martin Brudermuller, age 55, $798 total compensation
Head Greater China Asia Pacific ASEAN South and East Asia; Member Board of Executive Directors, Sanjeev Gandhi, age 50
Division Head Intermediates Monomers Petrochemicals and Process Research and Chemical Engineering, Wayne T. Smith, age 56
President BASF Information Services and Supply Chain Operations Division, Christoph Wegner
President Petrochemicals, Hartwig Michels, age 52
President Regional Division Europe, Markus Kramer, age 51
President Nutrition and Health, Melanie Maas-Brunner, age 47
President Coatings, Dirk Bremm
Vice Chairman, Michael Diekmann, age 62
Chairman, Jürgen Hambrecht, age 70

Vice Chairman, Robert Oswald, age 61
Auditors: KPMG AG

LOCATIONS

HQ: BASF SE
Carl-Bosch-Strasse 38, Ludwigshafen D-67056
Phone: (49) 621 60 0   **Fax:** (49) 621 602525
Web: www.basf.com

2015 Sales

	% of total
Europe	
Germany	40
Other Countries	15
North America	22
Asia Pacific	17
South America Africa Middle East	6
Total	**100**

PRODUCTS/OPERATIONS

2015 Sales

	% of total
Functional Materials & Solutions	26
Performance Products	22
Chemicals	21
Oil & Gas	19
Agricultural Solutions	8
Other	4
Total	**100**

Selected Products

Oil and Gas
  Crude oil and natural gas exploration
  Natural gas distribution and trading
Chemicals
  Inorganics
  Ammonia
  Formaldehyde
  Melamine
  Sulfuric acid
  Urea
  Intermediates
  Performance chemicals
  Water-based resins
  Petrochemicals
  Feedstocks
  Industrial gases
  Plasticizers
  Specialty chemicals
Plastics
  Engineering plastics
  Foams
  Polyamides and intermediates
  Polyurethanes
  Styrenics
Functional Solutions
  Catalysts
  Battery materials
  Chemical catalysts
  Coatings
  Automotive coatings
  Decorative paints
  Industrial coatings
  Pigments
  Construction chemicals
Performance Products
  Automotive fluids
  Care chemicals
  Paper chemicals
  Pharma ingredients
  Textile chemicals
Agricultural Solutions
  Crop protection
  Fungicides
  Herbicides
  Insecticides

COMPETITORS

3M	Evonik Degussa
Air Products	Exxon Mobil
Akzo Nobel	FMC
Albemarle	Formosa Plastics
Ashland Inc.	Henkel
BP	LANXESS
Bayer AG	LG Group
Cargill	Monsanto Company
DSM	Royal Dutch Shell

Dow Chemical   SABIC
DuPont   TOTAL
Eastman Chemical   Taminco

HISTORICAL FINANCIALS

Company Type: Public

Income Statement

FYE: December 31

	REVENUE ($ mil.)	NET INCOME ($ mil.)	NET PROFIT MARGIN	EMPLOYEES
12/15	76,733	4,342	5.7%	112,435
12/14	90,343	6,265	6.9%	113,292
12/13	101,841	6,666	6.5%	112,206
12/12	103,768	6,430	6.2%	113,262
12/11	95,064	8,003	8.4%	111,141
Annual Growth	(5.2%)	(14.2%)	—	0.3%

2015 Year-End Financials

Debt ratio: 6.2%
Return on equity: 13.6%
Cash ($ mil.): 2,440
Current ratio: 1.73
Long-term debt ($ mil.): —

No. of shares (mil.): 918
Dividends
  Yield: 2.9%
  Payout: —
Market value ($ mil.): 69,818

	STOCK PRICE ($) FY Close	P/E High/Low	PER SHARE ($) Earnings	Dividends	Book Value
12/15	76.02	24 17	4.72	2.26	36.66
12/14	83.39	19 14	6.81	2.72	36.54
12/13	107.79	21 17	7.26	2.47	40.64
12/12	95.00	18 13	7.00	2.41	35.27
12/11	69.73	13 8	8.70	0.00	33.99
Annual Growth	2.2%	—	— (14.2%)	—	1.9%

Bayer AG

You could get a headache trying to name all of Bayer's products. The company which created aspirin in 1897 makes prescription products and works in oncology and radiology through its Pharmaceuticals division; OTC products like Claritin and Canesten via its Consumer Health division; and crop protection and pest control via its Crop Science division. Its top selling pharmaceuticals include oral anticoagulent Xarelto and blood-clotting medicine Kogenate. Bayer also operates an animal health business unit; its top-seller is Advantage a flea medicine. Also known as Bayer Group the firm has some 300 operating subsidiaries worldwide; it operates in the US through Bayer Corporation. The company spun off its material science division in 2015 but retains 69% ownership.

Operations

Pharmaceuticals the largest segment by revenue at around a third deals in prescription products especially for women's health care and cardiology and on specialty therapeutics in the areas of oncology hematology and opthamology.

The Consumer Health business includes consumer care and medical care and makes primarily non-prescription and OTC medicines supplements and dermatology products such as Aspirin (for which it owns the trademark in 80 countries) Berocca and Aleve. In 2016 it completed the sale of its Diabetes Care unit to Panasonic Healthcare.

The Crop Science segment does business in seeds crop protection and non-agricultural pest control and accounted for 22% of revenue in 2015. In 2016 Bayer made a record $66 billion takeover bid for Monsanto the American GM crop producer.

Covestro develops and markets high-tech polymer materials and specialty chemicals; it also makes inorganic base chemicals. Its operating units are polyurethanes polycarbonates and coatings adhesives and specialties. It accounted for 30% of revenue in 2014.

The company also operates an animal health business.

Geographic Reach

Europe is Bayer's largest region at about a third of sales but the company also generates significant revenue in North American and the Asia-Pacific region. Most of the company's core manufacturing facilities are in Germany and the US. The company also has operations Latin America Africa and the Middle East.

The Bayer Group comprises about 300 consolidated companies operating in 77 countries around the world.

Sales and Marketing

Pharmaceuticals products are distributed primarily through wholesalers hospitals and pharmacy chains while Crop Science products are sold through wholesalers and regional distributors. The Consumer Health division's well-known and established brands are sold through major supermarket chains and pharmacies.

Financial Performance

Note: Growth rates may differ after conversion to US Dollars.

The company recorded its fifth consecutive year of sales growth in 2015: revenue grew 12% to euro 46.3 billion on the back of higher sales and earnings growth. Consumer Heath grew across all its divisions with HealthCare in particular showing strong growth. In the Pharmaceuticals segment the Xarelto Eylea Stivarga Xofigo and Adempas brands added euro 1.3 billion to sales in prior year and helped the company overcome declining prices. These brands are doing especially well in Germany Japan and the US.

Net income grew 20% to euro 4.1 billion despite special charges nearly doubling to euro 819 million mostly as a result of integration and re-structuring costs. These costs were offset to an extent by a favorable litigation settlement with Dow AgroSciences to the sum of euro 300 million.

Cash from continuing operations climbed 4.4% in 2015 to euro 7.0 billion.

Net income of euro 4.1 billion was 20% higher on prior year mostly due to an increase in sales.

Strategy

In 2015 Bayer undertook steps to realign itself as purely a life sciences company or one that works in biology be it pharmaceuticals biomedical technologies or plant science among other things. Bayer floated Covestro its materials science division (2015 revenue euro 12 billion) on the stock market as a fully independent company in September 2015 (although Bayer Group retains 69% ownership). SeedWorks India was acquired in July 2015 to strengthen Bayer's position in the vegetable seed business in India. Radiology joined Pharmaceuticals making Consumer Health consist entirely of the consumer care business. The lagging Diabetes Care business was sold to Panasonic for around euro 1 billion for financial reasons.

Bayer has substantially upped its R&D spend nearly tripling it since 2011 to euro 4.3 billion.

Bayer hopes that an expanding global population expected to reach 9.7 billion by 2050 will rapidly expand the demand for GM foods as a solution to difficult agriculture conditions. In mid-2016 the company agreed to an ambitious $66 billion takeover bid for US GM-food company Monsanto which will help Bayer makes gains in GM-resistant Europe. Historically GM foods have been produced almost exclusively in the US. The acquisition (which will be the largest all-cash corporate trans-

action to date) would bring Crop Sciences to almost half of Bayer revenue.

Shortly following the bid for Monsanto the company agreed to sell its consumer crop protection to French crop protection firm SBM Developpement to focus on commercial crop protection.

Mergers and Acquisitions

Acquisition activity was down substantially to almost nil in 2015 after a busy 2014 (euro 8 million vs euro 13741 million). In 2015 Bayer bought Thermoplast Composite to expand its range of polycarbonate materials. It also bought SeedWorks India to strengthen its vegetable seed business in the territory.

Acquisitions in 2014 in the health arena include the purchase of Merck's consumer care business which brought well-known brands including Claritin MiraLAX Coppertone and Dr. Scholl's under the Bayer umbrella. The company paid about $14.2 billion for the deal and moved into second place globally among OTC companies between a Novartis-GlaxoSmithKline joint venture and Johnson & Johnson.

Bayer also bought dermatology product specialist Dihon Pharmaceutical Group in China and former cancer drug Xofigo partner Algeta in Norway. CropScience purchases included Argentina's Biagro group (organic seed treatments and crop protection products) and the seed business of Paraguayan firm Granar. Altogether the company spent euro 13.5 billion on acquisitions in 2014.

HISTORY

Company Background

Friedrich Bayer founded Bayer in Germany in 1863 to make synthetic dyes. Research led to such discoveries as Antinonin (synthetic pesticide 1892) aspirin (1897) and synthetic rubber (1915).

Under Carl Duisberg Bayer allegedly made the first poison gas used by Germany in WWI. During the war the US seized Bayer's US operations and trademark rights and sold them to Sterling Drug.

In 1925 Bayer BASF Hoechst and other German chemical concerns merged to form I.G. Farben Trust. Their photography businesses combined as Agfa also joined the trust. Between wars Bayer developed polyurethanes and the first sulfa drug Prontosil (1935).

During WWII the trust took over chemical plants of Nazi-occupied countries used slave labor and helped make Zyklon B gas used to kill people at Auschwitz. At war's end Bayer lost its 50% of Winthrop Laboratories (US) and Bayer of Canada (to Sterling Drug). The 1945 Potsdam Agreement called for the breakup of I.G. Farben and Bayer AG emerged in 1951 as an independent company with many of its original operations including Agfa.

After rebuilding in West Germany Bayer AG and Monsanto formed a joint venture (Mobay 1954); Bayer AG later bought Monsanto's share (1967). In the 1960s the company offered more dyes plastics and polyurethanes and added factories worldwide. Agfa merged with Gevaert (photography Belgium) in 1964; Bayer AG retained 60%. Over the next 25 years it acquired Miles Labs (Alka-Seltzer US 1978) the rest of Agfa-Gevaert (1981) Compugraphic (electronic imaging US 1989) and Nova's Polysar (rubber Canada 1990).

Bayer AG integrated its US holdings under the name Miles in 1992 (renamed Bayer Corporation in 1995). The next year it introduced its first genetically engineered product Kogenate hemophilia treatment. It regained US rights to the Bayer brand and logo in 1994 by paying SmithKline Beecham $1 billion for the North American business of Sterling Winthrop.

EXECUTIVES

Chairman Board of Management, Werner Baumann, age 54

Member Board of Management Human Resources Technology and Sustainability, Hartmut Klusik

Member Board of Management Innovation and Latin America, Kemal Malik, age 54

Member Board of Management and Head of the Crop Science Division, Liam Condon

Member Board of Management and Head of the Consumer Health Division, Erica L. Mann

President Bayer North American Animal Health, Joyce Lee

Member Board of Management and Head of the Pharmaceuticals Division, Dieter Weinand

President and CEO Bayer Crop Science LP, James Blome

CFO and Asia Pacific, Johannes Dietsch, age 55

President Pharmaceuticals Americas, Carsten Brunn

Chairman Supervisory Board, Werner Wenning, age 70

Vice Chairman Supervisory Board, Oliver Z hlke, age 48

Auditors: PricewaterhouseCoopers Aktiengesellschaft Wirtschaftspruefungsgesellschaft

LOCATIONS

HQ: Bayer AG
Kaiser-Wilhelm Allee, Leverkusen D-51368
Phone: (49) 214 30 1   **Fax:** (49) 214 30 71985
Web: www.bayer.com

2015 Sales

	% of total
Europe	34
North America	27
Asia/Pacific	22
Latin America/Africa/Middle East	16
Total	**100**

PRODUCTS/OPERATIONS

2015 Sales

	% of total
Life Sciences	
Pharmaceuticals	33
Crop Science	22
Consumer Health	13
Animal Health	3
Other	2
Covestro	26
Total	**100**

Selected Operations and Products

HealthCare
Animal health products
Diabetes care products
Consumer care products (over-the-counter drugs)
Pharmaceuticals
MaterialScience
Coatings
Colorants
Plastics
Polyurethanes
CropScience
BioScience (biotechnology and seeds)
Crop protection (insecticides and herbicides)
Environmental science (lawn care and non-agricultural pesticides)

Selected Brands

HealthCare
Adalat (cardiovascular medication)
Advantage (animal health)
Aleve/Flanax (analgesic)
Alka-Seltzer (analgesic and antacid)
Aspirin (analgesic)
Aspirin Cardio (cardiovascular)
Avalox/Avelox (antibiotic)
Bepanthen/Bepanthol (skin care treatment)
Betaferon/Betaseron (multiple sclerosis medication)
Baytril (animal health infections)
Breeze/Contour (diabetes care glucose meters)

Canesten (antifungal)
Cipro/Ciprobay (antibiotic)
Glucobay (diabetes treatment)
Iopamiron (diagnostic imaging)
Kogenate (hematology/cardiology)
Levitra (impotence drug)
Magnevist (diagnostic imaging)
Mirena (contraceptive)
Nexavar (oncology)
One-A-Day (vitamins)
Supradyn (multivitamin)
Ultravist (diagnostic imaging)
Yasmin/Yasminelle/YAZ (contraceptive)
MaterialScience
Baydur/Bayflex/Bayblend (polyurethane)
Desmodur/Desmophen (isocyanates polyesters and polyols for polyurethanes)
Makrolon (polycarbonate resin)
CropScience
Betanal (herbicides)
Confidor/Gaucho/Admire/Merit (insecticides/seed treatment)
Decis (insecticides)
Flint/Stratego/Sphere/Nativo (fungicides)
Folicur/Raxil (fungicides/seed treatment)
Poncho (seed treatment)
Proline (fungicides)
Puma (herbicides)

COMPETITORS

3M	Evonik Degussa
Abbott Labs	GE Healthcare
Akzo Nobel	GlaxoSmithKline
Allergan plc	Johnson & Johnson
AstraZeneca	Merck
BASF SE	Merck KGaA
Baxter International	Mitsubishi Chemical
Boehringer Ingelheim	Holdings
Boston Scientific	Monsanto Company
Bristol-Myers Squibb	Novartis
Celanese	Pfizer
DSM	Rhodia
Dow Chemical	Roche Holding
DuPont	Sanofi
Eastman Chemical	Syngenta
Eli Lilly	Teva

HISTORICAL FINANCIALS

Company Type: Public

Income Statement

FYE: December 31

	REVENUE ($ mil.)	NET INCOME ($ mil.)	NET PROFIT MARGIN	EMPLOYEES
12/15	50,456	4,476	8.9%	116,800
12/14	51,341	4,164	8.1%	118,888
12/13	55,285	4,390	7.9%	113,200
12/12	52,405	3,223	6.2%	110,500
12/11	47,247	3,194	6.8%	111,800
Annual Growth	**1.7%**	**8.8%**	**—**	**1.1%**

2015 Year-End Financials

Debt ratio: 5.0%
Return on equity: 18.5%
Cash ($ mil.): 2,024
Current ratio: 1.40
Long-term debt ($ mil.): —

No. of shares (mil.): 826
Dividends
  Yield: 1.4%
  Payout: 32.3%
Market value ($ mil.): 103,232

	STOCK PRICE ($) FY Close	P/E High/Low		PER SHARE ($) Earnings	Dividends	Book Value
12/15	124.84	32	24	5.41	1.79	31.96
12/14	136.84	35	27	5.03	2.11	29.55
12/13	142.00	37	25	5.31	1.80	34.49
12/12	95.92	32	22	3.90	1.56	29.44
12/11	63.80	25	16	3.87	1.42	30.05
Annual Growth	**18.3%**	**—**	**—**	**8.8%**	**6.0%**	**1.6%**

Bayer Motoren WK

Auditors: KPMG AG Wirtschaftsprüfungsgesellschaft

LOCATIONS

HQ: Bayer Motoren WK
Petuelring 130, Munchen 80788
Phone: (49) 89 382 24544   **Fax:** (49) 89 382 24418
Web: www.bmwgroup.com

HISTORICAL FINANCIALS

Company Type: Public

Income Statement

FYE: December 31

	REVENUE ($ mil.)	NET INCOME ($ mil.)	NET PROFIT MARGIN	EMPLOYEES
12/15	100,398	6,937	6.9%	122,244
12/14	97,727	7,047	7.2%	116,324
12/13	104,711	7,315	7.0%	110,351
12/12	101,289	6,702	6.6%	105,876
Annual Growth	**(0.3%)**	**1.2%**	**—**	**4.9%**

2015 Year-End Financials

Debt ratio: —
Return on equity: 15.9%
Cash ($ mil.): 6,668
Current ratio: 0.94
Long-term debt ($ mil.): —

No. of shares (mil.): 602
Dividends
  Yield: —
  Payout: —
Market value ($ mil.): —

	STOCK PRICE ($) FY Close	P/E High/Low		PER SHARE ($) Earnings	Dividends	Book Value
12/15	0.00	—	—	10.57	0.00	76.95
Annual Growth	**—**	**—**		**—**	**—**	**—**

Bayerische Landesbank (Germany)

Bayerische Landesbank (BayernLB) acts as the principal bank to the state of Bavaria as well as the central clearing house for the more than 70 Bavarian sparkassen (savings banks). Also serving corporations national and local governments financial institutions and real estate firms the bank offers a variety of services including financing security underwriting and trading and risk management. Its Internet bank Deutsche Kreditbank (DKB) provides retail and private banking services to more than three million customers in Germany and also targets infrastructure customers in eastern Europe. Tracing its roots back to 1884 BayernLB is jointly owned by the State of Bavaria (75%) and the Association of Bavarian Savings Banks (25%).

OperationsBayernLB operates four core businesses: Corporates and Mittlestand (mid-market companies) which also offers structured and trade finance services; Real Estate & Savings Banks/Association which serves commercial real estate customers and provides a variety of tailored services to its network of savings banks (which partly own BayernLB) including payment services as well as assistance on investment securities and cross-border transactions; online bank Deutsche Kreditbank (DKB); and Financial Markets which offers asset management capital market treasury group treasury products and financial institution-based products and services. Broadly speaking the bank generated 86% of its total revenue from interest income (mostly from credit and money market transactions but also in hedge accounting and economic hedge derivatives) during 2014 while another 8% came from commission income. The rest of its revenue came from gains on financial investments (5%) and other income (1%).

Geographic Reach

Munich-based BayernLB has offices in Germany (Nuremberg Dusseldorf and DKB Berlin) Europe (London Milan Paris and representative office in Moscow) and America (New York).

Sales and MarketingThe bank serves retail and affluent individuals as well as corporations national and local governments financial institutions and real estate firms. In late 2014 the company said its average business relationship with large corporate customers has lasted 17 years. It also said that 28 out of the 30 DAX-listed companies are its customers.

Financial Performance

Note: Growth rates may differ after conversion to US dollars. This analysis uses financials from the company's annual report. BayernLB has struggled to grow its annual revenue over the past several years as interest margins on its loans have been shrinking. The bank's revenue fell 5% to euro 8.3 billion ($10.1 billion) during 2014 due to lower interest income in the low-interest environment and a decline in fair value measurements which were spawned as a result. The bank suffered a euro 1.3 billion ($1.58 billion) loss in 2014 mostly as it took heavy losses on its sale of MKB Bank to the Hungarian Government. Not counting this item BayernLB's profit operations used euro 366 million ($444.87 million) in cash mostly due to its operating losses during the year.

Strategy

BayernLB has been working on cutting its cost base and optimizing its efficiency ever since it hashed out a restructuring plan with the European Commission and launched its KSP cost-cutting programme in 2013. Stating that 2014 would "go down in Bayern LB's history as the year we put the legacy problems from the financial markets behind us" the bank focused on implementing the cost-cutting KSP program in the first half of 2014 and switched to strengthening and increasing its sales activities through long-term full-service customer relationships in the second half of the year. Toward its long-term profitability the bank hopes to leverage its wide variety of services to cross-sell and upsell to its existing customers. It also looks to digitize its sales channels to cut operating costs.As part of its restructuring BayernLB in 2014 sold its Hungarian subsidiary MKB Bank Zrt Budapest (MKB) and its ABS portfolio to strengthen its risk profile. It also sold its 44% stake in Landesbank Saar Saarbrucken (SaarLB).

Ownership

BayernLB is jointly owned by the State of Bavaria (75%) and the Association of Bavarian Savings Banks.

HISTORY

Company BackgroundBayerische Landesbank Girozentrale (the Bavarian regional bank clearinghouse) was formed by the government in 1972 from the merger of Bayerische Landesbodenkreditanstalt (the state authority for funding projects in Bavaria formed 1884) and Bayerische Gemeindebank (Girozentrale) Öffentliche Bankanstalt (the central institution for local public authorities established 1914).

Amid the oil crisis of the 1970s the bank known as BayernLB joined with Commerzbank Dresdner Bank and other West German banks in a consortium to buy from Deutsche Bank a 25% stake in Daimler-Benz; then-Chancellor Helmut Schmidt

wished to keep the automaker out of Iranian hands.

BayernLB began expanding outside Germany in the late 1970s; it opened an office in New York City by 1981. Three years later the bank joined with Westdeutsche Landesbank Commerzbank Deutsche Bank and Dresdner Bank to create the venture capital firm Deutsche Wagnisfinanzierung.

During the mid-1980s talk of merging West Germany's fragmented system of 11 Landesbanken and savings banks (a byproduct of post-WWII banking reforms) led BayernLB and Landesbank Stuttgart to consider merging to form a southern Landesbank. However by 1989 the bank had rallied against plans by the centralized Deutscher Sparkassen- und Giroverband to consolidate the operations of the various Landesbanken. That year it held indecisive merger talks with Landesbank Rheinland-Palatine.

Later the bank eschewed mergers and began looking eastward. In 1991 it acquired Czech bank Interbanka. BayernLB first sought out the Hungarian privatization authority in 1992 and by 1994 BayernLB purchased a one-quarter stake in the then-privatizing Hungarian Foreign Trade Bank (MKB; 75%-owned by 1999). The bank also looked to Asia opening an offshore banking branch in Malaysia in 1995. The bank gained assets closer to home by taking a 31% stake in the Austrian Bank für Arbeit und Wirtschaft (Bawag; increased to nearly half by 1999).

BayernLB opened another offshore branch in Thailand in 1996 but two years later began to see negative consequences to its expansion in the East when the Asian currency crisis hit walloping the bank's normally stellar credit rating.

In 2000 the European Commission said it would take action against the German government over the role of the Landesbanken claiming a breach of antitrust laws. The legal threat laid the groundwork for strategic cooperation —and even talks of a merger —between BayernLB and Landesbank Hessen-Thüringen. Bavaria's government also pressured BayernLB raiding the bank in search of evidence related to alleged embezzlement in Singapore.

In 2001 BayernLB after much European Union antitrust scrutiny announced a partial privatization plan. The next year BayernLB changed its legal name from Bayerische Landesbank Girozentrale to simply Bayerische Landesbank.

When the global economy fell into crisis in 2008 BayernLB was the first German bank to take money from the country's bailout program. It received euro 4.5 billion ($6.9 billion) from the German government's euro 80 billion rescue fund and raised another euro 1 billion from two state-backed shareholders. The bank which has branches in Asia North America and other parts of Europe to complement its offices in Germany restructured in order to focus on its core European markets and cut approximately 30% of its workforce.

Gerd Häusler was named BayernLB's CEO in 2010. He succeeded Stefan Ermisch who served on an interim basis for four months following the resignation of Michael Kemmer. Häusler was most recently a manager and board member of financial investment firm RHJ International.

Michael Kemmer resigned after the company announced it would write off its investment in Austria's Hypo Alpe-Adria-Bank which was nationalized in late 2009 to prevent collapse. BayernLB had acquired a majority stake in the bank in 2007 as part of an ill-timed international expansion of its retail banking operations.

In 2010 the bank sold its 75%-owned Landesbank Saar subsidiary which operated in the German state of Saarland and in France. That year BayernLB also ended merger talks with WestLB an-

other central bank in recovery. The combined entity would've become Germany's third-largest bank. However BayernLB's management didn't find that deal presented good enough advantages.

EXECUTIVES

CEO, Gerd H ¤usler, age 65
COO and CFO, Stephan Winkelmeier, age 48
Member Board of Management Head Corporate & Mittelstand, Michael B cker, age 54
Chief Risk Officer, Marcus Kramer, age 52
Deputy CEO, Edgar Zoller, age 59
Member Management Board Markets, Nils Niermann, age 47
Chairman, Michael Schneider
Deputy Chairman, Walter Strohmaier

LOCATIONS

HQ: Bayerische Landesbank (Germany)
Brienner Strasse 18, Munich D-80333
Phone: (49) 89 21 71 01   **Fax:** (49) 89 21 71 2 35 79
Web: www.bayernlb.de

PRODUCTS/OPERATIONS

2015

	Revenue %
Interest income	86
Commission income	8
Gains or losses on financial investments	5
Other income	1
Total	**100**

Selected Subsidiaries

Banque LBLux S.A. (Luxembourg)
BayTech Venture Capital Beratungs GmbH
Bayern Consult Unternehmensberatung GmbH
Bayernimmo KG
BayernLB Private Equity
BayernInvest Luxembourg S.A.
Deutsche Kreditbank AG

COMPETITORS

Aareal Bank	Landesbank Berlin
Commerzbank	UniCredit Bank AG
DZ BANK	WGZ BANK
Deutsche Bank	WestLB
Deutsche Postbank	Wstenrot &
KfW	Wrttembergische
Landesbank Baden-Wrttemberg	

HISTORICAL FINANCIALS

Company Type: Public

Income Statement

FYE: December 31

	ASSETS ($ mil.)	NET INCOME ($ mil.)	INCOME AS % OF ASSETS	EMPLOYEES
12/15	234,954	531	0.2%	7,082
12/14	282,147	(1,604)	—	6,842
12/13	351,894	165	0.0%	8,568
12/12	378,046	1,004	0.3%	9,932
12/11	399,862	134	0.0%	10,893
Annual Growth	(12.4%)	41.0%	—	(10.2%)

2015 Year-End Financials

Return on assets: 0.2%	Dividends
Return on equity: 4.2%	Yield: —
Long-term debt ($ mil.): —	Payout: —
No. of shares (mil.): —	Market value ($ mil.): —
Sales ($ mil): 8,064	

Bayerische Motoren Werke AG

Bayerische Motoren Werke better known as BMW is among the top 10 automakers in the world. It manufactures premium brand cars and off-road vehicles under the BMW MINI and Rolls-Royce names as well as motorcycles under the BMW and Husqvarna names. Spare parts and accessories are also offered. Its vehicles and products are sold worldwide through company branches independent dealers subsidiaries and importers. BMW's financial services segment offers car leasing and credit financing for both retail and corporate fleet customers; dealer financing; insurance; and deposit banking.

Geographic Reach

BMW operates in more than 140 countries and operates 30 production and assembly facilities in 14 countries. It generates about half of its revenue in Europe while the remainder is well dispersed among the Americas (mainly the US) China and other parts of the world.

Operations

To support global markets BMW has 30 production facilities in 14 countries. It also has about 12 R&D centers in Austria Germany the US Japan and China. Some assembly is undertaken with external partners in emerging markets including India Malaysia Thailand and Russia.

Sales and Marketing

The company has a global sales network that spans more than 140 countries. BMW and MINI brand products are sold in Germany through the company's own branches and independent authorized dealers. Sales outside of Germany are carried out mainly by subsidiaries and in certain markets by independent importers. Rolls-Royce brand vehicles are sold in the US by a subsidiary and elsewhere by dealers. At year end 2014 BMW's car sales network was made up of 3250 BMW 1550 MINI and 130 Rolls-Royce dealerships cover 650 locations worldwide.

Financial Performance

(Note: growth rates differ after conversion to US dollar.) BMW in 2014 experienced a 6% rise in sales primarily by the continued upward trend in sales volumes across all segments. It also experienced an uptick in external revenues from the sale of BMW MINI and Rolls-Royce brand cars. Revenue from its Automotive segment grew by 6% Motorcycles by 12% and Financial Services by 4%.

In addition to revenue growth BMW posted a surge in profits from 2013 to 2014 due to the revenue increase coupled with improvement from other operating income and expenses. Its operating cash flow however decreased during 2014 primarily due to higher cash outflows for taxes.

Strategy

BMW is in the midst of what it call its Number ONE strategy an initiative begun in 2007 that continues today to boost profitability and enable expansion of its global production and sales networks. From 2007 to 2014 the company expanded from 23 production facilities to 30. More recent manufacturing plants have been opened in China through its BMW Brilliance joint venture with Brilliance China Automotive. BMW's goal is to sell more than 2 million BMW MINI and Rolls-Royce vehicles by 2016 —up from the 2.1 million cars it sold in fiscal 2014.

From an environmental perspective BMW's strategy is to invest in and develop technologies that support making its vehicle fleet more fuel efficient and reducing carbon dioxide emissions by 25% between 2008 and 2020. To this end it is increasing R&D expenditures in part to support continued development of a new fuel efficient engine family called Efficient Dynamics and improvement of a hybrid technology called ActiveHybrid. New vehicle models like the pure electric BMWi family were launched in late 2013.

In other areas of its business BMW is dealing with contracting motorcycle markets worldwide and is therefore changing strategic course. In early 2013 it sold its Husqvarna motorcycle business to Austrian company Pierer Industrie AG in order

HISTORY

Company Background

BMW's logo speaks to its origin: a propeller in blue and white the colors of Bavaria. In 1913 Karl Rapp opened an aircraft-engine design shop near Munich. He named it Bayerische Motoren Werke (BMW) in 1917. The end of WWI brought German aircraft production to a halt and BMW shifted to making railway brakes until the 1930s. BMW debuted its first motorcycle the R32 in 1923 and the company began making automobiles in 1928 after buying small-car company Fahrzeugwerke Eisenach.

In 1933 BMW launched a line of larger cars. The company built aircraft engines for Hitler's Luftwaffe in the 1930s and stopped all auto and motorcycle production in 1941. BMW chief Josef Popp resisted and was ousted. Under the Nazis the company operated in occupied countries built rockets and developed the world's first production jet engine.

With its factories dismantled after WWII BMW survived by making kitchen and garden equipment. In 1948 it introduced a one-cylinder motorcycle which sold well as cheap transportation in postwar Germany. BMW autos in the 1950s were large and expensive and sold poorly. When motorcycle sales dropped the company escaped demise in the mid-1950s by launching the Isetta a seven-foot three-wheeled "bubble car."

In the 1970s BMW's European exports soared and the company set up a distribution subsidiary in the US. The company also produced larger cars that put BMW on par with Mercedes-Benz.

EXECUTIVES

Member Management Board Production, Norbert Reithofer, age 61, $840,000 total compensation
Member Management Board Sales and Marketing, Ian Robertson, age 59, $420,000 total compensation
Member Management Board Production, Harald Kr ger, age 52, $420,000 total compensation
Member Management Board Purchasing and Supplier Network, Klaus Draeger, age 61, $430,000 total compensation
Member Management Board Development, Herbert Diess, age 59, $420,000 total compensation
CEO ReachNow, Steve Banfield
Board of Management Member Finance, Nicolas Peter
Deputy Chairman Supervisory Board, Manfred Schoch
Chairman Supervisory Board, Joachim Milberg, age 73
Deputy Chairman Supervisory Board, Karl-Ludwig Kley, age 65
Deputy Chairman Supervisory Board, Stefan Quandt
Deputy Chairman Supervisory Board, Stefan Schmid
Auditors: KPMG AG

LOCATIONS

HQ: Bayerische Motoren Werke AG
  Petuelring 130, Munich 80788
Phone: (49) 89 3 82 0   **Fax:** (49) 89 3895 5858
Web: www.bmwgroup.com

2014 Sales

	% of total
Europe	
Germany	16
Rest of Europe	30
Americas	
US	17
Rest of Americas	4
Asia	
China	19
Other	14
Total	**100**

PRODUCTS/OPERATIONS

Selected Products
Automobiles
  BMW
  1 Series
  3-door
  5-door
  Convertible
  Coupe
  3 Series
  Convertible
  Coupe
  Sedan
  Touring
  5 Series
  Gran Turismo
  Sedan
  Touring
  6 Series
  Convertible
  Coupe
  Gran Coupe
  7 Series
  Sedan
  X3 X5 X6 sports utility vehicles
  M Models
  M3 Convertible
  M3 Coupe
  M3 Sedan
  M6 Convertible
  M6 Coupe
  Z4
  Coupe
  Roadster
  MINI
  John Cooper Works (Hardtop Convertible Clubman)
  MINI Cooper
  MINI Cooper Clubman
  MINI Cooper Convertible
  MINI Cooper S
  MINI Cooper S Clubman
  MINI Cooper S Convertible
  Rolls-Royce
  Ghost
  Phantom
  Phantom Coupe
Motorcycles
  BMW

2014 Sales

	% of total
Automobiles	93
Financial services	26
Motorcycles	2
Elimination	(21)
Total	**100**

COMPETITORS

Daimler	Mitsubishi Motors
Ducati	Nissan
FCA US	Porsche
Fiat Chrysler	Renault
Ford Motor	Suzuki Motor
General Motors	Toyota
Harley-Davidson	Ultra Motorcycle
Honda	Volkswagen

Kawasaki Heavy Industries
Mazda
Yamaha
Yamaha Motor

HISTORICAL FINANCIALS

Company Type: Public

Income Statement

FYE: December 31

	REVENUE ($ mil.)	NET INCOME ($ mil.)	NET PROFIT MARGIN	EMPLOYEES
12/15	100,398	6,937	6.9%	122,244
12/14	97,727	7,047	7.2%	116,324
12/13	104,711	7,315	7.0%	110,351
12/12	101,289	6,716	6.6%	105,876
12/11	89,016	6,313	7.1%	100,306
Annual Growth	3.1%	2.4%	—	5.1%

2015 Year-End Financials

Debt ratio: 58.0%
Return on equity: 15.9%
Cash ($ mil.): 6,668
Current ratio: 0.94
Long-term debt ($ mil.): 53,941

No. of shares (mil.): 602
Dividends
  Yield: —
  Payout: —
Market value ($ mil.): —

BAYWA Bayerische Warenvermittlung Landwirtschaftlicher Genossenschaften AG

BayWa's roots are in Bavarian farming but its interests are branching out. BayWa (pronounced bay-vah) is divided into several business units: agricultural (grain and oil fruit trading fertilizers insecticides feed seed fresh fruit production) agricultural equipment (farm machinery tools) building materials (building components and equipment) renewable energy products and services (wind solar) and energy (gas stations heating oil lubricants mineral oils). BayWa sold its do-it-yourself (DIY) and garden centers business in 2011. The company was founded as Bavarian Trading Co. in 1923 when it split from the Bavarian Savings & Loan.

BayWa sold its chain of 56 DIY and garden centers to Semer Beteiligungs-gesellschaft for euro 28 million ($39 million) to form a new company. Semer which initially holds a 50% stake in the new business will gradually raise its stake to 100%. BayWa continues to own the property on which the stores sit and leases it to the new company. BayWa cited intense competition in the DIY store business and the lack of critical mass as reasons for exiting the DIY business. Previously BayWa in mid-2010 sold a 75% stake in Frisch & Frost its Austria-based food producing subsidiary. The business was bought by food retailer Lamb Weston/Meijer. BayWa retained the remaining 25% stake.

BayWa's agricultural segment generates some 44% of its total revenues however tough economic times in Europe have put a damper on demand in recent years. The company's agricultural segment revenues increased by some 7% in 2010 compared to 2009. Higher prices for agricultural produce supplemented the increase in revenues with fertilizers and feedstuff increasing year-over-year by

around 15% in 2010. The company's fruit business gained close to 25% in 2010.

Revenues from the company's energy and construction businesses benefited from the economic stimulus programs and residential recovery programs. The energy segment which accounted for around 30% of revenues in 2010 was caused due in part to higher prices for heating oil and carburetor fuel. Its traditional energy and renewable businesses commanded revenue growth as well. In 2011 BayWa acquired a 70% stake in wind power developer WKN USA a subsidiary of WKN AG enabling its development of renewable energies and expanding its global presence. The company purchased a 95% stake in Schradenbiogas a Germany-based operator of biogas plants for euro 6 million in 2010. The construction segment which accounted for some 24% of revenues in 2010 was helped by BayWa's acquisition of German building materials and supplier Brands + Schnitzler for euro 20 million.

Both German and Austria were solid contributors to the company's growth accounting for roughly 92% of revenues.

HISTORY

BayWa was founded in 1923 when the Bavarian Trading Company separated from the Bavarian Savings & Loan Bank amid the hyperinflation that swept Germany in the 1920s.

Despite the economic turmoil of the 1920s and 1930s the co-operative established itself helping Bavarian farmers cope with rampant inflation. During WWII and thereafter BayWa helped stabilize the Bavarian economy by catering to the agricultural sector.

As part of Germany's postwar economic miracle BayWa innovated in tractor and combine manufacturing. The company also diversified into construction materials the house and garden markets and mineral oils.

In the 1970s BayWa opened its first retail stores followed by gas stations and heating oil depots. In 1972 the original name of Bayerischewarenhandelsgesellschaft was shortened to BayWa.

After German reunification in 1990 BayWa expanded in the East. Former East German companies looked for partners willing to transfer technology.

Spurred by regional and international competition in the 1990s BayWa expanded abroad starting in neighboring Austria.

EXECUTIVES

Management Board MemberBayWa Agri Services, Roland Schuler, age 60
Chairman Board of Management and CEO, Klaus J. Lutz, age 57
Deputy Chairman and Chairman General Works Council, Gunnar Metz
CFO, Andreas Helber
Member Board of Management renewable energy GmbH, Matthias Taft, age 49
Member Board of Management RWA Raiffeisen Ware Austria AG, Reinhard Wolf, age 56
Auditors: Deloitte & Touche GmbH Wirtschaftspraefungsgesellschaft

LOCATIONS

HQ: BAYWA Bayerische Warenvermittlung Landwirtschaftlicher Genossenschaften AG Arabellastrasse 4, Munich D-81925
Phone: (49) 89 9222 3887   **Fax:** (49) 89 9212 3887
Web: www.baywa.de

2015 Sales

	% of total
Germany	43
Austria	15

Other	42
Total	**100**

2014 Sales

	% of total
Germany	46
Austria	16
Netherlands	13
Other	25
Total	**100**

PRODUCTS/OPERATIONS

2015 Sales

	% of total
Agriculture	68
Energy	22
Building materials	10
Other activities	-
Total	**100**

COMPETITORS

ADM	Italmobiliare
BASF SE	METRO AG
BP	Mitsubishi Corp.
Cargill	Monsanto Company
Chevron	Origin Enterprises
Deere	REWE
Dole Food	Royal Dutch Shell
Dow Chemical	SMA Solar Technology
DuPont	Saint-Gobain
Exxon Mobil	Toyota
Ford Motor	Vestas Wind Systems
Franz Haniel	Wal-Mart
General Motors	ZF Friedrichshafen
Hanson Limited	

HISTORICAL FINANCIALS

Company Type: Public

Income Statement

FYE: December 31

	REVENUE ($ mil.)	NET INCOME ($ mil.)	NET PROFIT MARGIN	EMPLOYEES
12/15	16,358	52	0.3%	16,229
12/14	18,431	85	0.5%	16,432
12/13	22,010	135	0.6%	16,834
12/12	13,939	127	0.9%	32,239
12/11	12,516	66	0.5%	32,425
Annual Growth	6.9%	(5.7%)	—	(15.9%)

2015 Year-End Financials

Debt ratio: 45.9%
Return on equity: 5.7%
Cash ($ mil.): 91
Current ratio: 1.35
Long-term debt ($ mil.): 1,336

No. of shares (mil.): 34
Dividends
  Yield: —
  Payout: —
Market value ($ mil.): —

BCE Inc

BCE is Canada's Biggest Communications Enterprise. The company (BCE stands for Bell Canada Enterprises) owns Bell Canada the incumbent provider of long-distance and local telephone access in Ontario and Quebec (together the provinces contain 61% of Canada's population with more than 9 million lines in service. It also provides broadband Internet access to about 3.3 million subscribers under the Bell Internet banner and digital video subscriptions to more than 2 million viewers via Bell TV. BCE's mobile holdings include wireless carrier Bell Mobility and subsidiary Virgin Mobile Canada (more that 7 million subscribers). It owns 44% of Bell Aliant which serves more than 2.5 million local phone and 840000+ broadband Internet customers in eastern Canada.

Operations

Bell Wireline which generates 46% of BCE's sales provides data including Internet access and TV local and long distance telephone and serves Bell's residential small and medium-sized business and enterprise customers in Ontario's and Quebec's metro areas.

Bell Wireless accounted for 28% of BCE's with its wireless voice and data communication products and services to Bell's residential small and medium-sized business and large enterprise customers across Canada.

Bell Aliant and Bell Media brought in 13% of BCE's revenue.

Financial Performance

BCE's revenue increased 4% in 2014 from 2014 on stronger performances at Bell Wireless and Bell Media up 7% and 15% respectively. Bell Wireless revenue slipped 1%.

BCE's revenue growth helped push profit higher by 14% for 2014. The increase in the net income was due to higher revenue and lower costs for severance and acquisitions and depreciation and amortization.

Strategy

In 2014 BCE launched CraveTV a service delivered via set-tops boxes to subscribers of Pay-TV channels. CraveTV offers viewers a range of television choices and BCE is devoting more resources to expand its distribution. An issue that might cut into future profit is higher rates for sports broadcasts as a new round of bidding opens.

BCE has grown through the use of acquisitions. In late 2014 BCE agreed to acquire Glentel a major seller of cell phones in Canada and the US for $586 million. The important deal would push BCE into the US where Glentel runs more than 700 stores under the Wireless Zone and Diamond Wireless names two of Verizon Communications' six national premium retailers.

BCE in 2013 put up $3 billion to acquire Montreal-based broadcaster Astral Media Canada's top pay TV provider. The deal expanded BCE's presence in Quebec's French-speaking market where BCE gained 20 TV channels including MusiquePlus and Super Ecran. Additionally Astral Media owns more than 80 radio stations in 50 markets and it is Canada's number three outdoor advertising company.

Mergers and Acquisitions

BCE offered to acquire Manitoba Telecom Services for $2.4 billion (C$3.1 billion). The deal which received approval from Canadian regulators in early 2017 would expand BCE's operations in the west of Canada adding around 49'0000 Manitoba Telecom subscribers. In OKing the combination regulators told BCE to sell some wireless spectrum some retail stores and about 24000 wireless subscribers to Xplornet. BCE had already agreed to sell about a third of Manitoba's customers to Telus Corp. BCE intends to invest in building out wireless and internet networks in Manitoba.

HISTORY

Early History

Alexander Graham Bell experimented with the telephone in his native Canada before moving to the US in the mid-1870s. His father sold his Canadian patent rights to National Bell Telephone which combined with Canada's Hamilton District Telegraph to form Bell Telephone Company of Canada. Known as Bell Canada it received a charter in 1880 and settled in Montreal. By 1882 it had 40 exchanges. AT&T owned 48% of the company in 1890 but by 1925 Canadians owned 95% of Bell Canada. (AT&T severed all ties in 1975.)

EXECUTIVES

Chief Brand Officer Bell Canada; President Bell Mobility, Wade Oosterman
President and CEO BCE and Bell Canada, George A. Cope, age 55, $900,000 total compensation
EVP and CFO, Siim A. Vanaselja, $526,667 total compensation
President The Source, Charles Brown
EVP and CIO, Michael Cole
President Bell Media, Mary Ann Turcke
President Bell Business Markets, Tom Little
EVP Customer Operations, John Watson
SVP and CTO Bell Mobility, Stephen Howe
EVP and Chief Legal and Regulatory Officer, Mirko Bibic
EVP Corporate Services, Bernard le Duc
Auditors: Deloitte LLP

LOCATIONS

HQ: BCE Inc
1 Carrefour Alexander-Graham-Bell, Verdun, Quebec
H3E 3B3
Phone: 514 786-8424   **Fax:** 514 766-8161
Web: www.bce.ca

PRODUCTS/OPERATIONS

2014 Sales

	% of total
Bell	
Bell Wireline	46
Bell Wireless	28
Bell Media	13
Bell Aliant	13
Total	**100**

2014 Sales

	% of total
Data	28
Wireless	27
Bell Aliant	13
Media	12
Local and access	11
Equipment and others	5
Lond distance	3
Inter-segment revenues	1
Total	**100**

COMPETITORS

Allstream	Shaw Communications
COGECO	Skype
Canada Payphone	Sprint Communications
Globalive	TELUS
HC2 Holdings	Vonage
Quebecor	Yak Communications
Rogers Communications	
Shaw Broadcast Services	

HISTORICAL FINANCIALS

Company Type: Public

Income Statement

FYE: December 31

	REVENUE ($ mil.)	NET INCOME ($ mil.)	NET PROFIT MARGIN	EMPLOYEES
12/15	15,489	1,818	11.7%	49,968
12/14	18,170	2,040	11.2%	57,234
12/13	19,184	1,857	9.7%	55,830
12/12	20,083	2,638	13.1%	55,500
12/11	19,112	2,177	11.4%	55,250
Annual Growth	**(5.1%)**	**(4.4%)**	**—**	**(2.5%)**

2015 Year-End Financials

Debt ratio: 30.4%	No. of shares (mil.): 865
Return on equity: 15.8%	Dividends
Cash ($ mil.): 441	Yield: 6.7%
Current ratio: 0.48	Payout: 87.2%
Long-term debt ($ mil.): 11,080	Market value ($ mil.): 33,430

	STOCK PRICE ($) FY Close	P/E High/Low	PER SHARE ($) Earnings	Dividends	Book Value
12/15	38.62	14 12	2.15	2.01	14.16
12/14	45.86	16 13	2.56	2.22	15.36
12/13	43.29	18 15	2.39	2.26	18.19
12/12	42.94	13 13	3.41	2.23	17.99
12/11	41.67	14 12	2.82	2.00	17.42
Annual Growth	**(1.9%)**	**— —**	**(6.6%)**	**0.0%**	**(5.0%)**

BDO Unibank Inc.

BDO could stand for "Big Darn Operation" but instead it's short for Banco de Oro Unibank the latest iteration of a merger that took place in 2007 between two Filipino entities Banco de Oro Universal Bank and Equitable PCI Bank. Since 1968 Banco de Oro has provided corporate commercial retail and investment banking services throughout the country. Established in 1938 Equitable PCI brings to the coupling its commercial banking small and middle market lending trust leasing and remittances expertise. Combined BDO operates a network of more than 680 branches and some 1200 ATMs in Metro Manila as well as the Luzon Mindanao and Visayas provinces.

BDO —the largest bank in the Philippines by assets —has utilized partnerships with other lenders to foster its own growth. In 2009 the company made a deal with GE Capital in which BDO acquired the local arm of GE Money Bank; GE Capital in turn took a 10% stake of BDO. Two years earlier the bank acquired the American Express Bank Philippines giving it the exclusive right to issue American Express credit cards in the Philippines.

SM Prime Holdings —one of the largest conglomerates in the Philippines with interests in shopping malls real estate development tourism entertainment and financial services —owns more than a third of BDO.

The firm strengthened its business franchise in 2008 with the consolidation of its wholly-owned subsidiaries thrift banks Equitable Savings Bank (ESB) and BDO Elite Savings Bank (BDO Elite) and investment house PCI Capital Corp. into BDO. The four-way merger optimizes BDO's capital structure and streamlines operations in the bank's network.

EXECUTIVES

President and Chief Executive, Nestor Tan
Director & Chairman, Teresita Sy
Auditors: Punongbayan & Araullo

LOCATIONS

HQ: BDO Unibank Inc.
BDO Corporate Center, 7899 Makati Avenue, Makati City 0726
Phone: (63) 2 840 7000
Web: www.bdo.com.ph

COMPETITORS

Bank of the Philippine Islands	Philippine National Bank
Citibank	
Metropolitan Bank and Trust	

HISTORICAL FINANCIALS

Company Type: Public

Income Statement

FYE: December 31

	ASSETS ($ mil.)	NET INCOME ($ mil.)	INCOME AS % OF ASSETS	EMPLOYEES
12/15	43,356	533	1.2%	28,217
12/14	41,665	509	1.2%	24,779
12/13	37,666	509	1.4%	23,227
12/12	30,343	348	1.1%	21,746
12/11	25,065	240	1.0%	0
Annual Growth	14.7%	22.1%	—	—

2015 Year-End Financials

Return on assets: 1.2%
Return on equity: 13.2%
Long-term debt ($ mil.): —
No. of shares (mil.): —
Sales ($ mil): 2,221

Dividends
Yield: 0.0%
Payout: 26.3%
Market value ($ mil.): —

	STOCK PRICE ($) FY Close	P/E High/Low		PER SHARE ($) Earnings	Dividends	Book Value
12/15	2.04	0	0	0.15	0.04	1.17
12/14	1.83	0	0	0.14	0.05	1.12
12/13	1.59	0	0	0.14	0.05	1.03
Annual Growth	13.4%	—	—	1.2%	(5.1%)	3.1%

Bertelsmann AG (Germany, Fed. Rep.)

A company so big it takes up space on the bookshelf the magazine stand and on television Bertelsmann is one of the world's leading media conglomerates. It owns RTL Group Europe's #1 TV broadcaster with more than 40 channels operating in a dozen countries and Penguin Random House the world's top trade book publisher. In addition to these two heavyweights it owns magazine publisher Gruner Jahr services unit Arvato BMG the music business as well as Bertelsmann Printing Group Education Group and Investments. Carl Bertelsmann founded the company in 1835.

Operations

One unique quality of Bertelsmann is that its divisions operate more like stand-alone businesses rather than being integrated with one another in a fashion similar to Time Warner or News Corporation. Within its home market of Germany Bertelsmann competes most directly with publisher Axel Springer and broadcaster ProSiebenSat.

While Bertelsmann is certainly one of the largest European media conglomerates it is also one of very few: while its TV and publishing businesses range across dozens of countries most of the company's nearest competitors restrict their activities to just one or two.

RTL brings in over a third of revenue Arvato around 30% and Penguin Random House 20%. A restructure took effect on 1 January 2016 that reformed the struggling Be Printers (alongside other interests) as Bertelsmann Printing Group and split out Corporate Investments as independently functioning Bertelsmann Education Group Bertelsmann Investments and BMG the music business. The four units together account for around 10% of revenue.

Geographic Reach

Bertelsmann operates in more than 50 countries worldwide and the core markets are Germany France and the UK as well as the US. Germany is the biggest market at over a third of revenue while the strongly-growing US makes some 22%. The company is looking to increase its presence in emerging markets notable India China and Brazil.

Financial Performance

Note: Growth rates may differ after conversion to US Dollars.

In 2015 revenue for the year grew 2% to euro 17.1 billion. Part of this growth was down to positive exchange rate effects but earnings also grew in Penguin Random House (by 12%) on the back of strength in the US and in television in Germany BMG and Relias Learning an online education resource.

The latter helped the group record a huge leap in sales from digital platforms: for RTL in particular digital revenue increased 72% to upwards of euro 500 million doubling its contribution to total revenue.

Be Printer the struggling print business reporting under the Bertelsmann Printing Group umbrella as of January 2016 continued on its downward trajectory in 2015. It shrank 25.5% on prior year as digital printing and shorter print runs for magazines eat into revenue.

Net income rose 27% on prior year to euro 538 million due largely to a lower charge from special items. In 2015 special items which included sales of various businesses including Be Printers Spain amounted to euro -190 million up on euro -620 million.

Cash flow from operating activities nudged up 7% to euro 1.6 billion on the back of higher overall net working capital.

Strategy

Bertelsmann's strategy rests on two key tenets of embracing the digital transformation and expanding into regions with the biggest growth opportunities. The company also divides its businesses into growth and declining businesses and allocates investment as appropriate. For instance the company recognizes that the printing industry is undergoing a structural downsizing and has thus sold Barcelona-based Rotocobrhi and Eurohueco to British firm Walstead Capital in 2015. Gruner + Jahr departed the Italian market amid poor prospects selling its 50% stake in its joint venture with Mondadori.

Bertelsmann Education Group was created as part of the restructuring that took place on 1 January 2016 and has been supported by the expansion and acquisition of a variety of online education platforms. These include the expanded Relias Learning business and the acquired Affero Lab Udacity HotChalk and Alliant International University.

A fragmentation of RTL's audience as digital drives a wider variety of choice risks eating into the company's advertising revenue. The company has responded by investing in online video advertising for instance in the purchase of student marketing startup Employour and by developing non-advertising revenue such as distribution revenue. RTL found success in the US and Europe with 'Deutschland 83'.

China India and Brazil are Bertelsmann's biggest targets for revenue growth. In China the company invested in a large number of startups in Brazil it bought aforementioned internet learning platform Affero Lab and in India the company invested in Saavn the country's biggest music streaming service.

Random House merged with Penguin Group in 2013 to create the world's biggest book publisher. The merger came about amid an intensification of competition from online retailers (Amazon in particular) and supermarkets and this disruption to the market brought by the adoption of e-books.

Mergers & Acquisitions

Bertelsmann makes a large number of acquisitions each year to adapt to shifting media currents but also has to be aware of antitrust laws given its leading market position in many lines of business. The company made a series of acquisitions in the online learning space including Relias Learning Udacity HotChalk and Alliant International University as well as Saavn.

At year-end G+J acquired the student marketing specialist Employour.

HISTORY

Carl Bertelsmann founded his publishing company C. Bertelsmann Verlag in Gütersloh Germany in 1835. The company primarily published hymnals and religious materials expanding into newspapers during the 1860s. Heinrich Mohn a fourth-generation descendant took over the company in 1921 and expanded its operations to include popular fiction which helped Bertelsmann expand to more than 400 employees by 1939.

During WWII the company published books and propaganda material for the German army but was closed by the Nazi government in 1944 as it was not considered important to the war effort. (The company had maintained for decades it was closed because it produced religious materials but contrary evidence was uncovered in 2000 by historians working at the behest of the company.) After WWII Mohn's son Reinhard (who had been captured by the Allies and interned in a Kansas POW camp) returned to Germany determined to rebuild the company.

Bertelsmann boosted book sales by launching book clubs in Germany during the 1950s and bought Germany's UFA (TV and film production) in 1964. It took a minority interest in publisher Gruner + Jahr in 1969 taking a controlling stake in 1973. In the US Bertelsmann bought 51% of Bantam Books in 1977 (and the rest in 1981) and Arista Records in 1979. In 1986 it took control of Doubleday Publishing and bought RCA Records (forming Bertelsmann Music Group the next year). Mohn transferred substantial non-voting shares in the company to the Bertelsmann Foundation (Bertelsmann Stiftung) in 1993.

The company teamed up with AOL in 1995 to form AOL Europe and with Luxembourg broadcaster CLT it launched CLT-Ufa in 1997. Bertelsmann acquired book publisher Random House the next year. The company also took a 50% stake in online bookseller barnesandnoble.com (retaining nearly 40% after an IPO in 1999). In addition Thomas Middelhoff became chairman and CEO in 1998. The next year Bertelsmann acquired some 85% of scientific publisher Springer Verlag. Also in 1999 Reinhard Mohn transferred his controlling shares in the company to Bertelsmann Verwaltungsgesellschaft a firm controlled by Bertelsmann executives and the Mohn family.

In 2000 Bertelsmann announced that it would sell its half-interest in AOL Europe back to AOL by mid-2002; it also spun off Lycos Europe (retaining 27% now about 20%). It later merged CLT-Ufa with Pearson TV to form RTL Group. (Bertelsmann got a 37% stake.) That year Bertelsmann bought online music retailer CDNOW and began negotiating a merger between BMG and EMI Group. (Those talks fell apart in 2001.) Late in 2000 the company formed an alliance with online music service Napster loaning the company startup cash and allowing it to use the BMG music catalog to develop a subscription-based service. (Bertelsmann later tried to acquire Napster but a bankruptcy court quashed the deal. Napster went out of business shortly after although its name was acquired by Roxio now Napster.)

Bertelsmann bought Groupe Bruxelles Lambert's 30% stake in RTL Group in 2001. As part of the deal Bruxelles gained a 25% stake in Bertelsmann —with the understanding that it would be able to float its interest to the public in four years. Bertelsmann combined RTL's Ufa Sports unit with French sports-rights company Jean-Claude Darmon in exchange for a 40% stake in the combined company now called Sportfive. Later that year it sold its stake in online music venture GetMusic to Universal Music Group. Also that year it bought Pearson's 22% stake in RTL Group.

The company's board fired Middelhoff in 2002 citing disagreements over the direction of the company. He was replaced by Gunter Thielen chairman of Bertelsmann's arvato business unit. The following year Bertelsmann sold its science publishing subsidiary BertelsmannSpringer. Music subsidiary BMG Entertainment merged with Sony Music in 2004 to create Sony BMG Music Entertainment a joint venture with Sony Corporation.

After a contentious few months in 2006 when Groupe Bruxelles Lambert almost forced an IPO of the notoriously private media firm the Mohn family bought out Lambert's interest in the company for $5.7 billion (leaving the Mohns with a 23% interest in Bertelsmann and the Bertelsmann Foundation owning the rest). Later that year the company sold BMG Music Publishing (which was not part of the BMG-Sony Music merger) to Universal Music Group for $2.1 billion.

Thielen stepped down as CEO of Bertelsmann at the beginning of 2008 and was replaced by Hartmut Ostrowski. Later that year Bertelsmann sold its stake in Sony BMG Music Entertainment to Sony for $1.2 billion in cash and stock. (The music business then changed its name to Sony Music Entertainment.)

EXECUTIVES

Chairman and CEO Random House Group UK, Gail Rebuck, age 64

EVP Bertelsmann US (BInc.), Rob Sorrentino

CFO, Elmar Heggen, age 48

Executive Vice President Regional Operations & Business Development CEE and Asia, Andreas Rudas, age 63

President & CEO Random House of Canada, R. Bradley (Brad) Martin

Chief Executive Officer Penguin Random House, Markus Dohle, age 47

CEO Bertelsmann China Corporate Center; Managing Director Bertelsmann Asia Investments, Annabelle Yu Long

EVP Financial Reporting and Accounting, Martin Rembde

President Corporate Development and New Business, Thomas Hesse

Co-CEO RTL Group, Guillaume de Posch

Co-CEO RTL Group, Anke Sch ¤ferkordt

CEO Gruner + Jahr, Julia J ¤kel

CEO Be Printers Prinovis, Bertram Stausberg

CEO Arvato AG, Achim Berg

Auditors: PricewaterhouseCoopers Aktiengesellschaft Wirtschaftpruefungsgesellschaft

LOCATIONS

HQ: Bertelsmann AG (Germany, Fed. Rep.)
Carl-Bertelsmann-Strasse 270, Guetersloh D-33311
Phone: (49) 5241 80 0   **Fax:** (49) 5241 80 66 13
Web: www.bertelsmann.com

2015 Sales

	% total
Germany	34
US	21
Other Europe	18
France	13
Other Countries	7
UK	7
Total	**0**

PRODUCTS/OPERATIONS

2015 Sales

	% total
RTL Group	35
Arvato	28
Penguin Random House	21
Gruner + Jahr	9
Be Printers	4
Corporate Investments	3
Total	**100**

Selected Operations

arvato
Be Printers
Gruner + Jahr
Penguin Random House
RTL Group

COMPETITORS

21st Century Fox	ITV
Amazon.com	Lagard¨ re
Axel Springer	NBCUniversal
Bauer Verlagsgruppe	ProSiebenSat
CANAL+	Time Warner
Cinram	Verlagsgruppe Georg
Disney	von Holtzbrinck
Hearst Corporation	Viacom

HISTORICAL FINANCIALS

Company Type: Public

Income Statement

FYE: December 31

	REVENUE ($ mil.)	NET INCOME ($ mil.)	NET PROFIT MARGIN	EMPLOYEES
12/15	18,984	737	3.9%	117,249
12/14	20,629	198	1.0%	112,037
12/13	22,830	685	3.0%	111,763
12/12	21,489	637	3.0%	104,286
12/11	20,038	601	3.0%	100,626
Annual Growth	(1.3%)	5.2%	—	3.9%

2015 Year-End Financials

Debt ratio: 19.3%
Return on equity: 9.6%
Cash ($ mil.): 1,426
Current ratio: 1.08
Long-term debt ($ mil.): 3,349

No. of shares (mil.): 0
Dividends
   Yield: —
   Payout: —
Market value ($ mil.): —

Bharat Petroleum Corp Ltd. (India)

Auditors: Haribhakti & Co. LLP

LOCATIONS

HQ: Bharat Petroleum Corp Ltd. (India)
Bharat Bhavan, 4 & 6 Currimbhoy Road, Ballard Estate, Mumbai 400 001
Phone: (91) 22 2271 3000   **Fax:** (91) 22 2271 3688
Web: www.bharatpetroleum.in

HISTORICAL FINANCIALS

Company Type: Public

Income Statement

FYE: March 31

	REVENUE ($ mil.)	NET INCOME ($ mil.)	NET PROFIT MARGIN	EMPLOYEES
03/15	39,127	768	2.0%	12,687
03/14	44,267	651	1.5%	13,214
03/13	44,894	346	0.8%	13,213
03/12	41,984	153	0.4%	13,429
03/11	34,835	366	1.1%	13,915
Annual Growth	2.9%	20.3%	—	(2.3%)

2015 Year-End Financials

Debt ratio: 0.3%
Return on equity: 22.8%
Cash ($ mil.): 551
Current ratio: 0.90
Long-term debt ($ mil.): 3,092

No. of shares (mil.): 723
Dividends
   Yield: —
   Payout: —
Market value ($ mil.): —

Bharti Airtel Ltd

Bharti Airtel is the biggest telecommunications provider in India with the most revenue and subscribers and among the top 10 global carriers. It generates most of its revenue from its mobile segment. Bharti Airtel which operates in South Asia and Africa as well as India also offers broadband telephone and digital television services. It has 240 million customers in India and 328 million overall.

Operations

Bharti Airtel's mobile business in India is its biggest revenue generator ringing up 52% of revenue. Its mobile operation in Africa accounts for 27% of revenue. The company's other businesses —mobile service in South Asia Airtel Business Telemedia tower services and Digital TV services — make up the other 21% of revenue.

Geographic Reach

Most of Bharti Airtel's business is in India where it has 240 million customers. It also has operations in Sri Lanka Bangladesh Burkina Faso Democratic Republic of Congo Kenya Malawi Mali Nigeria Rwanda Sierra Leone Tanzania and Zambia.

Financial Performance

Bharti Airtel revenue increased 7% in 2015 (ended March) from 2014. It posted higher sales of mobile services in India as well as in Telemedia Digital TV and Business. Revenue from mobile operations in Africa and South Asia fell off from 2014. Net income zoomed 87% higher in 2015.

Strategy

With its business in growing regions with young populations Bharti Airtel is positioned to benefit from the transition from fixed-line telecommunications to mobile. Even more the increasing use of data services in India and Africa bodes well for the company as customers use their phones and other wireless devices to do more.

In India Bharti Airtel is working across several segments to keep customers it has get new ones and provide more data services to encourage customers to consume more data. The company opened its online 1 Rupee Entertainment Store to attract new users of data. Users can download services such as music games videos and photos for one rupee. It previously opened Re 1 Entertainment store which offers content in bundles of songs videos pictures and services.

To make sure it has the capability to deliver services the company has bought additional spectrum that gives it 4-G coverage across India.

In Africa Bharti Airtel wants to engage in the market for banking via mobile devices. Its airtel Airtel money service allows customers to pay bills transfer money and conduct other transactions from their phones. The company has agreements with insurance companies banks utilities stores and government agencies to accept airtel money transactions. B

EXECUTIVES

Managing Director and CEO (India and South Asia), Gopal Vittal, age 50
CFO, Niljan Roy
CIO, Harmeen Mehta
CEO Global Voice and Data Business and Director, Ajay Chitkara
CEO DTH, Shashi Arora
CEO Retail, Vani Venkatesh
CEO DTH, Sunil Taldar
Chief Executive Airtel Kenya, Prasanta Das Sarma
Chairman, Sunil Bharti Mittal, age 56

LOCATIONS

HQ: Bharti Airtel Ltd
Bharti Crescent, 1, Nelson Mandela Road, Vasant Kunj, Phase ? II, New Delhi 110 070
Phone:
Web: www.airtel.com

2011 Sales

	% of total
India	95
Other countries	5
Total	**100**

PRODUCTS/OPERATIONS

2015 Sales

	% of total
Mobile services India	52
Mobile services Africa	27
Airtel Business	7
Tower Services	5
Telemedia services	4
Digital TV Services	3
Mobile Services South Asia	2
Total	**100**

COMPETITORS

Aditya Birla Management	RPG Enterprises
Bharat Sanchar Nigam	Reliance Communications
Cable & Wireless Communications	Sify Technologies
Idea Cellular	Tata Communications
Mahanagar Telephone Nigam	Tata Teleservices
	Vodafone India

HISTORICAL FINANCIALS

Company Type: Public

Income Statement

FYE: March 31

	REVENUE ($ mil.)	NET INCOME ($ mil.)	NET PROFIT MARGIN	EMPLOYEES
03/15	15,243	828	5.4%	0
03/14	14,559	461	3.2%	0
03/13	14,333	419	2.9%	0
03/12	14,105	837	5.9%	0
03/11	26,784	1,356	5.1%	0
Annual Growth	(13.1%)	(11.6%)	—	—

2015 Year-End Financials

Debt ratio: 0.5%	No. of shares (mil.): —
Return on equity: 8.5%	Dividends
Cash ($ mil.): 187	Yield: —
Current ratio: 0.42	Payout: —
Long-term debt ($ mil.): 7,517	Market value ($ mil.): —

BHP Billiton Ltd.

Two heads (or headquarters) are better than one. Aussie minerals and oil company BHP Limited acquired UK miner Billiton plc in 2001. The result: a two-headquartered dual-listed company run as a single entity with the same board of directors and management. The Melbourne side is BHP Billiton Limited the London side is BHP Billiton Plc; collectively they are known as BHP Billiton. One of the largest diversified natural resources companies it ranks among the world's top producers of iron ore and coal (thermal and metallurgical). Other products include aluminum copper manganese nickel silver uranium and potash. BHP also has crude oil and natural gas holdings.

Geographic Reach

The company has far-flung operations. In Canada's Saskatchewan province BHP produces potash a primary raw material used to manufacture fertilizers and a top priority for the global titans of mining. In Australia it operates a coal-producing joint venture with Mitsubishi that has mining projects in Australia. Its Australian minerals businesses include not only iron ore coal and potash but also copper and uranium. Its Chilean operations include a 58% stake in the Escondida mine one of the world's largest and lowest-cost copper producers. BHP's oil and gas operations are worldwide ranging from its Shenzi deepwater oil and gas field in the Gulf of Mexico to onshore natural gas production in Pakistan.

Operations

The group operates four businesses aligned with the commodities it extracts and markets:

The Petroleum and Potash business headquartered in Houston is engaged unconventional and non-conventional oil and gas operations and a potash project based in Saskatchewan Canada. Headquartered in Santiago Chile BHP's Copper business is one of the world's leading producers of copper concentrate and cathode uranium oxide and a producer of zinc concentrate. It's portfolio of mining operations includes the Escondida mine in Chile a leading producer of copper and Olympic Dam in South Australia a major producer of copper and uranium oxide. The company's Coal Business headquartered in Brisbane is the world's largest supplier of seaborne metallurgical coal a key input in steel production. It is also a large supplier of seaborne energy coal (thermal or steaming coal) and a domestic energy coal supplier in the countries where its mines are located. BHP's Iron Ore Business based in Perth Australia is one of the world's leading iron ore producers. It sells lump and fine products produced in Australia and produces pellets from its operations in Brazil.

Sales and Marketing

Due to its proximity to customers in Asia the primary hub for BHP's marketing activities is Singapore while marketing of oil and gas is based in Houston. In addition it has marketing teams located close to customers in nine cities around the world. Financial Performance 2014 BHP's fiscal revenues have been restated due to the company's 2015 spinoff of a selection of assets that included BHP's interests in its integrated aluminum business Energy Coal South Africa the Illawarra metallurgical coal the manganese business the Cerro Matoso nickel operation and the Cannington silver-lead-zinc mine. In fiscal 2015 the company's net sales decreased by 34% due to lower revenues across all businesses but mainly in the Iron Ore and Petroleum and Potash Businesses.

The slump in Iron Ore sales was primarily due to a 41% decline in the average realized price of iron ore which more than offset a 13% volume in-crease from its Western Australia Iron Ore operations as a result of continued improvement in the performance of integrated supply chain and the successful ramp-up of the Jimblebar mining hub. The decrease in Petroleum revenues was primarily driven by lower realized prices. In fiscal 2015 BHP's net income decreased by 86% due to a decline in revenues and loss from discontinued operations. The company's operating cash inflow decreased by 25% due to net loss and a change in working capital.

Strategy

BHP's strategy is to own and operate large long-life low-cost expandable upstream assets diversified by commodity geography and market. The company has created a diversified portfolio of tier one natural resources by investing in large high-quality low-cost assets. In addition to strategic acquisitions BHP seeks organic growth through investments in major projects for its segments. Its diversified portfolio of high-quality assets gives it resilience and flexibility to enhance value throughout the commodity cycle. In 2015 BHP spun off a selection of its aluminum coal manganese nickel and silver-lead-zinc assets to create an independent metals and mining company South32.

In late 2015 the Brazilian government demanded $5 billion in compensation from BHP and Vale over flooding from a dam collapse at joint venture Samarco's mine which resulted in one of the worst environmental disasters in Brazil's history.

HISTORY

Company Background

In 1883 Charles Rasp a boundary rider for the Mt. Gipps sheep station believed valuable ore lay in the Broken Hill outcrop in New South Wales Australia. He gathered a few young speculators and The Broken Hill Proprietary Company (BHP) was incorporated in 1885. BHP immediately found a massive lode of silver lead and zinc. None of the founders knew how to run a mine so they recruited US engineers William Patton and Herman Schlapp. From the beginning labor and management clashed. The founding directors set up the head office in Melbourne far from the mine and gambled with gold sovereigns in the boardroom. But the miners worked in dangerous conditions. An 1892 labor strike was the first of BHP's bitter strikes.

In 1902 the new general manager Guillaume Delprat invented a flotation process that recovered valuable metals from iron ore waste. Delprat also foresaw a future in steel although Australia had no steel industry. BHP commissioned the Newcastle steelworks in 1915 and soon became the country's largest steel producer. BHP's 1935 purchase of Australian Iron and Steel its only competitor gave it a virtual steel monopoly while high tariffs protected it from outside competition. Its exhausted Broken Hill mine was closed that year.

In the 1960s BHP got into oil when it partnered with Esso Standard the Australian subsidiary of Standard Oil of New Jersey for offshore exploration. In 1967 the partners found oil in the Bass Strait which soon supplied 70% of Australia's petroleum. In the 1960s and 1970s BHP began expanding its iron ore manganese and coal interests. Meanwhile public opposition mounted to BHP's market power and labor practices and in 1972 the government took steps to limit BHP's power removing some subsidies and tax breaks.

The weak steel market of the 1970s and 1980s caused BHP to lay off almost a third of its steelworkers in 1983 but with government intervention BHP radically improved its steel productivity. In 1984 BHP bought Utah International's mining assets from General Electric (including Chile's rich Escondida copper mine). In 1986 corporate raider Robert Holmes à Court took a run at BHP;

BHP decided to become an international mining company to prevent further raids. Its acquisitions in the late 1980s included ERG Inc. and Monsanto Oil (combined into BHP Americas) Aquila Steel and Pacific Refining in Hawaii.

A peace deal with Holmes à Court gave BHP about 37% of Foster's Brewing but in 1992 BHP took a $700 million write-down after Foster's stock declined. BHP also bought Arizona-based Magma Copper in 1996 but plunging world copper prices forced a $420 million write-down.

With new worries over Asia's economic troubles BHP soon was struggling. In 1997 BHP sold most of its stake in Foster's and three senior executives resigned. In 1998 the company unloaded Pacific Refining which was acquired by Tesoro Petroleum for about $275 million.

As BHP's woes continued CEO John Prescott resigned; Paul Anderson was recruited from Duke Energy to succeed Prescott. In 1999 D. R. Argus took over as chairman replacing Jeremy Ellis. In a restructuring move the company sold its engineering power insurance and information technology businesses in 1999 and 2000. BHP began to sell $2 billion worth of steel operations (including its long product unit OneSteel which was later renamed Arrium). In 2000 the company shortened its official name to BHP Limited.

BHP acquired Billiton in 2001 forming BHP Billiton Ltd. and BHP Billiton plc. The combined BHP Billiton had sales of almost $20 billion and a market capitalization approaching $30 billion. In addition BHP paid $436 million for Dia Met Minerals which owned 29% of Canada's only producing diamond mine Ekati.

Also in 2001 BHP Billiton and Alcoa combined their North American metals distribution businesses as joint venture Integris Metals (subsequently sold and integrated into Ryerson). In order to focus on its minerals and oil and gas operations in 2002 BHP Billiton spun off its steel business as BHP Steel (now called Bluescope Steel).

In 2005 BHP Billiton acquired metals and minerals company WMC Resources which had been the subject of much takeover speculation and the target of the Swiss mining heavyweight Xstrata (since renamed Glencore). Its offer of $7.3 billion surpassed Xstrata's and was accepted and endorsed by the WMC board which had turned down the two earlier proposals by Xstrata. The addition of WMC added significantly to BHP Billiton's copper nickel and uranium operations.

In 2008 BHP Billiton Mitsubishi Alliance (BMA) spent $2.4 billion to buy the Saraji East metallurgical coal project from New Hope Corporation. Each of BMA's owners paid $1.2 billion to New Hope for the project which lies adjacent to one of BMA's coal mines.

Though the global recession of 2008-2009 certainly pushed the company's fortunes down BHP Billiton experienced eyebrow-raising growth thanks in part to generally high commodity prices and the emerging Asian economies. China for example represented 20% of the company's total sales in 2007 doubling its share from just three years prior. The continent as a whole accounted for more than half of sales.

Due to the strong demand BHP Billiton increased production of iron ore coking coal and manganese. The shifting nature of the market though changed the company's highest-grossing segments. In 2009 high coal prices helped that business immensely while conversely the Base Metals business of copper lead zinc and precious metals mining suffered from low prices driving down the unit's revenues. On the petroleum side the company continued to acquire oil and gas exploration leases in the Gulf of Mexico.

Two failed deals by BHP Billiton occurred in 2010: a $39 billion takeover of Potash Corpora-

tion of Saskatchewan and a proposed joint venture with Rio Tinto Ltd. BHP Billiton's offer for Potash Corporation was first rejected by that company's board as inadequate and then by Canadian regulators who ruled the offer to be anticompetitive. After a $150 billion bid to buy Rio Tinto fell through due to the global economic meltdown the companies proposed a joint iron ore venture in Western Australia which also failed because of opposition from European regulatory authorities.

In 2010 BHP Billiton acquired Athabasca Potash Inc. (API) for about $320 million. API's projects are located in Saskatchewan close to BHP Billiton's own potash operations.

In 2011 BHP acquired Chesapeake Energy's Fayetteville shale gas holdings in Arkansas for $4.75 billion. That year it also acquired Petrohawk Energy another US-based gas producer with projects in the Eagle Ford and Haynesville shale plays for $15.1 billion. In 2012 natural gas prices began to plummet. Although the company defended the long-term growth outlook for the shale assets it did not rule out a possible writedown later that year for those investments.

Following the Petrohawk announcement in 2011 BHP acquired three subsidiaries of HWE Mining a company owned by Leighton Holdings for $735 million. The HWE Mining subsidiaries provide contract iron ore mining services in Western Australia to BHP and the acquisition allows the company to both own and operate the mines.

In 2012 it sold its 51% stake in the Chidliak diamond exploration project in Canada's Baffin Island to the project operator Peregrine Diamonds giving it full ownership. The sale follows BHP's review of its diamond businesses to determine whether they fit in its strategy. The company also owns an 80% stake in Canada's EKATI diamond mine which is still under review. The company could receive less than $500 million for the sale of the mine.

EXECUTIVES

CEO, Andrew Mackenzie
President Iron Ore, Jimmy Wilson
President Coal, Mike Henry
President Petroleum and Potash, Tim Cutt
President HSE Marketing and Technology, Dean Della Valle
President Copper, Daniel Malchuk
CFO, Peter Beaven
President Corporate Affairs, Tony Cudmore
Interim President Copper, Edgar Basto
President Human Resources, Mike Fraser
Chairman, Jacques A. (Jac) Nasser, age 67
Auditors: KPMG

LOCATIONS

HQ: BHP Billiton Ltd.
BHP Billiton Centre, Level 16, 171 Collins Street, Melbourne, Victoria 3000
Phone: (61) 3 9609 3333   **Fax:** (61) 3 9609 3015
Web: www.bhpbilliton.com

2015 Sales

	% of total
Asia Pacific	
China	36
Japan	11
South Korea	6
Australia	5
India	4
Rest of Asia	11
Europe	
United Kingdom	1
Rest of Europe	5
North America	17
South America	3
Rest of the world	1
Total	**100**

PRODUCTS/OPERATIONS

2015 Sales

	% of total
Iron ore	33
Petroleum and Potash	26
Copper	26
Coal	13
Group and unallocated items	2
Total	**100**

Selected Divisions

Coal
  Metallurgical
  Energy
Iron ore
Petroleum
  Crude oil
  Ethane
  LPG
  Natural gas
Base metals
  Copper
  Gold
  Lead
  Silver
  Zinc
Aluminum
  Alumina
  Aluminum
  Bauxite
Manganese
Stainless steel materials
  Cobalt
  Ferrochrome
  Nickel
Diamonds and specialty products
  Diamonds
  Potash
  Titanium minerals

COMPETITORS

Anglo American
ArcelorMittal
Arconic
BP
Chevron
Chinalco
Codelco
ConocoPhillips
Exxon Mobil
Fortescue Metals
Freeport-McMoRan
Koch Industries Inc.
Kumba Iron Ore
Marathon Oil
Newmont Mining
Nippon Steel & Sumitomo Metal Corporation
Norsk Hydro ASA
Repsol
Rio Tinto Limited
Royal Dutch Shell
TOTAL
Tata Europe
Teck
Vale

HISTORICAL FINANCIALS

Company Type: Public

Income Statement

FYE: June 30

	REVENUE ($ mil.)	NET INCOME ($ mil.)	NET PROFIT MARGIN	EMPLOYEES
06/16	30,912	(6,385)	—	26,827
06/15	44,636	1,910	4.3%	29,670
06/14	67,206	13,832	20.6%	47,044
06/13	65,968	10,876	16.5%	49,496
06/12	72,226	15,417	21.3%	46,370
Annual Growth	(19.1%)			(12.8%)

2016 Year-End Financials

Debt ratio: 30.6%
Return on equity: (-10.7%)
Cash ($ mil.): 10,319
Current ratio: 1.44
Long-term debt ($ mil.): 31,768

No. of shares (mil.): —
Dividends
Yield: 5.4%
Payout: —
Market value ($ mil.): —

	STOCK PRICE ($) FY Close	P/E High/Low	PER SHARE ($) Earnings	Dividends	Book Value
06/16	28.56	— —	(1.20)	1.56	10.20
06/15	40.71	205 116	0.36	2.48	12.17
06/14	68.45	28 22	2.59	2.36	14.87
06/13	57.66	39 28	2.04	2.28	13.28
06/12	65.30	33 21	2.88	2.20	12.38
Annual Growth	(18.7%)	— —	—	(8.2%)	(4.7%)

BHP Billiton Plc

BHP Billiton Plc is one half of a dual-listed mining giant. It is headquartered in London; the other part of the company BHP Billiton Limited is based in Australia. Although they maintain separate listings the companies are managed as a single entity and have the same management team and board of directors. One of the largest diversified natural resources companies it ranks among the world's top producers of iron ore and coal (thermal and metallurgical). Other products include aluminum copper manganese nickel silver uranium and potash. BHP also has crude oil and natural gas holdings. For detailed information on the company's operations and history refer to Hoover's BHP Billiton Limited profile.

HISTORY

After starting out on its own in 1860 Billiton was subsequently bought first by Royal Dutch Shell and then by Gencor only to end up on its own once again. In 1860 a group of Dutch shareholders formed Billiton NV. The company bought the rich tin deposits of Billiton island (now part of Indonesia) for which it was named. The business grew to include tin and lead smelting in the Netherlands. Billiton NV began mining bauxite in the 1940s but WWII caused a production slowdown.

While demand for petroleum products exploded in the 1950s and 1960s in 1970 the industry nosedived. Royal Dutch Shell (formed from the merger of Royal Dutch and Shell Transport and Trading) responded by diversifying buying Billiton NV which it renamed Billiton International. Shell had gotten its start in commodities in the 1880s selling Russian oil of the Rothschilds to the Far East. Royal Dutch formed in 1890 after buying the rights to drill for oil in the Dutch East Indies. The two companies merged in 1907.

The 1970 Billiton purchase helped Royal Dutch Shell make up for the 1970s oil shortage and rationing that had resulted from OPEC's crude oil price hikes. Slow worldwide economic growth a major recession and oil and chemicals overcapacity impacted the company in the late 1970s and early 1980s.

Royal Dutch Shell sold Billiton in 1994 to Gencor which had been formed in 1980 by the merger of General Mining and Finance Corporation and Union Corporation. General Mining began mining gold in South Africa in the 1890s and Gencor continued its predecessors' metals and manufacturing operations. Gencor however spent the early 1980s focused on manufacturing because it anticipated a

downturn in base metals. But the recession inflation and high interest rates stifled Gencor's success and the company became known as an unfocused conglomerate. In 1986 a newly appointed chairman separated Gencor's manufacturing and mining interests.

By 1989 Gencor had cut its staff and reorganized. That year it bought 31% of South Africa's Richards Bay aluminum smelter. Within two years Gencor had become a holding company with a primary interest in mining. In 1993 the firm unbundled its non-mining activities. With the end of apartheid in 1994 Gencor was able to expand abroad. Its purchase of Billiton catapulted its presence into 13 countries but in 1996 the metals market spiraled downward.

Billiton was spun off by Gencor in 1997. It took over all of Gencor's nonprecious metal interests including its aluminum titanium ferroalloy and coal assets. That year Billiton combined its nickel interests with QNI of Australia. Making good on its plan to buy new base metals assets Billiton entered a joint venture in 1998 to explore for lead and zinc with Ireland's Ennex. Billiton also sold its metals brokerage subsidiary to Metallgesellschaft AG (Germany).

In 1999 Billiton announced that it would invest in smaller companies with promising properties and limit its own in-house exploration operations. It entered joint ventures with PT Taraco Mining to explore for coal in Indonesia and with Comet Resources to develop the Ravensthorpe Nickel Project in Western Australia.

Billiton's offer for a 21% stake in the Gove bauxite-alumina project in Australia was bested by Alcan in 2000. The company agreed to pay Alcoa about $1.5 billion for its majority stake in the Worsley alumina refinery in Australia. With Anglo American and Glencore International (now Glencore Xstrata) it acquired a 50% stake in Colombia's Cerrejon Zona Norte coal mine for $384 million; it then bought Canadian mining company Rio Algom (copper molybdenum uranium and coal) for $1.2 billion.

In 2001 Billiton closed the purchase of Alcoa's share of the Worsley smelter. The same year Billiton agreed to be acquired by Aussie natural resources company BHP Ltd. to form a dual-listed entity —known collectively as BHP Billiton —consisting of BHP Billiton Limited (run from Melbourne) and BHP Billiton plc (run from London). The deal closed in June 2001.

EXECUTIVES

CEO, Andrew Mackenzie, $1,120,620 total compensation
President Copper, Peter Beaven
CFO, Graham Kerr
President Iron Ore, Jimmy Wilson
President Marketing & Technology, Mike Henry
President Production BHP Billiton Petroleum, Tim Cutt
President Aluminium Manganese & Nickel, Daniel Malchuk
President Coal, Dean Della Valle
President Aluminium Manganese & Nickel, Daniel MalchukBE
Auditors: KPMG LLP

LOCATIONS

HQ: BHP Billiton Plc
  Neathouse Place, Victoria, London SW1V 1BH
Phone: (44) 20 7802 4000   **Fax:** (44) 20 7802 4111
Web: www.bhpbilliton.com

2015 Sales

	% of total
Australia	5
United Kingdom	1

Rest of Europe	5
China	36
Japan	11
Rest of Asia	11
North America	17
South America	3
Southern Africa	-
Rest of world	1
India	4
South Korea	6
Total	**100**

PRODUCTS/OPERATIONS

2015 Sales

	% of total
Iron Ore	33
Petroleum and Potash	26
Copper	26
Coal	13
Group and unallocated items	2
Total	**100**

COMPETITORS

Anglo American	Norilsk Nickel
Arconic	Norsk Hydro ASA
BP	Rio Tinto plc
Chevron	Vale
Newmont Mining	

HISTORICAL FINANCIALS

Company Type: Public

Income Statement

FYE: June 30

	REVENUE ($ mil.)	NET INCOME ($ mil.)	NET PROFIT MARGIN	EMPLOYEES
06/16	30,912	(6,385)	—	26,827
06/15	44,636	1,910	4.3%	29,670
06/14	67,206	13,832	20.6%	47,044
06/13	65,968	10,876	16.5%	49,496
06/12	72,226	15,417	21.3%	46,370
Annual Growth	(19.1%)	—		(12.8%)

2016 Year-End Financials

Debt ratio: 30.6%
Return on equity: (-10.7%)
Cash ($ mil.): 10,319
Current ratio: 1.44
Long-term debt ($ mil.): 31,768

No. of shares (mil.): —
Dividends
Yield: 6.1%
Payout: —
Market value ($ mil.): —

	STOCK PRICE ($) FY Close	P/E High/Low	PER SHARE ($) Earnings	Dividends	Book Value
06/16	25.38	— —	(1.20)	1.56	10.20
06/15	39.56	198 110	0.36	2.48	12.17
06/14	65.23	26 19	2.59	2.36	14.87
06/13	51.27	35 25	2.04	2.28	13.28
06/12	57.19	28 18	2.88	2.20	12.38
Annual Growth	(18.4%)	— —	—	(8.2%)	(4.7%)

BNP Paribas (France)

One of Europe's largest banks BNP Paribas and its many subsidiaries specialize in retail banking corporate and investment banking and investment services across more than 75 countries mostly in Europe but also in North America Africa and Asia. BNP Paribas operates in Italy through BNL banca commerciale. The French banking giant also owns Belgium's BNP Paribas Fortis which operates more than 1000 branches in Europe and the US. In the western US the company owns BancWest (the parent of Bank of the West and First Hawaiian Bank). BNP Paribas earns over 75% of its revenue from customers in Europe (mainly in Belgium France Italy and Luxembourg).

Operations

BNP Paribas operates three core businesses: Retail Banking Investment Solutions (IS) and Corporate and Investment Banking (CIB). Retail banking operates more than 7000 branches in 49 countries and accounted for more than 60% of the bank's total revenue in 2014. The segment consists of its domestic retail banking operations in France Italy (BNL banca commerciale) Belgium and Luxembourg (BNP Paribas Fortis and BGL BNP Paribas) and its international retail banking operations which are outside the euro zone including the Europe Mediterranean and the US (including BancWest). The segment also operates the Personal Finance unit through BNP Paribas Personal Finance (PF) which is a consumer credit specialist and also holds a residential mortgage lending business (which it's winding down). The Corporate and Investment Banking segment (22% of revenue) includes its Advisory & Capital Markets (equities and equity derivatives fixed income and forex and corporate finance) and Corporate Banking (lending specialty financing as well as cash management and international trade services across Europe Asia Americas Middle East Africa) businesses.

BNP Paribas' Investment Solutions segment (17% of revenue) provides wealth management asset management securities services insurance and real estate services. Some of its subsidiaries include BNP Paribas Securities BNP Paribas Wealth Management and insurance firms BNP Paribas Cardif and Pinnacle Insurance (Cardif Pinnacle). Other holdings include private bank BNP Paribas Banque Privee consumer lender Cetelem online brokerage Consorsbank (formerly Cortal Consors) and BNP Paribas Asset Management.

Broadly speaking about 51% of the bank's net operating income came from interest income (mostly from loans) in 2014. Another 19% came from commission income. The rest of its net operating income came from non-recurring sources such as net gains on financial instruments available for sale financial assets and other activities.

Geographic Reach

While it caters to more than 75 countries the Paris-based bank focuses mainly on four domestic markets: Belgium France Italy and Luxembourg. Europe is the bank's largest market accounting for more than 75% of revenue in 2014. North America contributed about 10% while the Asia-Pacific and Africa region and other countries each contributed more than 5%.

Financial Performance

Note: Growth rates may differ after conversion to US dollars. This analysis uses financials from the company's annual report.

BNP Paribas has struggled to grow its revenue and profits over the past several years as the European economy has faced headwinds toward consistent growth.

The bank's revenues (net of operating expenses) rose 2% to euro 39.2 billion ($47.6 billion) in 2014 thanks mostly to a 4% increase in net interest income as loan business grew 7% during the year. An 8% rise in commission income and a 21% jump in net gains on available-for-sale financial assets and other financial assets not measured at fair value also helped buoy the bank's top-line growth. All of the segments grew with Retail Banking growing by 2% (driving most of the firm's overall growth) Investment solutions up 3.7% and Corporate and Investment Banking up 2.1%.

Despite revenue growth in 2014 BNP Paribas' net income plummeted 97% to euro 157 million ($190.8 million) mostly due to a euro 6 billion

($7.3 billion) settlement charge with US authorities related "to violations of certain US laws and regulations regarding economic sanctions against certain countries and related recordkeeping" according to BNP. The group's operating cash levels nearly doubled to euro 16.5 billion ($20 billion) in 2014 mostly thanks to a net increase in cash related to transactions with credit institutions.

Strategy

While retail banking has remained relatively strong BNP Paribas has seen declines in its corporate and investment banking unit due to poor market conditions and losses on sales of sovereign bond debt. As a result the bank is engaged in ongoing cost cutting and the implementation of 2014-2016 business development plan. The plan includes three fundamental programs: Simple & Efficient a reorganization and efficiency program now under way; the Asia Pacific plan intended to increase revenues at Corporate and Investment Banking and Investment Solutions; and Hello bank! aimed at developing the digital bank.

Using its Simple & Efficient plan (which began in 2013) as a blueprint BNP Paribas has taken a number of cost-cutting and growth initiative measures in recent years to boost profits amidst an increasingly regulated industry. Indeed by late 2015 BNP reported that its transformation costs (investments in efficiency improvements) of around euro 620 million had led to savings of more than euro 2.514 billion per year in costs about 84% of what it aimed to save annually by the end of 2016 (and beyond).

Since launching Hello bank! in 2013 and acquiring DAB Bank through its Consorbank subsidiary in late 2014 BNP Paribas has been moving toward digital banking channels that are quickly taking the industry by storm allowing the bank to slow expensive branch-expansion plans and cut operating costs significantly while giving customers faster access to banking services. In late 2015 in the German market for example the bank noted that between DAB Bank and Consorbank BNP Paribas was the country's 3rd-largest digital bank with some 1.5 million customers as well as the largest online broker in the country.

Mergers and Acquisitions

In November 2013 BNP acquired Belgium's 25% share in its local consumer-banking unit BNP Paribas Fortis for 3.25 billion euros ($4.37 billion) as the country works to cut public debt. It also acquired Poland's Bank BGZ from Rabobank Group in 2013.

HISTORY

Company BackgroundBNP Paribas Group's predecessor Banque Nationale de Paris (BNP) is the progeny of two state banks with parallel histories; each was set up to jump-start the economy after a revolution in 1848.

For a century Paris-based Comptoir National d'Escompte de Paris (CNEP) bounced between private and public status depending on government whim. It was the #3 bank in France from the late 19th century through the 1950s.

Banque National pour le Commerce et l'Industrie (BNCI) started in Alsace a region that was part of Germany from the Franco-Prussian War until WWI. BNCI served as an economic bridge between Germany and France which had to give the bank governmental resuscitation during the Depression. By the 1960s BNCI had passed CNEP in size.

French leader Charles de Gaulle expected banking to drive post-WWII reconstruction and in 1945 CNEP and BNCI were nationalized. In 1966 France's finance minister merged them and they became BNP. That year the company started an association with Dresdner Bank of Germany under

which the two still operate joint ventures primarily in Eastern Europe.

By 1993 privatization was again in vogue and BNP was cut loose by the government. It expanded outside France to ameliorate the influences of the French economy and government. Even before it was privatized BNP was involved in such politically charged actions as the bailout of OPEC money repository Banque Arabe and the extension of credit to Algeria's state oil company Sonatrach.

The privatized BNP looked overseas in the late 1990s. In 1997 alone it won the right to operate in New Zealand bought Laurentian Bank and Trust of the Bahamas took control of its joint venture with Egypt's Banque du Caire and opened a subsidiary in Brazil.

BNP bought failed Peregrine Investment's Chinese operations in 1998. That year the bank also expanded in Peru opened an office in Algeria opened a representative office in Uzbekistan set up an investment banking subsidiary in India and bought Australian stock brokerage operations from Prudential.

After a decade of globe-trotting BNP brought it on home in 1999 and set off a year of tumult in French banking. As France's other two large banks (Societe Generale and Paribas) made plans to merge BNP decided it would absorb both banks as a means to get a bigger chunk of the to-be-privatized Credit Lyonnais and to protect France from Euro-megabank penetration by creating the globe's largest bank.

Executives at Societe Generale (SG) had other ideas forming a cartel called "Action Against the BNP Raid." Meanwhile BNP tried to boost to controlling stakes its holdings in the two banks. (In Europe's cross-ownership tradition the target banks also owned part of BNP.) France's central bank tried unsuccessfully to negotiate a deal (the government supported the triumvirate merger). A war of words was played out in the media and finally shareholders had to vote on the proposals. In the end BNP won control of Paribas but not SG. As BNP prepared to integrate a reluctant Paribas into its operations regulators ordered BNP to relinquish its stake in SG. The newly merged company was dubbed BNP Paribas Group.

In 2000 BNP Paribas and Avis Group launched a fleet-management joint venture. BNP also bought 150 shopping centers from French retailer Carrefour and the 40% of merchant bank Cobepa that it didn't already own. In 2001 BNP Paribas took full control of US-based BancWest. The company bought United California Bank from UFJ Holdings (now part of Mitsubishi UFJ Financial Group) the following year.

The bank opened up a second "home market" when it bought Italy's Banca Nazionale del Lavoro (BNL) for $11 billion in 2006.

Two of the French bank's most transformative acquisitions included the deal to buy Italian bank Banca Nazionale del Lavoro in 2006 and the 75% purchase of Fortis Bank (which also included a 25% stake in Fortis Insurance). Both deals boosted BNP Paribas' retail banking business across Europe. Retail banking is now responsible for more than 60% of BNP Paribas' revenues.

In addition to the Fortis and BNL acquisitions BNP Paribas looked to grow in new markets. BNP Paribas acquired Sahara Bank in Libya and a 51% stake in UkrSibbank one of Ukraine's leading banks. In 2008 as the world's economies struggled to stay afloat the French government agreed to inject euro 10.5 billion ($14 billion) into the nation's top six banks including BNP Paribas. The government didn't receive shares in the banks it assisted; rather the capital injections were meant to help reenergize lending activities in France. A year after receiving the cash BNP Paribas announced plans to repay the government's aid.

In 2009 after a couple of false starts and a seven-month saga BNP Paribas acquired control of Fortis Banque (also known as Fortis Bank). Fortis' Dutch operations were excluded from the transaction. The deal further cemented BNP Paribas as a top European bank. Fortis Bank was nationalized in October 2008 to prevent its collapse and the takeover by BNP Paribas was delayed and revised to satisfy Fortis shareholders and other interested parties. Upon the closing of the deal BNP Paribas became the market leader in Belgium and Luxembourg. The Belgian government gained more than 10% of BNP Paribas in the transaction.

BNP Paribas complimented its 2009 acquisition of Fortis with the purchase of private bank Insinger de Beaufort.

In 2011 BNP Paribas continued its strategy of expanding in high growth markets and acquired a majority of South Africa's Cadiz Securities. BNP Paribas also owns Banque Internationale pour le Commerce et l'Industrie which is active in six African nations and a majority of Türk Ekonomi Bankasi in Turkey. BNP Paribas has been expanding in China Egypt Israel and Russia as well.

In 2012 the company sold the bulk of its controlling stake in real estate firm Klepierre to US mall owner Simon for some euro 1.5 billion (around $2 billion) to further raise its capital levels.

EXECUTIVES

Deputy COO, Michel Konczaty
Head of Group Development and Finance, Philippe Bordenave
Chairman and CEO BNP Paribas Fortis, Maxime (Max) Jadot, age 60
Deputy COO and Head International Financial Services, Jacques d'Estais, age 57
Deputy COO and Group General Manager North America; Head Corporate and Institutional Banking, Alain Papiasse, age 57
Head International Retail Banking, Stefaan Decraene, age 51
CEO and Director BNL, Andrea Munari, age 53
Chairman BNP Paribas' Group Management Board; Group Head BNP Paribas Germany, Lutz Diederichs
Head Asia-Pacific Region, ric Raynaud
CEO, Jean-Laurent Bonnafe
Head French Retail Banking, Marie-Claire Capobianco
Head Compliance, Eric Martin
Head Corporate and Investment Banking, Yann Gerardin
Head of Group Risk Management, Frank Roncey
Deputy COO and Head Domestic Markets, Thierry Laborde
CEO BNP Paribas Personal Finance, Laurent David
Head Personal Investors, Beatrice Cossa Dumurgier
Head Retail and SME Banking, Franciska Decuypere
General Management Large Clients, Thierry Var ̈ ne
CEO BNP Paribas Cardif, Renaud Dumora
CEO and Country Head Netherlands, Daniel Thielemans
Finance Director BNP Paribas Cardif Biztos t l Zrt., M ̈ rk Istv ̈ n Kiss
Chairman, Jean Lemierre, age 67
Auditors: Deloitte & Associés

LOCATIONS

HQ: BNP Paribas (France)
16, Boulevard des Italiens, Paris 75009
Phone: (33) 1 42 98 46 45   **Fax:** (33) 1 42 98 21 22
Web: www.invest.bnpparibas.com

2013 Revenue

	% of total
Europe	77
North America	10
Asia-Pacific & Africa	7
Other	6
Total	**100**

PRODUCTS/OPERATIONS

2013 Sales by Segment

	% of total
Retail banking	62
Corporate and investment banking	22
Investment solutions	16
Total	**100**

COMPETITORS

ABN AMRO Group	HSBC
BBVA	JPMorgan Chase
Banco Popular Espa±ol	Natixis
Bank of America	Societe Generale
Barclays	U.S. Bancorp
Citigroup	UBS
Credit Agricole	Wells Fargo
Deutsche Bank	

HISTORICAL FINANCIALS

Company Type: Public

Income Statement

FYE: December 31

	ASSETS ($ mil.)	NET INCOME ($ mil.)	INCOME AS % OF ASSETS	EMPLOYEES
12/15	2,172,096	7,291	0.3%	189,077
12/14	2,525,526	190	0.0%	187,903
12/13	2,478,315	6,652	0.3%	184,545
12/12	2,513,902	8,637	0.3%	188,551
12/11	2,541,999	7,825	0.3%	198,423
Annual Growth	**(3.9%)**	**(1.8%)**	**—**	**(1.2%)**

2015 Year-End Financials

Return on assets: 0.3%
Return on equity: 7.2%
Long-term debt ($ mil.): —
No. of shares (mil.): 1,244
Sales ($ mil) 111,240

Dividends
Yield: 2.9%
Payout: 14.2%
Market value ($ mil.): 35,177

	STOCK PRICE ($) FY Close	P/E High/Low		PER SHARE ($) Earnings	Dividends	Book Value
12/15	28.26	6	5	5.59	0.83	84.24
12/14	29.38	—	—	(0.09)	1.02	87.43
12/13	39.20	11	7	5.07	0.97	97.06
12/12	29.21	6	3	6.79	0.75	91.38
12/11	19.65	8	3	6.22	1.34	81.80
Annual Growth	**9.5%**			**(2.7%)**	**(11.4%)**	**0.7%**

Boc Hong Kong Holdings Ltd

BOC Hong Kong (Holdings) is the parent of Bank of China (Hong Kong) which has about 300 branches in Hong Kong as well as on mainland China. The bank serves local businesses and consumers providing loans deposit accounts and other standard services as well as securities brokerage wealth management and project financing and syndication. It also prints currency. In addition Bank of China (Hong Kong) owns Nanyang Commercial Bank and some 70% of Chiyu Banking Corporation (both are also based in Hong Kong) as well as BOC Credit Card (International). Bank of China which is controlled by the Chinese government owns about two-thirds of BOC Hong Kong.

Strategy

The company wants to diversify its revenue mix by focusing on increasing its business in wealth management insurance and corporate finance. It is looking to China for growth and has plans to expand to other parts of Asia as well.

In line with those efforts in 2016 parent company Bank of China which is restructuring its Southeast Asia operations agreed to sell Bank of China (Thai) and Bank of China (Malaysia) to BOC Hong Kong for HK$3.1 billion and HK$3.8 billion respectively.

EXECUTIVES

Vice Chairman and CEO, Yue Yi, age 59
CFO, Sui Yang, age 41
COO, Zhong Xiangqun
Deputy Chief Executive Corporate Banking Financial Institutions and Product Management Corporate Credit Management Centre and China Business, Lin Jingzhen, age 51
Deputy Chief Executive Personal Banking and Product Management Channel Management Private Banking and BOCCC, Kung Yeung (Ann) Yun Chi, age 53
Vice Chairman, Chen Siqing, age 55
Chairman, Guoli Tian, age 54
Auditors: Ernst & Young

LOCATIONS

HQ: Boc Hong Kong Holdings Ltd
52nd Floor, Bank of China Tower, 1 Garden Road,
Phone: (852) 2846 2700   **Fax:** (852) 2810 5830
Web: www.bochk.com

PRODUCTS/OPERATIONS

2014 Sales

	% of total
Interest income	58
Fee and commission income	17
Gross earned premiums	20
Net trading gain	3
Others	2
Total	**100**

COMPETITORS

AXA Asia Pacific	Citigroup
Bank of Communications	Dah Sing Financial
Bank of East Asia	Holdings Limited
CITIC International	HSBC
Financial	Hang Seng Bank
Chong Hing Bank	Standard Chartered

HISTORICAL FINANCIALS

Company Type: Public

Income Statement

FYE: December 31

	ASSETS ($ mil.)	NET INCOME ($ mil.)	INCOME AS % OF ASSETS	EMPLOYEES
12/15	305,493	3,457	1.1%	15,000
12/14	282,309	3,169	1.1%	14,926
12/13	263,989	2,869	1.1%	14,647
12/12	236,174	2,700	1.1%	14,638
12/11	223,804	2,630	1.2%	14,475
Annual Growth	**8.1%**	**7.1%**	**—**	**0.9%**

2015 Year-End Financials

Return on assets: 1.1%
Return on equity: 14.5%
Long-term debt ($ mil.): —
No. of shares (mil.): —
Sales ($ mil) 9,158

Dividends
Yield: 4.6%
Payout: 871.4%
Market value ($ mil.): —

	STOCK PRICE ($)	P/E	PER SHARE ($)		
	FY Close	High/Low	Earnings	Dividends	Book Value
12/15	60.72	34 23	0.33	2.85	2.35
12/14	67.01	31 24	0.30	2.56	2.16
12/13	64.52	34 29	0.27	3.15	1.94
12/12	63.05	33 24	0.26	2.80	1.84
12/11	47.16	37 19	0.25	3.05	1.58
Annual Growth	6.5%	— —		7.1%	(1.7%) 10.4%

Bombardier Inc.

Canada's Bombardier is the world's only manufacturer of both planes and trains (but no automobiles). The company's Aerospace division manufactures business (Learjet) commercial (CSeries) and amphibious military (Bombardier 415) aircraft while overseas its Germany-based Transportation division manufactures rail vehicles including monorails light rails metros commuter trains high-speed trains (including the very high speed ZEFIRO) and locomotives. Both are industry-leading businesses. A third division Flexjet offers fractional jet ownership and charter services. (In late 2013 Bombardier announced it was selling Flexjet.)

Strategy

Over the next decade industry forecasts show sustained growth in business and commercial aircraft markets. As a result Bombardier's Aerospace unit continues to invest in and develop new state-of-the art aircraft lines such as its CSeries commercial aircraft family which is aiming to be the world's greenest and most fuel efficient mainliner.

The Aerospace division made one of its largest business aircraft sales in its history in late 2012 when luxury aviation company VistaJet signed a deal for up to 142 Global family business jets for $7.8 billion if all options are exercised. Deliveries of these aircraft will begin in 2014. Prior to that in mid-2012 Bombardier Aerospace won another landmark business jet order from NetJets for a whopping $7.3 billion.

On the rail transportation side demand for sturdy and efficient trains continues to be driven by urban and suburban development worldwide as well as ongoing demand for reliable public transportation. In South America's largest metropolis Sao Paulo Brazil Bombardier's Transportation division is undertaking a notable project to build the world's largest largest mass transit monorail to deal with the city's congestion. The monorail is due to begin operating in early 2014. The project is part of a broader effort by Bombardier to gain a stronger foothold in emerging markets with high growth potential; others include China India and Russia.

Bombardier's Transportation division is actively involved in China's development of urban mass transit and advanced rail networks. Demand is strong there as the growing popularity of rail transportation is actually eating into the profits of regional aviation companies. Bombardier Transportation has three joint ventures in China as well as several wholly owned foreign enterprises and offices in Beijing Guangzhou Shanghai and Hong Kong. One of its key contracts is a $4 billion order from China's Ministry of Railways (MOR) to deliver of several different types of ZEFIRO very high speed trains.

Ownership

The company is controlled by the Bombardier family.

Company Background

Bombardier engineers and industrial designers spent two years designing the Vancouver 2010 Olympic torch. To ensure the flame would not extinguish in temperatures reaching minus 36 degrees Celsius (minus 96.8 degrees Fahrenheit) the company blended propane and isobutane a mixture that supports fire at extremely cold temperatures. It manufactured 12000 torches each with a side vent to allow the flame to unfurl like a flag.

HISTORY

Bombardier got its start in the 1920s when mechanic Joseph-Armand Bombardier began converting old cars into snowmobiles. He founded L'Auto-Neige Bombardier Limited in 1942 to make commercial snow vehicles. In 1959 Bombardier introduced the first personal snowmobile the Ski-Doo.

At age 27 Laurent Beaudoin became the company's president in 1966. Bombardier went public in 1969. When the bottom dropped out of the snowmobile business due to the energy crisis in 1973 Beaudoin diversified and in 1974 Bombardier won its first mass transit contract to build Montreal subway cars. Expanding further into mass transportation Bombardier merged with MLW-Worthington Limited a builder of diesel engines and diesel-electric locomotives. In 1978 the company became Bombardier Inc.

During the 1980s Bombardier continued to diversify. It expanded into military vehicles and became the leading supplier to the North American rail transit industry. The company entered the European railcar market in 1986 the same year it acquired Canadair Canada's largest aerospace company from the national government.

Founded in 1920 as the aircraft division of Canadian Vickers Canadair became a separate company producing military and civilian aircraft in 1944. Acquired by Electric Boat (which became part of General Dynamics) in 1947 it was nationalized by the Canadian government in 1976. In 1978 Canadair introduced its Challenger 600 business jet which became a major seller.

Bombardier began development of a commuter aircraft the Canadian Regional Jet (a 50-seat derivative of the Challenger) in 1989. In 1990 the company bought US-based Learjet and its service centers and two years later it acquired a stake in de Havilland a regional aircraft maker which it jointly owned with the Province of Ontario. The company bought German railroad equipment maker Waggonfabrik Talbot in 1995.

Amtrak selected an international consortium in 1996 headed by Bombardier to produce high-speed trains electric locomotives and train maintenance facilities. Also that year the Global Express business jet made its first flight.

Bombardier doubled the size of its European operations in 1998 by buying German railcar maker Deutsche Waggonbau. In 1999 Bombardier announced the launch of its all-new business jet the eight-passenger Continental.

The company sold its 50% stake in Shorts Missile Systems to Thomson-CSF (now Thales) in 2000. Also that year Bombardier landed an $817 million contract to supply Spanish carrier Air Nostrum with 44 planes. It also inked a $2 billion deal to make 94 regional jets for Delta Air Lines; the Delta order included options for an additional 406 aircraft through 2010.

Bombardier signed a deal with SkyWest in 2001 worth about $1.4 billion for 64 Canadair regional jets. It was also selected by a bankruptcy court as winning bidder for Outboard Marine's Evinrude and Johnson outboard marine engine assets. Completing an agreement made the year before Bombardier acquired DaimlerChrysler's Adtranz rail systems unit for about $725 million making it part

of its Bombardier Transportation division. Later in the year the company announced that it would take a charge of about $600 million and lay off about 10% of its aerospace workforce (it also said that it would cut another 7% of that workforce if demand did not grow).

Bombardier sought about $870 million in damages in 2002 from DaimlerChrysler (now Daimler) over the Adtranz deal claiming that the level of equity in Adtranz was overstated and that the costs related to third-party contracts were higher than stated at the time of the deal. Later that year Bombardier temporarily suspended business jet production. Bombardier divested its Recreational Products unit (snowmobiles and personal watercraft) in 2003.

Bombardier announced in 2004 that it was considering building a family (CSeries) of 100- to 130-seat jets that would compete directly with Boeing and Airbus. The next year the company's board approved the larger CSeries planes but it deferred its final decision; in 2006 Bombardier announced that it would focus instead on 80- to 100-seat passenger planes. In 2007 the company announced the new project's official name —the CRJ1000. That same year Bombardier began a performance improvement project at its Transportation division. The project which aimed to improve performance by trimming costs —chiefly procurement costs — began to show signs of effectiveness in 2007. The company continued to seek the right mix of suppliers for parts including low-cost sources.

CEO Paul Tellier resigned in 2004 amid rumored boardroom differences with Laurent Beaudoin who assumed the CEO duties. A year later in 2005 the company sold its inventory finance division which provided equipment financing to GE Commercial Finance for $2.4 billion ($1.4 billion in cash and $1 billion in assumed liabilities).

Deliveries and orders were booming for Bombardier's line of business jets before the worldwide credit crisis and recession hit in 2008. The company had 232 deliveries for business jets in fiscal 2008 compared with 212 in 2007 and 197 in 2006.

Laurent Beaudoin maintained his role as chairman when in 2008 he handed over the president and CEO titles to his son Pierre.

The business and civil aircraft markets experienced their most turbulent conditions since the aftermath of September 11 due to the global recession and credit crisis in 2009. The perpetually dicey financial condition of the airline industry —due to fluctuating fuel prices and shifts in consumer spending —affected demand for commercial aircraft. Bombardier's limited number of customers many of which are government agencies or publicly held companies watched as their own revenues fell due to the recession.

Bombardier adapted by reducing its production of business jets and CRJ regional aircraft and reducing its workforce by 4700 (about 13%). The company also took the opportunity to build on its customer services opening a service center in Europe and a third service center in the US.

EXECUTIVES

President and CEO, Alain M. Bellemare, age 54
President Bombardier Commercial Aircraft, Fred S. Cromer
President Division Western Europe Middle East and Africa Transportation, Laurent Troger
President Bombardier Business Aircraft, David M. Coleal
President Bombardier Aerostructures & Engineering Services, Jean Seguin
SVP and CFO, John DiBert
President Bombardier China, Jianwei Zhang
Vice Chairman, Jean-Louis Fontaine, age 76

Vice Chairman, J. R. Andre Bombardier, age 73
Chairman, Pierre Beaudoin, age 53
Auditors: Ernst & Young LLP

LOCATIONS

HQ: Bombardier Inc.
800 Rene-Levesque Blvd. West, 29th Floor, Montreal,
Quebec H3B 1Y8
Phone: 514 861-9481   Fax: 514 861-2629
Web: www.bombardier.com

2011 Aircraft Sales

	% of total
North America	
US	38
Europe	30
Asia/Pacific	17
Other regions	15
Total	**100**

2011 Transportation Sales

	% of total
Europe	65
Asia/Pacific	18
North America	13
Other regions	4
Total	**100**

PRODUCTS/OPERATIONS

2011 Sales by Segment

	% of total
Transportation	51
Aerospace	49
Total	**100**

2011 Sales by Industry

	% of total
Manufacturing	73
Services	16
Other	11
Total	**100**

2011 Aerospace Sales by Market

	% of total
Business aircraft	44
Commercial aircraft	25
Services	18
Other	13
Total	**100**

2011 Transportation Sales by Market

	% of total
Rolling stock	70
Services	15
System and signaling	15
Total	**100**

Selected Operations

Aerospace
  Amphibious aircraft
  415
  415 MP
  Business aircraft
  Challenger
  Global
  Learjet
  Commercial aircraft
  CRJ Series
  CSeries
  Q-Series
  Flying training
  Military aircraft technical service
  Specialized aircraft modified for special missions
  Training and aircraft services
  Maintenance
  Parts
  Technical support
  Training
Flexjet
  Fractional ownership
  Whole aircraft ownership and management
Transportation
  Customized transportation systems
  Propulsion and controls
  Rail control systems

Rail vehicles
Automated people movers
Commuter/regional trains
Intercity/high-speed trains
Light rail vehicles
Locomotives
Metros
Monorails
Rapid transit
Services
Fleet maintenance
Material management
Operations and maintenance
Vehicle refurbishment and modernization

COMPETITORS

ALSTOM	Gulfstream Aerospace
AeroCentury	Kawasaki Rail Car
Airbus	Leonardo
Airbus Group	Mitsubishi Heavy
Blue Star Jets	Industries
Boeing	NetJets
COMAC	Piper Aircraft
Dassault Aviation	Siemens AG
Embraer	Thales
Flight Options	XOJET

HISTORICAL FINANCIALS

Company Type: Public

Income Statement

FYE: December 31

	REVENUE ($ mil.)	NET INCOME ($ mil.)	NET PROFIT MARGIN	EMPLOYEES
12/15	18,172	(5,347)	—	70,900
12/14	20,111	(1,260)	—	74,000
12/13	18,151	564	3.1%	76,400
12/12	16,768	588	3.5%	71,500
12/11	18,347	837	4.6%	70,000
Annual Growth	**(0.2%)**	**—**	**—**	**0.3%**

2015 Year-End Financials

Debt ratio: 38.8%
Return on equity: ***,***.*%
Cash ($ mil.): 2,720
Current ratio: 1.02
Long-term debt ($ mil.): 8,908

No. of shares (mil.): —
Dividends
  Yield: —
  Payout: —
Market value ($ mil.): —

	STOCK PRICE ($) FY Close	P/E High/Low		Earnings	PER SHARE ($) Dividends	Book Value
12/15	0.96	—	—	(2.58)	0.00	(1.83)
12/14	3.59	—	—	(0.74)	0.09	0.02
12/13	4.35	17	12	0.31	0.10	1.39
12/12	3.81	15	9	0.32	0.13	0.77
12/11	3.95	16	7	0.47	0.10	0.37
Annual Growth	**(29.9%)**	**—**	**—**	**—**	**—**	**—**

Bosch (Robert) GmbH (Germany Fed. Rep.)

Robert Bosch has spent more than a century establishing a name for really "boss" automobile and industrial equipment as well as consumer goods and building systems. Bosch operates via 440 subsidiaries in 60 countries; its core lines include mobility (auto) systems from diesel/hybrid drive to steering starter motors and generators electronics and brakes. Subsidiary Bosch Rexroth makes electric hydraulic and pneumatic machinery for industrial use. Bosch Security makes various protection systems. Bosch also makes photovoltaic and wind-turbine components heat pumps for buildings and home appliances through Bosch-Siemens Hausgerate. Charitable foundation Robert Bosch Stiftung controls the company.

Geographic Reach
The company has operations in 60 countries and plies its wares globally. Europe accounted for 53% of the revenue in 2014. The company also operates in Americas and Asia/Pacific. Bouncing back from the global recession which hit the automotive industry particularly hard Bosch has been expanding in the Asia Pacific region where recession effects were minimal or delayed.

Operations
Bosch divides its business into four main categories. The company's Mobility Solutions group is the world's largest independent auto parts supplier. The Industrial Technology segment includes Drive and Control Technology and Packaging Technology which supply the mechanical engineering and packaging and process engineering sectors respectively. Consumer Goods provides Power Tools and Household Appliances and the Energy and Building Technology segment offers HVAC solar energy and security systems products and services.

Sales and Marketing
Bosch is represented in about 150 countries.

Financial Performance
The company's revenues increased by 6% in 2014 due to an increase in Mobility Solutions' sales as the result of a strong demand for modern gasoline direct injection systems transmission control systems and continuously variable transmissions. In Europe and China Bosch's diesel technology business benefited from the ramp-up of new injection systems. Consumer Goods sales increased by 5% due to a growth in sales from the Power Tools division; Energy and Building Technology revenues increased by 2%. Bosch's net income increased by 111% as the result of higher revenues and the positive effects from changes in exchange rates and improved investment results.

Operating cash flow decreased by 10% due to an increase in cash used in inventories receivables and other assets.

Strategy
Bosch's strategic focus is on energy efficiency. Drivers include the growing demand for energy ever tighter climate-protection regulations and the finite nature of fossil fuels. The company generates 40% of its sales from products that contribute to energy efficiency environmental protection and resource conservation. These products account for more than half of the company's current research and development expenditure.

To deal with the economic woes of recent years and position itself for growth Bosch has been investing in Asia. By 2020 the company aims to double its sales in Asia/Pacific and the Americas compared with 2013 to grow faster than the market in Europe and to increase its annual sales in Africa to 2 billion euros.

Streamlining its operations for future growth Bosch plans to set up a new division in 2016 Bosch Global Service Solutions to bring together all the internal and external services offered by the company. The division will emerge from the Service Solutions business unit which is run by Bosch Sicherheitssysteme GmbH.Global expansion is a key aspect of the company's strategy. Bosch is focusing on the growing African market and is continuing to expand its presence on that continent. In 2015 it opened a new sales and service company in Lagos Nigeria.

That year Bosch also laid the foundation stone for its new plant in Russia. In 2014 the company opened a new research and technology center opened in Bangalore (India) its first center for software development and engineering services in North America in Guadalajara (Mexico) and its second automotive technology manufacturing plant in Romania. Bosch is also expanding its presence in Turkey.

Bosch applied for some 4600 patents worldwide in 2014.

Mergers and Acquisitions

Broadening its portfolio in 2015 in the US Bosch acquired Climatec a provider of energy efficiency building automation security and life-safety solutions and Osgood Industries a filling and packaging machine specialist.

In 2015 the company acquired ProSyst which specializes in the development of gateway software and middleware and planned to merge it with Bosch Software Innovations GmbH the software and systems unit of Bosch. Strengthening Bosch's consumer goods business in 2014 the company acquired 50/50 joint ventures BSH Bosch und Siemens Hausgeräte GmbH (for euro 3 billion) and ZF Lenksysteme GmbH.

The company in 2013 acquired software firm Bauer Optimierungstechnik. The company which is part of Bosch's Energy and Building Solutions group makes software-based air conditioning and ventilation control systems.

Ownership

Bosch is unique not only in that it is large (with ties to almost every automobile enterprise in the world) but that it is heavy influenced by a charitable foundation. Robert Bosch Stiftung holds 92% of shares in the company. (More than 90% of voting rights are held by Robert Bosch Industrietreuhand an industrial trust.) The remaining shares are held by the Bosch family and other investors.

HISTORY

Company Background

Self-taught electrical engineer Robert Bosch opened a Stuttgart workshop in 1886 and the following year produced the world's first alternator for a stationary engine. In 1897 his company built the first automobile alternator. Later electrical automotive product launches included spark plugs (1902) starters (1912) and regulators (1913). Bosch believed in treating employees well and shortened their workday to eight hours (extraordinary for 1906).

US operations begun in 1909 were confiscated during WWI as part of a trade embargo against Germany. Bosch survived the German depression of the 1920s introduced power tools (1928) and appliances (1933) and bought Blaupunkt (car radios 1933). Industrial and military demand for the company's products continued from the 1930s until WWII. Bosch died in 1942 and left 90% of his company to charity.

Bosch suffered severe damage in WWII and its US operations were again confiscated. It rebuilt after the war and enjoyed growing demand for its appliances and automotive products as postwar incomes increased worldwide. In 1963 Hans Merkle took the helm. Believing fuel efficiency and pollution control would be important issues in the future Bosch invested heavily to develop automotive components that would raise gas mileage and lower emissions. The company made the world's first electronic fuel-injection (EFI) system in 1967. Also that year Bosch and Siemens (West Germany) formed Bosch-Siemens Hausgerate to make home appliances.

The oil crisis of the 1970s increased awareness of fuel efficiency and benefited sales of EFI systems. Buying a plant in Charleston South Carolina Bosch re-entered the US in 1974 to make fuel-injection systems. It introduced the first antilock braking system in 1978.

A 1984 strike against Bosch in Germany disrupted automobile production throughout Europe. In the late 1980s the company developed technology for multiplexing (employing one wire to replace many by using semiconductor controllers) in automobiles established it as an industry standard and licensed it to chip makers Intel (US) Philips (the Netherlands) and Motorola (US). Throughout the 1980s and into the 1990s Bosch acquired various telecommunications companies.

In 1993 Bosch's sales dropped for the first time since 1967. In response the company cut its workforce. In 1996 Bosch bought Emerson's half of joint venture S-B Power Tool Co. which makes Bosch Dremel and Skil brand tools. Further consolidating its position as a world leader in braking systems Bosch also purchased AlliedSignal's struggling light-vehicle braking unit. The company sold its private mobile radio business to Motorola in 1997 and to speed its business for mobile phones bought Dancall Telecom (a maker of mobile-phone handsets) from UK-based Amstrad.

In 1998 the company's Bosch-Siemens Hausgerate joint venture opened a plant in the US and bought Masco's Thermador unit (cooktops ovens and ranges). In 1999 Bosch sold its US-based telecom unit to a joint venture of Motorola and Cisco Systems. The next year UK-based General Electric Company (now Marconi) bought the German operations of Bosch's telecom unit.

Early in 2000 the company sold its mobile-phone business to Siemens AG. That year the company's joint venture with Siemens bought Rexroth AG (Atecs Mannesmann AG's automation and packaging technology group) for about $9.2 billion. The new division was named Bosch Rexroth AG. In 2001 Bosch bought out Siemens' stake in Bosch Rexroth and consolidated its operations as a wholly owned subsidiary.

In 2006 Robert Bosch purchased Telex Communications for $420 million. Telex is a provider of audio wireless communications and safety equipment with applications in large public places including stadiums and airports.

Bosch along with the entire automotive industry was hard hit in the global economic crisis of 2008 and 2009. Bosch struggled to stay in the public's favor by avoiding cuts in headcount as it worked to shore up net earnings which waned more than 85% in 2008 from 2007 and plunged to a loss of euro 1214 ($1.6 billion) in 2009. In response Bosch shed weaker units. North American sales which declined more than 10% in 2009 from 2008 were partially offset by Bosch's hammering out a sale with Akebono Brake Industry. The Japanese manufacturer of brakes bought Bosch's North American foundation brake production. (Bosch's significant stake in Akebono gave the German auto parts maker a solid position.) The transaction included Bosch assets to manufacture corner modules drum brakes disc brakes and related parts at plants in Michigan Tennessee and South Carolina.

In late 2008 Bosch sold its "car infotainment" business branded Blaupunkt to Aurelius a German investment group. The deal comprised the trade name and portfolio of car radio hi-fi component and advanced navigation devices. Also that same year it bought a majority stake in ersol Solar Energy (renamed Bosch Solar Energy in 2009) a German manufacturer of wafer-based mono- and polycrystalline silicon solar cells and thin-film solar modules used to generate electricity from sunlight.

In 2012 the Bosch Automotive Aftermarket division spent about $120 million euros in a spark plug and brake pad manufacturing facility in Nanjing China. The facility which represents Bosch's largest investment anywhere houses testing and R&D operations. The move put Bosch in the cen-

ter of fast growing Asia and positioned it close to many of its automotive OEM customers.

EXECUTIVES

Member Management Board, Uwe Raschke, age 58
Chairman and CTO, Volkmar Denner, age 60
President Gasoline Systems, Peter Tyroller, age 59
Member Management Board, Wolf-Henning Scheider
Member Management Board, Werner Struth
Deputy Chairman, Stefan Asenkerschbaumer, age 60
President Automotive Electronics, Christoph Kuebel
Member Management Board, Stefan Hartung
Member Management Board, Dirk Hoheisel
Member Management Board, Rolf Bulander, age 58
Auditors: PricewaterhouseCoopers Aktiengesellschaft Wirtschaftprüfungsgesellschaft

LOCATIONS

HQ: Bosch (Robert) GmbH (Germany Fed. Rep.)
Postfach 10 60 50, Stuttgart D-70049
Phone: (49) 711 811 0   **Fax:** (49) 711 811 6630
Web: www.bosch.com

2014 Sales

	% of total
Europe	53
Asia	25
Americas	20
Other region	2
Total	**100**

PRODUCTS/OPERATIONS

2014 Sales

	% of total
Mobility Solutions	68
Industrial technology	14
Energy and building technology	9
Consumer goods	9
Total	**100**

Selected Divisions and Products

Automotive Technology
  Car multimedia
  Chassis systems brakes
  Chassis systmes control
  Diesel systems
  Electrical drives
  Gasoline systems
  Starter motors and generators
  Steering systems
Consumer Goods and Building Technology
  Household appliances
  Power tools
  Security systems
  Thermotechnology (gas-fired hot water heating systems)
Industrial Technology
  Drive and control technology
  Packaging technology
  Solar energy

COMPETITORS

BorgWarner	Pioneer Corporation
DENSO	Prestolite Electric
Dana	Senior plc
Delphi Automotive Systems	Snap-on
Electrolux	Standard Motor Products
Emerson Electric	Stanley Black and Decker
Federal-Mogul	Tenneco
GE	Trane Inc.
Honeywell International	Valeo
Ingersoll-Rand	Visteon
Johnson Controls	Whirlpool
Magna International	

HISTORICAL FINANCIALS
Company Type: Public

Income Statement
FYE: December 31

	REVENUE ($ mil.)	NET INCOME ($ mil.)	NET PROFIT MARGIN	EMPLOYEES
12/15	76,905	3,477	4.5%	374,778
12/14	59,500	2,929	4.9%	290,183
12/13	63,423	1,508	2.4%	281,381
12/12	69,150	2,980	4.3%	305,877
12/11	66,605	2,258	3.4%	302,519
Annual Growth	3.7%	11.4%	—	5.5%

2015 Year-End Financials

Debt ratio: 10.6%
Return on equity: 10.4%
Cash ($ mil.): 4,037
Current ratio: 1.69
Long-term debt ($ mil.): 5,819

No. of shares (mil.): —
Dividends
Yield: —
Payout: —
Market value ($ mil.): —

Boule Diagnostics AB

LOCATIONS

HQ: Boule Diagnostics AB
Domnarvsgatan 4, Spanga SE-163 53
Phone: (46) 8 744 7700   **Fax:** (46) 8 744 7720
Web: www.boule.se

HISTORICAL FINANCIALS
Company Type: Public

Income Statement
FYE: December 31

	REVENUE ($ mil.)	NET INCOME ($ mil.)	NET PROFIT MARGIN	EMPLOYEES
12/15	39,310	1,821	4.6%	168
12/14	39,673	3,915	9.9%	179
Annual Growth	(0.9%)	(53.5%)	—	(6.1%)

2015 Year-End Financials

Debt ratio: 2.3%
Return on equity: 8.5%
Cash ($ mil.): 5,977
Current ratio: 1.49
Long-term debt ($ mil.): 874

No. of shares (mil.): 4
Dividends
Yield: —
Payout: —
Market value ($ mil.): —

	STOCK PRICE ($) FY Close	P/E High/Low		PER SHARE ($) Earnings	Dividends	Book Value
12/15 4,750.46	0.00	—	—	0.38	0.00	
12/14 4,671.75 /0.00	0.00	—	—	0.83	0.00	
	—	—	—(0.00)	0.00	(0.00)	
Annual Growth	—	—	—	—	—	—

Bouygues S.A.

If all roads lead to Bouygues that's because the company built them. Bouygues (pronounced "bweeg") operates in three primary business areas: construction telecommunications and media. Its road work buildings and property development contracting services account for about 80% of the group's sales and operate through road builder Colas (about 35% of sales) Bouygues Construction (35%) and Bouygues Immobilier (10%) which de-velops commercial and residential properties. The group also owns a 90% stake in Bouygues Tele-com (France's #3 mobile phone carrier) more than 40% of TF1 (France's #1 TV channel) and 29% of industrial group ALSTOM.

Operations

Bouygues SA is a diversified industrial group with five main business segments: Construction through Bouygues Construction (building civil works energy and services); Property through Bouygues Immobilier (property); Roads through road builder Colas; Telecoms through Bouygues Telecom; and Media through TF1 (Television Française 1 SA).

Subsidiary Bouygues Construction is a force in itself with several subsidiaries performing civil con-struction and electrical/maintenance work. The group focuses on public-private partnerships those lucrative partnerships that governments use to build roads prisons schools and other infrastruc-ture. Bouygues has increasingly participated in sustainable development projects with investments in training research and resources.

The French conglomerate also has a 29% stake in Alstom (making it the largest shareholder) which builds rail cars ships and power plants.

Geographic Reach

Paris-based Bouygues' largest market is France which accounts for about 60% of its total sales. The European Union and the rest of Europe con-tributes about 15%. The firm is also active in Africa Asia Central America the Middle East North Amer-ica and South America. Overall the group does business in about 80 countries worldwide.

Financial Performance

Note: Growth rates may differ after conversion to US dollars.

Bouygues revenues have been steadily rising over the past few years thanks to strengthened de-mand for construction projects and property devel-opment. Profits however have been in decline due to impairment losses on the company's struggling Alstom business.

The company's revenue was mostly flat in 2014 inching up by less than 1% to euro 33.12 million ($40.3 million) with growth overseas and declin-ing business in France. Its construction business' sales grew by 2% mostly thanks to a higher vol-ume of international construction projects through its Bouygues Construction division. Bouygues Im-mobilier grew by 11% as commercial property sales doubled over the prior years' results. Its Colas business shrank by 3% as its project sales in France slipped by double digits while its TF1 sub-sidiary and Bouygues Telecom shrank by 9% and 5% respectively.

Bouygues' net income rebounded sharply to euro 807 million ($980.9 million) from a $1 billion loss in 2013 mostly due to the absence of a non-recurring euro 1.4 billion ($1.7 billion) impairment loss on its Alstom business that it incurred in 2013 and because of non-recurring gains on the sale of the company's equity interests in Cofi route and Eurosport International. Not counting these non-recurring items Bouygues' net income would have declined by euro 158 million during the year.

The company's operating cash fell by 13% to euro 1.9 billion for the year as it collected less from its share of profits from its joint ventures and associates.

Strategy

Bouygues completed a strong collection of high-value projects in 2014. Bouygues Construction completed the Tuen Mun-Chek Lap Kok tunnel in Hong Kong Zagreb Airport in Croatia and the L2 bypass in Marseille. Meanwhile Colas put the final touches on the Tangier-Kenitra high-speed rail link in Morocco the Santiago metro in Chile and a roads maintenance contract in London. In late 2014 Bouygues Construction began its first civil works contract in Azerbaijan; its Bouygues Travaux Publics subsidiary secured a euro 147 million contract to design and build the "28 May" station of the capital Baku's metro line; and its Dragages Hong Kong and Bouygues Travex Publics subsidiaries won a euro 490 million-con-tract with MTR Corporation to build two twin-tube tunnels on the 6-km extension of the Shatin to Central Link metro line.

To reduce its dependence on its home country and Europe the French firm is expanding in inter-national markets especially Asia and the Middle East. As of 2015 Bouygues Construction gener-ated 46% of its sales outside France while Colas generates 43% in international markets.

Mergers and Acquisitions

In December 2014 Bouygues Immobilier ac-quired Loticis to to expand its urban-planning-subdivision business in the Paris region. Also in 2014 subsidiary Bouygues Energies et Services bought an 85% equity stake in Toronto-based Plan Group.

Ownership

Bouygues SA is controlled by the founding Bouygues family and led by billionaire Martin Bouygues. Holding company SCDM owned a 21% stake in the company at the end of 2014. Com-pany Background Looking to grow its telecoms business Bouygues in 2014 bid euro 10.5 billion ($14.4 billion) in cash to acquire the telecoms arm of Vivendi SFR and 46% of the new company in a planned spin-off. It lost out to French cable op-erator SFR. A tie-up between SFR and Bouygues would have created Europe's seventh-biggest tele-com group by sales and in France would rank ahead of market leader Orange in market share.

HISTORY

Company BackgroundWith the equivalent of $1700 in borrowed money Francis Bouygues son of a Paris engineer started Entreprise Francis Bouygues in 1952 as an industrial works and con-struction firm in the Paris region of France. Within four years his firm had expanded into property de-velopment.

By the mid-1960s Bouygues had entered the civil engineering and public works sectors and de-veloped regional construction units across France. In 1970 it was listed on the Paris stock exchange. Four years later the company established Bouygues Offshore to build oil platforms.

In 1978 the firm built Terminal 2 of Paris' Charles de Gaulle airport. Three years later it won the contract to construct the University of Riyadh in Saudi Arabia (then the world's largest building project at 3.2 million sq. ft.) which was completed in 1984. That year Bouygues acquired France's #3 water supply company Saur and power transmis-sion and supply firm ETDE.

Expansion continued in 1986 with the purchase of the Screg Group which included Colas France's top highway contractor. The next year the com-pany led a consortium to buy 50% of newly priva-tized network Societe Television Française 1 (TF1). Bouygues became the largest shareholder with a 25% stake (increased to 40% by 1999). In 1988 the company began building the Channel Tunnel (completed 1994) and moved into its new ultramodern headquarters dubbed Challenger in Saint-Quentin-en-Yvelines outside Paris.

After rumors of failing health Francis Bouygues resigned as chairman in 1989. His son Martin took over as chairman and CEO although the patriarch called France's "Emperor of Concrete" remained on the board until his death in 1993.

Despite fears that the group would suffer with-out its founder's leadership Bouygues continued to grow with the 1989 acquisition of a majority inter-est in Grands Moulins de Paris France's largest flour milling firm (sold 1998). In 1990 it purchased Swiss construction group Losinger.

The company entered the telecom industry in 1993 with a national paging network and added a mobile phone license a year later. In 1996 the group listed 40% of Bouygues Offshore's shares on the New York and Paris stock exchanges. Also that year it launched mobile phone operator Bouygues Telecom and entered a partnership with Telecom Italia.

By 1999 Bouygues Telecom had reached 2 million customers and Bouygues bought back a 20% share held by the UK's Cable and Wireless to increase its stake to nearly 54%. That year Bouygues Offshore bought Norwegian engineering firm Kvaerner and the group spun off its construction sector creating Bouygues Construction.

After word circulated that Deutsche Telekom wanted to acquire the group's telecom unit Bouygues became the target of takeover rumors. Francois Pinault France's richest businessman became Bouygues' largest non-family shareholder when he increased his stake to 14% (later reduced to about 2%). Pinault's biggest rival Bernard Arnault upped his stake to more than 9% of the group fueling speculation of a battle over control of the board.

In 2001 the company pulled out of France's auction for a third-generation wireless license and remained the only European incumbent mobile carrier without a major domestic investment in 3G technology (until 2009). The next year the company agreed to buy Telecom Italia's stake in Bouygues Telecom increasing Bouygues' ownership in the mobile operator from 54% to more than 65%. In 2002 the company sold its 51% stake in oil field platform construction unit Bouygues Offshore to Italian oil services group Saipem which announced plans to bid for the remaining shares. However talks with German utility giant E. ON over the sale of Bouygues' Saur subsidiary failed that year after E.ON decided to focus instead on its electricity and gas operations.

In 2005 Bouygues was more successful when it sought to sell Saur piecemeal. It sold several divisions of the subsidiary (Coved Saur France Saur International and Stereau) to French private equity firm PAI Partners but retained the African and Italian (Sigesa-Crea) divisions of the firm.

Bouygues bought the French government's 21% stake in ALSTOM for $2.5 billion in 2006. The deal was approved on the condition that it not try to control the company for at least three years. Bouygues did build up its holding after the acquisition though eventually holding 29% of the shares.

In 2008 property developer Bouygues Immobilier expanded with the acquisition of Urbis a French rival. That year Colas bought the Gouyer Group of companies (distribution of construction materials) in Martinique and Guadeloupe while Bouygues Telecom acquired a fixed-line network that allowed it to launch the Bbox broadband router and Internet services that include VoIP e-mail Internet access and television; the telecom unit also gained the previously denied right to offer the iPhone 3G.

EXECUTIVES

Deputy CEO, Olivier Bouygues, age 66, $920,000 total compensation
Chairman and CEO, Martin Bouygues, age 64, $920,000 total compensation
Chairman and CEO TF1, Nonce Paolini, age 67
Chairman and CEO Bouygues Construction, Yves Gabriel, age 66, $850,000 total compensation
Chairman and CEO Bouygues Telecom, Olivier Roussat, age 52
CFO, Philippe Marien, age 60

Chairman and CEO Bouygues Immobilier; Director, Francois Bertiere, age 66
Chairman and CEO Colas; Director, Herve Le Bouc, age 65
Auditors: Mazars

LOCATIONS

HQ: Bouygues S.A.
32 avenue Hoche, Paris, Cedex 08 75378
Phone: (33) 1 44 20 10 00
Web: www.bouygues.com

2014 Sales

	% of total
Europe	
France	62
Other countries	16
North America	9
Asia/Pacific	6
Africa & Middle East	5
Central & South America	1
Oceania	1
Total	**100**

PRODUCTS/OPERATIONS

2014 Sales by Segment

	% of total
Construction	80
Telecoms	13
Media	7
Total	**100**

2014 Sales

	% of total
Colas	37
Bouygues Construction	35
Bouygues Telecom	13
TF1	7
Bouygues Immobilier	8
Total	**100**

Selected Subsidiaries and Affiliates

Construction
  Autoroute de liaison Seine-Sarthe SA (33%)
  Bouygues Bâtiment Ile-de-France SA (99.9%)
  Bati-Rénov SA (99.3%)
  Bouygues Bâtiment International SA (99.9%)
  Bouygues Thaï Ltd (49%)
  DTP Singapour Pte Ltd (99.9%)
  Kohler Investment SA (Luxembourg 99.9%)
  Bouygues Construction SA (99.9%)
  ETDE SA (99.9%)
  Exprimm IT (99.9%)
  Icel Maidstone Ltd (UK 99.9%)
  Quille SA (99.9%)
  Westminster Local Education Partnership Ltd (UK 80%)
Media
  Métro France Publications (15%)
  Télévision Française 1 SA (TF1 43%)
  TF1 Vidéo (43%)
  TV Breizh (43%)
Property
  Bouygues Immobilier
  Parque Empresearial Cristalia SL
  SNC Bouygues Immobilier Entreprises Île-de-France
Roads
  Cofiroute (16%)
  Colas Guadeloupe (97%)
  Colas Hungaria (97%)
  Colas Polska (97%)
  Colas SA (96%)
  Spac (97%)
Telecommunications
  Bouygues Telecom SA (90%)

COMPETITORS

Alarko	Fluor
Amec Foster Wheeler	Groupe SNEF
Anglian Water Group	HOCHTIEF
Atlantia	Hyundai Engineering
Balfour Beatty	and Construction
Bechtel	MWH Global
Bilfinger	Orange
CANAL+	Orange Switzerland
CSCEC	SUEZ Environnement
Dragados	Severn Trent
EIFFAGE	Skanska
Engie	Technip
FCC Barcelona	VINCI

HISTORICAL FINANCIALS

Company Type: Public

Income Statement

FYE: December 31

	REVENUE ($ mil.)	NET INCOME ($ mil.)	NET PROFIT MARGIN	EMPLOYEES
12/15	35,421	438	1.2%	120,254
12/14	40,409	980	2.4%	127,470
12/13	46,039	(1,042)	—	128,067
12/12	44,357	834	1.9%	133,780
12/11	42,483	1,383	3.3%	130,827
Annual Growth	**(4.4%)**	**(25.0%)**	**—**	**(2.1%)**

2015 Year-End Financials

Debt ratio: 20.3%	No. of shares (mil.): 345
Return on equity: 5.1%	Dividends
Cash ($ mil.): 4,122	Yield: —
Current ratio: 0.92	Payout: 135.5%
Long-term debt ($ mil.): 5,778	Market value ($ mil.): —

BP p.l.c.

BP is also BO (Big Oil). It is the world's #3 publicly traded integrated oil concern behind Royal Dutch Shell and Exxon Mobil. BP explores for oil and gas in 28 countries and has proved reserves of 17 billion barrels of oil equivalent. The company is the largest oil and gas producer in the US and a top refiner with 15 plants processing more than 3.2 million barrels of crude oil per day; it is also a major producer of petrochemicals. The company supplies fuel and related convenience services to consumers at some 17200 BP-branded retail sites worldwide and markets its products in more than 50 countries.

Geographic Reach

The company operates in 80 countries primarily in North America Europe and Asia but it also manufactures and markets products in Australasia Africa and Central and South America. BP's upstream activities in North America takes place in four main areas: deep-water Gulf of Mexico Lower 48 states Alaska and Canada.

Operations

BP's downstream segment includes fuels lubricants and Petrochemicals. The Upstream segment operates oil and natural gas exploration field development and production and midstream transportation storage and processing. BP also markets and trade natural gas including liquefied natural gas power and natural gas liquids.

Sales and Marketing

The company supplies fuel and related retail services to consumers through company-owned and franchised retail sites as well as other channels including dealer wholesalers and jobbers. BP also supplies commercial customers in the transport and industrial sectors.

Financial Performance

In 2014 BP's net revenues decreased by 7% due to lower liquids realizations partially offset by higher production in higher-margin areas higher gas realizations and higher gas marketing and trading revenues.

The company's net income decreased by 84% in 2014 due to lower net revenues higher impairment charges and losses on sale of businesses and fixed assets stemming from adjustments to prior year disposals in Canada and the North Sea and costs associated with the decision to cease refining operations at Bulwer Island in Australia. Other factors included the write-off of expenses related to unsuccessful drilling activities or lease expiration. In 2014 the company's cash inflow increased by 55% due to changes in working capital as a result of a decline in inventories a drop in other current and non-current assets and a decrease in other current and non-current liabilities.

Strategy

The company took a major hit in 2010 when one of its Gulf of Mexico oil rigs exploded and killed 11 workers. Millions of gallons of crude spilled into the Gulf and BP was forced to set aside $20 billion to pay for related damages in 2011 and 2012.

The spill developed into a major political economic and public relations crisis for the company as it struggled to cap the leaking well clean up the massive spill and mollify Gulf Coast communities which saw their fishing industry decimated and their coastlines inundated by oil. To address the growing crisis in 2010 the company established an escrow account of $20 billion managed by a third party to reimburse claims from people and businesses financially damaged by the oil spill. (It settled with individual and business plaintiffs for $7.8 billion in 2012 but still faced federal state and local government charges). In a plea deal with the US government in 2012 BP pled guilty to criminal misconduct (12 felony counts) and in 2013 agreed to pay $4.5 billion in damages.

A federal court found BP grossly negligent in 2014 for its role in the 2010 spill. In 2015 BP agreed to pay a record $20.8 billion in damages to the US government and five Gulf Coast states that resolved years of litigation over the 2010 Gulf of Mexico oil spill.

The company continues to jettison non-core assets to raise cash. In 2015 BP announced plans to sell its oil storage terminal in Amsterdam. It also agreed to sell its equity in the Central Area Transmission System business in the UK North Sea to Antin Infrastructure Partners for £324 million ($545 million).

After the costly Gulf spill BP embarked on a "shrink to grow" strategy of selling older oilfields around the world to generate cash for settlements and simplify its upstream operations. All told the company has sold about $37 billion in assets. Completed divestitures include one of the largest transactions in the Gulf of Mexico –BP's sale of a number of oil and gas fields in the deepwater Gulf of Mexico region to Plains Exploration & Production for $5.55 billion in 2012. That year it also sold assets in Canada Egypt and the Permian Basin in the US to fellow explorer Apache for about $7 billion. The deal included BP receiving a $5 billion cash advance. (In 2011 BP sold its Colombian assets to Talisman Energy and Ecopetrol for $1.9 billion and properties in Venezuela and Vietnam to its Russian joint venture TNK-BP for $1.8 billion.)

TNK-BP was BP's longtime drilling venture with several Russian partners. After years of feuding with those partners in 2013 BP sold that business to Russian state oil company Rosneft as part of a complex package of deals worth a whopping $55 billion. The transaction gave BP a nearly 20% stake in Rosneft and about $12.3 billion in cash allowing it to pursue offshore drilling opportunities in the Arctic Ocean and settle billions of dollars in US Gulf spill penalties. Several BP competitors

Exxon Mobil Italy's Eni and Norway's Statoil already have Russian Arctic drilling deals.

In 2014 the company agreed to sell interests in four BP-operated oilfields on the North Slope of Alaska to Hilcorp and its specialist global Aviation Turbine Oils business to Eastman Chemical Company.

On the growth side in 2015 BP signed a deal to sell to China Huadian Corporation up to 1 million tons of liquefied natural gas per year worth up to $10 billion over the next 20 years.

In 2016 BP agreed to acquire stakes in exploration blocks in Mauritania and Senegal from Kosmos Energy for $916 million.

Mergers and Acquisitions

As part of its strategy to be a leading purified terephthalic acid (PTA) regional player in 2014 BP acquired PT Amoco Mitsui PTA Indonesia (AMI). The deal allows the company to assess future opportunities to lower the cost of the production facilities by upgrading to the latest technology as well as opportunities for expansion in the Indonesian market.

HISTORY

Company Background

The company which was formed in 1998 from the merger of British Petroleum and Amoco grew by buying Atlantic Richfield Company.

BP (formerly BP Amoco) was born on two sides of the Atlantic. In the US Amoco emerged from Standard Oil Trust organized by John D. Rockefeller in 1882. In 1886 he bought Lima (Ohio) oil a high-sulfur crude anticipating the discovery of a sulfur-removing process. Such a process was indeed patented in 1887 and in 1889 Standard organized Standard Oil of Indiana which later established such innovations as company-owned service stations and a research lab at the refinery.

Overseas British Petroleum (BP) was a twinkle in the eye of English adventurer William D'Arcy who began oil exploration of Persia in 1901. In 1908 bankrolled by Burmah Oil D'Arcy's firm was the first to strike oil in the Middle East. D'Arcy and Burmah Oil formed Anglo-Persian Oil in 1909 and the British government took a 51% stake in 1914.

Back in the US Standard was broken up into 34 independent oil companies in 1911. Standard Oil of Indiana kept its oil refining and US marketing operations. In 1925 it added a few Mexican and Venezuelan firms including Pan American Petroleum and Transport which held half of American Oil Co. known for Amoco antiknock gasoline. It began Amoco Chemicals in 1945.

Anglo-Persian took the BP name in 1954 and bought its own Standard Oil: After making a strike in Alaska in 1969 BP swapped Alaskan reserves for a 25% interest (later upped to 55%) in Standard Oil of Ohio (SOHIO). BP also struck North Sea oil in 1970. But falling oil and copper prices in the mid-1980s and a dry hole in the Beaufort Sea hurt earnings. Under Robert Horton SOHIO sold off units. BP also bought livestock feed producer Purina Mills (1986 sold 1998) and the rest of SOHIO (1987).

Standard Oil of Indiana had its own problems including being kicked out of Iran after the Islamic revolution and causing a major oil spill off the French coast in 1978. The firm which became Amoco in 1985 bought Canada's Dome Petroleum in 1988 making it the largest private owner of North American gas reserves but the big purchase proved hard to swallow.

In 1992 Amoco hurled itself into overseas oil exploration. It was the first foreign oil company to explore the Chinese mainland. But by 1995 production was down. That year John Browne often compared to Rockefeller became BP's CEO. In 1996 BP and Mobil merged their European fuel

and lubricants operations and the British government sold its remaining stake in BP.

As oil prices tumbled in 1998 BP merged with Amoco in a $52 billion deal that formed BP Amoco. The new oil major agreed the following year to buy US-based Atlantic Richfield (ARCO) in a deal that closed in 2000. BP Amoco sold ARCO's Alaskan properties to Phillips (later ConocoPhillips) for $7 billion to gain regulatory approval for the purchase.

Its stake in Siberian oil fields was nearly taken away in a controversial 1999 bankruptcy sale before BP Amoco and Russia's Tyumen Oil agreed to cooperate. In 2000 BP Amoco and Shell Oil sold their stakes in Altura Energy to Occidental Petroleum for $3.6 billion. Also that year BP Amoco bought motor-oil maker Burmah Castrol for $4.7 billion. It paid $1.5 billion for the 18% of former ARCO exploration and production unit Vastar Resources that it didn't already own.

The company adopted BP as its main worldwide brand in 2000 and it officially shortened its name the next year.

In 2001 BP agreed to swap control of its stake in German natural gas supplier Ruhrgas plus $1.6 billion in cash and $950 million in assumed debt to German utility giant E.ON for a majority interest in Veba Oel owner of Germany's largest gas station chain. Regulators moved to keep E.ON from acquiring the Ruhrgas stake but BP agreed to make up the difference in cash if necessary and the deal proceeded. The agreement allowed BP to take full ownership of Veba Oel in 2002. To recoup some of its investment BP (with E.ON's consent) sold Veba Oel's exploration and production operations to Petro-Canada.

That year BP increased it stake in Russian oil and gas producer Sidanco from 10% to 25%.

In 2003 BP sold its Boqueron field and Desarrollo Zulia Occidental assets both located in Venezuela to Europe's Perenco. In late 2005 BP sold its petrochemical unit Innovene to INEOS for a reported $9 billion.

An explosion and fire in 2005 at BP's Texas City refinery killed 15 workers and injured many more.

In 2006 the company sold its remaining producing properties on the Outer Continental Shelf of the Gulf of Mexico to Apache Corporation for $845 million. That year BP sold its 28% stake in the Shenzi field in the Gulf of Mexico to Repsol for $2.2 billion. It also acquired a $1 billion stake in Rosneft.

In 2006 the discovery of corrosion in a major oil pipeline forced BP to close down part of its Prudhoe Bay oilfield (which represents 8% of daily US crude production) for several weeks.

That year the company also announced plans to invest $3 billion to reconfigure its Whiting Refinery in Indiana to process Canadian heavy crude oil.

In 2007 the company sold its Coryton refinery in the UK to Petroplus Holdings for $1.4 billion. That year BP acquired Chevron's 31% stake in a Netherlands-based refinery and other assets for $900 million.

BP's long-term chief executive John Browne was forced to step down in 2007 over a personal scandal and was replaced by BP veteran Tony Hayward. That year the company announced a major restructuring with a focus on core divisions Exploration & Production and Refining & Marketing and a new Alternative Energy unit dedicated to solar power wind energy and carbon capture technology.

In 2007 BP agreed to pay US authorities $373.5 million in fines relating to the 2005 Texas City refinery explosion the 2006 Alaska oil spill and a propane price-fixing scandal.

In 2008 the company signed a deal with Enbridge to pipe oil sands crude from Canada to the Texas Gulf Coast. Enbridge and BP will spend up to $2 billion to expand existing pipelines and build new connections to deliver up to 250000 barrels a day to Gulf Coast refiners by 2012. In another oil sands move BP and Husky Energy teamed up that same year to create an integrated North American oil sands business through two joint ventures BP-Husky Refinery LLC operated by BP and the Sunrise Oil Sands Partnership (SOSP) operated by Husky. BP committed $2.8 billion to create SOSP.

In 2008 BP acquired 90000 net acres of natural gas assets in the Arkoma Basin Woodford Shale play in the US from Chesapeake Energy for $1.75 billion. It subsequently bought a 25% stake in that company's Fayetteville Shale assets in Arkansas for $1.9 billion.

Boosting its North Sea assets in 2010 the company agreed to buy two oil fields in the Norwegian sector from TOTAL for $991 million. That year BP acquired Devon Energy's international assets for $7 billion in a deal that among other things gave BP a foothold in the emerging major oil play off the coast of Brazil. The company also gained properties in Azerbaijan and the Gulf of Mexico. (In 2010 it agreed to sell four of these mature deepwater oil and gas fields in Gulf of Mexico to Marubeni Oil and Gas for $650 million in order to pay down debt.)

The global recession and the slump in demand for oil and gas products saw BP's revenues (along with those of its industry peers) plummet in 2009. Improved market conditions in 2010 lifted revenues. However the company reported a $4.9 billion loss for 2010 as a result of the Gulf oil spill and its aftermath the cost of which was pegged at almost $41 billion.

EXECUTIVES

Group Chief Executive, Robert W. (Bob) Dudley, age 60, $750,000 total compensation
Chief Executive Alternative Energy and EVP Regions, Dev Sanyal, age 50
CEO US Lower 48 Onshore, David C. Lawler, age 48
Deputy Group Chief Executive, H. Lamar McKay, age 57
Group Operating Officer Strategy and Regions Upstream, Andy Hopwood, age 58
EVP Safety and Operational Risk, Bob Fryar, age 52
Chief Executive Upstream, Bernard Looney, age 45
EVP and Group Human Resources Director, Helmut Schuster, age 55
CFO, Brian Gilvary, age 54
President Russia, David Campbell
President Oman, Yousuf al Ojaili
Chief Executive Downstream, Tufan Erginbilgic, age 56
Treasurer, Alan Haywood
Chairman, Carl-Henric Svanberg, age 64
Auditors: Ernst & Young LLP

LOCATIONS

HQ: BP p.l.c.
1 St. James Square, London SW1Y 4PD
Phone: (44) 20 7496 4000   **Fax:** (44) 20 7496 4570
Web: www.bp.com

PRODUCTS/OPERATIONS

2014 Sales

	% of total
Upstream	8
Downstream	92
Other businesses and corporate	.
Total	**100**

2014 Sales

	% of total
US	35

Other countries	65
Total	**100**

Major Operations
Refining and marketing
  Marketing
  Refining
  Supply and trading
  Transportation and shipping
Exploration and production
  Field development
  Gas processing and marketing
  Oil and gas exploration
  Pipelines and transportation
Gas and power
  Natural gas marketing and trading
  Natural gas liquids
Chemicals
  Chemical intermediates
  Feedstock
  Performance products
  Polymers
Other
  Coal mining
  Solar power

Selected Subsidiaries

Atlantic Richfield Co
BP America Inc. (US)
BP Amoco Chemcal Company (US)
BP Oil Australia
BP Exploration Operating Company
BP Espa?a (Spain)
BP International
BP Norge (Norway)
BP Oil New Zealand
BP Shipping
BP Southern Africa (South Africa)
Burmah Castrol
The Standard Oil Company (US)

COMPETITORS

Apache	Koch Industries Inc.
Ashland Inc.	Marathon Oil
BASF SE	Norsk Hydro ASA
BG Group	Occidental Petroleum
BHP Billiton	PEMEX
Chevron	PETROBRAS
ConocoPhillips	Petrłeos de
Dow Chemical	Venezuela
DuPont	Repsol
Eni	Royal Dutch Shell
Exxon Mobil	Sinclair Oil
Hess Corporation	Sunoco
Huntsman International	TOTAL
Imperial Oil	Valero Energy

HISTORICAL FINANCIALS

Company Type: Public

Income Statement

	REVENUE ($ mil.)	NET INCOME ($ mil.)	NET PROFIT MARGIN	EMPLOYEES
				FYE: December 31
12/15	225,316	(6,482)	—	79,800
12/14	357,783	3,780	1.1%	84,500
12/13	383,102	23,451	6.1%	83,900
12/12	381,589	11,582	3.0%	85,700
12/11	382,333	25,700	6.7%	83,400
Annual Growth	**(12.4%)**	**—**	**—**	**(1.1%)**

2015 Year-End Financials

Debt ratio: 20.3%	No. of shares (mil.): —
Return on equity: (-6.2%)	Dividends
Cash ($ mil.): 26,389	Yield: 7.6%
Current ratio: 1.29	Payout: —
Long-term debt ($ mil.): 46,224	Market value ($ mil.): —

	STOCK PRICE ($) FY Close	P/E High/Low	Earnings	PER SHARE ($) Dividends	Book Value
12/15	31.26	— —	(0.35)	2.39	5.30
12/14	38.12	260170	0.20	2.34	6.12
12/13	48.61	39 32	1.23	2.19	6.95
12/12	41.64	79 60	0.60	1.98	6.19
12/11	42.74	36 26	1.34	1.68	5.87
Annual Growth	**(7.5%)**	**— —**	**—**	**9.2%**	**(2.6%)**

BPER Banca SpA

LOCATIONS

HQ: BPER Banca SpA
Via San Carlo, 8/20, Modena 41100
Phone: (39) 059 2021111   **Fax:** (39) 059 2022033
Web: www.bper.it

HISTORICAL FINANCIALS

Company Type: Public

Income Statement

FYE: December 31

	ASSETS ($ mil.)	NET INCOME ($ mil.)	INCOME AS % OF ASSETS	EMPLOYEES
12/15	66,726	240	0.4%	11,447
12/14	73,723	17	0.0%	11,593
12/13	85,024	9	0.0%	11,718
12/12	81,241	(14)	—	11,834
12/11	78,238	277	0.4%	11,965
Annual Growth	**(3.9%)**	**(3.5%)**	**—**	**(1.1%)**

2015 Year-End Financials

Return on assets: 0.3%	Dividends
Return on equity: 4.4%	Yield: 0.0%
Long-term debt ($ mil.): —	Payout: 5.7%
No. of shares (mil.): 480	Market value ($ mil.): 7,450
Sales ($ mil): 3,022	

	STOCK PRICE ($) FY Close	P/E High/Low	Earnings	PER SHARE ($) Dividends	Book Value
12/15	15.49	40 32	0.50	0.03	11.38
Annual Growth	**—**	**— —**	**—**	**—**	**—**

Bridgestone Corp (Japan)

Auditors: Deloitte Touche Tohmatsu LLC

LOCATIONS

HQ: Bridgestone Corp (Japan)
3-1-1 Kyobashi, Chuo-ku, Tokyo 104-8340
Phone: (81) 3 6836 3162
Web: www.bridgestone.co.jp

HISTORICAL FINANCIALS

Company Type: Public

Income Statement

FYE: December 31

	REVENUE ($ mil.)	NET INCOME ($ mil.)	NET PROFIT MARGIN	EMPLOYEES
12/15	31,485	2,361	7.5%	144,303
12/14	30,792	2,519	8.2%	144,632
12/13	33,991	1,924	5.7%	145,029
12/12	35,292	1,992	5.6%	143,448
12/11	39,081	1,330	3.4%	143,124
Annual Growth	(5.3%)	15.4%	—	0.2%

2015 Year-End Financials

Debt ratio: 0.1%
Return on equity: 13.2%
Cash ($ mil.): 3,220
Current ratio: 2.17
Long-term debt ($ mil.): 2,363

No. of shares (mil.): 783
Dividends
Yield: 2.9%
Payout: —
Market value ($ mil.): 13,381

	STOCK PRICE ($) FY Close	P/E High/Low	PER SHARE ($) Earnings	Dividends	Book Value
12/15	17.09	— —	3.01	0.50	24.20
12/14	17.41	— —	3.21	0.34	22.97
12/13	19.10	— —	2.46	0.22	22.67
12/12	51.67	— —	2.54	0.70	21.05
12/11	45.00	— —	1.70	0.00	19.25
Annual Growth	(21.5%)	— —	15.4%	—	5.9%

British American Tobacco Plc (United Kingdom)

When people pick up smoking British American Tobacco (BAT) picks up steam. BAT is the world's second-largest publicly-traded tobacco company by market share (after Philip Morris International). The company rolls more than 660 billion cigarettes a year sold in 200 markets across 60-plus countries. BAT's five global cigarette brands –Dunhill Kent Rothmans Lucky Strike and Pall Mall — account for more than a third of group sales. BAT also produces loose tobacco and regional cigarette brands giving it a portfolio of more than 200 brands overall. It owns 42% of Reynolds American the #2 US cigarette maker created by the merger of BAT's Brown & Williamson unit with R.J. Reynolds Tobacco. BAT holds about 30% of India's ITC as well.

OperationsThe company sources its product from more than 100000 tobacco farmers worldwide. BAT contributed about £30 billion worth of excise and other taxes to governments worldwide in 2014.

BAT's five Global Drive Brands (GDBs) include Dunhill Kent Lucky Strike Pall Mall and Rothmans.

Geographic Reach

BAT generated 28% of its total revenue from sales in the Asia-Pacific region in 2014 while sales from the Americas; Western Europe; and Eastern Europe Middle East and Africa (EMEA) regions contributed 21% 24% and 27% to total revenue respectively.

Sales and Marketing

BAT sells its product through retailers wholesalers distributors and logistics providers. About 50% of its global volume is sold by retailers that are supplied by direct distribution or exclusive distributors. Financial PerformanceNote: Growth rates may differ after conversion to US dollars.

BAT has struggled to grow its revenues and profits over the past few years as cigarette and tobacco product sales have been dampened worldwide with decreasing use rates.

The company's revenue fell by 8% to £13.97 billion ($21.7 billion) in 2014 mostly because of unfavorable foreign exchange rates across its international markets. Not counting this however BAT's revenue rose by nearly 3% as its price mix increased by 4% during the year. The cigarette maker recorded volume growth in Bangladesh China Iran Pakistan Turkey Ukraine and Venezuela; while cigarette sales volumes in Brazil Russia Vietnam and Western Europe shrank by around 1%. The strength of its GDBs drove its share growth higher by 10 basis points in key markets.

Declining revenue in 2014 caused BAT's net income to fall by nearly 20% to £3.39 billion ($5 billion) while the company's operating cash fell by 8% to £4.9 billion ($7.6 billion) as cash earnings shrank during the year.

Strategy

BAT in 2015 continued to invest in high-growth markets with a focus on Eastern Europe Africa the Middle East and the Asia/Pacific regions. It also pledged to continue introducing differentiated products and next-generation tobacco products such as its recent Vype brand e-cigarettes and Voke a nicotine inhalation product licensed as medicine in the UK; the company reported that its innovations made up nearly 50% of its Global Drive Brand (GDBs) volume during 2014. The company planned to launch its new tobacco heating product in test markets in 2016.

Faced with struggling sales in recent years the firm has had to cut back operations in several markets to keep its profits stable. In 2014 it closed factories in Australia Colombia and Congo while restructuring factories in Argentina Canada Germany Indonesia and Switzerland. In past years the company has cut costs by closing and downsizing its operations in other countries including Australia Denmark Italy Poland as well as combining businesses in Belgium Luxembourg and the Netherlands. All told the cigarette maker has scaled back the number of factories it operates to 44 from 83 (including acquisitions) in 2000.

The cigarette industry continues to consolidate adding possible challenges for BAT in the future. BAT's equity stake in rival Reynolds helps to hedge its bets but it comes with its own set of challenges. In 2014 for example Reynolds American Inc. acquired smaller cigarette maker Lorillard forcing BAT to make a $4.7 billion investment to keep its 42% equity stake in the enlarged Reynolds.

To mitigate this challenge and bolster its market presence in the tobacco industry in 2016 the company agreed to acquire the remaining shares in Reynolds American about 58% for $49.4 billion.

Mergers & Acquisitions

In 2016 the company agreed to acquire the remaining shares in Reynolds American about 58% for $49.4 billion. The deal upon approval will bring BAT 100% ownership of Reynolds' Camel Doral Eclipse Pall Mall and Newport cigarette brands as well as other tobacco products. Company BackgroundIn fall 2011 it purchased Colombia's second-largest cigarette maker Productora Tabacalera de Colombia (Protabaco) for $452 million. Protabaco's brands include Mustang (the country's #2 selling cigarette) Premier and President. The deal elevates BAT from third place to second in Colombia's cigarette market.

HISTORY

After a year of vicious price-cutting between Imperial Tobacco (UK) and James Buchanan Duke's American Tobacco in the UK Imperial counterattacked in the US. To end the cigarette price war in the UK the firms created British American Tobacco (BAT) in 1902. The truce granted Imperial the British market American the US market and they jointly owned BAT in the rest of the world.

With Duke in control BAT expanded into new markets. In China it was selling 25 billion cigarettes a year by 1920. When the Communist revolution ended BAT's operations in China the company lost more than 25% of its sales (although China later reemerged as a major export market for the company's cigarettes).

A 1911 US antitrust action forced American to sell its interest in BAT and opened the US market to the company. BAT purchased US cigarette manufacturer Brown & Williamson in 1927 and continued to grow through geographic expansion until the 1960s. In 1973 BAT and Imperial each regained control of its own brands in the UK and Continental Europe. Imperial sold the last of its stake in BAT in 1980.

Fearing that mounting public concern over smoking would limit the cigarette market BAT acquired nontobacco businesses; it changed its name to B.A.T Industries in 1976. The acquisitions of retailers Saks (1973) Argos (UK 1979) Marshall Field (1982) and later insurance firms diversified the company's sales base. After a 1989 hostile takeover bid from Sir James Goldsmith it sold its retail operations and retained its tobacco and financial services.

In 1994 B.A.T acquired the former American Tobacco for $1 billion. In 1997 the company acquired Cigarrera de Moderna (with 50% of Mexico's cigarette sales) and formed a joint venture with the Turkish tobacco state enterprise Tekel.

B.A.T's tobacco operations were spun off in 1998 as British American Tobacco (BAT). The financial services operations were merged with Zurich Insurance in a transaction that created two holding companies: Allied Zurich (UK) and Zurich Allied (Switzerland). With the changes Martin Broughton became chairman of BAT.

The company in 1999 paid $8.2 billion to buy Dutch cigarette company Rothmans International (Rothmans Dunhill) from Switzerland's Compagnie Financiere Richemont and South Africa's Rembrandt Group —both controlled by Anton Rupert. With the purchase BAT received a controlling stake in Canada's Rothmans Benson & Hedges (RBH).

In early 2000 BAT bought the 58% of Canada's Imasco it didn't already own. Imasco sold off its financial services and BAT received Imasco's Imperial Tobacco unit (not related to the UK's Imperial Brands) in the deal. (Formerly called Imperial Tobacco Company of Canada Imasco was created in 1908 with help from BAT.) BAT also unloaded its share of RBH via a public offering.

In 2001 BAT bought the 40.5% of its BAT Australasia subsidiary (formed in 1999 through the Rothmans merger) it didn't already own. Broughton announced that year that the Chinese government had approved development plans that would allow the company to build a factory in China. The company also announced it would build the first foreign-owned cigarette factory in South Korea at that time the world's #8 tobacco market.

Increasing its Latin American regional presence BAT purchased a controlling stake in Peru's top tobacco company Tabacalera Nacional and several of its suppliers in 2003. However two months later BAT said it would not make the million-dollar investment in the company. The announcement came soon after Peru raised taxes on cigarettes. By the end of the year BAT had purchased tobacco manufacturer Ente Tabacchi Italiani S.p.A. from the Italian government. BAT sold the distribution end of its Italian business to Compañia de Distribucion Integral Logista in 2004 the same year that Broughton retired; the company named Jan du Plessis as chairman and Paul Adams as CEO.

In June 2009 the company acquired an 85% stake in Indonesia's fourth largest cigarette maker PT Bentoel Internasional Investama Tbk for £303 million ($494 million) from Rajawali Group. Later that year Richard Burrows became chairman; he replaced du Plessis who had become chairman of Rio Tinto. Replacing Adams Nicandro Durante became CEO in early 2011. BAT in fall 2011 acquired Colombia's second-largest cigarette maker Productora Tabacalera de Colombia (Protabaco) for $452 million.

EXECUTIVES

President Souza Cruz, Nicandro Durante, age 59, $516,791 total compensation
Finance Director, Ben Stevens, age 56, $528,901 total compensation
Director Special Projects, Jean-Marc Levy
Regional Director Asia-Pacific, Jack Bowles, age 52
Managing Director Next Generation Products, Des Naughton, age 49
Regional Director Western Europe, Naresh Sethi
Director Operations, Alan Davy
Regional Director Americas, Ricardo Oberlander
Chairman, Richard Burrows, age 71
Auditors: KPMG LLP

LOCATIONS

HQ: British American Tobacco Plc (United Kingdom)
   Globe House, 4 Temple Place, London WC2R 2PG
Phone: (44) 20 7845 1000   **Fax:** (44) 20 7240 0555
Web: www.bat.com

PRODUCTS/OPERATIONS

2014 Cigarettes Sold

	Billion
Pall Mall	92
Kent	64
Dunhill	55
Rothmans	36
Lucky Strike	31
Total	**278**

2014 Sales

	% of total
Asia-Pacific	28
EEMEA	27
Western Europe	24
Americas	21
Total	**100**

Selected Brands

Benson & Hedges (Asia/Pacific Middle East Africa)
Craven ' A'
Dunhill
John Player Gold Leaf
Kent
Kool
Lucky Strike
Pall Mall
Peter Stuyvesant
Player' s Gold Lead
Rothmans
State Express 555
Viceroy
Vogue

COMPETITORS

Altria	Santa Fe Natural
Imperial Brands	Tobacco

Japan Tobacco
Philip Morris
   International
Reemtsma
   Cigarettenfabriken

Swedish Match
Swisher International
Universal Corporation
Vector Group

HISTORICAL FINANCIALS

Company Type: Public

Income Statement

FYE: December 31

	REVENUE ($ mil.)	NET INCOME ($ mil.)	NET PROFIT MARGIN	EMPLOYEES
12/15	19,419	6,357	32.7%	87,577
12/14	21,809	4,862	22.3%	90,118
12/13	25,218	6,451	25.6%	89,820
12/12	24,484	6,191	25.3%	87,485
12/11	23,789	4,781	20.1%	87,813
Annual Growth	**(4.9%)**	**7.4%**	**—**	**(0.1%)**

2015 Year-End Financials

Debt ratio: 79.9%	No. of shares (mil.): 2,026
Return on equity: 82.4%	Dividends
Cash ($ mil.): 2,909	Yield: 4.1%
Current ratio: 1.09	Payout: 132.9%
Long-term debt ($ mil.): 21,941	Market value ($ mil.): 223,867

	STOCK PRICE ($) FY Close	P/E High/Low		PER SHARE ($) Earnings	Dividends	Book Value
12/15	110.45	50	42	3.41	2.27	3.58
12/14	107.82	70	54	2.60	2.41	4.24
12/13	107.42	61	50	3.38	2.16	5.41
12/12	101.25	57	47	3.18	2.11	5.94
12/11	94.88	61	45	2.41	3.64	6.23
Annual Growth	**3.9%**	**—**	**—**	**9.1%**	**(11.2%)**	
(12.9%)						

Brookfield Asset Management Inc

Brookfield Asset Management sees the money flowing in from real estate. The company has approximately $200 billion in assets under management including commercial properties power generation interests and infrastructure holdings. It owns commercial retail residential and development properties in the Americas Europe Asia Pacific and the Middle East. Through its Brookfield Office Properties subsidiary it is one of the largest commercial landlords in Lower Manhattan. Brookfield also owns some 200 power-generating facilities including hydroelectric and wind plants through its 63% stake in Brookfield Renewable Energy. Other assets include a minority stake in mall owner General Growth Properties(GGP).

Operations
The company has seven core business segments: Property Service Activities Residential Development Private Equity Infrastructure Renewable Energy and Asset Management. Brookfield is especially focused on developing owning and operating real estate assets including property (office residential industrial and hotels) infrastructure (utilities transport energy timberland and agriculture) and renewable energy (hydroelectric and wind power facilities) —activities that make up nearly 50% of its revenue.

The company's Service Activities segment (which made up 19% of revenue in 2014) provides construction management and contracting services

---

as well as global corporate relocation facilities management and residential brokerage services. The Residential Development segment (15% of revenue) builds homes and condos and develops land. Its Private Equity segment (14% of revenue) typically invests in "out-of-favor sectors" and distressed or under-performing companies in Canada or the US in need of restructuring or redirection or provides event-driven financing to mid-market companies in the two regions.

Geographic Reach
Toronto-based Brookfield has a wide variety of holdings around the world with operations in Asia Australia Europe the Middle East North America and South America. About 33% of its revenue came from its business in the US in 2014 while its next largest markets were in Canada (19% of revenue) Australia (17% of revenue) Europe (12%) and Brazil (10% of revenue).

Sales and Marketing
The fund's institutional investors include sovereign wealth funds insurance companies and pension plans.

Financial Performance
The company's revenues and profits have been trending higher over the past few years as it's acquired more property assets and as property and portfolio-company valuations have risen in the strengthened economy. Brookfield's revenue reversed course in 2014 however falling 12% to $18.4 billion mostly as its Private Equity income declined 38% after it sold off two of its revenue-generating forest product investments. Its Asset Management income also shrank 35% mostly because in 2013 it had recognized a large non-recurring large client investment gain. Despite revenue declines in 2014 the firm's net income jumped 47% to $3.11 billion mostly thanks to a $3 billion-increase in fair value gains on its investment properties and equity investments in office and retail properties which benefited from lower discount rates and higher rental income. Brookfield's operating cash levels grew by more than 10% to $2.6 billion for the year thanks to higher cash earnings.

Strategy
Brookfield Asset Management is always on the lookout for acquisition opportunities and other ways to invest in out-of-favor promising markets with high barriers to entry as well as opportunities to sell assets to raise more capital. A key investment strategy for 2015 included investing in commodities and commodity-related businesses in Brazil (where there is a lack of capital in the market) and in Europe (where governments companies and banks continue to aggressively deleverage). The firm is also hopeful that the types of investments it specializes in —especially property power and infrastructure assets —will only grow in value as the world real estate markets continue to heat up.

Brookfield regularly performs fund offerings to raise capital for future investments. In 2013 the company closed on its Brookfield Infrastructure Fund II with commitments of $7 billion (easily exceeding its original target of $5 billion). Also that year Brookfield closed on its Timberlands Fund V with commitments of $1 billion. That fund will invest in timberlands around the world with an emphasis on the US Brazil and Australia.

Mergers and Acquisitions
In 2017 Brookfield offered to buy TerraForm Power for about $1.6 billion. The company already held a 12% stake in the power provider.

In February 2016 Brookfield Asset Management agreed to buy Rouse Properties for $2.8 billion. The deal was expected to close by the third quarter of 2016.

In January 2015 Brookfield Asset Management expanded its exposure to its second- and third-largest markets after it agreed to buy the remaining 50% stake of the Canadian and Australia facilities management business that it didn't own from joint-venture partner Johnson Controls Inc for $200 million. In early 2014 the company privatized its Brookfield Office Properties subsidiary after acquiring the 51% share stake that it didn't already own. The company kept itself busy in 2013 with a string of widely varied acquisitions. Major purchases that year included a minority stake in warehouse/distribution parks developer EZW Gazeley (with extensive holdings in Europe); an increase of its positions in mall owners General Growth Properties and Rouse Properties; all of Los Angeles commercial property owner MPG Office Trust (for $443 million); and all of business park developer Industrial Developments International ($595 million). It bought a portfolio of 19 apartment communities in North Carolina South Carolina and Virginia from Babcock & Brown Residential further boosting its multifamily portfolio.

The company also launched refrigeration unit Brookfield Cold Storage in 2013 after acquiring the Canadian logistics operations of Millard Refrigerated Services. The deal included more than 16 million cu. ft. of storage space in two facilities located in Toronto and Calgary.

EXECUTIVES

Senior Managing Partner Property Group and President Brookfield Properties, Steven J. (Steve) Douglas

Senior Managing Partner CEO and Director, J. Bruce Flatt, age 50, $485,450 total compensation

Senior Managing Partner and Head of Infrastructure Activities, Samuel J. B. (Sam) Pollock, $755,788 total compensation

Senior Managing Partner Chief Financial Officer, Brian D. Lawson, age 57, $485,450 total compensation

Senior Managing Partner and global head of real estate at Brookfield CEO of Brookfield Property Partners chairman of Rouse Properties and a member of the board of director of General Growth Properties, Richard B. (Ric) Clark, age 57

Managing Partner Corporate Operations, Brett M. Fox

Senior Managing Partner; Chairman Brookfield Power and Utilities, Harry A. Goldgut

Senior Managing Partner; President and CEO Brookfield Renewable Energy Partners, Richard Legault

Managing Partner Human Resources, Lori Pearson

Managing Partner Private Funds Group, Leo van den Thillart

Senior Managing Partner; President and CEO Brookfield Brazil, Luiz Ildefonso Sim ţes Lopes

Senior Managing Partner and Global Chief Investment Officer Brookfield Property Group, Brian Kingston

Senior Managing Partner Risk and Treasury, William Powell

Senior Managing Partner Brookfield Asset Management and Chief Investment Officer for Brookfield in South America, Ben Vaughan

Chair of the Board of Directors, Frank J. McKenna, age 68

Auditors: Deloitte LLP

LOCATIONS

HQ: Brookfield Asset Management Inc
Brookfield Asset Management Inc., Suite 300, Brookfield Place, 181 Bay Street, Toronto, Ontario M5J 2T3

Phone: 416 363-9491   **Fax:** 416 365-9642
Web: www.brookfield.com

2014 Sales

	% of total
US	33
Canada	19
Australia	17
Europe	12
Brazil	10
Others	9
Total	**100**

PRODUCTS/OPERATIONS

2014 Sales

	% of total
Property	26
Service Activities	19
Residential development	15
Private equity	14
Infrastructure	12
Renewable power	9
Asset management	4
Others	1
Total	**100**

Selected Subsidiaries

Brookfield Brasil S.A.
Brookfield Infrastructure Partners L.P. (29%)
Brookfield Multiplex Australia
Brookfield Office Properties Inc. (51%)
Brookfield Renewable Energy Partners L.P. (73%)
Brookfield Residential Properties (73%)
Norbord Inc. (52%)

COMPETITORS

Berkshire Hathaway	Equity Office
Blackstone Group	Pinetree Capital
CBRE Group	RREEF Funds
Dundee Corp.	
Equity Group Investments	

HISTORICAL FINANCIALS

Company Type: Public

Income Statement

FYE: December 31

	REVENUE ($ mil.)	NET INCOME ($ mil.)	NET PROFIT MARGIN	EMPLOYEES
12/15	19,913	2,341	11.8%	55,700
12/14	18,364	3,110	16.9%	30,000
12/13	20,830	2,120	10.2%	28,000
12/12	18,697	1,380	7.4%	24,000
12/11	4,100	1,957	47.7%	23,000
Annual Growth	48.5%	4.6%	—	24.7%

2015 Year-End Financials

Debt ratio: 41.7%
Return on equity: 9.5%
Cash ($ mil.): 2,774
Current ratio: 1.42
Long-term debt ($ mil.): 58,283

No. of shares (mil.): 961
Dividends
 Yield: 1.5%
 Payout: 20.9%
Market value ($ mil.): 30,310

	STOCK PRICE ($) FY Close	P/E High/Low	PER SHARE ($) Earnings	Dividends	Book Value
12/15	31.53	25 13	2.26	0.47	26.33
12/14	50.13	16 11	3.11	0.45	25.53
12/13	38.83	19 16	2.08	0.39	22.62
12/12	36.65	28 21	1.31	0.37	22.66
12/11	27.48	17 13	1.93	0.35	20.34
Annual Growth	3.5%	—	4.1%	8.1%	6.7%

BT Group Plc

BT Group offers local and long-distance phone service and provides internet access and other data and IT services. The UK-based company operates through several divisions: corporate clients are served through its BT Global Services unit BT Business provides communications and IT services in the UK and the Republic of Ireland and BT Consumer offers consumer fixed-voice and broadband services in the UK. The BT Wholesale and Openreach divisions are devoted to the broadband and local network needs of other carriers. BT Group which traces its history back to 1879 introduced its distinctive red phone booths around London and other service areas in 1936. The company acquired mobile network EE for £12.5 billion in 2016.

Operations
BT Global Services the group's enterprise telecommunications division is its largest segment by sales accounting for about 38% of revenue in 2015 (ended March). It provides voice and data communications as well as managed network and IT services to corporate and public sector customers in more than 170 countries; the UK government is the company's largest client. BT Global Services also operates customer contact and data centers and offers customer relationship management and managed network security.

BT Business serves small and medium-sized enterprises (SMEs) in fixed-voice and data; mobility; and IT services. The company has a market share of around 30% in fixed-voice and data but just 1% in mobility and 6% in IT services. The segment accounts for 15% of the BT Group's revenue.

BT Consumer provides broadband TV sports channels and mobile services. The unit also sells services through its Plusnet brand. The segment generates about a quarter of revenue.

BT Wholesale provides network services to more than 1400 communications service providers in the UK. It operates the only network that covers the entire country and many competitors pay to use its network to enable their own services. BT Wholesale manages the network infrastructure for Virgin Media and KCOM while O2 and Vodafone use its fixed-line network for their business customers. It has about 12% of the BT Group's sales.

Openreach is the group's smallest segment with 11% of sales. It was created in 2006 as part of a settlement with regulatory agency Ofcom to ensure that other companies have full access to BT's network. About 500 communications service providers including BT divisions rely on Openreach for network communications.

Geographic Reach
The UK is London-based BT Group's largest market accounting for more than three-quarters of its annual sales. Key European markets for the company include Italy Germany and Spain. In North America BT serves customers from offices in 25 cities. The firm also has a presence in high-growth regions in Asia Pacific Latin America the Middle East and Africa. Overall BT Group has operations in about 170 countries.

Financial Performance
BT Group's revenue declined 2% in 2015 (ended March) versus the prior year to £17.8 billion. BT Global's revenue dropped 7% because of the negative impact from foreign exchange and lower transit revenue. BT Business underlying revenue excluding transit was down with lower call and line volumes as customers moved to broadband and IP services. BT Wholesale underlying revenue fell 7%.

Net income grew 15% in 2015 versus 2014 while cash flow was flat year-to-year.

Strategy
BT Group is looking to spruce up its infrastructure and making improvements to its UK broadband network. The network is more resilient and has the capacity to comfortably accommodate increases in traffic. With its mobile virtual network

operator (MVNO) partner EE BT Group is developing new mobile services that enable BT Consumer's jump back into mobile.

Mergers and Acquisitions

In early 2016 BT Group acquired major mobile network EE. The £12.5 billion mega-deal is the latest in the UK's 'quad-play' wars a tussle between media communications companies to offer triple-play —television broadband and telephone —plus mobile. The acquisition of EE adds the mobile segment to BT's pre-existing triple-play offering and has the potential to alter to UK's telecommunications landscape and put pressure on smaller rivals.

Ownership

Asset manager Invesco owns about 10% of BT Group's stock.

HISTORY

Early History

In 1879 the British Post Office (now known as Royal Mail and formerly Consignia) got the exclusive right to operate telegraph systems. When private firms tried to offer phone service the government objected arguing in court that its telegraph monopoly was imperiled. The courts agreed and the Post Office was empowered to license private phone companies collect a 10% royalty and operate its own systems.

The private National Telephone Company emerged as the leading phone outfit competing with the Post Office. When National's license expired in 1911 the Post Office took over and became the monopoly phone company. In 1936 the phone system introduced its familiar red phone booths designed for King George V's jubilee.

Under a 1981 law telecommunications were split from the Post Office and placed under the new British Telecommunications (BT). The government also allowed competitor Mercury Communications —formerly One 2 One and now known as T-Mobile (UK) —to compete. The Thatcher government soon called for BT's privatization.

EXECUTIVES

Group Finance Director, Simon Lowth, age 55
CEO, Gavin Patterson, age 49
General Counsel and Secretary, Dan Fitz
CIO, J. Howard Watson, age 54
CEO Openreach, Clive Selley
CEO - BT Global Services, Luis Alvarez
Chairman, Michael D. V. (Mike) Rake, age 68
Auditors: PricewaterhouseCoopers LLP

LOCATIONS

HQ: BT Group Plc
BT Centre, 81 Newgate Street, London EC1A 7AJ
Phone: (44) 20 7356 5000   **Fax:** (44) 20 7356 5520
Web: www.bt.com

2015 Sales

	% of total
Europe Middle East & Africa	
UK	78
Other countries	13
Americas	6
Asia Pacific	3
Total	**100**

PRODUCTS/OPERATIONS

2015 Sales

	% of total
BT Global Services	38
BT consumer	24
BT business	15
BT wholesale	12
Openreach	11

Total	**100**

2015 Sales by Market

	%
ICT & managed networks	36
Calls & lines	33
Broadband & convergence	21
Transit	3
Other	7
Total	**100**

Selected Subsidiaries and Affiliates

Basilica Computing Limited (IT services)
British Telecommunications plc (telecommunication related services and products)
BT Americas Inc. (telecommunication related services and products US)
BT Australasia Pty Limited (telecommunication related services and products Australia)
BT Centre Nominee 2 Limited (property holding company)
BT Communications Ireland Limited (telecommunications services)
BT Conferencing Inc. (Audio video and Web conferencing services US)
BT Convergent Solutions Limited (communications related services and products)
BT ESPAÑA Compaía de Servicios Globales de Telecomunicaciones S.A. (telecommunication related services and products Spain)
BT Fleet Limited (fleet management)
BT France SA (telecommunication related services and products)
BT Frontline Pte Ltd (communications related services and products Singapore)
BT (Germany) GmbH & Co. oHG (telecommunication related services and products)
BT Global Services Limited (international telecommunications network systems)
BT Holdings Limited (investment holding company)
BT Hong Kong Limited (telecommunication related services and products)
BT Infrastructures Critiques (IT systems and network services France)
BT INS Inc (Information telecommunication consulting and software US)
BT Italia SpA (telecommunications related services and products Italy 97%)
BT Limited (international telecommunication network systems provider)
BT Nederland NV (telecommunication related services and products The Netherlands)
BT US Investments Limited (investments holding company US)
Communications Global Network Services Limited (telecommunication related services and products Bermuda)
Communication Networking Services (UK) (telecommunication related services and products)
Infonet Services Corporation (global managed network services provider US)
Infonet USA Corporation (global managed network services provider US)
Radianz Americas Inc. (global managed network services provider US)

COMPETITORS

Accenture	Sky plc
COLT Group	THUS Ltd.
Cable & Wireless	TalkTalk
Capgemini	Telecom Italia
Deutsche Telekom	Telecom plus
Easynet	Telefnica
IBM Global Services	Telenor
KCOM Group	TeliaSonera
KPN	Verizon Enterprise
Orange	Solutions
Orange Business	Virgin Media
Services	Vodafone

HISTORICAL FINANCIALS

Company Type: Public

Income Statement

FYE: March 31

	REVENUE ($ mil.)	NET INCOME ($ mil.)	NET PROFIT MARGIN	EMPLOYEES
03/16	27,409	3,725	13.6%	102,500
03/15	26,571	3,155	11.9%	88,500
03/14	30,444	3,359	11.0%	87,800
03/13	27,379	3,177	11.6%	87,900
03/12	30,280	3,208	10.6%	89,000
Annual Growth	**(2.5%)**	**3.8%**	**—**	**3.6%**

2016 Year-End Financials

Debt ratio: 48.2%
Return on equity: 46.1%
Cash ($ mil.): 715
Current ratio: 0.74
Long-term debt ($ mil.): 15,879

No. of shares (mil.): —
Dividends
  Yield: 2.9%
  Payout: 204.1%
Market value ($ mil.): —

	STOCK PRICE ($) FY Close	P/E High/Low		PER SHARE ($)	
			Earnings	Dividends	Book Value
03/16	32.08	240 106	0.43	0.94	1.50
03/15	65.17	262 199	0.39	0.88	0.14
03/14	63.85	271 172	0.41	0.76	(0.12)
03/13	42.03	159 113	0.39	0.64	(0.05)
03/12	36.16	145 100	0.39	0.58	0.25
Annual Growth	**(2.9%)**	**— —**	**2.4%**	**12.6%**	**55.7%**

Caisse des Depots et Consignations (France)

Caisse des Depôts et Consignations (CDC) serves as an investment manager for the French government and oversees tax-exempt funds collected by savings banks (caisses d'epargne) and the post office. The group invests its deposits in public projects including subsidized housing and semi-public companies formed with local governments for urban development. CDC manages retirement plans for government employees who are not part of the civil service system. Created by a French law passed in 1816 the public financial institution is under the supervision and guarantee of Parliament.

Operations

The company operates in five segments: Caisse des Depôts; Banking Insurance and La Poste; Corporate Finance; Real Estate and Tourism; and Infrastructure Transport and Environment.

Of these five segments the Caisse des Depôts segment generates the majority of revenue and consists of four divisions of its own including: Banking services savings funds the pensions and solidarity sector and regional development. Its Banking services division provides specialized banking services for third-party funds handled by regulated legal professions. It acts as banker to ACOSS the central body for France's social security system providing essential treasury management functions for agencies responsible for collecting mandatory contributions. It also provides banking administrative and financial services. The Pensions and Solidarity division provides asset management services for pension and solidarity funds for some 75000 public-sector employers including local regional and national government entities and hospitals. This division manages 47 funds covering 7.3 million active employees and 3.5 million old age pensioners (or 1 out of every 5 pensioners in France). CDC's Savings Funds division is France's top investor in social housing projects and funds the building and renovation of social housing units and care homes for populations at risk (through urban renewal projects transport infrastructure universities hospitals high-speed Internet access projects water supply networks and public building renovation projects).

The Regional and Local Development and Network division partners local and regional development projects. It funds economic development social cohesion projects (including urban planning and development) and supports the switch to alternative and renewable energy sources.

Geographic Reach

CDC's Caisse des Depôts group has a network of 25 regional offices in metropolitan France and operates through its subsidiaries in more than 90 countries.

Financial Performance

After spending years slowly recovering from the financial crisis CDC reports that its profits have been "virtually restored to to pre-financial crisis levels." CDC's net revenue grew by 2% to euro 7.1 billion (about $9.77 billion) in 2013 thanks to gains from financial instruments and available-for-sale financial assets. The group's interest and fee income however fell from the year before as the group had fewer interest-earning assets after these security sales.

The higher revenue and slightly lower operating costs helped net income jump to euro 2.3 billion (around $3.2 billion) a considerable improvement from last year's euro 1.32 billion (around $1.82 billion) loss. Despite higher earnings operations used euro 4.18 billion (roughly $5.75 billion) in 2013 spending significantly more cash than in 2012 when operations provided euro 3.02 billion (around $4 billion). This is mostly because the group used a net euro 13.2 billion (roughly $18.2 billion) toward interbank loans in 2013 whereas in 2012 it received more cash from other banks than it lent.

Strategy

CDC invests in development project needs that the market alone can't respond to. Rather than using contributions from the state budget or taxpayers the public institution finances all of its activities itself. Its profits come from stable diversified contracts with and on behalf of the public sector its subsidiary companies and strategic holdings. It has an extensive regional network and deep local roots through its subsidiaries which helps it partner and drive forward public policy projects across France.As part of the French government's Investments for the Future initiative CDC group has been entrusted to manage a euro 100 million (about $114 million) endowment that will go toward employment integration and other social programs designed to stimulate the French economy with the goal of adding 40000 to 60000 new jobs. Most of CDC's current investments are in projects relating to its strategic priorities of economic development higher education and training research industrial sectors and small to medium enterprises sustainable development (involving housing infrastructure energy efficiency and renewable energy) and digital developments.

While it mostly holds French and European financial assets CDC is beginning to invest more internationally to diversify into other vibrant economies. In 2014 for example CDC's investment arm (CDC International Capital) teamed up with Abu Dhabi-based Mubadala Development Company to launch a euro 300 million co-investment platform to pursue investment opportunities targeting equity stakes in private companies. In 2013

CDC International Capital and RDIF launched euro 1bn the Russia-France Investment Fund to seek attractive investments in broad range of sectors and asset classes.

In 2013 the French Minister of Finance la Banque Postale the Dexia group and CDC set up Societe de Financement Local (SFIL) as a development bank. The French State CDC and La Banque Postale own 75% 20% and 5% respectively of SFIL. The local development bank provided medium and long-term reﬁnancing — via its mortgage credit arm (Caisse Française de Financement Local) for the loans granted by La Banque Postale in partnership with CDC to local authorities and their business groups and to hospitals and healthcare organizations.

HISTORY

When Louis XVIII restored the monarchy in France in 1815 its government was deeply in debt and had problems raising money. To help remedy the situation the government in 1816 formed Caisse des Depôts et Consignations (CDC) to guarantee and invest deposits collected in escrow accounts and civil servants' retirement funds and by the post offices; because repayments had to be ready upon demand the organization put the money in short-term investments. The investments help stabilize France's economy and make its debt more attractive to foreign investors in the 1820s when it began underwriting municipal bonds.

In 1837 the CDC was given control over deposits in the government-owned savings banks (caisses d'epargne) and allowed to invest in government stocks and other issues growing its asset base and expanding its lending capabilities. Throughout the turbulent 19th century the organization faced the ebb and flow of deposits and rising and falling interest rates that threatened its liquidity and assets. In the mid-1880s CDC turned its eye to social welfare taking over all civil servant pensions in 1850 (only to have the responsibility revoked three years later) and launching cut-rate life insurance (1868). It also expanded its assets including more military pension funds and gaming taxes collected for charity; the group began lending to housing companies in 1894. By the dawn of the 20th century CDC began investing in foreign securities.

During the early 20th century the group watched its assets grow as deposits increased and interest rates were robust. In 1931 CDC began investing in industrial and commercial stocks. The Depression however put a drain on deposits and cut back its lending. By 1935 it was dormant after spending its resources to lower interest rates. The government helped revive the group just in time for WWII. During the war it ran a compensation fund for companies damaged during air bombings and took control of French Jews' assets under the order of the Vichy government. (In the late 1990s CDC began researching and returning these assets to their rightful owners.)

As France reformed after its liberation so did CDC. It became a lead underwriting manager in the 1960s and rising interest rates coupled with growing investments in government stock helped make up for losses on loans to the housing sector. In the 1970s it raised money in the foreign markets for France's toll road agency and began forming urban development subsidiaries. In the 1980s CDC was using about 60% of its assets in long-term housing loans a business that was threatened as the French moved their money from stagnant savings accounts to riskier investments.

With its asset base shrinking and competition encroaching the group began to diversify in the 1990s moving into venture capital investing in

transportation and expanding around the world. In the late 1990s it took over Credit Foncier de France the failed government property bank. In 2000 CDC reorganized its operations into three major subsidiaries: CDC Ixis (markets and financing asset management and banking and securities services) CNP Assurances (personal insurance) and C3D (real estate tourism transportation environmental services and infrastructure engineering).

CDC sold its stakes in CDC Ixis and in Eulia to La Caisse Nationale des Caisses d'Epargne (in which CDC also held a stake) in 2004. Two years later the company sold its CNCE holdings.

In 2007 the firm entered an alliance with NYSE Euronext to provide a carbon trading marketplace through Powernext Carbon a subsidiary of electricity trader Powernext.

The global financial crisis hit CDC hard in 2008. That year the company reported the first annual losses in its history. Contributing to those losses was the company's bailout of troubled Franco/Belgian bank Dexia through which CDC became the bank's largest shareholder.

In 2009 the company joined with France's national meteorological service Meteo-France and NYSE Euronext to take control of MetNext a climate and weather risk management firm.

EXECUTIVES

Chairman and CEO Egis, Nicolas Jachiet, age 58
CEO CDC Climat, Pierre Ducret, age 61
CEO, Pierre-Rene Lemas, age 66
Deputy CEO; Director Savings Funds, Odile Renaud-Basso, age 51
Banking Services Director, Nathalie Gilly, age 52
Group Finance Director, Olivier Mareuse, age 53
Head Financial Transactions Processing Caisse des Dep´ts; General Financial Officer, Andre Laurent Michelson, age 61
Chairman Qualium Investissement, Jean Eichenlaub, age 49
Chairman and CEO CDC Biodiversite, Laurent Piermont, age 64
CEO CDC Infrastructure, Patrick Vandevoorde, age 67
Chairman and CEO CDC International Capital, Laurent Vigier, age 47
Chairman, Henri Emmanuelli

LOCATIONS

HQ: Caisse des Depots et Consignations (France)
  56, rue de Lille, Paris, 07 SP 75356
Phone: (33) 1 58 50 00 00   **Fax:** (33) 1 58 50 80 90
Web: www.groupecaissedesdepots.fr

PRODUCTS/OPERATIONS

2012 Sales

	% of total
Banking insurance and La Poste	61
Infrastructure transport & environment	17
Real Estate & tourism	12
Casse des Depots	9
Corporate finance	1
Total	**100**

2012 Sales

	% of total
Interest income	20
Gains and losses on financial instruments at fair value through profit and loss net	3
Gains and losses on available for sale financial assets net	3
Income from other activites	74
Fee and commision income	
Total	**100**

Selected Subsidiaries

Belambra vvf (leisure housing and tour operations)
CDC Capital Investissement (development capital)

CDC Entreprises (private equity)
CNP Assurances (insurance)
Compagnie des Alpes (ski areas and leisure parks)
EGIS (engineering and infrastructure operations)
Sociéténationale Immobilière (housing management)
ICADE (REIT)
Transdev (mass transit networks especially streetcars)

COMPETITORS

AllianceBernstein	DB Advisors
Allianz Global	FMR
Investors	Goldman Sachs
Barclays Capital	HSBC France
Citigroup Global	ING
Markets	Societe Generale
Credit Suisse	UBS

HISTORICAL FINANCIALS
Company Type: Public

Income Statement
FYE: December 31

	ASSETS ($ mil.)	NET INCOME ($ mil.)	INCOME AS % OF ASSETS	EMPLOYEES
12/15	169,746	1,493	0.9%	25,179
12/14	181,534	2,179	1.2%	24,227
12/13	196,995	2,942	1.5%	25,146
12/12	377,816	(603)	—	75,995
12/11	339,224	266	0.1%	77,425
Annual Growth	(15.9%)	53.9%	—	(24.5%)

2015 Year-End Financials
Return on assets: 0.9%
Return on equity: 4.4%
Long-term debt ($ mil.): —
No. of shares (mil.): —
Sales ($ mil): 8,347

Dividends
Yield: —
Payout: —
Market value ($ mil.): —

Caixa Geral de Depositos, S.A.

Caixa Geral de Depositos (CGD) wants to hold what's left in Portuguese pockets and pocketbooks. As one of Portugal's largest banks CGD and its subsidiaries offer retail banking commercial banking investment banking venture capital asset management insurance and credit services to four million customers from its more than 750 branches in Portugal. The bank has an additional 450-plus branches in 22 other countries across Africa the Americas Asia and Europe. Boasting more than $110 billion in assets the bank enjoys market-leading shares in the Portuguese deposit and lending markets among corporations and individuals.

OperationsAround 50% of CGD's net operating income came from net interest income (around 75% of which comes from loans the rest from securities) as of the end of September 2015 while another nearly 45% came from non-interest income (more than half of which was from net commission income). The company had a staff of 16200 employees.

Geographic Reach

CGD boasted more than 1230 branches at the end of September 2015 with around 60% of its branches located in Portugal. The rest of its branches were located in 22 other countries across Africa the Americas Asia and Europe.

Strategy

Boasting more than $110 billion in assets (as of the end of September 30 2015) CGD enjoys market-leading shares in the Portuguese deposit and lending markets among corporations and individuals. The bank controlled 22% of the credit market in Portugal including 17% of the corporate loan market and 23% of the individual loan market. CGD also controlled 28% of the deposit market in late 2015 including a 32% share of the individual deposit market and 11% of the corporate deposit market.

EXECUTIVES

Vice-Chairman and CEO, Jose Agostinho Martins de Matos

Chairman, Ivaro Jose Barrigas do Nascimento, age 50

LOCATIONS

HQ: Caixa Geral de Depositos, S.A.
Av. Joao XXI, 63, Lisbon 1000-300
Phone: (351) 21 795 3000   **Fax:** (351) 21 790 5051
Web: www.cgd.pt

2012 Branches

	No.
Portugal	848
International	463
Total	**1,311**

COMPETITORS

Allianz France	Citigroup
Allianz S.p.A.	Credit Suisse
BBVA	Espirito Santo
BNP Paribas	Investment Bank
Banco BPI	Grupo Santander
Banco Comercial	UBS
Portugus	

HISTORICAL FINANCIALS
Company Type: Public

Income Statement
FYE: December 31

	ASSETS ($ mil.)	NET INCOME ($ mil.)	INCOME AS % OF ASSETS	EMPLOYEES
12/15	109,902	(186)	—	16,058
12/14	121,735	(423)	—	0
12/13	155,519	(792)	—	19,601
12/12	154,022	(520)	—	22,964
12/11	155,945	(631)	—	23,135
Annual Growth	(8.4%)	—	—	(8.7%)

2015 Year-End Financials
Return on assets: (-0.1%)
Return on equity: (-3.1%)
Long-term debt ($ mil.): —
No. of shares (mil.): 1,180
Sales ($ mil): 4,424

Dividends
Yield: —
Payout: —
Market value ($ mil.): —

Canadian Imperial Bank of Commerce

Canadian Imperial Bank of Commerce (CIBC) is both Canadian and imperial when it comes to growing its business. CIBC has more than 1100 domestic branches that offer a range of consumer and business financial services including deposits loans investments and insurance. Its largest segment is Retail and Business Banking which handles consumer and small business banking and credit card services. It also provides a full suite of services through its wholesale banking and wealth management divisions. Founded in 1867 CIBC's assets are worth more than $400 billion making it one of the five largest banks in Canada.

OperationsCIBC operates three main divisions: Retail and Business Banking Wealth Management and Wholesale Banking. The Retail and Business Banking division brings in nearly 65% of total revenue and provides financial advice along with banking investment and authorized insurance products.

CIBC's Wealth Management division generates nearly 20% of revenue and offers advisory services and a variety of investment solutions for institutions retail and high net worth clients. The business encompasses asset management retail brokerage and private wealth management activities and is delivered through more than 1500 advisors across Canada and the US.

Wholesale Banking accounts for another 15% of revenues and offers credit and capital market products and services investment banking advisory services and research for corporate institutional and government clients from around the world.

Sales and Marketing

The bank provides financial products and services to 11 million individual small business commercial corporate and institutional clients from Canada and around the world. CIBC has been increasing its advertising spend over the past few years to go toward strategic initiatives and developing its enhanced travel rewards program. The bank spent C$285 million toward advertising and business development in fiscal 2014 up 21% from its spend in 2013 and up 22% from what it spent in 2012.

Financial Performance

Note: Growth rates may differ after conversion to US dollars.

CIBC has enjoyed steady top-line growth over the past few years thanks to higher non-interest fee and commission-based income from its banking insurance and investing-related products and services. Revenue grew by 2% to C$17.4 billion ($15.5 billion) in fiscal 2014 (ended October) thanks to higher fee income from investment management custodial and mutual fund products. The bank was able to generate higher fees as its assets under management grew from its recent acquisition of Atlantic Trust and because asset values rose along with the rising stock market.

Despite higher revenue net income fell by 4% to C$3.22 billion ($2.88 billion) in fiscal 2014 after three straight years of profit growth. This is mostly because CIBC incurred significant impairment charges as the CIBC FirstCarribean division's loan assets fell in value in the struggling Carribean economy. The bank also paid employees more in performance-based compensation and spent more on computer software and office equipment.

Operations used C$16.57 billion in fiscal 2014 significantly more than in 2013 when operations provided C$5.19 billion mostly as the bank used more cash toward loans and securities purchased under resale agreements. From fiscal 2011 to fiscal 2013 operations had provided more cash than it spent.

Strategy

To grow its Retail and Business Banking division CIBC has shifted its strategy to a client-oriented focus. To do this CIBC aims to make banking easy personalized and flexible which it hopes will deepen client relationships and grow its client base further. Making moves toward this long-term goal in recent years CIBC was the first of Canada's five largest banks to launch eDeposit services for personal and business banking clients. It also took steps to achieve the third-largest branch and ATM network in Canada.

Toward CIBC's goal of expanding its wealth management business in North America CIBC in 2013 acquired Atlantic Trust an integrated wealth management solutions provider for high-net worth individuals families foundations and endowments in the US. The purchase helped CIBC broaden its reach into the US private wealth market where high-net-worth personal financial assets were growing 50% faster than those of the average US household. The acquisition also built upon the bank's 2012 purchase of the private-wealth business MFS McLean Budden in Canada which managed more than $1.4 billion in assets.

Looking to focus more on its core operations CIBC sold its stake in trust and custody services provider CIBC Mellon to its partner in the joint venture The Bank of New York Mellon for an undisclosed amount in late 2013.

Mergers and AcquisitionsIn 2013 CIBC acquired Atlanta-based Atlantic Trust from Invesco for C$224 million (or $210 million) to expand its Wealth Management business in North America.

The company is now buying Chicago-based PrivateBancorp for C$4.9 billion ($3.8 billion). That purchase will allow CIBC to offer commercial banking services in the US (and specifically to its Atlantic Trust customers).

HISTORY

In 1858 Bank of Canada was chartered; Toronto financier William McMaster bought the charter in 1866 when investors failed to raise enough money to open it and changed the name to Canadian Bank of Commerce.

The firm opened in 1867 bought the Gore Bank of Hamilton (1870) and expanded within seven years to 24 branches in Ontario as well as Montreal and New York. Led by Edmund Walker the bank spread west of the Great Lakes with the opening of a Winnipeg Manitoba branch in 1893 and joined the Gold Rush with branches in Dawson City Yukon Territory and Skagway Alaska in 1898.

As the new century began the bank's purchases spanned the breadth of Canada from the Bank of British Columbia (1901) to Halifax Banking (1903) and the Merchants Bank of Prince Edward Island (1906). More buys followed in the 1920s; the bank's assets peaked in 1929 and then plunged during the Depression. It recovered during WWII.

In 1961 Canadian Bank of Commerce merged with Imperial Bank of Canada to become Canadian Imperial Bank of Canada (CIBC). Imperial Bank was founded in 1875 by Henry Howland; it went west to Calgary and Edmonton and became known as "The Mining Bank." It bought Barclays Bank (Canada) in 1956.

As the energy and agriculture sectors declined in the early 1980s two of CIBC's largest borrowers Dome Petroleum and tractor maker Massey-Ferguson defaulted on their loans. Deregulation opened investment banking to CIBC which in 1988 bought a majority share of Wood Gundy one of Canada's largest investment dealers; CIBC also purchased Merrill Lynch Canada's retail brokerage business.

In 1992 CIBC added substantially to its loss reserves (resulting in an earnings drop of 98%) to cover real estate losses from developer Olympia & York and others. This launched more cost-cutting as the company reorganized by operating segments.

Deregulation allowed CIBC to begin selling insurance in 1993; the company built a collection of life credit personal property/casualty and nonmedical health companies.

In 1996 the bank formed Intria a processing and technical support subsidiary. The next year CIBC Wood Gundy became CIBC World Markets and CIBC bought securities firm Oppenheimer & Co. and added its stock underwriting and brokerage abilities to CIBC World Markets.

In 1998 increasing foreign competition prompted CIBC and Toronto-Dominion to plan a merger (as did Royal Bank of Canada and Bank of Montreal); the government halted both plans citing Canada's already highly concentrated banking industry.

Spurned the bank overhauled its operations to spark growth in the late 1990s. To cut costs it eliminated some 4000 jobs and sold its more than $1-billion real estate portfolio. It teamed with the Winn-Dixie (1999) and Safeway (2000) supermarket chains to operate electronic branches in the US. The firm scaled back its disappointing international operations and began selling its insurance units.

In 2000 CIBC created Amicus as a holding company for CIBC World Markets' retail electronic banking business. The following year the bank sold its merchant card services business to US-based Global Payments.

In 2002 the company snagged US-based Merrill Lynch's Canadian retail brokerage asset management and securities operations renaming it CIBC Asset Management Inc. That same year CIBC merged its Caribbean banking business with that of UK-based Barclays to create FirstCaribbean Bank.

The next year CIBC sold the Oppenheimer private client and asset-management divisions to Fahnestock Viner (now Oppenheimer Holdings). It sold Juniper Financial a Delaware-based credit card issuer to Barclays for some $293 million in 2004.

In 2004 and again in 2006 CIBC was sued by creditors of Internet telecommunications company Global Crossing stating that the bank had engaged in insider trading to the tune of $2 billion. Creditors demanded a return of the proceeds. CIBC denied the claims but in 2006 two units of the bank agreed to pay $17.4 million to investors in the ill-fated telecom.

More trouble came in 2005 when CIBC agreed to pay some $2.4 billion in an investor class-action suit to resolve claims that the company helped notorious energy trader Enron to conceal losses.

EXECUTIVES

SEVP Chief Administrative Officer and General Counsel, Michael G. Capatides
SEVP and Group Head Wealth Management, Stephen (Steve) Geist
EVP Brand Corporate and Client Relationships, Stephen J. Forbes
President and CEO, Victor Dodig
CEO CIBC FirstCaribbean International Bank, Rik Parkhill
Managing Director and Group Co-Head Wholesale Banking, Harry Culham
SVP and Chief Auditor, Kevin J. Patterson
SVP Retail Markets, Christina Kramer
SEVP and Group Head Retail and Business Banking, J. David Williamson, age 56, $348,657 total compensation
SEVP and Chief Risk Officer, Laura Dottori-Attanasio
EVP Human Resources, Jacqueline C. Moss
Managing Director and Head Equity Markets, Roman Dubczak
SEVP and CFO, Kevin Glass
Managing Director and Head U.S. Region/Risk CIBC World Markets; President and CEO CIBC World Markets, Gary W. Brown
Managing Director and Head Capital Markets Trading, Christian Exshaw

Managing Director and Head CIBC Wood Gundy, Monique Gravel
EVP Human Resources, Sandy Sharman
Chairman and CEO Atlantic Trust, Jack Markwalter
Senior Executive Vice-President Managing Director, Richard E. Venn
Chairman, Charles Sirois, age 62
Auditors: Ernst & Young LLP

LOCATIONS

HQ: Canadian Imperial Bank of Commerce
Commerce Court, Toronto, Ontario M5L 1A2
Phone: 416 980-2211
Web: www.cibc.com

PRODUCTS/OPERATIONS

2014 Sales

	% of total
Interest	
Loans	55
Securities & other	11
Noninterest	
Mutual fund fees	7
Deposits and payments fees	5
Investment management & custodial fees	4
Underwriting & advisory fees	3
Credit fees	3
Card fees	2
insurance fees	2
Commissions on securities transactions	2
Available-for-sale securities gains	1
Other	5
Total	**100**

2014 Revenue by Segment

	% of total
Retail and business banking	63
Wealth management	18
Wholesale banking	15
Corporate and other	4
Total	**100**

COMPETITORS

BMO Financial Group	JPMorgan Chase
Barclays	National Bank of
Caisses centrale	Canada
Desjardins	RBC Financial Group
Citigroup	Scotiabank
Goldman Sachs	TD Bank

HISTORICAL FINANCIALS

Company Type: Public

Income Statement

FYE: October 31

	ASSETS ($ mil.)	NET INCOME ($ mil.)	INCOME AS % OF ASSETS	EMPLOYEES
10/16	374,749	3,195	0.9%	43,213
10/15	352,088	2,717	0.8%	44,201
10/14	370,794	2,875	0.8%	44,424
10/13	380,892	3,253	0.9%	43,039
10/12	394,456	3,340	0.8%	42,595
Annual Growth	**(1.3%)**	**(1.1%)**	**—**	**0.4%**

2016 Year-End Financials

Return on assets: 0.8%
Return on equity: 19.0%
Long-term debt ($ mil.): —
No. of shares (mil.): 397
Sales ($ mil): 14,023

Dividends
Yield: 6.3%
Payout: 74.1%
Market value ($ mil.): 29,764

	STOCK PRICE ($) FY Close	P/E High/Low		Earnings	PER SHARE ($) Dividends	Book Value
10/16	74.96	7	6	8.00	3.58	44.19
10/15	76.55	9	7	6.74	3.27	40.86
10/14	91.35	12	10	7.02	3.62	41.91
10/13	85.15	10	9	7.87	3.71	43.71
10/12	78.58	10	9	7.87	3.61	41.81
Annual Growth	**(1.2%)**	**—**	**—**	**0.4%**	**(0.2%)**	**1.4%**

Canon, Inc.

Auditors: Ernst & Young ShinNihon LLC

LOCATIONS

HQ: Canon, Inc.
30-2, Shimomaruko 3-chome, Ohta-ku, Tokyo 146-8501
Phone: (81) 3 3758 2111
Web: www.canon.jp

HISTORICAL FINANCIALS

Company Type: Public

Income Statement

FYE: December 31

	REVENUE ($ mil.)	NET INCOME ($ mil.)	NET PROFIT MARGIN	EMPLOYEES
12/15	31,569	1,829	5.8%	189,571
12/14	31,239	2,135	6.8%	191,889
12/13	35,546	2,195	6.2%	194,151
12/12	40,401	2,607	6.5%	196,968
12/11	45,969	3,212	7.0%	198,307
Annual Growth	(9.0%)	(13.1%)	—	(1.1%)

2015 Year-End Financials

Debt ratio: 0.0%
Return on equity: 7.4%
Cash ($ mil.): 5,263
Current ratio: 2.52
Long-term debt ($ mil.): 7

No. of shares (mil.): 1,092
Dividends
  Yield: 4.4%
  Payout: 37.4%
Market value ($ mil.): 32,904

	STOCK PRICE ($) FY Close	P/E High/Low		PER SHARE ($) Earnings	Dividends	Book Value
12/15	30.13	0	0	1.68	1.34	22.56
12/14	31.66	0	0	1.92	1.96	22.86
12/13	32.00	0	0	1.91	1.41	24.38
12/12	39.21	0	0	2.22	1.49	26.17
12/11	44.04	0	0	2.64	1.64	27.44
Annual Growth	(9.1%)	—	—	(10.8%)	(5.0%)	(4.8%)

Carnival Plc

No one offers more floating fun than Carnival. Operating as a dual-listed company with US-based Carnival Corporation it is the #1 cruise line operator in the world with about a dozen cruise lines a fleet of more than 100 ships and a total passenger capacity of more than 215000. Carnival serves UK passengers (and Australia) primarily through P&O Cruises while brands such as AIDA and Costa Cruises serve travelers across the rest of Europe. In North America Carnival operates Princess Cruise Lines Holland America and its flagship Carnival Cruise Lines. Carnival also owns ocean liner operator Cunard which sails the Queen Victoria and Queen Elizabeth.

Geographic ReachCarnival's largest market is North America which represents more than 50% of sales. Other major markets include Europe (33%) and Australia and Asia (combined 14%).

Operations

Carnival's fleet of cruise liners caters to a variety of global markets and demographics. Its Carnival Cruises and Princess brands serve upper middle class families retirees and others with competitively priced cruise packages to such destinations as the Caribbean the Mexican Riviera and Alaska. P&O Cruises chases after a similar cus-

tomer in the UK with trips to the Mediterranean and Scandinavia. (P&O also operates out of Australia and New Zealand.) Holland America delivers scenic getaways in New England Canada and along the Pacific coast; the company offers trips within the Asian market through its Costa Cruises.

Known as the Fun Ship and for its casual cruising the company also serves customers who require high-end touches on the high seas. Carnival's Seabourn brand operates luxury cruises to upscale travelers and caters to them with fine food personalized service and exotic destinations worldwide. Similarly its Swan Hellenic premium brand sails throughout Europe and Asia and Cunard offers a variety of cruises in addition to its liner services.

Financial PerformanceAfter posting record revenues of $15.9 billion in 2014 Carnival saw its revenues dip by 1% to %15.7 billion in 2015. The marginal revenue decrease for 2015 was attributed to decreased sales from its EAA cruise brands mainly due to the impact of unfavorable foreign currency translations.

Carnival's profits surged 44% from 2014 to 2015 primarily due to a major decrease in fuel costs. In addition in 2015 its operating cash flow increased by 33% compared to 2014 primarily due to favorable changes in accrued and other liabilities and the benefit of timely customer deposits.

Strategy

In 2016 Carnival has a total of 17 cruise ships scheduled to be delivered between 2016 and 2020. Some of these ships will replace existing capacity as less efficient ships exit its fleet. Since 2006 it has removed 17 ships from its fleet and will remove one more ship in 2016.

To fill its expanding inventory of passenger berths Carnival has also been shifting its marketing efforts from print media to online and social media utilizing Facebook YouTube Twitter Flickr and Podcasts. Its goal is to engage in two-way conversations with consumers and create brand fans. Also the company has expanded its number of homeports to put cruising possibilities closer to customers.

The cruise firm's strategy is to grow in China due to its large and growing middle-class population and expansion of its international tourism. In 2015 it formed a strategic joint venture by partnering with state-owned China State Shipbuilding Company and China Investment Corporation to launch a new cruise brand in the Chinese vacation region.

EXECUTIVES

President and CEO Carnival Cruise Lines, Gerald R. (Gerry) Cahill, age 64, $775,000 total compensation
Vice Chairman and COO, Howard S. Frank, age 74, $780,000 total compensation
President Seabourn, Rick Meadows
President and CEO, Arnold W. Donald, age 61
President and CEO Princess Cruises, Alan B. Buckelew, age 68
Managing Director P&O Cruises, David K. Dingle, age 59
Chairman Costa Crociere, Pier Luigi Foschi, age 70, $1,296,750 total compensation
SVP and CFO, David Bernstein, age 59, $500,000 total compensation
President and CEO Holland America Line, Stein Kruse, age 58
CEO Costa Crociere, Michael Thamm, age 50
Chairman, Micky Arison, age 67
Auditors: PRICEWATERHOUSECOOPERS LLP

LOCATIONS

HQ: Carnival Plc
Carnival House, 100 Harbour Parade, Southhampton SO15 1ST
Phone: (44) 23 8065 5000
Web: www.carnivalplc.com

2015 Sales

	$ mil.	% of total
North America Cruise Brands	9,866	62
EAA Cruise Brands	5,636	36
Cruise support	119	1
Tour & other	226	1
Adjustments	(133)	-
Total	**15,714**	**100**

2015 Sales

	$ mil.	% of total
North America	8,015	51
Europe	5,133	33
Australia & Asia	2,256	14
Others	310	2
Total	**15,714**	**100**

PRODUCTS/OPERATIONS

2015 Sales

	$ mil.	% of total
Cruise		
Passenger tickets	11,601	74
Onboard & other	3,887	25
Tour & other	226	1
Total	**15,714**	**100**

Selected Cruise Ships

AIDA
  AIDAaura (launched in 2003; 1266 passengers)
  AIDAbella (2008; 2050)
  AIDAcara (1996; 1180)
  AIDAdiva (2007; 2050)
  AIDAvita (2002; 1266)
Carnival Cruise Lines
  Carnival Conquest (2002; 2966)
  Carnival Destiny (1996; 2634)
  Carnival Freedom (2007; 2966)
  Carnival Glory (2003; 2966)
  Carnival Legend (2002; 2118)
  Carnival Liberty (2005; 2966)
  Carnival Miracle (2004; 2118)
  Carnival Pride (2001; 2118)
  Carnival Spirit (2001; 2118)
  Carnival Splendor (2008; 2998)
  Carnival Triumph (1999; 2750)
  Carnival Valor (2004; 2966)
  Carnival Victory (2000; 2750)
  Ecstasy (1991; 2050)
  Elation (1998; 2050)
  Fantasy (1990; 2054)
  Fascination (1994; 2050)
  Holiday (1985; 1450)
  Imagination (1995; 2050)
  Inspiration (1996; 2050)
  Paradise (1998; 2048)
  Sensation (1993; 2050)
Costa Cruises
  Costa Allegra (1992; 784)
  Costa Atlantica (2000; 2114)
  Costa Classica (1991; 1302)
  Costa Europa (1986; 1488)
  Costa Fortuna (2003; 2702)
  Costa Magica (2004; 2702)
  Costa Marina (1990; 762)
  Costa Mediterranea (2003; 2114)
  Costa Romantica (1993; 1344)
  Costa Serena (2007; 2978)
  Costa Victoria (1996; 1928)
Cunard Line
  Queen Mary 2 (2003; 2592)
  Queen Victoria (2007; 1980)
  Queen Elizabeth (2010; 2092)
Holland America Line
  Amsterdam (2000; 1380)
  Eurodam (2008; 2104)
  Maasdam (1993; 1258)
  Noordam (2006; 1918)
  Oosterdam (2003; 1848)
  Prinsendam (1988; 792)
  Rotterdam (1997; 1316)

Ryndam (1994; 1260)
Statendam (1993; 1258)
Veendam (1996; 1258)
Volendam (1999; 1432)
Westerdam (2004; 1916)
Zaandam (2000; 1432)
Zuiderdam (2002; 1848)
Ibero Cruises
Grand Celebration (1987; 1494)
Grand Mistral (1999; 1244)
Grand Voyager (2000; 834)
Ocean Village
Ocean Village (1989; 1578)
Ocean Village Two (1990; 1708)
P&O Cruises
Arcadia (2005; 2016)
Artemis (1984; 1200)
Aurora (2000; 1870)
Oceana (2000; 2016)
Oriana (1995; 1818)
Ventura (2008; 3078)
P&O Cruises Australia
Pacific Dawn (1991; 1596)
Pacific Sun (1986; 1480)
Princess Cruise Lines
Caribbean Princess (2004; 3100)
Coral Princess (2002; 1974)
Crown Princess (2006; 3080)
Dawn Princess (1997; 1998)
Diamond Princess (2004; 2678)
Emerald Princess (2007; 3080)
Golden Princess (2001; 2598)
Grand Princess (1998; 2592)
Island Princess (2003; 1974)
Pacific Princess (1999; 676)
Royal Princess (2001; 710)
Ruby Princess (2008; 3080)
Sapphire Princess (2004; 2678)
Sea Princess (1998; 2016)
Star Princess (2002; 2598)
Sun Princess (1995; 2022)
Tahitian Princess (2000; 676)
Seabourn
Seabourn Legend (1992; 208)
Seabourn Pride (1988; 208)
Seabourn Spirit (1989; 208)

COMPETITORS

Carlson Companies	NYK Line
Club Med	Royal Caribbean
Disney Parks & Resorts	Cruises
Genting Hong Kong	Saga plc
Mediterranean Shipping	TUI
Company	

HISTORICAL FINANCIALS

Company Type: Public

Income Statement
FYE: November 30

	REVENUE ($ mil.)	NET INCOME ($ mil.)	NET PROFIT MARGIN	EMPLOYEES
11/16	16,389	2,779	17.0%	97,200
11/15	15,714	1,757	11.2%	94,600
11/14	15,884	1,236	7.8%	94,100
11/13	15,456	1,078	7.0%	92,700
11/12	15,382	1,298	8.4%	89,700
Annual Growth	1.6%	21.0%	—	2.0%

2016 Year-End Financials

Debt ratio: 24.2%	No. of shares (mil.): 726
Return on equity: 11.9%	Dividends
Cash ($ mil.): 603	Yield: 2.6%
Current ratio: 0.24	Payout: 46.7%
Long-term debt ($ mil.): 8,357	Market value ($ mil.): 37,048

	STOCK PRICE ($) FY Close	P/E High/Low	PER SHARE ($) Earnings	Dividends	Book Value
11/16	51.03	15 12	3.72	1.35	31.13
11/15	52.17	25 19	2.26	1.10	30.79
11/14	44.08	28 21	1.59	1.00	31.26
11/13	36.51	30 23	1.39	1.50	31.64
11/12	40.50	24 17	1.67	1.00	30.84
Annual Growth	5.9%	— —	22.2%	7.8%	0.2%

Carrefour S.A.

At the junction of groceries merchandise and services you'll find Carrefour (which means "crossroads" in French). Among the world's largest retailers by revenue and the largest in France Carrefour operates around 12200 stores under various banners including hypermarkets (Carrefour) supermarkets (Carrefour Market) convenience stores (including City Contact and Express) and cash-and-carry outlets (Promocash) in more than 35 countries in Europe Latin America and Asia. Its core markets are Belgium France Italy and Spain.

Operations
Carrefour which pioneered the hypermarket format operates about 1480 of its huge general merchandise and grocery stores on three continents. Hypermarkets accounts for the majority of its sales. It also operates more than 3450 supermarkets in 19 countries under the Carrefour market banner.

The French retail giant runs a growing number of more than 7180 convenience stores under the City Contact Express Montagne Proxi and 8 à Huit names 90% of which operate under franchising agreements. Its cash & carry stores mostly located in France combine wholesaling and hypermarkets and offer goods in larger quantities to cater to professionals and industrial consumers.

Carrefour also sells food and nonfood items online in France Brazil Spain and other countries.

Geographic Reach
France is Carrefour's largest market accounting for 47% of sales in 2015. Other countries in Europe including Belgium Italy Poland Romania and Spain contributed about 25% of its total sales. Carrefour is strong in Latin America and has leading market positions in Argentina and Brazil and the region as a whole contributes about 19% to group sales. Asia (including China) accounts for 9% of total revenue.

Carrefour does not have a presence in either the UK or the US.

Financial Performance
Note: Growth rates may differ after conversion to US Dollars.

Sales climbed 3% in 2015 to euro 76.9 billion. Growth was led by an increase in sales in France as well as in Europe as a whole for the first time in seven years due to increased competitiveness. Growth in Latin America also contributed sharply increasing 16%.

Net income fell euro 205 million to euro 977 million with the increase in sales offset by a rise in expenses which include an increase in fuel costs in Brazil among other things.

Cash flow from operations increased 8% to euro 2.7 billion due primarily to an increase in working capital.

Strategy
Carrefour experienced an alarming sales slump in 2012 and its strategy since then has been to arrest the fall (which it achieved in 2013) and latterly consolidate its return to profitable growth. It achieved this by refocusing and strengthening in its core European markets as well as in Brazil and Argentina where it retains a leading market share.

In this context Carrefour bought Spanish supermarket chain Dia's network of French stores (750 initially of which Carrefour sold off 100 due to insufficient profitability). It is in the process of bringing them under its owned banners -- Market (supermarkets) and City Express Contact and Bio (convenience stores).

Also in Spain the group signed an agreement in 2016 to buy 36 of Eroski's compact hypermarkets with a total floor space of 235000 sq. meters. The acquisition also includes eight shopping malls and 22 gas stations adjacent to the stores. It will bring 27 new cities into the fold and strengthen Carrefour's omnichannel offering.

In 2016 Carrefour acquired Rue de Commerce a key player in nonfood e-commerce from Altarea Cogedim. The acquisition is hoped to strengthen Carrefour's omnichannel approach in France.

Carrefour is struggling to reverse a decade-long sales slump at home while expanding in fast-growing emerging markets in Asia and Latin America. In Brazil the Carrefour network added 11 Atacadão stores a Brazillian wholesaler purchased by the company in 2007 a hypermarket a supermarket and 17 convenience stores.

Mergers and Acquisitions
The company made a number of recent acquisitions recently as part of its campaign to strengthen in Europe. In 2016 Carrefour acquired Rue de Commerce a key player in nonfood e-commerce from Altarea Cogedim. The acquisition is hoped to strengthen Carrefour's omnichannel approach in France.

Also that year Carrefour agreed to buy 36 of Spanish supermarket chain Eroski's company hypermarkets and the acquisition will give Carrefour access to 27 new cities.

In late 2014 Carrefour acquired Dia France from Spain's Dia. Carrefour picked up more than 800 Dia stores but it must sell about 55 to satisfy antitrust regulators. (Carrefour previously owned Dia but spun it off in 2011 when the company was listed on the Spanish stock exchange.)

In 2014 Carrefour's convenience store business acquired 128 stores from the Coop Alsace network and bought the RAST supermarket chain of 10 stores in Poland.

HISTORY

Although its predecessor was actually a supermarket opened by Marcel Fournier and Louis Defforey in a Fournier's department store basement in Annecy France the first Carrefour supermarket was founded in 1963 at the intersection of five roads (Carrefour means "crossroads"). That year Carrefour opened a vast store dubbed a "hypermarket" by the media in Sainte-Geneviève-des-Bois outside Paris.

The company opened additional outlets in France and moved into other countries including Belgium (1969) Switzerland (1970 —the year it went public) Italy and the UK (1972) and Spain (1973). Carrefour stepped up international expansion during the mid-1970s after French legislation limited its growth within the country.

Carrefour exported its French-style hypermarkets to the US (Philadelphia) in 1988. Scant advertising limited selection and a union strike led Carrefour to close its US operations in 1993. Carrefour opened its first hypermarket in Taiwan in 1989. The next year it formed Carma a 50-50 joint venture with Groupama to sell insurance. Carrefour paid over $1 billion for two rival chains (the bankrupt Montlaur chain and Euromarche) in 1991.

Daniel Bernard replaced Michel Bon the hard-charging expansion architect in 1992 after a 50% drop in first-half profits. A year later Carrefour partnered with Mexican retailer Gigante to open a chain of hypermarkets in Mexico. (In 1998 Carrefour bought Gigante's share of the joint venture.) In 1996 the company bought a 41% stake in rival GMB (Cora hypermarket chain) and sold its 11% stake in US warehouse retailer Costco (it now owns 20% of Costco UK). The next year Carrefour allowed 16 hypermarkets owned by Guyenne et Gascogne Coop Atlantique and Chareton to operate under the Carrefour name. It expanded into Poland in 1997 and the Czech Republic in 1998.

Its biggest acquisition (at the time) came in 1998 when Carrefour acquired French supermarket operator Comptoirs Modernes (with about 800 stores under the Stoc Comod and Marche Plus flags). Carrefour also entered the Indonesian market that year.

In August 1999 Carrefour announced a deal even bigger than the one for Comptoirs Modernes —a $16.3 billion merger with fellow French grocer Promodès which operated more than 6000 hypermarkets supermarkets convenience stores and discount stores in Europe. Paul-Auguste Halley and Leonor Duval Lemonnier founded Promodès in Normandy France in 1961. Initially a wholesale food distributor Promodès opened its first supermarket in 1962. This was followed by a cash-and-carry wholesale outlet (1964) a hypermarket (1970) and convenience stores (Shopi and 8 à Huit during the 1970s). To gain regulatory approval for the acquisition Carrefour divested its stake in the Cora chain and sold nearly 40 other stores in France and Spain. The Promodès acquisition was completed in 2000.

The company joined with US retailer Sears and software maker Oracle among others to form internet-based supply exchange GlobalNetXchange in early 2000. Also that year Carrefour bought Belgian retailer GB (about 500 stores).

In 2001 Carrefour sold its 74% stake in Picard Surgeles (frozen food stores). Carrefour also opened its first Japanese grocery store near Tokyo that year.

The grocer sold its 10% stake in PetSmart Inc. in a public offering in July 2002. That December Carrefour acquired the remaining 20% of the shares of Centro Comerciales Carrefour its Spanish subsidiary it didn't already own in a public tender offer.

In February 2003 Carrefour acquired two hypermarkets in Italy from Hyparlo. In October it entered the Scandinavian market through a franchise partnership and supply agreement with Norwegian grocer NorgesGruppen. Soon after Carrefour Poland acquired two hypermarkets there from troubled Dutch retailer Royal Ahold. In late 2003 Carrefour's discount chain Ed acquired 44 Treff Marche shops in France from German retailer Edeka.

The company sold its seven-hypermarket Chilean division in January 2004 to Distribucion Y Servicio. In April Carrefour opened its first Champion supermarket in Beijing. In September it entered Norway with six Meny Champion discount supermarkets in Oslo in partnership with Norway's NorgesGruppen.

In February 2005 Luc Vandevelde the former chairman of troubled British retailer Marks and Spencer succeeded Daniel Bernard as nonexecutive chairman of Carrefour. Bernard had been with Carrefour for 13 years. No stranger to the company Vandevelde was chief executive of Promodès when it merged with Carrefour

in 1999. Concurrently ex-CFO Jose-Luis Duran was named CEO. In March Carrefour sold its 29 hypermarkets in Mexico to Grupo Comercial Chedraui for an undisclosed sum. Also in March Carrefour exited the Japanese market with the sale of its eight hypermarkets there to Japanese retail giant AEON CO. On the plus side Carrefour completed the acquisition of Chris Cash & Carry of Cyprus through its Greek subsidiary Carrefour Marinopoulos. In November the French retailer acquired full ownership of three of its Chinese hypermarket joint ventures from its local partners: Kunming Department Store Co. a unit of China's Kunming Sinobright (Group) Co.; Hunan Yiyou Commercial Trade Co.; and Xinjiang Grandscape Investment Co. Also in 2005 Carrefour swapped 15 of its hypermarkets in Slovakia and the Czech Republic for five outlets in Taiwan operated by rival Tesco exiting both countries.

Carrefour increased its ownership stake in Groupe Hyparlo in late 2005 to 49% (up from 20% in 2004).

In 2006 the company pulled out of South Korea where it held a relatively weak market position. Carrefour sold its 32 stores there to local fashion retailer E.

Land for about $1.9 billion. In July Carrefour acquired 98% of the share capital and 99% of the voting rights of Hyparlo which operates stores under the Carrefour banner in France and Romania. The retailer launched its own mobile phone service Carrefour Mobile at all 218 of its hypermarkets in France in late 2006. (Rival Auchan launched a similar product earlier in the year.)

Vandevelde resigned his position in 2007 as non-executive chairman after a falling out with the controlling Halley family. In July Carrefour acquired 250 Spanish discount supermarkets trading under the PLUS banner for about $275 million. About the same time it sold a dozen hypermarkets in Portugal to Sonae the country's largest retailer for about $920 million. In October Carrefour added to its holdings in Romania with the purchase of the Artima supermarket chain there from Polish-based private equity firm Enterprise Investors for about $87 million.

In March 2008 the Halley family split its 13% stake in Carrefour into two separate holding companies —Halley Participations SAS and Comet BV —thereby ceding control of the French retail giant to Blue Capital. In May Robert Halley stepped down as chairman of the company's supervisory board and was replaced by the deputy chairman Amaury de Seze. Blue Capital which recently was granted two seats on the company's supervisory board won a third with the appointment of Bernard Arnault.

Duran stepped down in January 2009 and Lars Olofsson took over as top executive. In June the company opened its first location in Russia: a hypermarket in Moscow. A second Russian store debuted in September.

In November 2010 Carrefour sold its 42 stores in Thailand to Casino Guichard-Perrachon's Big C affiliate there for some euro 868 million ($1.17 billion).

At Carrefour's annual meeting in June 2011 chairman Amaury de Seze stepped down and Olofsson added the chairman's title. Olofsson retired in May 2012 and was succeeded by Georges Plassat who joined Carrefour as COO in April 2012.

EXECUTIVES

Chairman and CEO, Georges Plassat
Executive Director China and Taiwan, Thierry Garnier, age 49
Executive Director Group Merchandise, ric Legros
Executive Director Spain, No ël Prioux, age 56
Executive Director Belgium, Gerard Lavinay
Executive Director Turkey, Guillaume de Colonges
Executive Director Poland, Jean Anthoine
Executive Director Brazil, Luiz Fazzio
Executive Director Europe (excluding France), Thomas M. H bner, age 58
CFO, Pierre-Jean Sivignon
Executive Director Spain, Pascal Clouzard
Executive Director India, Jean-No ël Bironneau
Executive Director Argentina, Daniel Fernandez
Executive Director Taiwan, Patrick Ganaye
Executive Director Romania, Fran çis Melchior de Polignac
Executive Director International Partnerships, Stephane Thouin
Vice Chairman, Georges Ralli, age 68
Auditors: Deloitte & Associés

LOCATIONS

HQ: Carrefour S.A.
33, avenue Emile-Zola, TSA 55 555, Boulogne-Billancourt 92100
Phone: (33) 1 41 04 26 00   **Fax:** (22) 1 41 04 26 01
Web: www.carrefour.com

2015 Sales

	% of total
France	47
Europe	26
Latin America	19
Asia	9
Total	**100**

PRODUCTS/OPERATIONS

2015 Stores

	No.
Convenience	7,181
Supermarkets	3,462
Hypermarkets	1,481
Cash & Carry	172
Total	**12,296**

Selected Operations and Banners

Hypermarkets
　Carrefour
Supermarkets
　Champion
　GB
　Globi
　GS
　Marinopoulos
　Norte
　Super GB
　Super GS
　Unic
Hard discount stores
　Ed
　Minipreco
Other stores
　Cash-and-carry stores
　Docks Market
　Promocash
　Puntocash
Convenience stores
　8 à Huit
　Di per Di
　GB Express
　Marché Plus
　Proxi
　Shopi
Other Operations
Carfuel (petroleum products)
Comptoirs Modernes (supermarkets)
Costco UK (20% warehouse club)
Erteco (hard-discount stores)
Financiera Pryca (46% consumer credit Spain)
Fourcar B.V. (investments The Netherlands)
GlobalNetXchange (Internet-based supply exchange joint venture)
Ooshop (online shopping)
Prodirest (catering)
Providange (auto centers)
S2P (60% consumer credit)

COMPETITORS

AEON	La Rinascente
ALDI	Lianhua Supermarket
Ahold Delhaize	Lidl
Auchan	Lotteshopping
Brasiliera de	METRO AG
Distribui§o	Marui Group
Casino Guichard	Migros
China Nepstar	REWE
Dairy Farm	Rallye
International	SHV Holdings
E.Leclerc	Super Indo
Edeka Zentrale	Tengelmann
Eroski	Tesco
Falabella	Viavarejo
Galeries Lafayette	Wal-Mart
H&M	WuMart
ITM Entreprises	Zara
Ito-Yokado	

HISTORICAL FINANCIALS

Company Type: Public

Income Statement

FYE: December 31

	REVENUE ($ mil.)	NET INCOME ($ mil.)	NET PROFIT MARGIN	EMPLOYEES
12/15	85,891	1,067	1.2%	380,920
12/14	92,764	1,518	1.6%	381,227
12/13	105,561	1,738	1.6%	364,795
12/12	103,414	1,625	1.6%	364,969
12/11	107,051	479	0.4%	412,443
Annual Growth	(5.4%)	22.1%	—	(2.0%)

2015 Year-End Financials

Debt ratio: 31.1%	No. of shares (mil.): 727
Return on equity: 10.4%	Dividends
Cash ($ mil.): 2,967	Yield: 1.6%
Current ratio: 0.78	Payout: 6.0%
Long-term debt ($ mil.): 9,348	Market value ($ mil.): 4,161

	STOCK PRICE ($) FY Close	P/E High	P/E Low	PER SHARE ($) Earnings	PER SHARE ($) Dividends	PER SHARE ($) Book Value
12/15	5.72	5	4	1.48	0.09	14.42
12/14	6.02	4	3	2.15	0.17	15.70
12/13	7.88	4	3	2.51	0.28	15.40
12/12	5.15	3	2	2.39	0.90	14.38
12/11	4.48	14	7	0.72	0.99	12.71
Annual Growth	6.3%	—	—	19.6%	(44.7%)	3.2%

Casino Guichard Perrachon S.A.

You're unlikely to hit the jackpot at Casino Guichard-Perrachon but odds are you'll go home with the groceries. One of the world's leading food retailers Casino Group owns and operates more than 15300 stores including hypermarkets (mostly Geant) supermarkets (Casino and Monoprix to name a few) restaurants (Casino Cafeteria) and discount stores (Leader Price). It is the third-largest food retailer (behind Carrefour and Auchan) and the #1 convenience store operator in France (primarily Petit Casino but other banners include Franprix Vival and Spar). Most of its stores are in France but it has outlets in 8 countries in Asia and South America including Brazil Colombia Thailand and Vietnam.

Operations

Its retail operations bring in the bulk of revenue at around 73% but it also earns significant revenue from electronics and through e-commerce.

Of its 10627 stores 6917 are convenience stores 867 Franprix 810 Leader Price 698 Monoprix 441 Casino supermarkets 146 Indian Ocean and 128 Casino hypermarkets. It also operates 621 stores in other activities.

Geographic Reach

The company is headquartered in France. It has more than 250 affiliated stores in 45 countries including France Belgium Colombia Brazil Argentina Uruguay Thailand Vietnam Senegal Cote d'Ivoire Cameroon Madagascar and Mauritius.

Sales and Marketing

The company deals in physical retail and e-commerce.

Financial Performance

Note: Growth rates may differ after conversion to US Dollars.

Sales fell 5% to euro 46.1 billion primarily due to a decrease in revenue from Latin American electronics sales.

Strategy

Casino Group is pursuing a strategy of geographic diversification with a particular focus on Latin America. It combined its Latam operations into a single structure under the ?xito subsidiary. In Asia the Group continued to expand across all formats during the year supporting the development of modern retailing in the region.

Casino Group is also expanding its affiliate network through long-term agreements with local partners. The company opened 15 stores in 2015 raising the number of total stores outside France to 266.

In 2016 Casino Group disposed of its stake in Big C Supercenter PCL to BJC Group a subsidiary of Thailand's TCC Group for proceeds amounting to euro 3.1 billion. The disposal is part of the constant policy to the acquisition of key assets and the disposal of mature assets that the Group has conducted over the past ten years. In addition to the Big C disposal Cnova the Group's French e-commerce business disposed of its interests in Cdiscount Thailand also to BJC Group for euro 28 million.

Company Background

Casino is controlled by Euris which is controlled by Jean-Charles Naouri Casino's chairman and CEO.

HISTORY

Frenchman Geoffroy Guichard married Antonia Perrachon a grocer's daughter in 1889 in Saint-?tienne France. Three years later Geoffroy took over his father-in-law's general store (a converted "casino" or musical hall). In 1898 the company became Societe des Magasins du Casino. By 1900 when it became a joint stock company Casino had 50 stores; it opened its 100th store in 1904. That year the company introduced its first private-label product: canned sardines. In 1917 Guichard named his two sons Mario and Jean as managers.

By WWI there were about 215 branches more than 50 in Saint-?tienne. From 1919 to the early 1920s the company opened several factories to manufacture goods such as food soap and perfumes. In 1925 the elder Guichard retired leaving the day-to-day operations of Casino to his two sons. (Geoffroy died in 1940.) WWII took a heavy toll on the company: About 70 Casino stores were leveled and another 450 were damaged.

The company began opening cafeterias in 1967 and in 1976 it formed Casino USA to run them. Casino USA bought an interest in the California-based Thriftimart volume retailer in 1983 renaming the company after Thriftimart's Smart & Final warehouse stores.

Casino grew by acquiring companies across France including CEDIS (16 hypermarkets 116 supermarkets and 722 smaller stores in eastern France; 1985) and La Ruche Meridionale (18 hypermarkets and 112 supermarkets in southern France 1990). Casino bought nearly 300 hypermarkets and supermarkets from Rallye SA in 1992 giving Rallye about 30% of the company. The company opened its first hypermarket in Warsaw Poland in 1996.

Rival Promodès made a roughly $4.5 billion hostile takeover bid for Casino in 1997. Guichard family members voted against the Promodès offer instead backing a $3.9 billion friendly offer from Rallye (increasing their stake to nearly 50%). Casino also launched a massive counterattack —buying more than 600 Franprix and Leader Price supermarket stores from food manufacturer TLC Beatrice and acquiring a 21% stake in hypermarket chain Monoprix. Promodès withdrew its bid four months later.

Casino expanded internationally in the late 1990s acquiring stakes in food retailers in Argentina (Libertad) Uruguay (Disco) Colombia (Almacenes Exito SA) Brazil (Companhia Brasileira de Distribuição) and Thailand (Big C the country's largest retailer). It also opened its first hypermarket in Taichung Taiwan.

Expansion in France included a joint venture (called Opera) formed in 1999 with retailer Cora SA to buy food and nonfood goods for the Casino and Cora stores and the acquisition of 100 convenience stores (converted to the Petit Casino banner) in southwest France from retailer Guyenne et Gascogne.

Casino acquired 100 Proxi convenience stores in southeast France in 2000 from Montagne (most became Vival franchises) and more than 400 convenience stores (Eco Service and others) from Auchan. Casino also bought 51% of French online retailer Cdiscount.com (CDs videos CD-ROMs and DVDs) and upped its ownership in several of its international supermarket operations including gaining 100% ownership of Libertad. It also increased its ownership of Monoprix to 49%.

In July 2002 Casino bought a 38% stake in Laurus NV its financially troubled Dutch rival. Laurus operates nearly 2000 supermarkets in the Netherlands Spain and Belgium. (Soon after Casino sold Laurus's unprofitable stores in Spain and Belgium.) Also in 2002 the company sold its wine division Les Chais Beaucairois to wine and spirits company Marie Brizard for $22 million.

Chief executive Pierre Bouchut unexpectedly left Casino in March 2005. Jean-Charles Naouri the company's chairman and controlling shareholder replaced him. In May Casino took joint control of Brazil's leading food retailer Companhia Brasileira de Distribuição along with the family of Abilio Diniz. Previously Casino held a minority stake in the supermarket chain. Casino spun off some of its shopping center assets in an October IPO for part of its real estate assets in France including shopping mall properties adjacent to its hypermarket and supermarkets as well as the land under its cafeterias.

In 2006 the French supermarket operator spun off its property company Mercialys. (Following the IPO Casino holds about a 60% stake in Mercialys.) In January 2006 Casino increased its stake in Colombia's biggest retailer Exito to nearly 39%. The company in July sold its 19 hypermarkets in Poland to METRO AG its German rival for about $1.1 billion as part of its asset disposal program. In September Casino sold its 50% stake in its Taiwanese subsidiary Far Eastern Geant to its joint venture partner Far Eastern Department Stores.

Real estate sales continued in late 2007 with the announcement that Casino plans to sell nearly $930 million in assets including 255 grocery stores in France. The retailer says it plans to use the proceeds from the sale of these "mature" assets for high-potential projects in France and abroad. In May 2007 Casino sold its 55% stake of the California-based Smart & Final warehouse grocery chain to Apollo Management for $813 million thereby exiting the US market.

Casino acquired in July 2008 about 90% of the French textile maker International Textiles Associes (or INTEXA) from members of the Broyer family. Also Casino exercised its option in 2008 to increase its share in Dutch supermarket operator Super de Boer (formerly Laurus acquired in 2002) to a majority stake. However in December 2009 Casino sold its 57% stake in Super de Boer to Dutch rival Jumbo Groep Holding for euro 552.5 (nearly $800 million).

In November 2009 Casino acquired the remaining shares of Leader Price and Franprix chains from the Baud family bringing its ownership stake up to 100% in both chains.

EXECUTIVES

Finance Director, Antoine Giscard d'Estaing
Chairman, Jean-Charles Naouri, age 67
Auditors: Deloitte & Associés

LOCATIONS

HQ: Casino Guichard Perrachon S.A.
1, Esplanade de France, B.P. 306, Saint-Etienne, Cedex 2 42008
Phone: (33) 4 77 45 31 31   **Fax:** (33) 4 77 45 38 38
Web: www.groupe-casino.fr/en/

PRODUCTS/OPERATIONS

2015 Stores

	No.
France	10,627
International	
Argentina	27
Uruguay	65
Brazil	2,181
Colombia	1,668
Thailand	734
Vietnam	42
Total	**15,344**

2015 type of Stores (France)

	No.
Casino hypermarket	128
Supermarkets	441
Monoprix	698
Franprix	867
Leader price	810
Convenience stores	6,916
Indian ocean	146
Other Activities	621
Total	**10,627**

2015 Sales

	% of Total
France Retail	41
Latam Retail	32
Latam Electronics	11
Asia	9
E-Commerce	7
Total	**100**

Selected Operations

Banque du Groupe Casino (60% financial services)
Big C (36% Thailand)
Casino Enterprise (non-food operations)
Cativen (66% Venezuela)
Cdiscount.com (67% e-commerce)
Companhia Brasileira de Distribuito (34% Brazil)
Devoto (97% supermarkets Uruguay)
Exito Colombia SA (55% supermarkets)
Franprix (supermarkets)
Géant (hypermarkets)
Imagica (photo and digital imaging processing)
Leader Price (supermarkets)
Libertad (hypermarkets Argentina)

Vindémia (supermarkets; Madagascar Mauritius Réunion)

COMPETITORS

ALDI	ITM Entreprises
Auchan	Kingfisher
Carrefour	METRO AG
E.Leclerc	Migros
Groupe Flo	Tesco
Guyenne et Gascogne	Wal-Mart Brazil
IGA	

HISTORICAL FINANCIALS

Company Type: Public

Income Statement

FYE: December 31

	REVENUE ($ mil.)	NET INCOME ($ mil.)	NET PROFIT MARGIN	EMPLOYEES
12/15	50,261	(46)	—	325,820
12/14	58,943	305	0.5%	335,436
12/13	66,971	1,171	1.7%	329,355
12/12	55,319	1,399	2.5%	318,600
12/11	44,444	734	1.7%	223,050
Annual Growth	**3.1%**	**—**	**—**	**9.9%**

2015 Year-End Financials

Debt ratio: 32.0%
Return on equity: (-0.6%)
Cash ($ mil.): 4,997
Current ratio: 0.89
Long-term debt ($ mil.): 10,449

No. of shares (mil.): 111
Dividends
Yield: 7.6%
Payout: —
Market value ($ mil.): 1,026

	STOCK PRICE ($) FY Close	P/E High/Low		PER SHARE ($) Earnings	Dividends	Book Value
12/15	9.22	—	—	(1.30)	0.70	57.54
12/14	18.49	12	9	2.03	0.86	82.78
12/13	22.95	3	3	10.16	1.55	93.43
12/12	19.37	2	2	12.38	0.79	87.88
Annual Growth(21.9%) (10.0%)		**—**	**—**	**—**	**(3.0%)**	

Cathay Financial Holding Co

One of the largest financial services firms in Taiwan Cathay Financial Holding Co. owns companies involved in banking insurance brokerage and more. Its holdings include life accident and health insurer Cathay Life; property/casualty coverage provider Cathay Century; brokerage firm Cathay Securities; and Cathay United Bank which offers consumer banking services such as deposit accounts home mortgages credit cards and car loans as well as international banking and trust services. Cathay Financial Group also has units devoted to venture capital investing. All told the company has more than 700 locations and claims a customer base of more than ten million.

EXECUTIVES

Director; Chairman Cathay Insurance (China), Fa-Te Chang
Director; President Cathay Life Insurance, Ming-Ho Hsiung
Chairman Cathay Financial Holdings and Cathay Life Insurance, Hong-Tu Tsai

Vice Chairman; Chairman Cathay United Bank, Gregory K.H. Wang
President and Director, Chang-Ken Lee
CFO and First Deputy Spokesperson, Grace Chen
Director; Managing Director Cathay Life Insurance, Cheng-Ta Tsai
Director; Chairman Cathay Century Insurance, Cheng-Chiu Tsai
Director; Vice Chairman Cathay United Bank, Tsu-Pei Chen
Director; President Cathay Century Insurance, J. H. Hsu
EVP and Director; Chairman Cathay Securities Corporation, David P. Sun
EVP and Spokesperson, Alan Lee
Auditors: Ernst & Young

LOCATIONS

HQ: Cathay Financial Holding Co
No. 296, Sec. 4, Ren Ai Road, Da' an District, Taipei 106
Phone: (886) 2 2708 7698   **Fax:** (886) 2 2325 2488
Web: www.cathayholdings.com.tw

COMPETITORS

Bank of China	Hua Nan Financial
Chang Hwa Bank	Mega Financial
Chinatrust Financial	Shin Kong
E.Sun	SinoPac Holdings
First Financial Holding	Taishin
	Taiwan Business Bank

HISTORICAL FINANCIALS

Company Type: Public

Income Statement

FYE: December 31

	ASSETS ($ mil.)	NET INCOME ($ mil.)	INCOME AS % OF ASSETS	EMPLOYEES
12/15	230,339	1,750	0.8%	46,633
12/14	219,329	1,563	0.7%	44,542
12/13	203,777	966	0.5%	44,487
12/12	189,889	555	0.3%	44,678
12/11	165,140	372	0.2%	43,904
Annual Growth	**8.7%**	**47.2%**	**—**	**1.5%**

2015 Year-End Financials

Return on assets: 0.7%
Return on equity: 12.9%
Long-term debt ($ mil.): —
No. of shares (mil.): —
Sales ($ mil): 13,632

Dividends
Yield: —
Payout: —
Market value ($ mil.): —

	STOCK PRICE ($) FY Close	P/E High/Low		PER SHARE ($) Earnings	Dividends	Book Value
12/15	0.00	—	—	0.14	0.46	1.10
12/14	10.10	—	—	0.12	0.34	1.09
12/13	10.10	—	—	0.08	0.15	0.79
12/12	10.10	9	7	0.05	0.10	0.78
Annual Growth	**—**	**—**	**—**	**30.1%**	**46.6%**	**9.2%**

Celesio AG

Celesio likes being a middleman when it comes to pharmaceuticals. The company is one of Europe's largest drug wholesalers holding market-leading positions in several of the countries it serves. Its largest wholesale markets are France Germany and the UK. In addition to more than 130 wholesale distribution branches serving 65000 pharmacies Celesio owns retail chains consisting of 2200 pharmacies in Europe including Norway Italy and the UK. Celesio which was founded in 1835 and was acquired by North American pharmaceuticals distributor McKesson in 2014 has a presence in 14 countries.

Change in Company Type

McKesson purchased Celesio in 2014 in an $8.3 billion deal to expand its operations into Europe. Through an expanded global presence McKesson aims to increase globalization in a rapidly changing health care market; the combined entity is expected to benefit from increased purchasing power technology resources supply chain efficiencies and global sourcing capabilities.

Mergers and Acquisitions

In 2015 Celesio's LloydsPharmacy agreed to acquire UK grocer Sainsbury's pharmacy business for £125 million. The deal includes 281 locations including 277 in-store pharmacies and four hospital pharmacies; they will all be rebranded as LloydsPharmacy.

EXECUTIVES

President McKesson Specialty Health, Marc E. Owen, age 55
SVP and CFO McKesson U.S. Pharmaceutical, Alain Vachon
Chairman, John H. Hammergren, age 57
Deputy Chairman Supervisory Board, Ihno Goldenstein, age 43
Auditors: Deloitte & Touche GmbH Wirtschaftspraefungsgesellschaft

LOCATIONS

HQ: Celesio AG
Neckartalstrasse 155, Stuttgart D-70376
Phone: (49) 711 50 01 00   **Fax:** (49) 711 50 01 12 60
Web: www.celesio.com

2013 Sales

	% of total
France	30
UK	22
Germany	21
Brazil	9
Other	18
Total	**100**

PRODUCTS/OPERATIONS

2013 Sales

	% of total
Pharmacy solutions	84
Customer solutions	16
Total	**100**

Selected Subsidiaries

Pharmacy Solutions (wholesale distribution division)
AAH Pharmaceuticals Ltd. (UK)
AFM S.p.A. (Italy)
Cahill May Roberts Group Ltd (Ireland)
GEHE Pharma Handel GmbH (Germany)
GEHE Pharma Praha spol. S r.o. (Czech Republic)
Herba Chemosan Apotheker AG (Austria)
Kemofarmacija d.d. (Slovenia Romania and Croatia)
Laboratoria Flandria NV (Belgian)
Norsk Medisinaldepot AS (Norway)
OCP Repartition (France)
OCP Portugal Produtos Farmacêuticos SA (Portugal)
Panpharma Participacoes S.A. (54% Brazil)
Pharma Belgium SA
Rudolf Spiegel GmbH (Germany)
Tjellesen Max Jenne A/S (Denmark)
Patient and Consumer Solutions (retail pharmacies division)
Admenta Italia S.p.A.
Apotheke DocMorris (retail franchise)
Brocacef (45% Netherlands)
DocMorris Kooperationen GmbH (mail order)
Lékárny Lloyds s.r.o. (Czech Republic)

Lloyds Pharmacy Limited (UK)
Lloydspharma SA (Belgium)
Unicare Pharmacy Limited (Ireland)
Vitusapotek AS (Norway)

COMPETITORS

Cardinal Health	Sigma Pharmaceuticals
Co-operative Group	Superdrug
Mawdsleys	UDG Healthcare
Mediq	Walgreen
PHOENIX Pharma	Waymade
Profarma Distribuidora	

HISTORICAL FINANCIALS

Company Type: Public

Income Statement

FYE: March 31

	REVENUE ($ mil.)	NET INCOME ($ mil.)	NET PROFIT MARGIN	EMPLOYEES
03/16	24,388	447	1.8%	23,404
03/15*	5,657	(239)	—	25,118
12/14	25,096	59	0.2%	24,929
12/13	29,472	220	0.7%	28,653
12/12	29,354	(205)	—	28,877
Annual Growth	**(6.0%)**	—		**(6.8%)**

*Fiscal year change

2016 Year-End Financials

Debt ratio: 21.4%	No. of shares (mil.): 203
Return on equity: 14.9%	Dividends
Cash ($ mil.): 482	Yield: 0.0%
Current ratio: 1.35	Payout: 7.0%
Long-term debt ($ mil.): 1,328	Market value ($ mil.): 1,148

	STOCK PRICE ($) FY Close	P/E High/Low		PER SHARE ($) Earnings	Dividends	Book Value
03/16	5.65	3	3	2.20	0.16	15.32
03/15*	5.80	—	—	(1.18)	0.04	13.31
12/14	6.40	27	21	0.29	0.04	16.41
12/13	6.28	7	4	1.27	0.05	17.47
12/12	3.35	—	—	(1.21)	0.04	16.75
Annual Growth	**14.0%**	—	—	—	**55.0%**	**(2.9%)**

*Fiscal year change

Cementos Bio-Bio S.A. (Chile)

LOCATIONS

HQ: Cementos Bio-Bio S.A. (Chile)
Avenida Barros Errazuriz 1968, Piso 9, Providencia
Phone: (56) 41 546 000   **Fax:** (56) 41 546 010
Web: www.biobio.cl

HISTORICAL FINANCIALS

Company Type: Public

Income Statement

FYE: December 31

	REVENUE ($ mil.)	NET INCOME ($ mil.)	NET PROFIT MARGIN	EMPLOYEES
12/15	296,137	21,141	7.1%	3,337
12/14	283,525	20,295	7.2%	3,310
12/13	289,236	13,173	4.6%	3,553
12/12	310,346	(28,175)	—	3,485
12/11	317,739	(47,546)	—	4,523
Annual Growth	**(1.7%)**	—		**(7.3%)**

2015 Year-End Financials

Debt ratio: —	No. of shares (mil.): 264
Return on equity: 9.7%	Dividends
Cash ($ mil.): 21,777	Yield: —
Current ratio: 1.57	Payout: —
Long-term debt ($ mil.): —	Market value ($ mil.): —

Cencosud SA

Cencosud feeds and outfits its customers in Argentina Brazil Chile Colombia and Peru. One of Latin America's largest and most acquisitive retailers the multi-format retailer operates 760-plus supermarkets under the Santa Isabel banner in Chile Disco and Vea names in Argentina GBarbosa brand in Brazil and Wong banner in Peru. It also runs more than 35 hypermarkets in Chile and Argentina under the Jumbo banner. Fast-growing Cencosud's other retail activities include convenience and home improvement stores and some 40 Paris department stores located in Chile. Other activities include shopping centers travel agencies and banking. Cencosud is expanding rapidly in Brazil Latin America's largest economy.

Engaging in a bit of discount shopping Cencosud in late 2011 purchased an 85% stake in the financially-troubled retailer Johnson's SA for $64 million marked down from an initial $99.7 million. Johnson's operates 40 stores catering to middle- and lower-income families.

Brazil has grown to account for about 25% of Cencosud's consolidated sales up from just 11% in 2009. In 2011 it acquired the Prezunic supermarket chain in Rio de Janeiro. Cencosud in fall 2010 acquired Brazil's Supermercados Bretas in a deal valued at about $810 million. The purchase add the states of Minas Gerais and Goias to its portfolio and included more than 60 supermarkets 10 service stations and three distribution centers. (In late 2007 Cencosud acquired GBarbosa the largest supermarket retailer in the northeast region of Brazil.) While Cencosud sees Brazil as a growth opportunity so do some other foreign retailers including US-based Wal-Mart Stores and France's Carrefour and Groupe Casino. Cencosud expects to invest nearly $1 billion in South America in 2011.

Indeed Latin America is high on Wal-Mart's itinerary for expansion. It recently acquired Santa Isabel's main rival in Chile Distribucion y Servicio D&S and is expanding in Brazil where it operates Wal-Mart Brazil. Carrefour the world's second-largest retailer after Wal-Mart is also active in Latin America where it operates more than 1000 hypermarkets in Argentina Brazil and Colombia.

Cencosud sold a 38% stake in its retail subsidiary in Argentina to Swiss bank UBS for $442 million. Jumbo Retail Argentina which operates the Jumbo hypermarkets and Disco and Super Vea supermarket chains in Argentina contributed about 20% of Cencosud's sales in 2010. Cencosud retained the option to buy back the 38% stake within two years.

EXECUTIVES

Financial Retail Managing Director, Patricio Rivas, age 53
Corporate Risk Managing Director, Marcelo Reyes, age 49
CEO, Jaime Soler Bottinelli, age 44
CFO, Rodrigo Larrain, age 44
Managing Director Regional Shopping Centers, Carlos Madina, age 49
Home Improvement Stores Managing Director, Antonio Ureta, age 42
Department Stores Managing Director, Ricardo Bennett, age 41
CIO, Andres Artigas, age 50
Chairman, Horst Paulmann Kemna, age 80
Auditors: PricewaterhouseCoopers

LOCATIONS

HQ: Cencosud SA
Avenida Kennedy 9001, Piso 4, Santiago, Las Condes 4144
Phone: (56) 22 959 0545 **Fax:** (56) 22 959 0368
Web: www.cencosud.cl

2013 Sales

	% of total
Chile	38
Argentina	25
Brazil	19
Colombia	10
Peru	8
Total	**100**

2013 Supermarkets

	No.
Argentina	269
Chile	187
Brazil	221
Peru	87
Total	**764**

COMPETITORS

Brasileira de Distribui§o
Carrefour Espa±a
Casino Guichard
Falabella
Hipermarc
Lojas Americanas
Wal-Mart

HISTORICAL FINANCIALS

Company Type: Public

Income Statement

FYE: December 31

	REVENUE ($ mil.)	NET INCOME ($ mil.)	NET PROFIT MARGIN	EMPLOYEES
12/15	15,510	327	2.1%	143,813
12/14	17,685	272	1.5%	149,955
12/13	19,674	475	2.4%	154,424
12/12	19,038	520	2.7%	142,675
12/11	14,556	549	3.8%	128,029
Annual Growth	1.6%	(12.2%)	—	2.9%

2015 Year-End Financials

Debt ratio: 0.0%
Return on equity: 5.6%
Cash ($ mil.): 378
Current ratio: 1.03
Long-term debt ($ mil.): 4,126
No. of shares (mil.): —
Dividends
Yield: 1.4%
Payout: 72.0%
Market value ($ mil.): —

	STOCK PRICE ($) FY Close	P/E High	P/E Low	PER SHARE ($) Earnings	Dividends	Book Value
12/15	6.18	0	0	0.11	0.09	1.98
12/14	7.69	0	0	0.10	0.07	2.51
12/13	10.89	0	0	0.17	0.24	2.87
12/12	16.33	0	0	0.22	0.06	2.82
Annual Growth	(27.7%)	—	—	(15.2%)	11.0%	(8.4%)

Central Japan Railway Co.

Central Japan Railway known as JR Central provides passenger transportation throughout a network of some 1970 km (1221 miles) of track and more than 400 stations. The company's shinkansen (high-speed) lines connect the metropolitan areas of Tokyo Nagoya and Osaka. In addition JR Central operates a dozen conventional rail lines mainly in the Nagoya and Shizuoka areas and provides bus services. The company also earns revenue from department store and hotel operations; food and beverage sales; leasing real estate near its train stations; and travel agency services. JR Central was one of seven companies formed in the 1987 privatization of Japanese National Railways.

Geographic Reach

The company has its head office in Nagoya and Tokyo. Branch offices reside in Shizuoka Mie and regional offices are located in Osaka; Washington DC; London; and Sydney.

Operations

JR Central's operations are divided across four main segments: Transportation (70%) Merchandise and Other (12%) Real Estate (4%) and Other (14%).

Financial Performance

JR Central's revenues jumped 4% from 2013 to 2014. The growth was driven by increased revenue across all its segments: Transportation (3%) Merchandise and Other (5%) Real Estate (4%) and Other (7%). In addition to the revenue growth JR Central experienced net income growth of 28% in 2014 compared to to 2013 primarily due to the additional revenue coupled with a reduction in operating expenses.

StrategyIn order to increase the number of the travelers from the Kansai and Nagoya regions to the Tokyo Metropolitan area JR Central is utilizing promote package tours collaborated with popular tourist spots through its “Tokyo Bookmark” online campaign as a way to increase demand of trend-conscious young women.Also with the country striving to attract more foreign travelers to visit Japan JR Central is working with travel agencies and local municipalities along train lines to augment the tourist demand for the Tokaido Shinkansen.

EXECUTIVES

Executive Director, Yoshiomi Yamada
EVP, Tsutomu Morimura
Senior Corporate Executive Officer, Masaki Seki
Senior Corporate Executive Officer, Sumio Kudo
Senior Corporate Executive Officer, Noriyuki Shirakuni
Senior Corporate Executive Officer, Yutaka Osada
EVP, Koei Tsuge
EVP, Shin Kaneko
EVP, Naotoshi Yoshikawa
Senior Corporate Executive Officer, Katsumi Miyazawa
Chairman, Yoshiyuki Kasai
Auditors: Deloitte Touche Tohmatsu LLC

LOCATIONS

HQ: Central Japan Railway Co.
1-1-4 Meieki, Nakamura-ku, Nagoya, Aichi 450-6101
Phone: (81) 52 564 2620
Web: www.jr-central.co.jp

PRODUCTS/OPERATIONS

2014 Sales

	% of total
Transportation	70
Merchandise & other	12
Real Estate	4
Other	14
Total	**100**

COMPETITORS

East Japan Railway
Keihin Electric Express Railway
Keio Corporation
Keisei Electric Railway
Nagoya Railroad
Odakyu Electric Railway
Tobu Railway
West Japan Railway

HISTORICAL FINANCIALS

Company Type: Public

Income Statement

FYE: March 31

	REVENUE ($ mil.)	NET INCOME ($ mil.)	NET PROFIT MARGIN	EMPLOYEES
03/16	15,480	3,004	19.4%	36,758
03/15	13,938	2,201	15.8%	36,518
03/14	16,010	2,477	15.5%	28,619
03/13	16,848	2,125	12.6%	28,348
03/12	18,387	1,618	8.8%	28,082
Annual Growth	(4.2%)	16.7%	—	7.0%

2016 Year-End Financials

Debt ratio: 0.2%
Return on equity: 15.5%
Cash ($ mil.): 1,468
Current ratio: 0.83
Long-term debt ($ mil.): 10,697
No. of shares (mil.): 197
Dividends
Yield: 0.5%
Payout: —
Market value ($ mil.): 3,479

	STOCK PRICE ($) FY Close	P/E High	P/E Low	PER SHARE ($) Earnings	Dividends	Book Value
03/16	17.66	0	0	15.27	0.10	104.71
03/15	18.10	0	0	11.19	0.11	85.47
03/14	11.71	—	—	12.59	0.11	88.64
03/13	10.66	—	—	10.80	0.00	84.06
03/12	8.20	—	—	8.23	0.00	84.37
Annual Growth	21.1%	—	—	16.7%	—	5.5%

Centrica Plc

Centrica is centered on energy in the UK and North America via five major brands: British Gas Bord Gais Energy Centrica Energy Centrica Storage and Direct Energy. The UK's largest gas supplier British Gas serves about 11 million homes and 1 million businesses with electricity gas and energy-related services. Direct Energy supplies gas and power to residential customers in Canada and the US. Bord Gais supplies Irish customers. Centrica is also engaged in gas exploration and production and storage operations. Other activities include gas and electricity production wholesale energy marketing international retail energy marketing drain cleaning services (the Dyno Group) and appliance sales.

Geographic Reach

The company operates in North America Ireland the UK Norway the Netherlands and Trinidad and Tobago.

Operations

The company operates through British Gas Direct Energy Centrica Energy Centrica Storage and Bord Gais Energy.

In addition leading energy supplier and provides energy and/or services to around 11million homes in Britain British Gas provides energy to more than 9000000 UK business supply points. British Gas Services installs repairs and maintains boilers and heating systems. Direct Energy provides of electricity natural gas. and home services across North America via three lines of business: Residential energy supply; Business energy supply; and Residential and business services.

Centrica Energy produces natural gas on the UK continental shelf and has a significant international operating portfolio in Norway the Netherlands and North America. It also operate a fleet of gas-fired power stations and offshore wind farms in the UK and holds a 20% stake in eight nuclear power stations in the UK. Centrica Storage store gas on behalf of utilities gas traders and gas producers. Bord Gais Energy supplies gas and electricity to more than 600000 customers in the Republic of Ireland.

Financial Performance

The company's net revenues have grown over the last few years. Revenues increased by 11% in 2014 due to stronger Direct Energy sales reflecting a full year of revenues from the Hess Energy Marketing acquisition (completed in November 2013).

In 2014 Centrica posted a net loss of euro 1.01 billion (compared to net income of euro 950.00 million in 2013) due to higher cost of sales as a result of changes in cost of sales before exceptional items and certain re-measurements and changes in the re-measurement of energy contracts.

The company's cash inflow decreased by 59% in 2014 due to a net loss and changes in working capital as a result of changes in receivables and payables.

Strategy

A major aspect of the company's strategy includes growing its core British Gas business and upstream operations (including gas supply storage and renewables) while establishing a leadership position as an integrated North American energy business. Centrica also intends to increase its gas production by 50% –to around 75 million barrels of oil equivalent over the next three to five years — by extending its geographic reach. The company also looks to investing in power generation using offshore wind nuclear and biomass technologies to supply its customers' needs.

In 2015 the company plans to continue to develop its leading position in smart metering innovation and connected homes in the UK. In North America it is looking to expand its offerings to the more valuable customer segments through joint energy and services products solar and innovative partnership agreements. Centrica is also working on reducing capital expenditure through driving efficiencies on in-flight projects and putting a hold on certain new projects.

That year Direct Energy agreed to sell its Ontario home services business to EnerCare for C$550 million. In 2014 Centrica sold its 50% non-operated interest in the 90 MW Barrow Offshore Wind Farm located in the East Irish Sea for £50 million. In 2013 the company signed an agreement to sell its Race Bank offshore wind farm project to DONG Energy Power (UK) Limited for £50 million. Centrica will retain equity interests totaling 290 MW in four operational wind farms in the UK.

In 2013 Centrica entered into a 4½ year LNG supply agreement with Qatargas for the purchase of up to 3 million tons of liquefied natural gas (LNG) per year. The £4.4 billion deal builds on Centrica's existing agreement with Qatargas signed in February 2011 and could provide gas to meet approximately 13% per cent of UK annual residential gas demand. With increasing global competition from emerging economies for LNG and declining North Sea production this transaction secures important gas supplies for Centrica and the UK to the end of 2018.

Mergers and Acquisitions

In 2015 British Gas acquired AlertMe a UK-based connected homes company that provides innovative energy management products and services. The acquisition gives British Gas ownership of a scalable technology platform software development capability data analytics and a patent portfolio enabling further development of connected homes products and services in other parts of the Centrica Group through Direct Energy in North America and Bord Gais in Ireland.

In 2014 Centrica and Qatar Petroleum International agreed to acquire a package of natural gas assets in the Foothills region of Alberta from Shell Canada Energy for C$50 millionExpanding its geographic presence in 2014 Centrica acquired Bord Gais Energy's gas and electricity supply business in Ireland and the Whitegate gas-fired power station. In 2013 Direct Energy acquired Texas-based electricity retailer Bounce Energy.

HISTORY

Company Background

William Murdock invented gas lighting in 1792. In 1812 the Gas Light and Coke Company of London was formed as the world's first gas supplier to the public and by 1829 the UK had 200 gas companies.

In the second half of the 19th century the gas industry began looking for new uses for the fuel. Gas stoves were introduced in 1851 the geyser water heater was invented in 1868 and in 1880 the first gas units to heat individual rooms were developed.

Gas companies countered the emerging electricity industry by renting gas stoves at low prices and installing gas fittings (stove pipe and lights) in poor homes with no installation charges or deposits. By 1914 the UK had 1500 gas suppliers.

The electricity industry soon made major strikes against the gas industry's dominance. In 1926 the government began reorganizing the fragmented electricity supply industry building a national power grid and establishing the Central Electricity Generating Board to oversee it.

The gas industry was nationalized in 1949 and 1050 gas suppliers were brought under the control of the British Gas Council. Still the gas industry was losing. Supplying gas was more expensive than generating electricity: Gas was seen as a power supply of the past. The Gas Council sought to change that image through an aggressive marketing campaign in the 1960s touting gas as a modern clean fuel. Other factors played a part in its re-emergence: The Clean Air Act of 1956 steadily reduced the use of coal for home heating liquefied natural gas was discovered in the North Sea and OPEC raised oil prices in the 1970s. When natural gas was introduced most of the old gasworks were demolished and the British Gas Council (which became the British Gas Corp. in 1973) set about converting free of charge every gas appliance in the UK to natural gas.

As Margaret Thatcher's government began privatizing state industries the British Gas Corp. was taken public in 1986. Freed from government control British Gas expanded its international exploration and production activities. When the US gas industry began deregulating British Gas formed joint venture Accord Energy in 1994 with US gas trader Natural Gas Clearinghouse (now NGC) to sell gas on the wholesale market.

With the opening of the UK gas-supply market (which began regionally in 1996 and went nationwide in 1998) British Gas split into two public companies to avoid a conflict of interest between its supply business and its monopoly transportation business. In 1997 it spun off Centrica the retail operations and BG (now BG Group) which received the transportation business and the international exploration and production operations.

The UK electricity supply market began opening up to competition in 1998 and Centrica won 750000 UK electricity customers most of them also gas customers. In 1999 it bought The Automobile Association which it sold to venture capitalists in 2004. In 2000 Centrica began offering telecom services in the UK.

Centrica moved into North America in 2000 by purchasing two Canadian companies: natural gas retailer Direct Energy Marketing and gas production company Avalanche Energy. It gained a 28% stake in US marketing firm Energy America through the Direct Energy transaction and purchased the remaining 72% from US firm Sempra Energy the next year. Continuing its non-domestic strategy Centrica bought a 50% interest in Belgium energy supplier Luminus.

The firm purchased 60% of the 1260-MW Humber Power station in 2001 its first domestic power plant interest. It also acquired the UK operations of Australia's One.

Tel and it bought Enron's European retail supply business Enron Direct for $137 million.

In 2002 Centrica purchased the retail energy services business of Canadian pipeline company Enbridge for $637 million; it also agreed to acquire another Enron-controlled company US retail energy supplier NewPower Holdings for $130 million. But Centrica withdrew its offer to buy NewPower a month after the deal was announced because of concerns about NewPower's potential Enron-related liabilities. Later that year Centrica acquired 200000 retail customer accounts in Ohio and Pennsylvania from NewPower.

In 2004 the company brought all its UK upstream activities together under Centrica Energy.

In 2005 Centrica acquired Oxxio the Netherlands #4 energy supplier.

To pursue green energy options in 2007 British Gas launched British Gas New Energy.

In 2007 Centrica acquired Newfield Exploration's North Sea assets for $486 million and in 2008 it acquired its first gas and oil assets in the Norwegian North Sea for $375 million (from Marathon Oil).

Growing it retail business in 2008 Centrica acquired Electricity Direct a UK commercial retail supplier serving nearly 1 million customers.

In 2008 Centrica's British Gas unit acquired 40000 small and mid-sized business customers from UK retail energy provider BizzEnergy in the wake of the latter's sudden financial collapse.

Centrica began in 2012 a program to save £500 million ($788 million) in costs over the next two years by identifying efficiencies. Although the company plans to continue investing for further growth it has already started cutting

2300 positions company-wide as well as implementing a pay freeze across much of the group. It set out to develop a better relationship with its customers by simplifying the purchase of gas and electricity. It also decided to make the cost of delivery more transparent by giving its customers a breakdown on their bill of the actual costs of providing the energy.

Through its aggressive acquisition strategy in North America the company has gained more than 6 million retail power and gas supply customers in less than a decade as part of its Direct Energy operations. Building on its portfolio of offerings in 2011 it acquired Illinois-based Home Warranty of America (HWA) for £30 million ($48 million). HWA provides whole home warranty plans to more than 70000 customers through a network of 4000 contractors.

Direct Energy also made three acquisitions in 2011 for its residential energy supply business in North America: Gateway Energy Services First Choice Power and Vectren Retail. The deals part of the company's strategy of acquiring smaller suppliers and buying in deregulated markets added more than 750000 customers.

In a major move to grow its upstream business and its Norwegian operations Centrica completed a £936 million ($1.5 billion) deal in 2012 to acquire Norwegian assets from Statoil and ConocoPhillips. Combined the new assets will increase the company's reserves by almost 40% and its production by more than 30%. The acquisition includes proved and probable reserves of 117 million barrels of oil equivalent and production of 34000 barrels of oil evalent per day. The buy also makes Centrica one of Norway's fastest growing companies with a third of its gas and oil production originating from that region. The company's upstream operations also have a presence in Trinidad and the Netherlands.

In spite of the growth of Centrica's gas assets the company decided to raise its gas and electricity prices by 17% in late 2011 to cover the rising wholesale commodity prices in the first half of the year. Mild weather that year led to a decline per household averaging 21% less in gas and 4% less in electricity consumption. With lower residential demand customer bills were 4% lower on average in 2011. Consumer complaints over higher prices for heating homes in the UK led to protests at the offices of utility companies and at town halls early in 2012.

EXECUTIVES

Interim Managing Director British Gas, Ian Peters
CEO, Iain C. Conn
Managing Director International Upstream, Mark Hanafin
CFO, Jeff Bell
Chairman, Richard (Rick) Haythornthwaite
Auditors: PricewaterhouseCoopers LLP

LOCATIONS

HQ: Centrica Plc
Millstream, Maidenhead Road, Windsor, Berkshire SL4 5GD
Phone:
Web: www.centrica.com

2011 Sales

	% of total
UK	69
US	17
Canada	9
Other countries	5
Total	**100**

PRODUCTS/OPERATIONS

2011 Sales

	% of total
UK	
Downstream	
Residential energy supply	36
Business energy supply & services	12
Residential services	7
Upstream	
Gas	13
Power	6
Storage	1
North America	
Business energy supply	12
Residential energy supply	10
Residential & business services	2
Upstream & wholesale energy	1
Total	**100**

COMPETITORS

AGL Resources	IBERDROLA
Community Energy	RWE npower
Constellation Energy Group	STASCO
	Scottish and Southern
Dominion Resources	Energy
E.ON UK	Southern Company
EDF Energy	United Utilities
Electrabel	Viridian Group
Gasunie	Western Power
Green Mountain Energy	Distribution

HISTORICAL FINANCIALS

Company Type: Public

Income Statement
FYE: December 31

	REVENUE ($ mil.)	NET INCOME ($ mil.)	NET PROFIT MARGIN	EMPLOYEES
12/15	41,451	(1,107)	—	38,848
12/14	45,906	(1,579)	—	37,530
12/13	43,910	1,569	3.6%	36,966
12/12	38,591	2,051	5.3%	38,642
12/11	35,259	650	1.8%	39,432
Annual Growth	4.1%	—	—	(0.4%)

2015 Year-End Financials

Debt ratio: 50.8%	No. of shares (mil.): —
Return on equity: (-38.1%)	Dividends
Cash ($ mil.): 1,274	Yield: 0.0%
Current ratio: 0.93	Payout: —
Long-term debt ($ mil.): 8,881	Market value ($ mil.): —

	STOCK PRICE ($) FY Close	P/E High/Low		Earnings	PER SHARE ($) Dividends	Book Value
12/15	12.75	—	—	(0.22)	0.70	0.34
12/14	17.26	—	—	(0.32)	1.04	0.86
12/13	23.18	145	116	0.30	1.09	1.69
12/12	22.00	90	74	0.39	0.96	1.84
12/11	17.82	262	209	0.13	0.87	1.67
Annual Growth	(8.0%) (32.6%)	—	—	—	(5.5%)	

Chiba Bank, Ltd

Auditors: Ernst & Young ShinNihon LLC

LOCATIONS

HQ: Chiba Bank, Ltd
1-2 Chiba-Minato, Chuo-ku, Chiba 260-8720
Phone: (81) 43 245 1111
Web: www.chibabank.co.jp

HISTORICAL FINANCIALS

Company Type: Public

Income Statement
FYE: March 31

	ASSETS ($ mil.)	NET INCOME ($ mil.)	INCOME AS % OF ASSETS	EMPLOYEES
03/16	118,737	493	0.4%	7,040
03/15	108,097	475	0.4%	7,038
03/14	116,486	449	0.4%	4,399
03/13	120,878	469	0.4%	4,454
03/12	133,082	497	0.4%	4,491
Annual Growth	(2.8%)	(0.2%)	—	11.9%

2016 Year-End Financials

Return on assets: 0.4%	Dividends
Return on equity: 6.4%	Yield: 0.0%
Long-term debt ($ mil.): —	Payout: 103.6%
No. of shares (mil.): 821	Market value ($ mil.): 19,958
Sales ($ mil.): 2,013	

	STOCK PRICE ($) FY Close	P/E High/Low		Earnings	PER SHARE ($) Dividends	Book Value
03/16	24.29	1	0	0.60	0.62	9.39
03/15	33.15	0	0	0.57	0.25	8.59
03/14	30.94	—	—	0.53	0.00	8.77
03/13	28.90	—	—	0.54	0.00	9.01
03/12	29.50	—	—	0.57	0.00	9.21
Annual Growth	(4.7%)	—	—	1.3%	—	0.5%

China Citic Bank Corp Ltd

Auditors: PricewaterhouseCoopers Zhong Tian LLP

LOCATIONS

HQ: China Citic Bank Corp Ltd
No.9 Chaoyangmen Beidajie, Dongcheng District, Beijing 100010
Phone: (86) 10 85230010   **Fax:** (86) 10 85230079
Web: www.bank.ecitic.com

HISTORICAL FINANCIALS

Company Type: Public

Income Statement
FYE: December 31

	REVENUE ($ mil.)	NET INCOME ($ mil.)	NET PROFIT MARGIN	EMPLOYEES
12/15	39,839	6,337	15.9%	56,489
12/14	38,250	6,556	17.1%	50,735
12/13	30,388	6,471	21.3%	46,822
12/12	24,705	4,977	20.1%	41,365
12/11	18,945	4,896	25.8%	37,195
Annual Growth	20.4%	6.7%	—	11.0%

2015 Year-End Financials

Debt ratio: —	No. of shares (mil.): —
Return on equity: 14.2%	Dividends
Cash ($ mil.): 78,710	Yield: —
Current ratio: —	Payout: —
Long-term debt ($ mil.): —	Market value ($ mil.): —

	STOCK PRICE ($) FY Close	P/E High/Low	PER SHARE ($) Earnings	Dividends	Book Value
12/15	13.16	21 14	0.14	0.00	1.00
12/14	13.28	15 11	0.14	0.69	0.89
12/13	10.48	15 11	0.14	0.40	0.80
Annual Growth	12.1%	— —	(0.6%)	—	5.8%

China Communications Constructions Group Ltd

EXECUTIVES

Chairman, Yusheng Chen
Auditors: PricewaterhouseCoopers Zhong Tian LLP

LOCATIONS

HQ: China Communications Constructions Group Ltd
85 De Sheng Men Wai Street, Xicheng District, Beijing
100088
Phone: (86) 10 8201 6562   **Fax:** (86) 10 8201 6524
Web: www.ccccltd.cn

HISTORICAL FINANCIALS
Company Type: Public

Income Statement
FYE: December 31

	REVENUE ($ mil.)	NET INCOME ($ mil.)	NET PROFIT MARGIN	EMPLOYEES
12/15	62,146	2,437	3.9%	115,179
12/14	58,978	2,253	3.8%	103,357
12/13	54,807	2,076	3.8%	100,874
12/12	47,370	1,964	4.1%	94,629
12/11	46,752	1,869	4.0%	90,674
Annual Growth	7.4%	6.9%	—	6.2%

2015 Year-End Financials
Debt ratio: 5.3%
Return on equity: 12.0%
Cash ($ mil.): 14,621
Current ratio: 1.05
Long-term debt ($ mil.): 25,956
No. of shares (mil.): —
Dividends
Yield: 2.2%
Payout: 293.2%
Market value ($ mil.): —

	STOCK PRICE ($) FY Close	P/E High/Low	PER SHARE ($) Earnings	Dividends	Book Value
12/15	20.21	41 21	0.15	0.45	1.40
12/14	23.92	29 14	0.14	0.50	1.16
12/13	16.21	29 18	0.13	0.48	0.97
12/12	19.80	27 19	0.12	0.46	0.86
12/11	15.78	25 17	0.13	0.41	0.75
Annual Growth	6.4%	— —	4.2%	2.5%	16.7%

China Construction Bank Corp

Auditors: PricewaterhouseCoopers Zhong Tian LLP

LOCATIONS

HQ: China Construction Bank Corp
No. 25, Financial Street, Xicheng District, Beijing
100033
Phone: (86) 10 6621 5533   **Fax:** (86) 10 6621 8888
Web: www.ccb.com

HISTORICAL FINANCIALS
Company Type: Public

Income Statement
FYE: December 31

	ASSETS ($ mil.)	NET INCOME ($ mil.)	INCOME AS % OF ASSETS	EMPLOYEES
12/15	2,825,371	35,128	1.2%	369,183
12/14	2,697,894	36,709	1.4%	372,321
12/13	2,537,740	35,457	1.4%	368,410
12/12	2,241,301	30,986	1.4%	355,290
12/11	1,951,231	26,890	1.4%	329,438
Annual Growth	9.7%	6.9%	—	2.9%

2015 Year-End Financials
Return on assets: 1.3%
Return on equity: 17.0%
Long-term debt ($ mil.): —
No. of shares (mil.): —
Sales ($ mil): 143,166
Dividends
Yield: 6.1%
Payout: 570.3%
Market value ($ mil.): —

	STOCK PRICE ($) FY Close	P/E High/Low	PER SHARE ($) Earnings	Dividends	Book Value
12/15	13.61	22 14	0.14	0.84	0.88
12/14	16.45	18 14	0.15	0.83	0.80
12/13	15.18	21 15	0.14	0.73	0.70
12/12	16.23	22 16	0.12	0.62	0.60
12/11	13.94	30 17	0.11	0.55	0.52
Annual Growth	(0.6%)	— —	6.7%	10.8%	14.4%

China Everbright Bank Co Ltd

Auditors: KPMG Huazhen LLP

LOCATIONS

HQ: China Everbright Bank Co Ltd
China Everbright Center, No. 25, Taipingqiao Ave.,
Xicheng District, Beijing
Phone: (86) 010 63636363   **Fax:** (86) 010 63636713
Web: www.cebbank.com

HISTORICAL FINANCIALS
Company Type: Public

Income Statement
FYE: December 31

	ASSETS ($ mil.)	NET INCOME ($ mil.)	INCOME AS % OF ASSETS	EMPLOYEES
12/15	487,749	4,546	0.9%	0
12/14	441,000	4,653	1.1%	0
12/13	398,930	4,412	1.1%	0
12/12	365,608	3,784	1.0%	0
12/11	275,378	2,870	1.0%	0
Annual Growth	15.4%	12.2%	—	—

2015 Year-End Financials
Return on assets: 1.0%
Return on equity: 14.6%
Long-term debt ($ mil.): —
No. of shares (mil.): —
Sales ($ mil): 26,215
Dividends
Yield: —
Payout: —
Market value ($ mil.): —

	STOCK PRICE ($) FY Close	P/E High/Low	PER SHARE ($) Earnings	Dividends	Book Value
12/15	0.43	1 1	0.10	0.00	0.74
Annual Growth	—	— —	—	—	—

China Evergrande Group

Evergrande's urban developments aim to mimic Neverland. Evergrande (formerly Hengda Real Estate Group) is a residential real estate developer in mainland China. Its multi-phase Jinbi development in Guangdong Province has more than 20000 apartments in dozens of high-rise buildings. (Real estate agency E-House leases the apartments). Now the group has more than 50 other developments planned for 25 cities across China including resort complexes with hotels sports arenas and other tourist-related activities. Founded in 1996 the company began trading on the Hong Kong Stock Exchange in late 2009.

Despite the volatile market the company managed to raise $506 million in private funding by July. New World Development's chairman Cheng Yu-Tung ponied up $150 million for a 3.9% stake in the company and the Kuwait Investment Authority (that country's investment arm) put up $146 million for a 3.8% stake. Five other partners including Merrill Lynch and Deutsche Bank AG gave a total of $210 million.

EXECUTIVES

VP and Chairman Evergrande Cultural Industry Group, Tao Huang
VP and Director Combating Bureaucracy, Yuzhi Liu
EVP and Chairman EvergrandeFinance Group, Huofa Qin
CFO, Darong Pan
VP and Chairman HengTen NetworksGroup, Xiaohua Zhang
EVP, Weikang Liang
VP and Chairman EvergrandeHotel Management Group, Chuan Wang
EVP, Zhaohui Tan
VP and Director Poverty Alleviation Office, Dong Yao
EVP and Chairman Evergrande Tourism Group, Shawn Siu
Chairman, Ka Yan Hui
Vice Chairman, Haijun Xia
Auditors: PricewaterhouseCoopers

LOCATIONS

HQ: China Evergrande Group
43rd Floor, Evergrande Center, No. 78 Huangpu Avenue West, Guangzhou, Guangdong Province 510620
Phone: (852) 2287 9208
Web: www.evergrande.com

COMPETITORS

China Vanke	New World China Land
Citychamp Dartong	Shanghai Forte Land
Gree Group	Xiamen C&D
Guangzhou R&F Properties	Xinyuan
	Yanlord Land

HISTORICAL FINANCIALS

Company Type: Public

Income Statement

FYE: December 31

	REVENUE ($ mil.)	NET INCOME ($ mil.)	NET PROFIT MARGIN	EMPLOYEES
12/15	20,498	1,610	7.9%	83,372
12/14	17,949	2,030	11.3%	77,057
12/13	15,472	2,083	13.5%	47,330
12/12	10,468	1,471	14.1%	38,463
12/11	9,837	1,808	18.4%	32,644
Annual Growth	20.1%	(2.9%)	—	26.4%

2015 Year-End Financials

Debt ratio: 6.0%	No. of shares (mil.): —
Return on equity: 9.0%	Dividends
Cash ($ mil.): 15,873	Yield: 0.1%
Current ratio: 1.34	Payout: 1,508.2%
Long-term debt ($ mil.): 21,273	Market value ($ mil.): —

	STOCK PRICE ($) FY Close	P/E High/Low	Earnings	Dividends	Book Value
12/15	21.73	30 17	0.11	1.63	1.41
Annual Growth	—		—	—	—

China Life Insurance Co Ltd

Controlling about half of its home country's life insurance market China Life Insurance Company is the insurance beast from the East. The firm is by far China's largest life insurance company providing annuity products and life insurance for both individuals and groups. It has more than 90 million individual and group policies in force. China Life sells its individual products primarily through about 640000 of its own agents who are spread across the country at roughly 15000 branch locations; another direct sales force handles marketing of its group policies. In addition to life insurance the company provides asset management services and health and accident insurance.

China Life was formed in 2003 when its state-owned predecessor China Life Insurance (Group) Company (or CLIC) spun off some of its more attractive assets in an IPO on the New York Stock Exchange. CLIC still owns about 68% of China Life with public investors owning the rest of the company.

Though its formidable force of exclusive sales agents is still the firm's core means for selling its products China Life has been diversifying its distribution channels using alliances with banks travel agencies brokerages and others to reach additional customers.

In 2009 the company announced it would buy a stake in China Development Bank as part of China Life's strategy of investing in banks as a way to build a distribution network for its policies. The purchase also matches the company's strategy of buying into unlisted companies.

China Life is also implementing market segmentation initiatives designing products and marketing plans tailored for different income and education levels. China's booming middle and upper classes are among the company's key customer targets.

Through its controlling interest in China Life Insurance Assets Management China Life is the largest insurance asset management company and one of the largest institutional investors in China.

HISTORY

China Life listed on the NYSE in what would become one of the largest IPOs of 2003 valued at more than $3 billion. The company's IPO however was tarnished by subsequent revelations of improper accounting prior to the company's going public; several US lawsuits were filed but in 2006 the SEC's investigation came to an end with no action taken.

EXECUTIVES

Vice Chairman and President, Miao Jianmin, age 51
Chairman and Executive Director, Yang Mingsheng, age 60
CFO, Zhao Lijun
Auditors: Ernst & Young Hua Ming LLP

LOCATIONS

HQ: China Life Insurance Co Ltd
16 Financial Street, Xicheng District, Beijing 100033
Phone: (86) 10 63631191   **Fax:** (86) 10 66575112
Web: www.e-chinalife.com

COMPETITORS

AEGON	ING
AXA	John Hancock Financial
Allianz	Services
Aviva	Manulife Financial
Bank of China	MetLife
CIGNA	PICC Property
China Minsheng Banking	Ping An Insurance
China Pacific	Skandia
Insurance	Sun Life
Generali	

HISTORICAL FINANCIALS

Company Type: Public

Income Statement

FYE: December 31

	ASSETS ($ mil.)	NET INCOME ($ mil.)	INCOME AS % OF ASSETS	EMPLOYEES
12/15	376,980	5,342	1.4%	98,823
12/14	361,977	5,189	1.4%	101,972
12/13	325,896	4,090	1.3%	100,310
12/12	304,594	1,774	0.6%	100,340
12/11	251,637	2,912	1.2%	100,319
Annual Growth	10.6%	16.4%	—	(0.4%)

2015 Year-End Financials

Return on assets: 1.4%	Dividends
Return on equity: 11.4%	Yield: 2.0%
Long-term debt ($ mil.): —	Payout: 163.6%
No. of shares (mil.): —	Market value ($ mil.): —
Sales ($ mil): 78,438	

	STOCK PRICE ($) FY Close	P/E High/Low	Earnings	Dividends	Book Value
12/15	15.99	62 12	0.19	0.32	1.76
12/14	58.71	52 34	0.18	0.64	1.62
12/13	47.25	62 39	0.15	0.29	1.29
12/12	49.69	122 88	0.06	0.47	1.25
12/11	36.97	102 52	0.10	0.28	1.08
Annual Growth	(18.9%)	— —	16.1%	3.5%	13.0%

China Merchants Bank Co Ltd

Auditors: KPMG Certified Public Accountants

LOCATIONS

HQ: China Merchants Bank Co Ltd
7088 Shennan Boulevard, Futian District, Shenzhen, Guangdong Province 518040
Phone: (86) 755 83198888   **Fax:** (86) 755 83195109
Web: www.cmbchina.com

HISTORICAL FINANCIALS

Company Type: Public

Income Statement

FYE: December 31

	ASSETS ($ mil.)	NET INCOME ($ mil.)	INCOME AS % OF ASSETS	EMPLOYEES
12/15	843,012	8,883	1.1%	76,192
12/14	762,415	9,008	1.2%	75,109
12/13	663,440	8,547	1.3%	68,078
12/12	546,693	7,261	1.3%	59,340
12/11	444,040	5,739	1.3%	45,344
Annual Growth	17.4%	11.5%	—	13.9%

2015 Year-End Financials

Return on assets: 1.1%	Dividends
Return on equity: 17.0%	Yield: 3.7%
Long-term debt ($ mil.): —	Payout: 120.1%
No. of shares (mil.): —	Market value ($ mil.): —
Sales ($ mil.): 46,912	

	STOCK PRICE ($) FY Close	P/E High/Low	Earnings	Dividends	Book Value
12/15	11.78	7 5	0.35	0.44	2.20
12/14	12.47	6 4	0.36	0.70	2.01
12/13	10.76	5 4	0.38	0.71	1.74
12/12	11.25	6 4	0.34	0.27	1.49
12/11	10.12	9 4	0.27	0.19	1.21
Annual Growth	3.9%	— —	7.4%	24.0%	16.0%

China Minsheng Banking Corp Ltd

Auditors: KPMG Huazhen LLP

LOCATIONS

HQ: China Minsheng Banking Corp Ltd
No. 2, Fuxingmennei Avenue, Xicheng District, Beijing 100031
Phone: (86) 10 68946790   **Fax:** (86) 10 58560720
Web: www.cmbc.com.cn

HISTORICAL FINANCIALS
Company Type: Public

Income Statement
FYE: December 31

	ASSETS ($ mil.)	NET INCOME ($ mil.)	INCOME AS % OF ASSETS	EMPLOYEES
12/15	696,075	7,099	1.0%	59,510
12/14	646,937	7,177	1.1%	59,659
12/13	532,914	6,983	1.3%	54,927
12/12	515,218	6,025	1.2%	49,227
12/11	354,134	4,435	1.3%	40,820
Annual Growth	18.4%	12.5%	—	9.9%

2015 Year-End Financials

Return on assets: 1.0%
Return on equity: 17.0%
Long-term debt ($ mil.): —
No. of shares (mil.): —
Sales ($ mill): 41,075

Dividends
Yield: 0.0%
Payout: 69.4%
Market value ($ mil.): —

	STOCK PRICE ($) FY Close	P/E High/Low		Earnings	PER SHARE ($) Dividends	Book Value
12/15	9.91	11	7	0.20	0.14	1.27
12/14	13.14	10	7	0.20	0.17	1.13
12/13	11.00	13	8	0.20	0.33	0.96
12/12	11.67	10	7	0.18	0.48	0.77
12/11	8.61	12	6	0.14	0.00	0.64
Annual Growth	3.6%			8.9%	—	18.6%

China Mobile Limited

China Mobile Limited sees unlimited potential. The company is China's (and the world's) leading wireless operator by subscribers which total some 800 million. In terms of sales it trails UK-based global leader Vodafone Group. China Mobile offers domestic and international phone service text messaging and other mobile data services. In addition to its flagship postpaid GoTone brand the company targets the youth and budget-conscious markets with M-Zone and Easy Own prepaid services. State-controlled China Mobile Communications Corporation (CMCC) indirectly holds a majority stake of 75% through intermediary subsidiary China Mobile (Hong Kong) Group Limited.

Revenue rose more than 7% in 2010 over 2009 thanks mainly to upticks in voice usage volume and value-added business besides the more obvious factor of subscriber growth. In the company's main segment of usage and monthly fees (64% of revenue) revenue went up about 4% in 2010 over 2009 a trend that could continue because of tariff decreases that may bring more business. The value-added services segment (31% of revenue) enjoyed an increase of more than 15% in 2010 over 2009 owing mainly to the launch of new products and other business-development efforts.

Like any other major telecom company 3G (Third Generation) and LTE (Long Term Evolution) development have kept China Mobile Limited buzzing recently. After initiating 3G service in 2009 the company has signed up about 27 million customers for it. Efforts to keep 3G service up to speed could result in significant capital expenditures. In addition to that China Mobile has been helping its parent CMCC roll out the LTE network in six Chinese cities as well as installing a demonstration LTE network in Beijing.

Meanwhile China Mobile Limited's organic growth has been fueled in part by the adoption of mobile communications in rural areas that previously had no wired or wireless telephone services. Additionally the company has catered increasingly to corporate clients in a search for higher-margin contracts.

Other efforts to grow its business include the $35.9 million acquisition in 2011 of China Topssion Communication a seller of mobile phones and other electronic devices to build its distribution and retail operations. China Mobile bought state-run fixed-line carrier China Tietong Telecommunications in 2008 as part of a broader restructuring of the telecom industry in China which also involved former rival China Unicom selling its wireless operations to China Telecom. The previous year it grew globally as well with the acquisition of nearly 90% of Pakistani wireless company Paktel Ltd. for about $284 million.

These purchases continued the company's history of using acquisitions to expand operations. From 1998 to 2004 China Mobile purchased 29 regional telecom service providers. The company acquired China Resources Peoples Telephone (later renamed China Mobile Peoples Telephone) a Hong Kong-based telecom service provider for $436 million in 2006.

EXECUTIVES

CEO, Li Yue, age 56
VP and CFO, Xue Taohai, age 59
VP and Executive Director, Sha Yuejia, age 58
VP and Executive Director, Liu Aili, age 53
Chairman, Shang Bing, age 60
Auditors: PricewaterhouseCoopers Zhong Tian LLP

LOCATIONS

HQ: China Mobile Limited
60/F, The Center, 99 Queen's Road Central,
Phone: (852) 3121 8888　　**Fax:** (852) 3121 8809
Web: www.chinamobileltd.com

PRODUCTS/OPERATIONS

2015 Sales

	% of total
Telecommunication Services	
Voice Services	56
Data Services	33
Other	5
Other products & services	6
Total	100

2015 Sales

	% of total
Revenue from telecommunications services	87
Revenue from sales of products and others	13
Total	100

COMPETITORS

China Telecom
　Corporation Limited
China Unicom
City Telecom
Hutchison
　Telecommunications
PCCW Ltd.
Vodafone

HISTORICAL FINANCIALS
Company Type: Public

Income Statement
FYE: December 31

	REVENUE ($ mil.)	NET INCOME ($ mil.)	NET PROFIT MARGIN	EMPLOYEES
12/15	102,907	16,712	16.2%	438,645
12/14	103,353	17,607	17.0%	241,550
12/13	104,094	20,101	19.3%	197,030
12/12	89,892	20,736	23.1%	182,487
12/11	83,883	19,997	23.8%	175,336
Annual Growth	5.2%	(4.4%)	—	25.8%

2015 Year-End Financials

Debt ratio: 0.0%
Return on equity: 12.2%
Cash ($ mil.): 12,293
Current ratio: 0.98
Long-term debt ($ mil.): 769

No. of shares (mil.): —
Dividends
Yield: 2.9%
Payout: 199.8%
Market value ($ mil.): —

	STOCK PRICE ($) FY Close	P/E High/Low		Earnings	PER SHARE ($) Dividends	Book Value
12/15	56.33	14	10	0.82	1.69	6.90
12/14	58.82	12	8	0.86	1.83	6.75
12/13	52.29	10	8	0.99	2.02	6.48
12/12	58.72	9	8	1.02	1.96	5.77
12/11	48.49	8	7	0.99	1.88	5.14
Annual Growth	3.8%			(4.6%)	(2.7%)	7.6%

China National Building Material Company Limited

EXECUTIVES

Chairman, Zhiping Song
Auditors: Baker Tilly China Certified Public Accountants

LOCATIONS

HQ: China National Building Material Company Limited
21st Floor, Tower 2 (Building B), Guohai Plaza, No. 17 Fuxing Road, Haidian District, Beijing 100036
Phone: (86) 10 68138300　　**Fax:** (86) 10 68138388
Web: www.cnbmltd.com

HISTORICAL FINANCIALS
Company Type: Public

Income Statement
FYE: December 31

	REVENUE ($ mil.)	NET INCOME ($ mil.)	NET PROFIT MARGIN	EMPLOYEES
12/15	15,442	156	1.0%	134,158
12/14	19,659	953	4.9%	141,813
12/13	19,440	951	4.9%	134,780
12/12	13,990	894	6.4%	121,657
12/11	12,719	1,273	10.0%	82,352
Annual Growth	5.0%	(40.7%)	—	13.0%

2015 Year-End Financials

Debt ratio: 9.2%
Return on equity: 2.0%
Cash ($ mil.): 1,628
Current ratio: 0.57
Long-term debt ($ mil.): 7,491

No. of shares (mil.): —
Dividends
Yield: —
Payout: —
Market value ($ mil.): —

China Overseas Land & Investment Ltd.

China Overseas Land & Investment (COLI) builds upon its bricks-and-mortar aspirations both in Hong Kong and mainland China. The property developer and investor specializes in high-rise apartment buildings and commercial structures.

Its property investment operations bring in rental and property management income from commercial and retail space. Other businesses include construction design and property management. The company targets its investment and development efforts in 48 major cities including Beijing Guangzhou Hong Kong and Shanghai. The company is exiting the infrastructure business. Having already sold the Nanchang Bridge and Laizhou Port it is looking to sell its other infrastructure holdings.

Operations

Known as China Overseas Property in mainland China the company operates through three primary segments: Property Development Property Investments and Other Operations (including real estate agency and management services and construction and building design consultancy services). The largest segment Property Development accounts for 97% of total revenue.

Geographic Reach

COLI has a strong presence in the Hua Nan and Hua Dong regions which brought in 30% and 25% of revenues in 2014 respectively. To a lesser extent it also operates in the Northern Region Hua Bei Region Western Region Macau and Hong Kong.

Financial Performance

NOTE: Growth rates may differ after conversion to US dollars.

Revenue has been on the rise for the past five years with 2014 earnings continuing the trend. That year net revenue increased 46% to HK$119.9 billion on higher property sales and rental income (due to rising occupancy and market rates). However property management revenue experienced a decline that year.

Net income rose 20% to HD$27.7 billion in 2014 largely due to the increase in net revenue as well as a decrease in operating expenses. Cash flow from operations fell 55% to HK$4.5 billion due to changes in inventories and an increase in trade.

Strategy

COLI has some 30 million sq. meters of area under development a record for the company. Its main focus is on residential development projects with property investment serving in a supporting role.

The move away from the infrastructure business is part of COLI's strategy to get rid of its non-core assets and focus on its property business. The money earned from the sales will go toward the purchase and development of other properties.

Mergers and Acquisitions

The company has been busy buying up parcels of developable land in locations including Tianjin and Beijing. In one of its largest recent deals COLI in 2015 agreed to buy a portfolio of property projects in China and London from state-owned China State Construction Engineering Corporation (CSCEC which also controls some 55% of COLI) for some HK$42.8 billion.

Company Background

Through China Overseas Holding COLI is the flagship subsidiary of state-owned China State Construction Engineering Corporation (CSCEC) which owns about 55% of the company. COLI was incorporated in Hong Kong in 1979.

EXECUTIVES

Executive Director and Qualified Accountant, Paul M. K. Wang, age 59
Chairman, Kong Qingping, age 60
Vice Chairman, Xiao Xiao, age 59
Auditors: PricewaterhouseCoopers

LOCATIONS

HQ: China Overseas Land & Investment Ltd.
 10/F., Three Pacific Place, 1 Queens Road East,
Phone: (852) 2823 7888   **Fax:** (852) 2865 5939
Web: www.coli.com.hk

PRODUCTS/OPERATIONS

2014 Sales

	% of total
Property development	97
Property investment	1
Other operations	2
Total	**100**

OPERATIONS

Property development
Property investment
Property-related business
 Construction design
 Property management

COMPETITORS

China Vanke
Chinese Estates
Hang Lung Group
Hongkong Land
Kowloon Development Company

New World Development
Orient Overseas
Sun Hung Kai
 Properties

HISTORICAL FINANCIALS

Company Type: Public

Income Statement

FYE: December 31

	REVENUE ($ mil.)	NET INCOME ($ mil.)	NET PROFIT MARGIN	EMPLOYEES
12/15	19,104	4,297	22.5%	5,300
12/14	15,473	3,569	23.1%	25,705
12/13	10,635	2,971	27.9%	20,772
12/12	8,331	2,415	29.0%	18,849
12/11	6,254	1,934	30.9%	15,822
Annual Growth	32.2%	22.1%	—	(23.9%)

2015 Year-End Financials

Debt ratio: 3.4%
Return on equity: 20.5%
Cash ($ mil.): 13,217
Current ratio: 3.00
Long-term debt ($ mil.): 13,957

No. of shares (mil.): —
Dividends
 Yield: 0.0%
 Payout: 668.0%
Market value ($ mil.): —

	STOCK PRICE ($) FY Close	P/E High/Low		PER SHARE ($) Earnings	Dividends	Book Value
12/15	103.27	35	22	0.47	3.11	2.51
12/14	87.65	27	20	0.44	1.80	2.10
12/13	84.00	35	25	0.36	1.53	1.74
12/12	88.90	40	26	0.30	1.33	1.38
12/11	44.00	35	23	0.24	1.06	1.11
Annual Growth	23.8%			— — 18.4%	31.0%	22.7%

China Pacific Insurance (Group) Co., Ltd.

Auditors: PricewaterhouseCoopers Zhong Tian LLP

LOCATIONS

HQ: China Pacific Insurance (Group) Co., Ltd.
 South Tower, Bank of Communications, Financial Building, 190 Central Yincheng Road, Pudong New District, Shanghai 200120
Phone: (86) 21 58767282   **Fax:** (86) 21 68870791
Web: www.cpic.com.cn

HISTORICAL FINANCIALS

Company Type: Public

Income Statement

FYE: December 31

	REVENUE ($ mil.)	NET INCOME ($ mil.)	NET PROFIT MARGIN	EMPLOYEES
12/15	29,159	2,729	9.4%	0
12/14	34,835	1,780	5.1%	90,829
12/13	31,750	1,529	4.8%	86,893
12/12	26,812	814	3.0%	85,137
12/11	24,707	1,320	5.3%	82,456
Annual Growth	4.2%	19.9%	—	—

2015 Year-End Financials

Debt ratio: 0.3%
Return on equity: 14.1%
Cash ($ mil.): 1,462
Current ratio: 6.38
Long-term debt ($ mil.): 3,002

No. of shares (mil.): —
Dividends
 Yield: 0.0%
 Payout: 25.9%
Market value ($ mil.): —

	STOCK PRICE ($) FY Close	P/E High/Low		PER SHARE ($) Earnings	Dividends	Book Value
12/15	4.20	3	2	0.30	0.08	(0.00)
12/14	3.60	3	3	0.20	0.06	2.08
12/13	3.59	4	3	0.17	0.00	1.80
12/12	3.30	6	5	0.09	0.00	1.70
12/11	2.74	5	3	0.15	0.00	1.42
Annual Growth	11.3%			— — 18.3%	—	—

China Petroleum & Chemical Corp. Inc

China Petroleum and Chemical Corporation (Sinopec Corp.) is China's largest producer and supplier of refined oil products and its second-largest crude oil producer. It is also China's largest petrochemicals producer and distributor and the world's fourth-largest ethylene producer. Operations include oil and gas exploration and production; crude oil processing; oil products trading transportation distribution and marketing; and petrochemicals manufacturing. In 2010 it reported proved reserves of 2.9 billion barrels of oil and 6.5 trillion cu. ft. of natural gas; it also owns more than 29600 gas stations and 34 refineries. China's government controls about 76% of the company through Sinopec Group.

Sinopec Corp. is committed to growing its oil and gas reserves to keep pace with the energy demands from China's booming industrial economy and growing population. The company operates 16 oil and gas production fields in China and also owns vast reserves in Africa. In 2010 the company produced an average of more than 1 billion barrels of oil equivalent per day. For the past few years it has been buying up resources across the globe as it competes with other developing countries for oil and gas reserves.

In late 2011 the company acquired Canada's Daylight Energy for $2.1 billion which gave it access to 69 oil and natural gas assets in the western provinces of British Columbia and Alberta. Daylight is being integrated within an indirect subsidiary of Sinopec Corp. and will operate as Sinopec Daylight Energy. The purchase was made on the heels of the acquisition of OPTI Canada in November by competitor CNOOC another Chinese state-owned company.

In 2013 it purchased a 50% undivided interest in 850000 of Chesapeake's net oil and natural gas leasehold acres in the Mississippi Lime play in northern Oklahoma (425000 acres net to Sinopec) for $1.02 billion.

The acquisitions follow several other purchases Sinopec has made since 2009 including shelling out $7.1 billion for Repsol's assets in Brazil $2.5 billion for Occidental Petroleum's assets in Argentina; $4.7 billion for ConocoPhillips' 9% stake in Syncrude; and $7.5 billion for Addax Petroleum which had reserves in Africa and the Middle East. In late 2010 the company also signed a deal with Chevron to help develop the $6 billion-plus Gendalo-Gehem deepwater natural gas project off the coast of Indonesia.

The shopping spree for oil and gas resources paid off in 2010 when Sinopec Corp. achieved record sales. The company's sales spiked 47% over the previous year and its net income grew by more than 20%. Its exploration and production operations not only grew exponentially but the official launch of the Sichuan-East China Gas project in 2010 also accelerated the company's growth. The pipeline has the capacity to produce about 12 billion cu. meters of gas per year.

Sinopec Corp.'s parent state-owned China Petrochemical (Sinopec Group) reorganized in 2000 and pooled the best of its assets as Sinopec Corp.

EXECUTIVES

Vice Chairman of the Board; President, Wang Tianpu, age 53, $726,000 total compensation
Vice Chairman and President, Dai Houliang, age 53, $721,000 total compensation
VP and Director General Development and Planning Department, Lei Dianwu, age 53, $362,000 total compensation
Chairman, Wang Yupu
CFO, Wang Dehua
Vice Chairman, Zhang Yaocang, age 62
Auditors: PricewaterhouseCoopers Zhong Tian LLP

LOCATIONS

HQ: China Petroleum & Chemical Corp. Inc
22 Chaoyangmen North Street, Chaoyang District, Beijing 100728
Phone: (86) 10 5996 0028   **Fax:** (86) 10 5996 0386
Web: www.sinopec.com

2015 Sales

	% of total
Mainland China	78
Others	22
Total	**100**

PRODUCTS/OPERATIONS

2015 Sales

	% of total
Marketing and distribution	34
Refining	28
Chemicals	10
Exploration and production	4
Corporate and others	24
Total	**100**

COMPETITORS

BASF SE	Chevron
BP	Exxon Mobil
Bangchak Petroleum	Furmanite
Public	PetroChina
CNOOC	Royal Dutch Shell
CPC	TOTAL

HISTORICAL FINANCIALS

Company Type: Public

Income Statement

FYE: December 31

	REVENUE ($ mil.)	NET INCOME ($ mil.)	NET PROFIT MARGIN	EMPLOYEES
12/15	310,858	4,994	1.6%	351,019
12/14	455,324	7,486	1.6%	358,571
12/13	475,778	10,923	2.3%	368,953
12/12	446,893	10,246	2.3%	376,201
12/11	398,081	11,633	2.9%	377,235
Annual Growth	**(6.0%)**	**(19.1%)**	**—**	**(1.8%)**

2015 Year-End Financials

Debt ratio: 2.7%
Return on equity: 5.1%
Cash ($ mil.): 10,556
Current ratio: 0.72
Long-term debt ($ mil.): 21,517
No. of shares (mil.): —
Dividends
Yield: 4.7%
Payout: 6,620.5%
Market value ($ mil.): —

	STOCK PRICE ($) FY Close	P/E High/Low		PER SHARE ($) Earnings	Dividends	Book Value
12/15	59.98	341	205	0.04	2.85	0.86
12/14	81.01	260	182	0.06	3.47	0.81
12/13	82.17	221	120	0.09	3.27	0.81
12/12	114.92	222	152	0.09	4.25	0.73
12/11	105.05	179	131	0.10	2.49	0.67
Annual Growth	**(13.1%)**		**—**	**(19.5%)**	**3.4%**	**6.5%**

China Railway Construction Corp Ltd

Auditors: Ernst & Young Hua Ming LLP

LOCATIONS

HQ: China Railway Construction Corp Ltd
East, No. 40 Fuxing Road, Haidian District, Beijing 100855
Phone: (86) 10 5268 8600   **Fax:** (86) 10 5268 8302
Web: www.crcc.cn

HISTORICAL FINANCIALS

Company Type: Public

Income Statement

FYE: December 31

	REVENUE ($ mil.)	NET INCOME ($ mil.)	NET PROFIT MARGIN	EMPLOYEES
12/15	92,468	1,947	2.1%	254,366
12/14	95,380	1,827	1.9%	249,624
12/13	96,927	1,708	1.8%	246,736
12/12	77,685	1,360	1.8%	244,523
12/11	72,662	1,247	1.7%	241,621
Annual Growth	**6.2%**	**11.8%**	**—**	**1.3%**

2015 Year-End Financials

Debt ratio: 3.5%
Return on equity: 12.4%
Cash ($ mil.): 18,774
Current ratio: 1.19
Long-term debt ($ mil.): 12,312
No. of shares (mil.): —
Dividends
Yield: 0.0%
Payout: —
Market value ($ mil.): —

	STOCK PRICE ($) FY Close	P/E High/Low		PER SHARE ($) Earnings	Dividends	Book Value
12/15	12.31	21	10	0.15	0.18	1.27
12/14	12.60	14	8	0.15	0.17	1.19
12/13	10.00	15	10	0.14	0.14	1.08
12/12	11.39	17	8	0.11	0.13	0.94
12/11	5.29	21	7	0.10	0.12	0.83
Annual Growth	**23.5%**		**—**	**10.4%**	**10.1%**	**11.0%**

China Railway Group Ltd

China Railway Group keeps its infrastructure construction projects on the right track. A subsidiary of state-owned China Railway Engineering Corporation the company designs and constructs railways roads bridges tunnels subways and other structures. It also offers related consulting and engineering services as well as property development and construction services for commercial and residential buildings and other projects. In addition to its core transportation-related projects the company pursues projects from municipal and energy entities in China and abroad. Some of those projects have included hydroelectricity facilities ports and docks.

Operations
China Railway Group operates through five main segments. Its Infrastructure Construction segment generated 82% of its total sales in 2014 and works on railways highways bridges railways irrigation works dams docks airports and municipal works among other projects. Its Property Development segment (5% of revenue) is its next largest and sells or manages residential and commercial properties. The other segments include Survey Design and Consulting Services (2%); Engineering Equipment and Component Manufacturing (2%); and other (9%).

Geographic Reach
Beyond China the group has worked on construction projects in the Americas Europe Africa and the Asia Pacific. Still the group generated 96% of its total revenue from China in 2014.

Sales and Marketing
China Railway Group's largest customer is the China Railway Corporation which accounted for 32% of its total revenue in 2014. Its four next largest customers combined made up another 2.5% of its total revenue.

Financial PerformanceNote: Growth rates may differ after conversion to US dollars. This analysis uses financials from the company's annual report.

China Railway Group's annual revenues and profits have grown more than 30% since 2011 thanks mostly to increased demand for infrastructure construction in China with the growing economy.

The group's revenue climbed 9% to RMB$590.2 billion ($95.9 billion) during 2014 mostly driven by double-digit growth in its infrastructure construction business with more demand for railways highways building construction and urban rail work. The group's Survey Design and Consulting Services business grew 12% due to a rise in infrastructure project activity while its manufacturing and property development businesses each grew by 6% during the year.

Strong revenue growth in 2014 drove China Railway Group's net income higher by 9% to RMB$10.26 billion ($1.67 billion). The group's operating cash levels more than doubled to RMB$19.4 billion ($3.16 billion) in FY2014 mostly as it was able to collect more of its trade receivables with stronger management initiatives.

Strategy

Buoyed by an influx of infrastructure funds from the Chinese government's "One Belt and One Road" policy the group in 2015 planned to build a new China brand for high speed rail and expand its construction projects globally (through its "Go Global" campaign) in new infrastructure markets such as Russia and Israel. The group also planned to invest more in Research Development and Technological Achievements creating some 957 new research projects during 2014 with support from national funds amounting to nearly RMB$29 million.

Despite a strategy to expand internationally most of China Railway Group' work still originates in China. Recent projects include new light rail systems and highways in some of China's larger cities. Ultimately a state-owned company China Railway Group receives much of its funding for projects from the Chinese government which has been pushing to expand the country's public transportation infrastructure.

Company Background

China Railway Group traces its roots back to the 1950s. It has completed hundreds of infrastructure projects in more than 50 countries since the 1970s.

EXECUTIVES

President and Director, Zhang Zongyan
Chairman and Executive Director, Shi Dahua
Auditors: Deloitte Touche Tohmatsu CPA LLP

LOCATIONS

HQ: China Railway Group Ltd
918, Block 1, No. 128 South 4th Ring Road West,
Fengtai District, Beijing 100070
Phone:
Web: www.crec.cn

PRODUCTS/OPERATIONS

2015 Sales

	% of total
Infrastructure Construction	85
Property Development	5
Survey Design and Consulting Services	2
Engineering Equipment and Component Manufacturing	2
Other Businesses	6
Total	**100**

COMPETITORS

Bechtel	CSCEC
Beijing Urban Construction	Hyundai Engineering and Construction
Bouygues	Shimizu
CCCC	Zhejiang Expressway

HISTORICAL FINANCIALS

Company Type: Public

Income Statement

FYE: December 31

	REVENUE ($ mil.)	NET INCOME ($ mil.)	NET PROFIT MARGIN	EMPLOYEES
12/15	92,376	1,797	1.9%	291,149
12/14	95,090	1,653	1.7%	293,592
12/13	89,263	1,548	1.7%	289,547
12/12	74,688	1,179	1.6%	289,343
12/11	70,255	1,062	1.5%	294,761
Annual Growth	**7.1%**	**14.0%**	**—**	**(0.3%)**

2015 Year-End Financials

Debt ratio: 3.9%
Return on equity: 10.2%
Cash ($ mil.): 14,366
Current ratio: 1.20
Long-term debt ($ mil.): 14,890
No. of shares (mil.): —
Dividends
　Yield: 0.0%
　Payout: —
Market value ($ mil.): —

	STOCK PRICE ($) FY Close	P/E High/Low		PER SHARE ($) Earnings	Dividends	Book Value
12/15	19.16	67	32	0.08	0.23	0.88
12/14	17.77	38	21	0.08	0.22	0.75
12/13	12.81	37	25	0.07	0.17	0.67
12/12	14.14	41	24	0.06	0.16	0.59
12/11	7.82	64	15	0.05	0.18	0.54
Annual Growth	**25.1%**	**—**	**—**	**13.1%**	**7.1%**	**13.2%**

China Shenhua Energy Co., Ltd.

China Shenhua Energy Company (CSEC) is an integrated coal mining company in China. CSEC operates four mining groups —two underground and two surface mining projects —in western and northern China. The Shendong Mines account for close to two-thirds of its total coal production which is more than 180 million tons a year. It also markets coal mined by other companies making a total of more than 230 million tons sold annually. CSEC owns and operates four railway lines and port facilities for the transportation of its coal. The company also operates more than a dozen power plants with a total installed capacity of close to 18000 MW. Shenhua Group holds about 75% of the company.

The group announced in early 2006 that it plans to funnel all of its coal-related activities into Shenhua Energy. Shenhua Group's other businesses include power station construction coal chemicals manufacturing and coal-to-oil production.

EXECUTIVES

CFO, Zhang Kehui, age 50
Executive Director and President, Han Jianguo
Director, Zhang Yuzhuo, age 54
Vice chairman and Executive director, Ling Wen, age 53
Auditors: Deloitte Touche Tohmatsu Certified Public Accountants LLP

LOCATIONS

HQ: China Shenhua Energy Co., Ltd.
22 Andingmen Xibinhe Road, Dongcheng District, Beijing 100011
Phone: (86) 10 5813 3399　　**Fax:** (86) 10 5813 1804
Web: www.csec.com

2008 Sales

	% of total
China	91
Other countries	9
Total	**100**

COMPETITORS

China Yangtze Power	Yankuang
Peabody Energy	Yanzhou Coal
Rio Tinto Limited	
U.S. China Mining Group	

HISTORICAL FINANCIALS

Company Type: Public

Income Statement

FYE: December 31

	REVENUE ($ mil.)	NET INCOME ($ mil.)	NET PROFIT MARGIN	EMPLOYEES
12/15	27,264	2,717	10.0%	95,498
12/14	40,016	6,233	15.6%	92,738
12/13	46,878	7,446	15.9%	91,487
12/12	40,142	7,837	19.5%	89,144
12/11	33,076	7,256	21.9%	82,260
Annual Growth	**(4.7%)**	**(21.8%)**		**3.8%**

2015 Year-End Financials

Debt ratio: 2.9%
Return on equity: 5.9%
Cash ($ mil.): 6,516
Current ratio: 1.19
Long-term debt ($ mil.): 13,670
No. of shares (mil.): —
Dividends
　Yield: 13.9%
　Payout: —
Market value ($ mil.): —

	STOCK PRICE ($) FY Close	P/E High/Low		PER SHARE ($) Earnings	Dividends	Book Value
12/15	6.23	13	6	0.14	0.87	2.31
12/14	11.90	6	5	0.31	0.48	2.41
12/13	12.60	8	4	0.37	0.51	2.30
12/12	17.90	19	6	0.39	0.49	2.07
12/11	43.03	23	15	0.36	0.41	1.80
Annual Growth	**(38.3%)**	**—**	**—**	**(21.8%)**	**20.6%**	**6.4%**

China Southern Airlines Co Ltd

One of China's top three airline companies along with China Eastern Airlines and Air China China Southern Airlines operates a fleet of more than 600 passenger and cargo transport aircraft including Boeing models 787，777 757& 737 and Airbus models A380 330 321 320 319 from its hub in Guangzhou and more than a dozen regional bases. China Southern Airlines oversees 2000 daily flights to 207 destinations in 40 countries and regions across the world primarily in the Asia/Pacific region. Government-owned China Southern Air Holding Company owns just over 40% of China Southern Airlines.

Operations

To expand its global reach China Southern Airlines has joined the SkyTeam marketing and code-sharing alliance which along with Delta and KLM includes such carriers as Air France and Korean Air Lines. (Code-sharing allows airlines to sell tickets on one another's flights and thus offer potential passengers more destinations.)

EXECUTIVES

EVP, Liu Qian, age 51
Vice Chairman and President, Tan Wan Geng, age 53, $542,000 total compensation
EVP and Director, Zhang Zi Fang, age 59
EVP and Senior Engineer, Ren Ji Dong, age 52
CFO, Xiao Li Xin, age 49
EVP and Chief Pilot and Chairman Zhuhai Airlines Company Limited, Wang Zhi Xue
COO Marketing and Sales, Guo Zhi Qiang, age 52
COO Flight Safety, Feng Hua Nan, age 53
Chairman, Wang Changshun, age 56
Auditors: PricewaterhouseCoopers Zhong Tian LLP

LOCATIONS

HQ: China Southern Airlines Co Ltd
278 Ji Chang Road, Guangzhou, Guangdong Province
510405
Phone: (86) 20 8612 4462   **Fax:** (86) 20 8665 9040
Web: www.csair.com

2014 Sales

	% of total
Domestic	77
International	21
Hong Kong Macau & Taiwan	2
Total	**100**

PRODUCTS/OPERATIONS

2014 Sales

	% of total
Traffic revenue	96
Other	4
Total	**100**

Selected Services

Excess baggage
Carry-on baggage
Delayed/damaged/lost baggage
Checked Baggage
Restrictions on baggage transportation
Special baggage

COMPETITORS

ANA Holdings	Guangshen Railway
Air China	Hainan Airlines
Air India	Korean Air
Air Philippines	Lufthansa
American Airlines	Lung Cheong
Group	Malaysian Airlines
Cathay Pacific	Qantas
China Airlines	Singapore Airlines
China Eastern Airlines	Swire Pacific
Dragonair	Thai Airways
EVA Air	United Continental

HISTORICAL FINANCIALS

Company Type: Public

Income Statement

FYE: December 31

	REVENUE ($ mil.)	NET INCOME ($ mil.)	NET PROFIT MARGIN	EMPLOYEES
12/15	17,191	575	3.3%	87,202
12/14	17,495	286	1.6%	82,132
12/13	16,278	328	2.0%	80,175
12/12	15,962	420	2.6%	73,668
12/11	14,361	811	5.7%	54,326
Annual Growth	**4.6%**	**(8.3%)**	**—**	**12.6%**

2015 Year-End Financials

Debt ratio: 8.4%
Return on equity: 9.9%
Cash ($ mil.): 702
Current ratio: 0.22
Long-term debt ($ mil.): 10,053
No. of shares (mil.): —
Dividends
 Yield: 0.7%
 Payout: 448.1%
Market value ($ mil.): —

	STOCK PRICE ($) FY Close	P/E High/Low	Earnings	PER SHARE ($) Dividends	Book Value
12/15	38.15	159 57	0.06	0.27	0.61
12/14	23.90	139 81	0.03	0.27	0.59
12/13	19.74	154 86	0.03	1.77	0.58
12/12	25.85	112 76	0.04	1.42	0.54
12/11	25.45	69 40	0.08	0.00	0.52
Annual Growth	**10.7%**	**— —**	**(8.3%)**	**—**	**4.1%**

China Taiping Insurance Holding Co., Ltd.

EXECUTIVES

Chairman, Fan Lin
Auditors: PricewaterhouseCoopers

LOCATIONS

HQ: China Taiping Insurance Holding Co., Ltd.
22nd Floor, China Taiping Tower Phase I, 8 Sunning Road, Causeway Bay,
Phone: (852) 2854 6100   **Fax:** (852) 2544 5269
Web: www.ctih.cntaiping.com

HISTORICAL FINANCIALS

Company Type: Public

Income Statement

FYE: December 31

	ASSETS ($ mil.)	NET INCOME ($ mil.)	INCOME AS % OF ASSETS	EMPLOYEES
12/15	62,964	818	1.3%	53,682
12/14	57,193	521	0.9%	43,933
12/13	40,627	197	0.5%	40,827
12/12	31,339	120	0.4%	37,187
12/11	24,635	63	0.3%	31,661
Annual Growth	**26.4%**	**89.3%**	**—**	**14.1%**

2015 Year-End Financials

Return on assets: 1.3%
Return on equity: 12.6%
Long-term debt ($ mil.): —
No. of shares (mil.): —
Sales ($ mil): 20,728
Dividends
 Yield: —
 Payout: —
Market value ($ mil.): —

	STOCK PRICE ($) FY Close	P/E High/Low	Earnings	PER SHARE ($) Dividends	Book Value
12/15	74.86	59 42	0.23	0.00	2.14
Annual Growth	**—**	**— —**	**—**	**—**	**—**

China Telecom Corp Ltd

Auditors: Deloitte Touche Tohmatsu

LOCATIONS

HQ: China Telecom Corp Ltd
31 Jinrong Street, Xicheng District, Beijing 100033
Phone: (86) 10 6642 8166   **Fax:** (86) 10 6601 0728
Web: www.chinatelecom-h.com

HISTORICAL FINANCIALS

Company Type: Public

Income Statement

FYE: December 31

	REVENUE ($ mil.)	NET INCOME ($ mil.)	NET PROFIT MARGIN	EMPLOYEES
12/15	50,996	3,087	6.1%	291,526
12/14	52,267	2,848	5.5%	300,960
12/13	53,120	2,898	5.5%	306,545
12/12	45,406	2,394	5.3%	305,676
12/11	38,930	2,621	6.7%	309,799
Annual Growth	**7.0%**	**4.2%**	**—**	**(1.5%)**

2015 Year-End Financials

Debt ratio: 2.8%
Return on equity: 6.7%
Cash ($ mil.): 4,907
Current ratio: 0.31
Long-term debt ($ mil.): 9,994
No. of shares (mil.): —
Dividends
 Yield: 2.3%
 Payout: —
Market value ($ mil.): —

	STOCK PRICE ($) FY Close	P/E High/Low	Earnings	PER SHARE ($) Dividends	Book Value
12/15	46.45	299174	0.04	1.10	0.58
12/14	58.71	300182	0.04	1.10	0.58
12/13	50.57	271209	0.04	0.99	0.57
12/12	56.85	357238	0.03	0.99	0.53
12/11	57.13	345274	0.03	1.02	0.50
Annual Growth	**(5.0%)**	**— —**	**4.9%**	**2.0%**	**3.5%**

China Unicom (Hong Kong) Ltd

China Unicom (Hong Kong) Limited has brought competition to the world's largest telecommunications market. The Chinese government set up China Unicom in 1994 as the first competitor to another government-owned telecommunications monopoly. The state-controlled company provides 437 million subscribers long-distance broadband data and mobile communications services in 31 provinces cities and other regions throughout China. It is the country's #2 mobile phone operator behind former monopoly China Mobile Communications. China Unicom (Hong Kong) Limited operates primarily in the Chinese northern provinces; major cities served include Beijing and Tianjin.

EXECUTIVES

Chairman and CEO, Chang Xiaobing, age 59
Executive Director and President, Lu Yimin, age 52
Executive Director and CFO, Li Fushen, age 53
Auditors: KPMG

LOCATIONS

HQ: China Unicom (Hong Kong) Ltd
75th Floor, The Center, 99 Queen's Road Central,
Phone: (852) 2126 2018   **Fax:** (852) 2126 2016
Web: www.chinaunicom.com.hk

PRODUCTS/OPERATIONS

2013 Sales

	% of total
Mobile	51
Fixed-line	30
Telecommunication products	19
Total	**100**

COMPETITORS

Beijing Mobile	China Tietong
China Mobile	Hunan Telecom
China Mobile	Pacnet
Communications	Shanghai Mobile
China Telecom	
Corporation Limited	

HISTORICAL FINANCIALS
Company Type: Public

Income Statement
FYE: December 31

	REVENUE ($ mil.)	NET INCOME ($ mil.)	NET PROFIT MARGIN	EMPLOYEES
12/15	42,658	1,626	3.8%	268,887
12/14	45,869	1,942	4.2%	281,403
12/13	48,735	1,719	3.5%	283,596
12/12	39,928	1,138	2.9%	289,015
12/11	33,230	671	2.0%	297,210
Annual Growth	6.4%	24.7%	—	(2.5%)

2015 Year-End Financials
Debt ratio: 3.7%
Return on equity: 4.6%
Cash ($ mil.): 3,349
Current ratio: 0.17
Long-term debt ($ mil.): 6,263

No. of shares (mil.): —
Dividends
  Yield: 2.4%
  Payout: 415.3%
Market value ($ mil.): —

	STOCK PRICE ($) FY Close	P/E High/Low		PER SHARE ($) Earnings	Dividends	Book Value
12/15	12.06	43	26	0.07	0.29	1.49
12/14	13.45	35	23	0.08	0.41	1.53
12/13	15.06	41	28	0.07	0.17	1.52
12/12	16.29	73	42	0.05	0.14	1.43
12/11	21.13	126	83	0.03	0.11	1.39
Annual Growth	(13.1%)	—		24.1%	26.7%	1.7%

China United Network Communications Ltd

Auditors: PricewaterhouseCoopers Zhongtian Certified Public Accountants Co., Ltd.

LOCATIONS
HQ: China United Network Communications Ltd
  29th Floor, No. 1033, Changning Road, Changning District, Shanghai 200050
Phone: (86) 21 52732228   Fax: (86) 21 52732220
Web: www.chinaunicom-a.com

HISTORICAL FINANCIALS
Company Type: Public

Income Statement
FYE: December 31

	REVENUE ($ mil.)	NET INCOME ($ mil.)	NET PROFIT MARGIN	EMPLOYEES
12/15	42,658	534	1.3%	0
12/14	46,495	641	1.4%	0
12/13	50,170	568	1.1%	0
12/12	41,105	379	0.9%	0
12/11	34,239	224	0.7%	215,954
Annual Growth	5.6%	24.2%	—	—

2015 Year-End Financials
Debt ratio: 3.2%
Return on equity: 4.4%
Cash ($ mil.): 3,388
Current ratio: 0.18
Long-term debt ($ mil.): 6,263

No. of shares (mil.): —
Dividends
  Yield: —
  Payout: —
Market value ($ mil.): —

China Vanke Co Ltd

China Vanke (known as Vanke) helps the country's emerging middle class become yezhu (homeowners). Vanke is China's largest mainland residential real estate developer. Its high-rise apartment towers single-story suburban developments and luxury gated communities can be seen in 60 cities across the Pearl River Delta the Yangtze River Delta and the Bohai Rim region. Vanke has developed hundreds of properties and has a land bank of more than 18 million square meters. The company was founded in 1984 by chairman Shi Wang and in 1991 it became the second company to list on the Shenzhen Stock Exchange. China Vanke's largest shareholder is China Resources (Holdings) Co. with a stake of about 15%.

China Vanke said in late 2007 it was considering an IPO on the Hong Kong Stock Exchange which would give it more access to international investors than the Shenzhen Stock Exchange.

While the company does provide property management services that segment only accounts for around 1% of revenues. Vanke announced a joint venture with CBRE in 2008 to provide management services at its high-end properties.

Over the years China Vanke has grown through acquisitions. The company has about 180 subsidiaries of mostly property development companies. In 2007 alone it bought 13 companies either outright or through stock purchases.

EXECUTIVES
Deputy Chairman, Lin Song, age 54
Chairman, Shi Wang, age 65
Auditors: KPMG Huazhen Certified Public Accountants

LOCATIONS
HQ: China Vanke Co Ltd
  Vanke Center, No. 33, Huanmei Road, Dameisha, Yantian District, Shenzhen, Guangdong Province 518083
Phone: (86) 755 25606666   Fax: (86) 755 25531696
Web: www.vanke.com

PRODUCTS/OPERATIONS

2015 Sales
	% of total
Property development	97
Property service	2
Other	1
Total	100

COMPETITORS
CapitaLand	New World China Land
China Overseas Land & Investment	New World Development
	SRE Group
China Resources Land	Shanghai Forte Land
Chinese Estates	Singapore Land
Evergrande Real Estate Group	Xinyuan
	Yanlord Land

HISTORICAL FINANCIALS
Company Type: Public

Income Statement
FYE: December 31

	REVENUE ($ mil.)	NET INCOME ($ mil.)	NET PROFIT MARGIN	EMPLOYEES
12/15	30,109	2,789	9.3%	0
12/14	23,586	2,536	10.8%	0
12/13	22,368	2,497	11.2%	35,330
12/12	16,540	2,013	12.2%	31,019
12/11	10,757	1,529	14.2%	27,951
Annual Growth	29.3%	16.2%	—	—

2015 Year-End Financials
Debt ratio: 2.0%
Return on equity: 19.2%
Cash ($ mil.): 8,188
Current ratio: 1.30
Long-term debt ($ mil.): 8,136

No. of shares (mil.): —
Dividends
  Yield: —
  Payout: —
Market value ($ mil.): —

Chongqing Rural Commercial Bank Co., Ltd.

EXECUTIVES
Chairman, Jianzhong Liu
Auditors: PricewaterhouseCoopers Zhong Tian LLP

LOCATIONS
HQ: Chongqing Rural Commercial Bank Co., Ltd.
  No. 10 East Yanghe Road, Jiangbei District, Chongqing City 400020
Phone: (86) 23 6763 7929   Fax: (86) 23 6763 7932
Web: www.cqrcb.com

HISTORICAL FINANCIALS
Company Type: Public

Income Statement
FYE: December 31

	ASSETS ($ mil.)	NET INCOME ($ mil.)	INCOME AS % OF ASSETS	EMPLOYEES
12/15	110,370	1,112	1.0%	16,182
12/14	99,718	1,100	1.1%	15,740
12/13	82,995	989	1.2%	15,443
12/12	69,586	860	1.2%	14,800
12/11	54,782	674	1.2%	13,524
Annual Growth	19.1%	13.3%	—	4.6%

2015 Year-End Financials
Return on assets: 1.0%
Return on equity: 16.3%
Long-term debt ($ mil.): —
No. of shares (mil.): —
Sales ($ mil): 5,694

Dividends
  Yield: —
  Payout: —
Market value ($ mil.): —

Christian Dior SA

Put yourself in Christian Dior's shoes and you might never want to take them off. Through its operating unit Christian Dior Couture the fashion giant designs and makes some of the world's most coveted haute couture as well as luxury ready-to-wear fashion and accessories for men and women. Christian Dior Couture operates more than 194 boutique stores worldwide with plans to open more. The company holds a roughly 41% stake in luxury goods giant LVMH through which it operates around 3700 more. Chairman and LVMH CEO Bernard Arnault and family control Christian Dior.

Operations

The group's main interest is its 41% stake in LVMH which brings in the bulk of its revenue. Dior also operates Christian Dior Couture its own brand fashion house that wholly owns. The Group's brands and trade names are organized into seven business groups: Christian Dior Couture Wines and Spirits Fashion and Leather Goods Perfumes and Cosmetics Watches & Jewelry Selective Retailing and Other activities.

The Selective Retailing business comprises the Group's own-label retailing activities.

Other activities covers operations that fall outside the above categories and includes activities such as the Les Echos media group Royal Van Lent yachts hotel and real estate and holding companies.

Fashion and Leather Goods business group accounted the largest of about 33% of total net sales in fiscal 2015. Selective Retailing business group accounted 29%. Wines and Spirits and Perfumes and Cosmetics business groups each accounted for 12% respectively. Watches and Jewelry 9% and Christian Dior Couture accounted the remaining.

Geographic Reach

Headquartered in France Christian Dior operates more than 235 boutiques worldwide. It sells its upscale items in Europe the US Asia and internationally. Some 37% of its revenue comes from Asia followed by Europe's 30% and another 22% from the US.

The Group also owns industrial and office buildings wineries cellars warehouses and visitor and customer centers for each of its main champagne brands or production operations in France California Argentina Australia Spain Brazil and New Zealand as well as distilleries and warehouses in Cognac the United Kingdom and Poland.

Sales and Marketing

Revenue mostly comes from sales in the store network and through agents and distributors. Sales are made directly to customers through retail stores in Fashion and Leather Goods Selective Retailing and Christian Dior Couture as well as certain Watches and Jewelry and Perfumes and Cosmetics brands.

Besides its network of luxury boutiques Christian Dior sells its products online.

Financial Performance

Note: Growth rates may differ after conversion to US Dollars.

In 2015 sales grew 14% to euro 35 billion a euro 4.2 billion increase. The main bright spots of growth were Fashion & Leather Goods and Selective Retailing the former bolstered by strong performances in Louis Vuitton Fendi Celine Kenzo Givenchy and Berluti and the latter by strong growth in its Sephora business.

Net income increased 67% on prior year to euro 2.3 billion due to the increase in net sales partially offset by an increase in marketing expenses.

Cash flow from operating activities also grew by 21% to euro 938 million.

Strategy

Demand for luxury goods in developing markets is up strongly outpacing weak overall global growth. Dior is looking to build on successes in China and the Middle East.

As part of its geographical diversification strategy DFS (Duty Free Stores) is preparing to open stores in Siem Reap Cambodia and Venice Italy slated for 2016.

In the US Christian Dior plans to open a 10000-sq.-ft. flagship store in San Francisco's Union Square in 2016.

In 2016 the new face of the City of Dreams store in Macao will showcase the company's appetite for innovation and expertise in luxury.

HISTORY

Christian Dior a trained architect opened his own fashion house in 1947 with the backing of flamboyant textile king Marcel Boussac. Dior brightened up a bleak postwar Paris in 1948 when he launched his "New Look" designs. After years of slim cuts (to conserve fabric) and drab colors Dior's looks were feminine glamorous and opulent (skirts often used 40 or more yards of fabric).

Dior opened a store in New York in 1948 and pioneered the concept of licensing with hosiery and ties. Dior died unexpectedly from a stroke in 1957 and was succeeded by 21-year-old assistant Yves Saint-Laurent. By 1960 when Marc Bohan succeeded Saint-Laurent the house of Dior had dressed such famous women as Brigitte Bardot Marlene Dietrich and Eva Peron.

But mismanagement by Boussac took its toll and the company sold its trademark for perfume and cosmetics —potentially its most lucrative licenses —to Moët-Hennessy in 1972. Boussac drained the profits from Dior to finance his company's other struggling divisions and in 1978 the Boussac group was purchased by (also struggling) textile and retailing company Agache-Willot. Agache-Willot wound up in the hands of the French government with the dubious distinction of being France's largest bankruptcy since the war.

In 1984 ambitious but little-known real estate executive Bernard Arnault beat out several more prominent suitors to buy Agache-Willot from the French government; he put up $15 million of his own money and $45 million from investors and renamed the company Financiere Agache. He then laid off 9000 people sold factories and made the company profitable within three years.

Christian Dior SA was born in 1988 when Arnault sold 42% of it to the public to finance his victorious battle for control of newly formed luxury goods conglomerate LVMH Moët Hennessy Louis Vuitton. Meanwhile Arnault had to deal with the fact that Christian Dior's traditional business Dior Couture was losing its luster. Part of the problem was overlicensing —more than 250 licenses existed for everything Dior from sunglasses to sheets. What's more Dior Couture simply looked dowdy compared to other hot young designers.

To turn things around Arnault lured Beatrice Bongibault from Chanel and made her managing director of Dior Couture. She quickly cut nearly a quarter of the company's licenses and centralized control of those that remained improving quality and cutting costs. (Her techniques were quickly copied by other design houses.) She also replaced designer Bohan with Italian Gianfranco Ferre in 1989. Arnault ousted Bongibault in 1990. Dior Couture accused her of embezzlement but the parties settled out of court.

Dior Couture bought back most of its remaining licenses in 1994 and 1995. In 1996 Dior Couture turned to controversial designer John Galliano —already head of LVMH's house of Givenchy —to capitalize on the publicity that followed Galliano's eccentric sometimes bizarre creations.

Aided by its retail expansion Dior Couture bounced back from a 1997 loss with a profit in 1998. The fashion house opened 19 more boutiques in 2000 and introduced the Dior Homme collection of menswear —designed by Hedi Slimane —in January 2001 (now designed by Kris Van Assche).

In 2005 the company launched the perfume brands Miss Dior Cherie and Dior Homme. Christian Dior reclaimed the Baby Dior business in 2006 which had been operated under license. The fashion house celebrated its 60th anniversary in 2007.

In 2008 Christian Dior Couture acquired 87% of the shares of John Galliano SA a company specializing in the creation and concession of fashions and luxury items by the designer. To mark its entrance into the Chinese market the company hosted a major exhibition in Beijing.

Following allegations of anti-Semitic remarks made by its longtime and lucrative designer Christian Dior in March 2011 parted ways with Galliano.

EXECUTIVES

Chairman and CEO, Bernard Arnault, age 67
President Dior Hommes, Serge Brunschwig, age 55
Group Managing Director, Sidney Toledano, age 65
Vice Chairman, Eric Guerlain, age 76
Auditors: ERNST & YOUNG et Autres

LOCATIONS

HQ: Christian Dior SA
30, avenue Montaigne, Paris 75008
Phone: (33) 1 44 13 22 22   **Fax:** (33) 1 44 12 22 23
Web: www.dior-finance.com

2015 Sales

	% of total
Asia	
Japan	7
Rest of Asia	28
Europe	
France	10
Rest of Europe	19
US	24
Other regions	12
Total	**100**

PRODUCTS/OPERATIONS

2015 Product Sales

	% of total
Fashion & leather goods	33
Selective retailing	29
Wine & spirits	12
Perfumes & cosmetics	12
Watches & jewelry	9
Christian Dior Couture	5
Other activities & eliminations	-
Total	**100**

Principal Holdings
Christian Dior Couture SA
  Accessories
  Haute couture
  Luxury ready-to-wear
LVMH Moët Hennessy Louis Vuitton (42%)
  Fragrances and cosmetics
  Leather and fashion
  Retailing
  Watches and jewelry
  Wine and spirits

COMPETITORS

Armani	L' Oreal
Bill Blass	Oscar de la Renta
Calvin Klein	Prada
Chanel	Puig
Dolce & Gabbana	Ralph Lauren
Escada	Richemont
Estee Lauder	Salvatore Ferragamo
Gianni Versace	Shiseido
Hermès	Valentino Fashion
Kering	Vera Wang
Krizia	

HISTORICAL FINANCIALS
Company Type: Public

Income Statement
FYE: June 30

	REVENUE ($ mil.)	NET INCOME ($ mil.)	NET PROFIT MARGIN	EMPLOYEES
06/16	42,167	1,742	4.1%	131,523
06/15	39,192	2,656	6.8%	122,736
06/14	42,306	1,945	4.6%	117,806
06/13*	6,231	282	4.5%	108,837
04/13	39,076	1,871	4.8%	108,546
Annual Growth	2.6%	(2.3%)	—	6.6%

*Fiscal year change

2016 Year-End Financials

Debt ratio: 18.3%	No. of shares (mil.): 179
Return on equity: 14.6%	Dividends
Cash ($ mil.): 3,370	Yield: 0.0%
Current ratio: 1.44	Payout: 9.5%
Long-term debt ($ mil.): 6,056	Market value ($ mil.): 7,173

	STOCK PRICE ($) FY Close	P/E High/Low		PER SHARE ($) Earnings	Dividends	Book Value
06/16	40.00	6	4	9.65	0.92	68.54
06/15	51.14	4	3	14.73	5.61	64.09
06/14	49.70	6	5	10.79	1.02	91.44
06/13*	41.59	38	33	1.57	0.43	80.51
04/13	41.50	6	5	10.33	0.43	80.29
Annual Growth	(0.9%)	—	—	(2.2%)	28.7%	(5.1%)

*Fiscal year change

Chubb Ltd

Through subsidiaries Chubb Limited (formerly ACE Limited) sells property/casualty insurance life insurance and reinsurance through subsidiaries around the globe. It primarily provides property/casualty insurance to commercial and personal customers. Policies offered include general liability homeowners auto accident workers' compensation and specialty crop and marine coverage. The company's ACE Tempest Re businesses provide reinsurance to property/casualty insurers in North America and Europe. In early 2016 the former ACE Limited acquired the US's Chubb Corporation for $28 billion and took the Chubb name.

Geographic Reach

The North American insurance segment which includes property/casualty subsidiaries ACE USA ACE Bermuda and ACE Canada is Chubb's largest business segment accounting for about 40% of revenue. The company's ACE International and ACE Global Markets property/casualty insurance units reach into the rest of the world while its smaller ACE Life insurance division primarily operates in emerging markets in Asia Europe and the Americas. ACE Private Risk Services is a property/casualty division catering to high-net-worth individuals

With its operating subsidiaries located in more than 50 countries Chubb serves customers in more than 170 nations.

ACE moved its place of incorporation home from the Caymans to Switzerland in 2008. It kept executive offices in Bermuda and New York.

Strategy

Chubb regularly looks to expand its product offerings and geographical presence through acquisitions and organic measures.

To expand in high-growth geographic markets it established new offices in Turkey and Panama

in 2009 and 2008. Then in early 2012 the company opened a representative office in Kiev that will allow it to directly engage in the Ukrainian insurance market.

Mergers and Acquisitions

In recent years Chubb has focused its geographic expansion on smaller acquisitions in emerging global marketplaces. In 2011 it entered two new markets for life insurance in North Asia after acquiring New York Life's life insurance operations in Hong Kong and South Korea for about $425 million.

In 2012 Chubb acquired Indonesian general insurance firm Asuransi Jaya Proteksi for some $130 million. It closed its purchase of Mexican surety insurer Fianzas Monterrey from New York Life for $285 million in 2013 as well as its purchase of another Mexican insurance firm ABA Seguros from Ally Financial for $865 million.

In 2015 the company acquired the Fireman's Fund US personal lines business catering to high-net-worth customers. The deal valued at $365 million and providing access to more than 120000 premier personal lines customers expanded Chubb's position as one of the largest personal lines insurers catering to wealthy individuals.

Later that year the company announced a much larger deal with plans to acquire insurer Chubb which specialized in serving wealthy clients for $28.3 billion. The combined company which operates under the Chubb name became one of the world's largest property/casualty firms. ACE shareholders own 70% of the new company.

EXECUTIVES

VP and Division President North America Agriculture, Michael J. Coleman, age 72
SVP and Division President Westchester, Bruce L. Kessler
EVP Global Underwriting, Jacques Q. Bonneau
EVP and Chief Investment Officer, Timothy A. Boroughs
Chairman and CEO, Evan G. Greenberg, age 61, $1,351,538 total compensation
EVP and CFO, Philip V. Bancroft, age 57, $750,000 total compensation
EVP and President North America Commercial and Per, Paul J. Krump, age 56
EVP Global Accident and Health and Life, Edward (Ed) Clancy
SVP and Chief Claims Officer, Frank Lattal
Vice Chairman Chubb Limited and Chubb Group and President North America Major Accounts and Specialty Insurance, John J. Lupica, $775,000 total compensation
EVP Chief Risk Officer and Chief Actuary, Sean Ringsted, $575,000 total compensation
SVP; President ACE Life, Russell G. Bundschuh
SVP and President European Group, Andrew Kendrick
VP and Division President Bermuda and Global Accounts, Joseph S. (Joe) Clabby
SVP; President Chubb Tempest Re Group, James E. Wixtead
Vice Chairman and COO; Chairman Insurance Overseas General, John W. Keogh, age 52, $885,000 total compensation
EVP and President Overseas General Insurance, Juan C. Andrade, age 48
SVP; Regional President ACE Latin America, Jorge L. Cazar
SVP; Division President Accident and Health ACE Overseas General, Edward Levin
SVP and Division President North America Insurance Field Operations, Harold L. Morrison, age 59
SVP; President Combined Insurance, Brad Bennett
SVP and Division President North America Commercial Insurance, Steven R. Pozzi, age 59

VP and Division President Commercial Property and Casualty Overseas General Insurance, David Furby
VP and CIO, Kevin Shearan
SVP; Regional President ACE Asia/Pacific, Juan L. Ortega
VP and Division President Personal Insurance Overseas General Insurance, Darryl Page
EVP and General Counsel, Joseph Wayland
SVP and Division President North America Major Accounts, Christopher A. (Chris) Maleno
SVP and Division President North America Personal Risk Services, Frances D. O'Brien
SVP and Regional President Asia Pacific, Juan Luis Ortega
VP and Chief Reinsurance Officer, Michael Kessler
VP and Division President North America Small Commercial Insurance, James Williamson
Auditors: PricewaterhouseCoopers LLP

LOCATIONS

HQ: Chubb Ltd
Baerengasse 32, Zurich CH-8001
Phone: (41) 43 456 76 00
Web: www.acegroup.com

PRODUCTS/OPERATIONS

2015 Sales

	% of total
Insurance - North American P&C	34
Insurance - Overseas General	34
Net investment income	11
Life	10
Insurance - North American Agriculture	7
Global Reinsurance	4
Net realized losses	-
Total	100

2015 Sales

	% of total
Property & all Other	34
Casualty	32
Life Accident & Health	23
Net investment income	11
Net realized losses	-
Total	100

COMPETITORS

AEGON	ING
AIG	Liberty Mutual
AXA	Loews
Aetna	MetLife
Allianz	Munich Re America
Allstate	Munich Re Group
American Financial Group	Old Republic
Berkshire Hathaway	Swiss Re
CNA Surety	The Hartford
Fairfax Financial Holdings	Travelers Companies
General Re	W. R. Berkley
Hannover Re	White Mountains Insurance Group
Humana	XL Group plc

HISTORICAL FINANCIALS
Company Type: Public

Income Statement
FYE: December 31

	ASSETS ($ mil.)	NET INCOME ($ mil.)	INCOME AS % OF ASSETS	EMPLOYEES
12/15	102,366	2,834	2.8%	22,000
12/14	98,248	2,853	2.9%	21,000
12/13	94,510	3,758	4.0%	20,000
12/12	92,545	2,706	2.9%	17,000
12/11	87,505	1,585	1.8%	16,500
Annual Growth	4.0%	15.6%	—	7.5%

Return on assets: 2.8%
Return on equity: 9.6%
Long-term debt ($ mil.): —
No. of shares (mil.): 324
Sales ($ mil): 18,987

Dividends
Yield: 2.2%
Payout: 29.8%
Market value ($ mil.): 37,925

	STOCK PRICE ($) FY Close	P/E High/Low	PER SHARE ($) Earnings	Dividends	Book Value
12/15	116.85	14 11	8.62	2.66	89.77
12/14	114.88	14 11	8.42	3.21	90.02
12/13	103.53	9 7	10.92	2.00	84.83
12/12	79.80	10 9	7.89	2.41	80.90
12/11	70.12	16 13	4.65	1.03	72.76
Annual Growth	13.6%	— —	16.7%	26.8%	5.4%

Chubu Electric Power Co., Inc.

Chubu Electric Power is Japan's third-largest electric utility after Tokyo Electric and Kansai Electric. The company supplies power to about 16 million people in central Japan's Chubu region a leading manufacturing region in Japan that includes Nagoya one of the country's largest cities. It has thermal (LNG and coal) hydroelectric nuclear wind and solar power generating facilities that together have a capacity of more than 33170 MW. It also has power transmission and distribution facilities. In response to deregulation Chubu Electric Power has moved into newer industries including IT natural gas supply real estate management and overseas consulting.

Operations

Chubu Electric Power has three reporting segments —Electric Power Energy and Other.

Electric Power (90% of total revenue) has about 210 power generation facilities in Japan a transmission line that runs more than 12200 kilometers a distribution line that runs more than 133300 kilometers and nearly 940 transformer substations.

Energy provides energy services such as the sale of gas and liquefied natural gas (LNG) and the provision of co-generation systems. Geographic Reach In addition to Japan the company has offices in Australia Canada Indonesia Philippines Mexico Oman Thailand Taiwan Qatar Vietnam and the US. Sales and Marketing The company supplies electricity to residential commercial and industrial customers via transmission and distribution line.

Financial Performance

Note: Growth rates may differ after conversion to US Dollars.

Chubu Electric's revenue decreased to ¥2854 billion in fiscal 2016 (ends March) from ¥3103.6 billion a year earlier primarily due to lower electricity sales as power demand eased due to warmer-than-usual winter weather and a drop in automobile production.

Net income increased to ¥169.7 billion (a ¥130.9 billion improvement on the previous year) due to lower fuel costs (favorable fuel cost adjustment rates and a drop in thermal fuel costs thanks to higher use of hydropower) and company-wide cost reduction efforts.

Strategy

Like other Japanese power companies Chubu Electric has been struggling to get back to growth following the shut down of its nuclear plant operations. Chubu Electric suspended operations at the Hamaoka nuclear power station in mid-2011 at the request of the national government due to rising concerns over safety after the massive tsunami and Fukushima Daiichi nuclear power plant disaster in March 2011.

In order to get its profitability back on track and ensure a stable supply of electricity Chubu Electric is working on a tsunami countermeasure initiative to improve the safety of its power generation facilities including Hamaoka at a cost of about $1.5 billion. Its main efforts to this end are developing flooding prevention measures and enhancing emergency measures.

Although tight conditions at the company are expected to continue until the Hamaoka station resumes operations Chubu Electric's longer-term goals are to continue developing and buying more renewable energy and increase revenues by advancing energy-related infrastructure businesses including power generation outside of the Chubu region and in other countries. In 2016 it was responsible for generating about 3000 MW of power in a dozen countries around the world including Thailand Qatar and Australia.

EXECUTIVES

President, Akihisa Mizuno
EVP, Tomohiko Ohno
EVP, Masatoshi Sakaguchi
EVP, Kazuhiro Matsubara
EVP, Satoru Katsuno
Senior Managing Executive Officer, Ryosuke Mizutani
Senior Managing Executive Officer, Yutaka Watanabe
Senior Managing Executive Officer, Satoshi Onoda
Senior Managing Executive Officer, Masanori Matsuura
Chairman, Toshio Mita
Auditors: KPMG AZSA LLC

LOCATIONS

HQ: Chubu Electric Power Co., Inc.
1 Higashi-Shincho, Higashi-ku, Nagoya, Aichi 461-8680
Phone: (81) 52 951 8211   **Fax:** (81) 52 962 4624
Web: www.chuden.co.jp

PRODUCTS/OPERATIONS

2016 Sales

	% of total
Electric power	90
Energy	3
Other	7
Total	**100**

COMPETITORS

Chugoku Electric Power	Kyushu Electric Power
Hokkaido Electric Power	Osaka Gas
	Shikoku Electric
Hokuriku Electric Power	Tohoku Electric Power
	Tokyo Electric
KEPCO	Tokyo Gas

HISTORICAL FINANCIALS

Company Type: Public

Income Statement

FYE: March 31

	REVENUE ($ mil.)	NET INCOME ($ mil.)	NET PROFIT MARGIN	EMPLOYEES
03/16	25,415	1,511	5.9%	30,659
03/15	25,867	323	1.3%	30,848
03/14	27,535	(632)	—	30,888
03/13	28,153	(341)	—	30,847
03/12	29,858	(1,123)	—	29,859
Annual Growth	(3.9%)	—		0.7%

Debt ratio: 0.4%
Return on equity: 11.0%
Cash ($ mil.): 1,281
Current ratio: 0.63
Long-term debt ($ mil.): 16,988

No. of shares (mil.): 757
Dividends
Yield: —
Payout: —
Market value ($ mil.): 10,406

	STOCK PRICE ($) FY Close	P/E High/Low	PER SHARE ($) Earnings	Dividends	Book Value
03/16	13.74	0 0	2.00	0.00	18.81
03/15	11.82	0 0	0.43	0.00	16.17
03/14	11.86	— —	(0.84)	0.00	18.38
03/13	12.60	— —	(0.45)	0.00	20.92
03/12	18.94	— —	(1.48)	0.00	24.91
Annual Growth	(7.7%)	— —	—	—	(6.8%)

Chugoku Bank, Ltd. (The)

Chugoku Bank hopes to attract individuals and businesses who are looking to bank on the sunny side. The Japanese regional bank serves the Okayama prefecture (known as “the sunny land”) and the neighboring areas of Ehime Hiroshima Hyogo Kagawa and Tottori through some 150 offices and a network of ATMs. The bank also boasts overseas operations with offices in China Hong Kong Singapore and the US. Chugoku Bank subsidiaries and affiliates are involved in such businesses as asset management credit cards credit guarantees financing leasing and pre-paid cards. Japan Trustee Services Bank Ltd. owns a majority stake in the bank.

EXECUTIVES

President, MASATO MIYANAGA
Executive Vice President, Kenichiro Ohara
Vice Chairman, Ryosuke Yamada
Auditors: KPMG AZSA LLC

LOCATIONS

HQ: Chugoku Bank, Ltd. (The)
1-15-20 Marunouchi, Kita-ku, Okayama 700-8628
Phone: (81) 86 223 3111
Web: www.chugin.co.jp

PRODUCTS/OPERATIONS

Selected Subsidiaries
CBS Company Limited
Chugin Asset Management Company Limited
Chugin Securities Co. Ltd.
The Chugin Card Company Limited
The Chugin Credit Guarantee Co. Limited
The Chugin Lease Company Limited
The Chugin Operation Center Co. Limited

COMPETITORS

Awa Bank	Mizuho Financial
Hiroshima Bank	Norinchukin Bank
Hyakujushi Bank	Resona
Mitsubishi UFJ Financial Group	Sumitomo Mitsui

HISTORICAL FINANCIALS
Company Type: Public

Income Statement
FYE: March 31

	ASSETS ($ mil.)	NET INCOME ($ mil.)	INCOME AS % OF ASSETS	EMPLOYEES
03/16	69,459	242	0.3%	5,134
03/15	63,517	205	0.3%	5,061
03/14	67,627	278	0.4%	3,558
03/13	72,051	195	0.3%	3,570
03/12	77,278	232	0.3%	3,574
Annual Growth	(2.6%)	1.1%	—	9.5%

2016 Year-End Financials
Return on assets: 0.3%
Return on equity: 5.2%
Long-term debt ($ mil.): —
No. of shares (mil.): 194
Sales ($ mil): 1,114
Dividends
Yield: —
Payout: —
Market value ($ mil.): —

CIMB Group Holdings Bhd

CIMB Group is the second-largest financial services firm in Malaysia behind Maybank. It is the holding company for CIMB Bank CIMB Investment Bank and CIMB Islamic which provide retail and commercial banking and financial services to 13 million customers throughout Southeast Asia. While it has a presence in 17 countries (including a CIMB Securities office in New York City) the bank's main markets are Malaysia Indonesia Singapore Thailand and Cambodia. Altogether the group has more than 1050 branches. CIMB Group's offerings include corporate and consumer banking investment banking Islamic banking stock brokerage asset management and insurance. It was established in 1924 as Bian Chiang Bank.

Mergers and Acquisitions

CIMB Investment Bank became one of the largest investment banking franchises in Asia in 2012 with the acquisition of most of the Asian investment banking business of the Royal Bank of Scotland. The acquisition gave CIMB a presence in Taiwan and Australia and expanded its operations in Hong Kong India and China. RBS kept its business in South Korea.
Auditors: PricewaterhouseCoopers

LOCATIONS

HQ: CIMB Group Holdings Bhd
Level 13, Menara CIMB, Jalan Stesen Sentral 2, Kuala Lumpur Sentral, Kuala Lumpur 50470
Phone: (60) 3 2261 0085   **Fax:** (60) 3 2261 0099
Web: www.cimb.com

PRODUCTS/OPERATIONS

COMPETITORS

AmBank Group	Hong Leong Bank
Bank Muamalat	Malaysian Industrial
Bank Negara	Development Finance
Bank Pembangunan	Maybank
DBS Group Holdings	Public Bank
Edaran Otomobil	RHB Bank Berhad
Guoco	RHB Capital

HISTORICAL FINANCIALS
Company Type: Public

Income Statement
FYE: December 31

	ASSETS ($ mil.)	NET INCOME ($ mil.)	INCOME AS % OF ASSETS	EMPLOYEES
12/15	107,219	661	0.6%	40,545
12/14	118,440	888	0.8%	41,669
12/13	113,225	1,386	1.2%	40,804
12/12	110,085	1,419	1.3%	41,993
12/11	94,731	1,271	1.3%	40,244
Annual Growth	3.1%	(15.1%)	—	0.2%

2015 Year-End Financials
Return on assets: 0.6%
Return on equity: 7.2%
Long-term debt ($ mil.): —
No. of shares (mil.): —
Sales ($ mil): 5,767
Dividends
Yield: —
Payout: —
Market value ($ mil.): —

CITIC Ltd

CITIC Limited (formerly CITIC Pacific) is a chip off the old Communist bloc. The group has investments in steel real estate energy aviation and communications. With stakes in steel plants with an annual capacity of more than 7 million tons CITIC is China's largest producer of specialty steel (heat-resistant anti-corrosion and other enhanced steel). CITIC also owns stakes in facilities that produce raw materials needed in steel production including iron ore mines and coking coal plants. Property developments include office and residential towers and the group owns several land banks in and around Shanghai. State-owned CITIC Group owns more than half of CITIC Limited.

Geographic Reach

The company's headquarters are located in Hong Kong. It performs operations in different parts of China including Beijing Chongqing Guangzhou Hainan Hong Kong Shanghai and Tianjin.

Operations

CITIC's primary businesses are specialty steel manufacturing iron ore mining and property development in mainland China. These three businesses constituted over 70% of total assets at the end of 2012.

Financial Performance

The company's total annual revenue has been strong in recent fiscal years. After claiming a little more than $9 billion in revenue during fiscal 2010 its revenue spiked to $12.8 billion in fiscal 2011 and leveled off at about $12.0 billion in fiscal 2012.

EXECUTIVES

Executive Director and VP, Dou Jianzhong, age 61
Vice Chairman and President, Wang Jiong, age 56
VP, Zhang Jijing, age 60
executive Vice President of CITIC Pacific, Kwok Leung
Chairman, Chang Zhenming, age 59
Auditors: PricewaterhouseCoopers

LOCATIONS

HQ: CITIC Ltd
32nd Floor, CITIC Tower, 1 Tim Mei Avenue, Central,
Phone: (852) 2820 2111   **Fax:** (852) 2877 2771
Web: www.citic.com

2015 Sales

	% of total
Mainland China	87
Hong Kong and Macau	6
Overseas	7
Total	100

PRODUCTS/OPERATIONS

2015 Sales

	% of total
Financial Services	49
Manufacturing	14
Resources and energy	11
Real estate	7
Engineering contracting	4
Others	15
Total	100

COMPETITORS

CK Hutchison	Shanghai Industrial
Guangdong Investment	Sino Land
Henderson Investment	Sun Hung Kai
Jardine Matheson	Properties
New World Development	Wing Tai

HISTORICAL FINANCIALS
Company Type: Public

Income Statement
FYE: December 31

	REVENUE ($ mil.)	NET INCOME ($ mil.)	NET PROFIT MARGIN	EMPLOYEES
12/15	71,937	5,394	7.5%	133,526
12/14	70,093	5,136	7.3%	125,273
12/13	11,354	978	8.6%	36,512
12/12	12,032	897	7.5%	34,781
12/11	12,884	1,188	9.2%	33,295
Annual Growth	53.7%	46.0%	—	41.5%

2015 Year-End Financials
Debt ratio: —
Return on equity: 9.0%
Cash ($ mil.): 103,421
Current ratio: —
Long-term debt ($ mil.): —
No. of shares (mil.): —
Dividends
Yield: 17.4%
Payout: —
Market value ($ mil.): —

	STOCK PRICE ($) FY Close	P/E High	P/E Low	PER SHARE ($) Earnings	PER SHARE ($) Dividends	PER SHARE ($) Book Value
12/15	8.83	7	5	0.20	0.04	2.19
12/14	8.50	7	4	0.21	0.00	2.24
12/13	7.58	4	2	0.27	0.05	3.60
12/12	7.52	5	3	0.25	0.06	2.99
12/11	8.99	6	3	0.33	0.00	2.86
Annual Growth	(0.4%)	—	—	(11.2%)	—	(6.5%)

CJ Corp (Korea)

CJ Corporation wants to bring Korea to the world via four areas: food home shopping and logistics entertainment and biotechnology. Its food and food services unit owns such brands as Dashida (seasoning) Beksul (sugar flour salt) Haechandeul (sauces) and Spam (canned ham) as well as dumpling and tofu labels. The unit provides dining-out service too through restaurants and franchises. Using TV the Internet and other retail channels CJ's shopping and logistics unit pushes lifestyle health and beauty items as well as global delivery services. In addition the company is one of Korea's top entertainment content providers and has increasing interests in biopharmaceutical manufacturing (animal nutrition MSG).

EXECUTIVES

President, Gyeong Sik Son
President, Chae Wuk Lee
Chairman Of The Board, Jae Hyeon Lee
Auditors: Samil Accounting Corporation (A Member Firm of PircewaterhouseCoopers)

LOCATIONS

HQ: CJ Corp (Korea)
12 Sowol-ro 2-gil Jung-gu, Seoul 100-802
Phone: (82) 2 726 8114   **Fax:** (82) 2 726 8112
Web: www.cj.net

COMPETITORS

AOL	Nestle
Ajinomoto	Nongshim
Amazon.com	Overstock.com
Amgen	Samsung Group
Bayer AG	Sanofi
Buy.com	Shopzilla
Daesang	Sony
Daewoo E&C	Starbucks
Disney	Subway
GlaxoSmithKline	Tate & Lyle
Google	Time Warner
Hitachi	Wal-Mart
Hyundai Engineering	Walgreen
and Construction	Wendy' s International
Ito-Yokado	Inc.
McDonald' s	Yahoo!

HISTORICAL FINANCIALS
Company Type: Public

Income Statement				FYE: December 31
	REVENUE ($ mil.)	NET INCOME ($ mil.)	NET PROFIT MARGIN	EMPLOYEES
12/15	17,990	174	1.0%	56
12/14	17,888	191	1.1%	48
12/13	17,925	142	0.8%	43
12/12	16,510	206	1.3%	48
12/11	11,453	318	2.8%	108
Annual Growth	12.0%	(13.9%)	—	(15.1%)

2015 Year-End Financials

Debt ratio: 0.0%	No. of shares (mil.): 26
Return on equity: 5.8%	Dividends
Cash ($ mil.): 1,015	Yield: —
Current ratio: 0.90	Payout: —
Long-term debt ($ mil.): 3,894	Market value ($ mil.): —

Clydesdale Bank PLC (United Kingdom)

Clydesdale Bank won't horse around with your money. Founded in 1838 the full-service Scotland-based financial institution is owned by National Australia Bank. Along with standard personal and commercial services such as deposit accounts lending credit cards and financial advice the bank also dabbles in agribusiness and private banking. Clydesdale Bank has some 140 retail branches in Scotland and England. It is one of the only banks in Scotland that issues its own notes. Sister firm Yorkshire Bank also operates as a National Australia Bank brand in the UK.

OperationsClydesdale Bank reports under National Australia Bank's retail and commercial "UK Banking" business. UK Banking consists of banking and wealth management activities operating under the "Clydesdale Bank" and "Yorkshire Bank" brands. Together the two UK brands offer services through a network of retail branches direct banking business and private banking centers and broker channels.

The UK Banking business operates under two main segments: Business & Private Banking and Retail Banking. The Retail Banking segment generates nearly 60% of the UK Banking revenues. It provides products and services to personal customers including savings and deposit accounts mortgages overdraft lines of credit personal loans insurance and financial planning.

The remaining 40% of revenues come from the Business & Private Banking business which includes business banking centers small business and private banking customers and offers loans wealth management international services treasury solutions and day to day banking services.

Geographic Reach

Clydesdale Bank operates 140 retail branches and a network of business and private banking centers in Scotland and across the UK. The bank added two new UK branches in mid-2014 in Princes Square and in Perth.

Financial Performance

The UK Banking group (which reports the combined results of Clydesdale Bank and Yorkshire Bank) grew its revenue –defined as net interest income plus non-interest income — by 2% to £963 million in fiscal 2014. This is mostly from a 2% increase in net interest income thanks to a combination of higher interest margins increased mortgage business from the Retail segment and low rates of deposit paid to its customers. Non-interest income also grew by 4% in 2014 primarily thanks to gains in the fair value of the bank's investment holdings and hedging ineffectiveness.

Despite revenue growth the UK Banking group's profits continued to be hindered by "legacy conduct" expenses in 2014 as the bank had to set aside millions for customers that were allegedly mislead by the firm's sales payment protection insurance and interest rate hedging products. Because the UK Banking group had £433 million more in such expenses than in 2013 the group suffered a net loss of £178 million — more than four times what it lost in 2013.

Cash from operations also suffered with a net outflow of £629 million in 2014 compared to a net inflow of £3.8 billion the year before. While the £162 million drop in before-tax net income played a role the bank also used £1.19 billion toward operating assets in 2014 as it lent out significantly more for mortgage loans. By comparison in 2013 operating assets provided £6.13 billion in cash as the bank sold off many of its assets held for sale.

Strategy

The UK Banking group which includes Clydesdale Bank and Yorkshire Bank is dedicated to being a strong customer focused bank for the communities it serves. With this in mind and for the sake of turning around two years of losses the group will continue to follow a few key strategic objectives.

It's first objective is customer and cost oriented and involves the reshaping of the group's Retail Branch network. In March 2014 the group announced that it would close 28 unsustainable branches and relocate three of them to more targeted locations. The group also announced that it would invest in six new flagship branches in heartland locations that would provide access to new in-house facilities services and technology. To that end in mid-2014 Clydesdale Bank opened two new branches (in Perth and Princes Square) that will highlight the bank's new technology and register customers for internet and mobile banking assist with product discussions and collect customer feedback.

In addition the group plans to control its lending risk by creating a better framework for its management teams and intends to grow its credit portfolio with sustainable types of loans such as mortgages. The group has already seen lower risk and higher returns from its Retail Banking segment in 2014 as mortgage lending and interest margins on loans provided £23 million more net interest income compared the prior year. In December 2014 to further this initiative the group announced an aggressive £1000 cash back mortgage offer to new home-buying customers.

EXECUTIVES

COO, Debbie Crosbie
CEO and Director, David Duffy, age 54
CFO, Ian Smith
Chairman, James (Jim) Pettigrew, age 56
Auditors: Ernst & Young LLP

LOCATIONS

HQ: Clydesdale Bank PLC (United Kingdom)
30 St. Vincent Place, Glasgow, Scotland G1 2HL
Phone: (44) 0141 248 7070   **Fax:** (44) 0141 204 0828
Web: www.cbonline.co.uk

COMPETITORS

AIB	Nationwide Building
Barclays	Society
Co-operative Bank	Royal Bank of Scotland
HSBC	Santander UK
Lloyds Banking Group	

HISTORICAL FINANCIALS
Company Type: Public

Income Statement				FYE: September 30
	ASSETS ($ mil.)	NET INCOME ($ mil.)	INCOME AS % OF ASSETS	EMPLOYEES
09/16	51,777	(722)	—	6,718
09/15	58,740	(377)	—	4,616
09/14	60,013	(288)	—	4,521
09/13	58,906	(71)	—	4,570
09/05	39,322	219	0.6%	6,176
Annual Growth	2.5%	—	—	0.8%

2016 Year-End Financials

Return on assets: (-1.4%)	Dividends
Return on equity: (-16.6%)	Yield: —
Long-term debt ($ mil.): —	Payout: —
No. of shares (mil.): —	Market value ($ mil.): —
Sales ($ mil): 1,673	

CNH Industrial NV

Auditors: Ernst & Young LLP

LOCATIONS

HQ: CNH Industrial NV
25 St. Jame' s Street, London SW1A 1HA
Phone:
Web: www.cnhindustrial.com

Company Type: Public

Income Statement

FYE: December 31

	REVENUE ($ mil.)	NET INCOME ($ mil.)	NET PROFIT MARGIN	EMPLOYEES
12/15	25,912	253	1.0%	64,391
12/14	32,555	710	2.2%	69,207
12/13	33,836	677	2.0%	71,192
12/12	33,985	1,067	3.1%	68,257
12/11	31,416	807	2.6%	66,998
Annual Growth	(4.7%)	(25.2%)	—	(1.0%)

2015 Year-End Financials

Debt ratio: 56.4%	No. of shares (mil.): 1,362
Return on equity: 5.2%	Dividends
Cash ($ mil.): 6,311	Yield: 2.9%
Current ratio: 5.91	Payout: 112.9%
Long-term debt ($ mil.): 26,388	Market value ($ mil.): 9,316

	STOCK PRICE ($) FY Close	P/E High/Low	PER SHARE ($) Earnings	Dividends	Book Value
12/15	6.84	51 34	0.19	0.21	3.53
12/14	8.06	23 14	0.52	0.28	3.63
12/13	11.35	24 19	0.54	0.29	(0.00)
Annual Growth	(22.4%)	— —	(23.0%)	(7.5%)	—

Cnooc Ltd.

CNOOC Limited manages China's offshore oil and gas exploration and production activities in partnership with international oil and gas firms. Under Chinese government-regulated production sharing contracts CNOOC Limited has the sole right to acquire up to 51% of any successful discovery offshore China made by foreign partners. CNOOC Limited has 2.6 billion barrels of oil equivalent in estimated proved reserves primarily in the South China Sea. CNOOC Limited is also engaged in oil refining natural gas processing and refined products marketing. The oil producer has a net production of 469.4 barrels of oil equivalent per day. To grow it global assets in 2012 the company agreed to buy Nexen for $15 billion.

The deal gives CNOOC access to major oil and gas plays including Canadian oil sands and conventional fields in western Canada the North Sea the Gulf of Mexico and Nigeria.

Growin its North American assets in 2010 the company paid about $1.1 billion for a one-third stake in Chesapeake Energy's 600000 oil and natural gas acres in the Eagle Ford shale project in South Texas. It boosted its shale holdings further in 2011 agreeing to spend $570 million to buy a one-third stake in Chesapeake Energy's drilling assets in a shale oil field in northeast Colorado and southeast Wyoming. It also bought oil sands producer OPTI Canada for $2.1 billion.

In another major expansion that year the company acquired a 33% stake in an onshore oilfield in Uganda from Tullow Oil for $1.5 billion.

CNOOC Limited is 64%-owned by China National Offshore Oil Corporation.

EXECUTIVES

Chairman and CEO, Yang Hua, age 55
EVP Development Production and Sales, Chen Bi, age 55
President and Director, Yuan Guangyu, age 58

SVP and General Manager CNOOC China Limited Shanghai Branch, Zhang Guohua, age 57
EVP Chief Geologist and General Manager Exploration Department, Zhu Weilin, age 61
CFO, Zhong Hua
Vice Chairman, Liu Jian, age 58
Auditors: Deloitte Touche Tohmatsu

LOCATIONS

HQ: Cnooc Ltd.
65th Floor, Bank of China Tower, One Garden Road,
Phone: (852) 2213 2500   **Fax:** (852) 2525 9322
Web: www.cnoocltd.com

2007 Sales

	% of total
China	86
Other countries	14
Total	**100**

PRODUCTS/OPERATIONS

2015 Sales

	% of total
Exploration and Production	87
Trading business	13
Total	**100**

2015 Sales

	% of Total
Oil and gas sales	86
Marketing revenues	12
Other income	2
Total	**100**

Selected Subsidiaries

CNOOC China Limited (China)
CNOOC Finance (2002) Limited (British Virgin Islands)
CNOOC Finance (2003) Limited (British Virgin Islands)
CNOOC International Limited (British Virgin Islands)
CNOOC Offshore Oil (Singapore) Pte. Ltd.

COMPETITORS

Anadarko Petroleum	Exxon Mobil
Apache	PetroChina
BP	Royal Dutch Shell
Chevron	Sinopec Corp.

HISTORICAL FINANCIALS

Company Type: Public

Income Statement

FYE: December 31

	REVENUE ($ mil.)	NET INCOME ($ mil.)	NET PROFIT MARGIN	EMPLOYEES
12/15	26,397	3,117	11.8%	20,585
12/14	44,250	9,699	21.9%	21,046
12/13	47,218	9,326	19.8%	17,553
12/12	39,720	10,216	25.7%	10,063
12/11	38,279	11,161	29.2%	5,377
Annual Growth	(8.9%)	(27.3%)	—	39.9%

2015 Year-End Financials

Debt ratio: 3.8%	No. of shares (mil.): —
Return on equity: 5.2%	Dividends
Cash ($ mil.): 4,600	Yield: 6.3%
Current ratio: 1.66	Payout: 9,222.7%
Long-term debt ($ mil.): 20,180	Market value ($ mil.): —

	STOCK PRICE ($) FY Close	P/E High/Low	PER SHARE ($) Earnings	Dividends	Book Value
12/15	104.38	372215	0.07	6.62	1.33
12/14	135.44	148 94	0.22	6.62	1.37
12/13	187.66	185128	0.21	6.62	1.26
12/12	220.00	163124	0.23	4.99	1.11
12/11	174.68	179 94	0.25	5.92	0.94
Annual Growth	(12.1%)	— —	(27.4%)	2.8%	9.2%

CNP Assurances S.A.

Running to the post office and the bank? Buy some insurance while you're out. CNP Assurances is France's top personal life insurer. In addition to life insurance and other savings products it sells health death and disability and other personal risk coverage and pensions. CNP sells its products primarily through the outlets of La Poste the French postal service and Groupe BPCE the state savings banks; together these two channels account for about 65% of CNP's sales. These partners are also shareholders in the company together owning about 35%. Another French paragovernmental organization Caisse des Depôts et Consignations owns 40%.

Operations

CNP operates in three segments: Savings Pensions and Personal Risk. It offers its products to 27 million customers under personal risk and protection policies and 14 million savings and pensions policyholders around the world.

Geographic Reach

The company operates in 14 nations in Europe and Latin America; France accounts for some 80% of its total premium income.

Sales and Marketing

CNP sells its products through private banks family offices asset management centers and management companies. Through La Poste and BPCE CNP has 12000 points of sale in France. In Latin America Caixa Econômica Federal helps middle-class and lower-income customers buy insurance; it has 60000 points of sale in Brazil including 12500 lottery ticket sales booths.

Financial Performance

Revenues declined in 2010 and 2011 but have since recovered. In 2014 revenue rose 6% to euro 44.9 billion due to growth in premiums in France. La Poste premiums grew due to a rise in unit-linked sales and protection insurance premiums as well as improvements in the personal risk and protection segment. BPCE premiums performed strongly due to a 50% jump in business with wealthy individuals and a 24% jump in premiums from policies sold to the general public. Business in Italy also grew in 2014.

Net income has followed revenue trends in the past five years. It increased 5% to euro 1.4 billion due to the higher premiums and a change in the fair value of intangible assets. Cash flow from operations fell to euro 7.3 billion as a result of a change in securities sold and purchased.

Strategy

CNP's strategy for growth includes forging new partnerships developing new products and moving towards digital to broaden access to its products. It continues to focus on business in core markets including France and Brazil where it is undergoing a massive digital initiative but is also seeking to grow its presence in Latin America. Colombia Chile and Peru are among its new growth candidates.

Expanding its business in Europe CNP signed a 20-year strategic partnership with Santander in 2014; it acquired a 51% stake in the bank's Consumer Finance's life and property/casualty insurance subsidiaries and inked an exclusive distribution agreement. That deal broadens its business in 10 countries including Germany Poland Italy and Austria.

In 2014 the company launched a couple of savings products targeted towards wealthy individuals. The following year it introduced CNP One a premium savings life insurance contract.

The company sold its 50% stake in Spain-based CNP Barclays Vida y Pensiones to Barclays for euro 453 million.

Mergers and Acquisitions

In 2014 CNP acquired dental insurer Tempo Dental in Brazil.

HISTORY

Company Background

CNP Assurances traces its origins to three government insurance entities established in the mid-19th century. Caisse nationale d'assurance en cas d'accident ("accident insurance") was formed in 1868. Caisse nationale d'assurance en cas de decès ("death and disability insurance") was formed in 1848 while Caisse de retraite pour la vieillesse ("retirement pensions") followed two years later. These two organizations were merged in 1949 forming Caisse nationale d'assurance sur la vie. Ten years later it was merged with the government's accident insurance bureau to form Caisse Nationale de Prevoyance ("provident society"). CNP was put under the domain of the French government's investment banking arm Caisse des Depôts et Consignations (CDC).

Over the years CNP earned a reputation for specializing in certain risks introducing a variety of life and personal risk insurance and pension and savings products. During the 1980s the company enjoyed a healthy growth rate around 20% annually as more French individuals and companies began investing in insurance products.

In 1987 CNP became a national public establishment making it independent from though still owned by the government. The next year the company teamed with Centre National des Caisses d'Epargne et de Prevoyance (now La Caisse Nationale des Caisses d'Epargne or Caisses d'Epargne) to form Ecureuil-Vie a joint venture to sell CNP's insurance and savings products in the national savings banks. That year it partnered with Portugal's Caixa Geral de Depositos to create new products.

In the early 1990s CNP was among several entities the government announced it would privatize. To prepare for the change the company reorganized and became CNP Assurances; the government sold a large chunk of the firm to CDC La Poste and Caisses d'Epargne reducing its stake to 42%. During this time CNP passed rival Union des Assurances de Paris (now part of AXA) to become France's top life insurer.

Privatization lurched along until 1995 when it was put on hold for elections; the Socialist government that came to power was less enthusiastic about the sale of government assets than its predecessor. The process hit another snag two years later when some workers protested fearing they'd lose their status as civil servants and the perks associated with it. Also in 1997 CNP became the major shareholder of Polish life insurer Polisa-Zycie when it raised its stake from 26% (purchased 1996) to 46%. By 1998 privatization was back on track and the government sold a 22% stake in CNP to the public. CDC La Poste and Caisses d'Epargne raised their interests to their current levels. Before the year's end CNP bought majority stakes in Portuguese insurers Global and Global Vida.

Expansion abroad continued in 1999 when CNP announced plans to set up operations in China. That year it teamed with the UK's Prudential for cobranded insurance products. In 2000 the company extended its selling arrangement with Caisses d'Epargne to 2005. In 2003 it sold off its share of Italian bancassurance company Carivita.

EXECUTIVES

CEO, Gilles Benoist, age 68
Director International Operations and Deputy CEO, Xavier Larnaudie-Eiffel
Director Finance and Deputy CEO, Antoine Lissowski
Director Programmes Organisation and Information Systems and Deputy CEO, Michel Bois, age 56

LOCATIONS

HQ: CNP Assurances S.A.
4, place Raoul Dautry, Paris, Cedex 15 75716
Phone: (33) 1 42 18 88 88
Web: www.cnp.fr

2014 Premium by Country

	% of total
France	80
Brazil	9
Italy	9
Others	2
Total	**100**

PRODUCTS/OPERATIONS

2014 Premiums by Business Segments

	% of total
Savings	70
Pensions	9
Term creditor imsurance	11
Personal risk	7
Health Insurance	2
Property & casulty	1
Total	**100**

Selected Subsidiaries

Barclays Vida y Pensiones (50% Spain)
Caixa Seguros (52% insurance Brazil)
CNP Europe Life Ltd (Ireland)
CNP Holding Brasil
CNP IAM
CNP Seguros de Vida (76% insurance Argentina)
CNP UniCredit Vita (57% insurance Italy)
CNP Vida (94% insurance Spain)
Global (83% insurance Portugal)
Global Vida (83% insurance Portugal)
ITV
La Banque Postale Prévoyance (50% insurance)
Marfin Insurance Holdings Ltd. (50% insurance Cyprus)
Préviposte

COMPETITORS

AXA	BNP Paribas
Achmea	Credit Agricole
Allianz	Groupama
Allianz France	ING
April Group	

HISTORICAL FINANCIALS

Company Type: Public

Income Statement

FYE: December 31

	ASSETS ($ mil.)	NET INCOME ($ mil.)	INCOME AS % OF ASSETS	EMPLOYEES
12/15	428,857	1,231	0.3%	4,740
12/14	480,612	1,312	0.3%	4,705
12/13	503,862	1,418	0.3%	4,809
12/12	465,555	1,253	0.3%	4,842
12/11	415,211	1,127	0.3%	3,077
Annual Growth	**0.8%**	**2.2%**	**—**	**11.4%**

2015 Year-End Financials

Return on assets: 0.2%
Return on equity: 6.6%
Long-term debt ($ mil.): —
No. of shares (mil.): 685
Sales ($ mil): 48,439

Dividends
Yield: 0.0%
Payout: 25.0%
Market value ($ mil.): 4,635

	STOCK PRICE ($) FY Close	P/E High/Low		PER SHARE ($) Earnings	Dividends	Book Value
12/15	6.76	6	4	1.68	0.42	27.19
12/14	8.56	6	6	1.81	0.53	29.55
12/13	7.41	6	5	2.01	0.33	29.35
12/12	7.90	6	4	1.92	0.31	29.03
Annual Growth	**(5.1%)**	**—**	**—**	**(3.4%)**	**7.6%**	**(1.6%)**

Co-operative Bank plc

In business for well over a century The Co-operative Bank provides individuals and business with traditional services (checking and savings accounts mortgages loans and credit cards) along with such ethical financial services products as credit cards that benefit charities. The bank also offers insurance (through sister firm Co-operative Insurance Society) and investments such as ISAs unit trusts pensions and trust funds. The institution which has more than 300 branches throughout the UK also operates Internet banking business smile. Founded in 1872 by what is now Co-operative Group the bank was incorporated in 1970.

The group's financial service offerings (Co-Operative Bank Co-operative Insurance online bank smile) are operated under the aegis of holding company Co-operative Banking Group (formerly Co-operative Financial Services). They account for about one-fifth of Co-operative Group's revenues.

Co-operative Financial Services merged in 2009 with the second-largest building society in the UK Britannia Building Society creating a "super-mutual" financial institution as an alternative to the country's floundering shareholder-owned banks. The combined firm is a wholly owned subsidiary of Co-operative Group.As it complete the integration process Co-operative Bank is also investing in its CFS transformation plan. The group plans to spend some Â729 million over the course of three years to update its banking systems and infrastructure. As part of that transformation Co-operative Bank rolled out online banking in 2010.

The Financial Times named Co-operative the world's most sustainable bank in 2010.

EXECUTIVES

CEO, Niall S. K. Booker, age 57
CFO, John Baines
COO, R. G. (Bob) Rickert
Managing Director CoAM, Grahame McGirr
Chief Information Officer, Steve Friedlos
Chairman, Dennis Holt, age 68
Auditors: Ernst & Young LLP

LOCATIONS

HQ: Co-operative Bank plc
1 Balloon Street, Manchester M60 4EP
Phone: (44) 161 832 3456   **Fax:** (44) 161 829 4475
Web: www.co-operativebank.co.uk

PRODUCTS/OPERATIONS

2011 Sales

	% of total
Interest & similar	61
Earned premiums	28
Fees & commissions	11
Total	**100**

COMPETITORS

Bank of England
Barclays
HSBC
Lloyds Banking Group
Nationwide Building
  Society

Royal Bank of Scotland
Santander UK
Standard Life Bank

HISTORICAL FINANCIALS
Company Type: Public

Income Statement   FYE: December 31

	ASSETS ($ mil.)	NET INCOME ($ mil.)	INCOME AS % OF ASSETS	EMPLOYEES
12/15	43,018	(923)	—	5,714
12/14	58,667	(353)	—	6,402
12/13	71,715	(1,237)	—	7,526
12/12	79,905	(820)	—	7,754
12/11	75,629	74	0.1%	8,528
Annual Growth	(13.2%)	—	—	(9.5%)

2015 Year-End Financials

Return on assets: (-1.8%)
Return on equity: (-37.2%)
Long-term debt ($ mil.): —
No. of shares (mil.): 451
Sales ($ mil): 1,220

Dividends
Yield: —
Payout: —
Market value ($ mil.): —

Commerzbank AG (Germany, Fed. Rep.)

Auditors: PricewaterhouseCoopers Aktiengesellschaft

LOCATIONS

HQ: Commerzbank AG (Germany, Fed. Rep.)
  Kaiserplatz, Frankfurt am Main D-60261
Phone: (49) 69 136 20   **Fax:** (49) 69 28 53 89
Web: www.commerzbank.com

HISTORICAL FINANCIALS
Company Type: Public

Income Statement   FYE: December 31

	ASSETS ($ mil.)	NET INCOME ($ mil.)	INCOME AS % OF ASSETS	EMPLOYEES
12/15	580,158	1,156	0.2%	51,305
12/14	677,776	320	0.0%	52,103
12/13	756,737	107	0.0%	52,944
12/12	838,118	7	0.0%	53,601
12/11	855,958	825	0.1%	49,215
Annual Growth	(9.3%)	8.8%	—	1.0%

2015 Year-End Financials

Return on assets: 0.1%
Return on equity: 3.8%
Long-term debt ($ mil.): —
No. of shares (mil.): 1,252
Sales ($ mil): 17,690

Dividends
Yield: —
Payout: —
Market value ($ mil.): 12,962

	STOCK PRICE ($) FY Close	P/E High/Low	PER SHARE ($) Earnings	Dividends	Book Value
12/15	10.35	16 11	0.96	0.00	25.57
12/14	13.06	76 55	0.28	0.00	27.82
12/13	16.30	— —	(0.12)	3.63	31.42
12/12	1.98	— —	(0.53)	0.00	59.13
12/11	1.69	5 1	2.33	0.00	60.98
Annual Growth	57.3% (19.5%)	— —	(19.9%)	—	

Commonwealth Bank of Australia

Commonwealth Bank of Australia (CBA) one of Australia's Big Four banks offers retail private business and institutional banking services funds management insurance and investment services. CBA's brands include Bankwest wealth manager Colonial First State master trust services provider FirstChoice online brokerage CommSec ASB Bank which provides banking investment and financial services in New Zealand. CBA has more than 1100 branch offices in Australia (plus over 3600 Australia Post locations) as well as operations that reach Asia Europe and the US. CBA is also one of the largest life insurers in Australia and a leading provider of home loans there.

Operations

Broadly speaking CBA generated 75% of its revenue from interest income from its various banking divisions and New Zealand operations in fiscal 2015 (ended June 30) while its insurance premiums and fund management income (from its Wealth Management New Zealand and IFS and other divisions) made up 11% of revenue. The rest came from other banking income and investment revenue.

CBA operates seven divisions. Its Retail Banking unit which made up 40% of its revenue in FY2015 provides deposit home loan and consumer loan products to retail customers and small businesses. The Business and Private Banking division (16% of revenue) provides personalized banking services to Agribusiness customers and high-net-worth individuals as well as margin lending through CommSec. Institutional Banking and Markets (12% of revenue) provides debt and equity capital raising financial and commodities price risk management and transactional banking services to corporate institutional and government clients. Its Wealth Management division (10% of revenue) includes its Global Asset Management business (including operations in Asia and Europe) as well as its Platform Administration and Life and General Insurance businesses in Australia. The rest of its revenue comes from its operations in New Zealand (9% of revenue) Bankwest (8% of revenue) and IFS and other divisions (5% of revenue). In addition to banking CBA has life insurance operations in New Zealand (Sovereign) Indonesia (Commonwealth Life) and a joint venture in China called BoCommLife. Its investment products include funds offered by CBA or through its master trust product FirstChoice the largest retail platform in Australia. CBA is one of the country's largest managers of Australian funds.

Geographic Reach

CBA generated 83% of its revenue from customers in Australia in FY2015 while its business

in New Zealand brought in another 11% of revenue. The bank operates retail banks in New Zealand (ASB) and Indonesia (Commonwealth Bank of Indonesia). It has minority investments in two banks in China and one in Vietnam. It also has banking branch offices in London New York Tokyo Hong Kong Shanghai Singapore Auckland Ho Chi Minh City and Mumbai.

Financial Performance

Note: Growth rates may differ after conversion to US dollars.

CBA's revenues and profits have been rising in recent years thanks to growing loan business (especially retail loans for homes) lower interest expense on deposits amidst the low-interest environment and declining loan loss provisions.

The bank's revenue rose 2% to A$45.3 billion (around $34 billion) in fiscal 2015 (ended June 30) mostly thanks to higher card and loan commissions from higher transaction volumes and higher trading income stemming from strong market sales and trading volumes. Its interest income inched up by 1% on continued loan business growth.

Higher revenue in 2014 drove CBA's net income up 5% to A$9 billion (roughly $7 billion) despite headwinds of higher staff costs and salary increases and regulatory tightening. The bank's operating cash levels jumped 81% to A$7.1 billion ($5.5 billion) on higher cash earnings and favorable changes in working capital.

Strategy

CBA in 2015 continued its focus on four "strategic priorities": people technology productivity and strength. In line with these priorities CBA has been moving toward digital banking channels that are quickly taking the industry by storm allowing the bank to slow expensive branch-expansion plans and cut operating costs significantly while giving customers faster access to banking services. During 2014 it continued improving its CommBank app on mobile phones and introduced the app for smartwatches which allowed customers to find ATMs and view balances and even pay for items with its "Cardless Cash" feature. That year it also introduced its Innovation Lab in Sydney to provide a place for employees and customers to create new solutions and launched "Albert" its tablet device allowing businesses to create email receipts and invoices split bills up to nine ways record and track payments and collect real-time analytics and business insights. Mergers and AcquisitionsIn 2014 CBA purchased TYME (Take Your Money Everywhere) a South African-based digital banking technology designer and builder. The deal follows the bank's digitization strategy and is expected to unlock opportunities in its emerging markets businesses.

HISTORY

Company BackgroundThe Commonwealth Bank Act of 1911 allowed banks to conduct both savings bank and central bank functions and paved the way for the founding of the Commonwealth Bank of Australia the next year. The bank initially operated through a single main office and in nearly 500 post offices in Victoria; it spread out through the entire country over the next few years.

The young bank was drafted during WWI to help the federal government organize war loans and a merchant shipping fleet. In 1919 the bank took over responsibility for issuing notes from the Federal Treasury. In 1928 it created the Commonwealth Savings Bank from its savings department.

Australia —heavily indebted to British lenders — was devastated by the Great Depression. As banks failed the Commonwealth Bank picked up several other institutions including the state banks in Western Australia and New South Wales. During those years Commonwealth took on more and more of the functions of a central bank.

During WWII the bank again came to the aid of its country acting as an agent for the federal government. After the war when the Australian economy stabilized the bank began offering home loans.

After years of controversy in 1959 two bank acts formally separated the Commonwealth Bank's central bank and savings functions. The Reserve Bank of Australia took over the central bank functions in 1960 and the trading and savings operations were taken over by the new Commonwealth Development Bank later renamed the Commonwealth Banking Corporation (a subsidiary of Commonwealth Bank of Australia).

The bank concentrated on expansion and diversification in the 1970s establishing travel home insurance and financing (CBFC 1978); it set its sights on technology in the 1980s expanding its credit card offerings and introducing electronic banking.

The US's 1987 stock market crash again affected Australia's banks which spent almost a decade recovering. Luckily for Commonwealth Bank it wasn't the hardest hit.

In 1988 Commonwealth Bank moved into life insurance and investment services forming subsidiaries Commonwealth Life and Commonwealth Management Services (now together known as CBA Financial Services). In 1989 the bank bought 75% of New Zealand-based ASB Bank.

Commonwealth faced a bevy of challenges including banking deregulation that began in 1982 foreign competition and 1990's banking-law amendments allowing banks to be publicly traded. All of these factors influenced Commonwealth's decision to reorganize. The government sold approximately 30% of its stake in 1991 in part to help Commonwealth fund its acquisition of the State Bank of Victoria. The government sold the rest of its stake in 1996.

That year the company's push into electronic banking bore fruit —some 60% of all its banking transactions were online; that figure later rose to 80%. The company moved into e-commerce in 1999 putting out a call for an overseas partner; Commonwealth's stated goal was to generate one-quarter of its income outside Australia. Also that year Commonwealth and a division of The Bank of Nova Scotia joined forces to form a commodities trading group specializing in metals. In 2000 the company bought Australian financial services firm Colonial Limited.

In late 2008 the company acquired Australia-based BankWest from British bank HBOS (now part of Lloyds Banking Group). The US$1.5 billion deal included insurer and asset manager St. Andrew's (which was later sold) and bolstered CBA's presence in western Australia. Its 2008 acquisitions of BankWest from HBOS bolstered its position in western Australia. In 2010 CBA entered the Chinese insurance market with the launch of a joint venture with Bank of Communications. In 2011 the bank opened branches in China India and Indonesia and bought a 20% sake in Vietnam International Bank. Also that year the bank continued to strengthen its ties to China signing a referral agreement with Agricultural Bank of China to capture potential customers.

EXECUTIVES

CFO, David Craig
Group Chief Risk Officer, David Cohen
Group Executive Chief Executive and Managing Director ASB, Barbara Chapman
Managing Director and CEO, Ian Narev, age 48
Group Executive Wealth Management, Annabel F. Spring

Group Executive Retail Banking Services, Matt Comyn
Group Executive Enterprise Services and CIO, David Whiteing
Group Executive Institutional Banking and Markets, Kelly Bayer Rosmarin
Group Executive Marketing and Strategy, Vittoria Shortt
Chairman, Catherine B. Livingstone, age 61
Auditors: PricewaterhouseCoopers

LOCATIONS

HQ: Commonwealth Bank of Australia
Ground Floor, Tower 1, 201 Sussex Street, Sydney, New South Wales 2000
Phone: (61) 2 9378 2000   **Fax:** (61) 2 9118 7192
Web: www.commbank.com.au

2015

	%
Australia	83
New Zealand	11
Other locations	5
Total	**100**

PRODUCTS/OPERATIONS

2015

	%
Interest income	75
Other banking income	11
Premiums from insurance contracts	6
Funds management income	5
Investment revenue	2
Investment revenue	1
Total	**100**

2015 Sales by Segment

	% of total
Retail banking services	40
Business & private banking	16
Institutional banking & markets	12
Wealth Management	10
New Zealand	9
Bankwest	8
IFS and Other Divisions	5
Total	**100**

Selected Brands

ASB (New Zealand)
Bankwest
Colonial First State
CommInsure
CommSec
FirstChoice
Sovereign

COMPETITORS

AMP Limited	Macquarie Group
AXA Asia Pacific	National Australia
Asteron	Bank
Australia and New	QBE
Zealand Banking	Suncorp-Metway
HSBC	Westpac Banking
Lloyds Banking Group	

HISTORICAL FINANCIALS

Company Type: Public

Income Statement

FYE: June 30

	ASSETS ($ mil.)	NET INCOME ($ mil.)	INCOME AS % OF ASSETS	EMPLOYEES
06/16	694,231	6,865	1.0%	45,129
06/15	671,217	6,964	1.0%	45,948
06/14	743,668	8,109	1.1%	44,329
06/13	695,355	7,081	1.0%	44,969
06/12	731,444	7,220	1.0%	44,844
Annual Growth	**(1.3%)**	**(1.3%)**	**—**	**0.2%**

2016 Year-End Financials

Return on assets: 1.0%
Return on equity: 16.3%
Long-term debt ($ mil.): —
No. of shares (mil.): 1,711
Sales ($ mil.): 32,619
Dividends
Yield: 5.7%
Payout: 84.1%
Market value ($ mil.): 95,563

	STOCK PRICE ($) FY Close	P/E High/Low		PER SHARE ($) Earnings	Dividends	Book Value
06/16	55.85	12	10	3.94	3.22	26.18
06/15	65.62	14	10	4.17	3.36	24.83
06/14	76.50	15	12	4.90	3.53	28.38
06/13	63.35	14	10	4.28	3.26	25.82
06/12	53.69	12	9	4.41	3.08	26.37
Annual Growth	**1.0%**	**—**	**—**	**(2.8%)**	**1.1%**	**(0.2%)**

Compagnie de Saint-Gobain

Auditors: PricewaterhouseCoopers Audit

LOCATIONS

HQ: Compagnie de Saint-Gobain
Les Miroirs, 18, avenue d' Alsace, Courbevoie 92400
Phone: (33) 1 47 62 30 00
Web: www.saint-gobain.com

HISTORICAL FINANCIALS

Company Type: Public

Income Statement

FYE: December 31

	REVENUE ($ mil.)	NET INCOME ($ mil.)	NET PROFIT MARGIN	EMPLOYEES
12/15	43,204	1,410	3.3%	168,114
12/14	49,957	1,158	2.3%	178,799
12/13	57,857	819	1.4%	185,634
12/12	56,937	1,009	1.8%	192,781
12/11	54,475	1,660	3.0%	194,658
Annual Growth	**(5.6%)**	**(4.0%)**	**—**	**(3.6%)**

2015 Year-End Financials

Debt ratio: 24.7%
Return on equity: 7.0%
Cash ($ mil.): 5,859
Current ratio: 1.39
Long-term debt ($ mil.): 7,983
No. of shares (mil.): 558
Dividends
Yield: 3.1%
Payout: 10.5%
Market value ($ mil.): 4,829

	STOCK PRICE ($) FY Close	P/E High/Low		PER SHARE ($) Earnings	Dividends	Book Value
12/15	8.65	4	3	2.49	0.27	36.96
12/14	8.34	6	4	2.07	0.34	39.07
Annual Growth	**3.7%**	**—**	**—**	**4.8%**	**(5.2%)**	**(1.4%)**

Compagnie Generale des Etablissements Michelin (France)

Auditors: Deloitte & Associés

LOCATIONS

HQ: Compagnie Generale des Etablissements Michelin (France)
23, place des Carmes-Dechaux, Clermont-Ferrand, Cedex 9 63040
Phone: (33) 4 73 32 20 00
Web: www.michelin.com

HISTORICAL FINANCIALS
Company Type: Public

Income Statement
FYE: December 31

	REVENUE ($ mil.)	NET INCOME ($ mil.)	NET PROFIT MARGIN	EMPLOYEES
12/15	23,090	1,272	5.5%	111,700
12/14	23,766	1,253	5.3%	112,300
12/13	27,874	1,551	5.6%	112,199
12/12	28,303	2,069	7.3%	107,302
12/11	26,799	1,891	7.1%	115,000
Annual Growth	(3.7%)	(9.4%)	—	(0.7%)

2015 Year-End Financials

Debt ratio: 13.6%
Return on equity: 12.2%
Cash ($ mil.): 1,690
Current ratio: 1.91
Long-term debt ($ mil.): 2,662

No. of shares (mil.): 181
Dividends
　Yield: 2.8%
　Payout: 7.9%
Market value ($ mil.): 3,468

	STOCK PRICE ($) FY Close	P/E High/Low		Earnings	PER SHARE ($) Dividends	Book Value
12/15	19.07	4	2	6.74	0.54	56.82
12/14	18.04	4	3	6.62	0.68	62.25
12/13	21.35	4	3	8.23	0.63	68.56
12/12	19.19	2	1	11.08	0.53	61.36
12/11	11.72	2	1	10.31	0.46	58.19
Annual Growth	12.9%		—	(10.1%)	4.2%	(0.6%)

Compal Electronics Inc

Compal Electronics is one of the world's largest notebook computer manufacturers counting Dell Lenovo and Acer as customers. Compal also makes mobile phone handsets LCD and 3D TVs computer displays as well as a growing list of server computers tablets and media players. The company does most of its manufacturing in China. It gets about a third of sales from customers in the US.

Operations
Compal gets 98% of its revenue from its IT segment which develops and manufactures computers TVs and telecommunications equipment. The other 2% is from its Strategically Integrated Products segment which works on wireless networking products.

Geographic Reach

Based in Taiwan Compal has sites in China the US Vietnam Brazil and Poland. Compal's main manufacturing facilities are in Kunshan and Nanjing China. The biggest geographic market for Compal is the US which supplies 32% of revenue. China is its other double-digit percentage customer at 16%.

Sales and Marketing
Two of Compal's biggest customers are Dell and Lenovo for which it makes notebooks and servers. Huawei is also a customer. Compal's four biggest customers account for 72% of revenue with the top customer topping out at 32% of total revenue.

Financial Performance
Compal reported flat revenue for 2015 from 2014 while profit rose 24%. The profit increase resulted from a lower impairment loss for 2015 compared to 2014. Cash flow from operation increased from 2014 to 2015.

Strategy
Compal is acting to diversity its product mix and its customers. It is moving into production of higher-end servers used to power cloud computing data centers. The company is working with customers such as Dell and Lenovo who also face the prospect of declining notebook sales to find higher value computer products. Huawei is another server customer. Compal has jumped into the Apple supply chain producing the iPad mini. It also has partnered with Ingenu to make devices for the internet of things.

In 2016 Compal agreed to sell a TV assembly plant in Poland to Vestel Ticaret based in Turkey.

EXECUTIVES

SVP and CFO, Gary Lu
Auditors: KPMG

LOCATIONS

HQ: Compal Electronics Inc
No. 581, Ruiguang Road, Neihu District, Taipei 11492
Phone: (886) 2 8797 8588   **Fax:** (886) 2 2658 5001
Web: www.compal.com

2015 Sales

	% of total
United States	32
Mainland China	16
Netherlands	8
Japan	4
England	4
Others	36
Total	**100**

PRODUCTS/OPERATIONS

2015 Sales

	% of total
IT Product Segment	98
Strategically Integrated Product Segment	2
Total	**100**

2015 Sales

	% of total
5C Electronic Products	100
Others	-
Total	**100**

COMPETITORS

ASUSTeK	Jabil
BenQ	MiTAC
Celestica	Pegatron
China Techfaith	Quanta Computer
First International Computer	Sanmina
Flextronics	Tatung
Hon Hai	TriGem
Inventec	Wistron

HISTORICAL FINANCIALS
Company Type: Public

Income Statement
FYE: December 31

	REVENUE ($ mil.)	NET INCOME ($ mil.)	NET PROFIT MARGIN	EMPLOYEES
12/15	25,785	264	1.0%	0
12/14	26,708	222	0.8%	0
12/13	23,230	82	0.4%	0
12/12	23,565	220	0.9%	67,156
12/11	22,867	366	1.6%	62,357
Annual Growth	3.0%	(7.8%)	—	—

2015 Year-End Financials

Debt ratio: 0.5%
Return on equity: 8.4%
Cash ($ mil.): 1,909
Current ratio: 1.37
Long-term debt ($ mil.): 436

No. of shares (mil.): —
Dividends
　Yield: —
　Payout: 321.5%
Market value ($ mil.): —

	STOCK PRICE ($) FY Close	P/E High/Low		Earnings	PER SHARE ($) Dividends	Book Value
12/15	0.00	—	—	0.06	0.19	0.71
12/14	0.00	2	2	0.05	0.14	0.72
12/13	3.60	7	6	0.02	0.12	0.72
Annual Growth	—	—	—	33.1%	13.7%	(0.5%)

Compass Group PLC (United Kingdom)

Look in almost any direction and you'll likely see a foodservice operation run by this company. Compass Group is the world's largest contract foodservices provider with operations in more than 50 countries. It provides hospitality and foodservice for a variety of businesses and such public-sector clients as cultural institutions hospitals and schools. It also offers vending catering concessions and security services for a number of events and sports venues. Its foodservice brands include Chartwells Crothall and Levy Restaurants. In addition Compass is a franchisee of such well-known chains as Burger King and Starbucks.

EXECUTIVES

Group Chief Executive, Richard J. Cousins, age 57, $313,000 total compensation
Group COO North America, Gary R. Green, age 59
COO Europe, Dominic Blakemore, age 46
Finance Director, Johnny Thompson
Chairman, Paul S. Walsh, age 61
Auditors: KPMG LLP

LOCATIONS

HQ: Compass Group PLC (United Kingdom)
Compass House, Guildford Street, Chertsey, Surrey KT16 9BQ
Phone: (44) 1932 573 000   **Fax:** (44) 1932 569 956
Web: www.compass-group.com

PRODUCTS/OPERATIONS

Selected Operating Units

All Leisure (sports and leisure venues)
Bon Appétit Management Company (on-site dining services)
Canteen (vending services)

Chartwells (education foodservices)
Crothall (health care facilities management)
ESS (offshore and remote foodservices)
Eurest (corporate foodservice)
FLIK (upscale foodservices)
Levy Restaurants (fine dining sports and leisure events)
Medirest (health care services)
Morrison Management Specialists (health care foodservice)
Restaurant Associates Managed Services (corporate dining and sporting and leisure events)
Scolarest (education foodservices)

COMPETITORS

ARAMARK	Healthcare Services
Autogrill	Legion Group
Centerplate	Reliance Security
Delaware North	Sodexo
Elior	
Farsight Security Services	

HISTORICAL FINANCIALS
Company Type: Public

Income Statement
FYE: September 30

	REVENUE ($ mil.)	NET INCOME ($ mil.)	NET PROFIT MARGIN	EMPLOYEES
09/16	25,400	1,285	5.1%	527,180
09/15	26,698	1,318	4.9%	515,864
09/14	27,605	1,399	5.1%	514,718
09/13	28,340	692	2.4%	506,699
09/12	27,378	979	3.6%	508,714
Annual Growth	(1.9%)	7.0%	—	0.9%

2016 Year-End Financials

Debt ratio: 41.7%	No. of shares (mil.): 1,654
Return on equity: 44.5%	Dividends
Cash ($ mil.): 448	Yield: 1.9%
Current ratio: 0.75	Payout: 44.0%
Long-term debt ($ mil.): 3,984	Market value ($ mil.): 32,117

	STOCK PRICE ($) FY Close	P/E High/Low	PER SHARE ($) Earnings	Dividends	Book Value
09/16	19.41	33 22	0.78	0.38	1.96
09/15	16.09	36 27	0.79	0.39	1.77
09/14	16.07	35 27	0.79	0.00	1.78
09/13	13.71	63 46	0.38	0.00	2.49
09/12	11.05	37 26	0.52	0.00	2.82
Annual Growth	15.1%	— —	10.9%	—	(8.7%)

Continental AG (Germany, Fed. Rep.)

Continental AG keeps rolling along as one of Europe's largest manufacturers of tires for cars trucks bicycles and agricultural products. Its Automotive Group is Continental's largest segment manufacturing brake and traction control systems passive safety products sensors and chassis and powertrain products. The Rubber Group comprises its Tires division (sold under the Continental Uniroyal and General brands) as well as its ContiTech division which produces vibration control and power transmission systems as well as conveyor belts. Germany-based bearing and clutch manufacturer Schaeffler controls 46% of Continental AG's shares.

Operations

Continental's Automotive Group generates about 60% of total sales each year while its Rubber Group hauls in the remaining 40%. Automotive comprises the Interior Chassis and Safety and Powertrain segments. Each segment operates through about 80 to 90 locations in about 20 countries.

Financial PerformanceThe company's revenues increased by 4% from 2013 to 2014. The primary reason was a surge in the production of cars station wagons and light commercial vehicles combined with a more favorable vehicle mix. The growth in its automotive division was strongest in NAFTA and in Asia particularly in China. Continental's net income also increased 24% from 2013 to 2014 due to the higher revenue volumes coupled with lower depreciation and amortization costs.

Strategy

For its growth strategy Continental has identified about 25 of the fastest growing automotive groups including navigation systems turbochargers and systems used for reducing emissions. The decision to diversify product lines is also part of the company's strategy to keep its dependence on the automotive industry in check by generating additional sales in industries other than automotive. Continental also intends to tighten its grip in emerging markets in Asia where it already generates about 20% of its total sales. Throughout 2005 it additionally announced initiatives to expand its tire research and development capabilities in both China and Bangalore.

Mergers and Acquisitions

In 2015 Continental bought US-based rubber and plastics maker Veyance Technologies from financial investment firm Carlyle for about EUR 1.4 billion (or US $1.9 billion). The company will integrate Veyance into its ContiTech division.

HISTORY

Company Background

A group of financiers and industrialists with interests in the rubber industry founded Continental-Caoutchouc und Gutta-Percha Compagnie in Hanover Germany in 1871. The company's products included solid tires for carriages and bicycles rubberized fabrics and various consumer items.

In 1892 Continental was the first German maker of pneumatic bicycle tires. During this period the budding automobile and motorcycle industries created fresh demand for solid tires. Continental began producing pneumatic tires for automobiles in 1898. By 1904 Continental was first to develop a treaded tire. Between 1905 and 1913 Continental expanded into Australia Denmark Italy Norway Romania Sweden and the UK by forming marketing subsidiaries. However the onset of WWI caused a shift to military production and the overseas sales network dissolved.

Poor overall economic conditions atrophied postwar tire industry growth and by the late 1920s the company merged several German rubber firms to create a much larger and stronger Continental. In 1929 the company changed its name to Continental Gummi-Werke AG.

EXECUTIVES

Chairman Executive Board, Elmar Degenhart, age 58
Executive Board Member Human Resources and Personnel, Heinz-Gerhard Wente, age 65
Member Executive Board Chassis and Safety, Ralf Cramer, age 50
Member Executive Board Interior, Helmut Matschi, age 53
Member Executive Board Tire Division, Nikolai Setzer, age 45

Member Executive Board Finance Controlling Compliance Law and IT, Wolfgang Sch ¤fer, age 57
Member Executive Board Powertrain Division, Jose A. Avila, age 61
Chairman Supervisory Board, Wolfgang H. Reitzle, age 67
Deputy Chairman Supervisory Board, Werner Bischoff, age 69
Auditors: KPMG AG Wirtschaftsprufungsgesellschaft

LOCATIONS

HQ: Continental AG (Germany, Fed. Rep.)
Vahrenwalder Strasse 9, Hanover 30165
Phone: (49) 511 938 01   **Fax:** (49) 511 938 81 770
Web: www.continental-corporation.com

2014 Sales

	% of total
Europe	
Germany	23
Other countries	30
North America	22
Asia	20
Other regions	5
Total	100

PRODUCTS/OPERATIONS

2014 Sales

	% of total
Automotive Group	
Chassis & safety	22
Interior	20
Powertrain	19
Rubber Group	
Tires (passenger & light truck)	28
ContiTech	11
Other/Consolidation	0
Total	100

Selected Automotive Group Products

Chassis and Safety
  Chassis components
  Electronic brake systems
  Hydraulic brake systems
  Passive safety and ADAS
  Sensors
Interior
  Body and security
  Commercial vehicles and aftermarket
  Connectivity
  Instrumentation and displays
  Interior modules
  Multimedia
Powertrain
  Engine systems
  Fuel supply
  Hybrid electric vehicle
  Sensors and actuators
  Transmissions

Selected Rubber Group Products

ContiTech
  Air spring systems
  Benecke-Kaliko group
  Conveyor belt group
  Elastomer coatings
  Fluid technology
  Power transmission group
  Vibration control
Tires
  Commercial vehicle
  Passenger and light truck

COMPETITORS

A.G. Simpson	Magna International
AirBoss of America	McLaren Performance
Bridgestone	Meritor
China Enterprises	Michelin
Cooper Tire & Rubber	Nokian Tyres
DENSO	Pirelli
Dana	Robert Bosch
Delphi Automotive Systems	Standard Motor Products

HISTORICAL FINANCIALS
Company Type: Public

Income Statement
FYE: December 31

	REVENUE ($ mil.)	NET INCOME ($ mil.)	NET PROFIT MARGIN	EMPLOYEES
12/15	42,731	2,970	7.0%	207,899
12/14	41,941	2,887	6.9%	189,168
12/13	45,887	2,647	5.8%	177,762
12/12	43,147	2,482	5.8%	169,639
12/11	39,456	1,606	4.1%	163,788
Annual Growth	2.0%	16.6%	—	6.1%

2015 Year-End Financials

Debt ratio: 17.4%
Return on equity: 23.2%
Cash ($ mil.): 1,766
Current ratio: 1.09
Long-term debt ($ mil.): 3,458
No. of shares (mil.): 200
Dividends
  Yield: 1.0%
  Payout: 3.5%
Market value ($ mil.): 9,621

	STOCK PRICE ($) FY Close	P/E High/Low		PER SHARE ($) Earnings	Dividends	Book Value
12/15	48.11	4	3	14.86	0.52	69.63
12/14	41.83	4	3	14.44	0.50	64.86
12/13	44.42	23	5	13.24	0.43	62.03
12/12	117.10	12	7	12.42	0.29	57.78
12/11	62.00	16	8	8.03	0.00	46.21
Annual Growth	(6.1%)	—	—	16.6%	—	10.8%

Coop Switzerland (Switzerland)

EXECUTIVES

Managing Director, Gerhard Metz
Auditors: PricewaterhouseCoopers AG

LOCATIONS

HQ: Coop Switzerland (Switzerland)
Thiersteinerallee 12, Postfach 2550, Basel CH-4002
Phone: (41) 61 336 66 66   **Fax:** (41) 61 336 60 40
Web: www.coop.ch

HISTORICAL FINANCIALS
Company Type: Public

Income Statement
FYE: December 31

	REVENUE ($ mil.)	NET INCOME ($ mil.)	NET PROFIT MARGIN	EMPLOYEES
12/15	26,074	418	1.6%	79,953
12/14	27,459	475	1.7%	77,087
12/13	30,264	518	1.7%	74,955
12/12	29,160	493	1.7%	75,309
12/11	28,316	459	1.6%	75,296
Annual Growth	(2.0%)	(2.3%)	—	1.5%

Country Garden Holdings Co., Ltd.

Country Garden builds residential properties in China. The group primarily develops large-scale apartment communities and townhouses in China's suburbs. Its more than 170 projects boast an aggregate completed gross floor area (GFA) of 45.7 million square meters. Country Garden manages 20 completed properties and has 45 more under construction totaling 48000 units. The company also owns nine hotels with more under construction. It was founded in 1997 in Guangdong Province by Chairman and CEO Yang Guoqiang (also known as Yeung Kwok Keung). His daughter Yang Huiyan a director with the firm owns 59% of Country Garden and is China's richest woman. Country Garden listed on the Hong Kong Stock Exchange in 2007.

Country Garden's development strategy is to build middle-class developments outside of smaller cities experiencing first-time growth and low property values. The majority of its projects are in Guangdong Province but Country Garden has expanded to the provinces of Hunan Hubei Jiangsu Anhui and Liaoning as well as Mongolia and Chongquing municipality. In June 2008 the company applied to 20 towns in those provinces seeking to build affordable housing.

EXECUTIVES

CFO, Wu Jianbin, age 54
Chairman and CEO, Yeung Kwok Keung, age 62
President and Executive Director, Mo Bin, age 50
Associate President and Executive Director, Zhu Rongbin
CFO, Wu Bijun, age 43
Vice Chairman, Yang Huiyan, age 35
Auditors: PricewaterhouseCoopers

LOCATIONS

HQ: Country Garden Holdings Co., Ltd.
Suite 1702, 17/F., Dina House, Ruttonjee Centre, 11 Duddell Street, Central,
Phone:
Web: www.countrygarden.com.cn

PRODUCTS/OPERATIONS

2013 Sales

	% of total
Property development	96
Hotel operations	2
Construction fitting & decoration	1
Property management	1
Total	100

Selected Projects

Country Garden - Galaxy Palace
Country Garden - Grand Garden
Country Garden - Springs City
Country Garden - Ten Miles Coast
Country Garden City Garden
Country Garden Grand Lake
Country Garden Phoenix City
Dalang Country Garden
Heshan Country Garden
Holiday Island
Malaysia Project
Tianjin Country Garden

COMPETITORS

China Overseas Land & Investment
China Vanke

Shanghai Forte Land
Sino Land
Xinyuan

Evergrande Real Estate Group
Guangzhou R&F Properties

Yanlord Land

HISTORICAL FINANCIALS
Company Type: Public

Income Statement
FYE: December 31

	REVENUE ($ mil.)	NET INCOME ($ mil.)	NET PROFIT MARGIN	EMPLOYEES
12/15	17,433	1,428	8.2%	68,150
12/14	13,622	1,648	12.1%	64,869
12/13	10,353	1,406	13.6%	64,772
12/12	6,719	1,099	16.4%	40,243
12/11	5,520	923	16.7%	35,206
Annual Growth	33.3%	11.5%	—	18.0%

2015 Year-End Financials

Debt ratio: 3.8%
Return on equity: 15.2%
Cash ($ mil.): 5,580
Current ratio: 1.35
Long-term debt ($ mil.): 10,311
No. of shares (mil.): —
Dividends
  Yield: 66.4%
  Payout: 50.4%
Market value ($ mil.): —

CPC Corporation, Taiwan

The Chinese petroleum handled by this company is in the other China —Taiwan. CPC (formerly Chinese Petroleum Corporation) is engaged in the exploration production refining storage transportation and the sale of oil and oil products in Taiwan. To supplement oil supply to hydrocarbon-poor Taiwan the state-owned monopoly has stakes in oil and gas exploration ventures in Australia Chad Ecuador Indonesia Libya the US and Venezuela. Its refineries produce natural gas kerosene fuel oil ethylene propylene and other refined products. CPC owns and operates more than 2030 gas stations as well as boat and aviation refueling stations. The Taiwanese government has CPC on track for privatization.

Geographic Reach

CPC has operations in Taiwan and in 21 active fields in seven countries including Block 16 and 17 in Ecuador; Sanga Sanga Bulungan Amborip VI and Sanga Sanga coal bed methane in Indonesia; Gulf of Paria East and Gulf of Paria West in Venezuela (negotiations are in progress in regard to confiscated prospects); Block AC/P21 and NT/P76 in Australia; Caviar Manahuilla Estrella Garden City Field and Hurricane Creek (Big Horn Shorts Creek Danub Yellowstone) Blocks in the USS; the Murzuq 162 Block in Libya; and the BCO III/BCS 11/BLT I Blocks in Chad. In tandem with CNPC it is also seeking to exploit the Agadem block in Niger.

OperationsIn 2011 CPC sold a total of 15.28 billion cubic meters of natural gas mainly for power generation co-generation industrial and household use in Taiwan.

Financial Performance

In 2011 CPC's revenues increased by 10% and net income decreased by 302%.

Strategy

Because of its dependency of foreign oil and gas sources CPC plans to increase investment in domestic exploration and production in order to protect Taiwan from the rising costs of crude oil imports. In 2012 it signed a joint exploration and production agreement with Husky Energyto develop the deep water oil and gas reserve in the Tainan Basin in the Taiwan Strait southwest of Kaohsiung City.

Growing its marketing presence in 2012 CPC set up CPCI new subsidiary of the company's Overseas Petroleum and Investment Corporation (OPIC) Group as the first ever overseas oil trading unit in Singapore.

The company is also investing in upgrading its refinery infrastructure to increase its processing capacity and efficiency. To streamline refinery configuration and boost value-added profiles in 2012 CPC built a residue fluid catalytic cracking unit with a capacity of 80000 barrels per stream day. To meet the increase in ethylene demand by the local petrochemical industry that year CPC built a naphtha cracker unit with an annual capacity of 600000 metric tons of ethylene.

To comply with environmental regulations and to upgrade gasoline quality in 2011 CPC set up an alkylation unit with a capacity of 14000 barrels per stream day.

Company Background

Boosting its LNG supply base in 2008 CPC signed a deal whereby Woodside Petroleum agreed to supply 2-3 million tons per year for 15 to 20 years.

EXECUTIVES

Chairman, Sheng-Chung Lin
CEO Natural Gas Business Division, J. Y. Chen
President, Arthur H. Kung
VP; CEO Petrochemical Business Division, J. S. Yang
CEO Marketing Business Division, Cheng-Hsie Liu
CEO Solvent and Chemical Business Division, Jimmy Chang
VP, Ray-Chung Chang
VP, Shane S. I. Lin
VP, Ming-Huei Chen
CEO Exploration and Production Business Division, Jong-Chang Wu
CEO Refining Business Division, Ching-Yang Wu
CEO LPG Business Division, Jung-Lieh Lin
Acting CEO Lubricants Business Division, Ting Pang Chi
Director Refining & Manufacturing Research Institute, Vincent Y.S. Ho
Director Exploration & Development Research Institute, Shin-Tai Hu
Director Project & Construction Division and Acting Director LNG Project Division, Marc W.H. Lin
Director Green Technology Research Institute, Jung-Chung Wu
Director Material Testing & Certification Center, Ta-Tsung Yen
Auditors: Deloitte & Touche

LOCATIONS

HQ: CPC Corporation, Taiwan
No. 3, Songren Road, Sinyi District, Taipei 11010
Phone: (886) 2 8789 8989   **Fax:** (886) 2 8789 9000
Web: www.cpc.com.tw

PRODUCTS/OPERATIONS

Selected Products
Industrial Oil
LNG Product
LPG Product
Lube Oil
Marine Oil
Motor Oil
RBU Product
SNC Product

COMPETITORS

BP	Formosa Plastics
CNOOC	Royal Dutch Shell
Cosmo Oil	Sinopec Corp.
Exxon Mobil	TOTAL

HISTORICAL FINANCIALS
Company Type: Public

Income Statement
FYE: December 31

	REVENUE ($ mil.)	NET INCOME ($ mil.)	NET PROFIT MARGIN	EMPLOYEES
12/15	25,672	(43)	—	14,685
12/14	37,638	(1,066)	—	14,787
12/13	39,827	110	0.3%	14,819
12/12	39,529	(1,162)	—	14,977
12/11	33,977	(1,070)	—	15,219
Annual Growth	(6.8%)	—	—	(0.9%)

2015 Year-End Financials

Debt ratio: 1.4%
Return on equity: (-0.7%)
Cash ($ mil.): 69
Current ratio: 0.65
Long-term debt ($ mil.): 5,414

No. of shares (mil.): —
Dividends
  Yield: —
  Payout: —
Market value ($ mil.): —

CrediCorp Ltd.

Auditors: Gaveglio, Aparicio y Asociados S.C.R.L

LOCATIONS

HQ: CrediCorp Ltd.
Calle Centenario 156, La Molina, Lima 12
Phone: (51) 1 313 2014   **Fax:** (51) 1 313 2121
Web: www.credicorpnet.com

HISTORICAL FINANCIALS
Company Type: Public

Income Statement
FYE: December 31

	ASSETS ($ mil.)	NET INCOME ($ mil.)	INCOME AS % OF ASSETS	EMPLOYEES
12/15	45,668	908	2.0%	33,658
12/14	45,163	799	1.8%	32,313
12/13	40,820	567	1.4%	27,638
12/12	40,797	788	1.9%	26,541
12/11	30,732	709	2.3%	22,276
Annual Growth	10.4%	6.4%	—	10.9%

2015 Year-End Financials

Return on assets: 2.1%
Return on equity: 20.5%
Long-term debt ($ mil.): —
No. of shares (mil.): 79
Sales ($ mil.): 4,706

Dividends
  Yield: 2.2%
  Payout: 17.5%
Market value ($ mil.): 7,734

	STOCK PRICE ($) FY Close	P/E High/Low		PER SHARE ($) Earnings	Dividends	Book Value
12/15	97.32	4	2	11.41	2.19	59.61
12/14	160.18	6	4	9.80	1.90	58.91
12/13	132.73	23	16	7.12	2.60	53.25
12/12	146.56	15	11	9.90	2.30	52.50
12/11	109.47	13	9	8.90	1.95	42.76
Annual Growth	(2.9%)	—	—	6.4%	2.9%	8.7%

Credit Agricole Corporate & Investment Bank

Credit Agricole Corporate and Investment Bank (or Credit Agricole CIB) sows money for future growth. The bank is the corporate and investment banking arm of French superbank Credit Agricole. Through its six major divisions the investment bank is active in capital markets; offers mergers and acquisitions consultancy; provides equity debt and derivatives sales and underwriting; and provides foreign exchange services brokerage and structured finance. The bank has a global network (with an emphasis on Europe) and is active in more than 30 countries. It has some 1200 clients.

Operations

Credit Agricole CIB operates four business lines: financing activities capital markets and investment banking wealth management and corporate center.

Financing activities responsible for over 40% of revenue carries out corporate banking in France and internationally as well as structured finance activities including project finance aviation finance marine finance acquisition finance and property. Capital markets and investment banking (38% of revenue) conducts treasury foreign exchange interest rate derivatives debt market activities (capital markets); and mergers and acquisitions consulting and primary equity (investment banking).

Wealth management helps clients manage protect and pass on their wealth. Corporate Center carries out the nonoperational activities of the previous three segments.

Geographic Reach

Credit Agricole CIB is present in Europe the Americas the Asia/Pacific region and the Middle East. The wealth management business is active in France Belgium Switzerland Luxembourg Monaco Spain and Brazil.

Sales and Marketing

Credit Agricole CIB has 1200 clients and conducts financing activities in the natural resources (oil gas petrochem mines and metal bashing) sector electricity generation and distribution environmental services (water waste processing) and infrastructure (transport hospitals prisons schools and public services).

Financial Performance

Note: Growth rates may differ after conversion to US Dollars.

In fiscal 2015 revenue was up 20% to euro 5205 million while net income was down 9% to euro 958 million due to the impact of settlements with the Office of Foreign Assets Control (OFAC) and Union de Banques Arabes et Françaises (UBAF) for euro 350 million and euro 150 million respectively.

EXECUTIVES

President Directeur General, Philippe Jean BRASSAC
Board Member, Francois IMBAULT
Board Member, Marc KYRIACOU
Board Member, Francois Regis VEVERKA
Board Member, Jean-Frederic Marcel Ivan DREYFUS
Auditors: ERNST & YOUNG et Autres

LOCATIONS

HQ: Credit Agricole Corporate & Investment Bank
9, quai du President Paul Doumer, Paris La Defense,
Cedex 92920
Phone: (33) 1 41 89 00 00   **Fax:** (33) 1 41 89 12 77
Web: www.ca-cib.fr

COMPETITORS

CIBC World Markets	Lazard
Citigroup Global	Merrill Lynch
Markets Limited	Morgan Stanley
Cowen Group	N M Rothschild & Sons
Goldman Sachs	UBS Investment Bank
JPMorgan Chase	

HISTORICAL FINANCIALS

Company Type: Public

Income Statement   FYE: December 31

	ASSETS ($ mil.)	NET INCOME ($ mil.)	INCOME AS % OF ASSETS	EMPLOYEES
12/15	598,276	1,043	0.2%	9,899
12/14	782,903	1,275	0.2%	9,720
12/13	834,217	770	0.1%	9,993
12/12	1,193,217	(512)	—	12,154
12/11	1,068,396	882	0.1%	14,863
Annual Growth	(13.5%)	4.3%	—	(9.7%)

2015 Year-End Financials

Return on assets: 0.1%
Return on equity: 5.7%
Long-term debt ($ mil.): —
No. of shares (mil.): 268
Sales ($ mil): 9,543

Dividends
Yield: —
Payout: —
Market value ($ mil.): —

Credit Agricole SA

LOCATIONS

HQ: Credit Agricole SA
12 place des Etat-Unis, Montrouge, Cedex 92127
Phone: (33) 1 43 23 52 02
Web: www.credit-agricole.com

HISTORICAL FINANCIALS

Company Type: Public

Income Statement   FYE: December 31

	ASSETS ($ mil.)	NET INCOME ($ mil.)	INCOME AS % OF ASSETS	EMPLOYEES
12/15	1,665,723	3,829	0.2%	71,495
12/14	1,931,529	2,844	0.1%	72,567
12/13	2,115,867	3,448	0.2%	75,529
12/12	2,428,322	(8,529)	—	79,282
12/11	2,229,404	(1,901)	—	87,451
Annual Growth	(7.0%)	—	—	(4.9%)

2015 Year-End Financials

Return on assets: 0.2%
Return on equity: 6.7%
Long-term debt ($ mil.): —
No. of shares (mil.): —
Sales ($ mil): 84,289

Dividends
Yield: 3.3%
Payout: 14.4%
Market value ($ mil.): —

(Credit Agricole Corporate & Investment Bank stock/per share table)

	STOCK PRICE ($) FY Close	P/E High/Low		PER SHARE ($) Earnings	Dividends	Book Value
12/15	5.86	6	4	1.32	0.20	22.24
12/14	6.38	9	7	1.01	0.24	23.66
12/13	6.42	6	4	1.39	0.00	23.33
12/12	4.05	—	—	(3.44)	0.00	21.02
12/11	2.74	—	—	(0.78)	0.29	22.22
Annual Growth	20.9%		—	—	(9.7%)	0.0%

Credit Du Nord S.A. (France)

EXECUTIVES

President Directeur General, Jean-Francois
SAMMARCELLI
Auditors: ERNST & YOUNG et Autres

LOCATIONS

HQ: Credit Du Nord S.A. (France)
28, place Rihour, Lille 59000
Phone: (33) 1 40 22 40 22
Web: www.groupe-credit-du-nord.com

HISTORICAL FINANCIALS

Company Type: Public

Income Statement   FYE: December 31

	ASSETS ($ mil.)	NET INCOME ($ mil.)	INCOME AS % OF ASSETS	EMPLOYEES
12/15	64,536	422	0.7%	8,891
12/14	67,093	413	0.6%	9,033
12/13	78,114	507	0.7%	9,323
12/12	74,813	406	0.5%	9,689
12/11	71,343	407	0.6%	9,850
Annual Growth	(2.5%)	0.9%	—	(2.5%)

2015 Year-End Financials

Return on assets: 0.6%
Return on equity: 13.7%
Long-term debt ($ mil.): —
No. of shares (mil.): 111
Sales ($ mil): 2,839

Dividends
Yield: —
Payout: —
Market value ($ mil.): —

Credit Industriel et Commercial France

Auditors: ERNST & YOUNG et Autres

LOCATIONS

HQ: Credit Industriel et Commercial France
6 avenue de Provence, Paris 75009
Phone: (33) 1 45 96 96 96   **Fax:** (33) 1 45 96 96 66
Web: www.cic.fr

HISTORICAL FINANCIALS

Company Type: Public

Income Statement   FYE: December 31

	ASSETS ($ mil.)	NET INCOME ($ mil.)	INCOME AS % OF ASSETS	EMPLOYEES
12/15	276,633	1,210	0.4%	19,806
12/14	298,624	1,356	0.5%	19,893
12/13	320,669	1,163	0.4%	20,222
12/12	310,706	920	0.3%	20,654
12/11	301,740	717	0.2%	20,668
Annual Growth	(2.1%)	13.9%	—	(1.1%)

2015 Year-End Financials

Return on assets: 0.4%
Return on equity: 8.7%
Long-term debt ($ mil.): —
No. of shares (mil.): 37
Sales ($ mil): 12,243

Dividends
Yield: —
Payout: —
Market value ($ mil.): —

Credit Suisse Group

Credit Suisse is one of Switzerland's top financial services firms though a distant second to behemoth rival UBS. The group provides investment management private banking and asset management services to clients worldwide. Its investment banking offerings include debt and equity underwriting M&A advisory and other securities services. The group also provides wealth management services and asset management services to individual institutional and government clients. With more than 200 retail branches in Switzerland it operates in more than 50 countries (including the US and UK).

OperationsCredit Suisse operates through two main divisions that each contribute nearly 50% of total revenue: Private Banking & Wealth Management and Investment Banking.

The Private Banking & Wealth Management division provides advisory and financial services to private corporate and institutional clients and is made up of three businesses including: Wealth Management Clients Corporate & Institutional Clients and Asset Management businesses. Credit Suisse's Investment Banking division provides a range of financial products and services to client-driven flow-based and capital efficient businesses. Its services include: global securities sales trading and execution prime brokerage and capital raising services corporate advisory and comprehensive investment research. Its investment banking services are delivered through the company's regional and local teams based in major global financial centers. As part of Credit Suisse's integrated business model the Investment Banking division works closely with Private Banking & Wealth Management with the goal of providing customized financial solutions for each of Credit Suisse's clients.

Geographic Reach

Switzerland-based Credit Suisse boasts 530 offices and 22 booking centers in more than 50 countries. More than 40% of its revenue comes from the Americas while another 30% is generated in Switzerland. Other major regions include Europe Middle East and Africa (or EMEA which brings in more than 15% of revenue) and the Asia Pacific Region. Sales and MarketingCredit Suisse's Private Banking & Wealth Management business serves more than 2 million clients globally. The firm's Wealth Management Clients business serves ultra-high-net-worth and high-net-worth individuals worldwide as well as wealthy and retail clients in Switzerland. Its Corporate & Institutional Clients business caters to corporations and institutional clients mostly in Switzerland. The Asset Management business offers its investment products globally to governments institutions corporations and individuals.

The company's Investment Banking serves corporations governments and institutional investors (including pension and hedge funds) and private individuals.

Financial Performance

Note: Growth rates may differ after conversion to US dollars.

While Credit Suisse's financials have stabilized since its low-days in 2008 the bank has struggled to grow significantly in recent years. Revenue in 2014 remained mostly flat at CHF 26.24 billion ($26.52 billion). Fair value gains in the company's credit spreads (compared to credit spread losses in 2013) were the reason Credit Suisse did not lose revenue in 2014 as the Private Banking & Wealth Management division experienced a 6% decline in revenue as it earned lower net interest income and lower transaction- and performance-based revenue. Income from the group's Investment Banking division remained stable thanks to higher fixed income sales as well as higher fee income from trading underwriting and advisory activities. Net income plummeted by 19% to CHF 1.88 billion ($1.89 billion) in 2014 mostly because the bank incurred an 11% hike in general and administrative expenses which were primarily driven by a CHF 1.618 billion ($1.64 billion) litigation charge related to the final settlement of all outstanding US cross-border matters. Cash levels dropped significantly in 2014 with operations using CHF 17.62 billion ($17.81 billion) mostly due to the timing of its trading assets and liabilities which vary significantly in the normal course of business. Management believes that the capital it receives from operations available cash balances and short and long-term borrowings is sufficient to fund the company's operations.

Strategy

With the goal of creating a more client-focused capital-efficient strategy in the midst of a challenging regulatory environment Credit Suisse continues to sell off less profitable businesses to refocus its resources on higher-returning ones. In late 2014 the company sold its Private Banking & Wealth Management's local affluent and upper affluent businesses in Italy along with the associated euro 1.9 billion ($2.31 billion) in assets under management to Banca Generali S.p.A. It also exited a string of other small businesses in 2014 to free up cash resources including: its private equity fund of funds Customized Fund Investment Group; the group's mid-market leveraged buyout business DLJ Merchant Merchant Banking Partners; and its German-based private banking business in Germany selling the unit to Bethmann Bank AG.

That year it also exited its small commodities trading business (part of its global macro products business) planning to refocus instead on its more popular foreign exchange business and simplify it to satisfy client liquidity needs in cash products and derivatives. Additionally in 2014 the company agreed to sell its Prime Fund Services to BNP Paribas. In 2013 Credit Suisse sold its exchange traded funds (ETFs) business to private equity giant BlackRock Inc.

Credit Suisse also continues to make strategic acquisitions to grow the business. In 2014 the company purchased Morgan Stanley's private wealth management businesses in the EMEA region to expand its affluent client base across Europe. In 2012 the company acquired HSBC's private banking operations in Japan. Additionally the company has made moves to grow beyond its main

markets in the Americas and Switzerland. In 2015 the company launched its global digital private banking platform in Singapore with plans to provide digital wealth management services to the region while introducing a new 24-hour private banking service delivery model at the same time.

Mergers and Acquisitions

In 2014 Credit Suisse acquired Morgan Stanley's private wealth management businesses in the EMEA region (excluding Switzerland) which expanded its client base among high- and ultra-high-net-worth individual clients across the Europe.

Company Background

The bank has been plagued by litigation charges in recent years. In 2012 Credit Suisse handed over information to the US government as part of an investigation into hidden Swiss bank accounts that are used by wealthy Americans to evade taxes. Credit Suisse was among other Swiss banks that were being investigated. Swiss privacy laws have typically protected wealthy individuals who funnel money through offshore accounts.

HISTORY

In 1856 shortly after the creation of the Swiss federation Alfred Escher opened Credit Suisse (CS) in Zurich. Primarily a venture capital firm CS helped fund Swiss railroads and other industries. It later opened offices in Italy and helped establish the Swiss Bank Corporation.

CS shifted its focus to commercial banking in 1867 and sold most of its stock holdings. By 1871 it was Switzerland's largest bank buoyed by the nation's swift industrialization. In 1895 CS helped create the predecessor of Swiss utility Electrowatt. Foreign activity grew in the 1920s. A run on banks in the Depression forced CS to sell assets at a loss and dip into reserves of unreported retained profits.

Trade declined in WWII but neutrality left Switzerland's institutions intact and made it a major banking center partly due to CS's role as a conduit for the Nazis' plundered gold. Foreign exchange and gold trading became important activities for CS after WWII. Mortgage and consumer credit acquisitions fueled domestic growth in the 1970s.

In 1978 the bank took a stake in US investment bank First Boston and with it formed London-based Credit Suisse-First Boston (CSFB). CS created 44%-owned holding company Credit Suisse First Boston to own First Boston CSFB and Tokyo-based CS First Boston Pacific.

The stock market crash of 1987 led a damaged First Boston to merge with CSFB the next year. In 1990 CS (renamed CS Holding) injected $300 million into CSFB and shifted $470 million in bad loans from its books becoming the first foreign owner of a major Wall Street investment bank.

In the early 1990s CS Holding strengthened its insurance business with a Winterthur Insurance alliance. In 1993 and 1994 acquisitions helped it gain share in its overbanked home market.

In 1996 CS Holding reorganized as Credit Suisse Group and grew internationally including further merging the daredevil US investment banking operations into Credit Suisse's more staid and relationship-oriented corporate banking. It bought Winterthur (Switzerland's #2 insurer) in 1997 as well as Barclays' European investment banking business.

Credit Suisse and other Swiss banks came under fire in 1996 for refusing to relinquish assets from Jewish bank accounts from the Holocaust era and for gold trading with the Nazi regime. In 1997 the banks agreed to establish a humanitarian fund for Holocaust victims. A stream of lawsuits by American heirs and boycott threats from US states and cities led in 1998 to a tentative $1.25 billion set-

tlement (unpopular in Switzerland) with Credit Suisse on the hook for about a third of that.

CS in 1998 expanded its investment banking by buying Brazil's Banco de Investimentos Garantia; it also moved to expand US money management operations by allying with New York-based Warburg Pincus Asset Management. By 1999 that joint venture –which was to give the investment firm access to CS's mutual fund distribution channels in Europe and Asia –had morphed into CS's $650 million purchase of Warburg Pincus Asset Management.

Japan revoked the license of the company's financial products unit for obstructing an investigation (the harshest penalty ever given to a foreign firm at the time); it also accused the company of helping 60 others hide losses and cover up evidence.

In 2000 the company started a mortgage and home-buying Web site and decided to allow searches of Holocaust-era accounts. The next year as a part of its European expansion Credit Suisse acquired Spanish broker and asset manager General de Valores y Cambios.

Under former chairman and CEO Lukas Mühlemann the company expanded Credit Suisse First Boston when it bought US investment firm Donaldson Lufkin & Jenrette in 2000 and renamed it Credit Suisse First Boston (USA).

The collapse of Credit Suisse's share price along with what proved to be an over-ambitious acquisition strategy brought about the downfall of Mühlemann who was pressured out by shareholders in 2002.

In 2005 Credit Suisse merged with its Credit Suisse First Boston subsidiary creating a global Credit Suisse brand and in 2006 reorganized into three distinct operating segments –investment banking private banking and asset management along with insurance.

Credit Suisse sold insurance subsidiary Winterthur to AXA in 2006 for nearly $10 billion. A Winterthur sale had been on Credit Suisse's agenda for a while as a plan to divest noncore operations. Also that year Credit Suisse and General Electric jointly acquired a 50% stake in London City Airport which serves about 2 million travelers a year. The following year as a cost-saving measure Credit Suisse combined four private banks and one securities dealer into Clariden Leu.

The company named Brady Dougan CEO in 2007. Dugan was the first non-German speaker to hold the position.

Globally the investment banking industry was hit hard by the US subprime mortgage crisis and Credit Suisse was no exception. The company reported a net loss of euro 5.4 billion in 2008 the worst in its history. Credit Suisse turned down a bailout offer from the Swiss government in 2008 but it did receive a capital injection of CHF10 billion ($8.7 billion) from private investors. However the capital infusion couldn't prevent losses as global credit markets froze and consumer and shareholder confidence fell.

The company cut more than 5000 jobs or some 11% of its workforce mostly from its investment banking unit. It also reviewed its results for 2007 and among its findings discovered rogue traders in its ranks à la the beleaguered Societe Generale. Credit Suisse reduced its results accordingly.

In 2008 it bought an 80% stake in US firm Asset Management Finance Corporation a division of National Bank of Canada. Also in 2008 it expanded its Middle East franchise when it bought majority ownership in joint venture Saudi Swiss Securities which it renamed Credit Suisse Saudi Arabia. It has added Shariah-compliant banking for Islamic clients and has expanded in other markets including Brazil Kazakhstan and Turkey.

The following year Credit Suisse sold certain fund management assets and businesses to Aberdeen Asset Management in exchange for about 25% of Aberdeen's shares.

EXECUTIVES

President and CEO Credit Suisse Holdings (USA) Inc., Eric Varvel, age 53
CEO, Tidjane C. Thiam, age 54
CFO, David Mathers, age 52
CEO Asia Pacific, Helman Sitohang
COO, Pierre-Olivier Bouee
CEO Investment Banking and Capital Markets, James L. Amine
Chief Risk Officer, Joachim Oechslin, age 45
CEO Swiss Universal Bank, Thomas P. Gottstein
CEO International Wealth Management, Iqbal Khan
CEO Global Markets, Brian Chin
Head of Integration; Executive Vice Chairman Credit Suisse (USA), Richard E. Thornburgh, age 65
Chairman, Urs Rohner, age 57
Vice Chair and Lead Independent Director, Noreen Doyle, age 67
Auditors: KPMG AG

LOCATIONS

HQ: Credit Suisse Group
Paradeplatz 8, Zurich CH 8001
Phone: (41) 44 333 6607   **Fax:** (41) 44 333 1790
Web: www.credit-suisse.com

2014 Sales

	% total
Americas	42
Switzerland	31
EMEA	17
Asia Pacific	10
Total	**100**

PRODUCTS/OPERATIONS

2014 Sales

	% of total
Net interest income	35
Non-Interest	
Commissions & fees	50
Trading revenues	8
Other	7
Total	**100**

2014 Sales

	% of total
Private Banking & Wealth Management	48
Investment Banking	48
Non-Controlling interest with SEI	2
Corporte Center	2
Total	**100**

COMPETITORS

AEGON	JPMorgan Chase
Barclays	Mitsubishi UFJ
Citigroup	Financial Group
Deutsche Bank	Mizuho Financial
Goldman Sachs	Morgan Stanley
Grupo Santander	Nomura Securities
HSBC	TD Bank
ING	UBS

HISTORICAL FINANCIALS
Company Type: Public

Income Statement
FYE: December 31

	ASSETS ($ mil.)	NET INCOME ($ mil.)	INCOME AS % OF ASSETS	EMPLOYEES
12/15	826,505	(2,964)	—	48,200
12/14	931,534	1,895	0.2%	45,800
12/13	979,520	2,610	0.3%	46,000
12/12	1,008,171	1,617	0.2%	47,400
12/11	1,115,189	2,075	0.2%	49,700
Annual Growth	**(7.2%)**	—	—	**(0.8%)**

2015 Year-End Financials

Return on assets: (-0.3%)	Dividends
Return on equity: (-6.6%)	Yield: 5.5%
Long-term debt ($ mil.): —	Payout: —
No. of shares (mil.): 1,951	Market value ($ mil.): 42,327
Sales ($ mil): 23,962	

	STOCK PRICE ($) FY Close	P/E High/Low		PER SHARE ($) Earnings	Dividends	Book Value
12/15	21.69	—	—	(1.74)	1.20	22.90
12/14	25.08	28	22	1.08	0.79	27.78
12/13	31.04	28	21	1.37	0.14	29.74
12/12	24.56	33	19	0.98	0.82	30.04
12/11	23.48	35	15	1.45	1.36	29.33
Annual Growth	**(2.0%)**	—	—	—	**(3.1%)**	**(6.0%)**

Credito Emiliano Spa Credem Reggio Emilia

Being in the middle isn't always such a bad thing. Just ask Credito Emiliano one of Italy's leading midsized bank holding companies. Through its 20 financial subsidiaries and affiliates Credito Emiliano (also known as Credem) offers a host of retail commercial and institutional banking services through some 590 branches across Italy. In addition to its lending and deposit products the financial group offers life and liability insurance pensions asset management leasing and various corporate financial services. Credem Holding owned by the Maramotti family (known in fashion circles for its design house Max Mara) controls the company. Operations include Banca Euromobiliare (private banking and asset management) Abaxbank (investment banking) Credem International (based in Luxembourg) Credemleasing Credemfactor (factoring) Creacasa (mortgage lending) CredemVita (life insurance) and CredemAssicurazioni (insurance).

Credem which has been growing through the opening of new branches had been avoiding the consolidation wave sweeping its home country but planned to continue to open or buy new offices. The bank is focusing on further developing its services catering to SMEs (small and medium-sized enterprises) and individuals.

In 2008 Credem bought the remaining 50% of CredemAssicurazioni's share capital from Assurance Mutelles increasing its equity stake in the insurance company to 100%. That same year subsidiary Banca Euromobiliare acquired the asset management division of Citibank International involving the transfer of five Italian branches. Credem also acquired 33 branches and 2 corporate

centers from Banca Popolare di Verona-San Geminiano e San Prospero.

There's more than money in Credem's vaults: The bank also stores more than 440000 wheels of Parmesan cheese worth $187 million produced in the region. The practice dates back to 1953 when the bank began using cheese as loan collateral.

EXECUTIVES

President Titolare, GIORGIO FERRARI
Vice Presidente, FRANCO TERRACHINI
Vice Presidente, LUIGI MARAMOTTI
Vice Presidente, LUCIO IGINO ZANON DI VALGIURATA
Consigliere, BENEDETTO GIOVANNI MARIA RENDA
Consigliere, ROMANO ALFIERI
Consigliere, ENRICO CORRADI
Consigliere, Ugo Medici
Consigliere, VINCENZO CALANDRA BUONAURA

LOCATIONS

HQ: Credito Emiliano Spa Credem Reggio Emilia
Via Emilia San Pietro 4, Reggio Emilia 42100
Phone: (39) 522 5821   **Fax:** (39) 522 433969
Web: www.credem.it

2008 Sales

	% of total
Italy	
North-central	63
Southern & islands	35
Other countries	2
Total	**100**

PRODUCTS/OPERATIONS

2008 Sales

	% of total
Retail banking	59
Corporate loans	16
Investment banking	-
Wealth management	5
Other	20
Total	**100**

COMPETITORS

Antonveneta	Intesa Sanpaolo
BPER-Emilia Romagna	Mediobanca
Banca Popolare di	Monte dei Paschi di
Milano	Siena
Interbanca	UniCredit

HISTORICAL FINANCIALS
Company Type: Public

Income Statement
FYE: December 31

	ASSETS ($ mil.)	NET INCOME ($ mil.)	INCOME AS % OF ASSETS	EMPLOYEES
12/15	40,796	180	0.4%	5,516
12/14	42,292	184	0.4%	5,327
12/13	43,409	159	0.4%	6,186
12/12	40,528	159	0.4%	6,041
12/11	40,222	124	0.3%	5,051
Annual Growth	**0.4%**	**9.7%**	—	**2.2%**

2015 Year-End Financials

Return on assets: 0.4%	Dividends
Return on equity: 6.8%	Yield: —
Long-term debt ($ mil.): —	Payout: —
No. of shares (mil.): 331	Market value ($ mil.): —
Sales ($ mil): 2,207	

	STOCK PRICE ($) FY Close	P/E High/Low	PER SHARE ($) Earnings	Dividends	Book Value
12/15	0.00	—	0.54	0.00	8.14
Annual Growth	—	— —	—	—	—

CRH Plc

CRH has built its business upon building materials. Through subsidiaries (including Oldcastle) the international company makes and distributes cement concrete aggregate glass and asphalt for commercial residential and infrastructure projects across the globe. CRH has some 4000 operating locations and operates more than 700 wholesale and retail building supply stores under the Professional Builders Merchants GAMMA and Allied Building Products brands. With a presence in some 35 countries CRH has become the top supplier of building materials in North America and the third-largest worldwide.

OperationsCRH's operations are divided into six segments based on its largest service lines in the Americas and Europe. Its Europe Heavyside businesses (which make up 20% of CRH's total revenue) manufacture and supply cement aggregates precast and ready-mixed concrete concrete landscaping and asphalt products while its Americas Materials businesses (nearly 30% of revenue) provide similar products in the Americas. The company's Europe Distribution businesses (20% of revenue) consist of its Do-It-Yourself (DIY) General Merchants and Sanitary Heating and Plumbing (SHAP) businesses that supply bricks cement sanitary heating plumbing and other building products to consumers and small and medium-sized builders. Its Europe Lightside businesses (5% of revenue) make and sell construction accessories shutters and awnings fencing and composite access chambers.

CRH's Americas Products businesses (more than 15% of revenue) produce and sell concrete masonry and hardscapes clay brick packaged lawn and garden products cement mixes fencing utility drainage and other construction products. Its Americas Distribution businesses (nearly 10% of revenue) supply exterior products like roofing and siding as well as interior products like gypsum wallboard metal studs and acoustical ceiling systems. Geographic ReachWhile Ireland-based CRH operates in more than 35 countries it generates more than 50% of its sales in the US. More than 10% of sales come from countries in the Benelux region (mainly the Netherlands) while less than 2% of its sales come from its home country. The company also supplies materials in emerging markets in Asia Eastern Europe and South America. Financial PerformanceNote: Growth rates may differ after conversion to US dollars.

CRH has struggled to grow its revenues and profits in recent years as the sluggish housing markets and overall economies across Europe have held back demand for its products. CRH's sales rose by 5% to euro 18.9 billion ($23 billion) in 2014 mostly thanks to higher demand for its products in the US as the housing market and overall economy picked up steam. Business in Europe picked up as well thanks to favorable early season weather while like-for-like sales picked up by 6% in the region.

Higher sales and gains from the sale of discontinued operations in 2014 pushed CRH's profits up

to euro 582 million ($707 million) compared to a loss of euro 296 million in 2013. CRH's operating cash levels jumped by 13% to euro 1.2 billion ($1.46 billion) thanks to higher cash earnings.

Strategy

Since the company's formation in 1970 acquisitions have been a key part of CRH's growth strategy. The company has historically targeted growth across all business divisions in both developed and emerging regions making strategic bolt-on acquisitions each year. After a brief break from acquisitions after the financial crisis CRH has resumed making acquisitions making its biggest deal yet in 2015 after purchasing cement facilities from rivals Lafarge and Holcim to boost its production capacity and geographic reach.

While the company is growing in some areas it is making cuts in others –particularly in the US. In 2014 the company announced a multi-year divestment program intended to streamline operations to prepare for future growth and make acquisitions that align with that goal. That year it divested 16 units realizing total proceeds of euro 350 million; most had been bolt-on acquisitions for its existing operations in the Americas. Late in 2014 CRH also announced plans to sell its UK clay and concrete businesses and its US clay business to European funds managed by Bain Capital for £414 million.

Mergers and AcquisitionsIn August 2015 CRH purchased cement assets from Holcim Ltd. and Lafarge SA for a total of euro 6.5 billion ($7.3 billion) marking its largest acquisition to date. The deal bolstered the company's production capacity and expanded its operations in Canada Brazil the Philippines and several countries in Europe.

EXECUTIVES

Finance Director, Maeve Carton, age 57
Business Development Director Europe Materials Division, Albert Manifold, age 53
Chairman, Nicky Hartery, age 64
Auditors: Ernst & Young

LOCATIONS

HQ: CRH Plc
Belgard Castle, Clondalkin, Dublin 22
Phone: (353) 1 404 1000   **Fax:** (353) 1 404 1007
Web: www.crh.com

2014 Sales

	% of total
Europe	
Heavysie	21
Distribution	21
Lightside	5
Americas	
Materials	27
Products	17
Distribution	9
Total	**100**

PRODUCTS/OPERATIONS

Selected Activities and Products

Materials
  Aggregates
  Agricultural and chemical lime
  Asphalt
  Cement
  Concrete products
  Ready-mixed concrete
Products
  Architectural concrete
  Building products
  Building envelope products
  Construction accessories
  Clay facing bricks pavers and blocks
  Structural concrete
Distribution
  Builders merchants
  DIY stores

COMPETITORS

BUZZI UNICEM	Kingspan
Boral	LafargeHolcim
CEMEX	Marshalls
CIMPOR	Martin Marietta
Cementos de Chihuahua	Materials
Ciments Fran§ais	Saint-Gobain
Dyckerhoff	Tarmac
Grafton Group	Titan Cement
HeidelbergCement	Travis Perkins
Home Depot	Vulcan Materials
Imerys	Wienerberger
Italcementi	

HISTORICAL FINANCIALS
Company Type: Public

Income Statement
FYE: December 31

	REVENUE ($ mil.)	NET INCOME ($ mil.)	NET PROFIT MARGIN	EMPLOYEES
12/15	25,743	788	3.1%	78,106
12/14	22,987	707	3.1%	75,706
12/13	24,823	(407)	—	75,642
12/12	24,593	727	3.0%	76,175
12/11	23,386	763	3.3%	76,433
Annual Growth	**2.4%**	**0.8%**	**—**	**0.5%**

2015 Year-End Financials

Debt ratio: 31.3%
Return on equity: 6.2%
Cash ($ mil.): 2,742
Current ratio: 1.48
Long-term debt ($ mil.): 9,220
No. of shares (mil.): 823
Dividends
  Yield: 2.3%
  Payout: 70.1%
Market value ($ mil.): 23,722

	STOCK PRICE ($) FY Close	P/E High/Low	PER SHARE ($) Earnings	Dividends	Book Value
12/15	28.82	34 23	0.97	0.69	17.22
12/14	24.01	33 25	0.96	0.84	16.61
12/13	25.55	— —	(0.56)	0.82	18.14
12/12	20.34	29 23	1.01	0.80	19.12
12/11	19.82	27 17	1.07	0.81	18.91
Annual Growth	**9.8%**	**— —**	**(2.5%)**	**(4.0%)**	**(2.3%)**

CRRC Corp Ltd

Auditors: Deloitte Touche Tohmatsu Certified Public Accountants LLP

LOCATIONS

HQ: CRRC Corp Ltd
No. 16 Central West Fourth Ring Road, Haidian District, Beijing 100036
Phone: (86) 10 5186 2188   **Fax:** (86) 10 6398 4785
Web: www.crrcgc.cc

HISTORICAL FINANCIALS
Company Type: Public

Income Statement
FYE: December 31

	REVENUE ($ mil.)	NET INCOME ($ mil.)	NET PROFIT MARGIN	EMPLOYEES
12/15	36,612	1,819	5.0%	186,963
12/14	18,999	856	4.5%	88,925
12/13	15,944	683	4.3%	86,509
12/12	14,279	643	4.5%	85,181
12/11	12,632	613	4.9%	86,058
Annual Growth	**30.5%**	**31.2%**	**—**	**21.4%**

2015 Year-End Financials

Debt ratio: 1.4%
Return on equity: 17.2%
Cash ($ mil.): 5,351
Current ratio: 1.22
Long-term debt ($ mil.): 2,204

No. of shares (mil.): —
Dividends
  Yield: —
  Payout: —
Market value ($ mil.): —

STOCK PRICE ($) FY Close	P/E High/Low		PER SHARE ($) Earnings	Dividends	Book Value
12/15	1.22	3	2	0.07	0.00	0.55
Annual Growth	—	—	—	—	—	—

CTBC Financial Holding Co Ltd

Chinatrust Financial Holding (CFHC) is one of Taiwan's largest financial services groups. It operates Chinatrust Commercial Bank which has more than 140 domestic branches and more than 70 overseas. The group provides general banking services including corporate and consumer loans financial consulting checking and savings accounts letters of credit commercial drafts collections and payments and credit cards. It also offers property/casualty insurance life insurance investments and other related financial services. Overseas the bank operates subsidiaries in the US Canada the Philippines and Indonesia. The predecessor to the family-owned CFHC was founded in 1966.

EXECUTIVES

Head Global Capital Market Group, Larry Hsu
Head Legal and Compliance Division, Aaron King
President and CEO Global Institutional Banking, James Chen
CEO Global Retail Banking; Head International Private Banking Division, Albert Lee
CEO Cards and Payment, I. Cheng Liu
Head Global Risk Management Group, Jack T.K. Cheng
Head Taiwan Region Group Institutional Banking, Openmind Yeh
Acting Head Global General Administration Group, Yong Jin Chen
Head Cards and Payment Group, Amy H.C. Lin
Head Taiwan Region Group Retail Banking, Amy Yang
Head Japan Business Division, James Y.G. Chen
Head Public Relations and Public Welfare Division, Roger Kao
Chief Strategy Officer, Frank Shih
Head Overseas Division Retail Banking, Peter Wei
Acting Head Merchant Banking Division, Boshan Hsu
Head Cross-border Financial Business Division, Ching Chuan Chen
Acting Head Digital Banking Division, Meihsun Su
Head Information Service Division, William Chu
Chairman, Chao Chin Tung
Vice Chairman, Morris Li
Auditors: KPMG

LOCATIONS

HQ: CTBC Financial Holding Co Ltd
27 & 29F., No. 168, Jingmao 2nd Road, Nangang District, Taipei 115
Phone: (886) 2 3327 7777
Web: www.ctbcholding.com

COMPETITORS

Cathay Financial Holding	Fubon Financial
Chang Hwa Bank	Hua Nan Financial
E.Sun	Mega Financial
East West Bancorp	Shin Kong
First Financial Holding	SinoPac Holdings
	Taishin
	Taiwan Business Bank

HISTORICAL FINANCIALS

Company Type: Public

Income Statement

FYE: December 31

	ASSETS ($ mil.)	NET INCOME ($ mil.)	INCOME AS % OF ASSETS	EMPLOYEES
12/15	139,872	1,077	0.8%	0
12/14	115,418	1,245	1.1%	0
12/13	81,308	721	0.9%	0
12/12	72,825	733	1.0%	13,107
12/11	66,632	603	0.9%	12,568
Annual Growth	20.4%	15.6%	—	—

2015 Year-End Financials

Return on assets: 0.8%
Return on equity: 13.9%
Long-term debt ($ mil.): —
No. of shares (mil.): —
Sales ($ mil.): 7,211

Dividends
  Yield: —
  Payout: —
Market value ($ mil.): —

Dai-ichi Life Holdings Inc

Auditors: Ernst & Young ShinNihon LLC

LOCATIONS

HQ: Dai-ichi Life Holdings Inc
1-13-1 Yuraku-cho, Chiyoda-ku, Tokyo 100-8411
Phone: (81) 3 3216 1211
Web: www.dai-ichi-life.co.jp

HISTORICAL FINANCIALS

Company Type: Public

Income Statement

FYE: March 31

	REVENUE ($ mil.)	NET INCOME ($ mil.)	NET PROFIT MARGIN	EMPLOYEES
03/16	60,770	1,589	2.6%	61,446
03/15	59,160	1,187	2.0%	60,647
03/14	54,963	755	1.4%	59,512
03/13	52,947	344	0.7%	60,771
03/12	55,775	248	0.4%	60,305
Annual Growth	2.2%	59.1%	—	0.5%

2016 Year-End Financials

Debt ratio: —
Return on equity: 5.4%
Cash ($ mil.): 8,289
Current ratio: 12.27
Long-term debt ($ mil.): —
No. of shares (mil.): 1,191
Dividends
  Yield: 0.0%
  Payout: 18.6%
Market value ($ mil.): 14,711

	STOCK PRICE ($) FY Close	P/E High/Low		PER SHARE ($) Earnings	Dividends	Book Value
03/16	12.35	0	0	1.34	0.25	21.93
03/15	14.00	0	0	1.04	0.00	24.98
03/14	15.30	—	—	0.76	0.00	18.87
03/13	1,400.00	—	—	0.35	0.00	17.53
03/12	1,050.52	—	—	0.25	0.00	12.09
Annual Growth	(67.1%)	—	—	51.9%	—	16.0%

Daikin Industries, Ltd.

To "air" is human and to have air conditioning divine. Founded in 1924 Daikin Industries makes air conditioning and refrigeration products for residential and industrial use worldwide. Residential products include air cleaners dehumidifiers and air conditioners; industrial products range from infrared ceramic space heaters to marine vessel air conditioners. Daikin also has chemicals (fluorocarbons surfactants and mold-release agents) oil hydraulics and defense divisions; combined they account for close to 15% of revenues. The company's acquisition of O.Y.L. Industries made it the #1 air conditioning maker after Carrier.

Overall Daikin's air conditioning segment accounted for around 87% of sales in fiscal 2011. By becoming the world's top air conditioning and refrigeration manufacturer Daikin has moved into new markets and expanded its product lineup. The O.Y.L. acquisition allowed Daikin to expand into the US. The company plans to further strengthen its operations in North America as well as in Europe and Asia. Daikin has also set its sights on new markets such as Brazil China and India. To this end Daikin in November 2012 acquired Houston-based residential HVAC maker and distributor Goodman Global Group. The $3.7-billion deal gives Daikin a necessary foot in the door in North America's ducted-style residential unitary HVAC sector and a network of 900-plus distribution points.

In Brazil Daikin has announced the building of a new factory for air conditioning equipment in the city of Mogi das Cruzes located on the outskirts of Sao Paulo. Production will begin at the start of 2014. Now that the affluent class in Brazil is increasing the demand for residential use of air conditioning is expected to rapidly grow. According to Daikin the air conditioning market in Brazil experienced sales of roughly 180 billion yen ($2.2 billion) for fiscal 2010 but in 2015 the market is expected to increase to over 400 billion yen ($4.8 billion).

The company has already established itself in China's air conditioner market. Daikin teamed with China-based Gree Electric Appliances to manufacture economical residential air conditioners. The venture targets markets where penetration is low. The deal is also part of the company's plan to promote energy-efficient appliances such as inverter products and heat pump systems that use less energy.

Daikin has been manufacturing commercial air conditioners in India since fiscal 2010 and in April 2011 began marketing operations. The company has identified India as one of its most important strategic markets for the next five years.

Daikin's chemical segment which accounts for about 10% of sales makes a wide range of fluorochemicals. The company's strategic goal is to corner the fluorochemical segment especially China's expanding economy. To that end Daikin decided to manufacture fluoropolymer coatings through its Changshu factory part of the Daikin Fluorochemicals (China) Co. Ltd.. It will manufactures and sell fluorochemical products in China. Production will commence around June 2013.

EXECUTIVES

Senior Executive Officer Air Conditioning Business Director and Chairman Daikin Fluorochemicals (China) Co. Ltd, Ken Tayano, age 70
President and COO, Masanori Togawa, age 68
Senior Executive Officer Leader of the GRT Project and Director, Takashi Matsuzaki, age 58

Senior Executive Officer Air Conditioning Europe
Africa and Middle East (EMEA) and Director,
Masatsugu Minaka, age 63
Senior Executive Officer IT Development and
Director, Koichi Takahashi, age 60
Senior Executive Officer Leader of ATT Project
and Leader of SSJ Project and Director, Jiro
Tomita, age 67
Chairman and CEO, Noriyuki Inoue, age 81
Auditors: Deloitte Touche Tohmatsu LLC

LOCATIONS

HQ: Daikin Industries, Ltd.
  Umeda Center Bldg., 2-4-12 Nakazaki-Nishi, Kita-ku,
  Osaka 530-8323
Phone: (81) 6 6373 4356
Web: www.daikin.com

2015 sales

	% of total
Japan	26
USA	23
China	18
Europe	13
Asia and Oceania	14
Other regions	6
Total	100

PRODUCTS/OPERATIONS

2015 Sales

	% of total
Air conditioning	89
Chemicals	8
Other	3
Total	100

Selected Products and Operations

Air Conditioning and Refrigerator Division
  Commercial air cleaners
  Commercial air conditioners
  Container refrigeration
  Large-scale refrigerators
  Marine vessel air conditioners and refrigerators
  Marine-type container refrigeration units
  Room air cleaners
  Room air conditioners
Chemical Division
  Equipment and systems
  Fluorocarbon gas
  Synthesized products
Oil Hydraulics Division
  Centralized lubrication units and systems
  Oil hydraulic products for industrial machinery
  Oil hydraulic products for mobile equipment
Defense Systems Division
  Aircraft components
  Ammunition
  Warheads for aerial torpedoes

COMPETITORS

Brooks Automation	Lockheed Martin
Dyneon	Orbital ATK
Ingersoll-Rand Climate	Paloma Group
Solutions	Pribuss Engineering
Johnson Controls	Tecumseh Products
Lennox	Trane Inc.

HISTORICAL FINANCIALS

Company Type: Public

Income Statement

FYE: March 31

	REVENUE ($ mil.)	NET INCOME ($ mil.)	NET PROFIT MARGIN	EMPLOYEES
03/16	18,199	1,219	6.7%	68,598
03/15	15,961	997	6.2%	66,289
03/14	17,274	890	5.2%	56,240
03/13	13,719	463	3.4%	51,398
03/12	14,856	501	3.4%	44,110
Annual Growth	5.2%	24.9%	—	11.7%

2016 Year-End Financials

Debt ratio: 0.2%
Return on equity: 13.3%
Cash ($ mil.): 2,593
Current ratio: 1.89
Long-term debt ($ mil.): 4,269
No. of shares (mil.): 292
Dividends
  Yield: 1.2%
  Payout: 48.7%
Market value ($ mil.): 43,554

	STOCK PRICE ($) FY Close	P/E High/Low		PER SHARE ($) Earnings	Dividends	Book Value
03/16	149.14	0	0	4.18	1.87	30.97
03/15	134.25	0	0	3.42	1.20	29.30
03/14	112.78	—	—	3.05	0.81	27.37
03/13	79.00	—	—	1.59	0.00	23.22
03/12	53.72	—	—	1.72	0.00	21.61
Annual Growth	29.1%	—	—	24.8%	—	9.4%

Daimler AG

Daimler's cars may stop on a dime but they cost a little more than that. Daimler's passenger car business Mercedes-Benz includes luxury brands Mercedes and Maybach as well as compact hybrid and electric models including its smart brand. Other major auto brands include Freightliner Western Star BharatBenz Fuso Setra and Thomas Built Buses while financial services brands include Mercedes-Benz Bank Mercedes-Benz Financial moovel and car2go. Its Daimler Trucks North America unit manufactures heavy-trucks in the US. Daimler sells its vehicles in 40 countries but Europe represents around 35% of its net sales.

OperationsThe company operates through five business segments: Mercedes-Benz Cars (55% of net sales) Daimler Trucks (23%) Mercedes-Benz Vans (7%) Daimler Buses (3%) and Daimler Financial Services (12%). Daimler distributes its vehicles in around 200 countries worldwide.

Financial Performance

After posting four straight years of revenue growth Daimler saw its revenues dip 3% from $162 billion in 2013 to $158 billion in 2014. Profits also declined 10% from $9 billion to roughly $8.5 billion over that same time period due to higher interest tax rates and increased expenses.

Strategy

The company's blueprint for growth involves the strengthening of its core business within the emerging markets of Brazil Russia India and China. It is also focused on enhancing its green technologies and vehicular safety operations. It will invest approximately euro 11 billion in property plant and equipment throughout 2015 and 2016 as well as more than euro 13 billion in research and development projects.

With its continued focus on the Chinese markets the company in 2013 opened a new production plant for four-cylinder engines in China along with its biggest training center in the world in 2014. Daimler also plans to launch a new research and development center in Beijing.

For the Brazilian markets the company will begin manufacturing its C‑Class and the GLA brands for the local market in Brazil in 2016. The company will also establish its local bus manufacturing operations in India in 2015.

HISTORY

Company Background

Daimler-Benz was formed by the merger of two German motor companies –Daimler and Benz –in 1926. Daimler-Benz bought Auto Union (Audi) in 1958 (sold to Volkswagen in 1966). The company's Mercedes cars gained international fame and sales expanded worldwide in the 1970s.

Daimler-Benz diversified in the 1980s buying aerospace heavy truck (Freightliner) and consumer and industrial electrical companies. Although diversification continued sales slowed. Losses at its aerospace unit forced Daimler-Benz into the red in 1995. Also that year the company and ABB Asea Brown Boveri (now ABB) formed joint venture Adtranz the #1 train maker in the world and Jürgen Schrempp became chairman of the management board (CEO).

In 1998 Daimler-Benz acquired Chrysler and introduced a subcompact car the smart in Europe. The newly formed DaimlerChrysler rolled both companies' financial services units into Daimler-Chrysler Interservices (DEBIS) in 1999.

EXECUTIVES

Chairman Management Board; Head Mercedes-Benz Cars, Dieter Zetsche, age 63, $1,530,000 total compensation
Member Management Board; Head Daimler Trucks and Buses Division, Wolfgang Bernhard, age 56
Member Management Board Finance and Controlling Daimler Financial Services, Bodo Uebber, age 56, $660,000 total compensation
Member Management Board; Head Greater China, Hubertus Troska
Member Management Board; Head Marketing and Sales, Ola K ¤llenius
CEO Daimler Trucks Korea, Cho Kyu-Sang
President and CEO Daimler Middle East and Levant, Mark De Haes
Chairman Supervisory Board, Manfred Bischoff, age 74
Auditors: KPMG AG Wirtschaftsprufungsgesellschaft

LOCATIONS

HQ: Daimler AG
  Mercedesstrasse 137, Stuttgart D-70327
Phone: (49) 711 17 97875   Fax: (49) 711 17 94075
Web: www.daimler.com

PRODUCTS/OPERATIONS

Selected Divisions and Brands

Mercedes-Benz Cars
  Maybach
  Mercedes-Benz
  smart
Daimler Trucks
  Freightliner
  Mitsubishi Fuso
  Mercedez-Benz
  Western Star Trucks
Daimler Financial Services
  Banking (Mercedes-Benz Bank)
  Fleet management
  Insurance
  Leasing and financing
Mercedes-Benz Vans
Daimler Buses
  Mercedes-Benz (city buses coaches interurban minibuses)
  Mercedes-Benz chassis
  Mitsubishi Fuso (large buses midi-sized buses minibuses)
  Orion (city buses)
  Setra (coaches interurban buses)
  Thomas Built Buses (hybrid school bus school and activity buses)

COMPETITORS

BMW	PACCAR
Fiat Chrysler	PROTON Holdings
Ford Motor	Peugeot
Fuji Heavy Industries	Porsche

General Motors
Honda
Isuzu
Land Rover
MAN
Navistar International
Nissan
Renault
Scania
Toyota
Volkswagen
Volvo
ZAP

HISTORICAL FINANCIALS
Company Type: Public

Income Statement
FYE: December 31

	REVENUE ($ mil.)	NET INCOME ($ mil.)	NET PROFIT MARGIN	EMPLOYEES
12/15	162,801	9,175	5.6%	248,015
12/14	157,860	8,462	5.4%	279,972
12/13	162,430	9,419	5.8%	274,616
12/12	150,649	8,033	5.3%	275,087
12/11	137,804	7,329	5.3%	271,370
Annual Growth	4.3%	5.8%	—	(2.2%)

2015 Year-End Financials

Debt ratio: 50.7%
Return on equity: 17.3%
Cash ($ mil.): 10,822
Current ratio: 1.19
Long-term debt ($ mil.): 65,168
No. of shares (mil.): 1,069
Dividends
  Yield: 2.9%
  Payout: 31.1%
Market value ($ mil.): 89,492

	STOCK PRICE ($) FY Close	P/E High/Low		PER SHARE ($) Earnings	Dividends	Book Value
12/15	83.65	13	9	8.57	2.65	54.53
12/14	82.40	13	10	7.91	3.12	49.61
12/13	86.92	14	8	8.81	2.89	54.93
12/12	54.97	11	8	7.53	2.88	54.17
12/11	43.86	14	7	6.87	2.39	48.07
Annual Growth	17.5%	—	—	5.7%	2.6%	3.2%

Daishi Bank, Ltd.

If everything old is new again then Daishi Bank is hot off the presses. The regional bank which was founded in 1873 and lays claim to being the oldest in Japan serves primarily the Niigata prefecture through some 120 offices there. Daishi Bank also has about 10 additional offices (two in Tokyo and 10 in other prefectures). Daishi Bank and it subsidiaries offer individuals and businesses a range of traditional deposit banking and other products and services including business matching business consulting credit cards credit guarantee credit card settlement and processing financial advice investment banking investment products leasing and venture capital.

EXECUTIVES

President, FUJIO NAMIKI
Chairman, Masahide Nakamura
Auditors: KPMG AZSA LLC

LOCATIONS

HQ: Daishi Bank, Ltd.
  1071-1 Higashiborimae-dori 7-bancho, Chuo-ku, Niigata 951-8066
Phone: (81) 25 222 4111
Web: www.daishi-bank.co.jp

PRODUCTS/OPERATIONS

COMPETITORS

Hachijuni Bank
Hokuetsu Bank Ltd.
Mizuho Financial
Resona
Sumitomo Mitsui

HISTORICAL FINANCIALS
Company Type: Public

Income Statement
FYE: March 31

	ASSETS ($ mil.)	NET INCOME ($ mil.)	INCOME AS % OF ASSETS	EMPLOYEES
03/16	47,572	128	0.3%	3,686
03/15	43,288	118	0.3%	3,673
03/14	47,735	124	0.3%	2,610
03/13	52,032	114	0.2%	2,635
03/12	57,087	118	0.2%	2,651
Annual Growth	(4.5%)	2.0%		8.6%

2016 Year-End Financials

Return on assets: 0.2%
Return on equity: 4.7%
Long-term debt ($ mil.): —
No. of shares (mil.): 344
Sales ($ mil): 872
Dividends
  Yield: —
  Payout: —
Market value ($ mil.): —

Daiwa House Industry Co Ltd

More than a half-century ago Daiwa House Industry called its first prefabricated homes "Pipe Houses" because they were made from steel pipes. Today the group's eight businesses build lease sell and manage single-family houses condominiums and commercial buildings. Daiwa House's health and leisure segment manages and operates resort hotels golf courses fitness clubs and health care facilities. Other offerings include agency services of-fice relocation and staffing services and vehicle and equipment leasing. Daiwa House Industry has more than 100 branches and factories throughout Japan and in China and Vietnam.

Operations

The company has built leased and/or managed some 1.5 million single-family homes more than 30000 commercial facilities and more than 60000 health care facilities.

Financial Performance

Daiwa House's sales increased 35% to ¥2.7 trillion in fiscal 2013 (ended March). The rise was driven by commercial facilities and rental housing. Net income rose 54% to ¥102 billion over the same period largely due to the increased revenues. Cash flow from operations fell 52% to ¥78.5 billion largely as a result of changes in current assets and liabilities.

Strategy

In 2013 Daiwa House acquired Fujita Corp. a construction business active in Japan and beyond. The purchase strengthens Daiwa House's operations beyond Japan as Fujita is one of the top Japanese contractors in China and supports its Chinese clients operations abroad in countries such as Mexico and Vietnam. Daiwa plans to use Fujita's overseas platform to expand its own presence abroad as well as in the corporate and commercial construction markets.

Japan's aging and shrinking population doesn't favor new single-family home construction so Daiwa House has increasingly focused on in its commercial and hotel operations as well as rental housing condominiums and home renovations. The company also operates about a dozen Daiwa Roynet business hotels.

In fiscal 2015 Daiwa House entered into a part-nership with Malaysian developer Sunway Berhad to develop and sell prefabricated landed houses in Malaysia.

EXECUTIVES

EVP and CFO, Tetsuji Ogawa, age 75
President Nihon Jyutaku Ryutu, Minoru Fujita
President and COO, Naotake Ohno, age 68
Chairman and CEO, Takeo Higuchi, age 78
Senior Managing Executive Officer, Takuya Ishibashi, age 63
Senior Managing Executive Officer, Tatsushi Nishimura, age 67
President Daiwa Royal, Ken Harada
Senior Managing Executive Officer, Shigeru Numata, age 67
President Daiwa Logistics, Isamu Ogata, age 68
Senior Managing Executive Officer, Katsutomo Kawai, age 69
President Daiwa Lease, Shunsaku Morita
President Daiwa Odakyu Construction, Atsushi Kanakubo
President Daiwa Royal Golf, Seishu Umaoka
President Daiwa House Reform, Junichi Sugiura
President Daiwa House Life Support, Toshinori Inaguchi
President Osaka Marubiru, Haruyuki Yoshimoto
President Eneserve, Yoshio Kinoshita
President Higashi-Fuji, Masamichi Yagita
President Daiwa Energy, Hidekazu Matsushima
President Daiwa House Insurance, Shigeru Sasashita
President Fujita, Takuji Ueda
President Daiwa House Asset Management, Yuji Yamada
EVP, Tamio Ishibashi, age 61
President Daiwa Living Management, Masaru Akashi
President Daiwa Rakuda Industry, Masato Shima
President Daiwa Service, Tomoyuki Kido
President Global Community, Takashi Yamada
President Daiwa LifeNext, Yoshinori Watanabe
President Cosmos Initia, Yoshiyuki Takagi
President Daiwa Homes Online, Norio Togashi
President Daiwa Core Factory, Syuji Oda
President Daiwa Lantec, Kazuo Shimoe
President Daiwa Information Service, Katsuyuki Fujita
President Daiwa House REIT Management, Hirotaka Najima
President Media Tech, Mitsuo Adachi
President Daiyoshi Trust, Yoshihiro Oho
President Frameworx, Junichi Akiba
President Daiwa House Financial, Hiroshi Osada
President Royal Home Center, Masaaki Nakayama
President Daiwa Resort, Seiji Kushida
President Sports Club NAS, Yoshinari Shibayama
President Nishiwaki Royal Hotel, Hideaki Tomiyama
President Shinwa Agency, Nobuyuki Otsuji
President Daiwa House California, Takeshi Wakita
Auditors: Deloitte Touche Tohmatsu LLC

LOCATIONS

HQ: Daiwa House Industry Co Ltd
3-3-5 Umeda, Kita-ku, Osaka 530-8241
Phone: (81) 6 6342 1400   Fax: (81) 6 6342 1587
Web: www.daiwahouse.co.jp

PRODUCTS/OPERATIONS

2014 Sales

	% of total
Rental housing	24
Business and corporate facilities	21
Commercial facilities	15
Single-family housing	14
Condominiums	9
Existing homes	3
Other businesses	14
Total	**100**

COMPETITORS

HASEKO	Taisei
Nishimatsu Construction	Takenaka
Sekisui House	Toda
Shimizu	Tokyu Construction
Sumitomo Mitsui Construction	

HISTORICAL FINANCIALS

Company Type: Public

Income Statement

FYE: March 31

	REVENUE ($ mil.)	NET INCOME ($ mil.)	NET PROFIT MARGIN	EMPLOYEES
03/16	28,432	922	3.2%	57,095
03/15	23,426	976	4.2%	53,966
03/14	26,160	989	3.8%	32,628
03/13	21,340	704	3.3%	30,361
03/12	22,538	404	1.8%	27,130
Annual Growth	**6.0%**	**22.9%**	**—**	**20.4%**

2016 Year-End Financials

Debt ratio: 0.1%
Return on equity: 9.0%
Cash ($ mil.): 1,714
Current ratio: 1.36
Long-term debt ($ mil.): 3,524

No. of shares (mil.): 663
Dividends
Yield: 2.0%
Payout: 44.5%
Market value ($ mil.): 18,666

	STOCK PRICE ($) FY Close	P/E High/Low		PER SHARE ($) Earnings	Dividends	Book Value
03/16	28.12	0	0	1.39	0.57	15.70
03/15	19.72	1	0	1.48	0.51	13.95
03/14	169.35	—	—	1.56	5.47	14.59
03/13	196.35	—	—	1.22	0.00	13.50
03/12	131.71	—	—	0.70	0.00	13.86
Annual Growth	**(32.0%)**		**—**	**18.7%**	**—**	**3.2%**

Dalian Wanda Commercial Properties Co Ltd

Auditors: Ernst & Young

LOCATIONS

HQ: Dalian Wanda Commercial Properties Co Ltd
No. 539 Changjiang Road, Xigang District, Dalian, Liaoning Province
Phone: (86) 010 85853888 **Fax:** (86) 010 85853222
Web: www.wandaplazas.com

HISTORICAL FINANCIALS

Company Type: Public

Income Statement

FYE: December 31

	REVENUE ($ mil.)	NET INCOME ($ mil.)	NET PROFIT MARGIN	EMPLOYEES
12/15	19,124	4,614	24.1%	63,881
12/14	17,380	4,002	23.0%	60,674
12/13	14,333	4,060	28.3%	0
Annual Growth	**15.5%**	**6.6%**	**—**	**—**

2015 Year-End Financials

Debt ratio: 4.4%
Return on equity: 17.9%
Cash ($ mil.): 10,255
Current ratio: 0.97
Long-term debt ($ mil.): 22,282

No. of shares (mil.): —
Dividends
Yield: —
Payout: —
Market value ($ mil.): —

	STOCK PRICE ($) FY Close	P/E High/Low		PER SHARE ($) Earnings	Dividends	Book Value
12/15	5.65	1	1	1.02	0.00	6.14
12/14	0.00	—	—	1.05	0.00	5.50
12/13	0.00	—	—	1.09	0.00	4.79
Annual Growth	**—**	**—**	**—**	**(3.2%)**	**—**	**13.2%**

Danone

You say Danone I say Dannon; let's call the whole thing one of the largest dairy food and water producers in the world. The company is organized around four core activities: Fresh Dairy Products Waters Early Life Nutrition and Medical Nutrition. The #1 maker of fresh dairy products worldwide Danone sells dozens of global and regional yogurt brands including top-sellers Dannon and Activia functional brands like Actimel and DanActive and Greek yogurt brands Oikos and Danio. The company's evian Volvic Aqua water brands (among others) make it #2 worldwide in bottled water and Danone is also the world's #2 baby nutrition company. Its medical nutrition products are #1 in Europe. In 2016 Danone agreed to acquire organic food giant WhiteWave Foods for $12.5 billion.

HISTORY

In 1965 Antoine Riboud replaced his uncle as chairman of family-run Souchon-Neuvesel a Lyons France-based maker of glass bottles. Antoine quickly made a mark in this field —he merged the firm with Boussois a major French flat-glass manufacturer creating BSN in 1966.

Antoine enlarged BSN's glass business and filled the company's bottles by acquiring well-established beverage and food concerns. In 1970 BSN purchased Brasseries Kronenbourg (France's largest brewer) Societe Europeenne de Brasseries (another French brewer) and Evian (mineral water France). The 1972 acquisition of Glaverbel (Belgium) gave BSN 50% of Europe's flat-glass market. The next year BSN merged with France's Gervais Danone (yogurt cheese Panzani pasta; founded in 1919 and named after founder Isaac Carasso's son Daniel). This moved the company into pan-European brand-name foods.

Increasing energy costs depressed flat-glass earnings so BSN began divesting its flat-glass businesses. In the late 1970s it acquired interests in brewers in Belgium Spain and Italy.

BSN bought Dannon the leading US yogurt maker (co-founded by Daniel Carasso who had continued making Danone yogurt in France until WWII) in 1982. It established a strong presence in the Italian pasta market by buying stakes in Ponte (1985) and Agnesi (1986). BSN also purchased Generale Biscuit the world's #3 biscuit maker (1986) and RJR Nabisco's European cookie and snack-food business (1989).

In a series of acquisitions starting in 1986 BSN took over Italy and Spain's largest mineral water companies and several European pasta makers and other food companies. Adopting the name of its leading international brand BSN became Groupe Danone in 1994.

Antoine's son Franck succeeded him as chairman in 1996 and restructured the company to focus on three core businesses: dairy beverages (specifically water and beer) and biscuits. By 1997 Danone had begun shedding non-core grocery products. The company simultaneously stepped up acquisitions of dairy beer biscuit and water companies in developing markets.

The 1998 purchase of AquaPenn Spring Water for $112 million doubled its US water-bottling production capacity. Danone in 1999 completed a merger and subsequent sale of part of its BSN Emballage glass-packaging unit to UK buyout firm CVC Capital Partners for $1.2 billion; Danone retained 44% ownership. Thirsty for the #2 spot in US bottled water sales Danone gulped down McKesson Water (the #3 bottled water firm in the US after Nestle and Suntory) for $1.1 billion in 2000.

Also in 2000 Danone's joint venture Finalrealm (which includes several European equity firms) along with Burlington Biscuits Nabisco and HM Capital Partners (then called Hicks Muse Tate & Furst) acquired 87% of leading UK biscuit maker United Biscuits. Danone then bought Naya (bottled water Canada) and sold its brewing operations (#2 in Europe) to Scottish & Newcastle (later acquired by Heineken and Carlsberg) for more than $2.6 billion.

During 2001 Danone announced restructuring would shutter two LU biscuit plants and eliminate about 1800 jobs; the move met with strikes and legal battles. That same year having been bumped to the #2 spot in the US yogurt market (after General Mills' Yoplait brand) Danone acquired 40% of Stonyfield Farm the #4 yogurt brand in the US and ultimately came to own 84% of the company.

The company launched 2002 with a series of beverage acquisitions including Frucor (New Zealand) and Zywiec Zdroj (the top brand of water in Poland). Danone then struck a deal handing Coca-Cola the distribution and marketing of Evian in North America and formed a joint venture with Coke to distribute its lower-end water brands. Antoine Riboud died that same year at the age of 83.

Danone divested noncore companies during 2002 including the sale of its Italian meat and cheese business Galbani and its Kro Beer Brands (Kronenbourg 1664 brands) to Scottish & Newcastle. Then typical of its consolidation strategy later in 2002 Danone acquired the home and office water delivery companies Chateaud'eau (France) Patrimoine des Eaux du Quebec (Canada) and Canada's Sparkling Spring (now Aquaterra).

In 2004 Danone sold its 10% interest in the Australian dairy firm National Foods. Later that year it announced an alliance with Japanese dairy group Yakult Honsha to focus both companies' efforts with probiotics. Danone is a 20% shareholder of Yakult and has agreed not to increase its share holdings of Yakult for five years and not to pursue majority control for another five. Also in 2004 Danone acquired the Mexican bottled water company Arco Iris.

While its dairy and water businesses bubbled along nicely Danone found its cookies crumbling. Opting for a new recipe in 2004 it joined with Argentine food giant ARCOR Group to merge both companies' biscuits operations in South America. Later that same year Danone sold off its W&R Jacob Ltd. biscuits operations in Ireland to local company Fruitfield Foods. It also sold Italaquae its Italian bottled water business to LGR Holding.

Long after its departure from brewing in 2004 Danone was fined euro 1.5 million for forming a beer distribution cartel along with Heineken in 1996. In 2005 Danone and Coca-Cola ended their 2002 water-distribution joint venture with Coke buying out Danone's 49% share for about $100 million.

In 2005 Danone got out of the brewing business altogether with the sale of its 33% stake in Spanish brewer Mahou. It sold its HP Foods Group including Amoy Lea & Perrins and HP sauce brands to Heinz and its biscuits businesses in the UK and Ireland. That year it sold its US home and office water-delivery company DS Waters of America to investment firm Kelso & Company. Danone has increased its ownership of Russian dairy and beverage company Wimm-Bill-Dann Foods to almost 20%.

Due to slow sales for its chilled products and competition from lower-priced brands in 2006 Danone introduced Senjà (a soy-based yogurt) in France. It acquired Egyptian fresh dairy products company Olait (which it renamed Danone Dairy Egypt) and Algerian bottled water company Tessala. On the Asian front Danone acquired 23% of fruit-drink company China Huiyuan Juice Group and 51% of Wahaha. (It sold its interest in Huiyuan Juice in 2010.) In the Ukraine it bought fresh dairy company JSC Molochnyi Zavod. In the US it launched the Activia brand yogurt.

Because it wants to introduce more organic products in Europe in 2006 Danone announced the spending of $66 million on the expansion of its subsidiary Stonyfield Farm's New Hampshire production plant. (That year Stonyfield bought a 34% interest in Irish organic dairy Glenisk.)

In 2006 Danone sold its Amoy Asian sauce and chilled foods business to Ajinomoto exiting the sauce business altogether. It then sold virtually all of its grocery activities glass-container business its cheese and cured meat activities (Galbani) and its beer activities in Europe. It also sold New Zealand biscuits maker Griffins Food to investment firm Pacific Equity Partners.

Danone paid euro 12 billion (about $16 billion) for Numico maker of infant food and medical nutrition (nutritional bars and shakes) in 2007. The Numico products (Cow & Gate Dumex Mellin milupa NUTRICIA) joined Danone's bledina baby-food brand to create a wide array of well-known nutritional products for babies and adults. The purchase made Danone the largest baby-food maker in Europe.

Prior to announcing the Numico purchase Danone announced the sale of its cookie business to Kraft Foods; that deal closed in late 2007. At the time some analysts saw Danone as ripe for a takeover; hence the Numico deal was construed as a way for Danone to remain independent. (The acquisition was viewed as helping ward off predators who might have been attracted to the cash that Danone accrued as a result of the Kraft deal.) As part of its strategy to divest itself of all biscuit/cookie activities in 2009 the company ended its Indian joint venture with the Wadia Group. Danone sold its 50% interest in the operation ABI Holdings to Wadia.

Strengthening its business in Asia in 2007 Danone acquired all of the Japanese joint venture with Ajinomoto and Calpis that it did not already own. Renamed Danone Japan the operation man-

ufactures fresh products for the expanding Japanese dairy market.

Saying it wanted to "regain room for maneuver[ing]" in 2007 it sold off its 20% stake in and terminated its distribution agreement with Shanghai-based Bright Dairy. Danone cited no specifics surrounding the move but the company has had legal disputes with various joint-venture partners in China and India recently relating to how its brands are marketed and produced.

In late 2007 the company exited its joint venture with Chinese company Mengniu Dairy Group citing time frame and other condition difficulties. (Both companies agreed to the termination of the venture which was initiated in 2006.) Turning to South America that same year Danone acquired a 70% holding in Chile's fresh dairy company Vialat.

Among its divestments in 2008 in order to fulfill European Union requirements for its acquisition of Numico the company sold off its French baby milk and baby drinks businesses to Groupe Lactalis. That year it also sold its subsidiary Frucor a maker of non-alcoholic beverages in New Zealand and Australia as well as its international brands V and Mizone (with the exception of in China and Indonesia) to Suntory for some euro 600 million ($780 million).

Danone took full control of its South African joint venture Danone Clover in 2009. It purchased Clover's 45% stake for R1085 ($145 million). (Clover is one of South Africa's largest dairy companies.) Other partnerships include a joint venture with Weight Watchers formed in 2008. The 51% Weight Watchers-49% Danone operation provides weight-management services to the People's Republic of China.

Following its acquisition of a controlling interest in a venture with Russia's Unimilk in 2010 Danone sold its 18.4% stake in Wimm-Bill-Dann Foods back to the Russian dairy and juice producer for $470 million.

EXECUTIVES

Vice Chairman and Co-COO, Jacques Vincent, age 69, $1,529,800 total compensation
EVP Fresh Dairy Products, Thomas Kunz, age 59
CEO, Emmanuel Faber, age 53, $1,373,620 total compensation
Chairman President and CEO Stonyfield Farm, Gary Hirshberg
Deputy General Manager and Co-COO; Director, Bernard Hours, age 60, $2,863,620 total compensation
General Manager Medical Nutrition, Flemming Morgan, age 60
EVP Research and Development, Jean-Philippe Pare, age 58
Exec. VP Baby Nutrition; Member of the Executive Committee, Felix Garcia
EVP of Research & Development; Member of the Executive Committee, Jean-Philippe Pare
CFO and Member the Executive Committee, Pierre-Andre Terisse
General Manager South-Eastern Europe, Adrian Pascu
Chairman, Franck Riboud, age 60
Auditors: ERNST & YOUNG et Autres

LOCATIONS

HQ: Danone
17, Boulevard Haussmann, Paris 75009
Phone: (33) 1 44 35 20 20   **Fax:** (33) 1 44 35 26 95
Web: www.danone.com

2015 Sales

	% of total
Asia-Pacific Latin America Middle East & Africa	40
Europe	40
CIS & North America	20
Total	**100**

COMPETITORS

Abbott Nutrition	HP Hood
Ajinomoto	Heinz
Arla Foods	Kellogg
Associated British	Kerry Group
Foods	Lactalis
Beech-Nut	Leche Pascual
Blue Bell	Mead Johnson
China Mengniu Dairy	Metagenics
Coca-Cola	Nestle
Dairy Crest	Novartis
Dairy Farm	Ornua
International	Parmalat
Dairygold	PepsiCo
Dean Foods	Pfizer
Dr Pepper Snapple	Shanghai Bright Dairy
Group	& Food
Dreyer's	Sodiaal
Feihe	Unilever NV
Fonterra	Wells' Dairy
FrieslandCampina	Wessanen
General Mills	WhiteWave
Gerber Products	Wimm-Bill-Dann
Glanbia plc	Yili Group
Granarolo	

HISTORICAL FINANCIALS

Company Type: Public

Income Statement

FYE: December 31

	REVENUE ($ mil.)	NET INCOME ($ mil.)	NET PROFIT MARGIN	EMPLOYEES
12/15	24,411	1,396	5.7%	99,781
12/14	25,700	1,360	5.3%	99,927
12/13	29,321	1,957	6.7%	104,642
12/12	27,506	2,203	8.0%	102,401
12/11	24,986	2,161	8.7%	101,885
Annual Growth	(0.6%)	(10.3%)	—	(0.5%)

2015 Year-End Financials

Debt ratio: 36.8%	No. of shares (mil.): 615
Return on equity: 10.5%	Dividends
Cash ($ mil.): 565	Yield: 2.4%
Current ratio: 0.87	Payout: 14.4%
Long-term debt ($ mil.): 8,808	Market value ($ mil.): 8,373

	STOCK PRICE ($) FY Close	P/E High/Low		PER SHARE ($) Earnings	Dividends	Book Value
12/15	13.61	7	5	2.29	0.34	22.32
12/14	13.02	7	6	2.29	0.39	23.69
12/13	14.52	7	6	3.33	0.38	25.11
12/12	13.39	5	4	3.65	0.36	27.08
12/11	12.64	5	4	3.58	0.32	26.06
Annual Growth	1.9%	—	—	(10.6%)	1.3%	(3.8%)

Danske Bank A/S

When you're the largest bank in Denmark there's nowhere to grow but out. Danske Bank serves 3.7 million consumers and businesses through a network of 159 branches in Denmark; 45 branches in Finland (where it operates Sampo Bank); 39 branches in Sweden (Östgöta Enskilda Bank); 32 in Norway (Fokus Bank); and more than 50 branches in Ireland and Northern Ireland where it owns National Irish Bank and Northern Bank respectively. The company also has operations in Germany Poland Russia and the Baltic states. In addition to standard deposit and lending services Danske Bank offers asset management insurance leasing securities trading and research and real estate brokerage services.

Operations Danske Bank operates out of three divisions: Personal Banking Business Banking and Corporates & Institutions.

Personal Banking makes up more than 35% of revenue and serves personal and private banking customers with traditional banking services and financial advice to high-net worth clients respectively. Business Banking brings in another nearly 30% of revenue and provides financing investing cash management and risk management services to small and medium-sized businesses through the bank's network of finance centers branches contact centers and online channels. Corporates & Institutions makes up roughly 20% of revenue and provides wholesale banking services to the largest institutional and corporate customers in the Nordic region. The segment's products and services include cash management services; trade finance solutions; custody services; equity bond foreign exchange and derivatives products; corporate finance; and acquisition finance. The bank also offers life insurance and pensions (Danica Pension) services mortgage finance (Realkredit Danmark) asset management (Danske Capital) real estate (home) and leasing (Nordania Leasing) services.

Geographic ReachCopenhagen-based Danske Bank boasts roughly 330 branches in 15 countries with a major presence in Denmark Northern Ireland Finland Sweden Norway Estonia Lithuania and Latvia. It also has branches in London Hamburg Dublin and Warsaw and an office in New York City. Subsidiaries in Luxembourg and St. Petersburg serve private banking and corporate banking customers respectively.

Financial Performance

Note: Growth rates may differ after conversion to US dollars.After years of flat revenue Danske Bank's total income in 2014 jumped by 10% to D$43.9 billion ($7.17 billion) mostly thanks to a combination of: higher net interest income from lower funding costs as the bank paid down its borrowed debt an 11% rise in net fee income thanks to increased business from all banking units and positive developments at Danske Capital and the doubling of its insurance business resulting from the booking of the risk allowance to income (for all four interest rate groups) and booking of part of the shadow account balance. Despite higher revenue and lower operating expenses in 2014 the bank's net income fell by 46% to D$3.8 billion (roughly $620 million) mostly as it paid D$9.1 billion ($1.49 billion) worth of (non-recurring) goodwill impairment charges as a result of weaker long-term economic development expectations in Finland Northern Ireland and Estonia. Before counting these goodwill impairments net profit rose by 82%.

Cash levels in 2014 improved significantly with operations using D$7.48 billion ($1.22 billion) mostly as the bank raised more cash from its bonds issued by RealKredit Danmark and borrowed more from other credit institutions and central banks.

The bank grew its total loans by 2% to D$1.56 trillion ($255 billion) in 2014 while total deposits declined by 2% to D$763.4 billion ($124.63 billion).

Strategy

While Danske Bank expects slow and fragile economic growth and a continuation of low interest rate levels in its core markets in 2015 it still is optimistic about future profit growth. By the end of 2015 it expects revenue to remain flat but also expects that profit will rise above D$14 billion (roughly $2.15 billion) from lower deposit funding costs higher customer activity and significantly lower impairment charges (as it incurred significant goodwill impairment charges in 2014). The

bank plans to continue adding to its market share in its core markets where it controlled more than 25% of the deposit and lending markets in Denmark nearly 10% in Finland and roughly 5% in both the Sweden and Norway markets as of late 2014. In 2014 it built on its Personal Banking market positions in Sweden and Norway by strengthening its management team in both regions signing an agreement with the Akademikerne federation to offer services to more than 100000 of its members in Norway and positioning itself as a full-service bank in Sweden. It also plans to continue reducing its salary consultancy services marketing and other discretionary spending to boost profit. In late 2014 it planned to strengthen its workforce setup with Group Services operations in Lithuania and insourcing of activities in India to support cost reductions in the coming years. It also encouraged its clients to adopt its digital banking services which will help lessen the need for costly brick-and-mortar branch operations.

HISTORY

Company BackgroundLeathersmith-turned-stock trader Gottlieb Gedalia founded Den Danske Landmandsbank Hypothek- og Vexelbank i Kjøbenhavn (The Danish Farmer's Bank Mortgage and Exchange Bank of Copenhagen. It would change its name four times before finally settling on the less-verbose Danske Bank.

Even in its early years Danske Bank never restricted itself to purely agricultural concerns preferring to offer a wide range of banking services that appealed to farmers merchants and businessmen alike. Isak Glückstadt who managed the bank from 1872 until his death in 1910 guided the bank to prominence in Copenhagen's corporate landscape where it became a leading commercial bank. Glückstadt's son Emil succeeded his father as managing director in 1910. Despite his best efforts Danske Bank could not cope with the strains of WWI and the Depression; the Danish government had to rescue the firm from bankruptcy. But the bank survived German occupation during WWII mostly unscathed.

During the 1960s and 1970s Denmark's government encouraged Danish banks to expand internationally. Danske Bank pounced on the opportunity by forming consortium banks with such Nordic neighbors as Skandinaviska Enskilda Banken (aka S-E-Banken). Danske Bank stayed ahead of its competitors through acquisitions including the purchase of two large Danish banks in 1990 making it Denmark's largest bank.

By 1990 the bank also had made its presence felt worldwide but Asian economic crises in the early 1990s caused the bank's international subsidiaries to fall short of expectations. After restructuring its international business the bank focused more energy on its Nordic customers. It bought Sweden's Östgöta Enskilda in 1998 and Norway's Fokus Bank in 1999. In 2000 Danske bought fellow Danish Bank BG Bank. Danske also added a Finnish asset management company and a majority interest in Pol-Can Bank of Poland in the same year. In 2001 Danske and BG trimmed down redundant branches.

Danske Bank bought the banking operations of Finnish insurer Sampo for more than $5 billion in 2007. The acquisition brought in more than 150 branches in Finland Estonia Latvia and Lithuania. It followed Danske Bank's 2005 acquisitions of National Irish Bank and Northern Bank from National Australia Bank for some $1.8 billion.

EXECUTIVES

CEO, Thomas F. Borgen, age 52

Head Personal Banking, Tonny Thierry Andersen, age 52

SEVP Group HR and Communications, Lars Stensgaard M.rch, age 44

Head Corporates and Institutions, Glenn Soderholm, age 52

COO, Jim Ditmore, age 56

CFO Danica Pension, Jacob Aarup-Andersen, age 39

Vice Chairman, Trond . Westlie, age 55

Chairman, Ole G. Andersen, age 60

Auditors: Deloitte

LOCATIONS

HQ: Danske Bank A/S
2-12, Holmens Kanal, Copenhagen DK-1092
Phone: (45) 33 44 00 00   **Fax:** (45) 70 121 080
Web: www.danskebank.dk

PRODUCTS/OPERATIONS

2014 Sales

	% of total
Net Interest	53
Net fees	24
Net trading income	15
Net income from insurance business	3
Other	5
Total	**100**

2014 Sales by Segment

	% of total
Personal Banking	36
Business Banking	29
Corporate & Institutions	20
Danica Pension	7
Danske Capital	5
Other Activities	3
Total	**100**

COMPETITORS

ABN AMRO Group	ING
ABN AMRO Group	ING
Citigroup	Jyske
Citigroup	Jyske
Credit Suisse	Nordea Bank
Credit Suisse	Nordea Bank
Credit Agricole	SEB AB
Credit Agricole	SEB AB
Deutsche Bank	Svenska Handelsbanken
Deutsche Bank	Svenska Handelsbanken
DnB NOR	UniCredit Bank AG
DnB NOR	UniCredit Bank AG

HISTORICAL FINANCIALS

Company Type: Public

Income Statement

FYE: December 31

	REVENUE ($ mil.)	NET INCOME ($ mil.)	NET PROFIT MARGIN	EMPLOYEES
12/15	15,876	1,826	11.5%	19,049
12/14	19,008	627	3.3%	18,478
12/13	21,677	1,313	6.1%	19,122
12/12	22,473	838	3.7%	20,308
12/11	20,045	297	1.5%	21,320
Annual Growth	**(5.7%)**	**57.4%**	**—**	**(2.8%)**

2015 Year-End Financials

Debt ratio: —
Return on equity: 7.9%
Cash ($ mil.): 11,215
Current ratio: —
Long-term debt ($ mil.): —

No. of shares (mil.): 976
Dividends
  Yield: —
  Payout: 62.5%
Market value ($ mil.): —

Danske Bank AS (Denmark)

When you're the largest bank in Denmark there's nowhere to grow but out. Danske Bank serves 3.7 million consumers and businesses through a network of 159 branches in Denmark; 45 branches in Finland (where it operates Sampo Bank); 39 branches in Sweden (Östgöta Enskilda Bank); 32 in Norway (Fokus Bank); and more than 50 branches in Ireland and Northern Ireland where it owns National Irish Bank and Northern Bank respectively. The company also has operations in Germany Poland Russia and the Baltic states. In addition to standard deposit and lending services Danske Bank offers asset management insurance leasing securities trading and research and real estate brokerage services.

Operations Danske Bank operates out of three divisions: Personal Banking Business Banking and Corporates & Institutions.

Personal Banking makes up more than 35% of revenue and serves personal and private banking customers with traditional banking services and financial advice to high-net worth clients respectively. Business Banking brings in another nearly 30% of revenue and provides financing investing cash management and risk management services to small and medium-sized businesses through the bank's network of finance centers branches contact centers and online channels. Corporates & Institutions makes up roughly 20% of revenue and provides wholesale banking services to the largest institutional and corporate customers in the Nordic region. The segment's products and services include cash management services; trade finance solutions; custody services; equity bond foreign exchange and derivatives products; corporate finance; and acquisition finance. The bank also offers life insurance and pensions (Danica Pension) services mortgage finance (Realkredit Danmark) asset management (Danske Capital) real estate (home) and leasing (Nordania Leasing) services.

Geographic ReachCopenhagen-based Danske Bank boasts roughly 330 branches in 15 countries with a major presence in Denmark Northern Ireland Finland Sweden Norway Estonia Lithuania and Latvia. It also has branches in London Hamburg Dublin and Warsaw and an office in New York City. Subsidiaries in Luxembourg and St. Petersburg serve private banking and corporate banking customers respectively.

Financial Performance

Note: Growth rates may differ after conversion to US dollars.After years of flat revenue Danske Bank's total income in 2014 jumped by 10% to D$43.9 billion ($7.17 billion) mostly thanks to a combination of: higher net interest income from lower funding costs as the bank paid down its borrowed debt an 11% rise in net fee income thanks to increased business from all banking units and positive developments at Danske Capital and the doubling of its insurance business resulting from the booking of the risk allowance to income (for all four interest rate groups) and booking of part of the shadow account balance. Despite higher revenue and lower operating expenses in 2014 the bank's net income fell by 46% to D$3.8 billion (roughly $620 million) mostly as it paid D$9.1 billion ($1.49 billion) worth of (non-recurring) goodwill impairment charges as a result of weaker long-term economic development expectations in Finland Northern Ireland and Estonia. Before counting these goodwill impairments net profit rose by 82%.

Cash levels in 2014 improved significantly with operations using D$7.48 billion ($1.22 billion) mostly as the bank raised more cash from its bonds issued by RealKredit Danmark and borrowed more from other credit institutions and central banks.

The bank grew its total loans by 2% to D$1.56 trillion ($255 billion) in 2014 while total deposits declined by 2% to D$763.4 billion ($124.63 billion).

Strategy

While Danske Bank expects slow and fragile economic growth and a continuation of low interest rate levels in its core markets in 2015 it still is optimistic about future profit growth. By the end of 2015 it expects revenue to remain flat but also expects that profit will rise above D$14 billion (roughly $2.15 billion) from lower deposit funding costs higher customer activity and significantly lower impairment charges (as it incurred significant goodwill impairment charges in 2014). The bank plans to continue adding to its market share in its core markets where it controlled more than 25% of the deposit and lending markets in Denmark nearly 10% in Finland and roughly 5% in both the Sweden and Norway markets as of late 2014. In 2014 it built on its Personal Banking market positions in Sweden and Norway by strengthening its management team in both regions signing an agreement with the Akademikerne federation to offer services to more than 100000 of its members in Norway and positioning itself as a full-service bank in Sweden. It also plans to continue reducing its salary consultancy services marketing and other discretionary spending to boost profit. In late 2014 it planned to strengthen its workforce setup with Group Services operations in Lithuania and insourcing of activities in India to support cost reductions in the coming years. It also encouraged its clients to adopt its digital banking services which will help lessen the need for costly brick-and-mortar branch operations.

HISTORY

Company BackgroundLeathersmith-turned-stock trader Gottlieb Gedalia founded Den Danske Landmandsbank Hypothek- og Vexelbank i Kjøbenhavn (The Danish Farmer's Bank Mortgage and Exchange Bank of Copenhagen. It would change its name four times before finally settling on the less-verbose Danske Bank.

Even in its early years Danske Bank never restricted itself to purely agricultural concerns preferring to offer a wide range of banking services that appealed to farmers merchants and businessmen alike. Isak Glückstadt who managed the bank from 1872 until his death in 1910 guided the bank to prominence in Copenhagen's corporate landscape where it became a leading commercial bank. Glückstadt's son Emil succeeded his father as managing director in 1910. Despite his best efforts Danske Bank could not cope with the strains of WWI and the Depression; the Danish government had to rescue the firm from bankruptcy. But the bank survived German occupation during WWII mostly unscathed.

During the 1960s and 1970s Denmark's government encouraged Danish banks to expand internationally. Danske Bank pounced on the opportunity by forming consortium banks with such Nordic neighbors as Skandinaviska Enskilda Banken (aka S-E-Banken). Danske Bank stayed ahead of its competitors through acquisitions including the purchase of two large Danish banks in 1990 making it Denmark's largest bank.

By 1990 the bank also had made its presence felt worldwide but Asian economic crises in the early 1990s caused the bank's international subsidiaries to fall short of expectations. After restructuring its international business the bank focused more energy on its Nordic customers. It bought Sweden's Östgöta Enskilda in 1998 and Norway's Fokus Bank in 1999. In 2000 Danske bought fellow Danish Bank BG Bank. Danske also added a Finnish asset management company and a majority interest in Pol-Can Bank of Poland in the same year. In 2001 Danske and BG trimmed down redundant branches.

Danske Bank bought the banking operations of Finnish insurer Sampo for more than $5 billion in 2007. The acquisition brought in more than 150 branches in Finland Estonia Latvia and Lithuania. It followed Danske Bank's 2005 acquisitions of National Irish Bank and Northern Bank from National Australia Bank for some $1.8 billion.

EXECUTIVES

CEO, Thomas F. Borgen, age 52

Head Personal Banking, Tonny Thierry Andersen, age 52

SEVP Group HR and Communications, Lars Stensgaard M .rch, age 44

Head Corporates and Institutions, Glenn Soderholm, age 52

COO, Jim Ditmore, age 56

CFO Danica Pension, Jacob Aarup-Andersen, age 39

Vice Chairman, Trond . Westlie, age 55

Chairman, Ole G. Andersen, age 60

Auditors: Deloitte Statsautoriseret Revisionspartnerselskab

LOCATIONS

HQ: Danske Bank AS (Denmark)
Holmens Kanal 2-12, Copenhagen K DK-1092
Phone: (45) 33 44 00 00   **Fax:** 212 370-9564
Web: www.danskebank.com

PRODUCTS/OPERATIONS

2014 Sales

	% of total
Net Interest	53
Net fees	24
Net trading income	15
Net income from insurance business	3
Other	5
Total	**100**

2014 Sales by Segment

	% of total
Personal Banking	36
Business Banking	29
Corporate & Institutions	20
Danica Pension	7
Danske Capital	5
Other Activities	3
Total	**100**

COMPETITORS

ABN AMRO Group	ING
ABN AMRO Group	ING
Citigroup	Jyske
Citigroup	Jyske
Credit Suisse	Nordea Bank
Credit Suisse	Nordea Bank
Credit Agricole	SEB AB
Credit Agricole	SEB AB
Deutsche Bank	Svenska Handelsbanken
Deutsche Bank	Svenska Handelsbanken
DnB NOR	UniCredit Bank AG
DnB NOR	UniCredit Bank AG

HISTORICAL FINANCIALS

Company Type: Public

Income Statement
FYE: December 31

	ASSETS ($ mil.)	NET INCOME ($ mil.)	INCOME AS % OF ASSETS	EMPLOYEES
12/16	494,783	2,726	0.6%	19,303
12/15	480,623	1,826	0.4%	19,049
12/14	563,717	585	0.1%	18,478
12/13	595,590	1,313	0.2%	19,122
12/12	615,733	838	0.1%	20,308
Annual Growth	**(5.3%)**	**34.3%**	**—**	**(1.3%)**

2016 Year-End Financials

Return on assets: 0.5%
Return on equity: 11.6%
Long-term debt ($ mil.): —
No. of shares (mil.): 935
Sales ($ mil): 17,118

Dividends
Yield: —
Payout: —
Market value ($ mil.): —

DBS Group Holdings Ltd.

DBS Group is the holding company for DBS Bank the largest bank in Singapore and a significant presence throughout Southeast Asia. DBS Bank offers personal and private banking in addition to commercial banking services to small and midsized companies through some 80 branches in its home country. The company also has around 50 locations in Hong Kong plus operations in China India Indonesia Malaysia The Philippines Taiwan and Thailand. DBS Group owns a 20% stake in the Bank of the Philippine Islands (that country's second-largest bank) as well. Other activities include capital markets brokerage fund management private equity and equipment and trade finance.

DBS intends to continue its expansion in Asia. It has opened new branches in India and Indonesia and was the first Singapore bank to establish a local subsidiary in China. In 2011 the company bought the retail and commercial banking operations of Royal Bank of Scotland in China and plans to more than double its presence in that country by 2013.

In 2012 DBS announced plans to acquire PT Bank Danamon Indonesia. The deal would greatly expand DBS' presence in Indonesia and add about 1400 branches.

In addition to expanding geographically DBS is also placing more emphasis on small and midsized businesses large corporations and affluent consumers. Areas of focus include transaction services treasury and markets and wealth management.

The Singapore government (through Temasek) owns more than a quarter of DBS Group.

EXECUTIVES

Group Executive Institutional Banking Group DBS Bank, Jeanette Wong
CFO, Chng Sok Hui
Chief Risk Officer, Elbert Pattijn
CEO, Piyush Gupta, age 56
Managing Director and Head Group Technology and Operations, David Gledhill
Managing Director and Group Head Consumer Banking and Wealth Management, Tan Su Shan, age 48

President Director DBS Indonesia, Paulus Sutisna
Group Executive Singapore Country Head DBS Bank, Sim S Lim
CEO DBS Bank (Hong Kong) Limited, Sebastian Paredes
CEO DBS India, Surojit Shome
Chairman, Peter Seah Lim Huat, age 69
Auditors: PricewaterhouseCoopers LLP

LOCATIONS

HQ: DBS Group Holdings Ltd.
12 Marina Boulevard, Marina Bay Financial Centre Tower 3, 018982
Phone: (65) 6878 8888   **Fax:** 213 627-0228
Web: www.dbs.com

2014 Sales

	% of total
Singapore	62
Hong Kong	19
Rest of the greater China	10
South and Southeast Asia	6
Rest of the world	3
Total	**100**

PRODUCTS/OPERATIONS

2014 Sales

	% of total
Institutional Banking	51
Consumer Banking/wealth management	29
Treasury	11
Others	9
Total	**100**

2014 Sales

	% of total
Interest income	73
Net fee and commission income	16
Net Trading income	7
Net income from investment securities	2
Other income	2
Total	**100**

Selected Subsidiaries

DBS Bank
  Bank of the Philippines Islands (20.3%)
  Cholamandalam DBS Finance Limited (37.4%)
  DBS Asia Capital Limited
  DBS Asset Management Ltd
  DBS Diamond Holdings Ltd
  DBS Bank (Hong Kong) Limited
  Hutchison DBS Card Ltd (50%)
  DBSN Services Pte. Ltd.
  DBS Vickers Securities (Singapore) Pte Ltd
  The Islamic Bank of Asia Limited (50%)
  PT Bank DBS Indonesia (99%)

COMPETITORS

AmBank Group	Hong Leong Finance
Amara	Maybank
Bangkok Bank	Maybank Kim Eng
Bank Central Asia	Metropolitan Bank and Trust
Bank Mandiri	
Bank Rakyat	OCBC Bank
Bank of China	Standard Chartered
HSBC	United Overseas Bank

HISTORICAL FINANCIALS

Company Type: Public

Income Statement
FYE: December 31

	ASSETS ($ mil.)	NET INCOME ($ mil.)	INCOME AS % OF ASSETS	EMPLOYEES
12/15	323,906	3,151	1.0%	22,000
12/14	333,543	3,062	0.9%	0
12/13	318,213	2,906	0.9%	0
12/12	288,638	3,114	1.1%	0
12/11	262,255	2,335	0.9%	0
Annual Growth	**5.4%**	**7.8%**	**—**	**—**

2015 Year-End Financials

Return on assets: 0.9%
Return on equity: 11.4%
Long-term debt ($ mil.): —
No. of shares (mil.): —
Sales ($ mil): 9,537

Dividends
Yield: 5.1%
Payout: 131.1%
Market value ($ mil.): —

	STOCK PRICE ($) FY Close	P/E High/Low	PER SHARE ($) Earnings	Dividends	Book Value
12/15	46.70	34 26	1.25	0.44	11.43
12/14	62.23	38 29	1.22	0.46	11.54
12/13	54.27	38 30	1.17	0.44	11.09
12/12	49.06	31 24	1.28	0.45	10.66
12/11	35.42	37 26	0.97	1.62	9.47
Annual Growth	**7.2%**	**— —**	**6.6%**	**(27.9%)**	**4.8%**

DCC Plc

In the UK and Ireland DCC provides procurement sales marketing distribution and other business support services. In more than a dozen countries it supplies products from several industries such as energy (heating oil and liquefied petroleum gas) IT and consumer electronics healthcare (medical and surgical devices) and food and beverages. Products are distributed under the DCC brand and those of numerous third-party providers. DCC also offers supply-chain management through subsidiary SerCom and waste management for businesses. DCC acquired Pace Fuelcare in 2011; in 2014 is bought Esso Express and the Esso Motorway concessions in France as well as Williams Medical Holdings in Britain.

DCC has been expanding its energy unit through acquisitions. The 2011 acquisition of Pace Fuelcare one of the largest British independent fuel distributors added 19 widely disparsed depots and some 83 tankers to the DCC Energy business. In early 2010 the company bought Shell Direct Austria for euro 18.3 million (about $27.4 million) and its December 2009 acquisition of Scotland-based oil distributor Brogan Holdings Ltd for $69 million have solidified DCC's position as a leading oil distributor in Britain.

DCC is also fine-tuning its health care segment. In mid-2010 the company sold the rehabilitation businesses of DCC Healthcare to Patterson Medical an equipment unit of Patterson Companies. The deal involved the divesture of DCC Healthcare's Days Healthcare Physio Med Services Ausmedic Australia and Metron Holdings businesses which provided rehabilitation equipment and related supplies to hospitals care facilities and therapists. The disposal was part of DCC's strategy to focus its DCC Healthcare segment more on its larger DCC Hospital Supplies and Services and DCC Health & Beauty Solutions businesses it claimed are in a more prime position for growth.

Accounting for about half of DCC's overall sales fuel distribution represents the company's largest business and DCC hopes to expand in that area via both organic growth and acquisitions. In addition the company will be working to broaden the product lines of its other distribution businesses. DCC has operations in more than a dozen countries but the UK and Ireland account for the vast majority of the company's sales.

Jim Flavin founded DCC in 1976 and went on to lead the company's strategy for more than 30 years. In May 2008 he stepped down as executive chairman. Michael Buckley became the company's new chairman while Tommy Breen was named chief executive.

EXECUTIVES

Chief Executive and Board Member; Managing Director DCC Environmental, Tommy Breen, age 56, $514,000 total compensation
Head - Group Human Resources, Ann Keenan
Managing Director DCC Energy, Donal Murphy, age 51
Managing Director DCC Food and Beverage, Frank Fenn, age 50
Managing Director DCC Corporate Finance, Michael Scholefield
Group CIO, Peter Quinn
Finance and Development Director SerCom, Niall Ennis, age 45
Managing Director DCC Healthcare, Conor Costigan, age 44
Head - Group Treasury, Daphne Tease
Managing Director Oil DCC Energy, Eddie O'Brien
CFO and Executive Director, Fergal O'Dwyer
Head - Group Sustainability, John Barcroft
Head - Group Tax, Yvonne Divilly
Managing Director LPG DCC Energy, Henry Cubbon
Chairman, John J. Moloney, age 61
Deputy Chairman, David Byrne, age 68
Auditors: PricewaterhouseCoopers

LOCATIONS

HQ: DCC Plc
  DCC House, Leopardstown Road, Dublin, Foxrock
Phone: (353) 1 279 9400   **Fax:** (353) 1 283 1017
Web: www.dcc.ie

PRODUCTS/OPERATIONS

2014 Sales

	% of total
Energy	73
Technology	20
Healthcare	4
Food & Beverage	2
Environmental	1
Total	**100**

COMPETITORS

BP	Maxol Oil
Biffa	Shamrock Foods Limited
CEVA Logistics UK	Shell Oil
Cardinal Health	Sitel UK
Central Foods	UDG Healthcare
Computacenter	Waste Recycling
Ingram Micro UK	Wincanton

HISTORICAL FINANCIALS

Company Type: Public

Income Statement

FYE: March 31

	REVENUE ($ mil.)	NET INCOME ($ mil.)	NET PROFIT MARGIN	EMPLOYEES
03/16	15,259	256	1.7%	10,540
03/15	15,675	213	1.4%	10,220
03/14	18,698	201	1.1%	9,804
03/13	16,628	167	1.0%	9,153
03/12	14,266	136	1.0%	8,355
Annual Growth	**1.7%**	**17.0%**	**—**	**6.0%**

2016 Year-End Financials

Debt ratio: 43.6%
Return on equity: 15.4%
Cash ($ mil.): 1,701
Current ratio: 1.43
Long-term debt ($ mil.): 1,814
No. of shares (mil.): 88
Dividends
 Yield: —
 Payout: 31.3%
Market value ($ mil.): —

Dekabank Deutsche Girozentrale

EXECUTIVES

Chief Executive Officer, Michael R diger
Auditors: KPMG AG Wirtschaftspruefungsgesellschaft

LOCATIONS

HQ: Dekabank Deutsche Girozentrale
  Mainzer Landstrasse 16, Frankfurt 60325
Phone: (49) 69 7147 0   **Fax:** (49) 69 7147 1376
Web: www.dekabank.de

HISTORICAL FINANCIALS

Company Type: Public

Income Statement

FYE: December 31

	ASSETS ($ mil.)	NET INCOME ($ mil.)	INCOME AS % OF ASSETS	EMPLOYEES
12/15	117,613	359	0.3%	4,277
12/14	137,564	674	0.5%	4,183
12/13	159,801	407	0.3%	4,035
12/12	171,009	375	0.2%	4,040
12/11	172,983	337	0.2%	3,957
Annual Growth	**(9.2%)**	**1.6%**	**—**	**2.0%**

2015 Year-End Financials

Return on assets: 0.3%
Return on equity: 6.9%
Long-term debt ($ mil.): —
No. of shares (mil.): 191
Sales ($ mil): 3,775
Dividends
 Yield: —
 Payout: —
Market value ($ mil.): —

Delphi Automotive Plc

Delphi Automotive PLC predicts a profitable future. The UK-based company is one of the world's largest automotive parts makers churning out a vast array of parts for the automotive and commercial vehicle industries. Product lines include connection systems fuel cells electric vehicle parts infotainment displays safety mechanisms and powertrain systems among others. Spread across the globe it has operations in 44 countries and a list of customers comprising some of the biggest names in automotive. Delphi Automotive PLC was formed as the holding company of US-based Delphi Automotive LLP.

Operations

Delphi's business is organized into three divisions: Electrical/Electronic Architecture Powertrain Systems and Electronics and Safety.

The Electrical/Electronic Architecture segment which brings in more than 50% of net revenue designs electrical architecture including connectors wiring assemblies and harnesses electrical centers and hybrid high voltage and safety distribution systems.

Powertrain systems makes parts for gasoline and diesel engines including fuel handling and injection combustion electronic controls aftermarket and original equipment services. It accounts for around 30% of net sales.

The Electronics and Safety segment makes parts systems and software for purposes including passenger safety security comfort and infotainment. It also works in body controls hybrid vehicle power technologies displays and mechatronics. It brings in about 20%.

Geographic Reach

Headquartered in Gillingham UK the company has operations in 44 countries. It has 126 manufacturing facilities and 14 major technical centers. The US represents around 37% of revenue Europe the Middle East and Africa brings in around 35% and the Asia-Pacific region 25%. Latin America brings in 2%.

Sales and Marketing

The company's customer base includes all 25 of the largest automotive OEMs in the world; GM accounts for 14% of sales. Customers include Volkswagen Group Ford Motor Company Fiat Chrysler Automobiles Daimler Peugeot Citroen Shanghai General Motors Company and others.

Financial Performance

In fiscal 2015 revenue fell 2% to $15.2 billion as unfavorable currency movements impacted on sales in Powertrain Systems and Electronics and Safety. The divestiture of the company's Reception systems business also brought down revenue. Profitability was up for the year climbing 7% to $1.5 billion due to the gain on the sale of the company's Thermal Systems business while cash from operations fell around 20% due to changes in accounts receivable.

Strategy

The company is expanding in Asia and has set up six new manufacturing facilities in China since 2012. The difficulties the company endured for a six year spell from in the mid-2000s prompted a streamlining process and relocated a significant chunk of its US operations to Asia where labor costs are lower. Sales to the US market have also shrunk as a proportion of the whole.

Delphi has been busy selling off its underperforming units which in 2015 included its Electronics and Electrical Wiring businesses in Argentina its wholly owned Thermal Systems business and its Korean joint venture. In 2016 it sold off its Chinese automotive air conditioning joint venture.

Mergers and Acquisitions

In March 2016 Delphi acquired PureDepth Inc. a maker of 3D display technology for around $15 million.

In 2015 it acquired HellermannTyton a maker of cable-management products for $1.5 billion. In 2015 it also bought Control-Tec LLC a cloud-hosted data analytics provider and Ottomatika Inc. an automated vehicle developer for $104 million and $32 million respectively.

Company Background

The company's return to the public markets and eventual profitability hasn't been easy. Delphi has struggled financially for years; it was only sporadically profitable for after being spun off in 1999. Delphi filed for bankruptcy in 2005 and emerged four years later as a heavily indebted private company owned by its investors Elliot Management GM and Silver Point Capital. By that time it had laid off more than 75000 workers closed more than 70 sites reduced its products lines from 119 to 33 exited 11 businesses and had its pension (primarily for UAW workers) frozen and taken over by federal Pension Benefit Guaranty Corporation (PBGC). (In the end the union workers' pension was kept afloat by taxpayers as part of the 2009 auto industry bailout).

In 2011 Delphi was finally able to pay off GM for its $3.8 billion stake and PBGC for the $594 million it owed. The two transactions were funded with cash and $2.5 billion of new bank debt as part of a $3 billion credit facility from by investment bank J.P. Morgan Securities. The company makes about half of what it made five years ago and plans the use the proceeds from its IPO to fund operations buy equipment and repay more debt.

Paying off GM helped pave the way for the company's return to health and a new business strategy to show investors doesn't hurt either. Admittedly Delphi has much leaner operations after its restructuring and moved the bulk of its operations outside the US to emerging markets where overall costs especially labor costs are lower. Delphi no longer has any UAW employees on its payroll; outside the US it relies on non-salary and temporary workers to manage a flexible workforce.

EXECUTIVES

President CEO and Director, Kevin P. Clark, age 54
CTO and EVP, Jeffrey J. (Jeff) Owens, age 61
SVP and CFO, Joseph R. Massaro, age 46
SVP Marketing and Communications, J. Christopher (Chris) Preuss
SVP and President Powertrain Systems and Delphi Product & Service Solutions, Liam Butterworth
President Delphi Product and Service Solutions, Keith D. Stipp
SVP and President Electronics and Safety, Jugal K. Vijayvargiya
SVP and President Delphi Electrical/Electronic Architecture; President Delphi Asia Pacific, Majdi B. Abulaban
VP Sales and President Delphi Europe Middle East Africa and Russia, Michael Gassen
SVP Global Supply Management, Sidney Johnson
SVP and CIO, Matthew Peterson
SVP and CTO, Glen De Vos
VP Global Operations and President Delphi Mexico, William H. Guggina
Chairman, Rajiv L. (Raj) Gupta, age 70
Auditors: Ernst & Young LLP

LOCATIONS

HQ: Delphi Automotive Plc
Courteney Road, Hoath Way, Gillingham, Kent ME8 0RU
Phone: (011) 44 163 423 4422
Web: www.delphi.com

2015 Sales

	$ mil.	% of total
United States	5,536	37
Other North America	146	1
Europe Middle East & Africa	5,275	35
Asia Pacific	3,839	25
South America	369	2
Total	**15,165**	**100**

PRODUCTS/OPERATIONS

2015 Sales by Segment

	$ mil.	% of total
Electrical/Electronic Architecture	8,180	53
Powertrain Systems	4,377	29
Electronics and Safety	2,774	18
Eliminations and Other	(166)	-
Total	**15,165**	**100**

Selected Products

Automotive Industry
Body & Security
Connection Systems
Driver Interface
Electrical/Electronic Architecture
Hybrid & Electric Vehicle Products
Infotainment
Powertrain Systems
Safety Electronics
Sensors

COMPETITORS

Aisin Seiki	Magneti Marelli
Autoliv	Molex
BorgWarner	Motorola Solutions
Continental AG	Robert Bosch

DENSO	Sanden
Dana	Sumitomo Electric
Federal-Mogul	TE Connectivity
Johnson Controls Power Solutions	Valeo
	Visteon
LEONI	Yazaki
Lear Corp	ZF TRW Automotive
Magna International	

HISTORICAL FINANCIALS

Company Type: Public

Income Statement

FYE: December 31

	REVENUE ($ mil.)	NET INCOME ($ mil.)	NET PROFIT MARGIN	EMPLOYEES
12/16	16,661	1,257	7.5%	145,000
12/15	15,165	1,450	9.6%	139,000
12/14	17,023	1,351	7.9%	127,000
12/13	16,463	1,212	7.4%	117,000
12/12	15,519	1,077	6.9%	118,000
Annual Growth	**1.8%**	**3.9%**	**—**	**5.3%**

2016 Year-End Financials

Debt ratio: 32.3%
Return on equity: 53.9%
Cash ($ mil.): 838
Current ratio: 1.31
Long-term debt ($ mil.): 3,959
No. of shares (mil.): 269
Dividends
Yield: 0.0%
Payout: 25.2%
Market value ($ mil.): 18,170

	STOCK PRICE ($) FY Close	P/E High/Low	PER SHARE ($) Earnings	Dividends	Book Value
12/16	67.35	19 12	4.59	1.16	8.90
12/15	85.73	18 13	5.06	1.00	8.09
12/14	72.72	16 13	4.48	1.00	8.61
12/13	60.13	15 10	3.89	0.68	9.50
12/12	38.25	11 7	3.33	0.00	7.44
Annual Growth	**15.2%**	**— —**	**8.4%**	**—**	**4.6%**

Denso Corp. (Japan)

DENSO knows: When building cars the whole is very little without its parts. Among the world's largest automotive parts manufacturers DENSO supplies OEM and aftermarket components and systems for most of the world's carmakers. Its six product groups make systems for powertrain control information and safety electric electronic small motors and thermal systems. Its lines range from automotive air conditioning systems to radiators and spark plugs. The Information and Safety Systems arm develops car navigation and collision avoidance systems. Non-auto industrial systems and consumer products are also made; subsidiary DENSO WAVE makes bar code readers industrial robots and programmable logic controllers.

DENSO's holistic perspective is demonstrated in all aspects of its automotive business from product development and design to manufacturing and sales. The company touts collaborative efforts with local car manufacturers and suppliers that support each customer's specific regional requirements. Although the company has a global presence with more than 185 subsidiaries and operations in 35 countries more than half of its sales depend on Japanese manufacturers. US operations are overseen by DENSO International America which accounted for 14% of sales in fiscal 2011.

DENSO was spun off from Toyota Motor Corporation in 1949; its former parent remains the largest shareholder owning a 25% stake. Toyota

Industries Corporation owns almost 9% while an affiliate of German auto parts giant Robert Bosch owns another 6%. Toyota Motor Corporation is also its largest customer accounting for about 30% of sales in 2011.

Like other auto parts manufacturers DENSO is looking to expand in emerging markets in Brazil China and India. It built a new plant for car air conditioners in Changchun a city in northeast China that is also home to the China FAW Group. The plant will supply AC units to Toyota and Volkswagen models built by China FAW and is expected to open by 2013. It also expanded its car air conditioner and radiator plant in Brazil to increase production capacity and established a joint venture with Indian air conditioning company Subros. It introduced four low-cost heat exchangers for the Indian market. Elsewhere DENSO bought CTR an Italian company that sells air conditioners to aftermarket customers and opened its first sales office in Dubai for customers in the Middle East and North Africa.

With international operations representing about a quarter of overall sales the company is pinning its future growth foremost on product research and development to boost fuel efficiency and reduce carbon dioxide emissions. New products include engines for hybrid and electric vehicles. DENSO is working on cutting costs and improving performance in key products such as inverters DC-DC converters battery monitoring units and electric compressors. It is also developing new products such as battery packs that integrate motor generators batteries battery monitoring units and cooling fans. Its intelligent sensing monitoring and navigation technologies are advancing too with components that promise to help reduce car accidents.

Cost-control measures are playing an equally dominant role in DENSO's operations. The company is shifting its concentration from products for mature markets and premium vehicles to producing low-cost lines that cater to rising demand in developing markets particularly for compact cars which are common in Asia. Business systems at DENSO are evolving as well; more projects are addressed on an interdepartmental basis allowing resources to be pooled and leveraged. The company set a goal to halve the manufacturing costs of 23 key products sold in emerging markets by buying local parts and materials. For fiscal 2011 DENSO managed to cut costs by 40%.

HISTORY

Originally the in-house parts supplier for Toyota Nippondenso Co. (the predecessor to DENSO) was spun off by Toyota in 1949 because Toyota no longer wanted the burden of Nippondenso's troubled financial performance. Nippondenso remained dependent upon Toyota for sales and members of Toyota's controlling family the Toyodas remained involved in management. Nippondenso established a technological partnership with Germany's Robert Bosch in 1953.

As part of its plan to become a major supplier to North American carmakers in 1966 Nippondenso established a sales office in Chicago and branch offices in Los Angeles and Detroit. It then turned to Europe establishing a branch office in Stuttgart Germany in 1970. The following year the company established its first overseas subsidiary Nippondenso of Los Angeles (now DENSO Sales California). In 1972 the company established three more foreign subsidiaries in Australia Canada and Thailand. A European subsidiary (now DENSO Europe) was established in the Netherlands in 1973.

Nippondenso began consignment production for what is now known as Asmo Co. a maker of electric motors in 1978. In 1984 the company joined with Allen Bradley Co. (US) to develop factory automation equipment. That year the predecessor to DENSO Manufacturing Michigan one of the company's largest international subsidiaries was established. Nippondenso expanded into Spain in 1989 by opening a plant in Barcelona.

In 1990 the company formed NDM Manufacturing (now DENSO Manufacturing UK) a joint venture (25%-owned) with Magneti Marelli of Italy for the manufacture of automotive air conditioning and heating systems. The following year Nippondenso and AT&T formed a joint venture for the development of integrated circuit (IC) cards.

Nippondenso established several Chinese manufacturing joint ventures during the mid-1990s. In 1994 the company was recognized by the Guinness Book of Records as the maker of the world's smallest car the DENSO Micro Car.

The company changed its name to DENSO CORPORATION in 1996. In 1999 it acquired the rotating machines business of Magneti Marelli. The next year DENSO agreed to buy out Magneti Marelli's share in the companies' automotive air conditioning and heating joint venture (the deal was completed in 2001).

In 2001 DENSO ceased production of wireless phones in order to focus on making onboard car information systems. Also in 2001 the company merged its industrial equipment subsidiaries (bar code scanners and factory automation robots) and spun them off as majority-owned subsidiary DENSO Wave.

DENSO joined forces with Robert Bosch GmbH in 2003 to form a joint venture for the development of car navigation and multimedia systems.

In 2006 DENSO added four new Chinese production facilities that make navigation systems air conditioner compressors instrument panels and oil filters. It has also established technical centers in China and Thailand.

EXECUTIVES

EVP, Masahiko Miyaki
EVP, Haruya Maruyama
EVP, Yasushi Yamanaka
President and CEO, Koji Arima
CEO North America Thermal Systems Center, Steve Milam
President DENSO Manufacturing Canada, Rich van Oorschot
Vice Chairman, Koji Kobayashi
Chairman, Nobuaki Katoh
Auditors: Deloitte Touche Tohmatsu LLC

LOCATIONS

HQ: Denso Corp. (Japan)
1-1 Showa-cho, Kariya, Aichi 448-8661
Phone: (81) 566 25 5850   **Fax:** (81) 566 25 4913
Web: www.denso.co.jp

2016 Sales

	% of total
Japan	47
Asia	21
North America	20
Europe	11
Others	1
Total	**100**

PRODUCTS/OPERATIONS

Products & Services

Automotive Service Parts and Accessories
Consumer Products
Industrial Products
OEM Automotive Systems and Components
Services

COMPETITORS

APM Automotive	NGK SPARK PLUG
Adept Technology	Prestolite Electric
Aisin Seiki	Robert Bosch
Delphi Automotive Systems	Standard Motor Products
Garmin	Valeo
JTEKT	Visteon
Johnson Controls	Yazaki
KUKA	ZF TRW Automotive
Key Safety Systems	

HISTORICAL FINANCIALS

Company Type: Public

Income Statement

FYE: March 31

	REVENUE ($ mil.)	NET INCOME ($ mil.)	NET PROFIT MARGIN	EMPLOYEES
03/16	40,290	2,175	5.4%	182,229
03/15	35,921	2,153	6.0%	176,297
03/14	39,672	2,685	6.8%	167,139
03/13	38,057	1,930	5.1%	132,276
03/12	38,456	1,088	2.8%	126,036
Annual Growth	**1.2%**	**18.9%**	**—**	**9.7%**

2016 Year-End Financials

Debt ratio: 0.0%
Return on equity: 7.5%
Cash ($ mil.): 5,988
Current ratio: 1.91
Long-term debt ($ mil.): 1,911
No. of shares (mil.): 792
Dividends
 Yield: 2.5%
 Payout: 19.8%
Market value ($ mil.): 15,783

	STOCK PRICE ($) FY Close	P/E High/Low		PER SHARE ($) Earnings	Dividends	Book Value
03/16	19.91	0	0	2.74	0.50	35.09
03/15	22.87	0	0	2.70	0.48	34.78
03/14	23.99	0	0	3.37	0.42	34.03
03/13	21.24	—	—	2.41	0.00	32.43
03/12	16.82	—	—	1.35	0.00	32.03
Annual Growth	**4.3%**	**—**	**—**	**19.3%**	**—**	**2.3%**

Deutsche Bahn AG

One of Europe's largest transportation providers Deutsche Bahn gets freight and passengers from Punkt A to Punkt B. The company's DB Mobility Logistics group encompasses logistics and rail operations. About half of the company's sales come from freight transport and logistics led by Schenker AG. Its railway division carries 2.2-plus billion passengers yearly throughout Germany and into neighboring countries over a network of about 34000 km of track. Deutsche Bahn operates bus services in Germany and holds interests in passenger rail franchises dotting Europe. It also manage train stations and infrastructure services. State-owned Deutsche Bahn operates a handful of offices around the world.

Geographic Reach

By far the company's largest geographical segment is Germany representing 58% of total sales. Other European countries account for 31% while other major markets include the Asia/Pacific (6%) and North America (4%).

Mergers and Acquisitions

Deutsche Bahn often grows though the use of acquisitions. In 2013 its DB Schenker subsidiary purchased the assets of its long-standing partner Euro-Line Panamericana in Panama thereby expanding its network in one of the growth markets within Central America.

EXECUTIVES

Member Management Board; Infrastructure and Services, Volker Kefer, age 61
Member Management Board; Finance and Controlling, Richard Lutz, age 52
Chairman and CEO, R diger Grube, age 65
Member Management Board; Human Resources, Ulrich Weber, age 66
Member Management Board; Compliance Privacy Legal Affairs and Corp. Security, Gerd Becht, age 64
Member Management Board; Technology and Environment, Heike Hanagarth, age 57
Chairman Supervisory Board, Utz-Hellmuth Felcht
Auditors: PricewaterhouseCoopers Aktiengesellschaft Wirtschaftpruefungsgesellschaft

LOCATIONS

HQ: Deutsche Bahn AG
Potsdamer Platz 2, Berlin 10785
Phone: (49) 30 297 61030   **Fax:** (49) 30 297 61919
Web: www.deutschebahn.com

2013 Sales

	% of total
Europe	
Germany	58
Other countries	31
Asia/Pacific	6
North America	4
Other regions	1
Total	**100**

PRODUCTS/OPERATIONS

2013 Sales

	% of total
Transport & logistics	49
Passenger transport	43
Infrastructure	6
Other	2
Total	**100**

COMPETITORS

Air Berlin	Kuehne + Nagel International
Air France	Lufthansa
British Airways	National Express Group
DHL	Panalpina
Expeditors	SNCF
FedEx	UPS Supply Chain Solutions
Geodis	Veolia Environnement
KLM Royal Dutch Airlines	

HISTORICAL FINANCIALS

Company Type: Public

Income Statement

FYE: December 31

	REVENUE ($ mil.)	NET INCOME ($ mil.)	NET PROFIT MARGIN	EMPLOYEES
12/15	46,947	(1,443)	—	297,202
12/14	51,564	1,174	2.3%	295,763
12/13	57,486	904	1.6%	295,653
12/12	55,239	1,938	3.5%	299,005
12/11	52,302	1,706	3.3%	294,733
Annual Growth	**(2.7%)**	**—**	**—**	**0.2%**

2015 Year-End Financials

Debt ratio: 43.5%
Return on equity: (-9.5%)
Cash ($ mil.): 4,954
Current ratio: 0.75
Long-term debt ($ mil.): 21,515
No. of shares (mil.): 430
Dividends
 Yield: —
 Payout: —
Market value ($ mil.): —

Deutsche Bank AG

Deutsche Bank AG is one of the top financial groups in the world and the largest bank in Germany where it operates about 1845 retail branch locations. It has another 1000 branches in more than 70 countries in Europe the Americas Asia the Pacific Rim and Africa. Deutsche Bank's Corporate Banking & Securities division is its largest business while the Private & Business Clients segment is the next largest. The company's massive Deutsche Asset Management subsidiary which includes US-based companies Deutsche Bank Securities RREEF and DWS Investments serves private and institutional clients and boasts some euro 711 billion (some $804.8 billion) in assets under management.

OperationsDeutsche Bank operates through five main segments. Corporate Banking & Securities (CB&S) which makes up 40% of the company's total revenue is made up of the company's global Corporate Finance and Markets businesses which offer financial products such as underwriting of stocks and bonds trading services for investors and other company-tailored financial services.

The Private & Business Clients (PBC) segment brings in another 30% of revenue and is made up of all private and commercial banking operations under: the Deutsche Bank brand (in Germany); Advisory Banking International (in the rest of Europe); and under its joint-venture with Hua Xia Bank and Postbank which includes Postbank norisbank and BHW (in Asia).Global Transaction Banking (GTB) which makes up roughly 15% of revenue provides commercial banking products and services to corporate clients and financial institutions such as domestic and cross-border payments international trade financing and lending. It also offers provision of trust agency depositary custody and related services.

Its Deutsche Asset & Wealth Management (Deutsche AWM) division generates another 15% of overall revenue. Its asset management arm offers traditional active passive and alternative investments spanning all major asset classes to individuals and institutions worldwide. The division also offers wealth management and private banking services to high-net-worth and ultra-high-net-worth (UHNW) individuals and family offices.

The Non-Core Operations Unit (NCOU) which makes up roughly 1% of revenue operates alongside Deutsche Bank's core businesses and is designed to highlight the company's non-core positions for management-led risk decisions.

Geographic Reach

Deutsche Bank operates worldwide through nearly 2815 branches with two-thirds of those in Germany. Roughly 35% of revenue comes from Germany while the Americas generate another 25%. The UK is the next largest market generating 15%. Other large markets include the Asia Pacific region (more than 10% of revenue) the rest of Europe the Middle East and Africa.

Sales and Marketing

The bank serves both corporate clients and individuals. It spent euro 313 million on advertising in 2014 down from euro 314 million in 2013 and euro 362 million in 2012.

Financial Performance

Note: Growth rates may differ after conversion to US dollars.

Deutsche Bank's revenue has trended downward in recent years. Revenue in 2014 fell to euro 42.67 billion ($51.88 billion) mostly due to lower interest income from the NCOU division as the bank sold off some of its riskier assets as part of a long-term de-risking initiative. Its CB&S division

grew by 9% however thanks to better trading conditions in the bond market compared to a tough 2013 and favorable trading conditions in the equity derivatives market.

Despite falling revenue in 2014 profit rose for a second year with net income more than doubling to euro 1.69 billion ($2.02 billion). The profit boost was mostly driven by the de-risking activities during the year which reduced credit loss provisions by euro 931 million ($1.13 billion). The bank's general and administrative expenses also fell by euro 472 million ($573.71 million) mostly thanks to lower litigation costs as well as savings from its Operational Excellence (OpEx) program.

Cash levels fell in 2014 with operations using euro 630 million ($765.76 million). The drop was mostly because the bank had less inflow from interest-earning time deposits from its bank subsidiaries and other banks.

Strategy

Deutsche Bank has taken a number of cost-cutting and growth initiative measures in recent years to turn around its multi-year revenue decline. In 2014 for example the bank invested euro 4 billion (roughly $4.8 billion) into its Operational Excellence (OpEx) program which was designed to increase quality and flexibility as well as reinforce controls and establish a cost-efficiency culture in the bank. With plans to achieve euro 4.5 billion (around $5.1 billion) in annual cost savings by 2015's end the program saved a cumulative euro 3.3 billion ($4 billion) by the end of 2014 ahead of target.

Part of this cost-cutting plan has included investments in technology to streamline operations and transition away from costly brick-and-mortar banking. In early 2015 the company partnered with Hewlett-Packard IHP) in a 10-year multi-billion agreement to modernize its global information technology (IT) operations and significantly cut IT infrastructure costs by having HP provide on-demand data center services for the bank including storage platform and hosting. In mid-2014 the company invested euro 200 million ($272 million) toward its mobile and web-based banking options to allow its retail clients access to more services typically offered through its branches.

To raise badly needed capital Deutsche Bank agreed to sell its UK insurer Abbey Life to Phoenix Group for euro 1.1 billion in 2016. The move will help the company as it works to simplify operations.

The bank has also been leveraging its wide variety of services through its different divisions to add new customers and grow business with existing customers. In 2014 for example the bank cross-sold between its CB&S and GTB divisions to better serve multinational corporations in the US helping it obtain 66 new clients over the year.

Company Background

Hoping to take advantage of China's growing economy the company established an outpost there in 2008. It also built up its stake in the China-based mutual fund manager Harvest Fund and in 2009 became the largest single shareholder in Hua Xia Bank (with a 19.99% stake the maximum allowed for a foreign investor).

HISTORY

Company BackgroundGeorg von Siemens opened Deutsche Bank in Berlin in 1870. Three years later the firm opened an office in London and was soon buying other German banks. In the late 1800s Deutsche Bank helped finance Germany's electrification (carried out by Siemens AG) and railroad construction in the US and the Ottoman Empire. Von Siemens ran the bank until his death in 1901.

The bank survived post-WWI financial chaos by merging with Disconto-Gesellschaft and later helped finance the Nazi war machine. After the war the Allies split the company into 10 banks; it became extinct in Soviet-controlled East Germany.

The bank was reassembled in 1957 and primarily engaged in commercial banking often taking direct interests in its customers. It added retail services in the 1960s. In 1975 to prevent the Shah of Iran from gaining a stake in Daimler-Benz (now Daimler) the bank bought 29% of that company.

The firm opened an investment banking office in the US in 1971 and a branch office in 1978. In the 1980s it expanded geographically buying Bank of America's Italian subsidiary (1986) and UK merchant bank Morgan Grenfell (1989); it also moved into insurance creating life insurer DB Leben (1989).

Terrorists killed chairman Alfred Herrhausen a symbol of German big business in 1989. After German reunification in 1990 successor Hilmar Kopper oversaw the bank's reestablishment in eastern Germany.

In 1994 Deutsche Bank bought most of ITT's commercial finance unit. That year the company suffered scandal when real estate developer Jurgen Schneider borrowed more than DM1 billion and disappeared; he was later found and returned to Germany.

The company grew its global investment banking operations in 1995 under its Morgan Grenfell subsidiary. Corporate culture clashes prompted Deutsche Bank to take greater control of the unit and restructure it in 1998.

Deutsche Bank's global aspirations suffered a setback in 1998 when losses on investments in Russia trimmed its bottom line. Still trying to put WWII behind it the bank accepted responsibility for its wartime dealing in gold seized from Jews but has rejected liability to compensate victims of Nazi forced labor who toiled in industrial companies in which it holds stakes.

In 1999 the bank acquired Bankers Trust. Despite a decision to divest its industrial portfolio that year the company bought Tele Columbus the #2 cable network in Germany and Piaggio the Italian maker of the famed Vespa motor scooter. On the banking front Deutsche Bank bought Chase Manhattan's Dutch auction business and sought a foothold in Japan through alliances with Nippon Life Insurance and Sakura Bank (now part of Sumitomo Mitsui Banking).

In 2000 the company agreed to merge with Dresdner Bank (after which they would spin off their retail banking businesses) but the merger collapsed in part over the fate of investment banking subsidiary Dresdner Kleinwort Benson. German mega-insurer Allianz bought Dresdner in 2001. Deutsche Bank's reorganization plans the same year saw the bank eliminate 2600 jobs worldwide and realign its businesses into two divisions. Deutsche Bank also bought Banque Worms from French insurer AXA.

Looking for a steady supply of cash in 2001 Deutsche Bank's Morgan Grenfall Private Equity bought 3000 English pubs owned by UK-based conglomerate Whitbread plc. In 2002 more shuffling of the executive board members allowed Deutsche Bank to grow in the international Anglo-American style rather than as a domestic player.

In 2004 Deutsche Bank acquired Berkshire Mortgage (now Deutsche Bank Berkshire Mortgage) one of the top multifamily residential lenders in the US. The next year it bought Russian financial services company United Financial Group and combined its depositary business with its own.

The year 2006 was a bad year for the company from a public relations standpoint. Fallout from former chairman Rolf Breuer's remarks regarding the financial stability of banking client Kirch Holding led to a shake-up in the executive suite and the board that year. Later UK financial regulators charged the bank an $11.1 million fine for market misconduct related to trading activity in 2004. In the US the IRS investigated the bank for alleged abusive tax shelters.

The bank also took a public relations hit when its CEO Josef Ackermann went on trial for illegal bonuses during his tenure at Mannesmann.

To boost its lending operations in the US the company bought MortgageIT a real estate investment trust for some euro 285 million ($430 million) in 2007. The timing wasn't great: the subsidiary suffered a major loss a victim of the US subprime mortgage crisis. Also that year Deutsche Bank acquired Abbey Life from Lloyds Banking Group for some euro 1 billion ($2 billion.) This acquisition fared better than MortgageIT finishing out the year in the black.

Deutsche Bank's expansion was slowed in 2008 when its proposed acquisition of some of ABN AMRO's assets –including corporate and commercial units parts of Hollandische Bank Unie and a factoring company –from Fortis was canceled.

On the heels of a global expansion which began in earnest in 2002 Deutsche Bank was hit hard by the worldwide financial crisis. The company reported a fourth-quarter loss of euro 4.8 billion in 2008 largely due to declines in its trading and asset management businesses. Its Americas business primarily the US operations was hit the hardest by far.

But in 2009 Deutsche Bank's growth seemed to pick back up again as it acquired Dresdner Bank's global agency securities lending business from Commerzbank. The business was merged with Deutsche's trust and securities services unit. The deal expanded Deutsche Bank's custody platform.

EXECUTIVES

Co-CEO, J rgen Fitschen, age 68, $600,000 total compensation
CFO, Marcus Schenck, age 51
Co-CEO, John Cryan, age 56
CIO and Head of Operations Corporate and Investment Banking, Pascal Boillat
Chief Risk Officer, Stuart Lewis
COO, Kim Hammonds
Global Head Equities Trading; Head Equities EMEA, Rick Saunders
COO Global Equities Trading, Leonie Ryan
Head Global Markets, Garth Ritchie
CEO Middle East and Africa and Deutsche Securities Saudi Arabia, Jamal Al Kishi
Chairman, Paul Achleitner, age 60
Deputy Chairman, Alfred Herling, age 63
Auditors: KPMG AG Wirtschaftsprufungsgesellschaft

LOCATIONS

HQ: Deutsche Bank AG
Taunusanlage 12, Frankfurt am Main D-60325
Phone: (49) 69 910 00   **Fax:** (49) 69 910 34 225
Web: www.deutsche-bank.com

2014 Net Sales

	% of total
Europe Middle East & Africa	
Germany	34
UK	15
Other countries	14
Americas	25
Asia/Pacific	12
Total	**100**

PRODUCTS/OPERATIONS

2014 Sales

	% of total
Interest	
Loans & others	36
Financial assets at fair value through profit or loss	23
Noninterest	
Commission & fee income	29
Other	12
Total	**100**

2014 Sales

	% of total
Corporate Banking & Securities	42
Private & Business Clients	29
Deutsche Asset & Wealthmanagement	15
Global Transaction Banking	13
Non-Core Operations Unit	1
Total	**100**

COMPETITORS

BNP Paribas	KfW
Barclays	Landesbank Berlin
Citigroup	Merrill Lynch
Citigroup Global	Mizuho Financial
Markets	Morgan Stanley
Commerzbank	National Australia
Cortal Consors	Bank
Credit Suisse	Rabobank Group
Goldman Sachs	Societe Generale
Grupo Santander	TD Bank
HSBC	UBS
JPMorgan Chase	UniCredit Bank AG

HISTORICAL FINANCIALS

Company Type: Public

Income Statement

FYE: December 31

	ASSETS ($ mil.)	NET INCOME ($ mil.)	INCOME AS % OF ASSETS	EMPLOYEES
12/15	1,774,466	(7,400)	—	101,104
12/14	2,076,936	2,021	0.1%	98,138
12/13	2,218,471	916	0.0%	98,254
12/12	2,652,349	312	0.0%	98,219
12/11	2,799,163	5,344	0.2%	100,996
Annual Growth	**(10.8%)**	**—**	**—**	**0.0%**

2015 Year-End Financials

Return on assets: (-0.4%)
Return on equity: (-9.6%)
Long-term debt ($ mil.): —
No. of shares (mil.): 1,378
Sales ($ mil) 47,500

Dividends
Yield: 3.1%
Payout: —
Market value ($ mil.): 33,300

	STOCK PRICE ($) FY Close	P/E High/Low	PER SHARE ($) Earnings	Dividends	Book Value
12/15	24.15	— —	(5.51)	0.84	53.20
12/14	30.02	36 21	1.59	1.02	64.32
12/13	48.24	79 61	0.89	0.97	73.91
12/12	44.29	209 119	0.33	0.92	76.60
12/11	37.86	14 6	5.56	0.97	76.34
Annual Growth	**(10.6%)**	**— —**	**—**	**(3.6%)**	**(8.6%)**

Deutsche Bundesbank (Germany, Fed. Rep.)

Deutsche Bundesbank is not your local burg's bank. The central bank of Germany Deutsche Bundesbank is a major part of the European System of Central Banks (ESCB). Deutsche Bundesbank supervises the German banking system manages the country's monetary supply collects and publishes economic statistics advises the German government on monetary policy and settles cross-border euro transactions. With the ESCB it participates in monetary decisions for the European Union. Deutsche Bundesbank has nine regional offices that operate 35 branches throughout Germany.

OperationsThe bank generated 75% of its total revenue from interest income (mostly on the euro and foreign currencies) during 2014 while fee and commission income made up just 1%. Income from participating interest in the ECB the BIS and Liquiditats-Konsortia Bank (which was in liquidation) made up another 9% of the bank's total revenue while the rest came from realized gains from financial operations (9%) net result arising from allocation of monetary income (4%) and other income (2%). Geographic ReachFrankfurt-based Deutsche Bundesbank has a regional office in nine German cities including Berlin Düsseldorf Frankfurt am Main Hamburg Hanover Leipzig Mainz Munich and Stuttgart.

Financial Performance
Note: Growth rates may differ after conversion to US dollars. This analysis uses financials from the company's annual report. Deutsche Bundesbank's annual revenues have been declining over the past few years as low interest rates (and interest rate cuts) have eaten into its euro-based revenue.

The bank's revenue fell 37% to euro 5.38 billion ($6.54 billion) during 2014 mostly as lower key interest rates and a decline in Eurosystem-relevent balance sheet items caused its interest income on the euro to be cut nearly in half half. Key interest rates were just over two-thirds lower on an annual average. Falling revenue in 2014 coupled with moderately rising staff costs caused Deutsche's net income to tumble 36% to euro 2.95 billion ($3.59 billion) for the year. Strategy-Deutsche Bundesbank and the European Central Bank (ECB) have been cutting interest rates to spur economic growth in Germany and Europe in recent years. Indeed in December 2015 the ECB said it looked to reduce deposit interest rates at commercial banks from minus 0.2 percent to minus 0.3 percent which was intended to help bank lend more cash instead of leaving it at the central bank.

The bank has also becoming more digitized along with the rest of the banking industry to save on operating costs. It's reduced its branch count from a peak of 202 in 1991 to 61 branches in 2006 and has ultimately settled to 35 branches today (as of early 2016).

EXECUTIVES

Member Executive Board Information Technology and Markets, Hans-Helmut Kotz
Chairman Executive Board and President, Jens Weidmann, age 48
Auditors: KPMG AG Wirtschaftspruefungsgesellschaft

LOCATIONS

HQ: Deutsche Bundesbank (Germany, Fed. Rep.)
Wilhelm-Epstein-Strasse 14, Frankfurt am Main D-60431
Phone: (49) 69 9566 0   **Fax:** (49) 69 9566 3077
Web: www.bundesbank.de

PRODUCTS/OPERATIONS

2014 Sales

	% of total
Interest Income	75
Realized gain/losses arising from financial operations	9
Income from fees and commissions	1
Income from Participating interest	9
Net result arising from allocation of monetary income	4
Other income	2
Total	**100**

COMPETITORS

Bank of England
Federal Reserve

Reserve Bank of
Australia

HISTORICAL FINANCIALS

Company Type: Public

Income Statement
FYE: December 31

	ASSETS ($ mil.)	NET INCOME ($ mil.)	INCOME AS % OF ASSETS	EMPLOYEES
12/15	1,102,247	3,473	0.3%	11,001
12/14	936,962	3,590	0.4%	10,858
12/13	1,102,810	6,320	0.6%	10,822
12/12	1,351,404	875	0.1%	10,825
12/11	1,083,451	831	0.1%	9,743
Annual Growth	0.4%	43.0%	—	3.1%

2015 Year-End Financials

Return on assets: 0.3%
Return on equity: 2.8%
Long-term debt ($ mil.): —
No. of shares (mil.): —
Sales ($ mil): 4,314

Dividends
  Yield: —
  Payout: —
Market value ($ mil.): —

Deutsche Genossenschafts-Hypothekenbank (Germany, Fed. Rep.)

EXECUTIVES

Vorstandsvorsitzender, Frank Westhoff
Auditors: Ernst & Young GmbH

LOCATIONS

HQ: Deutsche Genossenschafts-Hypothekenbank
(Germany, Fed. Rep.)
Rosenstrasse 2, P.O. Box 10 14 46, Hamburg D-20095
Phone: (49) 40 33 34 0   **Fax:** (49) 40 33 34 11 11
Web: www.dghyp.de

HISTORICAL FINANCIALS

Company Type: Public

Income Statement
FYE: December 31

	ASSETS ($ mil.)	NET INCOME ($ mil.)	INCOME AS % OF ASSETS	EMPLOYEES
12/15	43,373	0	—	454
12/14	52,159	0	—	449
12/13	68,445	0	—	438
12/12	71,659	0	—	372
12/11	75,041	0	—	433
Annual Growth	(12.8%)	—	—	1.2%

Deutsche Lufthansa AG (Germany, Fed. Rep.)

Germany's air ambassador Deutsche Lufthansa rivals the world's largest airlines. Operating through some 540 subsidiaries and affiliated companies the global aviation group runs Europe's largest passenger airline. Lufthansa Passenger Airlines operates a global route network of 235 destinations in 78 countries with a fleet of more than 400 aircraft. Its logistics segment is also a market leader in international airfreight transportation through Lufthansa Cargo. The group's other main business segments deal in maintenance repair and overhaul (MRO) services through Lufthansa Technik; airline catering services through LSG Sky Chefs; and IT services through Lufthansa Systems.

Geographic Reach

The company's largest market is still Europe including the former CIS states. This region accounted for 67% of revenue in 2014.

Operations

Lufthansa's passenger airline business segment consists of Lufthansa (which includes Lufthansa Regional and Lufthansa Italia) Austrian Airlines SWISS and Germanwings as well as equity stakes in Brussels Airlines JetBlue and SunExpress. The company is considered to be a leading European premium carrier with hubs in Brussels Frankfurt Munich Vienna and Zurich.

The company is also a member of the Star Alliance a group of 27 member airlines and counting that together cover more than 1100 destinations across the globe and of Atlantic++ the largest transatlantic joint venture which was founded by Lufthansa Air Canada Continental Airlines and United Air Lines. With about 280 daily transatlantic flights Atlantic++ establishes a route network to North America from Europe the Middle East and Africa.

Lufthansa Cargo one of the largest cargo airlines in the world is seeing a dramatic earnings turnaround due to the recovering global economy and a boom in German exports. The Asia/Pacific region is Lufthansa Cargo's most important sales market generating about half of its total traffic revenue.

Lufthansa Technik serves a total of 3290 aircraft on an exclusive basis for almost 800 customers worldwide. It provides maintenance aircraft overhaul technical support for engines components and landing gear and special maintenance services for VIP aircraft. Lufthansa Technik

Financial Performance

In fiscal 2014 Lufthansa's net revenue was euro m 30 billion which remained stable compared to 2013. While most segments remained flat for 2014 the company's catering segment jumped by 6% and its MRO and IT services segments climbed 3% and 2% respectively.

Lufthansa's net income decreased by euro m 258 million in 2014 compared to 2013. This decrease was due to additional operating expenses driven by foreign exchanges losses and losses from non-disposable assets.

Strategy

An ongoing positive uptick in passenger air travel is expected to help Lufthansa return to normal economic growth. A fleet modernization program may also prove fruitful over the long-term as Lufthansa ordered 29 new aircraft to be delivered starting in 2014. Overall the Lufthansa Group's order list contains 263 aircraft for delivery by 2025.

HISTORY

Company Background

The Weimar government created Deutsche Luft Hansa (DLH) in 1926 by merging private German airlines Deutscher Aero Lloyd (founded 1919) and Junkers Luftverkehr (formed in 1921 by aircraft manufacturer Junkers Flugzeugwerke). DLH built what would become Europe's most comprehensive air route network by 1931. It served the USSR through Deruluft (formed 1921; dissolved 1941) an airline jointly owned by DLH and the Soviet government. In 1930 DLH and the Chinese government formed Eurasia Aviation Corporation to develop air transport in China.

DLH established the world's first trans-Atlantic airmail service from Berlin to Buenos Aires in 1934 and went on to develop air transport throughout South America. The outbreak of WWII ended operations in Europe and the Chinese government seized Eurasia Aviation in 1941. Klaus Bonhoeffer head of DLH's legal department led an unsuccessful coup against the Nazi leadership and was executed in 1945. Soon afterward all DLH operations ceased.

In 1954 the Allies allowed the recapitalization of Deutsche Lufthansa. The airline started with domestic routes returned to London and Paris (1955) and then re-entered South America (1956). In 1958 it made its first nonstop flight between Germany and New York and initiated service to Tokyo and Cairo. Meanwhile it started a charter airline with several partners in 1955. Lufthansa bought out its partners in 1959 and renamed the unit Condor two years later.

The carrier resumed service behind the Iron Curtain in 1966 with flights to Prague. The stable West German economy helped Lufthansa maintain profitability through most of the 1970s. The reunification of Germany in 1990 ended Allied control over Berlin airspace allowing Lufthansa which had bought Pan Am's Berlin routes to fly there under its own colors for the first time since the end of WWII.

EXECUTIVES

Chief Officer Hub Management, Harry Hohmeister, age 52
Chairman and CEO, Carsten Spohr, age 50
CEO Eurowings and Aviation Services, Karl U. Garnadt, age 60
CIO, Roland Sch tz, age 48
CFO, Simone Menne, age 57
CEO Austrian Airlines, Kay Kratky, age 58
Auditors: PricewaterhouseCoopers Aktiengesellschaft

LOCATIONS

HQ: Deutsche Lufthansa AG (Germany, Fed. Rep.)
Lufthansa Aviation Center, Airportring, Frankfurt 60546
Phone: (49) 69 696 28008   **Fax:** (49) 69 696 90990
Web: www.lufthansagroup.com

2014 Sales

	% of total
Europe	62
North America	17
Asia/Pacific	13
Middle East	3
Central & South America	3
Africa	2
Total	**100**

PRODUCTS/OPERATIONS

2014 Sales

	% of total
Passenger airline group	75
Maintenance repair & overhaul	9
Logistics	8
Catering	7
IT services	1
Total	**100**

COMPETITORS

AAR Corp.	IAG
Aer Lingus	ITA Software
Air Berlin	Japan Airlines
Air France-KLM	Jeppesen Sanderson
Alitalia	Korean Air
American Airlines	Qantas
Group	Ryanair
Aviall	SR Technics
British Airways	TIMCO Aviation
Delta Air Lines	Virgin Atlantic
Deutsche Bahn	Airways
Gate Gourmet	easyJet

HISTORICAL FINANCIALS

Company Type: Public

Income Statement
FYE: December 31

	REVENUE ($ mil.)	NET INCOME ($ mil.)	NET PROFIT MARGIN	EMPLOYEES
12/15	35,136	1,849	5.3%	120,652
12/14	36,736	66	0.2%	118,781
12/13	41,558	430	1.0%	117,343
12/12	39,868	1,304	3.3%	118,368
12/11	37,345	(16)	—	119,084
Annual Growth	(1.5%)	—	—	0.3%

2015 Year-End Financials

Debt ratio: 21.3%	No. of shares (mil.): 464
Return on equity: 34.8%	Dividends
Cash ($ mil.): 1,197	Yield: —
Current ratio: 0.72	Payout: —
Long-term debt ($ mil.): 5,479	Market value ($ mil.): 7,296

	STOCK PRICE ($) FY Close	P/E High/Low		Earnings	PER SHARE ($) Dividends	Book Value
12/15	15.71	5	3	4.00	0.00	13.52
12/14	16.66	206	110	0.15	0.44	10.42
12/13	21.39	34	26	0.94	0.00	18.08
12/12	19.29	9	5	2.85	0.22	23.61
12/11	11.78	—	—	(0.04)	0.55	22.45
Annual Growth	7.5%			—	—	—
(11.9%)						

Deutsche Post AG

Deutsche Post has outgrown its mailbox origins. Doing business as Deutsche Post DHL the company divides its operations between delivering the mail in Germany (Deutsche Post) and being one of the world's leading providers of express delivery and logistics services (DHL). As Deutsche Post it delivers about 64 million letters a day to more than 40 million customers (about half of the German population). DHL handles the international express delivery freight forwarding global mail and supply chain business. Overall DHL-branded business activities account for the majority of Deutsche Post DHL's sales. The company's largest market is Europe which accounts for about two-thirds of total sales.

Operations

Deutsche Post operates through four divisions: Express Freight Forwarding Global Mail and Supply Chain. Deutsche Post only encompasses the group's German mail service. And as electronic communication grows the company is reevaluating its legacy operations. Demand for mail delivery has trended downward; and while that's good for the earth it's bad for business.

The company expects the most growth to come from its DHL-branded services which handle the international express delivery freight forwarding global mail and supply chain business.

Financial Performance

Deutsche Post's revenue dropped marginally from 2012 to 2013 due to slight decreases in sales from European countries (other than Germany) the Americas and other regions. The company also experienced a revenue drop from its freight segment from 2012 to 2013. (Note: Growth rates may differ after conversion to US dollars.)

Strategy

The company is looking to strengthen its international express services and its freight business. In China DHL-Sinotrans International Air Courier operates as its joint venture with Sinotrans one of the country's top express delivery firms. Deutsche Post will also continue to focus on logistics as its core business with more than 85% of revenue coming from logistics by 2020. In addition it aims to secure its letter business in Germany while also further expanding its services within the e-commerce market.

HISTORY

Company Background

The German postal system was established in the 1490s when German emperor Maximilian I ordered a reliable and regular messenger service to be set up between Austria (Innsbruck where the emperor had his court) and the farther reaches of his Holy Roman Empire: the Netherlands France and Rome. The von Tassis (later renamed Taxis) family of Italy was responsible for running the network. Family members settled in major cities across Europe to expand the postal business.

Although the family operated what was officially an exclusively royal mail service by the early 1500s the company was also delivering messages for private patrons. In 1600 a family member who served as general postmaster was authorized to collect fees for private mail deliveries. By the early 19th century Thurn und Taxis as the company was then called was the leading postal service in the Holy Roman Empire serving more than 11 million people.

The dissolution of the Holy Roman Empire prompted by Napoleon's military adventures led to the creation of a federation of 39 independent German states. Thurn und Taxis had to make agreements with members of the separate states including Austria and Prussia. After Austria's defeat in 1866 by Prussia the confederation was dissolved and all Thurn und Taxis postal systems were absorbed by Prussia. When Bismarck's Prussian-led German Reich was established in 1870 the new postal administration (Reichspostverwaltung) began issuing postage stamps valid across Germany.

After Germany was defeated in WWII and split into two nations in 1949 two postal systems were established: Deutsche Post (East Germany) and Deutsche Bundespost (West Germany). The fall of the Berlin Wall in 1989 preceded a reunion of the two German states in 1990. That year Deutsche Post led by chairman Klaus Zumwinkel was integrated into Deutsche Bundespost.

EXECUTIVES

CEO, Frank Appel, age 55, $867,167 total compensation
CEO DHL Express, Ken Allen, age 61
CEO Post eCommerce Parcel, J rgen Gerdes, age 52, $357,500 total compensation
CEO DHL Supply Chain Williams Lea, John Gilbert
CFO, Melanie Kreis
Chair Supervisory Board, Wulf von Schimmelmann
Auditors: PricewaterhouseCoopers Aktiengesellschaft

LOCATIONS

HQ: Deutsche Post AG
Charles-de-Gaulle-Strasse 20, Bonn D-53113
Phone: (49) 228 182 0   **Fax:** (49) 228 14 88 72
Web: www.dpwn.de

2014 Sales

	% of total
Europe	
Germany	31
Other countries	33
Americas	16
Asia/Pacific	16
Other regions	4
Total	**100**

PRODUCTS/OPERATIONS

2014 Sales

	% of total
PeP	27
Supply Chain	26
Global Forwarding Freight	25
Express	21
Total	**100**

Selected Services

Air freight
Contract logistics
Dialog marketing services
European road freight
International express
National and international mail and parcel services
Ocean freight
Outsourcing and system solutions for the mail business

COMPETITORS

CEVA Logistics	Nippon Express
DB Schenker Rail AG	Panalpina
Expeditors	PostNL
FedEx	Poste Italiane
Geodis	Royal Mail
Kuehne + Nagel	TNT Express
International	UPS
La Poste	US Postal Service

HISTORICAL FINANCIALS

Company Type: Public

Income Statement
FYE: December 31

	REVENUE ($ mil.)	NET INCOME ($ mil.)	NET PROFIT MARGIN	EMPLOYEES
12/15	64,513	1,677	2.6%	497,745
12/14	68,834	2,517	3.7%	488,824
12/13	75,837	2,878	3.8%	479,212
12/12	73,167	2,185	3.0%	472,321
12/11	68,331	1,504	2.2%	467,188
Annual Growth	(1.4%)	2.8%	—	1.6%

2015 Year-End Financials

Debt ratio: —	No. of shares (mil.): 1,211
Return on equity: 14.7%	Dividends
Cash ($ mil.): 3,929	Yield: 3.2%
Current ratio: 1.02	Payout: 66.8%
Long-term debt ($ mil.): —	Market value ($ mil.): 33,647

	STOCK PRICE ($) FY Close	P/E High/Low		Earnings	PER SHARE ($) Dividends	Book Value
12/15	27.78	27	20	1.33	0.91	9.92
12/14	32.45	20	16	1.99	1.07	11.42
12/13	36.70	21	13	2.29	0.89	11.22
12/12	22.12	16	12	1.74	0.87	13.03
12/11	15.42	19	12	1.24	0.83	11.78
Annual Growth	15.9%			—	1.7%	2.4% (4.2%)

Deutsche Post RG

Auditors: PricewaterhouseCoopers Aktiengesellschaft Wirtschaftpruefungsgesellschaft

LOCATIONS

HQ: Deutsche Post RG
  Charles-de-Gaulle-Str. 20, Bonn 53113
Phone: (49) 228 182 0   **Fax:** (49) 228 182 98 80
Web: www.dp-dhl.com

HISTORICAL FINANCIALS

Company Type: Public

Income Statement

FYE: December 31

	REVENUE ($ mil.)	NET INCOME ($ mil.)	NET PROFIT MARGIN	EMPLOYEES
12/15	64,513	1,677	2.6%	497,745
12/14	68,834	2,517	3.7%	488,824
12/13	75,837	2,878	3.8%	480,006
12/12	73,167	2,185	3.0%	473,626
12/11	68,331	1,504	2.2%	471,654
Annual Growth	(1.4%)	2.8%	—	1.4%

2015 Year-End Financials

Debt ratio: —
Return on equity: 15.0%
Cash ($ mil.): 3,929
Current ratio: 1.02
Long-term debt ($ mil.): —

No. of shares (mil.): 1,211
Dividends
  Yield: —
  Payout: —
Market value ($ mil.): —

Deutsche Postbank AG

Deutsche Postbank is claiming its post as one of Germany's leading retail banks. Spun off from postal service provider Deutsche Post in 2004 the bank offers deposits loans and mortgages asset management insurance and commercial finance including factoring and leasing services through more than 850 branches; it also offers some services through post office locations. The bank performs payment processing services as well with rivals including Deutsche Bank among its biggest customers. Outside Germany Deutsche Postbank offers banking services in Luxembourg and structured finance products to companies in North America. Deutsche Bank controls just over half of the bank.

In 2008 there was renewed interest in the acquisition of Deutsche Postbank as its former parent company Deutsche Post sought to sell the bank in order to focus on mail express deliveries and logistics. German banking giant Deutsche Bank acquired 25% of Deutsche Postbank for some $4 billion in 2009; it later upped its stake to more than 50% the next year.

Stefan Juette was named CEO of Deutsche Postbank in 2009. He followed Wolfgang Klein who resigned following a clash with members of the board. Juette was a Deutsche Postbank board member responsible for lending and credit management.

EXECUTIVES

Member Management Board; Resources, Ralf Stemmer, age 55, $400,000 total compensation
Member Management Board; Branch Sales, Hans-Peter Schmid, age 58, $433,300 total compensation
CFO, Marc Hess, age 43
Chairman; Group Management and Sales, Frank Strauss, age 46

Member Management Board; Chief Risk Officer, Hanns-Peter Storr, age 57
COO, Ralph M ller, age 45
Member Management Board; Product, Susanne Kl ¶, age 52
Auditors: PricewaterhouseCoopers Aktiengesellschaft Wirtschaftpruefungsgesellschaft

LOCATIONS

HQ: Deutsche Postbank AG
  Friedrich-Ebert-Allee 114-126, Bonn D-53113
Phone: (49) 228 920 0   **Fax:** (49) 228 920 35151
Web: www.postbank.com

2007 Sales

	% of total
Europe	
Germany	94
Other countries	4
US & Asia	2
Total	**100**

PRODUCTS/OPERATIONS

2007 Sales by Segment

	% of total
Retail banking	77
Corporate banking	9
Transaction banking	8
Financial markets	6
Total	**100**

COMPETITORS

ABN AMRO Group	Erste Bank
Commerzbank	HSBC
DZ BANK	UniCredit Bank AG
Deutsche Bank	

HISTORICAL FINANCIALS

Company Type: Public

Income Statement

FYE: December 31

	ASSETS ($ mil.)	NET INCOME ($ mil.)	INCOME AS % OF ASSETS	EMPLOYEES
12/15	164,031	662	0.4%	14,758
12/14	188,946	337	0.2%	14,774
12/13	222,351	454	0.2%	18,223
12/12	255,466	367	0.1%	18,599
12/11	248,319	143	0.1%	19,232
Annual Growth	(9.8%)	46.5%	—	(6.4%)

2015 Year-End Financials

Return on assets: 0.4%
Return on equity: 8.8%
Long-term debt ($ mil.): —
No. of shares (mil.): 218
Sales ($ mil): 6,961

Dividends
  Yield: —
  Payout: —
Market value ($ mil.): —

Deutsche Telekom AG

Operating the autobahn on the global information superhighway Deutsche Telekom (DT) is a leading telecom company in Europe and one of the largest carriers in the world. The company's core business is its services and products for fixed-network and mobile communications services as well as for enterprise information and communication technology (ICT). Germany's #1 fixed-line telephone operator it provides domestic and international long-distance voice services. It is a leading ISP offering other data and multimedia services

such as its Entertain-branded Internet television. DT's T-Systems International delivers ICT services for businesses. About three-quarters of sales come from Europe.

Operations

DT offers goods and services through subsidiaries in 15 European countries including Austria Croatia the Czech Republic Greece (through a 30% stake in OTE) Hungary (Magyar Telekom) the Netherlands and Poland (Polska Telefonia Cyfrowa).

Outside Germany and Eastern Europe the company's key international wireless subsidiaries are T-Mobile USA and T-Mobile (UK). The UK is the group's third-largest market with about 17 million subscribers.

Geographic Reach

Deutsche Telekom (DT) operates through its subsidiary in more than 50 countries worldwide. The company gets about 60% of its revenue from outside Germany. While DT has an impressive global reach customers in Germany still comprise its largest single market accounting for almost 40% of sales; its customers in Europe are essentially in Eastern European countries.

Financial Performance

In 2014 DT's revenue rose 4% on the strength of 21% growth in the US which came from the addition of MetroPCS and new customers. In Germany the company posted a slight decrease in revenue. Revenue from its other European operations was hurt by regulatory decisions and price reductions driven by competition.

DT's net income jumped more than 200% in 2014 from 2013. The increase in product and service revenue was supplemented by a transaction between T-Mobile US and Verizon Communications concerning the acquisition and exchange of spectrum.

Mergers and Acquisitions

DT has built up its operations in Eastern Europe with acquisitions.

It acquired the 40% of T-Mobile Czech Republic it didn't own in order to combine the Czech operations of GTS Group and T-Mobile Czech Republic. In 2015 DT bought out the rest of Slovak Telekom. Those moves followed the previous acquisition of GTS Central Europe to offer telecom services across Europe.

Ownership

The German government and German state-owned development bank KfW together own about 32% of Deutsche Telekom.

HISTORY

Early History

Deutsche Telekom was formed by the 1989 separation of West Germany's telecommunications services from the nation's postal system Deutsche Post. Dating back to the 15th century (when the Thurn und Taxis private postal system was created for German principalities) the service expanded to cover Austria France the Netherlands and most of Germany by the 1850s. After the 1866 Austro-Prussian War it became part of the North German Postal Confederation. When the German Empire was formed in 1871 the postal operation became the Deutsche Reichspost (later the Bundespost). Shortly thereafter the newly invented telephone was introduced in Germany.

Post-WWI inflation shook the Bundespost and the government allowed it to try new organizational structures. A 1924 law allowed the state-run service to operate as a quasi-commercial company. After WWII the American-British zone returned postal authority to Germans and in 1949 the USSR established the state of East Germany.

Only by the 1960s did West Germany's postal and phone services meet modern standards. Privatization of the Bundespost became a political cause when many complained about the monopoly's cost and inefficiency. Efforts to privatize the agency (named Deutsche Telekom in 1989) intensified with the 1990 German reunification. Faced with updating the antiquated phone system of the former East Germany however political opposition to taking Deutsche Telekom public faded.

The company began operating T-D1 its mobile phone network in 1992 and the next year it launched T-Online now Germany's largest online service provider. In 1996 Deutsche Telekom finally went public and raised more than $13 billion in Europe's largest IPO. It also launched Global One with France Telecom (renamed Orange) and Sprint (now Sprint Nextel); as part of the partnership Deutsche Telekom took a 10% stake in Sprint.

In 1998 European Union (EU) member countries opened their phone markets to competition and Deutsche Telekom's long-distance market share quickly eroded. Under EU pressure in 1999 the company said it would sell its cable network which it divided into nine regional units.

EXECUTIVES

CTO, Bruno Jacobfeuerborn
Member Management Board Technology and Innovation, Claudia Nemat, age 48
CEO, Timotheus Hottges, age 55
Member Board of Management; T-Systems, Reinhard Clemens, age 57
Member Board of Management; Managing Director Telekom Deutschland GmbH, Niek Jan Van Damme, age 56
Member Board of Management; CFO, Thomas Dannenfeldt
Member Board of Management; Data Privacy Legal Affairs and Compliance Acting Chief Human Resources Officer, Thomas Kremer, age 59
Auditors: PricewaterhouseCoopers Aktiengesellschaft

LOCATIONS

HQ: Deutsche Telekom AG
Friedrich-Ebert-Allee 140, Bonn D-53113
Phone: (49) 228 181 4949   **Fax:** (49) 228 181 94004
Web: www.telekom.com

2014 Sales

	% of total
Europe	
Germany	40
Other European countries	23
North America	36
Other countries	1
Total	**100**

PRODUCTS/OPERATIONS

2014 Sales

	% of total
Rendering of services	86
Sale of goods & merchantise	13
The use of entity assets & other	1
Total	**100**

COMPETITORS

BT	Tele Columbus
COLT Group	Tele2
Cable & Wireless	Telecom Italia
Freenet	Telefnica
HP Enterprise Services	Telefnica O2 Germany
Invitel	Telekom Austria
KPN	Telenor
Orange	TeliaSonera
Proximus	United Internet
QSC	Versatel
Swisscom	Vodafone
TDC	Vodafone GmbH

HISTORICAL FINANCIALS
Company Type: Public

Income Statement

FYE: December 31

	REVENUE ($ mil.)	NET INCOME ($ mil.)	NET PROFIT MARGIN	EMPLOYEES
12/15	75,403	3,544	4.7%	225,243
12/14	76,161	3,554	4.7%	227,811
12/13	82,785	1,280	1.5%	228,586
12/12	76,669	(6,926)	—	229,686
12/11	75,864	720	0.9%	235,132
Annual Growth	(0.2%)	48.9%		(1.1%)

2015 Year-End Financials

Debt ratio: 47.2%
Return on equity: 11.8%
Cash ($ mil.): 7,512
Current ratio: 0.96
Long-term debt ($ mil.): 52,217
No. of shares (mil.): —
Dividends
  Yield: 2.9%
  Payout: 115.9%
Market value ($ mil.): —

	STOCK PRICE ($) FY Close	P/E High/Low		PER SHARE ($) Earnings	Dividends	Book Value
12/15	17.88	27	19	0.77	0.53	6.98
12/14	15.89	26	19	0.79	0.65	6.85
12/13	17.26	82	52	0.29	0.90	7.39
12/12	11.36	—	—	(1.61)	0.85	7.91
12/11	11.45	113	80	0.17	0.86	10.56
Annual Growth	11.8%			—	46.4%(11.4%)	(9.8%)

Deutscher Sparkassen- und Giroverband e.V. (Germany, Fed. Rep.)

LOCATIONS

HQ: Deutscher Sparkassen-und Giroverband e.V.
(Germany, Fed. Rep.)
Charlottenstrasse 47, Berlin 10117
Phone: (49) 30 20225 0   **Fax:** (49) 30 20225 250
Web: www.dsgv.de

HISTORICAL FINANCIALS
Company Type: Public

Income Statement

FYE: December 31

	REVENUE ($ mil.)	NET INCOME ($ mil.)	NET PROFIT MARGIN	EMPLOYEES
12/15	46,777	3,141	6.7%	324,200
12/14	51,729	233	0.5%	0
12/13	58,289	2,292	3.9%	349,500
12/12	56,879	2,763	4.9%	354,500
12/11	59,202	2,100	3.5%	360,300
Annual Growth	(5.7%)	10.6%	—	(2.6%)

2015 Year-End Financials

Debt ratio: —
Return on equity: 1.9%
Cash ($ mil.): 33,588
Current ratio: —
Long-term debt ($ mil.): —
No. of shares (mil.): —
Dividends
  Yield: —
  Payout: —
Market value ($ mil.): —

Dexia SA

Auditors: Deloitte Bedrijfsrevisoren / Reviseurs d' Entreprises

LOCATIONS

HQ: Dexia SA
Place du Champ de Mars, 5, Brussels B-1050
Phone: (32) 2 213 50 81
Web: www.dexia.com

HISTORICAL FINANCIALS
Company Type: Public

Income Statement

FYE: December 31

	ASSETS ($ mil.)	NET INCOME ($ mil.)	INCOME AS % OF ASSETS	EMPLOYEES
12/15	250,824	177	0.1%	1,203
12/14	300,375	(736)	—	1,290
12/13	306,923	(1,491)	—	1,405
12/12	470,820	(3,777)	—	2,429
12/11	533,884	(15,054)	—	14,181
Annual Growth	(17.2%)	—		(46.0%)

2015 Year-End Financials

Return on assets: 0.0%
Return on equity: 4.7%
Long-term debt ($ mil.): —
No. of shares (mil.): 1,948
Sales ($ mil): 12,467
Dividends
  Yield: —
  Payout: —
Market value ($ mil.): —

	STOCK PRICE ($) FY Close	P/E High/Low		PER SHARE ($) Earnings	Dividends	Book Value
12/15	0.00	—	—	0.01	0.00	2.30
12/14	0.16	—	—	(0.38)	0.00	1.69
12/13	0.00	—	—	(0.77)	0.00	2.46
12/12	0.00	—	—	(1.94)	0.00	1.93
Annual Growth	—			—	—	4.5%

DNB ASA

Financial services 'n real estate are what DnB NOR is for. One of the largest banks in Norway the company serves retail and corporate clients at more than 150 locations in 20 countries operating under the DnB NOR Bank Nordlandsbanken and Postbanken banners. In addition to traditional banking services such as deposits and loans it also provides life and pension insurance (through its Vital subsidiary) credit cards (through Cresco) and mutual funds and institutional asset management in Norway and Sweden (through DnB NOR Asset Management) as well as real estate brokerage and capital markets services. The Norwegian government owns about a third of DnB Nor.

DnB NOR also has banking and insurance operations in Sweden where it operates through Svensk Fastighetsförmedling and SalusAnsvar. Elsewhere it provides banking services in Poland Denmark and the Baltic States through DnB NORD and in Russia through DnB NOR Monchebank. The group's strategy for international growth is focused on large corporate clients particularly in the energy shipping and seafood industries. DnB NOR also has limited operations in the US and Asia.

The company acquired the 49% it didn't already own in DnB NORD from German venture partner Norddeutsche Landesbank Girozentrale (NordLB) in late 2010. NordLB had considered buying out DnB NOR in the Baltic venture which had been hit hard by the global economic crisis but ultimately chose not to. DnB NOR instead took over the unit. DnB NORD is still reeling from the downturn but its 2010 losses were about a third of 2009's.

To strengthen the group's identity and streamline operations DnB NOR is uniting itself under one brand. Among its planned changes is the eventual phasing out of the Postbanken name.

Also DnB NOR discontinued its mortgage lending business in Sweden in 2011. It sold its retail customer mortgage loan portfolio to SEB that year.

The Norwegian government owns about a third of DnB NOR.

EXECUTIVES

EVP DNB Markets, Ottar Ertzeid, age 51, $1,600,000 total compensation

EVP Finance, Bj‚rn Erik N¦ss, age 62

EVP Wealth Management, Tom Rathke, age 59, $2,604,000 total compensation

EVP IT and Operations, Liv Fiksdahl, age 52, $1,615,000 total compensation

EVP Products, Kari Olrud Moen, age 48

EVP Personal Banking Norway, Trond Bentestuen, age 47

EVP Large Corporates and International, Harald Serck-Hanssen

EVP Corporate Banking Norway, Kjerstin Braathen, age 47

EVP HR, Solveig Hellebust

EVP Risk Management, Terje Turnes

EVP Corporate Communications, Thomas Midteide

Chairman, Anne Carine Tanum, age 63

Vice Chairman, Tore Olaf Rimmereid, age 57

Auditors: Ernst & Young AS

LOCATIONS

HQ: DNB ASA
Dronning Eufemias gate 30, Oslo, Bjorvika N-0021
Phone: (47) 915 03000
Web: www.dnb.no/en

2013 Sales

	% of total
Norway	80
Other international operations	15
Baltics and Poland	5
Total	**100**

PRODUCTS/OPERATIONS

2013 Sales

	% of total
Large corporate and international customers	36
Personal customers	37
Small and medium-sized enterprises	16
Trading	6
Traditional pension products	5
Total	**100**

COMPETITORS

ABN AMRO Group	HSBC
BNP Paribas	Nordea Bank
Credit Suisse	SEB AB
Danske Bank	Svenska Handelsbanken
Deutsche Bank	UBS
Grupo Santander	

HISTORICAL FINANCIALS

Company Type: Public

Income Statement

FYE: December 31

	ASSETS ($ mil.)	NET INCOME ($ mil.)	INCOME AS % OF ASSETS	EMPLOYEES
12/15	294,845	2,767	0.9%	11,840
12/14	357,047	2,778	0.8%	12,064
12/13	393,236	2,884	0.7%	12,016
12/12	404,904	2,441	0.6%	13,291
12/11	353,609	2,158	0.6%	16,320
Annual Growth	**(4.4%)**	**6.4%**	**—**	**(7.7%)**

2015 Year-End Financials

Return on assets: 0.9%
Return on equity: 13.9%
Long-term debt ($ mil.): —
No. of shares (mil.): 1,628
Sales ($ mil): 8,999

Dividends
Yield: 4.1%
Payout: 50.7%
Market value ($ mil.): —

Dongfeng Motor Group Co Ltd

With a name that means "East Wind" Dongfeng Motor (DFM) is determined to prevail in the world of cars. Since its founding in 1969 the company has grown to rival as one of China's top three auto makers (China FAW Group and Shanghai Automotive Industry). The company manufactures and assembles commercial vehicles passenger cars as well as engines and automotive parts and components. DFM controls a sizable portion of China's medium and heavy truck markets. Its has manufacturing facilities in Shiyan Xiangfan Wuhan and Guangzhou and a sales and service network dots the country. DFM is owned by the Chinese government.

Operations

DFM's primary facilities are located in the cities of Shiyan Xiangfan Wuhan and Guangzhou. The car maker also has several branches located in Shanghai Liuzhou (Guangxi) Yancheng (Jiangsu) Nanchong (Sichuan) Zhengzhou (Henan) Urumchi (Xinjiang) Chaoyang (Liaoning) Hangzhou (Zhejiang) and Kunming (Yunnan).

Financial Performance

From 2010 to 2011 DFM experienced a 12% increase in its total sales.

Strategy

DFM competes in China's auto industry through a three-pronged approach. It continues to expand production capacity product mix and market placement. Partners underpin each; the company has more foreign partners than any other Chinese auto company. In the past DFM has set up joint ventures with US-based Cummins; Japanese automakers Nissan and Honda; South Korean car company Kia; and French manufacturer Peugeot.

EXECUTIVES

Chairman, Zhu Yanfeng, age 55
General Manager, Li Shaozhu
Deputy General Manager, Tong Dongcheng
Deputy General Manager, Ouyang Jie
Deputy General Manager, Liu Weidong
Auditors: PricewaterhouseCoopers Zhong Tian LLP

LOCATIONS

HQ: Dongfeng Motor Group Co Ltd
Special No. 1 Dongfeng Road, Wuhan Economic and Technology Development Zone, Wuhan, Hubei Province 430056
Phone: (86) 27 8428 5274   **Fax:** (86) 27 8428 5057
Web: www.dfmg.com.cn

PRODUCTS/OPERATIONS

Selected Subsidiaries and Operations

DFM Passenger Vehicle Company (Passenger car Department)
Donfeng (Shiyan) Industrial Company
Donfeng Yueda Kia Co Ltd
Dongfeng Automobile Trading Company
Dongfeng Chaoyang Siyi Co Ltd
Dongfeng Checheng Logistics Co Ltd
Dongfeng Design Institute Co Ltd
Dongfeng Hongtai Wuhan Holding Co Ltd
Dongfeng Motor Co Ltd
Dongfeng Nanchong Automobile Co Ltd
Dongfeng Well-off Motor Co Ltd
Dongfeng Yunnan Motor Co Ltd
Hubei Dongfeng TV Culture Media Co Ltd

COMPETITORS

AUDI	Honda
BYD	Hyundai Motor
Brilliance China	Kia Motors
Chang' an Automobile	Mazda
China FAW	Nissan
Daimler	SAIC Motor
Fiat Chrysler	Shanghai Automotive
General Motors	

HISTORICAL FINANCIALS

Company Type: Public

Income Statement

FYE: December 31

	REVENUE ($ mil.)	NET INCOME ($ mil.)	NET PROFIT MARGIN	EMPLOYEES
12/15	19,488	1,778	9.1%	129,885
12/14	13,043	2,069	15.9%	122,159
12/13	6,155	1,739	28.3%	114,365
12/12	19,895	1,458	7.3%	109,963
12/11	20,882	1,665	8.0%	102,219
Annual Growth	**(1.7%)**	**1.7%**	**—**	**6.2%**

2015 Year-End Financials

Debt ratio: 1.3%
Return on equity: 14.5%
Cash ($ mil.): 4,897
Current ratio: 1.39
Long-term debt ($ mil.): 1,163

No. of shares (mil.): —
Dividends
Yield: 0.0%
Payout: 647.1%
Market value ($ mil.): —

	STOCK PRICE ($) FY Close	P/E High/Low		PER SHARE ($)		
				Earnings	Dividends	Book Value
12/15	66.60	65	35	0.21	1.34	1.51
12/14	70.89	63	41	0.24	1.25	1.38
12/13	79.01	71	51	0.20	1.05	1.21
12/12	77.98	95	53	0.17	1.23	1.00
12/11	84.20	86	68	0.19	1.24	0.86
Annual Growth	**(5.7%)**	**—**	**—**	**1.7%**	**1.9%**	**15.3%**

Doosan Corp. (Korea)

Holding company Doosan Corporation maintains many different irons in even more fires but it is fanning the fires of its core competencies in electronics manufacturing and heavy construction. The company owns significant stakes in more than 100 companies primarily Asian businesses with operations in manufacturing real estate distribution and financing. Subsidiary Doosan Infracore acquired in 2005 from Daewoo is one of Korea's largest construction equipment manufacturers. Doosan Heavy Industries and Construction builds power plants desalination plants and engages in various civil and construction activities. Doosan was founded in 1933 as beer-maker Sohwa-Kirin Beer.

The company has divested operations to focus on its manufacturing holdings. In 2009 it sold its liquor business to Lotte Chilsung Beverage a part of LOTTE Holdings. Doosan used proceeds from the sale to reduce its debt and to aid in its conversion to a holding company that year. It previously sold its publishing operations.

To build its heavy industry business Doosan acquired small construction and utility equipment maker Bobcat in 2007. It also acquired HCNG Engine Technology that year.

EXECUTIVES

Chairman and CEO, Jeongwon Park
President, Hyunsoo Dong
Vice Chairman, Jae Kyung Lee
Vice Chairman, Geewon Park, age 51

LOCATIONS

HQ: Doosan Corp. (Korea)
275, Jangchungdan-ro Jung-gu, Seoul 100-730
Phone: (82) 2 3398 1181   **Fax:** (82) 2 3398 1135
Web: www.doosancorp.co.kr

2015 Sales

	% of total
Domestic	48
America	18
Europe	15
Asia	13
Middle East	6
Total	**100**

PRODUCTS/OPERATIONS

2015 Sales

	% of total
DI	42
DHC	31
DEC	8
Electro-Materials BG	4
Industrial Vehicle BG	4
DE	3
Mottrol BG	1
Information and Communication BU	1
Others	6
Total	**100**

2015 Sales

	% of total
Sales of goods	66
Construction contracts	32
Others	2
Total	**100**

COMPETITORS

Daelim Industrial	Mitsubishi Heavy
Hyundai Engineering	Industries
and Construction	Samsung C&T
Kajima	Shimizu
LG International	

HISTORICAL FINANCIALS
Company Type: Public

Income Statement
FYE: December 31

	REVENUE ($ mil.)	NET INCOME ($ mil.)	NET PROFIT MARGIN	EMPLOYEES
12/15	16,115	(332)	—	3,930
12/14	18,707	59	0.3%	3,940
12/13	20,859	117	0.6%	4,038
12/12	3,590	78	2.2%	3,363
12/11	3,480	304	8.7%	3,078
Annual Growth	**46.7%**	**—**	**—**	**6.3%**

2015 Year-End Financials

Debt ratio: 0.0%
Return on equity: (-14.3%)
Cash ($ mil.): 1,982
Current ratio: 0.86
Long-term debt ($ mil.): 5,535

No. of shares (mil.): 15
Dividends
  Yield: —
  Payout: —
Market value ($ mil.): —

Dubai Islamic Bank Ltd

EXECUTIVES

Chairman, H.E. Mohammad Ibrahim Abdulrahman Al Shaibani
Auditors: KPMG Lower Gulf Limited

LOCATIONS

HQ: Dubai Islamic Bank Ltd
P.O. Box 1080, Dubai
Phone: (971) 4 295 3000   **Fax:** (971) 4 295 4111
Web: www.alislami.ae

HISTORICAL FINANCIALS
Company Type: Public

Income Statement
FYE: December 31

	ASSETS ($ mil.)	NET INCOME ($ mil.)	INCOME AS % OF ASSETS	EMPLOYEES
12/16	47,635	979	2.1%	0
12/15	40,811	968	2.4%	0
12/14	33,731	724	2.1%	0
12/13	30,843	438	1.4%	0
12/12	25,961	313	1.2%	0
Annual Growth	**16.4%**	**33.0%**	**—**	**—**

2016 Year-End Financials

Return on assets: 2.2%
Return on equity: 15.9%
Long-term debt ($ mil.): —
No. of shares (mil.): —
Sales ($ mil): 1,840

Dividends
  Yield: —
  Payout: —
Market value ($ mil.): —

DZ Bank AG Deutsche Zentral-Genossenschaftsbank

DZ BANK is the central institution for 1000 local cooperative banks which serve 30 million customers from a combined 11000 branch offices across Germany. It provides administrative services for its member banks which are also the company's owners. Additionally DZ BANK provides corporate banking services including commercial lending for small to midsized businesses capital markets services retail and private banking and transaction banking. DZ Bank agreed to acquire WGZ Bank in late 2015 which would effectively make it Germany's third-largest financial institution and lender.

OperationsAs of early 2016 DZ Bank operated nine management units including: DZ BANK; Deutsche Genossenschafts-Hypothekenbank AG Hamburg (DG HYP); TeamBank AG Nürnberg (TeamBank); and the BSH; DVB; DZ PRIVATBANK; R+V; UMH; and VR LEASING subgroups.

Subsidiary Union Investment is one of Germany's top fund managers and had some euro 232 billion ($250 billion) in assets under management as of late 2015. ReiseBank another unit provides foreign cash exchange and transfers from about 100 locations around Germany. Other divisions offer credit processing for financial companies and specialist consumer financing.

Broadly speaking the bank made 25% of its total revenue from interest income during 2014 while another 10% came from fee and commission income. About 47% of its revenue came from premiums earned from its insurance businesses. The remainder of its revenue came from non-recurring gains mostly on its insurance business investments.
Geographic Reach

While the vast majority of its branches are in Germany the bank has representative offices and branches in London New York Singapore Hong Kong Dublin (subsidiaries) and other key financial centers around the world.
Sales and Marketing

The bank serves retail affluent individuals corporate and institutional clients. It spent euro 133 million ($161.7 million) on public relations and marketing expenses in 2014 down from euro 134 million ($184.5 million) in 2013. Financial PerformanceNote: Growth rates may differ after conversion to US dollars. This analysis uses financials from the company's annual report.

DZ Bank's annual revenues and profits have been trending higher over the past several years. The bank's revenue jumped 9% to euro 29.4 million ($35.7 million) during 2014 mostly thanks to a combination of gains on sold investments from its insurance companies which included selling shares in Natixis and selling asset-backed securities; coupled with higher insurance premium earnings as the company integrated its R+V subgroup into its cooperative financial network.

Strong revenue growth in 2014 combined with lower interest fee and commission expenses drove DZ Bank's net income higher by 48% to euro 1.7 billion ($2.1 billion). The company's operating cash levels doubled to euro 5.1 billion ($6.2 billion) as cash-based earnings rose for the year. StrategyDZ Bank has been moving toward digital banking channels that are quickly taking the industry by storm allowing the bank to slow expensive branch-expansion plans and cut operating costs significantly while giving customers faster access to banking services. As part of its local cooperative banks' omni-channel strategy DZ Bank launched its webErfolg (web success) project aimed at building its online sales channel in 2014. In 2015 it launched its follow-up Kundenfokus 2020 project which was designed to focus on a number of improvements for the bank including "interlinking the depth and breadth of the online and offline sales channels."DZ Bank sometimes acquires other banks to grow its branch reach loan and deposit business keeping the idea of cross-selling its variety of other services later. Its late 2015 announcement to buy WGZ Bank would take DZ Bank from being Germany's fourth-largest financial institution to its third largest.

Mergers and Acquisitions

In November 2015 DZ Bank planned to buy WGZ Bank in a deal that would create Germany's third-largest financial institution. With the acquisition slated for completion in August 2016 the newly merged DZ Bank would control total assets of nearly euro 500 billion ($535 billion) making it Germany's third-largest lender behind larger lenders Deutsche Bank and Commerzbank and ahead of development bank KfW. Company Background

In 2009 DZ BANK and WGZ BANK the second-largest central institution for Germany's cooperative banking network postponed merger discussions for the fourth time in three years. The deal would have created the third-largest bank in Germany. However the two companies have combined certain operations such as their investment advisory and private banking units.

In 2001 GZ-Bank and DG Bank –Germany's primary central institutions for cooperative lenders — merged to create today's DZ BANK.

HISTORY

Company BackgroundCreated as a public entity in 1895 DG Bank began as the Preussische Central Genossenschafts-Kasse (Preussenkasse). The bank controlled liquidity and also managed cashless payment transfers and securities business for central cooperative banks. By 1905 regional co-op banks had taken equity stakes in the Preussenkasse. In the years that followed more central banks began to work with the company and its influence spread to all areas of the cooperative movement as well as outside Prussian borders.

Even the German government took an interest in the Preussenkasse and by 1932 had taken it under its control and renamed it the Deutsche Zentralgenossenschaftskasse. The partition of Germany following WWII affected the bank in two ways: assets of companies in the Soviet zone were seized and the bank's headquarters located in the Soviet-occupied portion of Berlin had to be moved. The bank operated from Marburg and Hamburg until a new headquarters was chosen in 1949. This new bank was based in Frankfurt and called Deutsche Genossenschaftskasse. The entity had a similar structure and public mandate to Preussenkasse and Deutsche Zentralgenossenschaftskasse.

In the following decades the bank started accepting deposits and received trust investment status (1954) began issuing securities (1957) and expanded its investment portfolio. The Deutsche Genossenschaftsbank Act of 1975 formalized the company's development into a commercial bank and gave it the new name Deutsche Genossenschaftsbank to reflect this.

Throughout the late 1980s the bank underwent mergers that expanded its abilities as a cooperative central institution. During this time the bank arose as the central bank of Bavaria northern Germany and parts of Hesse. In 1987 the bank approached the trade union-owned Volksfursorge Group about merging with the R&V Versicherungsgruppe to form an insurance group in an effort to boost bank and insurance cross-marketing. The next year DG solicited a possible merger among West Germany's five cooperative banks. It also took a stake in its Spanish counterpart Cajas Rurales. Both offers fell through in 1989 as some of the other cooperatives dissented and management decided against acquiring a 75% stake in Volksfursorge.

In 1990 several French banks cried outrage over $3.5 billion in bonds that had sunk in value by about $350 million. Inflation and fears over the currency integration with East Germany were the culprits for the devaluation. A vice chairman of the company took responsibility for the dispute and resigned. By 1991 three key DG Bank executive had left or announced their resignations from the company. Bernd Thiemann took the helm to restore credibility to the company which had alienated itself from other cooperative banks and whose plans to be a universal bank made it overextend itself.

With the reunification of Germany in the early 1990s DG assumed the role of the central bank for former East German cooperatives as well as East Germany's Bank für Landwirtschaft und Nahrungsgüterwirtschaft der DDR (Agriculture and Food Industry Bank).

In 1995 the bank started to look outside Germany for expansion and by 1997 it was ready to open an office in Hong Kong. In addition DG purchased a majority stake in Magyar Takarekszovethezeti Bank of Hungary. That year DG Bank along with other state-owned banks in Germany came under fire from the European Commission for receiving illegal public aid.

DG became a publicly traded company in 1998. Early that year the bank began discussions with Rabobank and Credit Agricole (similarly organized banks in the Netherlands and France) about establishing a European cooperative bank.

In 2000 DG Bank began to securitize mortgages originated by its DG Hypothekenbank unit and scrapped its planned merger with the Netherlands-based Rabobank. DG Bank then found a merger partner in the fellow German cooperative bank GZ Bank. They formed DZ BANK in 2001.

EXECUTIVES

Managing Director, Albrecht Merz
CEO, Wolfgang Kirsch
President DZ Financial Markets, Gerhard Summerer
Managing Director DZ BANK Ireland, Mark Jacob
Managing Director DZ BANK Ireland, Tilmann Gerhards
Deputy Chairman of the Supervisory Board, Rolf Hildner
Deputy Chairman of the Supervisory Board, Helmut Gottschalk
Auditors: Ernst & Young GmbH Wirtschaftspruefungsgesellschaft

LOCATIONS

HQ: DZ Bank AG Deutsche Zentral-Genossenschaftsbank
Platz der Republik, Frankfurt am Main 60325
Phone: (49) 69 7447 01   **Fax:** (49) 69 7447 1685
Web: www.dzbank.com

PRODUCTS/OPERATIONS

2014 Sales

	% of total
Premiums earned	47
Interest income and current income and expense	25
Gains and losses on investments held by insurance companies	15
Fee and commission income	10
Others	3
Total	**100**

Selected Subsidiaries

Bausparkasse Schwäbisch Hall
Deutsche Genossenschafts-Hypothekenbank AG (DYG HYP)
DZ PRIVATBANK Group
R+V Versicherung AG
TeamBank
Union Investment Group
VR LEASING

COMPETITORS

BNP Paribas	Deutsche Bank
Barclays	HSBC
BayernLB	KBC
Citibank	UniCredit Bank AG
Commerzbank	WestLB

HISTORICAL FINANCIALS

Company Type: Public

Income Statement

FYE: December 31

	REVENUE ($ mil.)	NET INCOME ($ mil.)	NET PROFIT MARGIN	EMPLOYEES
12/15	30,683	1,542	5.0%	30,029
12/14	35,746	2,102	5.9%	29,596
12/13	37,220	1,609	4.3%	28,962
12/12	34,534	910	2.6%	28,227
12/11	31,051	497	1.6%	27,825
Annual Growth	(0.3%)	32.7%	—	1.9%

2015 Year-End Financials

Debt ratio: —	No. of shares (mil.): 1,402
Return on equity: 10.2%	Dividends
Cash ($ mil.): 7,125	Yield: —
Current ratio: —	Payout: —
Long-term debt ($ mil.): —	Market value ($ mil.): —

E.ON SE

E.ON has transformed itself from a regional conglomerate into a multi-utility and a global player with 26 million customers. Its diversified business consists of power generation natural gas energy trading retail and distribution operations. Subsidiary E.ON Energie is one of Germany's top two power companies (running neck and neck with RWE) with some 17 million electricity gas and water customers; the unit also has about 69000 MW of electric generating capacity across Germany and Central Europe. E.ON operates E.ON Ruhrgas Germany's #1 natural gas supplier. Non-German utility subsidiaries include E.ON UK and E.ON Nordic.

Geographic Reach

E.ON operates in Bulgaria the Czech Republic France Germany Hungary Italy the Netherlands Romania Russia Slovakia Spain Sweden and the UK.

Financial Analysis

In 2011 the company reported revenue growth of 22% thanks to a 2% increase in Generation revenue as a result of higher sales volume higher average transfer prices and positive currency-translation effects in Sweden's Nuclear sales. Other factors included high Fossil segment sales a 26% increase in the Renewables segment and an 8% increase in the Gas segment as a result of positive energy price developments. There was also a 50% jump in the Trading segment as a result of an increase in trading activity in power and gas and a 29% increase in Russian sales as a result of a growth in generating capacity coupled with higher power prices.

E.ON has a net loss of 130% in 2011 attributable to the 58% decrease in Net book gains compared to 2010 and euro 3 billion ($4.2 billion) in impairment charges on assets and goodwill mainly at its generation businesses. It also had impairment charges of euro 1.9 billion ($2.7 billion) in Spain and Italy due to poor regional economic forecasts for the long-term development of power prices regulatory intervention and reduced use of gas-fired and coal-fired power stations.

Strategy

The company is focusing on realigning its businesses to create greater efficiencies putting more emphasis on developing its renewable power operations and reducing its debt.

In response to tightening European regulations regarding carbon emissions E.ON has announced plans to obtain 24% of its generating capacity from renewable energy sources by 2030.

In 2012 the company started building the Wysoka (Wysoka 1 und 2) onshore wind farm in Poland growing E.ON's position as one of the leading players on the Polish wind energy market.

Creating a foothold in Brazil in 2012 the company formed a power generation joint venture with Brazilian company MPX to develop 20000 MW of capacity in Brazil and Chile.

E.ON is seeking to generate about euro 15 billion ($21 billion) through divestments by the end of 2013. Paying down debt in 2012 E.ON sold Open Grid Europe its gas transmission company in Germany to a consortium led by Macquarie European Infrastructure Fund 4 for about euro 3.2 billion ($4.5 billion).

In 2011 it sold its Italian natural gas distribution network unit (E.ON Rete) to a group of Italian and French investors for EUR290 million (US$392.3 million). It also sold its UK-based Central Networks unit to PPL for $5.7 billion

HISTORY

VEBA (originally Vereinigte Elektrizitats-und Bergwerks AG) was formed in 1929 in Berlin to consolidate Germany's state-owned electricity and mining interests. These operations included PreussenElektra an electric utility formed by the German government in 1927; Hibernia a coal mining firm founded in 1873; and Preussag a mining and smelting company founded in 1923.

In the 1930s VEBA produced synthetic gasoline (essential to the German war machine) from coal at its Hibernia plant. In 1938 the company and chemical cartel I. G. Farben set up Chemische Werke Hüls to make synthetic rubber. After WWII VEBA's assets in western Germany were transferred to the government and several executives were arrested. Preussag was spun off in 1959.

In 1965 the government spun off VEBA to the public. That year the company entered trading and transportation by buying Stinnes one of West Germany's largest industrial companies. In 1969 VEBA transferred its coal mining interests to Ruhrkohle and a few years later moved into oil exploration and development. The company shortened its name to VEBA in 1970.

The West German government sold its remaining stake in VEBA in 1987. In a changed regulatory environment large investors were able to accumulate big portions of stock and their dissatisfaction with the company's lackluster results made it a takeover target. In response new chairman Ulrich Hartmann began cutting noncore businesses and reducing staff.

In 1990 VEBA began accumulating mobile communications networking and cable TV companies. It allied with the UK's Cable and Wireless (C&W) in 1995 to develop a European mobile phone business but in 1997 C&W sold its interest to VEBA (as part of the deal VEBA gained a 10% stake in C&W which it sold in 1999). In anticipation of the 1998 deregulation of the German telecom market VEBA and RWE merged their German telecom businesses in 1997.

VEBA acquired a 36% stake in Degussa a specialty chemicals company in 1997; two years later Degussa merged with Hüls to form a separately traded chemical company called Degussa-

Hüls in which VEBA took a 62% stake. VEBA sold a 30% stake in Stinnes to the public in 1999. The company's telecom venture sold its fixed-line telephone business its cable TV unit and its stake in mobile phone operator E-Plus.

These moves however were just the prelude to a bigger deal: a $14 billion merger agreement between VEBA and fellow German conglomerate VIAG. The partners announced plans to dump noncore businesses and beef up their energy and chemicals holdings. VEBA and VIAG completed their merger in 2000 and the combined company adopted the name E.ON. The companies' utilities businesses were combined into E.ON Energie and their chemicals units were brought together as Degussa.

To gain regulatory approval to form E.ON VEBA and VIAG agreed to sell their stakes in German electric utilities Bewag and VEAG and coal producer LAUBAG. E.ON sold its VEAG and LAUBAG interests along with semiconductor and electronics distribution units in 2000 and sold Bewag in 2001.

In 2001 E.ON agreed to acquire UK electricity generator Powergen (now E.ON UK) and it sold off nonutility operations including Degussa and Veba Oel. E.ON swapped a 51% stake in Veba Oel for BP's 26% stake in German natural gas supplier Ruhrgas (now E.ON Ruhrgas). E.ON also sold Klöckner to UK steel trader Balli and sold its stake in silicon wafer maker MEMC to buyout firm Texas Pacific Group.

In 2002 E.ON sold its VAW Aluminum unit to Norwegian conglomerate Norsk Hydro in a $2.8 billion deal. Regulators moved to prevent E.ON from acquiring BP's stake in Ruhrgas in 2002 but BP agreed to pay for the Veba Oel stake in cash if necessary and the swap was completed later that year. E.ON also acquired Vodafone and ThyssenKrupp's stakes in Ruhrgas in 2002 and it sold its remaining stake in Veba Oel to BP.

Also in 2002 E.ON completed its purchase of Powergen (which included its US subsidiary LG&E Energy) for about $8 billion and it sold its 65% stake in logistics company Stinnes to German railroad operator Deutsche Bahn. In late 2002 E.ON acquired the UK energy supply and generation businesses of TXU Europe in a $2.5 billion deal.

The following year E.ON swapped its majority stake in chemical maker Degussa with coal group RAG for RAG's 18% interest in Ruhrgas. It completed its acquisition of Ruhrgas by purchasing the combined 40% stake held by Royal Dutch Shell Exxon Mobil and TUI (formerly Preussag). It also sold subsidiary Viterra's energy services unit (gas and water meters) to CVC Capital Partners.

In 2005 the company acquired the Enfield power station in the UK for $250.2 million.

In 2007 E.ON acquired Ireland-based wind farm company Airtricity for $1.4 billion.

Pursuing growth in new geographic markets in 2007 E.ON acquired Russia-based power utility OGK-4 for almost $6 billion. Outmaneuvered by its rivals in 2008 it dropped its $56 billion bid to buy Endesa S.A. Spain's largest electric utility settling for the purchase of a number of Endesa's generation assets in Spain and Italy.

In 2009 to counter EDF's acquisition of British Energy E.ON and RWE formed a joint venture to develop 6000 MW of nuclear power capacity in the UK.

That year prompted by the regulatory requirements of the European Commission E.ON and GDF SUEZ agreed to swap generating assets to allow for more competition in their major markets. It sold 860 MW of Germany-based conventional power plants 132 MW of hydroelectric plants and access to 770 MW of nuclear power. In return GDF SUEZ sold to E.ON a similar amount of power generation capacity in France and the Benelux

countries. In 2010 also to meet EU anti-monopoly regulations it sold grid operator Transpower to Dutch giant TenneT for $1.1 billion and it swapped 5000 MW of generation capacity with EDF and EnBW.

In 2010 the company sold E.ON U.S. which operates Kentucky's two major utilities for $7.6 billion. Its US assets were no longer considered a core part of its growth strategy and the sale helped to pay down debt. To raise cash that year it also sold its 3.5% stake in Gazprom to Russian investment bank Vnesheconombank for $4.4 billion.

EXECUTIVES

Chairman Uniper, Bernhard Reutersberg, age 63
CFO, Klaus Schäfer, age 49
CEO E.ON Deutschland and CEO E.ON Energie Deutschland, Robert Hienz
Chairman and CEO, Johannes Teyssen
Member Management Board - Human Resources and Generation, Mike Winkel
CEO E.ON E&P, Frank Sivertsen
SVP Technology and Innovation, Susana Quintana-Plaza
Member Management Board - Markets and Services, Ing. Leonhard Birnbaum
Chairman Supervisory Board, Karl-Ludwig Kley
Auditors: PricewaterhouseCoopers Aktiengesellschaft Wirtschaftspruefungsgesellschaft

LOCATIONS

HQ: E.ON SE
E.ON-Platz 1, Duesseldorf D-40479
Phone: (49) 211 45 79 0   **Fax:** (49) 211 45 79 5 01
Web: www.eon.com

2015 Sales

	% of total
Europe	
Germany	35
Europe (Other)	31
United Kingdom	30
Sweden	3
Other regions	1
Total	**100**

PRODUCTS/OPERATIONS

2015 Sales

	% of total
Gas	49
Electricity	47
Other	4
Total	**100**

Selected Business Areas

Power Generation
Energy Mix
Coal
Natural Gas and Oil
Nuclear
Water
Wind
Solar
Bio Energy
Gas Supply & Production
Exploration & Production
LNG
Sources of Supply
Security of Supply
Gas Storage & Transportation
Underground Storage Facilities
Nord Stream Pipeline
Trading
Power and Emissions Trading
Gas and Oil Trading
Coal Biofuels and Freight Trading
Market Activity
Market Development
Distribution
Power Distribution
Gas Distribution
Technology of the Future

COMPETITORS

BASF SE	EnBW
Bayer AG	Endesa S.A.
Business Group Benelux	Enel
Deutsche Telekom	Engie
Dow Chemical	Eni
DuPont	Orange
EVN	RWE
Electricite de France	Vattenfall

HISTORICAL FINANCIALS

Company Type: Public

Income Statement

FYE: December 31

	REVENUE ($ mil.)	NET INCOME ($ mil.)	NET PROFIT MARGIN	EMPLOYEES
12/15	127,118	(7,623)	—	56,490
12/14	135,942	(3,841)	—	59,301
12/13	169,067	2,948	1.7%	62,239
12/12	174,687	2,922	1.7%	72,083
12/11	146,751	(2,870)	—	78,889
Annual Growth	(3.5%)	—	—	(8.0%)

2015 Year-End Financials

Debt ratio: 17.0%
Return on equity: (-34.1%)
Cash ($ mil.): 8,920
Current ratio: 1.20
Long-term debt ($ mil.): 16,288

No. of shares (mil.): 1,952
Dividends
Yield: 4.2%
Payout: —
Market value ($ mil.): 18,577

	STOCK PRICE ($) FY Close	P/E High/Low	PER SHARE ($) Earnings	Dividends	Book Value
12/15	9.52	— —	(3.92)	0.41	9.17
12/14	17.00	— —	(1.99)	0.60	15.46
12/13	18.48	18 15	1.54	1.10	24.15
12/12	18.79	22 16	1.53	0.96	24.16
12/11	21.39	— —	(1.50)	1.39	24.26
Annual Growth (18.3%) (21.6%)		— —	—	(26.4%)	

E.Sun Financial Holdings Co Ltd

Here comes the E. Sun and I say it's providing banking and financial services in Taiwan. Established in 2002 to consolidate the operations of E.Sun Bank and other subsidiaries E.Sun provides commercial banking venture capital securities trading and other financial services to businesses and individuals throughout the country. The group depends on commercial banking services for its bread and butter (90% of annual revenues) and carries out additional financial operations through six subsidiaries. An attempt to acquire Taiwan Business Bank in 2005 broke down amid union protests. A year later the group allied with Singapore's Temasek which would eventually control 6% through Fullerton Financial Holdings.

EXECUTIVES

President, Yung Jen Huang
Auditors: Deloitte Taiwan

LOCATIONS

HQ: E.Sun Financial Holdings Co Ltd
14F., No.117 & 1F, No. 115, Sec.3, Minsheng E. Rd,
Songshan District, Taipei
Phone: (886) 2 2175 1313
Web: www.esunfhc.com.tw

COMPETITORS

Cathay Financial Holding	Hotung Investment Holdings
Chinatrust Financial	Taiwan Business Bank

HISTORICAL FINANCIALS

Company Type: Public

Income Statement

FYE: December 31

	ASSETS ($ mil.)	NET INCOME ($ mil.)	INCOME AS % OF ASSETS	EMPLOYEES
12/15	54,025	390	0.7%	8,457
12/14	49,468	332	0.7%	7,678
12/13	46,310	282	0.6%	7,164
12/12	42,931	242	0.6%	6,476
12/11	38,122	114	0.3%	6,009
Annual Growth	9.1%	35.7%	—	8.9%

2015 Year-End Financials

Return on assets: 0.7%
Return on equity: 11.2%
Long-term debt ($ mil.): —
No. of shares (mil.): —
Sales ($ mil): 1,551

Dividends
Yield: —
Payout: 505.6%
Market value ($ mil.): —

East Japan Railway Co.

If you want to ride the rails into Tokyo you could find yourself cruising at 168 mph aboard a bullet train operated by East Japan Railway known as JR East. The company serves 17 million people daily and carries passengers on more than 7510 km (4660 miles) of track in the eastern half of the Japanese mainland including the Tokyo area. JR East's shinkansen (bullet-train) lines connect metropolitan Tokyo with other major cities. Besides its transportation-related operations JR East gets revenue from leasing restaurant and retail space in its stations and from managing shopping centers and office buildings on property that has been developed near its stations.

Geographic Reach

The railway business of JR East spans the eastern half of Hons Shinkansen network which connects Tokyo with regional cities in five directions.

Operations

JR East operates through four segments. Transportation its core business accounted for around 68% of its total revenue for 2014. Station space utilization represented 15% of its sales while shopping centers and office buildings accounted for 9%. Other operations accounted for the remainder of revenue.

The company is one of the six passenger railway companies and serves eastern Honshu (Japan's main island). It operates 70 railway lines 1686 railway stations and 7512.6 operating kilometers.

Financial Performance

In the recent past JR East's balance sheet has been affected by many factors including the Great East Japan Earthquake a sizable strengthening of the yen rising oil prices and the financial debt crisis affecting Europe.

However net sales increased 1% from 2013 to 2014 due to growth from its transportation (1%) and shopping centers and office buildings (5%) segments. Its net income also spiked by 14% in 2014 due to decreased impairment losses on fixed assets and insurance proceeds related to the earthquake.

Strategy

To grow and to maintain consumers' confidence in the safety of its system JR East aims to continue to invest in its rail infrastructure. The company is preparing for higher-speed trains that will travel at 200 mph. It also sees opportunities for additional growth in revenue from its rail-related real estate operations and its electronic ticketing system Suica.

EXECUTIVES

President and CEO, Tetsuro Tomita
EVP Railway Operations Headquarters, Masaki Ogata
EVP, Yuji Fukasawa
EVP, Naomichi Yagishita
Chairman, Satoshi Seino
Auditors: KPMG AZSA LLC

LOCATIONS

HQ: East Japan Railway Co.
2-2-2 Yoyogi, Shibuya-ku, Tokyo 151-8578
Phone: (81) 3 5334 1111   **Fax:** (81) 3 5334 1110
Web: www.jreast.co.jp

PRODUCTS/OPERATIONS

2014 Sales

	% of total
Transportation	68
Station space utilization	15
Shopping centers & office buildings	9
Other	8
Total	100

COMPETITORS

FedEx	Kintetsu
Keihin Electric Express Railway	Odakyu Electric Railway
Keio Corporation	UPS
Keisei Electric Railway	

HISTORICAL FINANCIALS

Company Type: Public

Income Statement

FYE: March 31

	REVENUE ($ mil.)	NET INCOME ($ mil.)	NET PROFIT MARGIN	EMPLOYEES
03/16	25,532	2,184	8.6%	99,200
03/15	22,972	1,503	6.5%	100,642
03/14	26,186	1,937	7.4%	73,551
03/13	28,395	1,863	6.6%	73,017
03/12	30,868	1,325	4.3%	71,729
Annual Growth	(4.6%)	13.3%	—	8.4%

2016 Year-End Financials

Debt ratio: 0.3%
Return on equity: 10.3%
Cash ($ mil.): 2,132
Current ratio: 0.67
Long-term debt ($ mil.): 23,494

No. of shares (mil.): 392
Dividends
Yield: 1.1%
Payout: —
Market value ($ mil.): 5,612

	STOCK PRICE ($) FY Close	P/E High/Low	PER SHARE ($) Earnings	Dividends	Book Value
03/16	14.31	0 0	5.57	0.17	55.45
03/15	13.40	0 0	3.83	0.18	48.45
03/14	12.28	— —	4.91	0.20	53.99
03/13	13.60	— —	4.72	0.00	55.02
03/12	10.44	— —	3.35	0.00	58.25
Annual Growth 8.2%		— —	13.6%	—	(1.2%)

Eaton Corp plc

Auditors: Ernst & Young LLP

LOCATIONS

HQ: Eaton Corp plc
Eaton House, 30 Pembroke Road, Dublin 4 44114-2584
Phone: (1) 353 1637 2900
Web: www.eaton.com

HISTORICAL FINANCIALS
Company Type: Public

Income Statement   FYE: December 31

	REVENUE ($ mil.)	NET INCOME ($ mil.)	NET PROFIT MARGIN	EMPLOYEES
12/15	20,855	1,979	9.5%	97,000
12/14	22,552	1,793	8.0%	102,000
12/13	22,046	1,861	8.4%	102,000
12/12	16,311	1,217	7.5%	103,000
12/11	16,049	1,350	8.4%	73,000
Annual Growth	6.8%	10.0%	—	7.4%

2015 Year-End Financials

Debt ratio: 27.2%
Return on equity: 12.7%
Cash ($ mil.): 268
Current ratio: 1.43
Long-term debt ($ mil.): 7,781

No. of shares (mil.): 458
Dividends
Yield: 4.2%
Payout: 52.0%
Market value ($ mil.): 23,876

	STOCK PRICE ($) FY Close	P/E High/Low	PER SHARE ($) Earnings	Dividends	Book Value
12/15	52.04	17 12	4.23	2.20	33.10
12/14	67.96	21 15	3.76	1.96	33.74
12/13	76.12	20 14	3.90	1.68	35.34
12/12	54.18	15 10	3.46	1.52	32.05
12/11	43.53	28 9	3.93	1.36	22.34
Annual Growth	4.6%	— —	1.9%	12.8%	10.3%

Eaton Ltd (United Kingdom)

Auditors: Ernst & Young LLP

LOCATIONS

HQ: Eaton Ltd (United Kingdom)
Eaton House, 30 Pembroke Road, Dublin
Phone:
Web: www.eaton.com

HISTORICAL FINANCIALS
Company Type: Public

Income Statement   FYE: December 31

	REVENUE ($ mil.)	NET INCOME ($ mil.)	NET PROFIT MARGIN	EMPLOYEES
12/15	20,855	1,979	9.5%	97,169
12/14	22,552	1,793	8.0%	102,227
12/13	22,046	1,861	8.4%	0
12/12	16,311	1,217	7.5%	0
Annual Growth	8.5%	17.6%	—	—

2015 Year-End Financials

Debt ratio: 27.2%
Return on equity: 12.7%
Cash ($ mil.): 445
Current ratio: 1.43
Long-term debt ($ mil.): 7,781

No. of shares (mil.): 458
Dividends
Yield: —
Payout: 52.0%
Market value ($ mil.): —

	STOCK PRICE ($) FY Close	P/E High/Low	PER SHARE ($) Earnings	Dividends	Book Value
12/15	0.00	— —	4.23	2.20	33.10
Annual Growth	—	— —	—	—	—

Ecopetrol SA

Ecopetrol performs crude oil and natural gas exploration production refining and transportation. The largest company in Colombia (where it accounts for 60% of national production and is one of the world's 40 largest oil companies) Ecopetrol has two large refineries (Barrancabermeja and Cartagena) strategically located to supply the domestic market and to export oil and oil products to the southern US. Ecopetrol explores for oil and gas across Colombia and is expanding internationally through exploration partnerships in Brazil Peru and the US Gulf of Mexico. In 2013 the company reported proved reserves of more than 1.4 billion barrels of oil equivalent.

Geographic Reach

Headquartered in Bogota Colombia the company has exploration and production activities in Brazil Peru and the US (Gulf of Mexico). In 2013 it derived almost 40% of its revenues from Colombia and nearly 30% from the US.

Sales and Marketing

The company's crude oil export sales are made both in the spot market and through long-term contracts primarily to refiners in the US Gulf Coast Far East Europe and the U. West Coast. It sell natural gas to distribution companies through take-or-pay or swing contracts.

Strategy

The company has ambitious expansion plans including the doubling of refining capacity and the emergence of Ecopetrol as a leader in biofuels production. The company's goal is to produce 1 million barrels of oil equivalent per day by 2015 and 1.3 million of oil equivalent per day in 2020.

Ecopetrol's strategy is focused on supplying the local market and exporting crude oil refined products petrochemical products and natural gas to end-users including refineries and wholesalers in order to improve its margins. It also intends to increase its market participation in crude oil and refined products in Asia and Europe.

In an effort to enhance the strategic and logistical framework of Colombia's oil industry in response to the increase in hydrocarbon production and higher sales of crudes and refined products both within Colombia and on the international markets in 2012 the company established Cenit as a wholly-owned subsidiary specializing in logistics and transportation of hydrocarbons within Colombia.

During 2012 the company acquired 23908 kilometers of additional seismic equivalent which includes 13908 kilometers in the US Gulf Coast and 10000 kilometers in Brazil. During the first quarter of 2013 it drilled five stratigraphic wells out of which two exhibited evidence of hydrocarbons (Segua 1 and Circe 1).

EXECUTIVES

VP Production, Hector Manosalva Rojas
VP Refining, Federico Maya Molina
VP Innovation and Technology, Nestor Fernando Saavedra
VP Supply and Marketing, Camilo Marulanda, age 37
VP Exploration, Humberto Fuenzalida
VP Transportation, Jaime Bocanegra
CFO, Magda Manosalva
Manager Procurement, Jaime A. Pineda Dur‐n
CEO, Juan Carlos Echeverry
Auditors: PricewaterhouseCoopers Ltda.

LOCATIONS

HQ: Ecopetrol SA
Carrera 13 No. 36-24, Bogota
Phone: (57) 1 234 4000   **Fax:** (57) 1 234 5628
Web: www.ecopetrol.com.co

2013 Sales

	% of total
Colombia	38
US	29
Asia	16
Europe	7
Central America and Caribbean	5
South America	3
Others	2
Total	**100**

PRODUCTS/OPERATIONS

2013 Sales

	% of total
Exploration & production	59
Refining activities	34
Transportation & logistics	7
Total	**100**

COMPETITORS

BP	Hunt Oil
Exxon Mobil	Nexen
Gran Tierra Energy	Pacific Exploration
HKN	Repsol Oil & Gas
Houston American Energy	Royal Dutch Shell

HISTORICAL FINANCIALS
Company Type: Public

Income Statement   FYE: December 31

	REVENUE ($ mil.)	NET INCOME ($ mil.)	NET PROFIT MARGIN	EMPLOYEES
12/15	16,518	(2,270)	—	10,765
12/14	27,592	2,110	7.6%	11,069
12/13	36,501	6,792	18.6%	10,686
12/12	38,801	8,328	21.5%	9,701
12/11	33,928	7,973	23.5%	8,729
Annual Growth	(16.5%)	—	—	5.4%

2015 Year-End Financials

Debt ratio: 0.0%
Return on equity: (-16.3%)
Cash ($ mil.): 2,066
Current ratio: 1.15
Long-term debt ($ mil.): 15,351

No. of shares (mil.): —
Dividends
Yield: 14.8%
Payout: —
Market value ($ mil.): —

	STOCK PRICE ($) FY Close	P/E High/Low	PER SHARE ($) Earnings	Dividends	Book Value
12/15	7.01	— —	(0.06)	1.04	0.32
12/14	17.12	0 0	0.05	2.67	0.48
12/13	38.45	— —	0.17	3.15	0.90
12/12	59.67	— —	0.20	4.38	0.89
12/11	44.52	— —	0.20	0.00	0.69
Annual Growth	(37.0%) (17.6%)	— —	—	—	—

EDP Energias de Portugal S.A.

If you live in Portugal or Brazil you can plug into EDP - Energias de Portugal a state-controlled holding company for utilities that generate transmit and distribute electricity. EDP's distribution unit serves customers across Portugal and has stakes in Brazilian power distributors. EDP serves more than 9.7 million electric customers. Other operations include a majority stake in Spanish utility HC Energia gas distribution (more than 1 million customers) utility metering and billing engineering and water and wastewater projects. EDP (a major wind energy player) has a combined generating capacity of more than 22000 MW from its domestic hydroelectric fossil-fueled and wind-powered plants.

Geographic Reach

The company has facilities in Portugal Spain France Belgium Italy Brazil Poland Mexico the US Canada the UK China and Angola. Portugal accounted for 51% of EDP's sales in 2014.

Operations

EDP's transmission distribution and supply of electricity (including last resort activities and market facilitator) as well as the logistics of changes of supplier and organized markets management are subject to regulation by Entidade Reguladora dos Serviços Energeticos - ERSE (Energy Sector Regulator) which is responsible for the preparation issuance and enforcement of regulations and for establishing the tariffs and prices related to network usage access tariffs and electricity supply for clients in the regulated markets.

In the distribution activity for natural gas EDP Group develops its activity in Portugal through its subsidiary Portgas S.A. EDP Group is present in the commercialization of natural gas both in the regulated market (EDP Gas Serviço Universal) and the free market (EDP Commercial). Additionally the Group develops the supply business of propane gas through EDP Gas GPLS.A.

Branching out across the peninsula EDP has grown its interests in HC Energia from 40% to 97% by purchasing the shares owned by German utility Energie Baden-Württemberg and Spanish banks Cajastur and Caser. It also controls 95% of Spanish gas utility Naturgas.

Financial Performance

In 2014 net revenues (in euros) remained flat due to increased sales from electricity and network access of about 171 million euros was offset by lower gas sales.

EDP's net income increased by 6% due to higher financial income and decreased amortization and impairment charges and financial expenses. Net cash provided by operating activities decreased primarily due to a change in payments to suppliers and payments to personnel.

Strategy

The company is looking to grow its generating capacity primarily through the development of wind-powered generating plants through its EDP Renovaveis unit. In 2014 EDP Renovaveis. entered into an agreement with CWEI Brasil a subsidiary of China Three Gorges to sell an equity shareholding of 49% in its wind farm developments in Brazil. In 2014 EDP agreed with ACE Asia (an entity related to China Three Gorges) to sell 50% of subsidiary EDP Asia. EDP Asia holds a 21.2% stake of Companhia de Electricidade de Macau which has held the exclusive concession for the transmission distribution and commercialization of electricity in the Macao Special Administrative Region since 1985.

That year EDP and Cheniere Energy signed a binding agreement for the supply to EDP with 1 billion cubic meters of liquefied natural gas (LNG) per year for a 20 year period beginning in 2020. Cheniere is building a liquefaction plant in Corpus Christi in Texas.

HISTORY

Company Background

EDP - Energias de Portugal has its roots in the several power enterprises that sprouted throughout the country during the infancy of electricity. The first recorded event in Portugal's electrification was the import of six voltaic arc lamps in 1878. The nation's first large-scale project saw the light in 1893 when the city of Braga was illuminated by the Sociedade de Electricidade do Norte de Portugal.

Electricity grew throughout the 1900s in the form of municipal concession contracts for distribution and government-licensed power plants. Large-scale power stations were not in effect in Portugal until after 1947 when Companhia Nacional de Electricidade was formed to interconnect the small generating systems dotting the nation. From the 1950s to mid-1970s new companies were formed to bring electricity to various parts of Portugal.

The original Electricidade de Portugal was founded in the wake of a leftist revolution during the 1970s in Portugal. In what became known as the Captain's Revolution military officers overthrew the Portuguese government which had been a dictatorship since 1933. The new government dominated by Marxists nationalized Portugal's industries including its generation transmission and distribution companies in 1975. The next year the Portuguese government created Electricidade de Portugal to unify the recently nationalized companies.

A new Social Democrat government came to power in 1987 and decided to denationalize Portuguese industry including EDP. The company reorganized into four major sectors in 1994: production (headed by its CPPE subsidiary) transmission distribution and services (led by its REN subsidiary which operated the national grid four regional utilities and 10 services units). EDP was the holding company.

Seeking opportunities opened up by the privatization of Brazil's state-owned electricity distributor EDP joined a consortium with Spain's Endesa and Chile's Chilectra to buy 70% of Rio de Janeiro distributor CERJ in 1996. The next year EDP gained a license to help build a hydro plant in Brazil. By 1998 the Endesa-led consortium had gained control of another Brazilian distributor Coelce.

The Portuguese government floated 30% of EDP in 1997 raising $1.76 billion. In a joint venture with the UK's PowerGen and Germany's Siemens EDP formed Turbogas to operate a power plant that would produce 20% of Portugal's electricity.

In 1998 EDP forged an alliance with Spain's Iberdrola and bought 80% of Guatemalan utility EEGSA. That year EDP and São Paulo utility CPFL gained control of São Paulo distributor Bandeirante. In 1999 EDP acquired stakes in two other Brazilian distributors. It also joined the UK's Thames Water to develop projects in Portugal Chile and Brazil and bought 45% of Chilean water and sewage company Essel. (EDP exchanged its stake in Essel for Thames Water's interest in the Portuguese joint venture in 2002.) The Portuguese state reduced its stake in EDP to about 50% in 1999.

Stepping up its telecommunications activities in 2000 EDP made its telecom unit Onitelecom (ONI) fully operational and agreed to share a fiber-optic network on the Iberian Peninsula with Spain's Iberdrola. (In 2006 however the company sold its stake in ONI.) Also in 2000 the Portuguese government acquired a majority stake in EDP's REN unit and EDP combined its four power distribution utilities into one unit (EDP Distribuição).

In 2001 EDP and Spanish savings bank Cajastur jointly bid to buy Hidrocantabrico one of Spain's leading utilities. EDP won control of 20% of Hidrocantabrico while German utility Energie Baden-Württemberg (EnBW) won control of 60%. The following year after a fierce bidding war the two companies agreed that EDP would control the majority share (40%) while EnBW would own only 35%.

The company changed its name from EDP - Electricidade de Portugal to EDP - Energias de Portugal in 2004.

Since 2007 the company has sold much of its holdings in other firms to pay down debt. Divestment deals include a 30% stake in Portugal's national transmission grid operator Rede Electrica Nacional (REN); a 40% stake in TURBOGAS - Produtora Energetica the company behind the construction of gas power station Tapada do Outeiro; and a 27% stake in PORTUGEN - Energia which is in charge of operating Tapada do Outeiro. In 2011 it sold a 7.7% stake in Brazil's Ampla Energia to a subsidiary of Spain's Endesa for euro 85 million ($121 million).

EXECUTIVES

Executive Director and CFO, Nuno M. Pestana de Almeida Alves, age 58
CEO, Ant nio Lu s Guerra Nunes Mexia, age 56
Executive Director, Jo o Manuel Manso Neto, age 58
Executive Director, Ant nio Manuel Barreto Pita de Abreu
Executive Director, Ant nio Fernando Melo Martins da Costa, age 62
Executive Director, Jo o Manuel Ver ssimo Marques da Cruz, age 55
Executive Director, Miguel Stilwell de Andrade
Auditors: KPMG & Associados, SROC, S.A.

LOCATIONS

HQ: EDP Energias de Portugal S.A.
Praca Marques de Pombal 12, Lisbon 1250-162
Phone: (351) 21 001 25 00 **Fax:** (351) 21 001 14 03
Web: www.edp.pt

2014 Sales

	% of total
Portugal	51
Spain	27
Brazil	18
US	2
Other	2
Total	**100**

PRODUCTS/OPERATIONS

2014 Sales

	% of total
Electricity and Network access	87
Gas and Network access	10
Revenue from assets assigned to concessions	3
Sales of CO2 licences	0
Other	0
Total	**100**

COMPETITORS

AES	Endesa S.A.
Cemig	Enel

E.ON
ELETROBRS
Electrabel
Electricite de France

IBERDROLA
Jazztel
RWE

HISTORICAL FINANCIALS
Company Type: Public

Income Statement
FYE: December 31

	REVENUE ($ mil.)	NET INCOME ($ mil.)	NET PROFIT MARGIN	EMPLOYEES
12/15	16,901	994	5.9%	12,084
12/14	19,805	1,264	6.4%	11,798
12/13	22,169	1,383	6.2%	12,179
12/12	21,536	1,334	6.2%	12,275
12/11	19,558	1,454	7.4%	12,219
Annual Growth	(3.6%)	(9.1%)	—	(0.3%)

2015 Year-End Financials

Debt ratio: 49.3%
Return on equity: 10.5%
Cash ($ mil.): 1,356
Current ratio: 0.72
Long-term debt ($ mil.): 17,050

No. of shares (mil.): —
Dividends
Yield: 3.7%
Payout: 492.3%
Market value ($ mil.): —

	STOCK PRICE ($) FY Close	P/E High/Low		PER SHARE ($) Earnings	Dividends	Book Value
12/15	36.16	163	129	0.27	1.37	2.60
12/14	38.85	156	111	0.35	1.65	2.90
12/13	36.57	137	109	0.39	1.55	3.20
12/12	30.66	115	78	0.37	1.65	2.98
12/11	31.10	122	85	0.40	1.72	2.89
Annual Growth	3.8%	—	—	(9.2%)	(5.5%)	(2.7%)

Eiffage SA

EIFFAGE whips up bridges tunnels and roads the way others might whip cream. With dozens of subsidiaries the company builds infrastructure and commercial projects primarily in western Europe. The group is active in five sectors: concessions and public-private partnerships (PPPs); construction; public works; energy; and metal. Its construction activities include civil engineering new housing and commercial and industrial building and is split evenly between the public and private sectors. Major completed projects include the Perpignan-Figueras high speed rail link and the Millau Viaduct —the world's highest cable-stayed bridge. France accounts for the vast majority of EIFFAGE's business.

Geographic Reach

France is EIFFAGE SA's single largest market accounting for 85% of total revenue. International projects in some 15 mainly European countries accounts for the rest. Other areas of operation include Africa and Asia.

Operations

Europe's fourth-largest construction and concessions group EIFFAGE generates about 30% of its revenue from public works projects such as road and rail construction civil engineering drainage and earthworks. Energy including electrical engineering HVAC and process automation projects contributes about 20%. Construction projects include urban development property development construction and maintenance and facilities management. It brings in about 20% of EIFFAGE's revenue. The firm's concessions business (approximately 15% of annual revenue) erects and operates motorways and other large infrastructures and public facilities such as stadiums and buildings. EIFFAGE Construction Metallique and Eiffel Industrie which are engaged in metal work including sheet metal work values and pipework facades and offshore platform projects bring in the rest.

Financial Performance

The French group reported euro 14.4 billion ($19.6 billion) in revenue in 2013 up nearly 2% (before the effects of currency translation) versus 2012. The firm's net profit rose 17% to euro 257 million ($354 million). Contracting which accounted for 84% of the group's total annual revenue increased 1% year over year while revenue from EIFFAGE's concessions business rose 4%. The public works business outperformed the group's other activities posting a 7% gain. On a regional basis sales in France and the rest of Europe rose about 1% while other markets posted a 26% annual gain.

Cash flow generated by operations declined for the second consecutive year in 2013 on steeply rising capital expenditures.

Strategy

With its diverse line of businesses EIFFAGE is better-equipped than most to handle market fluctuations such as downturns in the construction industry or in government spending. By securing contracts for ambitious complex structures it gains multiple-year streams of revenue. It further sustains those revenues by providing maintenance and operations services. Recently awarded contracts include the Grand Stade Lille Metropole multi-use stadium which will house the Lille OSC soccer team. EIFFAGE was also selected to design build and operate the Brittany-Loire Valley high-speed rail link.

EIFFAGE has become the massive group it is through numerous acquisitions with a focus on Europe. Recent deals include the September 2013 purchase of the main companies of the Smulders Group by Eiffage's metals branch which strengthened its presence in the offshore energy market. Smulders is a key player in the wind energy market.

HISTORY

Fougerolle made its name in construction during the 1840s with the completion of the Nivernaise canal. Co-founded by Philippe and Jacques Fougerolle in 1844 the company went on to begin construction of Saint Gothard tunnel in the Swiss Alps which was completed in 1882.

By 1890 the company expanded its operations in France to include work on the metro line between Porte de Clichy and Place de la Trinite and internationally with construction of the Namur fortifications in Belgium. It completed the Adolphe bridge in Luxembourg in 1903 and was granted a contract to construct the Rio Grande do Sul port in Brazil in 1908.

During WWI the company was enlisted to help keep the flow of supplies steady between Paris and Amiens with the construction of a second railroad. After the war the company returned to its previous operations under the name Le Soliditit Français. It completed several airship hangars in Orly France in 1921.

During the 1920s and 1930s the company expanded its operations into French colonies building the port in Dakar (1927) and the Deir Ez Zor bridge over the Euphrates River on the Iraq-Syria border. Domestically the company constructed a series of fortifications making up the Maginot line to try to deter a German invasion. It also managed to complete one arm of the Parisian Metro before the Germans invaded in 1940.

The company resumed its operations and helped rebuild war-torn France. It bought up subsidiaries but remained a family-led company with a decentralized management —during a time when the French construction industry was beginning a shift toward larger government-influenced public conglomerates.

In 1954 it completed the Bin el Ouidane dam in Morocco and the Serre-Ponçon dam in the French Alps in 1960. The company reorganized under the name Societe des Entreprises Fougerolle Limousin in 1970. Aided by 20 years of economic growth in France the company acquired construction specialist Societe Nouvelle de Constructions et de Travaux (1973) and foundation specialist Gifor (1974).

A series of losses on projects in Iraq and Nigeria coupled with the collapse of the French construction market in the early 1980s nearly bankrupted the company. It was spared with the help of investment banking firm Paribas and oil company TOTALl in 1982. A third major investor Generale des Eaux attempted to acquire Fougerolle in the late 1980s but its efforts were thwarted by an employee-led buyout of the company headed by CEO Jean-François Roverato in 1989.

Fougerolle bolstered is operations with the acquisition of France's second largest-construction firm Societe Auxiliaire d'Entreprise (SAE) in 1992 and the combined companies were renamed Eiffage in 1993. The group began to consolidate the complementary operations of the two companies. In 1999 Fougerolle Quillery and SAE combined to form Eiffage Construction and Norelec and Forclum were formed into the group's electrical contracting arm. Eiffage's road construction operations were brought together as Appia in 2000. The next year Eiffage shareholders agreed to merge with its holding company Financière SAE-Fougerolle in order to reduce the company's debt.

In 2001 the company completed a leveraged management buyout that had begun in 1990. Employee ownership of the company was reduced to 23%. The next year Eiffage along with French construction giant VINCI acquired a stake in ASF Europe's second-largest toll road operator. In 2002 the group also gained control of Polish construction company Mitex.

That year EIFFAGE and rival French construction giant VINCI grabbed nearly 20% of Autoroutes du Sud de la France when it was partly privatized.

The company reorganized in 2004 shedding excess baggage and streamlining operations. It sold its stake in ASF to VINCI.

Spanish construction group Sacyr Vallehermoso acquired more than 30% of EIFFAGE in 2006 but —after a nearly two-year-long dispute between the rivals -- sold that stake to a group of French investors (including Caisse des Depôts and Groupama) in 2008.

EXECUTIVES
CEO, Max Roche
Interim Chairman, Jean-Fran ßis Roverato
Auditors: KPMG Audit IS

LOCATIONS
HQ: Eiffage SA
   Campus Pierre Berger, 3-7, place de l' Europe, Velizy-Villacoublay 78140
Phone: (33) 1 34 65 89 89
Web: www.eiffage.com

2013 Sales

	% of total
France	84
Rest of Europe	14
Other countries	2
Total	100

PRODUCTS/OPERATIONS

2013 Sales

	% of total
Public works	30
Energy	22
Construction	21
Concessions	16
Metal	6
Property development	5
Total	**100**

Major Subsidiaries
Clemessy
Eiffage Concessions (highway and other infrastructure operations)
Eiffage Construction (building industry and property development)
Eiffage Energie
Eiffage Travaux Publics (road and railway construction civil engineering and earthworks)
Eiffel (metallic construction and glass facades)
Forclum (electrical contracting and facilities management)

COMPETITORS

Ballast Nedam NV	Parsons Corporation
Bechtel	STRABAG SE
Bilfinger	Sacyr Vallehermoso
Bouygues	Schneider Electric
Colas	Skanska
Fluor	Taisei
HOCHTIEF	Technip
Hyundai Engineering and Construction	VINCI
Nishimatsu Construction	

HISTORICAL FINANCIALS

Company Type: Public

Income Statement

FYE: December 31

	REVENUE ($ mil.)	NET INCOME ($ mil.)	NET PROFIT MARGIN	EMPLOYEES
12/15	15,320	339	2.2%	50,854
12/14	16,961	334	2.0%	66,022
12/13	19,657	353	1.8%	67,329
12/12	18,497	289	1.6%	68,839
12/11	17,871	265	1.5%	70,221
Annual Growth	(3.8%)	6.4%	—	(7.8%)

2015 Year-End Financials

Debt ratio: 61.3%	No. of shares (mil.): 90
Return on equity: 10.2%	Dividends
Cash ($ mil.): 3,965	Yield: 0.0%
Current ratio: 0.95	Payout: 4.4%
Long-term debt ($ mil.): 13,993	Market value ($ mil.): 1,117

	STOCK PRICE ($) FY Close	P/E High/Low		PER SHARE ($) Earnings	Dividends	Book Value
12/15	12.31	4	3	3.61	0.16	38.37
12/14	9.60	4	3	3.67	0.18	39.57
12/13	10.60	4	3	3.99	0.21	42.64
12/12	6.10	3	3	3.33	0.20	35.80
12/11	9.00	—	—	2.95	0.00	35.49
Annual Growth	8.1%	—	—	5.2%	—	2.0%

Electricite de France

State-owned Electricite de France (EDF) has been quick to expand into global deregulated markets. One of the world's top electric utilities (as well as one of the last major state-controlled energy gi-

ants in Europe) EDF has a generating capacity of more than 654 TWh (primarily from nuclear sources) and provides power to 28.5 million French customers and 10 million customers in other countries. It's transmission and distribution subsidiaries in France operate 1.3 million km of low and medium voltage power lines and 100000 km of high and very high voltage networks. Its EDF Trading unit trades a range of energy products.

Geographic Reach

The company operates power plants in Europe Africa the Americas Asia and the Middle East.

Operations

EDF operates in three major segments: Generation/Supply –energy generation and energy sales to industry local authorities small businesses and residential consumers. This segment also includes commodity trading activities; Distribution –the management of the low and medium-voltage public distribution network; and Other –energy services (district heating thermal energy services etc.) for industry and local authorities and new businesses mainly aimed at boosting electricity generation through cogeneration and renewable energy sources.

Nuclear plants provide the vast majority of EDF's domestic power supply; other sources include hydroelectric and fossil-fueled plants. Making use of its extensive experience especially in developing nuclear power EDF builds power plants and provides plant management and consulting services worldwide.

In the UK EDF's units include EDF Energy Nuclear Generation Ltd and EDF Development Company Ltd. In Italy operations are led by the Edison subgroup TdE and Fenice.

EDF International and the other gas and electricity entities are located in continental Europe the US Latin America and Asia. Other activities include EDF Trading EDF ?nergies Nouvelles Dalkia Tiru ?lectricite de Strasbourg and EDF Investissements Groupe.

Financial Performance

EDF's net revenues increased by 1% in 2014 primarily due to an increase in Other activities driven by organic growth of euro 22 million as the result of the takeover of former joint venture Dalkia's activities in France in 2014.

Net income increased by 5% due to higher revenues changes in net increases in provisions for renewal of property plant and equipment operated under concessions and a share in net income of associates and joint ventures.

In 2014 the company's cash inflow decreased by 2% due to changes in working capital as a result of changes in net financial expenses disbursed and income taxes paid.

Strategy

EDF is investing aggressively outside of France.

In 2015 the EDF Energies Nouvelles entered into the South American market by setting up a local subsidiary in Brazil EDF EN do Brasil. EDF Energies Nouvelles purchased a portfolio of wind energy development projects from SOWITEC one of the leading international renewable energy developers with a total capacity of about 800 MW.

That year EDF announced additional capacity at the Arada-Montemuro (9.2 MW) and São Pedro (2 MW) wind farms in Portugal. These extensions increased the combined capacity of these two facilities to 133 MW. In 2015 EDF also signed an agreement with China General Nuclear Power Group to share their experience of plant operation and engineering support for existing nuclear fleets with the aim of preserving the highest safety levels and maintaining consistency between French and Chinese procedures and standards. It also signed an agreement with Huadian a leading Chi-

nese electric utility paving the way for future cooperation on joint projects in China and elsewhere.

In 2014 the company and the UK government agreed to build a new nuclear power station at Hinkley Point C in Somerset. That year EDF also signed an agreement with Constellation Energy Nuclear Group (CENG) delegating to Exelon operational management of the five nuclear reactors owned by CENG. Exelon also granted to EDF an option to sell its holding in CENG to Exelon between 2016 and 2022. After this deal EDF will continue to hold 49.99% of CENG whilst Exelon will hold 50.01%.

In 2013 EDF signed an agreement with Global Energy Holding Company (GEHC) for the creation of a joint venture in nuclear energy Riyadh. The JV will carry out feasibility studies in the context of the Saudi nuclear program based on French technology.

Ownership

The French government owns 85% of the company.

HISTORY

Company Background

The French government nationalized hundreds of regional private firms to form Electricite de France (EDF) in 1946 as part of an effort to rebuild the nation's badly shaken post-war economy. This was a marked difference from the notoriously complex and inefficient pre-war electrical industry.

By the 1950s EDF had taken advantage of the centralized control and developed massive hydroelectric projects. Hydroelectric power would account for more than 70% of EDF's power.

But in France as elsewhere hydro wasn't enough to keep up with the growing demand for electricity and fossil fuels became an increasingly important power source. Then came the oil shortages of the 1970s and France –with limited domestic supplies of oil and gas –began searching for alternatives to fossil-fueled plants. Nuclear power was determined to be the answer.

The government moved to invest billions of dollars in developing its relatively small nuclear power production facilities. Muddled with Malthusian predictions of power shortages and a preoccupation with having enough energy to be self-reliant France found its nuclear operations left the government with more energy than it could use and more debt than it wanted. The company began to build a cable connecting the Continent to the UK in 1981. With the power grids of the two countries connected in 1986 EDF was finally able to start exporting its power to the Brits.

The 1990s brought with them deregulation. EDF fought to keep the UK-France grid closed to other energy sellers. After the government forbade the utility from diversifying into areas other than electricity in 1995 the company turned its attention to foreign investment especially in Latin America.

The company faced increasing deregulatory pressures from without in the late 1990s. The newly formed European Union required open competition from member states. Begrudgingly and behind schedule EDF opened about 30% of its market to competition in 2000.

Other members of the EU complained that EDF was trying to play it both ways: It was making aggressive acquisitions in the UK liberalized market (it bought London Electricity in 1999) while resisting a competition-enabling breakup or even allowing a foreign competitor to buy a stake in the French market.

EDF in 2001 expanded its stake in Italy's Montedison a conglomerate with substantial energy holdings by forming a consortium (Italenergia) with

Italian automaker Fiat and some Italian banks to wrest control of Montedison from Italian bank MEDIOBANCA. Although the consortium owns 94% of Montedison EDF has only 2% of voting rights. (Montedison changed its name to Edison in 2002.)

EDF also purchased a 35% interest in German utility Energie Baden-Württemberg in 2001 and it merged its energy services unit with Dalkia a unit of Vivendi Environnement (now Veolia Environnement) taking a 34% stake in Dalkia (which will eventually be increased to 50%). EDF subsidiary London Electricity agreed to buy $2.4 billion in UK assets from TXU Europe that year including a 2000 MW power plant TXU's Eastern Electricity distribution unit and its interest in TXU/EDF joint venture 24seven; the deals were completed in 2001 and 2002.

In 2002 EDF increased its stake in Brazilian utility Light Serviços de Eletricidade to 88% by swapping Light's interest in São Paulo utility Eletropaulo for AES's 24% interest in Light. Later that year EDF purchased UK electric and gas utility SEEBOARD (1.9 million customers) from US utility AEP in a $2.2 billion deal.

Deregulation of 70% of the French market took effect in July 2004. Between 2000 and 2004 only 30% of the market was deregulated just more than the percentage required by European Union (EU) rulings.

EDF acquired Edison SpA (Italy's second-largest power group) in partnership with Italian utility company AEM SpA in 2005 for an estimated $15.4 billion.

Expanding its presence and its position as a nuclear power provider in the US in 2009 EDF unit EDF Development acquired 49.99% of Constellation Energy's Constellation Energy Nuclear Group LLC for $4.5 billion. (However another joint venture between these two parties aimed at developing new nuclear power plants in the US was terminated in 2010 after strategic disagreements between the principals).

In a move to boost its position as both a major energy and a nuclear power player in Europe in 2009 EDF acquired British Energy with its 1.1 million customer accounts for about $18 billion.

In 2010 EDF signed two new agreements with China National Nuclear Corporation and China Guangdong Nuclear Power Holding Company solidifying its role as a long term partner in China's nuclear development program. (The company has worked in China for 25 years.)

To help pay down debt to pay for its expansion in 2010 Hong Kong's Cheung Kong Infrastructure and Hongkong Electric both controlled by Hong Kong-based billionaire Li Ka-shing acquired EDF's three UK distribution UK grids in a deal valued at about $9 billion. In 2011 EDF sold its 45% stake in German power utility Energie Baden-Württemberg for $6.1 billion.

In 2012 EDF acquired the Italy-based energy group Edison by purchasing Delmi's entire investment (50%) in Transalpina Di Energia for a total of euro 784 million. Following this acquisition the Group held 78.96% of the capital and 80.64% of the voting rights in Edison.

Not to be left out in the competitive renewable energy market EDF is seeking to boost its wind and solar energy output from a few hundred MW in 2008 to 4000 MW (in 2012) and higher in 2013.

The company is working on a euro 6 billion Flamanville EPR construction project in France. In early 2013 the civil engineering work was 94% complete and 39% of the electro-mechanical equipment was in place. Its other projects included French offshore projects at Saint-Nazaire Courseulles-sur-Mer and Fecamp.

EXECUTIVES

Director Upstream-Downstream Optimisation and Trading Division, Philippe Torrion
SEVP HR, Marianne Laigneau
Chairman and CEO, Jean-Bernard Levy, age 60
Chief Executive EDF Energies Nouvelles, Antoine Cahuzac
SEVP Commerce Optimisation and Trading and Island Energy Systems, Henri Lafontaine
SEVP Gas and Southern Europe; Chief Executive Edison, Bruno Lescoeur
Chief Executive EDF Energy, Vincent de Rivaz
Director Hydraulic Production and Engineering Division, Xavier Ursat
Interim CFO, Xavier Girre
Auditors: Deloitte & Associés

LOCATIONS

HQ: Electricite de France
22-30 avenue de Wagram, Paris, Cedex 08 75382
Phone: (33) 1 40 42 22 22   **Fax:** (33) 1 40 42 32 17
Web: www.edf.com

2014 Sales

	% of total
France	55
Italy	17
UK	14
Other countries	8
Other activities	6
Total	**100**

COMPETITORS

Business Group Benelux	Hydro-Quebec
Centrica	IBERDROLA
E.ON	International Power
ELETROBRS	RWE
Endesa S.A.	Scottish and Southern
Enel	Energy
Energias de Portugal	Vattenfall
Engie	Veolia Environnement

HISTORICAL FINANCIALS

Company Type: Public

Income Statement

FYE: December 31

	REVENUE ($ mil.)	NET INCOME ($ mil.)	NET PROFIT MARGIN	EMPLOYEES
12/15	81,697	1,292	1.6%	159,112
12/14	88,578	4,498	5.1%	158,161
12/13	104,072	4,841	4.7%	158,467
12/12	95,860	4,370	4.6%	159,740
12/11	84,471	3,893	4.6%	151,804
Annual Growth	(0.8%)	(24.1%)	—	1.2%

2015 Year-End Financials

Debt ratio: 25.0%
Return on equity: 3.3%
Cash ($ mil.): 4,555
Current ratio: 1.30
Long-term debt ($ mil.): 57,383

No. of shares (mil.): 1,917
Dividends
Yield: 14.0%
Payout: 79.3%
Market value ($ mil.): 5,638

	STOCK PRICE ($) FY Close	P/E High/Low		PER SHARE ($) Earnings	Dividends	Book Value
12/15	2.94	17	8	0.35	0.41	19.74
12/14	5.43	4	3	2.16	0.33	23.02
12/13	7.01	4	2	2.53	0.33	25.34
12/12	3.71	3	2	2.37	0.29	18.46
12/11	4.81	5	3	2.11	0.30	21.40
Annual Growth	(11.6%)	—	—	(36.2%)	8.6%	(2.0%)

Electricity Generating Authority of Thailand

LOCATIONS

HQ: Electricity Generating Authority of Thailand
53 Moo 2,, Charansanitwong Road, Bang Kruai,
Nonthaburi 11130
Phone: (66) 2 436 1416   **Fax:** (66) 2 436 4832
Web: www.egat.co.th

HISTORICAL FINANCIALS

Company Type: Public

Income Statement

FYE: December 31

	REVENUE ($ mil.)	NET INCOME ($ mil.)	NET PROFIT MARGIN	EMPLOYEES
12/15	15,167	865	5.7%	22,776
12/14	16,962	1,180	7.0%	22,920
12/13	16,400	1,232	7.5%	22,957
12/12	16,764	1,267	7.6%	22,825
12/11	13,296	1,011	7.6%	22,981
Annual Growth	3.3%	(3.8%)	—	(0.2%)

2015 Year-End Financials

Debt ratio: 1.1%
Return on equity: 9.1%
Cash ($ mil.): 2,016
Current ratio: 1.66
Long-term debt ($ mil.): 9,438

No. of shares (mil.): —
Dividends
Yield: —
Payout: —
Market value ($ mil.): —

Empire Co Ltd

Decline and fall? Not for this Empire of supermarkets food distribution movie theaters and real estate. Empire Company owns Sobeys Canada's #2 grocery chain (after Loblaw). Sobeys runs some 1500 food and drug stores across Canada under names such as Sobeys IGA Foodland Price Chopper and Lawton's Drug; it distributes food to its company-owned stores and other retailers. Wholly owned Empire Theatres operates about 50 theaters (390 screens) in eight provinces and is the #2 movie exhibitor in Canada. Empire is also party to a joint venture with oil and gas properties in Alberta. Controlled by the Sobey family Empire also develops and manages commercial and to a lesser extent residential real estate.

Operations

While Sobeys has always been important to its parent company it has become even more so since Empire took the grocery chain private in 2007. Increasingly Empire's focus and capital resources are behind the food retailer and its underlying real estate. Indeed in fiscal 2012 (ends May) Sobeys represented the vast majority of Empire's sales (99%) and earnings (90%).

Beyond its core food retailing business Empire owns a large portfolio of commercial properties in Canada including millions of square feet in shopping centers in the maritime provinces. Its commercial real estate operations include wholly owned ECL Properties which develops shopping centers related to the Sobeys business. ECL has about 18 grocery-anchored shopping centers under development in Ontario Quebec and Atlantic Canada nearly all of which will be anchored by a Sobeys store. ECL also owns about 40% of Genstar Development Partnership (a developer of residential property headquartered in San Diego) and about 44% of Crombie REIT a Canadian real estate income trust investing in retail office and mixed-use properties in Canada. ETL Canada Holdings (better known as Empire Theatres) is the nation's second-largest movie exhibitor.

Financial Performance

Empire Company's consolidated fiscal 2012 (ends May) sales increased by about $292 million (nearly 2%) vs. the prior year to more than $16.2 billion after adjusting for the impact of the additional week of operations in fiscal 2011 and the purchase of 236 combination convenience store/gas station locations. Same-store sales at Sobeys stores increased 1.4% over the same period largely driven by merchandising initiatives. Empire's investment and other operations business segment (which includes Empire Theatres and its property development businesses) posted an increase in sales of about 1.5% in 2012 vs. the prior year.

In a bid to become a truly national company Empire is extending its reach beyond its stronghold in Atlantic Canada westward to Quebec Ontario and western Canada. To that end Empire has agreed to acquire US grocery giant Safeway's stores in Canada (Canada Safeway) for C$5.8 billion ($5.6 billion). Previously Sobeys in 2012 purchased 236 Shell retail gas locations and their associated convenience store operations located in Atlantic Canada and Quebec. The deal follows similar savvy geographic purchases such as the acquisition of British Columbia-based Thrifty Foods a food wholesaler and retailer with 20 supermarkets. The company's wholly owned Empire Theatres business is employing digital and 3D technologies in its cinemas to boost attendance. It is also presenting alternative programming including live NBA games in 3D to generate a buzz and ticket sales.

HISTORY

J. W. Sobey started a butcher shop and meat delivery business in Nova Scotia in 1907. In 1924 his son Frank —who had worked for his father from boyhood —persuaded J. W. to expand the business into a full grocery operation. The Sobeys had six grocery stores in Nova Scotia by 1939.

Frank Sobey known both for his knack for innovation and his fanatical attention to cost control helped the company grow by promising low prices and by introducing new products and concepts into the Sobey grocery business. On a trip through the US in the 1940s Sobey witnessed first-hand the operation of a new type of grocery store —the supermarket. He introduced the first Sobeys supermarket in Nova Scotia in 1947.

The business continued to grow during the 1950s and 1960s expanding throughout Canada's Maritime Provinces. By 1971 Frank Sobey's sons Bill David and Donald had taken over the operation of various aspects of the family business; the patriarch remained active as chairman of the company until his death in 1985.

As Bill and David Sobey continued to build the grocery operation Donald steered the growth of the family's business in real estate and investments — which was carried out as the Empire Company. Empire went public on the Toronto Stock Exchange in 1983. At the same time the family folded the Sobeys chain —which had been publicly traded since the 1950s —into Empire. In 1987 Sobeys opened its first store in Ontario; by the early 1990s Sobeys had expanded in Ontario and into Quebec.

The 1998 acquisition of The Oshawa Group (owner of the IGA and Price Chopper grocery chains) tripled the size of Sobeys and made its SERCA food service distributorship the largest in

Canada. Also in 1998 Paul Sobey —nephew of Empire chairman Donald Sobey —became president and CEO of Empire.

Late that year Empire took Sobeys public again retaining a majority stake in the grocery business. In 2000 Empire sold its 25% stake in US-based grocery retailer Hannaford Bros. Co. to Delhaize America for more than $800 million in cash and stock.

Early in 2001 the company announced that it would abandon parts of its SAP supply-chain management software; according to the company problems with the software led to grocery stock shortages during the 2000 holiday season that cost it tens of millions of dollars. Significant changes in senior management during fiscal 2001 included the appointment of Bill McEwan as President and CEO of Sobeys.

In 2002 Empire sold its SERCA Foodservice unit to US-based SYSCO to focus on its core retail operations.

In July 2003 Empire raised its stake in Sobeys to 63.8% paying nearly $42 million for an additional 1.2 million shares.

In September 2004 Robert Dexter succeeded Donald Sobey as chairman of Empire the first chairman from outside the Sobey family.

In fiscal 2006 Empire converted its Wajax equipment distribution business into an income fund and doubled the size of its Empire Theatres business with the acquisition of 28 movie theaters. (It sold off its Wajax stake in late 2010.)

In June 2007 Empire paid about $54 per share to acquire all of Sobeys' shares it did not already own thereby taking the grocery chain private. Sobeys was delisted from the Toronto Stock Exchange on June 18. 2007. In September Sobeys acquired Thrifty Foods a British Columbia-based chain of about 20 supermarkets for about $250 million.

Empire in October 2010 sold its 27% stake in Wajax Income Fund to focus on food retailing and real estate.

EXECUTIVES

President CEO and Director and President and CEO Sobeys Inc., Michael B. Medline
EVP, Fran $is Vimard
Interim CFO, Clinton Keay
Chairman, James M. (Jim) Dickson
Auditors: PricewaterhouseCoopers LLP

LOCATIONS

HQ: Empire Co Ltd
115 King Street, Stellarton, Nova Scotia B0K 1S0
Phone: 902 755-4440   **Fax:** 902 755-6477
Web: www.empireco.ca

COMPETITORS

AMC Entertainment	Loblaw
Cinemark	London Drugs
Costco Wholesale	METRO
Canada	Provigo
Couche-Tard	Shoppers Drug Mart
Jean Coutu	Wal-Mart Canada
Jim Pattison Group	Whole Foods
Katz Group	

HISTORICAL FINANCIALS
Company Type: Public

Income Statement
FYE: May 7

	REVENUE ($ mil.)	NET INCOME ($ mil.)	NET PROFIT MARGIN	EMPLOYEES
05/16	19,187	(1,655)	—	125,000
05/15	19,923	346	1.7%	0
05/14	19,216	214	1.1%	125,000
05/13	17,521	380	2.2%	47,000
05/12	16,529	343	2.1%	47,000
Annual Growth	3.8%	—	—	27.7%

2016 Year-End Financials

Debt ratio: 20.1%
Return on equity: (-43.6%)
Cash ($ mil.): 205
Current ratio: 0.96
Long-term debt ($ mil.): 1,562

No. of shares (mil.): 271
Dividends
  Yield: 0.0%
  Payout: —
Market value ($ mil.): 4,451

	STOCK PRICE ($) FY Close	P/E High/Low		PER SHARE ($) Earnings	Dividends	Book Value
05/16	16.38	—	—	(6.05)	0.31	10.36
05/15	71.34	52	36	1.25	0.30	17.85
05/14	62.18	77	61	0.89	0.32	18.79
05/13	66.03	35	24	1.87	0.32	18.08
05/12	60.16	38	33	1.68	0.30	16.86
Annual Growth(27.8%) (11.5%)		—	—	—	0.6%	

Empresas COPEC SA

Everything is copasetic at Copec as long as the gas and oil keep flowing. Empresas Copec (formerly known as Compa ±a de Petr leos de Chile) is the country's #1 importer and distributor of gasoline and petroleum by-products sold through several channels including its more than 600 gas stations. Copec's interests aren't single-minded though: The industrial conglomerate owns Celulosa Arauco y Constituci n (whose subsidiaries and affiliates cover the spectrum of forestry and wood products manufacturing) and fisheries businesses Corpesca and SouthPacific Korp or SPK. Other interests include mining electricity and retail holdings. Chile's Angelini family (through AntarChile) controls some 60% of Copec.

Empresas Copec seeks to keep its top dog position by maintaining an efficient cost structure and a conservative financial profile as it focuses on two major areas —natural resources and fuels.

EXECUTIVES

CEO Corpesca, Arturo Natho Gamboa
CEO Copec S.A., Lorenzo Gazmuri Schleyer
CFO, Rodrigo Huidobro Alvarado
CEO Sonacol, Roberto Hetz Vorpahl
CEO, Eduardo Navarro Beltr ̈n
EVP Celulosa Arauco y Constituci ín, Mat as Domeyko Cassel
CEO Abastible, Joaqu n Cruz Sanfiel
CEO Metrogas, V ctor Turpaud Fern ̈ndez
CEO Orizon, Rigoberto Rojo Rojas
CEO Alxar Miner a, Erwin Kaufmann Salinas
CEO Mina Invierno, Sebasti ̈n Gil Clasen
Chairman, Roberto Angelini Rossi

LOCATIONS

HQ: Empresas COPEC SA
Avenida El Golf 150, Piso 17, Santiago, comuna de Las Condes 6500586
Phone: (56) 2 461 7000   **Fax:** (56) 2 461 7070
Web: www.copec.cl

PRODUCTS/OPERATIONS

2007 Sales

	% of total
Fuels	73
Forestry	26
Fisheries	1
Total	**100**

COMPETITORS

Endesa S.A.	Petrobras
Enersis	Distribuidora
Falabella	Repsol
International Paper	Walmart Chile

HISTORICAL FINANCIALS

Company Type: Public

Income Statement

FYE: December 31

	REVENUE ($ mil.)	NET INCOME ($ mil.)	NET PROFIT MARGIN	EMPLOYEES
12/15	18,160	539	3.0%	25
12/14	23,840	855	3.6%	22
12/13	24,339	786	3.2%	23
12/12	22,761	409	1.8%	0
12/11	21,124	932	4.4%	0
Annual Growth	(3.7%)	(12.8%)	—	—

2015 Year-End Financials

Debt ratio: 28.7%
Return on equity: 5.6%
Cash ($ mil.): 1,584
Current ratio: 2.65
Long-term debt ($ mil.): 5,734
No. of shares (mil.): 1,299
Dividends
 Yield: —
 Payout: —
Market value ($ mil.): —

Enbridge Inc

Cold spells heated business for Enbridge in North America. Gas Pipelines Processing and Energy Services is Enbridge's largest segment but it also has interests in Gas Distribution Liquids Pipelines and Sponsored Investments. Its gas utilities provide natural gas to about 2 million customers primarily in Ontario and New York. Enbridge moves about 2.5 million barrels of crude oil a day and operates thousands of miles of natural gas pipeline including a 1500 mile system connecting Alberta and British Columbia to the Chicago area. In 2016 it agreed to merge with Spectra Energy. To free up cash for the deal the company sold pipelines and related assets in Saskatchewan and Manitoba for $1.1 billion.

Enbridge operates the world's longest crude oil and liquids pipeline system and transports 65% Western Canada's crude oil exports. It has natural gas gathering transmission and midstream operations and a power transmission business. The company also owns Canada's largest natural gas distribution operations. To meet clean air regulations Enbridge is also investing in geothermal hybrid fuel cell solar and wind power projects and has about 1000 MW of renewable and alternative energy generating capacity.

Enbridge operates in Canada and the US. It has gas distribution customers in Ontario Quebec New Brunswick and New York. Outside of North America the company provides natural gas distribution consulting services in more than 30 countries.

Embridge reported a 26% jump in revenues in 2011 thanks to an improving economy increased product sales and higher commodity oil and natural gas liquids prices. However net income grew by only 1.5% as higher gas commodity costs related to its gas pipelines processing and energy services segment trimmed back its profits.

In North America the company is investing heavily in pipeline construction to expand the reach of its oil and gas assets. In 2012 it teamed up with Spectra Energy and DTE Energy to develop the NEXUS Gas Transmission system a 250-mile pipeline to move natural gas from the Ohio Utica shale to markets in the US Midwest and Ontario. In 2011 Enbridge was eyeing $30 billion in growth opportunities under development extending pipelines from Canadian gas and oil sources for heavily populated markets in the Midwest and Southern US. In 2010 alone Enbridge put into service some $6.5 billion of growth projects including the $3.5 billion Alberta Clipper project the largest liquids pipeline project in the Enbridge's history which provides service between Hardisty Alberta and Superior Wisconsin.

In a major expansion in 2011 Enbridge acquired ConocoPhillips' 50% stake in the Seaway Crude Pipeline System for $1.15 billion and plans to reverse the direction of crude oil flows on the pipeline to enable it to ship oil from Cushing Oklahoma to Gulf Coast refineries.

In 2011 the company acquired Tonbridge Power for $20 million. Tonbridge Power is developing the Montana-Alberta Tie-Line power transmission project a 345-km transmission line from Great Falls Montana to Lethbridge Alberta.

Embridge has also agreed to work with PetroChina International Company to develop the Gateway Pipeline. The proposed pipeline would move 525000 barrels per day of oil sands production from Edmonton Alberta to a port in British Columbia where it would be shipped to California and on to China and other Asian markets.

Enbridge has cut back on its direct investments in international pipeline projects in order to focus on the growing demand and surer financing for pipeline expansion closer to home. (In 2009 Enbridge sold its quarter stake in Colombian pipeline operator Oleoducto Central S.A. to that country's national oil company Ecopetrol for $400 million. Cash from the deal was designated to fund North American crude oil pipeline expansion projects).

In 2016 the company announced the $538 million acquisition of Tupper Main and Tupper West gas plants and associated pipelines in northeastern British Columbiafrom the Canadian subsidiary of Murphy Oil.

EXECUTIVES

EVP Corporate Development, J. Richard Bird, age 67, $540,000 total compensation
President Gas Pipelines and Processing, C. Gregory (Greg) Harper, age 52
EVP and CFO, John K. Whelen
President CEO and Director, Al Monaco, age 57, $437,500 total compensation
EVP People and Partners, Karen L. Radford, age 47
EVP and Chief Legal Officer, David T. Robbottom
President Liquids Pipelines, Guy Jarvis
COO, Leon Zupan
President Enbridge Gas Distribution, Glenn Beaumont
Chairman, David A. Arledge, age 72
Auditors: PricewaterhouseCoopers LLP

LOCATIONS

HQ: Enbridge Inc
Suite 200, 425 - 1st Street S.W., Calgary, Alberta T2P 3L8
Phone: 403 231-5935   **Fax:** 403 231-5929
Web: www.enbridge.com

2015 Sales

	% of total
US	67
Canada	33
Total	**100**

PRODUCTS/OPERATIONS

2015 Sales

	% of total
Gas pipelines processing and energy services	62
Sponsored investments	23
Gas distribution	10
Liquids pipelines	5
Total	**100**

Selected Subsidiaries and Affiliates

Gas Pipelines Processing and Energy Services
  Aux Sable Liquids Products Inc. (43%)
  Alliance Pipeline Limited Partnership (50%)
  Tlbury Solar Project
  Vector Pipeline Limited Partnership (60%)
Gas Distribution
  Enbridge Gas Distribution
  Enbridge Gas New Brunswick (63%)
  Gazifère Inc.
  Niagara Gas Transmission Limited
Liquids Pipelines
  Chicap Pipe Line Company (44%)
  Enbridge Energy Partners L.P. (13%)
  Enbridge Pipelines (Athabasca) Inc.
  Enbridge Pipelines (North Dakota) Inc.
  Enbridge Pipelines (NW) Inc.
  Enbridge Pipelines (Toledo) Inc.
  Enbridge Pipelines Inc.
  Frontier Pipeline Company (78%)
  Mustang Pipe Line Partners (30%)
  Olympic Pipe Line (85%)
Sponsored Investments
  Enbridge Income Fund (72%)
  Enbridge Energy Partners L.P. (25.5%)
Corporate
  Noverco Inc. (39%)
  Gaz Métropolitain and Company Limited Partnership (71%)
  Vermont Gas Systems Inc.

COMPETITORS

Con Edison	New York Power
Dynegy	Authority
Hydro One	ONEOK Partners
Koch Industries Inc.	TransCanada
National Fuel Gas	Williams Companies

HISTORICAL FINANCIALS

Company Type: Public

Income Statement

FYE: December 31

	REVENUE ($ mil.)	NET INCOME ($ mil.)	NET PROFIT MARGIN	EMPLOYEES
12/15	24,331	180	0.7%	8,652
12/14	32,504	1,213	3.7%	11,000
12/13	30,957	591	1.9%	10,000
12/12	25,444	718	2.8%	7,828
12/11	19,019	984	5.2%	0
Annual Growth	6.4%	(34.5%)	—	—

2015 Year-End Financials

Debt ratio: 36.1%
Return on equity: 1.4%
Cash ($ mil.): 730
Current ratio: 0.70
Long-term debt ($ mil.): 28,468
No. of shares (mil.): 868
Dividends
 Yield: 5.6%
 Payout: —
Market value ($ mil.): 28,809

	STOCK PRICE ($) FY Close	P/E High/Low	PER SHARE ($) Earnings	Dividends	Book Value
12/15	33.19	— —	(0.03)	1.46	15.68
12/14	51.41	37 28	1.18	1.27	17.01
12/13	43.68	83 72	0.52	1.23	15.27
12/12	43.32	54 46	0.78	1.13	13.11
12/11	37.41	49 21	1.27	0.96	11.10
Annual Growth	(2.9%)	— —	—	11.1%	9.0%

ENBW Energie Baden-Wuerttemberg AG

One of Germany's largest utilities Energie Baden-Wü̈rttemberg (EnBW) is bathing its namesake region with light. EnBW distributes electricity in the state of Baden-Wü̈rttemberg; the company also provides natural gas and energy and environmental services. The company markets power to retail customers throughout Germany under subsidiary Yello Strom. EnBW also generates distributes and markets energy across Central Europe. The company has 5.5 million energy customers and about 15500 MW of electric generating capacity. EnBW is focusing on energy diversity improving the energy-efficiency of its fossil-fuel powered generation facilities while expanding its renewable power sources.

Geographic Reach

The company's core market is Baden-Wü̈rttemberg where it is the market leader. It also operates throughout Germany and across Europe.

Operations

As an integrated energy supply company EnBW operates four segments: Sales Grids Renewable Energies and Generation and Trading. The Sales segment encompasses the distribution of electricity and gas and the provision of energy-related services (invoicing energy supply and energy-saving contracting) 45% of EnBW's revenues in 2014.

The Grids segment encompasses the transmission and distribution of electricity and gas the provision of grid-related services (such as the operation of grids for third parties) and the supply of water. The Renewable Energies segment is engaged in power generation from renewable energy sources (wind power and hydropower). It is involved in project development construction the efficient operation of green energy plantsThe Generation and Trading segment encompasses the generation and trading of electricity the gas midstream business district heating environmental services and decommissioning of power plants. This business is primarily based on the generation of electricity and heat from thermal power plants (coal gas and pumped storage power plants and nuclear power plants).

Sales and Marketing

The company's core market is Baden-Wü̈rttemberg. It supplies customers all over Germany through subsidiaries Yello Strom GmbH and Sales & Solutions GmbH. EnBW serves private residential customers commercial enterprises the housing industry and agriculture major commercial enterprises industrial customers and redistributors municipal utilities local authorities and public entities.

Financial Performance

In 2014 EnBW's net revenues increased by 2% due to higher sales from Grids segment and Renewable Energies segment. Revenues in the Grids segment grew significantly as a result of higher EEG revenues while Renewable Energies segment was dueto the sale of two solar parks and higher organic sales.

Net income decreased by 417% due to increased amortization and depreciation costs partially offset by increased revenues. In 2014 net cash provided by the operating activities decreased by 7% as the result of a change in net balance of other assets and liabilities and trade receivables and payables.

Strategy

EnBW aims to more than double its share of renewable energies in its generation portfolio raising it from about 19% to more than 40% in 2020. Its capacities derived from onshore wind farms will be increased significantly in the target markets of Germany and Turkey. The company's innovation strategy pursues a goal of developing models for new business segments and rapidly moving them to commercialization.

EnBW invested nearly 2 billion euros in 2014 primarily in the Renewable Energies segment in the expansion of the company's electric grids. Other main areas of investment were the new power plants RDK 8 in Karlsruhe and Lausward in Dü̈sseldorf.

To raise cash to pay down debt and fund growth in 2014 EnBW Group sold 74.9% of the equity in SWS Netzinfrastruktur GmbH Stuttgart to Stadtwerke Stuttgart GmbH Stuttgart on 31 October 2014. The sale is connected with the City of Stuttgart's franchise award process. SWS Netzinfrastruktur GmbH owns the electricity and gas distribution grid in the Stuttgart franchise area. Following the sale of the interest SWS Netzinfrastruktur GmbH is now a joint venture in the EnBW Group and is consolidated using the equity method.

That year it also sold 49.98% of the equity in EnBW Onshore Portfolio GmbH Stuttgart in equal shares to Onshore Bü̈ndelgesellschaft 1 GmbH Stuttgart Onshore Bü̈ndelgesellschaft 2 GmbH Karlsruhe and Onshore Bü̈ndelgesellschaft 3 GmbH Stuttgart. As a result of the transaction our interest in EnBW Onshore Portfolio GmbH falls to 50.02%. EnBW continues to fully consolidate EnBW Onshore Portfolio GmbH in its consolidated financial statements.

In 2013 EnBW announced plans to shut down a total of four non-core power plant units with a total output of 668 MW at its power plant locations in Marbach and Walheim.

Mergers and Acquisitions

Expanding its Renewable Energies portfolio in 2015 EnBW bought wind power player PROKON Regenerative Energien GmbH. It also acquired the Albatros offshore wind farm project from the consortium partners STRABAG and the Norderland/ETANAX Group. This offshore wind project which has approval for 79 wind turbines of the 5-7 megawatt rating class is located 105 kilometers from the coast in the German sector of the North Sea.

In 2014 EnBW purchased a further 50% of the equity in EnBW Gas VerwaltungsgesellschaftmbH Karlsruhe (previously EnBW Eni Verwaltungsgesellschaft mbH Karlsruhe) and thus indirectly acquired a further 50% of GasVersorgung Sü̈ddeutschland GmbH Stuttgart and of terranets bw GmbH Stuttgart from the Italian energy group Eni S.p.A. The euro 197.9 million deal boosted EnBW's stake in EnBW Gas Verwaltungsgesellschaft mbH to 100%.

Company Background

As part of this green energy push in 2010 EnBW completed its Baltic 1 wind farm (which has 21 turbines and an installed output of 50 MW) just off of Germany's north coast. The company has additional wind farms under construction or in the planning stage.

It is also growing its renewables by acquisition. In 2011 EnBW acquired a 6 MW wind farm from ABO Wind AG through its renewable energy unit EnBW Erneuerbare Energien GmbH. The company had previously acquired a 15 MW wind farm from ABO Wind in 2010.

EnBW has also made selective international energy acquisitions (including renewable sources) to balance the growth of its core German operations. The company moved into Sweden in 2007 via Yello Strom. In 2008 EnBW made a domestic acquisition when it acquired a 26% stake in German gas and electricity distributor EWE for about $3 billion. It also bought stakes in two German coalfired power plants from E.ON in 2009.

Moving into the Turkish market in 2009 the company announced plans to build up generation capacities of 2000 MW of primarily renewable energy powered plants by 2020 in collaboration with Turkish industrial conglomerate Borusan Holding.

In 2010 with the global economy bouncing back the company benefited from higher commodity prices and greater industrial demand. EnBW saw its revenues and income grow robustly that year led by a 100% jump in its power generating and trading segment revenues.

Electricite de France (EDF) and Oberschwä̈bische Elektrizitä̈tswerke once each owned 45% of EnBW but in early 2011 EDF sold its stake to the state of Baden-Wü̈rttemberg for $6.1 billion to raise cash. Baden-Wü̈rttemberg increased its holdings to 47% in March 2011 through the acquisition of minority stakes.

EXECUTIVES

CTO, Ing. Hans-Josef Zimmer, age 58
CFO and Member the Management Board, Thomas Kusterer
Chairman and CEO, Frank Mastiaux, age 52
Deputy Chairman Supervisory Board, Dietrich Herd
Chairman Supervisory Board, Claus Dieter
Auditors: KPMG AG Wirtschaftspruefungsgesellschaft

LOCATIONS

HQ: ENBW Energie Baden-Wuerttemberg AG
Durlacher Allee 93, Karlsruhe D-76131
Phone: (49) 721 63 00   **Fax:** (49) 721 63 127 25
Web: www.enbw.com

2014 Revenue by Geography

	%
Germany	93
Europe	2
Rest of Europe	5
Total	**100**

PRODUCTS/OPERATIONS

2014 Sales

	% of total
Sales	43
Grids	30
Generation & trading	25
Renewable energies	2
Others	
Total	**100**

Selected Subsidiaries

EnBW Gas GmbH (natural gas distribution)
EnBW Vertriebs- und Servicegesellschaft mbH (electricity energy and environmental services)
EnBW Kraftwerke AG (electricity generation)
EnBW Regional AG (electricity distribution)
EnBW Trading GmbH (energy marketing)
EnBW Transportnetze AG (electricity transmission)
Yello Strom GmbH (electricity supply)

Gasversorgung Süddeutschland GmbH (GVS district heating and natural gas transmission and supply)

COMPETITORS

Business Group Benelux	Fortum
E.ON	Gasunie
Endesa S.A.	IBERDROLA
Enel	RWE
Energias de Portugal	Vattenfall Europe
Engie	

HISTORICAL FINANCIALS
Company Type: Public

Income Statement
FYE: December 31

	REVENUE ($ mil.)	NET INCOME ($ mil.)	NET PROFIT MARGIN	EMPLOYEES
12/15	23,153	136	0.6%	20,150
12/14	25,642	(547)	—	19,966
12/13	28,356	70	0.2%	19,822
12/12	25,410	624	2.5%	20,098
12/11	24,420	(1,121)	—	20,959
Annual Growth	(1.3%)	—	—	(1.0%)

2015 Year-End Financials

Debt ratio: 21.6%
Return on equity: 3.7%
Cash ($ mil.): 3,813
Current ratio: 1.36
Long-term debt ($ mil.): 7,417

No. of shares (mil.): 270
Dividends
  Yield: —
  Payout: —
Market value ($ mil.): —

Endesa S.A.

Endesa provides power to more than 26 million customers in 11 countries (50% customers in Spain) on three continents. A subsidiary of Italian power giant Enel Endesa is Spain's #1 electric utility and has a generating capacity of 39562 MW from nuclear fossil-fueled hydroelectric and renewable energy plants. Endesa is the primary electricity company in Chile Argentina Colombia and Peru and also operates in Brazil. It is a major player in the Mediterranean region especially Italy and is active in other countries. Endesa also serves natural gas customers in Spain. The company is also investing heavily in renewable energy to meet Spain's commitment to greenhouse gas reduction.

HISTORY

When dictator Francisco Franco set about rebuilding Spain after the Civil War Empresa Nacional de Electricidad (Endesa) was formed in 1944 under the state-run Instituto Nacional de Industria (INI). The nation's lack of power facilities sparked the company into building hydroelectric plants. In the 1950s the US fighting the Cold War financed Spain's industrial boom which Endesa aided by building coal-fired plants including Compostilla (on line in 1961).

When inflation plagued Spain in the late 1950s the government cut off INI's funding. INI and its companies then borrowed heavily from banks. Spain then passed the Stabilization Act in 1959 to make INI companies self-financing though they were still government-owned. In the 1960s many of Spain's rural areas were undeveloped so the government instituted and funded a plan to build power infrastructure.

In 1972 Endesa acquired the As Pontel and Teruel facilities where it began constructing fossil fuel plants. However the energy crisis of the early 1970s kept the plants from operating until 1976 and 1979 respectively.

After Franco's death in 1975 King Juan Carlos moved Spain into Europe's free market union. In preparation for the liberalization of the energy markets INI and Endesa reorganized in 1983 and shifted INI's holdings in regional electric utilities (Eneco Enher Gesa and Unelco) to Endesa.

After the government halted its nuclear power program in 1984 many private electric companies were left with bad investments. Endesa was brought in to bail them out by taking over power plants; to repay Endesa they were forced to buy Endesa's electricity. The 1985 asset swaps also brought regional power companies Erz and Fecsa into Endesa's grasp.

In 1986 Spain joined the European Community; two years later the government sold 20% of Endesa to the public. In the early 1990s Endesa went into coal production when it purchased EN-CASUR (1990) and it continued buying interests in private power companies including Viesgo and Sevillana.

The government floated more of the company in 1997 and the utility became Endesa S.A. Its eye on Latin American opportunity Endesa bought a 29% stake in Chile's largest power company Enersis. It also branched into telecommunications by grabbing a small stake in Retevision.

Endesa was fully privatized in 1998 the year Spain's deregulation process began. The next year Endesa paid some $2.6 billion to buy the outstanding shares of its regional units and merge them into the company as part of its larger effort to reorganize and cut its costs and workforce. Endesa also increased its stake in Enersis to more than 60%.

In 2000 Endesa began restructuring its regional electric utilities into separate generation and distribution units. Also that year Endesa Telecom Italia and Union Fenosa combined their Spanish telecom holdings to form the Auna joint venture. (Telecom Italia later sold its stake to Santander Central Hispano.) Endesa also agreed to acquire rival Spanish utility Iberdrola but the companies cancelled the transaction in 2001.

In 2001 Endesa completed the purchase of a 30% interest in French generation company SNET. The company also acquired one of Italian utility Enel's power production units (Elettrogen). Endesa sold its New Viesgo unit (a spinoff composed of regional electric utility Electra de Viesgo which served 500000 customers and had 2400 MW of generation assets) to Enel in 2002.

Endesa branched out into new territories to prepare for the deregulation of Spain's electric utility market which took full effect in 2003.

In 2005 Endesa sold its major stake in Auna to France Telecom (since renamed Orange).

The company found itself the target of takeover bids by other European power companies seeking to bulk up in the wake of the deregulation of the European power and gas markets. In 2007 E.ON and Gas Natural made bids of $47-plus billion and $26-plus billion respectively for Endesa. That year Enel and Acciona jumped into the fray buying about 70% and 25% of the company respectively when Gas Natural dropped out of the bidding. E.ON dropped out in 2008 in return for buying some power plants and shareholdings in Italy Spain and France from Endesa. In 2009 Enel bought Acciona's stake.

In 2009 Endesa had a generating capacity of more than 3700 MW of wind power or about 10% of the Spanish wind power market. In another major move to promote renewable energy in 2010 the company agreed to develop about 550 recharging locations in Barcelona Madrid and Seville to power electric cars.

EXECUTIVES

President, Prado Eulate Borja
Vicepresidente, Francesco Starace
Chief Executive Officer, Jose Damián Bogas Gálvez
Consejero, Alberto de Paoli
Consejero, Alejandro Echevarría Busquet
Consejero, Livio Gallo
Consejero, Ignacio Garralda Ruíz de Velasco
Consejero, Francisco Jose Queiroz de Barros de Lacerda
Consejero, Helena Revoredo Delvecchio
Consejero, Miquel Roca Junyent

LOCATIONS

HQ: Endesa S.A.
  Calle Ribera Del Loira 60, Madrid 28042
Phone: (34) 91 213 10 00   **Fax:** (34) 91 563 81 81
Web: www.endesa.es

2009 Sales

	% of total
Europe	
Spain & Portugal	68
Latin America	32
Total	**100**

COMPETITORS

AES	International Power
Business Group Benelux	PPL Corporation
E.ON	RWE
Edison	Red Electrica de
Electricite de France	España
Energias de Portugal	Sempra Energy
Gas Natural SDG	Telefnica
HC Energa	Tractebel Engineering
IBERDROLA	Vattenfall

HISTORICAL FINANCIALS
Company Type: Public

Income Statement
FYE: December 31

	REVENUE ($ mil.)	NET INCOME ($ mil.)	NET PROFIT MARGIN	EMPLOYEES
12/15	22,109	1,182	5.4%	10,000
12/14	26,147	4,056	15.5%	10,500
12/13	42,958	2,586	6.0%	22,995
12/12	44,725	2,680	6.0%	22,807
12/11	42,277	2,861	6.8%	22,877
Annual Growth	(15.0%)	(19.8%)	—	(18.7%)

2015 Year-End Financials

Debt ratio: 17.4%
Return on equity: 12.3%
Cash ($ mil.): 376
Current ratio: 0.85
Long-term debt ($ mil.): 5,097

No. of shares (mil.): 1,058
Dividends
  Yield: 74.6%
  Payout: 26.5%
Market value ($ mil.): 15,871

	STOCK PRICE ($) FY Close	P/E High/Low		PER SHARE ($) Earnings	Dividends	Book Value
12/15	14.99	15	9	1.12	18.45	9.30
12/14	9.75	5	3	3.83	6.80	9.85
12/13	13.41	8	7	2.44	0.75	26.68
Annual Growth	5.7%		—	—(17.6%)	122.5%	(23.2%)

Enel Societa Per Azioni

Arrivederci monopolio! Buongiorno diversified energy player. Italy's largest electric utility Enel has given up its monopoly status and raced into the deregulated global power marketplace. Operating in 32 countries Enel distributes electricity and gas to about 61 million customers and has more than 95000 MW of primarily fossil-fueled and hydroelectric generating capacity. The second largest gas distributor in Italy (after Italgas) Enel serves 3.2 million customers in Italy. It also has renewable and international power generation assets. The Italian government owns about a third of Enel.

Geographic Reach

Internationally Enel has built and acquired independent power plants primarily in Europe and the Americas. The company operates in 32 countries across four continents.

In 2014 Italy accounted for 39% of the company's revenues.

Operations

Enel operates through a number of segments. Its Sales Division sells to high-value mass market segments acquiring new electricity and gas customers. Italy-focused Enel Energia serves 55.8 million electricity customers and 4.6 million gas customers. The company's Generation and Energy Management Division generates about 283.1 TWh of power (30% of the Italian market) a year.

The Engineering and Innovation Division carries out numerous research and development initiatives and plant construction projects. The Infrastructure and Networks Division is engaged in energy distribution The Iberia and Latin America Division serve market in Spain and Portugal and South America.

Enel is strongly committed to renewable energy sources and to the research and development of new environmentally friendly technologies. Enel Green Power (the company's publicly listed renewable energy generation business) operating 9500 MW of net installed capacity of hydro wind geothermal solar biomass and co-generation sources in Europe the Americas and Africa.

Financial Performance

In 2014 Enel's revenues decreased by 3.6% due to lower sales of electricity largely due to a fall in amounts sold the adverse impact of changes in the currency exchange rates and the disposal of strategic equity interests.

Net income decreased by 84% due to a drop in revenues and increased depreciation amortization and impairment losses. The depreciation amortization and impairment losses reflected the net impact of an increase in impairment of Slovenske elektrarne (held for sale) an increase in impairment of property plant and equipment higher impairment of intangible assets and a decreased impairment of goodwill. In 2014 Enel's net cash provided by the operating activities increased by 39% due to a change in trade payables and receivables.

Strategy

The company is also growing its non-traditional power assets to meet EU regulation on carbon emissions. In 2015 Enel Green Power S.p.A. through its subsidiary Enel Green Power North America Inc. entered into a deal with General Electric Unit GE Energy Financial Services for the sale of a 49% stake in newly created EGPNA Renewable Energy Partners LLC for $440 million.

That year Enel Green Power begun construction of Nojoli wind farm which is located in the Eastern Cape Province in South Africa. The new wind farm will have a total installed capacity of 88 MW.

Enel was the first utility in the world to replace the traditional electromechanical meters with smart meters making it possible to measure consumption in real time and manage contractual relationships remotely. In 2015 some 32 million Italian retail customers are equipped with smart meters developed and installed by Enel. It is deploying an additional 13 million smart meters to its customer base in Spain as well as running pilot tests for the smart cities of Buzios (Brazil) and Santiago (Chile).

The company is also expanding in areas where it is already operating such as in Latin America and entering new countries. In 2015 Enel Green Power and Marubeni agreed to cooperate in evaluating potential business opportunities in renewable projects mainly in the Asia-Pacific Region. In 2014 Enel signed a framework agreement with ZTE Corporation a leading Chinese telecommunications equipment and systems company to kick-start cooperation between the two groups in the areas of electric mobility smart grids and renewable generation.

To raise cash in 2013 the company disposed of 51% of Buffalo Dunes Wind Project and its remaining stake in Enel Rete Gas.

It also disposed its entire 36.2% stake in LaGeo a geothermal generation company in El Salvador and 100% of Enel Green Power France a renewables generator.

The Italian government owns about a third of Enel. Italy's Ministry of Economy and Finance directly owns approximately 14% of Enel; it owns another 17% indirectly through the government-controlled bank Cassa Depositi e Prestiti.

HISTORY

Company Background

Italy's energy consumption doubled in the 1950s as the country experienced a period of rapid industrialization and urbanization. A tight-knit oligopoly controlled the electric power industry and included Edison SADE La Centale SME and Finelettrica. The economic boom pushed into the 1960s and the Italian government created Enel (Ente Nazionale per l'Energia Elettrica) in 1962 to nationalize the power industry. In 1963 Enel began gradually buying some 1250 electric utilities. About 160 municipal utilities and the larger independents such as Edison were left out of the takeover.

The company spent the late 1960s and early 1970s connecting Italy's unwieldy transmission network and building new power plants including the La Spezia thermoelectric plant (600 MW). Construction costs coupled with the high prices Enel was required to pay for its takeover targets caused the utility to become steeped in debt. The Arab oil embargoes of the early 1970s made matters worse and the Italian government helped Enel with an endowment in 1973.

The energy crisis also prompted Enel to build its first nuclear power plant Caorso which came on line in 1980. However nuclear power was short-lived in Italy: After the 1986 Chernobyl accident a national referendum forced Enel to deactivate its nukes in 1987. The firm also stepped up its development of renewable energy sources in the 1980s.

Meanwhile Enel opened its Centro Nazionale de Controllo (CNC) in Rome in 1985 to supervise Italy's power grid. The next year the company turned its first profit.

To begin disassembling Enel's monopoly the Italian government in 1992 opened the power generation market to outside producers and converted Enel into a joint stock company (with the state holding all of the shares). Following the European Union's 1997 directive to deregulate Europe's power industry Enel unbundled its utility activities and began trimming its staff.

Italy's Bersani Decree (passed in 1999) outlined the restructuring process: Enel was ordered to divest 25% of its capacity (15000 MW) and turn over a portion of its municipal distribution networks to local governments to enhance competition in the country's power market. Accordingly it transferred management of the national transmission grid to an independent government-owned operator Gestore della Rete di Trasmissione Nazionale (GRTN) and reduced its customer count by approximately

1 million through municipal distribution asset sales.

Enel had already begun to diversify. It started Wind Telecomunicazioni a joint venture with France Telecom —later renamed Orange —and Deutsche Telekom in 1998. (Deutsche Telekom sold its stake to the other partners in 2000.) Wind first offered fixed-line and mobile telecom services to corporations; it extended the services to residential users in 1999. In addition Enel began building water infrastructure to serve local distributors and purchased three water operations in southern Italy.

Also in 1999 the government floated 32% of Enel in one of the world's largest IPOs at the time. The next year the company bought Colombo Gas (a northern Italian gas distributor with about 75000 customers) and it transferred control of its transmission network to Gestore della Rete di Trasmissione Nazionale (an independent government-owned operator) while retaining ownership of the assets.

Enel bought fixed-line telephone company Infostrada from Vodafone in 2001 acquired two more Italian gas distributors and sold its 5400-MW Elettrogen generation unit to Spain's Endesa for $2.3 billion. That year Enel put its 7000-MW Eurogen generation unit on the auction block. The high bidder with a $2.6 billion offer was a consortium backed by Fiat and ?lectricite de France; the sale was completed in 2002.

Also in 2002 Enel merged Infostrada into Wind Telecomunicazioni to create one of Italy's top telecom companies it purchased Camuzzi Gazometri's gas distribution business (Italy's second-largest) for $870 million from Mill Hill Investments and it bought Endesa's Viesgo unit (2400 MW of generating capacity and 500000 power customers) for about $1.8 billion.

Enel sold its final generation divestment company Interpower (2600 MW) to a consortium of utilities (including Belgian utility Electrabel and Italian utility ACEA) for about $880 million in 2003.

That year Enel purchased France Telecom 's 27% stake in Wind for $1.4 billion making the unit a wholly owned subsidiary. (Enel had flirted with the idea of taking Wind public but instead sold the unit in 2006 to the Egypt-based Weather Investments consortium which had the backing of Orascom Telecom 's chairman and CEO Naguib Sawiris.)

The Italian government began the second round of Enel's privatization process in 2003 by selling a 7% stake to Morgan Stanley for more than $2.3 billion. In 2004 the government further reduced its stake by nearly 20% through a public offering of shares.

In 2005 it acquired power distribution and sales businesses in Romania and in 2006 in Slovakia.

With Italian regulators requiring that Enel divest 80% of its Terna subsidiary (which holds the company's power transmission assets) by 2007 Enel spun off 50% of the unit in an IPO in 2004. The following year it divested another 44% and the company reduced its holding to about 5% by January 2006. Grid management and operational functions were also transferred from GRTN back to Terna.

In 2008 the company set Enel Green Power to develop wind solar geothermal and biomass projects. By 2009 it was operating alternative energy plants worldwide with a generating capacity of 4700 MW. In 2010 Enel Green Power acquired Pagoda Wind Power which is developing 4000 MW of wind projects in California.

In what could have been a large cross-border deal Enel considered making a bid for France's SUEZ (now GDF SUEZ) utility company. Perhaps in reaction to the news of Enel's interest France's Gaz de France made a bid for SUEZ (consummated in 2008) a move that Italy called protectionist.

Unperturbed by its failure to secure SUEZ the company took control of Spain's power giant Endesa in 2007 increasing its market share as a European power player. Hoping to pay down what had become a heavy debt load the company in 2009 sold an 80% stake in gas distributor Enel Rete Gas for $666 million.

In 2012 Enel Green Power consolidated its position in the Greek renewable industry through the launching of two new plants - a wind farm and a photovoltaic plant - both located in the Peloponnese region.

EXECUTIVES

Chairman Enel Green Power, Francesco Starace, age 61
CFO, Alberto De Paoli, age 51
Chairman, Jorge Rosenblut
Auditors: Reconta Ernst & Young spa

LOCATIONS

HQ: Enel Societa Per Azioni
Viale Regina Margherita, 137, Rome I-00198
Phone: (39) 6 8509 3184   **Fax:** (39) 6 8509 5810
Web: www.enel.it

2014 Sales

	% of total
Europe	46
Italy	39
Americas	14
Asia	1
Africa	0
Total	**100**

PRODUCTS/OPERATIONS

2014 Sales

	% of total
Iberia & Latin America	40
Generation & energy management (Italy)	30
Sales (Italy)	20
Infrastructure & networks (Italy)	10
International	7
Renewable energy	4
Other (11)	
Total	**100**

COMPETITORS

A2A	Eni
ABB	HC Energa
ACEA	IBERDROLA
Acque Potabili	International Power
E.ON	Italgas
ERG S.p.A.	RWE
Edison	Risanamento
Electricite de France	Tractebel Engineering

HISTORICAL FINANCIALS

Company Type: Public

Income Statement

FYE: December 31

	REVENUE ($ mil.)	NET INCOME ($ mil.)	NET PROFIT MARGIN	EMPLOYEES
12/15	82,407	2,391	2.9%	67,914
12/14	92,124	628	0.7%	68,961
12/13	110,875	4,453	4.0%	71,394
12/12	111,966	313	0.3%	73,702
12/11	102,847	5,365	5.2%	75,360
Annual Growth	**(5.4%)**	**(18.3%)**	**—**	**(2.6%)**

2015 Year-End Financials

Debt ratio: 35.6%	No. of shares (mil.): —
Return on equity: 6.8%	Dividends
Cash ($ mil.): 11,588	Yield: 2.0%
Current ratio: 0.94	Payout: 32.9%
Long-term debt ($ mil.): 48,875	Market value ($ mil.): —

	STOCK PRICE ($) FY Close	P/E High/Low		PER SHARE ($) Earnings	Dividends	Book Value
12/15	4.14	21	16	0.25	0.09	3.75
12/14	4.42	107	75	0.06	0.11	4.07
12/13	4.34	13	9	0.47	0.14	5.26
12/12	4.14	142	87	0.04	0.22	5.01
12/11	4.00	14	8	0.57	0.22	5.34
Annual Growth	**0.9%**	**—**	**—**	**(18.5%)**	**(21.4%)**	**(8.4%)**

Engie SA

Engie channels its energy into being Europe's top power gas and infrastructure player. It is engaged in the purchasing production and marketing of natural gas and electricity; the development and maintenance of major natural gas and electricity infrastructures; and the creation and marketing of energy and environmental services. With operations in about 70 countries power producer Engie has 115.3 GW of installed capacity. It is Europe's top importer of liquefied natural gas (LNG) its largest supplier of natural gas the continent's leading supplier of multi-technical energy services and a leading global supplier of water and waste management services.

Geographic Reach

Engie operates around the world. France is the company's largest single market at euro 25.1 billion while Europe combined (including France) accounts for around 80% of revenue.

Operations

The company operates five business units: Energy Europe the largest at 32% of revenue; Energy Services; Energy International; Global Gas & LNG; and Infrastructures.

Electricity is Engie's biggest earner and Energy Europe and Energy International together bring in some 65% of sales; Engie is the fourth largest electricity producer in Europe and second in France after EDF. Global Gas & LNG carries out upstream activities in the gas value chain and Infrastructures comprises subsidiaries that operate gas transport and storage infrastructure in Germany and France.

Engie's renewables play a significant role: hydropower operations generate more than 13500MW a year in more than a dozen territories and comprises 14% of total installed capacity. Engie is the largest windpower player in France and Belgium and has more than 3500MW of installed capacity throughout the world.

Financial Performance

Note: Growth rates may differ after conversion to US Dollars.

Engie is vulnerable to fluctuations in commodity prices and the recent and ongoing commodity price collapse has been some cause of turbulence for the company in 2015 and into 2016. Consequently revenue fell in 2015 to euro 69.9 billion from euro 74.7 billion in 2014. The company also felt the effects of outages at its Doel 3 and Tihange 2 nuclear plants and the shut-down of the Doel 1 reactor in Belgium. The effects of the shutdowns were tempered to an extent by a return to cool temperatures in Europe after a mild 2014. The hardest-hit segments were Energy Europe down euro 3.2 billion and Global Gas & LNG down euro 2.7 billion.

Net income turned negative in 2015 with Engie recording a loss of euro 4.6 billion which resulted mostly from euro 8.7 billion in impairment losses and which were focused in the Global Gas & LNG Energy International and Energy Europe business lines.

Cash flow from operations rose euro 1.9 billion year on year to euro 9.8 billion mostly due to favorable change in working capital requirements after a difficult 2014.

Strategy

Changing dynamics in the global energy market has necessitated a shift in strategy. Engie sees Europe as being at the beginning of a move towards renewables and is thus ramping up its efforts to become the region's leading producer of clean energy. Part of this involves innovating in clean energy in cities and investing euro 1 billion in renewables in 2016-18 with hydropower at the forefront. It also purchased US electricity storage company Green Charge. The buyout is the latest in a series of purchases by big energy firms of electricity storage companies intended to overcome difficulties in storing renewable energy which is one of the biggest obstacles in the wider uptake of renewables.

As well as moving towards renewables Engie is also moving away from hydrocarbons particularly coal. It closed its 1000 MW coal-fired power plant in Staffordshire in the UK in 2016.

In 2017 ENGIE sold 8700 MW of thermal power plant assets in the US to Dynegy for an enterprise value of $3.3 billion.

Expansion into high-growth markets like the Middle East and Latin America is a priority and 90% of Engie's 15GW of energy capacity in development worldwide is focused in these high-growth markets.

Mergers and Acquisitions

Engie acquired Green Charge Networks in 2016. In addition in the same year Engie acquired C3 Resources a digital energy management company based in Plymouth UK which processes large volumes of energy and environmental data to improve energy control. It is hope the acquisition will improve Engie's capabilities in the digital sphere. Lastly the company agreed to sell its US power plants to Dynegy for $3.3 billion in order to reduce its exposure to low energy prices and to reduce debt.

HISTORY

The first canal in Egypt was dug in the 13th century BC but it was Napoleon who revived the idea of a shorter trade route to India: a canal through Egypt linking the Gulf of Suez with the Mediterranean. Former French diplomat and engineer Ferdinand de Lesseps formed Compagnie Universelle du Canal Maritime de Suez in 1858 to build and eventually operate the canal which opened 11 years later. Egypt's modernization had pushed it into debt and increased its ties to the British government which by 1875 had acquired a 44% stake in the company.

For more than 80 years the Suez Canal was a foreign enclave protected by the British Army since 1936. After Egypt's puppet government fell and as Gamal Abd Al-Nasser assumed power in 1956 British troops exited the Canal Zone which Egypt quickly nationalized. Israel Britain and France attacked but the UN arranged a truce and foreign forces withdrew leaving the Suez in Egypt's control.

With no canal to operate Universelle du Canal Maritime de Suez became Compagnie

Financière de Suez in 1958. A year later it created a bank (which became Banque Indosuez in 1974).

In 1967 Financière de Suez became the largest shareholder in Societe Lyonnaise des Eaux et de L'Eclairage a leading French water company. Formed in 1880 Lyonnaise des Eaux had stakes in water (Northumbrian Water) and energy (Elyo). After France's energy firms were nationalized in 1946 Lyonnaise des Eaux dipped deeper into the water industry by acquiring Degremont (now Ondeo-Degremont) in 1972. It also purchased stakes in waste management (SITA 1970) and heating systems (Cofreth 1975).

In the 1980s Lyonnaise des Eaux expanded in Spain the UK and the US and diversified into cable TV (1986) and broadcast TV (1987). It merged with construction firm Dumez in 1990.

Meanwhile Financière de Suez became a financial power when it won a controlling stake in Societe Generale de Belgique (SGB) in 1988 and bought Groupe Victoire in 1989. But the two buys left the firm (renamed Compagnie de Suez in 1990) deeply in debt.

Losing money Compagnie de Suez disposed of Victoire (1994) and then the valuable Banque Indosuez (1996). In 1996 the company bought a controlling stake in Belgium's top utility Tractebel (now SUEZ-TRACTEBEL). Compagnie de Suez and Lyonnaise des Eaux merged in 1997 to create Suez Lyonnaise des Eaux. The following year Suez Lyonnaise acquired the rest of SGB and bought the European and Asian operations of waste management giant Browning-Ferris Industries; it also began divesting noncore operations.

Suez Lyonnaise in 1999 expanded its core businesses primarily in the US. The company bought Calgon (water treatment US) and Nalco Chemical (water treatment chemicals US) then merged Calgon into Nalco to form Ondeo Nalco. (The company's name was changed back to Nalco when it was divested in 2003.)

In 2000 Suez Lyonnaise bought United Water Resources (now United Water) and acquired the rest of SITA. Through its Elyo subsidiary Suez Lyonnaise bought out minority shareholders in US-based Trigen Energy. The company also merged its construction unit Groupe GTM with French construction rival VINCI; Suez Lyonnaise then sold the VINCI shares that it received from the transaction.

The next year the company shortened its name to Suez (later modified to SUEZ) as part of a global rebranding effort. It also united its water services operations under the ONDEO brand. In 2002 SUEZ made Tractebel a wholly owned subsidiary by purchasing the remaining publicly held shares. Also in 2002 SUEZ sold minority stakes in communications equipment manufacturer Sagem (now SAFRAN) steelmaker Arcelor and motorway operator Autopistas Concesionaria Española (ACESA).

SUEZ divested most of its 11% stake in Belgian insurance firm Fortis for nearly $2 billion in 2003. It also sold its 79% stake in cable company Coditel that year. In 2003 the company merged Tractebel and SGB (Tractebel's former holding company) to form SUEZ-TRACTEBEL.Gaz de France was founded in 1946 by the French government to consolidate the more than 500 (mostly coal-fired) gas works that had existed before WWII. From 1949 on Gaz de France focused on upgrading gas plants and local transmission networks. Its first long-distance pipeline was built in 1953 linking Paris to the Lorraine coal gas fields. With the development of the Lacq gas field in southwestern France annual gas sales increased by 300% between 1957 and 1962.

By 1965 nearly half of the French population was supplied with natural gas. Spurred on by the loss of its Algerian colony which held major oil and gas assets the French government pushed for new gas supplies to supplement its Lacq resources. Gaz de France was able to secure a contract with Algerian natural gas supplier Sonatrach in 1965 and in 1967 it signed an import contract with Dutch supplier Gasunie. The company also diversified in the 1960s helping to build a natural gas liquefaction plant in Algeria and a receiving terminal in Le Havre. It also helped pioneer gas storage engineering.

Following the price shock of the Arab oil embargo of the early 1970s Gaz de France stepped up its search for alternative suppliers including contracts with Russia's largest gas producer Soyouzgazexport (in 1976 1980 and 1984) and four separate Norwegian producers Efofisk (1977) Stafjord (1985) Heimdal (1986) and Gullfaks (1987). The company also renewed contracts with its Dutch and Algerian suppliers.

During the 1990s Gaz de France expanded its international operations as deregulation in the industry accelerated. In 1994 the company gained a foothold in eastern Germany's gas sector by buying gas production and storage company Erdgas Erdol GmbH (EEG). Three years later Gaz de France acquired Italian heating and related services firm Agip Servizi and was awarded a joint venture contract to distribute gas in Berlin in 1997 and in the suburbs of Mexico City in 1998.

Through contracts for North Sea oil and gas with Elf Aquitaine (now owned by TOTAL FINA ELF) British-Borneo and Ruhrgas in 1999 the company increased its natural gas supplies. It also established new gas supply contracts with Nigeria and Qatar.

For the first time in its history Gaz de France became an offshore field operator in 2000 by acquiring exploration and production company TransCanada International Netherlands and a 39% stake in Noordgastransport BV an offshore gas pipeline operator.

In 2001 through the purchase of a 10% interest in Petronet LNG Gaz de France embarked on a project to import liquefied natural gas from Qatar to India.

France's energy and environmental services giants came together when SUEZ merged with Gaz de France in 2008 to form GDF SUEZ. As part of the merger agreement and in order to clear hurdles set up by the EU competition policy SUEZ then spun off its waste and water unit SUEZ Environnement.

Following the 2008 merger of Gaz de France with SUEZ in a move to expand geographically GDF SUEZ acquired a 90% stake in Izmit Gaz Dagitim San Ve Tic AS (Turkey's third-largest natural gas distributor) for $232 million.

In 2009 the company made further geographic realignments prompted by the regulatory requirements of the European Commission for GDF SUEZ and Germany's E.ON to allow for more competition in their major markets by swapping some generation capacity. It acquired from E.ON 860 MW of Germany-based conventional power plants 132 MW of hydroelectric plants and through subsidiary Electrabel access to 770 MW of nuclear power. In return GDF SUEZ sold to E.ON a similar amount of power generation capacity in France and the Benelux countries.

Ramping up its nuclear assets in 2011 GDF SUEZ formed a joint venture with IBERDROLA and Scottish and Southern Energy. NuGeneration planned to develop up to 3600 MW of nuclear power in the UK. Late in 2011 SSE announced plans to sell its 25 percent in NuGen to GDF SUEZ and IBERDROLA and return to its renewable energy strategy.

EXECUTIVES

Executive Vice-President Energy Service, Jerôme Tolot, age 65
EVP Global Gas and LNG Business Line, Jean-Marie Dauger, age 64
Executive Vice-President Communications Marketing and Sustainable Development, Valerie Bernis, age 58
Chairman and CEO; Chairman SUEZ-TRACTEBEL GDF SUEZ Energy Services and SUEZ Environnement, Gerard Mestrallet, age 67
EVP Electricity and Gas International; CEO Tractebel Electricity and Gas International, Dirk Beeuwsaert, age 69
Executive Vice-President Environment Business, Jean-Louis Chaussade, age 65
Vice Chairman and President, Jean-François Cirelli, age 58
EVP and COO, Isabelle Kocher, age 49
CEO of GDF SUEZ Energy International, Willem van Twembeke, age 51
Executive Vice-President Group Human Resources, Henri Ducre, age 60
Group CIO, Yves Le Gelard
Executive Vice-President Infrastructures, Jean-Claude Depail, age 68
Director of Group Purchasing, Claire Brabec-Lagrange
Director of the Group Sales and Marketing, Jean-Louis Blanc
CEO Elengy, Martin Lestang
EVP and CFO, Judith Hartmann
Auditors: Deloitte & Associés

LOCATIONS

HQ: Engie SA
1, Place Samuel de Champlain, Courbevoie 92400
Phone: (33) 1 44 22 00 00
Web: www.engie.com

2015 Sales

	% of total
Europe	
France	36
Belgium	13
Other EU countries	26
Other European countries	3
Asia Pacific & Middle East	9
North America	7
South America	6
Africa	0
Total	**100**

PRODUCTS/OPERATIONS

2015 Sales

	% of total
Energy Europe	46
Energy Services	23
Energy International	21
Global Gas & LNG	6
Infrastructures	4
Total	**100**

COMPETITORS

BG Group	Eni
Bouygues	Gas Natural SDG
CANAL+	Gasunie
Centrica	Gazprom
Covanta	Italgas
Dragados	National Grid
E.ON	RWE
Electricite de France	SABESP
Electricite de Strasbourg	United Utilities
	Vattenfall
Enel	Veolia Environnement

HISTORICAL FINANCIALS

Company Type: Public

Income Statement

FYE: December 31

	REVENUE ($ mil.)	NET INCOME ($ mil.)	NET PROFIT MARGIN	EMPLOYEES
12/15	76,632	(5,028)	—	154,935
12/14	91,317	2,965	3.2%	152,882
12/13	122,942	(12,788)	—	147,199
12/12	127,900	2,042	1.6%	139,781
12/11	117,281	5,177	4.4%	240,303
Annual Growth	(10.1%)	—	—	(10.4%)

2015 Year-End Financials

Debt ratio: 26.5%
Return on equity: (-9.9%)
Cash ($ mil.): 10,002
Current ratio: 1.12
Long-term debt ($ mil.): 30,631
No. of shares (mil.): —
Dividends
Yield: 6.3%
Payout: —
Market value ($ mil.): —

	STOCK PRICE ($) FY Close	P/E High/Low	PER SHARE ($) Earnings	Dividends	Book Value
12/15	17.60	— —	(2.17)	1.12	19.58
12/14	23.30	26 20	1.22	2.67	25.18
12/13	23.67	— —	(5.38)	1.99	27.97
12/12	21.04	42 29	0.88	3.00	33.41
12/11	27.17	22 13	2.33	1.87	36.77
Annual Growth (10.3%) (14.6%)		— —	—(12.1%)		

ENI S.p.A.

It's not teeny it's Eni —and it's huge. One of Italy's largest companies Eni operates in the oil and natural gas petrochemicals and oil field services industries and has expanded into power generation. Its main subsidiaries and affiliates include EniPower (power generation) Italgas (natural gas transmission) Saipem (oil field services) pipeline operator Snam Rete Gas and Snamprogetti (contracting engineering). As one of the world's leading oil enterprises in 2010 Eni had proved reserves of 6.8 billion barrels of oil equivalent most of it in Italy and in Africa. The Italian government owns 27% of Eni.

The company's oil and gas holdings and exploration and production efforts extend into more than 30 countries on five continents. Eni has expanded outside its traditional bases of Africa and Italy with ventures in the Americas the Asia/Pacific region Europe and the Middle East.

In response to the opening up of Italy's energy markets Eni is increasing its natural gas holdings and adding electricity generating power units. In 2007 the company bought Dominion Resources' US oil and gas assets in the Gulf of Mexico for $4.75 billion. To expand its Asian and Algerian holdings in 2008 Eni acquired Burren Energy and First Calgary Petroleums. It was able to benefit from SUEZ's acquisition of Gaz de France by buying up GDF SUEZ's majority stake in Belgian gas company Distrigas. Eni now owns 100% of Distrigas.

In 2009 to raise cash to pay down debt the company sold its 20% stake in Gazprom Neft to strategic partner Gazprom for $4.2 billion. To save operating costs that year Eni consolidated its gas divisions and sold Italgas and Stogit (gas storage) to subsidiary Snam Rete Gas.

Expanding its Central European market share in 2010 it acquired Exxon Mobil's 135 gas stations and other downstream assets in Austria.

In the wake of the global recession the company saw its revenues and income bounce back in 2010 thanks to higher commodity prices and stronger demand. The unrest in Libya in 2011 had a material impact of Eni which gets 15% of it production from the North African country. To compensate the company is investing heavily in growing production in other areas. Looking to expand in China in 2011 Eni signed a strategic alliance with Chinese oil major PetroChina.

In order to comply with an EU anti-trust ruling in 2011 the company sold its 89% stake in the TAG Pipeline (which transports gas from Russia to Italy) to Cassa Depositi e Prestiti for $986 million.

HISTORY

Although the Italian parliament formed Ente Nazionale Idrocarburi (National Hydrocarbon Agency) in 1953 Enrico Mattei is the true father of Eni. In 1945 Mattei a partisan leader during WWII was appointed northern commissioner of Agip a state-owned petroleum company founded in 1926 by Mussolini and ordered to liquidate the company. Mattei instead ordered the exploration of the Po Valley where workers found methane gas deposits in 1946.

When Eni was created in 1953 Mattei was named president. His job was to find energy resources for an oil-poor country. He initiated a series of joint ventures with several Middle Eastern and African nations offering better deals than his large oil company rivals which he dubbed the Seven Sisters.

Mattei didn't stick to energy: By the time he died in a mysterious plane crash in 1962 Eni had acquired machinery manufacturer Pignone finance company Sofid Milan newspaper Il Giorno and textile company Lane Rossi. Eni grew during the 1960s partly because of a deal made for Soviet crude in 1958 and a joint venture with Esso in 1963. It also expanded its chemical activities.

By the early 1970s losses in Eni's chemical and textile operations the oil crisis and the Italian government's dumping of unprofitable companies on Eni hurt its bottom line. Former finance minister Franco Reviglio took over in 1983 and began cutting inefficient operations.

EniChem merged with Montedison Italy's largest private chemical company in 1988 but clashes between the public agency and the private company made Montedison sell back its stake in 1990. Eni became a joint stock company in 1992 but the government retained a majority stake.

Franco Bernabe took over Eni following a 1993 bribery scandal and began cutting noncore businesses. The Italian government began selling Eni stock in 1995. In 1996 Eni signed on to develop Libyan gas resources and build a pipeline to Italy. A year later the company merged its Agipa exploration and production subsidiary into its main operations. Eni also took a 35% stake in Italian telecom company Albacom (which has since been sold to British Telecom Group).

The government cut its stake in Eni from 51% to 38% in 1998. That year Vittorio Mincato a company veteran succeeded Bernabe as CEO. In 1999 Eni and Russia's RAO Gazprom the world's largest natural gas production firm agreed to build a controversial $3 billion natural gas pipeline stretching from Russia to Turkey. Eni agreed to invest $5.5 billion to develop oil and gas reserves in Libya; it also sold interests in Saipem and Nuovo Pignone as well as some of its Italian service stations.

In 2000 Eni paid about $910 million for a 33% stake in Galp a Portuguese oil and gas company

that also has natural gas utility operations. Also that year Eni bought British-Borneo Oil & Gas in a $1.2 billion deal and in 2001 it paid $4 billion for UK independent exploration and production company LASMO topping a bid by US-based Amerada Hess.

The Italian government sold off another 5% of Eni in 2001 reducing its stake to about 30% and announced that it was considering selling its entire investment. In an effort to reduce noncore holdings the company sold property management subsidiary Immobiliare Metanopoli to Goldman Sachs. Also that year Eni sold a minority stake in its gas pipeline unit Snam Rete Gas to the public.

In 2002 Eni entered discussions to acquire Enterprise Oil but lost out to a rival bid from Royal Dutch Shell. Later that year Eni's oil field services unit Saipem gained control of Bouygues Offshore.

In 2006 Eni and Gazprom formed an international alliance to launch joint mid and downstream gas projects and collaborate in upstream and in technological activities.

EXECUTIVES

CEO, Claudio Descalzi, age 62
SEVP Corporate Affairs and Governance, Roberto Ulissi
SEVP Internal Audit, Marco Petracchini
SEVP Retail Market g&p, Angelo Zaccari
EVP Procurement Department, Rita Marino
EVP Government Affairs Department, Pasquale Salzano
EVP External Communication Department, Marco Bardazzi, age 50
Chairman, Emma Marcegaglia, age 52
Auditors: Reconta Ernst & Young S.p.A.

LOCATIONS

HQ: ENI S.p.A.
1, piazzale Enrico Mattei, Rome 00144
Phone: (39) 2 52041730   **Fax:** (39) 2 52041765
Web: www.eni.com

2014 Sales

	% of total
Europe	
Italy	27
Other EU countries	27
Other countries	11
Africa	11
Americas	8
Asia	15
Other Areas	1
Total	**100**

PRODUCTS/OPERATIONS

2014 Sales

	% of total
Refining & marketing	42
Gas & power	21
Exploration & production	22
Engineering & construction	10
Petrochemicals	4
Corporate & financial	1
Total	**100**

Selected Subsidiaries and Affiliates

Distrigas NV (gas Belgium)
EniPower SpA (power generation)
Italgas SpA (natural gas supply)
Saipem SpA (42.9% oil field services)
Snam Rete Gas SpA (52.5% gas pipeline)
Snamprogetti SpA (contracting and engineering)

COMPETITORS

A2A	Hellenic Petroleum
Ashland Inc.	Marathon Oil
BASF SE	Occidental Petroleum
BG Group	PEMEX

BP
Chevron
ConocoPhillips
ERG S.p.A.
Edison
Exxon Mobil

PETROBRAS
Petrleos de
  Venezuela
Royal Dutch Shell
Sunoco
TOTAL

HISTORICAL FINANCIALS

Company Type: Public

Income Statement

FYE: December 31

	REVENUE ($ mil.)	NET INCOME ($ mil.)	NET PROFIT MARGIN	EMPLOYEES
12/15	75,095	(9,566)	—	29,053
12/14	134,857	1,569	1.2%	84,405
12/13	159,816	7,103	4.4%	83,887
12/12	169,719	10,264	6.0%	77,838
12/11	142,954	8,873	6.2%	78,686
Annual Growth	(14.9%)	—	—	(22.0%)

2015 Year-End Financials

Debt ratio: 22.4%
Return on equity: (-15.7%)
Cash ($ mil.): 5,663
Current ratio: 1.35
Long-term debt ($ mil.): 21,123

No. of shares (mil.): —
Dividends
  Yield: 5.1%
  Payout: —
Market value ($ mil.): —

	STOCK PRICE ($) FY Close	P/E High/Low		PER SHARE ($) Earnings	Dividends	Book Value
12/15	29.80	—	—	(2.66)	1.53	15.65
12/14	34.91	137	89	0.44	2.24	20.17
12/13	48.49	38	30	1.95	2.31	22.12
12/12	49.14	23	19	2.83	2.14	21.54
12/11	41.27	25	16	2.44	1.91	19.81
Annual Growth	(7.8%)	—	—	—	(5.4%)	(5.7%)

Ericsson

Auditors: PricewaterhouseCoopers AB

LOCATIONS

HQ: Ericsson
  Torshamnsgatan 21, Kista, Stockholm SE-164 83
Phone: (46) 10 719 0000
Web: www.ericsson.com

HISTORICAL FINANCIALS

Company Type: Public

Income Statement

FYE: December 31

	REVENUE ($ mil.)	NET INCOME ($ mil.)	NET PROFIT MARGIN	EMPLOYEES
12/15	29,289	1,607	5.5%	116,281
12/14	29,492	1,496	5.1%	118,055
12/13	35,465	1,872	5.3%	114,340
12/12	34,964	886	2.5%	110,255
12/11	32,901	1,768	5.4%	104,525
Annual Growth	(2.9%)	(2.4%)	—	2.7%

2015 Year-End Financials

Debt ratio: 1.0%
Return on equity: 9.3%
Cash ($ mil.): 4,771
Current ratio: 2.18
Long-term debt ($ mil.): 2,697

No. of shares (mil.): —
Dividends
  Yield: 2.6%
  Payout: 65.0%
Market value ($ mil.): —

	STOCK PRICE ($) FY Close	P/E High/Low		PER SHARE ($) Earnings	Dividends	Book Value
12/15	9.61	3	2	0.49	0.25	5.26
12/14	12.10	3	3	0.46	0.30	5.65
12/13	12.24	4	3	0.58	0.77	6.77
12/12	10.10	6	5	0.27	0.35	6.52
12/11	10.13	4	2	0.55	0.00	6.46
Annual Growth	(1.3%)	—	—	(2.7%)	—	(5.0%)

Erste Group Bank AG

First there was Erste. Erste Group Bank is the holding company of Erste Bank Austria's first savings bank founded in 1819. However the company has grown beyond its home country to number some 2800 branches throughout Central and Eastern European that serve some 16.5 million customers. The company has operating subsidiaries in Austria Croatia the Czech Republic Montenegro Moldova Romania Serbia Slovakia and Hungary. Erste Group banks provide financial services such as savings and lending to individuals and small to medium-size businesses. It also has a private banking arm. Erste Bank is Austria's largest lender.

As Austrian banks consolidated the group increased its presence in surrounding nations. Since the early 2000s the holding company has expanded its market by purchasing stakes in or acquiring outright banks in Austria Bosnia Russia and the Ukraine. Each of its subsidiaries is focused on local operations.

Erste Group slowed its acquisitions during the economic downturn and focused instead on cutting costs and making good lending decisions. The choices helped the company weather the financial crisis rather well. Over the long term Central and Eastern European countries are expected to record economic growth. Erste Group expects loan growth and an increased demand for asset management services in those emerging countries.

The company has sharpened its focus on its core banking activities by selling non-core insurance subsidiaries. It sold most its insurance brokerage operations to Austrian firm GrECo International in 2010.

In 2011 Erste Group made its first acquisitions in several years when it took control of Intermarket Bank —the largest factoring bank in Austria. Erste Group already owned more than 20% of Intermarket Bank and it acquired an additional 56%. The transaction was part of Erste Group's strategy to offer broad services to corporate customers. Also in 2011 Erste offered to buy the rest of majority-held Romanian unit Banca Comerciala Romana it doesn't already own.

HISTORY

In 1819 a bank was born and its name was Erste oesterreichische Spar-Cassa. Called Die Erste for short the bank was Austria's first commercial and savings bank. Unlike Austria's community savings banks Die Erste was independent —not backed by government guarantees.

For more than 150 years Die Erste operated as a local savings bank serving Vienna. Then in 1979 the Austrian government passed a law that would alter the face of the banking industry in that country. The Banking Act of 1979 placed banks and savings institutions in direct competition with each other by allowing them both to take part in all aspects of the banking business. As a result of the enhanced competition Die Erste began expanding its domestic branch network.

Meanwhile the Austrian savings banks had established their own central institution in 1937 and called it Girovereinigung der österreichischen Sparkassen or Girozentrale for short. Girozentrale focused on managing the liquidity reserves of the savings banks and helping them with their syndication and securities businesses. The bank also endeavored to improve the non-cash payment system and to promote mortgage savings. Concentrating on international and investment banking rather than retail banking Girozentrale eventually became the country's third-largest bank.

Throughout the late 1980s and into the 1990s rumors began to spread about a possible merger between Girozentrale and Die Erste (both were associated with the nation's conservative People's Party). In 1992 Girozentrale merged with Österreichisches Credit-Institut (ÖCI) to create GiroCredit giving the central savings bank a branch network for the first time. But it also made GiroCredit a direct competitor with its two largest shareholders —Bank Austria (now part of HypoVereinsbank) and Die Erste who were also fierce competitors with each other.

Between 1992 and 1994 Die Erste and Bank Austria struggled to find a solution to the problem of GiroCredit's ownership. In 1994 Bank Austria emerged the victor by winning the majority stake in GiroCredit in a move that was characterized by Die Erste as "unfriendly."

Throughout the next two years Die Erste attempted to secure a stake in Creditanstalt Austria's second-biggest bank as the Austrian government began moves to privatize it. Die Erste acted as a part of a consortium of Austrian German and Italian entities interested in obtaining stakes in the bank. But in 1997 Bank Austria won that battle too managing to take over Creditanstalt. In turn Die Erste bought Bank Austria's majority stake in GiroCredit. The resulting company was given the name Erste Bank which went public that year in the largest stock issue in Austrian history. In 1998 it became the first major Austrian company to allow for the election of small shareholder representatives to its supervisory board.

In 2000 Erste Bank bought a majority stake in Ceska Sporitelna the largest retail bank in the Czech Republic from the Czech government. Later in the year the Slovak government allowed Erste Bank to become a major shareholder in the previously state-owned Slovenska sporitel'na. Erste Bank was also one of several Austrian banks to be accused by the European Commission of fixing foreign exchange fees.

In 2001 Erste Bank took control of Slovenska Sporitel'na and acquired majority ownership of Tiroler Sparkasse Bank AG. The following year Erste Bank took full control of Czech Republic-based Czeska Sporitelna. Ever acquisitive in 2005 the company completed its acquisition of Serbia's Novosadska banka.

Erste in 2006 acquiered Romanian bank Banca Comerciala Romana the largest bank in that country and previously state-owned.

Erste switched to a holding company structure in 2008. That year the company also sold most of its insurance business to Vienna Insurance Group.

EXECUTIVES

Chairman, Andreas Treichl, $1,245,000 total compensation
Management Board Member Controlling and Information Management, Gernot Mittendorfer, age 52

Management Board Member Enterprise wide Risk Management, Andreas Gottschling, age 49
Management Board Member Investment Banking and Steering and Operating Office Corporates, Jozef Sikela
First Vice Chairman, Georg Winckler, age 73
Chairman, Friedrich R – DLER, age 66
Second Vice Chairman, Jan Homan, age 69
Auditors: Ernst & Young Wirtschaftsprufungsgesellschaft

LOCATIONS

HQ: Erste Group Bank AG
Am Belvedere 1, Vienna A-1100
Phone: (43) 50100 10100   **Fax:** (43) 50100 9 13112
Web: www.erstegroup.com

PRODUCTS/OPERATIONS

2015 Sales

	% of total
Interest income	73
Fee & commission income	27
Total	**100**

Selected Subsidiaries

Banca Comerciala Romana S.A. (BCR)
Ceská Sporitelna (Czech Republic)
Erste Bank a.d. Novi Sad (Serbia)
Erste Bank Croatia (Erste & Steiermärkische Bank d.d.)
Erste Bank der oesterreichen Sparkassen AG
  Autoleasing EBV
  Sparkasse Salzburg
  Wohnbaubank
Erst Bank Hungary Nyrt.
Erste Bank Ukraine (formerly Bank Prestige)
Slovenská sporitelna a.s. (Slovakia)

COMPETITORS

BAWAG
Banca Comerciala Romana
Bank Austria
Credit Suisse
Deutsche Bank
Deutsche Post
Deutsche Postbank
Erste & Steierm¤rkische Bank
Investkredit
OTP Bank
Oberbank AG
RZB Group
UBS
UniCredit Bank AG

HISTORICAL FINANCIALS

Company Type: Public

Income Statement

FYE: December 31

	ASSETS ($ mil.)	NET INCOME ($ mil.)	INCOME AS % OF ASSETS	EMPLOYEES
12/15	217,562	1,054	0.5%	46,467
12/14	238,588	(1,752)	—	46,067
12/13	275,176	83	0.0%	45,670
12/12	281,830	637	0.2%	49,381
12/11	271,633	(929)	—	50,452
Annual Growth	**(5.4%)**	—	—	**(2.0%)**

2015 Year-End Financials

Return on assets: 0.4%	Dividends
Return on equity: 9.2%	Yield: —
Long-term debt ($ mil.): —	Payout: —
No. of shares (mil.): 410	Market value ($ mil.): 6,457
Sales ($ mil): 6,691	

STOCK PRICE ($) FY Close	P/E High/Low		PER SHARE ($) Earnings	Dividends	Book Value
12/15	15.73	7	4	2.47	0.00	29.20
12/14	11.45	—	—	(4.10)	0.13	29.17
12/13	17.60	—	—	(0.08)	0.21	37.56
12/12	16.05	19	9	1.15	0.00	45.10
12/11	8.65	—	—	(2.95)	0.00	41.92
Annual Growth	**16.1%**	—	—	—	—	**(8.6%)**

Eurobank Ergasias SA

Eurobank Ergasias has a lot of branches for shaking the money tree. The bank operates some 500 branches business centers and ATMs in its home country Greece and about 1250 more in about half-a-dozen other central and southeastern European countries. In addition to traditional retail banking and consumer lending Eurobank offers business banking factoring insurance leasing investment banking and wealth management services. The bank was founded in 1990 as Euromerchant Bank. Swiss-based EFG Bank European Financial Group owns about 44% of Eurobank.

Plans to merge with rival Alpha Bank fell through in 2012. The merger was aimed at strengthening both banks which hold much of Greece's troubled debt that caused fear of another worldwide recession. By joining forces the companies would have created the nation's largest lender. However Alpha scrapped merger plans after the Greek government restructured its sovereign debt.

Unlike many banks in Europe Eurobank increased its lending activity in 2008. It saw the biggest increases in mortgage small business and corporate loans to customers in its Eastern European and Greek markets.

In addition Eurobank saw a rise in deposit activity in 2008. The bank attributed this increase to its expansion of low-cost deposit products which brought in more consumer and professional customers. It also made heavy investments in products and services outside its home country and aims to become a banking leader in Romania Serbia Bulgaria Turkey Cyprus the Ukraine and other European countries.

In 2012 EFG Eurobank Ergasias sold a majority stake in its Polbank subsidiary in Poland. Raiffeisisen Bank International acquired 70% of Polbank for €490 million ($640 million).

EXECUTIVES

Chief Executive Officer, Fokion Christos Karavias
Chairman, Nikolaos Basil Karamouzis
Vice Chairman, Jawaid A Mirza
Auditors: PricewaterhouseCoopers SA

LOCATIONS

HQ: Eurobank Ergasias SA
8 Othonos Street, Athens 105 57
Phone: (30) 210 333 7000   **Fax:** (30) 210 323 3866
Web: www.eurobank.gr

COMPETITORS

Alpha Bank   Piraeus Bank S.A.
Emporiki Bank
National Bank of Greece

HISTORICAL FINANCIALS

Company Type: Public

Income Statement

FYE: December 31

	ASSETS ($ mil.)	NET INCOME ($ mil.)	INCOME AS % OF ASSETS	EMPLOYEES
12/15	80,114	(1,286)	—	17,521
12/14	91,792	(1,481)	—	18,428
12/13	106,815	(1,588)	—	20,053
12/12	89,170	(1,915)	—	17,662
12/11	99,365	(7,124)	—	19,156
Annual Growth	**(5.2%)**	—		**(2.2%)**

2015 Year-End Financials

Return on assets: (-1.5%)	Dividends
Return on equity: (-19.5%)	Yield: —
Long-term debt ($ mil.): —	Payout: —
No. of shares (mil.): —	Market value ($ mil.): —
Sales ($ mil): 3,336	

STOCK PRICE ($) FY Close	P/E High/Low		PER SHARE ($) Earnings	Dividends	Book Value
12/15	0.58	—	—	(4.38)	0.00	3.22
12/14	0.12	—	—	(13.37)	0.00	46.58
12/13	0.11	—	—	(56.45)	0.00	106.79
12/12	0.30	—	—	(303.15)	0.00	(223.20)
12/11	0.18	—	—	(1,310.27)	0.00	139.85
Annual Growth	**34.0%**	—	—	—	—	**(61.0%)**

European Investment Bank

The biggest international lovefest since Esperanto the European Investment Bank (EIB) is the financial backbone of the European Union (EU). Led by finance ministers from EU countries the bank makes loans for trans-European enterprise and infrastructure projects focusing on less-developed EU countries. About 90% of the loans go to projects located within the EU; major loan categories are transportation and energy. The bank also offers development aid to some non-European countries. The EIB owns a majority of the European Investment Fund (EIF) which invests in venture capital funds and debt financing for small businesses in the EU.

The EIB provides loans and finances the development of infrastructure and businesses according to the policies of the EU. Loan categories also include health care organizations educational ventures and housing throughout the EU and beyond. Most of the 150 non-European countries it makes loans to are former colonies of European countries. The EIB which loans more money annually than the World Bank has lending policies geared to foster economic integration and social cohesion among current and potential EU member nations.

A board of governors (consisting of EU member states' finance ministers) appoints a 28-person board of directors (along with 18 alternates) to manage the bank's affairs. One director and one alternate represent the European Commission. The board of directors meets once a month to approve loans review policies and suggest changes in the EIB's credit policy. The EIB also employs an audit committee and a management committee to oversee daily functions. The bank's president chairs the management committee's meetings.

Although the EIB enjoys unique legal and financial autonomy within the EU it must also remain competitive with private banks in the international market. The bank's concerns for economic parity among member nations sometimes pit it against the EU which seeks to bring Europe's poorer cousins of the east into the Union's political fold. Watchdog groups have called for the bank to be more open in its decision-making process and policies arguing that large infrastructure projects funded by EIB loans have a substantial environmental impact.

The EIB's clients include public entities EU and non-EU governments and large private corporations.

HISTORY

The European Investment Bank (EIB) has its roots in the Messina Conference of 1955 when the soon-to-be members of the European Economic Community (EEC) proposed a central public body to oversee the spread of wealth between rich and poor European nations.

In 1958 the Treaty of Rome established the EEC and the EIB was founded to make and guarantee loans that helped develop infrastructure and improvements in member countries. The six founding countries were Belgium France Italy Luxembourg the Netherlands and West Germany.

The Yaounde (Cameroon) Convention of 1963 saw the EIB expand its lending activities to 17 African former colonies of European countries. Under the Yaounde Convention these nations were provided financial aid and trading advantages.

In 1973 the UK Denmark and Ireland joined the EEC and the EIB grew in size assets and lending power. The Lome (Togo) Convention of 1975 expanded the Yaounde Convention to include 70 more African Caribbean and Pacific countries. Meanwhile the EEC continued to grow adding Greece (1981) and Spain and Portugal (1986). It became the more fully integrated European Union (EU) in 1993 (Finland Austria and Sweden were added in 1995). The bank's loans first exceeded those of the World Bank in 1992.

In 1994 the European Investment Fund (EIF) was created by the EIB the EU and private European banks to invest in venture capital funds and to guarantee financed debt.

Environmental groups denounced the EIB for loans they considered ecologically damaging in the mid-1990s; those included loans for a Sweden-Denmark bridge a gold mine in Papua New Guinea a water project in Lesotho (Africa) and a gas pipeline between Bolivia and Brazil.

In 2000 EIF realigned itself as the EIB's specialist risk capital arm while the EIB raised its stake to more then 50% of the fund.

EXECUTIVES

Chairman, Werner Hoyer

LOCATIONS

HQ: European Investment Bank
98-100, Boulevard Konrad Adenauer, Luxembourg L-2950
Phone: (352) 43 79 1   **Fax:** (352) 43 77 04
Web: www.eib.org
The EIB has offices in Australia Austria Belgium Egypt Finland France the French Caribbean Germany Greece Italy Kenya Luxembourg Morocco Poland Portugal Romania Senegal South Africa Spain Tunisia and the UK.

COMPETITORS

BNP Paribas	Deutsche Bank
Banco Comercial Portugus	National Bank of Greece
Banco Popular Espa±ol	Royal Bank of Scotland
Citigroup	UniCredit Bank AG

HISTORICAL FINANCIALS

Company Type: Public

Income Statement

FYE: December 31

	REVENUE ($ mil.)	NET INCOME ($ mil.)	NET PROFIT MARGIN	EMPLOYEES
12/15	26,529	4,658	17.6%	2,916
12/14	25,404	820	3.2%	2,557
12/13	32,068	3,505	10.9%	2,359
12/12	34,301	3,611	10.5%	0
12/11	32,379	2,964	9.2%	0
Annual Growth	(4.9%)	12.0%	—	—

2015 Year-End Financials

Debt ratio: —
Return on equity: 6.9%
Cash ($ mil.): 54,672
Current ratio: —
Long-term debt ($ mil.): —

No. of shares (mil.): —
Dividends
  Yield: —
  Payout: —
Market value ($ mil.): —

Fairfax Financial Holdings Ltd

Achieving a high rate of return is the main objective at Fairfax Financial Holdings. The holding company provides insurance reinsurance and other financial services. Its subsidiaries including Northbridge Financial Falcon Insurance and Crum & Forster focus on property/casualty coverage such as commercial auto liability trucking and accident insurance in Canada the US Singapore and Hong Kong. Fairfax's reinsurance operations span North America the UK Africa and Central Europe. Chairman and CEO Prem Watsa's unorthodox business strategies have been compared to those of Warren Buffett; he controls about half the voting rights of Fairfax Financial.

Operations

The majority of Fairfax Financial Holdings' operations are in the US and account for roughly half of its earned premiums. These include Crum & Forster (commercial and specialty insurance) and Odyssey Re (reinsurance). International operations include Asian firms Falcon Insurance First Capital Insurance and The Pacific Insurance Berhad.

The Resolution Group and the RiverStone Group tend to the company's runoff businesses in the US and UK respectively. International acquisitions and new operations are keeping the company lively overseas.

Strategy

One difference in the company's style is it pays less attention to its market share and more attention to its profitability. For this reason its subsidiaries might not be household names but unlike better-known competitors the company does not underwrite at a loss so its combined ratios came out of the financial recession in sturdier condition.

In 2015 Fairfax entered the African market when it acquired a minor stake in Africa Re. The following year it made a move to expand its presence on the continent when it agreed to buy

Zurich Insurance Company's South African and Botswana operations.

Mergers and Acquisitions

Fairfax typically likes to acquire a minority stake in a company and then if it likes what it sees goes ahead and works to acquire the balance.

In late 2014 the company agreed to buy QBE Insurance's operations in the Czech Republic Hungary and Slovakia. Late the following year it agreed to buy 80% of Greek insurer Eurolife ERB Insurance for euro 316 million.

In late 2016 Fairfax announced its largest deal to date agreeing to buy Swiss insurance firm Allied World Assurance for some $4.9 billion. Allied World provides such products as professional liability coverage environmental policies and reinsurance. The deal will boost Fairfax's investment portfolio –a strategy similar to that of Warren Buffett and his insurance activities.

Early the following year the company agreed to buy Tower Limited a property/casualty insurer operating in New Zealand and the Pacific Islands for around $144 million. That purchase will help Fairfax as it expands in that geographic market.

EXECUTIVES

VP International Operations, Jean Cloutier
President, Paul C. Rivett, age 48
Vice President and Chief Risk Officer, Peter Clarke
VP and CFO, David Bonham
Chairman and CEO, V.Prem Watsa
Auditors: PricewaterhouseCoopers LLP

LOCATIONS

HQ: Fairfax Financial Holdings Ltd
95 Wellington Street West, Suite 800, Toronto, Ontario M5J 2N7
Phone: 416 367-4941   **Fax:** 416 367-4946
Web: www.fairfax.ca

PRODUCTS/OPERATIONS

Selected Subsidiaries

Insurance
  Asian Insurance
  Falcon Insurance Company (Hong Kong) Ltd.
  First Capital Insurance Limited (Singapore)
  Canadian Insurance
  Northbridge Financial Corporation
  Commonwealth Insurance Company
  Federated Holdings of Canada Limited
  Lombard General Insurance Company of Canada
  Markel Insurance Company of Canada
  U.S. Insurance
  Crum & Forster Holdings Corporation
Reinsurance
  CRC (Bermuda) Reinsurance Limited
  Odyssey Re Holdings Corp.
  Polish Re (Poland)
  Wentworth Insurance Company Ltd. (Barbados)
Runoff
  nSpire Re Limited
  RiverStone Group LLC
  RiverStone Holdings Limited
  TRG Holding Corporation

COMPETITORS

AIG	Everest Re
Aviva	General Re
Baldwin & Lyons	ING
Berkshire Hathaway	Manulife Financial
Chubb Limited	Nationwide
Co-operators General Insurance	RenaissanceRe
Economical Insurance Group	Sun Life
	Travelers Companies
	Wawanesa Mutual

HISTORICAL FINANCIALS
Company Type: Public

Income Statement
FYE: December 31

	ASSETS ($ mil.)	NET INCOME ($ mil.)	INCOME AS % OF ASSETS	EMPLOYEES
12/15	41,529	567	1.4%	23,576
12/14	36,131	1,633	4.5%	11,484
12/13	35,958	(573)	—	10,938
12/12	36,941	532	1.4%	11,507
12/11	33,406	45	0.1%	38
Annual Growth	5.6%	88.4%	—	399.1%

2015 Year-End Financials

Return on assets: 1.4%	Dividends
Return on equity: 5.7%	Yield: 0.0%
Long-term debt ($ mil.): —	Payout: 0.5%
No. of shares (mil.): 23	Market value ($ mil.): 223
Sales ($ mil): 9,580	

	STOCK PRICE ($) FY Close	P/E High/Low	PER SHARE ($) Earnings	Dividends	Book Value
12/15	9.69	1 0	23.15	0.13	447.02
Annual Growth	—	— —	—	—	—

Fast Retailing Co., Ltd.

Since 1963 Fast Retailing has been working to fill the gap in Japan's casual wear market. The company operates 841 UNIGLO (a combination of the words unique and clothing) stores in Japan and another 798 UNIGLO shops in foreign markets including China France South Korea the UK and the US. Fast Retailing —often described as the "Gap of Japan"—sells functional basics (similar to US-based Old Navy or Spain's Zara but undercutting its competitors more drastically) for men women and children. The retail group also operates almost 1340 other stores under the Theory Comptoir des Cotonniers Princess TAM.

TAM and G.U. banners.

Operations The company operates in three business segments: UNIQLO Japan UNIQLO International and Global Brands. In 2015 UNIQLO Japan operated 841 stores and contributed about 46% of the company's total revenue. UNIQLO International (36%) operated 798 stores. Global brand (18%) had 1339 stores. Fast Retailing manages multiple brands worldwide including UNIQLO GU Theory and Comptoir des Cotonniers using an SPA (Specialty store retailer of Private label Apparel) business model that controls the entire process from design through manufacture and retail. UNIQLO the group's mainstay brand offers basic casualwear at reasonable prices via a network of 1700 stores. Some of the company's subsidiaries are Fast Retailing Co. LTD. Fast Retailing France S.A.S. Fast Retailing USA Inc Uniqlo Trading Co. LTD PT. Fast Retailing Indonesia and J Brand Japan Co. Ltd. Geographic Reach Based in Japan the company also operates in China Hong Kong Taiwan South Korea Singapore Malaysia Thailand Philippines Indonesia Australia the US Canada the UK France Germany Belgium and Russia. UNIQLO International's store count includes 467 stores in Greater China (Mainland China Hong Kong and Taiwan) 155 in South Korea and 108 in Southeast Asia and Oceania. Most products sold through group companies are made in China other Asian countries and Turkey. Sales and Marketing

UNIQLO sells products via stores and e-commerce. UNIQLO conducts promotional campaigns for core products and markets their products via TV commercial promotional flyer and online. Online sales in Japan accounted for 4.2% of Fast Retailing's total sales. It also has online sales in Mainland China Taiwan South Korea the UK the US Australia and Singapore among other places.

Financial Performance

Fast Retailing has recorded an increasing trend in net revenues over the last five years. In 2015 net revenue was ¥1681.7 billion up 22% on 2014 due to an increase in sales from UNIQLO Japan UNIQLO International and Global Brands. Revenue from UNIQLO Japan increased by 9% due to a same store sales increase of 6.2%. Sales from new stores opened in Japan also contributed to the increase in net revenue. Revenue from UNIQLO International increased by 46% as a result of higher sales from Greater China and South Korea (the main driver of group growth). Continued growth in same-store sales fueled significant gains at UNIQLO South Korea. In 2015 the company opened 93 stores in Greater China 22 in South Korea 23 in Southeast Asia 5 in Australia 5 in Europe and 17 in the US. Global Brands' revenue expanded 17.6% to ¥295.3 billion. Operating profit totaled ¥14.4 billion compared to a ¥4.1 billion loss in 2014. Significant increases in revenue and profit from the low-priced GU fashion casualwear brand drove segment growth.

In 2015 Fast Retailing's net income was ¥110.0 billion up 48% compared to 2014 due to higher sales an increase in finance income higher foreign exchange gains and a decrease in other expenses.

Strategy

Already Asia's largest apparel retailer Fast Retailing seeks no less than to become #1 in the world by 2020. To succeed it plans to leverage its successful model of combining quality and aggressive pricing of its private-label apparel with the international expansion of its Uniqlo chain and an active acquisition schedule. Indeed Fast's CEO and founder Tadashi Yanai has committed $11 billion to the company's global expansion plans with up to $3 billion allocated for mergers and acquisitions in the US and Europe.

It is also looking to integrate its physical stores and e-commerce operations to give customers a seamless experience.

Yanai and his family own about 22% of Fast Retailing.

EXECUTIVES
Chairman President and CEO, Tadashi Yanai, age 67
Group EVP, Shuichi Nakajima
Group EVP, Ning Pan
Group EVP, Takeshi Okazaki
Group EVP, Osamu Yunoki
Group EVP and Head Production Dept., Yoshihiro Kunii
Group EVP, Takahiro Wakabayashi
President Global Creative, John C. Jay
Group EVP, Takao Kuwahara
Group EVP, Taku Morikawa
Auditors: Ernst & Young ShinNihon LLC

LOCATIONS
HQ: Fast Retailing Co., Ltd.
Midtown Tower, 9-7-1 Akasaka, Minato-ku, Tokyo 107-6231
Phone: (81) 3 6865 0050
Web: www.fastretailing.com

PRODUCTS/OPERATIONS

2015 sales

	% of total
UNIQLO Japan	46
UNIQLO International	36
Global brand operations	18
Total	**100**

COMPETITORS

AEON	L.L. Bean
Benetton	Marui Group
Bloomingdale's	Mitsukoshi
Daiei	Otto Group
Daimaru	Seiyu
H&M	Takashimaya
Inditex	The Gap
Isetan	Tokyu Department Store
Isetan Mitsukoshi	Wal-Mart
Ito-Yokado	

HISTORICAL FINANCIALS
Company Type: Public

Income Statement
FYE: August 31

	REVENUE ($ mil.)	NET INCOME ($ mil.)	NET PROFIT MARGIN	EMPLOYEES
08/16	17,296	465	2.7%	69,921
08/15	13,862	906	6.5%	68,865
08/14	13,300	716	5.4%	56,153
08/13	11,629	1,064	9.2%	47,517
08/12	11,824	912	7.7%	18,854
Annual Growth	10.0%	(15.5%)	—	38.8%

2016 Year-End Financials

Debt ratio: —	No. of shares (mil.): 101
Return on equity: 7.2%	Dividends
Cash ($ mil.): 3,731	Yield: 0.8%
Current ratio: 2.74	Payout: 7.6%
Long-term debt ($ mil.): —	Market value ($ mil.): 3,587

	STOCK PRICE ($) FY Close	P/E High/Low	PER SHARE ($) Earnings	Dividends	Book Value
08/16	35.18	0 0	4.56	0.31	54.55
08/15	40.55	0 0	8.89	0.27	60.72
08/14	31.18	0 0	7.03	0.29	58.36
08/13	32.30	0 0	10.44	0.27	56.96
08/12	23.33	— —	8.95	0.27	49.36
Annual Growth	10.8%	—	(15.5%)	3.6%	2.5%

Faurecia S.A. (France)

Take a seat —Faurecia is one of the world's largest automotive seat makers. In addition to car seats it also manufactures emission control systems vehicle interiors and doors and front-end systems. Although Europe accounts for over 50% of sales it supplies most major carmakers including GM Ford and Volkswagen. Faurecia also deals in precious metals and ceramics for use in its catalytic converter businesses though Faurecia Exhaust Systems which together with EMCON Technologies makes emission control technologies in the US. Bertrand Faure and ECIA a Peugeot S.A. subsidiary merged in 1999 to create Faurecia. Faurecia has struggled to keep its CEO seat filled going through three executives in less than five years.

Operations

Faurecia operates four business units. Emission Control Technologies the largest segment accounting for around 36% of sales designs and manufactures exhaust systems; Automotive Seating representing 28% of sales designs and assembles vehicle seats seating frames and adjustable mechanisms; Interior Systems (25% of sales) makes instrument panels door panels and modules and acoustic components; and Automotive Exteriors (11%) designs and manufactures front ends and safety modules.

Geographic Reach

Faurecia has 330 sites including 30 R&D centers in 34 countries around the world. Europe is the company's largest market at some 55% of sales.

Sales and Marketing

Faurecia works with some of the biggest names in the automotive industry. Its five main customers represent 72% of sales. VW leads the way with 22.7% followed by Ford (15.9%) PSA (Peugeot Citroen 13.3%) GM (7.6%) and Daimler (7.1%).

Financial Performance

Note: Growth rates may differ after conversion to US Dollars.

In fiscal 2015 sales climbed 9% to euro 20.7 billion. Product sales (parts and components) were up 6.0% while sales of tooling R&D prototypes and other services were down 15.6%. Catalytic converter monolith sales (precious metals and ceramics used in emission control systems) were up 12.4%.

Net income was up 123% to euro 371.8 million due to higher margins in Europe and an upturn in product sales in North America partially offset by lower sales in South America as a result of the region's difficult economic climate and lower sales in Asia (despite reduced costs). The company's cash position strengthened markedly due mostly to the sale of the Automotive Exteriors business up to euro 1.25 billion from a low base.

Strategy

Faurecia signed a definitive agreement to sell its Automotive Exteriors business which had revenue of around euro 2.0 billion in fiscal 2015 to Plastic Omnium for euro 665 million. The deal does not include Faurecia's composites business its Smart plant in France or two joint ventures in Brazil and China. The sale of the business is to reduce debt which it will do almost entirely.

Faurecia has high hopes for its composites business as the automotive industry looks increasingly towards lightweighting in search of greater fuel efficiency.

In 2015 Faurecia formed a joint venture with Beijing WKW Automotive Parts in order to strengthen its position in China.

HISTORY

Bertrand Faure opened his workshop in Levallois-Perret France in 1914 to manufacture cushions and spring backs for automotive seats; spring pads were developed in 1929. The company diversified into bedding in 1954. The following year it opened a factory near Etampes.

Throughout the 1960s and 1970s Bertrand Faure continued to grow through geographic and product-line expansion. The company boosted its metal and foam seat-making operations in France and in 1971 it expanded into Germany with the purchase of automotive seating component manufacturer Schmitz. Faure bought French bedding maker Merinos in 1973 and then changed its company name to Epeda-Bertrand Faure. Between 1977 and 1978 Epeda-Bertrand Faure expanded its automotive seating business through acquisitions in Spain and Portugal.

Epeda-Bertrand Faure diversified into the luggage business with the 1982 purchase of Delsey. That year the company was floated on the French stock exchange. In 1983 Epeda-Bertrand Faure

further strengthened its car-seat business in France with the purchase of Autocoussin (structures and foam) and Cousin Frères (mechanisms). Another plant in Germany was opened in 1986 to supply BMW. That year Epeda-Bertrand Faure invested in Canadian CASE a leading North American maker of car-seat mechanisms. The company also reorganized its automotive activities under the name Bertrand Faure Automobile.

Epeda-Bertrand Faure acquired Luchaire a defense materials and aerospace and automotive equipment manufacturer in 1987. The following year the company bought automotive seating structures maker Sicam (Italy) and seating foam and structures firm Molaflex (Portugal). In 1989 the company forged joint ventures in the UK Japan and Canada for the manufacture of car seating.

By 1990 the company had reorganized into four product segments: automotive seats bedding luggage and aerospace equipment. The automotive seating business was conducted under the name Bertrand Faure while the rest of the group changed its name to EBF. Bertrand Faure purchased RHW a leading German maker of car seats in 1991.

The following year EBF's board of directors decided to focus the company on automotive seating and initiated a vast restructuring plan. EBF sold its bedding concerns in 1994. As part of its restructuring EBF changed its name back to Bertrand Faure. Two years later Bertrand Faure opened offices in Beijing and São Paulo.

Peugeot S.A. subsidiary ECIA and Bertrand Faure merged in 1999 to form Faurecia. In 2000 Faurecia bolstered its North American presence by purchasing US-based automotive exhaust system maker AP Automotive Systems; it renamed the subsidiary Faurecia Exhaust Systems. The company acquired Sommer Allibert's car interiors business early in 2001.

Expanding in Asia Faurecia purchased Chang Heung Precision Co. Ltd. a Korean maker of exhaust systems in 2003.

Since 2004 the headcount at high-cost Western European locations has been reduced while headcount in low-cost regions has increased.

In 2006 the company opened a new plant in China for the manufacture of automotive seats and interior modules for Ford.

In 2006 CEO Pierre Levi stepped down amid a corruption scandal involving Faurecia employees who allegedly offered kickbacks to managers at customers including Volkswagen and BMW. CFO Frank Imbert was named interim CEO then director Gregoire Olivier followed as CEO. Yann Delabrière succeeded him in early 2007.

In 2007 sales in North America grew by 42%. The company opened seven new plants in the US in 2006 and 2007 —in Michigan (seats interior modules front end modules) Ohio (interior modules and exhaust systems) and South Carolina (seats).

In Asia Faurecia's sales grew by 21% in 2007 over the previous year. To keep up momentum Faurecia continues to invest in the region.

EXECUTIVES

EVP Faurecia China, Jean-Michel Vallin, age 61
EVP Faurecia North America, Mark Stidham
EVP Faurecia Emissions Control Technologies, Christophe Schmitt
EVP Faurecia Group Human Resources, Jean-Pierre Sounillac
CEO, Patrick Koller
EVP Faurecia and Group CFO, Michel Favre
EVP Faurecia Interior Systems, Jean-Michel Renaudie
EVP Faurecia Group Strategy, Herve Guyot

EVP Faurecia Group Communications, Kate Philipps
EVP Faurecia Automotive Seating, Hagen Wiesner, age 55
EVP Group Operations, Eelco Spoelder, age 44
Chairman, Yann Delabriere
Auditors: PricewaterhouseCoopers Audit

LOCATIONS

HQ: Faurecia S.A. (France)
2, rue Hennape, Nanterre 92000
Phone: (33) 1 72 36 70 00   **Fax:** (33) 1 72 36 70 07
Web: www.faurecia.com

2015 Sales

	% of total
Europe	54
North America	27
Asia	15
South America	3
Other countries	1
Total	**100**

PRODUCTS/OPERATIONS

2015 Sales

€ mil % total

Emissions Control Systems	7,450	36
Automotive Seating	6,188	30
Interior Systems	5,018	24
Automotive Exteriors	2,035	10
Total	**20,691**	**100**

2015 Sales by Customer

	% of total
VW Group	23
Ford group	16
PSA Peugeot Citroën	13
GM	8
Daimler	7
Others	33
Total	**100**

COMPETITORS

Benteler Group	Magna International
DURA Automotive	Magneti Marelli
IAC Group	Meritor
Johnson Controls	Tenneco
Kongsberg Automotive	Visteon
Lear Corp	

HISTORICAL FINANCIALS

Company Type: Public

Income Statement

FYE: December 31

	REVENUE ($ mil.)	NET INCOME ($ mil.)	NET PROFIT MARGIN	EMPLOYEES
12/15	20,444	404	2.0%	102,869
12/14	22,886	201	0.9%	99,281
12/13	24,820	120	0.5%	97,419
12/12	22,887	187	0.8%	93,918
12/11	20,941	480	2.3%	84,179
Annual Growth	**(0.6%)**	**(4.2%)**	**—**	**5.1%**

2015 Year-End Financials

Debt ratio: 21.0%	No. of shares (mil.): 137
Return on equity: 18.0%	Dividends
Cash ($ mil.): 1,015	Yield: 0.0%
Current ratio: 0.79	Payout: 3.5%
Long-term debt ($ mil.): 1,052	Market value ($ mil.): 2,691

	STOCK PRICE ($) FY Close	P/E High/Low		PER SHARE ($) Earnings	Dividends	Book Value
12/15	19.62	8	5	3.23	0.12	19.04
12/14	14.38	—		1.63	0.11	16.84
12/13	14.38	19	17	1.09	0.00	18.36
Annual Growth	**16.8%**	**—**	**—**	**31.3%**	**—**	**0.9%**

Fiat Chrysler Automobiles NV

Auditors: Reconta Ernst & Young S.p.A.

LOCATIONS

HQ: Fiat Chrysler Automobiles NV
25 St. James' Street, London SW1A 1HA
Phone: (44) 20 776 0311
Web: www.fcagroup.com

HISTORICAL FINANCIALS
Company Type: Public

Income Statement
FYE: December 31

	REVENUE ($ mil.)	NET INCOME ($ mil.)	NET PROFIT MARGIN	EMPLOYEES
12/15	120,461	363	0.3%	234,621
12/14	116,797	690	0.6%	228,690
12/13	119,258	1,244	1.0%	229,053
12/12	110,406	57	0.1%	218,311
12/11	77,036	1,550	2.0%	197,021
Annual Growth	11.8%	(30.4%)	—	4.5%

2015 Year-End Financials

Debt ratio: 28.8%
Return on equity: 2.2%
Cash ($ mil.): 22,505
Current ratio: 1.30
Long-term debt ($ mil.): 30,264

No. of shares (mil.): 1,288
Dividends
  Yield: —
  Payout: —
Market value ($ mil.): 18,032

	STOCK PRICE ($) FY Close	P/E High/Low		PER SHARE ($) Earnings	Dividends	Book Value
12/15	13.99	78	47	0.24	0.00	13.60
12/14	11.58	29	18	0.56	0.00	12.70
Annual Growth	20.8%	—	—(19.0%)			1.7%

Finatis SA

Finatis finesses its way through a variety of activities. The French holding company has interests in commercial real estate including the leasing of shopping malls in France and Poland through a majority stake in Fonciere Euris. It is also involved in the distribution of food and sporting goods in France through retail giant Rallye owner of Groupe Casinoand Groupe Go Sport and food in South America through Companhia Brasileira de Distribui § o. Through Euristates Finatis has interests in US property investment funds. Groupe Euris founded by president Jean-Charles Naouri controls Finatis.

EXECUTIVES

Managing Director, Jean-Marie Grisard, age 73
Finance Director, Pierre Feraud
Chairman and CEO, Jean-Charles Naouri, age 67
Auditors: ERNST & YOUNG et Autres

LOCATIONS

HQ: Finatis SA
83, rue du Faubourg Saint-Honore, Paris 75008
Phone: (33) 1 44 71 14 00
Web: www.finatis.fr

COMPETITORS

Auchan	Klepierre
Carrefour	SFL
GECINA	Unibail-Rodamco
ITM Entreprises	

HISTORICAL FINANCIALS
Company Type: Public

Income Statement
FYE: December 31

	REVENUE ($ mil.)	NET INCOME ($ mil.)	NET PROFIT MARGIN	EMPLOYEES
12/15	51,946	(77)	—	330,433
12/14	60,481	(9)	—	340,060
12/13	68,383	108	0.2%	333,723
12/12	56,709	224	0.4%	321,386
12/11	45,885	(23)	—	227,997
Annual Growth	3.2%	—		9.7%

2015 Year-End Financials

Debt ratio: 40.2%
Return on equity: (-0.5%)
Cash ($ mil.): 5,153
Current ratio: 0.84
Long-term debt ($ mil.): 13,115

No. of shares (mil.): 5
Dividends
  Yield: —
  Payout: —
Market value ($ mil.): —

First Commercial Bank

EXECUTIVES

President, Ching Nien Tsai
Auditors: PricewaterhouseCoopers

LOCATIONS

HQ: First Commercial Bank
30, Chung-King S. Road, Sec. 1, Taipei 100-05
Phone: (886) 2 2348 1111   **Fax:** (886) 2 2361 0036
Web: www.firstbank.com.tw

HISTORICAL FINANCIALS
Company Type: Public

Income Statement
FYE: December 31

	ASSETS ($ mil.)	NET INCOME ($ mil.)	INCOME AS % OF ASSETS	EMPLOYEES
12/15	74,165	489	0.7%	7,428
12/14	72,533	422	0.6%	7,286
12/13	73,997	356	0.5%	7,207
12/12	71,424	357	0.5%	7,133
12/11	67,153	284	0.4%	7,279
Annual Growth	2.5%	14.6%	—	0.5%

2015 Year-End Financials

Return on assets: 0.6%
Return on equity: 9.5%
Long-term debt ($ mil.): —
No. of shares (mil.): —
Sales ($ mil): 1,611

Dividends
  Yield: —
  Payout: —
Market value ($ mil.): —

First Gulf Bank

EXECUTIVES

Director & Chairman, Sheikh Tahnoon Bin Zayed Al Nahyan
Auditors: Ernst & Young

LOCATIONS

HQ: First Gulf Bank
P.O. Box 6316, Abu Dhabi
Phone: (971) 2 681 6666   **Fax:** (971) 2 681 3169
Web: www.firstgulfbank.ae

HISTORICAL FINANCIALS
Company Type: Public

Income Statement
FYE: December 31

	ASSETS ($ mil.)	NET INCOME ($ mil.)	INCOME AS % OF ASSETS	EMPLOYEES
12/15	61,938	1,635	2.6%	0
12/14	57,767	1,539	2.7%	0
12/13	53,098	1,299	2.4%	1,452
12/12	47,650	1,130	2.4%	1,112
12/11	42,874	1,009	2.4%	930
Annual Growth	9.6%	12.8%		

2015 Year-End Financials

Return on assets: 2.7%
Return on equity: 17.1%
Long-term debt ($ mil.): —
No. of shares (mil.): —
Sales ($ mil): 3,074

Dividends
  Yield: —
  Payout: —
Market value ($ mil.): —

Flex Ltd

Having factories on four continents would make you flexible too. Flex International (it changed its name from Flextronics in 2015) offers turnkey manufacturing services to the world's leading electronics companies including Apple Cisco Ericsson HP Huawei Lenovo Microsoft BlackBerry and Xerox. The company's services range from design engineering through manufacturing and assembly to distribution and warehousing. It manufactures and assembles printed circuit boards electromechanical components subsystems and complete systems for a wide range of makers of networking and telecommunications equipment computers consumer electronics and medical instruments. The name change signals an expansion beyond electronics.

Operations

Flex divides its business into four segments.

The Communications & Enterprise Compute segment 36% of revenue makes equipment that includes radio access base stations remote radio heads and small cells for wireless infrastructure; optical routing broadcasting and switching products for the data and video networks; server and storage platforms for both enterprise and cloud based deployments; storage and security products; and data center servers and software defined networking products.

The Consumer Technologies Group 29% of revenue is oriented toward the user side of electronics. It turns out mobile devices such as smart phones; consumer electronics including wearable electronics; and computing products including notebook computers tablets and printers. Besides supplying supply chain services to those product groupings the CTG group has expanded its supply chain domain to non-electronics such as shoes and clothing.

The High Reliability Solutions group 19% of revenue makes products for medical application including consumer health digital health disposables drug delivery diagnostics life sciences and imaging equipment; automotive uses including vehicle electronics connectivity and clean technologies; and defense and aerospace in commercial aviation and military.

Operations under the Industrial & Emerging Industries segment 16% of revenue include semiconductor and capital equipment office equipment industrial automation and kiosks energy and metering and lighting.

Geographic Reach

Flex operates a network of more than 100 facilities in 30 countries. Its manufacturing facilities are Europe Eastern Europe Asia and the Americas. Customers in China account for about 35% of sales with customers in Mexico and US accounting for 15% and 11% respectively.

Sales and Marketing

Flex's top 10 customers account for 46% of its revenue. Lenovo/Motorola is the only Flex customer that provides more than 10% of its revenue.

Financial Performance

Flex's revenue shifted downward 6.6% in 2016 (ended March) to $24.4 billion from $26 billion in 2015. The consumer technologies group's revenue tumbled 22% (a $1.9 billion drop) in 2016 because of less business from a large mobile customer. The big communications segment's sales slipped 4% from less demand for servers and storage systems.

Net income dropped 26% to $4.4 billion in 2016 hurt not only by the sales declines but higher selling general and administrative costs related to research and design stock-based compensation and acquisitions. Cash from operations rose to $1.1 billion in 2016 from $794 million in 2015.

Strategy

Flex maintains standardized instruments and processes that are flexible in that they can be used in multiple ways. At the heart of Flex's strategy is its systematic process for innovation in its operations including manufacturing and logistics. That approach enables it to offer customers a set of common technologies that can be applied in endless combinations across industries. This extends the company's reach beyond electronics and into new industries. In one example Flex works with Nike to get its products to customers more quickly. In 2015 the company emphasized its expansion to new areas by dropping "tronics" from its name.

Mergers and Acquisitions

In 2015 Flex acquired Mirror Controls International (MCi) from the private equity firm Egeria for euro 457 million. MCi manufactures glass and powerfold mirror actuators for the automotive market and should improve Flex's prospects in that arena. In another 2015 deal Flex bought NEXTracker a designer and builder of single-axis PV trackers for $330 million. The acquisition expanded Flex's capabilities for solar processes in commercializing smart and connected energy technologies.

HISTORY

Flextronics International formed in 1990 followed two earlier contract manufacturers named Flextronics formed in 1969 and 1980. The latter iteration used acquisitions to expand throughout Asia and the US. In 1988 it opened the first US-managed contract electronics plant in China and that year sales topped $200 million.

But acquisitions burdened Flextronics with debt and left it with disparate operations. It divested its US-based manufacturing operations and laid off 75% of its workforce. The company brought in a management team to sell its healthy Asian operations to pay off debt. These operations formed the current incarnation of Flextronics International.

A revitalized Flextronics based in Singapore went public in 1994. It quickly joined the industry rush toward consolidation and globalization. Acquisitions included nCHIP (California 1996) FICO

Plastics (Hong Kong 1997) Neutronics Electronic Industries (Austria 1997) and Kyrel EMS Oyj (Finland and France 1999).

In 2000 Flextronics acquired rival The DII Group which propelled the company to the #4 spot in contract manufacturing (behind Solectron SCI Systems and Celestica). The company was also selected by Microsoft to build the software juggernaut's Xbox video game console. Later that year Motorola and Flextronics signed one of the largest outsourcing deals ever worth an estimated $30 billion over five years. The company expanded further in Asia when it acquired JIT Holdings a Singapore-based electronics manufacturer.

In 2001 Flextronics announced a deal with telecommunications giant Ericsson; under the pact Flextronics assumed management of Ericsson's mobile phone manufacturing operations worldwide. Later that year the company announced that it would cut its workforce by about 10% and that the multibillion-dollar deal with Motorola unraveled due to a continuing market slowdown. Flextronics also repurchased Motorola's 5% stake in the company.

Also that year Flextronics bought Telcom Global Solutions a supplier of planning and design services for telecommunications providers. Flextronics later announced a deal with Xerox to acquire Xerox facilities in Brazil Canada Malaysia and Mexico for about $220 million and to provide manufacturing services to Xerox for five years. Later that year the company laid off 10000 workers – about 15% of its staff –in a cost-cutting move. Flextronics also acquired a 91% stake in Orbiant a telephone network services spinoff of Swedish telecom giant Telia for $100 million in cash (along with future payments pegged to the unit's performance).

In 2002 the company made a deal with CASIO COMPUTER under which Flextronics bought two CASIO plants in Asia then supplied the Japanese electronics maker with finished products in a three-year pact. Also that year the company significantly expanded its presence in southern China with the purchase of Hong Kong-based NatSteel Broadway (printed circuit boards plastic and metal components) for about $367 million.

In 2004 Flextronics took over optical wireless and enterprise manufacturing as well as optical design operations from Nortel Networks in a four-year supply deal generating about $2.5 billion in annual revenues. Flextronics later closed several former Nortel facilities in Canada France and Northern Ireland.

Flextronics also acquired a majority ownership stake in India-based software services provider Hughes Software Systems (HSS) in 2004. The following year Flextronics purchased Agilent's mobile communications camera module business. The company sold its semiconductor division to AMIS Holdings (now part of ON Semiconductor) and its Flextronics Network Services division was merged with a company called Telavie and renamed Relacom; Flextronics retained a 30% stake.

Flextronics set plans in 2005 to build an industrial park in Chennai India to supplement its existing operations on the subcontinent where it previously employed more than 5000 people. The development added to the two manufacturing facilities and three design centers Flextronics had in India.

To focus on its core electronics manufacturing services business in 2006 Flextronics sold its Flextronics Software Systems business (renamed Aricent) to an affiliate of KKR for about $900 million in cash and notes. Flextronics retained a 15% equity interest in the software development business which was primarily based in India (it sold the remaining stake in 2009). Divestitures of its software and semiconductor businesses took a small chunk

out of the company's revenues –$278 million in fiscal 2006.

Flextronics then acquired International DisplayWorks a contract manufacturer of small LCDs and LCD modules for cell phones and other consumer electronics for stock valued at approximately $243 million. International DisplayWorks became a wholly owned subsidiary of Flextronics operating within the company's Components Group. Also in 2006 nLight Corp. acquired the assets of Flextronics Photonics including a line of fiber-coupled and hybrid microelectronic devices.

In 2007 Flextronics purchased rival contract manufacturer Solectron in a deal valued at $3.6 billion. The combination vaulted the company into the position of the second-largest contract electronics manufacturer in the world trailing only Hon Hai Precision Industry the maker of products for Apple Dell and many other companies.

The next year it bought contract disposable device maker Avail Medical Products a private company with around $250 million in sales to further the expansion of its Flextronics Medical segment. Also in 2008 Flextronics inked a deal to acquire Elcoteq's ZAO Elcoteq subsidiary and plant in St. Petersburg Russia. Flextronics however later terminated the transaction and was forced to pay a fee for noncompletion.

In 2009 it sold its stake in Aricent a privately held communications software company to investment firms KKR and CPP Investment Board for about $250 million. The sale was part of a plan to sell noncore assets as Flextronics tried to bolster its balance sheet during the economic downturn. At the end of the year it bought SloMedical S.R.O. a leading maker of disposable medical devices for the European market. In addition to adding disposable devices for the medical and surgical market in Eastern Europe SloMedical (based in Slovenia) gave Flextronics an FDA-compliant clean room-enabled production site with low production costs.

In 2012 Flextronics acquired Stellar Microelectronics an EMS provider based in California that specializes in custom packaging services for the aerospace defense and medical manufacturing markets as part of a plan to expand services for the highly regulated markets. Also that year Flextronics sold its Vista Point camera module business to Tessera Technologies' subsidiary DigitalOptics; the sale included the brand intellectual property and China-based manufacturing assets.

EXECUTIVES

EVP and General Counsel, Jonathan S. (Jon) Hoak, age 66, $500,000 total compensation

CEO, Michael M. (Mike) McNamara, age 59, $1,250,000 total compensation

President Automotive, Christopher J. Obey

President Innovation and New Ventures, Jeannine P. Sargent, age 51

CFO, Christopher (Chris) Collier, age 48, $538,750 total compensation

President Industrial and Emerging Industries, Douglas (Doug) Britt, age 51

President Power Solutions, Christopher Cook

President Global Operations and Components, Fran $is Barbier, age 57, $625,000 total compensation

President High Reliability Solutions, Paul Humphries, $625,000 total compensation

President Consumer Technologies Group, Mike Dennison

President Integrated Network Solutions, Caroline Dowling

President Manufacturing Operations, Tzahi Rodrig

CTO, Erik H. Volkerink

SVP and CIO, Gus Shahin

Chairman, H. Raymond Bingham

Auditors: Deloitte & Touche LLP

LOCATIONS

HQ: Flex Ltd
2 Changi South Lane, 486123
Phone: (65) 6876 9899
Web: www.flextronics.com

2016 Sales

	$ mil.	% of total
China	8,471	35
Mexico	3,645	15
US	2,767	11
Malaysia	2,241	9
Brazil	1,839	8
Other countries	5,453	22
Total	**24,418**	**100**

PRODUCTS/OPERATIONS

2016 Sales

	$ mil.	% of total
Communications & Enterprise Compute	8,841	36
Consumer Technologies Group	6,997	29
Industrial & emerging industries	4,680	19
High reliability solutions	3,899	16
Total	**24,418**	**100**

Selected Services

Assembly and manufacturing
  Box build (complete systems)
  Complex electromechanical components
  Printed circuit boards (PCBs)
  Subsystems (including those that incorporate PCBs)
Engineering
  Design
  Prototyping
  Test development
Materials procurement and management
  Planning
  Purchasing
  Warehousing
Network support
  Installation and maintenance of telecommunications
  systems and corporate networks
Packaging
Plastic and metal components
Product distribution
Recycling and refurbishment
Testing of PCBs subsystems and systems
Warranty repair

COMPETITORS

ASUSTeK	Pegatron
Benchmark Electronics	Plexus
Cal-Comp Electronics	Quanta Computer
Celestica	SYNNEX
Compal Electronics	Sanmina
Hon Hai	TTM Technologies
Jabil	Universal Scientific
Kimball International	Venture Corp.
MiTAC	Wistron
Nam Tai	

HISTORICAL FINANCIALS

Company Type: Public

Income Statement

FYE: March 31

	REVENUE ($ mil.)	NET INCOME ($ mil.)	NET PROFIT MARGIN	EMPLOYEES
03/16	24,418	444	1.8%	200,000
03/15	26,147	600	2.3%	150,000
03/14	26,108	365	1.4%	150,000
03/13	23,569	277	1.2%	149,000
03/12	29,387	488	1.7%	159,000
Annual Growth	**(4.5%)**	**(2.4%)**	**—**	**5.9%**

2016 Year-End Financials

Debt ratio: 22.4%
Return on equity: 17.9%
Cash ($ mil.): 1,607
Current ratio: 1.27
Long-term debt ($ mil.): 2,709

No. of shares (mil.): 544
Dividends
  Yield: —
  Payout: —
Market value ($ mil.): 6,571

	STOCK PRICE ($) FY Close	P/E High/Low	PER SHARE ($) Earnings	Dividends	Book Value
03/16	12.06	16 11	0.79	0.00	4.72
03/15	12.68	12 8	1.02	0.00	4.19
03/14	9.24	16 11	0.59	0.00	3.66
03/13	6.76	17 13	0.41	0.00	3.52
03/12	7.22	11 8	0.67	0.00	3.34
Annual Growth	**13.7%**	**— —**	**4.2%**	**—**	**9.0%**

Fomento Economico Mexicano, S.A.B. de C.V.

From soda pop to shops FEMSA is quenching Mexico's thirsty throats. Fomento Economico Mexicano or FEMSA is a top soft drink bottler and convenience store operator in Latin America. Its Coca-Cola FEMSA subsidiary is the world's largest Coca-Cola bottler. FEMSA bottles Coca-Cola Sprite other soft drinks juices and water in nine Latin American countries. FEMSA also owns more than 12800 OXXO convenience stores in 31 Mexican states primarily in the northern part of the country through its FEMSA Comercio subsidiary. FEMSA was a major beer brewer in Mexico and Brazil as well through its former FEMSA Cerveza subsidiary. (It sold the unit to Heineken in 2010 but gained a stake in Heineken in the process.)

Operations

FEMSA holds the second-largest stake (20%) in Heineken after selling FEMSA Cerveza. In addition to its beverage operations and retail holdings (The OXXO chain is the largest and fastest-growing in the Americas.) it provides logistics refrigeration services and plastics to internal and external customers.

Geographic Reach

FEMSA operates in Argentina Brazil Colombia Costa Rica the Philippines Guatemala Mexico Nicaragua Panama and Venezuela. Subsidiary Coca-Cola FEMSA operates in Argentina Brazil Central America Colombia Mexico the Philippines and Venezuela.

In 2014 Mexico and Central America provided most of the company's revenues.

Financial Performance

Revenues for FEMSA have been rising for the past four years. In 2014 revenue rose 2% to 263.4 billion pesos largely due to growth in the convenience store operations. Specifically FEMSA Comercio saw a 12% revenue increase as it opened more than 1100 net new stores that year.

Net income has generally been on the rise as well. It grew 2% to 22.6 billion pesos in fiscal 2014 on the rising revenue plus increases in Heineken. Cash flow from operations rose 30% to 37.3 billion pesos.

Strategy

To grow its convenience store network FEMSA Comercio carefully examines new possible locations ensuring sustainable expansion. Its organizational efforts include improving logistics utilizing more sophisticated information systems developing closer relationships with suppliers and expanding marketing capacity. During 2014 the company opened a record new 1132 stores bringing its portfolio to more than 12800 locations.

Coca-Cola FEMSA has been working to streamline operations in order to create a more limble lean business and prepare for future growth.

Mergers and Acquisitions

The company is investing in drug stores an industry that is attractive and highly fragmented. In 2014 FEMSA acquired drugstore operator Farmacias Farmacon which operates more than 200 stores in northwestern Mexico. The year before that it acquired Farmacias FM Moderna which has drugstores in the state of Sinaloa.

Branching into the restaurant business in 2013 it acquired quick-service restaurant operator Doña Tota (which has more than 200 locations in the US and Mexico).

HISTORY

FEMSA's 2005 purchase of Panamerican Beverages (Panamco) through its Coca-Cola subsidiary gave the company access to markets in Brazil Colombia Costa Rica Guatemala Nicaragua Panama and Venezuela.

EXECUTIVES

CEO Coca-Cola FEMSA, Carlos Salazar Lomel n, age 65
VP Corporate Development, Federico Reyes Garc a, age 71
CFO, Eduardo Padilla Silva, age 59
VP Administration and Corporate Control, Jose Gonz ˉlez Ornelas, age 65
CEO FEMSA Empaques, Alfonso Garza Garza, age 54
Chairman and CEO, Jose Antonio Fern ˉndez Carbajal
CEO FEMSA Comercio, Daniel Rodr guez Cofre
Auditors: Mancera, S.C. (member of Ernst & Young Global)

LOCATIONS

HQ: Fomento Economico Mexicano, S.A.B. de C.V.
  General Anaya 601 Poniente, Colonia Bella Vista,
  Monterrey, Nuevo Leon 64410
Phone: (52) 81 8328 6000   **Fax:** (52) 81 8328 6080
Web: www.femsa.com

2014

Geography mil (pesos) %

Mexico and Central America	186,736	71
South America	69,172	26
Venezuela	8,835	3
Consolidation adjustments	(1294)	-
Total	**263,449**	**100**

PRODUCTS/OPERATIONS

2014

Business Unit mil (pesos) %

Coca-Cola FEMSA	147,298	53
FEMSA Comercio	109,624	40
Other	20,069	7
Consolidation Adjustments	(13542)	-
Total	**263,449**	**100**

COMPETITORS

Andina	Empresas Polar
Arca Continental	Nestle Waters
Danone Water	Organizacin Cultiba
Dr Pepper Snapple Group	Pepsi Amercias Beverages

HISTORICAL FINANCIALS
Company Type: Public

Income Statement
FYE: December 31

	REVENUE ($ mil.)	NET INCOME ($ mil.)	NET PROFIT MARGIN	EMPLOYEES
12/15	17,935	1,017	5.7%	246,158
12/14	17,924	1,136	6.3%	216,740
12/13	19,709	1,215	6.2%	207,657
12/12	18,340	1,593	8.7%	182,260
12/11	14,427	1,097	7.6%	177,470
Annual Growth	5.6%	(1.9%)	—	8.5%

2015 Year-End Financials

Debt ratio: 1.2%
Return on equity: 10.0%
Cash ($ mil.): 1,692
Current ratio: 1.33
Long-term debt ($ mil.): 4,948

No. of shares (mil.): —
Dividends
  Yield: 1.4%
  Payout: 2,498.8%
Market value ($ mil.): —

	STOCK PRICE ($) FY Close	P/E High/Low	PER SHARE ($) Earnings	Dividends	Book Value
12/15	92.35	110 80	0.05	1.37	0.58
12/14	88.03	110 89	0.06	0.00	0.65
12/13	97.87	146 113	0.06	3.12	0.68
12/12	100.70	98 66	0.08	1.40	0.67
12/11	69.71	91 59	0.05	0.96	0.58
Annual Growth	7.3%	— —	(1.8%)	9.3%	0.3%

Fonciere Euris SA

Foncière Euris is a holding company that engages in specialty distribution and real estate. Through main majority held subsidiary Rallye Foncière Euris is involved in food distribution to supermarkets hypermarkets convenience stores and discount stores in France and abroad via Casino Guichard-Perrachon and sporting goods distribution in France and Poland via Groupe Go Sport. Foncière Euris also holds directly or indirectly a handful of shopping centers in operation and shopping centers under construction in France Germany and Poland. Most of the company's sales are made in France but it also generates significant sales in South America and to a lesser extent Asia among other regions.

Operations
Among Foncière Euris' property holdings are three shopping centers in operation in Tours France Lotz Poland and Frankfurt Germany. It has two shopping centers under construction in Paris and Gdynia Poland.

Ownership
Parent company Finatis controls about 80% of Foncière Euris.

EXECUTIVES
Chairman & Managing Director, Michel SAVART
Board Member, Jean-Louis BRUNET
Board Member, Christian PEENE
Board Member, Nicole Marie Ther̃se WIEDMER
Auditors: ERNST & YOUNG et Autres

LOCATIONS
HQ: Fonciere Euris SA
  83, rue du Faubourg Saint-Honore, Paris 75008
Phone: (33) 1 44 71 14 00
Web: www.fonciere-euris.fr

COMPETITORS
Bayerische Immobilien   SFL
Fonci̇̀re des Regions   Unibail-Rodamco
Klepierre

HISTORICAL FINANCIALS
Company Type: Public

Income Statement
FYE: December 31

	REVENUE ($ mil.)	NET INCOME ($ mil.)	NET PROFIT MARGIN	EMPLOYEES
12/15	51,946	(77)	—	330,433
12/14	60,481	2	0.0%	340,060
12/13	68,383	123	0.2%	333,723
12/12	56,709	242	0.4%	321,386
12/11	45,883	(12)	—	227,996
Annual Growth	3.2%	—	—	9.7%

2015 Year-End Financials

Debt ratio: 39.9%
Return on equity: (-0.5%)
Cash ($ mil.): 5,151
Current ratio: 0.84
Long-term debt ($ mil.): 12,995

No. of shares (mil.): 9
Dividends
  Yield: —
  Payout: —
Market value ($ mil.): —

Formosa Petrochemical Corp

Formosa Petrochemical Corporation (FPCC) is second only to Chinese Petroleum Corporation for oil refining in Taiwan. The company produces refined petroleum products (jet fuel liquid petroleum gas and gasoline) and petrochemicals (ethylene propylene and butadiene) from its naphtha cracking operations. It owns gas stations through subsidiary Formosa Oil. FPCC also sells electricity and steam from its co-generation plants. Its engineering and maintenance divisions carry out planning construction and daily maintenance services on behalf of group companies.

Geographic Segment
FPCC sells its products worldwide. In 2011 Taiwan accounted for 58% of the company's revenues.

Sales and Marketing
In 2011 Formosa Chemicals & Fibers accounted for 19% of sales; Formosa Plastics 13%.

Financial Performance
FPCC's revenues increased by 7% in 2011 and its net income decreased by 45%.

StrategyIn 2011 the company restarted its 700000 tons-per-year No. 1 naphtha cracker after a four-month shutdown due to a fire.

Ownership
Formosa Plastics owns 29% of FPCC; affiliates Formosa Chemicals & Fibers and Nan Ya Plastics also own 25% and 24% respectively.

Company Background
The three group companies formed FPCC in 1992 to build and run a giant integrated petrochemicals facility called the No. 6 Naphtha Cracking Project.

EXECUTIVES
President and Director, Wilfred Wang
Chief Financial Officer, Ming-Hsiung Shih
Chairman, Chen Bao-Lang
Auditors: Ernst & Young

LOCATIONS
HQ: Formosa Petrochemical Corp
  No. 1-1, Taisu Industrial Park, Mailiao Township,
  Yunlin County 638
Phone: (886) 5 681 2345
Web: www.fpcc.com.tw

COMPETITORS
BASF-YPC   OCI Company
CPC   Total Petrochemicals
ExxonMobil Chemical

HISTORICAL FINANCIALS
Company Type: Public

Income Statement
FYE: December 31

	REVENUE ($ mil.)	NET INCOME ($ mil.)	NET PROFIT MARGIN	EMPLOYEES
12/15	19,157	1,439	7.5%	4,891
12/14	28,836	286	1.0%	4,864
12/13	31,230	900	2.9%	3,978
12/12	30,817	93	0.3%	6,507
12/11	0	0	—	6,426
Annual Growth	—	—	—	(6.6%)

2015 Year-End Financials

Debt ratio: 0.8%
Return on equity: 18.6%
Cash ($ mil.): 1,389
Current ratio: 3.92
Long-term debt ($ mil.): 2,808

No. of shares (mil.): —
Dividends
  Yield: —
  Payout: —
Market value ($ mil.): —

Fresenius Medical Care AG & Co KGaA

Fresenius Medical Care provides products and services to refresh renal disease patients and their kidneys. The company is one of the largest dialysis providers in the world. Its staff treats approximately 2.8 million patients a year at some 3600 dialysis clinics worldwide about half of which are based in the US. In addition to performing dialysis Fresenius Medical Care makes dialysis machines dialyzers and other supplies that are sold to hospitals and clinics through internal sales efforts and independent distributors. It also offers dialysis support services including laboratory testing renal drug distribution and disease management programs. Fresenius SE owns a controlling stake in Fresenius Medical Care.

Operations
In addition to its core dialysis care operations (which account for more than 70% of sales) and its dialysis products unit Fresenius Medical Care offers services that support the dialysis process including customized patient-specific treatments through its UltraCare program and disease management programs for ESRD patients through subsidiary KidneyTel. It also provides laboratory testing to determine the best course of a patient's treatment through subsidiary Spectra Laboratories (in addition to the full-service laboratories associated with its dialysis centers).

Geographic Reach
With a majority of its operations in the US (North America accounts for about 60% of sales) Fresenius Medical Care is increasing its presence in other regions including Europe Latin America and the Middle East. Fresenius Medical Care's ex-

pansion efforts have already made it one of the largest dialysis providers in Asia. The company has dialysis clinic operations in about 45 countries while its dialysis products segment serves customers in 140 countries.

Sales and Marketing

Fresenius Medical Care's core dialysis care segment relies heavily on Medicare reimbursement; Medicare's end stage renal disease (ESRD) program accounts for about 45% of treatment revenues in the US. The firm has managed to decrease this percentage (and decrease its dependence on Medicare) in recent years by increasing the number of privately insured patients utilizing its services.

The company markets its dialysis products through local sales forces and independent distributors and dealers. Products are shipped from central and regional warehouse facilities to dialysis centers and patients' homes.

Financial Performance

Continuing a multi-year trend of growth Fresenius Medical care reported a revenue increase of 6% in 2011 to $12.8 billion due to increased revenues from both the dialysis care (5%) and dialysis products (10%) segments primarily in international markets. The growth was attributed to organic measures and acquisitions.

Strategy

The firm has been a leading consolidator of dialysis treatment (renal care) operations particularly in the US. It typically grows by opening or acquiring singular or small groups of dialysis locations in targeted regions. For example in 2011 it added about 120 new facilities; it also built 65 centers and sold 30 locations deemed as noncore.

The company is also looking to grow by offering new dialysis products and technologies including upgrades on its existing equipment lines. In 2011 it introduced several new hospital and home dialysis machines including the Cordiax dialyzers and the 5008 therapy system.

To further broaden its operations Fresenius Medical Care is expanding into additional areas beyond patient care and dialysis products such as dialysis medication (drugs regulating patient mineral and blood levels) and home therapies. It has formed partnerships with several drugmakers and is pursuing additional acquisitions and partnerships in those fields.

Mergers and Acquisitions

Fresenius Medical Care agreed to buy a majority stake in Australian day-hospital operator Cura Group. Cura operates about 20 outpatient hospitals that provide services in areas such as opthalmology and orthopedics. The purchase will set Fresenius Medical Care up for further expansion in Australia's dialysis market.

In late 2014 majority-owned subsidiary Sound Inpatient Physicians acquired US-based hospitalist group Cogent Healthcare to become the country's largest private provider of hospitalist and intensivist services. It serves more than 180 hospitals in 35 states with more than 2250 physicians and advanced care practitioners.

HISTORY

Fresenius Medical Care was formed in 1996 by the merger of Fresenius AG's dialysis systems division with National Medical Care (NMC). While Fresenius traces its roots back to the 1462 founding of Hirsch Pharmacy in Frankfurt (the Fresenius family gained control of the company in the 18th century) and its 1966 entry into the dialysis equipment market NMC was founded in 1968 by Constantine Hampers who recognized that for-profit companies could provide dialysis services more cheaply than not-for-profit hospitals. He opened his first clinic in Boston (it grew to some 600 clinics)

and took the company public in 1971. In 1984 he sold the company to chemical maker W. R. Grace which was on a diversification binge but attempted to buy it back after 10 contentious years.

The birth of Fresenius Medical was also mired in legal muck. NMC was under investigation for fraudulent Medicare billing and illegal kickbacks and its manufacturing operations were restricted by court order. Fresenius Medical put an end to the fraud but the ongoing investigation took its toll on its bottom line.

In 1997 a US federal court lifted the manufacturing injunction against NMC. That year Fresenius Medical grew its US clinic practices with the purchase of NEOMEDICA and expanded its laboratory services by buying Spectra Laboratories. The next year it sold its diagnostic services and home care divisions to concentrate on its core dialysis operations. In 1998 it also partnered with Kaiser Permanente a leading not-for-profit HMO to run dialysis clinics and provide other services to patients. Growth continued the next year with key acquisitions in such regions as western Europe South Korea and the US.

Fresenius Medical was finally able to put its NMC woes behind it in 2000 when it settled the Medicare fraud suit for some $425 million. Undaunted the firm also acquired the non-US operations of rival DaVita (formerly Total Renal Care). The next year it bought the perfusion services business of Edwards Lifesciences.

In 2005 the company transformed its structure from a corporation to a share-limited partnership; the restructuring included the formation of the company's general partner Fresenius Medical Care Management AG and a name change from Fresenius Medical Care AG to Fresenius Medical Care AG & Co. KGaA.

In a larger than usual transaction the company also acquired US rival Renal Care Group which had 460 locations. The deal was valued at $3.5 billion and made Fresenius Medical Care the top US dialysis center operator (despite the required divestiture of some 100 centers to clear the deal). Fresenius Medical Care also later sold the former RCG laboratory operations.

Also in 2006 the company purchased the 50% stake in venture Renaissance Health Care that it didn't already own and the 20% stake in Optimal Renal Care (a former venture with health care provider Kaiser Permanente) and merged Optimal Renal Care into Renaissance Health Care; the combined entity was renamed KidneyTel.

Fresenius Medical Care acquired its first dialysis medication the PhosLo brand calcium acetate and related assets from Nabi Biopharmaceuticals in 2006. The following year it acquired privately held Renal Solutions which makes filter cartridges that can be used in home dialysis a growing field in the hemodialysis market.

In 2007 the company sealed its position in the Asian dialysis market with the acquisition of a majority stake in Taiwan-based Jiate Excelsior.

In 2008 it entered drug distribution agreement with pharma companies Luitpold and Galenica to expand its therapeutic offerings.

To further cement its position in Asia in 2010 the company agreed to purchase Asia Renal Care from Bumrungrad International to expand its operations in Taiwan Singapore and other Asia/Pacific countries. It also established operations in countries including Japan Korea and Russia that year.

Also in 2010 it expanded its home care offerings by purchasing the peritoneal (abdominal) dialysis operation of Gambro and the assets of home therapy device development firm Xcorporeal.

Fresenius Medical Care continued its growth efforts in 2011 when it acquired Dutch firm Euromedic International's dialysis business Interna-

tional Dialysis Centers (IDC) for some euro 485 million ($647 million). The purchase gave Fresenius about 70 clinics in Central and Eastern Europe.

EXECUTIVES

Chairman Management Board and CEO, Rice Powell, age 60, $700,000 total compensation
CFO, Michael Brosnan, age 60
CEO Global Research and Development, Olaf Schermeier, age 42
CEO Global Manufacturing Operations, Kent Wanzek, age 55
CEO Europe Middle East and Africa (EMEA), Dominik Wehner, age 46
CEO North America, William (Bill) Valle, age 56
CEO Asia-Pacific, Harry de Wit, age 53
Chairman Supervisory Board, Gerd Krick, age 78
Vice Chairman, Dieter Schenk, age 64
Auditors: KPMG AG

LOCATIONS

HQ: Fresenius Medical Care AG & Co KGaA
 Else-Kroener-Strasse 1, Bad Homburg 61352
Phone: (49) 6172 609 2601   **Fax:** (49) 6172 609 2301
Web: www.fmc-ag.com

2011 Sales

	% of total
North America	
Dialysis care	57
Dialysis products	6
International	
Dialysis products	19
Dialysis care	17
Total	**100**

PRODUCTS/OPERATIONS

2011 Payer Breakdown

	% of total
Medicare ESRD program	46
Private/alternative payers	43
Medicaid & other government sources	6
Hospitals	5
Total	**100**

Selected Acquisitions

COMPETITORS

Amgen	MEDIVATORS
Asahi Kasei	Nephros
B. Braun Melsungen	NxStage
Baxter International	Quest Diagnostics
DaVita	Rockwell Medical
Dialysis Clinic Inc	Terumo
Gambro AB	Tivity Health
LabCorp	Toray Industries

HISTORICAL FINANCIALS

Company Type: Public

Income Statement

FYE: December 31

	REVENUE ($ mil.)	NET INCOME ($ mil.)	NET PROFIT MARGIN	EMPLOYEES
12/15	16,737	1,029	6.2%	104,033
12/14	15,831	1,045	6.6%	99,895
12/13	14,609	1,109	7.6%	90,690
12/12	13,800	1,186	8.6%	86,153
12/11	12,795	1,071	8.4%	79,159
Annual Growth	**6.9%**	**(1.0%)**	**—**	**7.1%**

2015 Year-End Financials

Debt ratio: 33.8%
Return on equity: 10.6%
Cash ($ mil.): 549
Current ratio: 1.67
Long-term debt ($ mil.): 7,853
No. of shares (mil.): 305
Dividends
Yield: 0.7%
Payout: 8.8%
Market value ($ mil.): 12,774

	STOCK PRICE ($) FY Close	P/E High/Low	PER SHARE ($) Earnings	Dividends	Book Value
12/15	41.84	14 11	3.38	0.30	32.38
12/14	37.14	11 9	3.46	0.37	31.11
12/13	35.58	10 8	3.65	0.33	30.63
12/12	34.30	20 9	3.87	0.31	29.54
12/11	67.98	23 16	3.51	0.33	26.32
Annual Growth	(11.4%)	— —	(0.9%)	(2.2%)	5.3%

Fresenius SE & Co KGaA

Fresenius offers a wide range of dialysis and infusion products and services through its four core business segments: Fresenius Medical Care Fresenius Kabi Fresenius Helios and Fresenius Vamed. The company's Medical Care division specializes in treating chronic kidney failure at some 3350 dialysis clinics worldwide. Fresenius Kabi provides nutrition infusion and IV therapies and related equipment. Fresenius Helios operates private hospitals in Germany while Fresenius Vamed offers facility management project development and other services to hospitals and health facilities. Fresenius has operations in more than 100 countries.

Operations

Fresenius Helios operates 110 hospitals (including 86 acute-care facilities and seven maximum-care hospitals) with more than 34000 beds in Germany. Fresemius Vamed provides project development planning technical and operation management and turnkey construction services to hospitals and other health care facilities around the world.

In addition to its four core segments the Corporate and Other segment comprises the holding activities of Fresenius as well as its internal IT service provider Fresenius Netcare.

Geographic Reach

North America and Europe are the German health care company's largest markets contributing 40% and 44% of annual revenue respectively. The Asia/Pacific region (China Japan) accounts for about 10% of revenue followed by Latin America (5%) and South Africa (2%).

The company also has production facilities in other European countries and in Latin America the Asia/Pacific region and South Africa.

Sales and Marketing

Fresenius offers its products and services to hospitals and other health care organizations.

Financial Performance

Fresenius has seen revenue growth over the past few years. In 2014 revenue rose 14% to euro 23.2 billion primarily due to 54% growth in the Helios segment which saw growth due to the addition of acquired hospitals from Rhön-Klinikum (which contributed euro 1.8 billion) as well as an increase of admissions and hospital services price increases. The Medical Care segment grew 8% that year while Kabi and Vamed rose 3% and 2% respectively.

The higher revenues led to a 6% increase in net income which reached euro 1.1 billion. Cash flow from operations also increased rising 11% to euro 2.5 billion; this was led by a decline in cash used in inventories and an increase in trade accounts payable accrued expenses and other liabilities.

Strategy

The company has been aggressively expanding its core operating segments through both organic growth and acquisitions. Its majority-owned Fresenius Medical Care subsidiary which accounts for more than half of the firm's revenues has expanded its dialysis service and its equipment manufacturing operations through acquisitions. Though Fresenius Medical Care primarily grows through purchases of single clinics or small dialysis groups it occasionally makes larger acquisitions. The division is also widening its operations in the fields of home dialysis and renal pharmaceuticals.

Fresenius Kabi is a market leader in infusion therapy and clinical nutrition in Europe and in key markets in the Asia/Pacific region and Latin America. Fresenius has expanded Kabi's operations through a number of acquisitions in recent years. In 2014 for instance Kabi acquired the privately held Brazilian pharmaceutical company Novafarma Industria Farmacêutica to further its strategy to expand its market presence in emerging markets. In addition Fresenius Kabi is working to expand in the generic injectables market by developing and releasing new IV pharmaceutical products and expanding distribution of existing drugs both in the US and international markets. Kabi is also working to increase its offerings of infusion and nutrition equipment such as feeding tubes and drug delivery pumps. In 2014 the unit was granted US approval for products in the fields of clinical nutrition and medical devices.

In 2015 Kabi sold subsidiary CFL a specialist in IV oncology drug compounding in order to focus on parenteral nutrition products.

Fresenius Vamed provides hospitals with engineering equipment planning and other upkeep-related services. Helios is seeking to increase brand recognition and add more facilities as Germany's hospitals become increasingly privatized while Vamed is focused on growth of engineering and other specialty services. A hard-won acquisition in 2014 of a rival German hospital operator has made Fresenius Helios the leading private hospital operator in Europe with 117 hospitals across Germany.

Mergers and Acquisitions

In a move that created the largest private hospital operator in Europe in February 2014 Fresenius Helios acquired 38 hospitals and 11 outpatient facilities from Rhön-Klinikum for $4.1 billion. The purchase gave Fresenius Helios 117 hospitals across Germany. The deal came a year after Fresenius attempted to acquire all of Rhön-Klinikum but failed. The purchase will add about euro 2 billion in annual sales.

Later that year Fresenius Medical Care acquired US-based Cogent Healthcare to become the nation's largest private provider of hospitalist and intensivist services. Its majority-owned Sound Inpatient Physicians division now serves more than 180 hospitals.

Also in 2014 Fresenius bought National Cardiovascular Partners which provides endovascular vascular and cardiovascular services in outpatient settings.

HISTORY

Company Background

Fresenius was founded as the Hirsch Pharmacy in 1462. The Fresenius family took over its ownership in the 18th century and converted it into a pharmaceutical manufacturing entity in 1912.

Fresenius entered the dialysis equipment market in 1966. The company formed its Fresenius Medical Care unit in 1996 when it merged its dialysis systems division with National Medical Care (NMC).

In 1999 Fresenius formed its Fresenius Kabi division by combining its infusion pharmaceutical operations with the former infusion solution business of drugmaker Pharmacia & Upjohn which it acquired the previous year.

The company conducted a number of expansion efforts within the Kabi division in the following decade including the 2007 purchase of IV drug manufacturing firms Labesfal (Portugal) and Filaxis (Argentina) as well as German medical device maker Clinico. Also that year the company bought the artificial colloid product business of Kyorin to build up a presence in the Tokyo market.

It then purchased Indian oncology drug manufacturer Dabur Pharma in 2008. Also that year the unit expanded its reach in the US market for injectable drugs by acquiring US generics maker APP Pharmaceuticals for $3.7 billion plus debt.

Following the acquisition of German private clinic operator Helios Kliniken Fresenius refreshed its acute care operations by separating its hospital division (Fresenius ProServe) into two business segments Fresenius Helios and Fresenius Vamed in 2008.

EXECUTIVES

CEO Fresenius Medical Care, Rice Powell, age 60
CEO, Stephan Sturm, age 53
CEO Fresenius Kabi AG, Mats Henriksson, age 49
CEO Fresenius Helios, Francesco De Meo, age 52
CEO Fresenius Vamed, Ernst Wastler, age 57
Deputy Chairman, Gerhard Rupprecht, age 68
Chairman, Gerd Krick, age 78
Auditors: KPMG AG

LOCATIONS

HQ: Fresenius SE & Co KGaA
Else-Kroener-Strasse 1, Bad Homburg D-61352
Phone: (49) 6172 608 0 **Fax:** (49) 6172 608 2488
Web: www.fresenius.com

2014 Sales

	% of total
North America	40
Europe	44
Asia Pacific	9
Latin America & other regions	7
Total	**100**

PRODUCTS/OPERATIONS

2014 Sales

	% of total
Fresenius Medical Care	51
Fresenius Kabi	22
Fresenius Helios	23
Fresenius Vamed	4
Total	**100**

Selected Services

Fresenius Medical Care
  Dialysis facility operation
  Disease management
  Disposable dialysis supplies
  Hemodialysis equipment
  Peritoneal dialysis equipment
Fresenius Kabi
  Blood volume replacement
  Enteral nutrition
  Infusion and IV devices
  Infusion therapies
  IV generic drugs
  Parenteral nutrition
  Tranfusion products
Fresenius Helios
  HELIOS Kliniken Group (61 private hospitals Germany)
Fresenius Vamed
  Construction management
  Facility planning
  Maintenance services
  Operational management
  Project development
  Staff recruitment and training

COMPETITORS

Asahi Kasei	Hospira
B. Braun Melsungen	Johnson & Johnson
Baxter International	NxStage
Becton Dickinson	Renal Advantage
Bio-Reference Labs	Terumo
DaVita	Teva
Dialysis Clinic Inc	

HISTORICAL FINANCIALS

Company Type: Public

Income Statement

FYE: December 31

	REVENUE ($ mil.)	NET INCOME ($ mil.)	NET PROFIT MARGIN	EMPLOYEES
12/15	30,090	1,479	4.9%	222,305
12/14	28,237	1,296	4.6%	216,275
12/13	27,990	1,391	5.0%	178,331
12/12	25,425	1,220	4.8%	169,324
12/11	21,370	892	4.2%	149,351
Annual Growth	8.9%	13.5%	—	10.5%

2015 Year-End Financials

Debt ratio: 37.2%
Return on equity: 14.5%
Cash ($ mil.): 1,137
Current ratio: 1.47
Long-term debt ($ mil.): 14,820

No. of shares (mil.): 545
Dividends
Yield: 0.4%
Payout: 3.3%
Market value ($ mil.): 9,741

	STOCK PRICE ($) FY Close	P/E High/Low		PER SHARE ($) Earnings	Dividends	Book Value
12/15	17.85	8	5	2.70	0.08	21.83
12/14	12.97	9	6	2.38	0.14	20.95
12/13	19.35	10	7	2.58	0.12	20.93
12/12	14.40	9	7	2.32	0.10	18.82
12/11	11.70	8	8	1.80	0.00	15.77
Annual Growth	11.1%	—	—	10.6%	—	8.5%

Fuji Heavy Industries Ltd

Fuji Heavy Industries (FHI) is the parent of Subaru of America the automotive company known for its all-wheel-drive (AWD) technology found in cross-over vehicles (a sedan drive with SUV looks) such as the Forester and Outback and in the Impreza Legacy and Tribeca models. Through some 80 subsidiaries FHI has manufacturing operations in China Japan Taiwan and the US where it operates through Subaru of America. Other FHI businesses include Aerospace (aircraft and structural components) and Industrial Products (general-purpose engines agricultural machinery and machine tools). However its core business is Subaru automobiles representing more than 90% of sales.

Financial Performance

Strong momentum at Subaru of America the company's core business is driving sales and profit growth for Fuji Heavy Industries (FHI). Indeed in fiscal 2014 (ended March) FHI reported sales of $23.4 billion up 15% versus the prior year. Net income rose 59% to $2 billion over the same period. Subaru sold 424683 vehicles in the US in 2013 and the company expects to sell at least 500000 in 2014 marking its fifth straight year of record sales here. Subaru represented 93% of FHI's total fiscal 2014 revenue while the Aerospace business accounted for 5%.

FHI's Aerospace arm posted a 40% increase in sales in fiscal 2014 versus the prior year while the Industrial Products division saw its sales dip 1%. The company credited increased sales to Japan's Ministry of Defense and Boeing to support the Boeing 777 and 787 jetliners for the rise in its Aerospace business.

Strategy

The company is focused on advancing transportation technology with innovations that include the horizontally-opposed Boxer Engine Symmetrical All-Wheel drive the advanced driving support system "EyeSight" in the automotive business and the unmanned aircraft system in its aerospace business.

Fuji Industrial Products holds a large share in the global general-purpose engine market with more than 2000 models one of which is the Robin engine which is sold in more than 70 countries. Fuji's Eco Technologies supplies vehicles (Fuji Mighty sanitation truck) used to collect and transport waste products as well as wind-power systems. Its Clean Robot division was the first to commercialize floor-cleaning robots for high-rise buildings.

Fuji Aerospace manufactures main wings and other structural aircraft components. It is the primary contractor of the AH-64D combat helicopter to the Japan Defense Agency (JDA). Fuji Aerospace also supplies JDA with fixed-wing aircraft and primary trainers and manufactures components for Boeing aircraft (767/777); its center wing box is part of the Boeing 787 Dreamliner. Other technology includes unmanned aircraft and development of a Fuji Aerial Robot (FABOT) system that uses GPS navigation and handles takeoffs and landings by small fixed-wing aircraft.

HISTORY

Chikuhei Nakajima started the Aircraft Research Laboratory north of Tokyo in 1917 renaming it the Nakajima Aircraft Company in 1931. Amid the ashes of WWII Nakajima formed Fuji Sangyo to make products with aircraft technology in 1945. His motor scooters used bomber tail wheels and he later added buses with unibody frames. Nakajima died in 1949.

Fuji Sangyo joined four other firms in 1953 and Fuji Heavy Industries was born. The Subaru car division debuted in 1958 and FHI went public two years later. The firm expanded product lines throughout the 1960s and in 1968 Nissan Motor invested in FHI. The relationship lasted more than 30 years.

Subaru expanded to the US in 1968 with the help of furniture retailer Harvey Lamm. Lamm visiting Japan saw Subaru's utilitarian front-wheel-drive station wagon and recognized its potential. He convinced FHI to make him its US importer and he set up Subaru of America. Lamm ultimately became chairman and CEO of the US subsidiary.

In 1975 FHI exported the four-wheel-drive Subaru GF to the US; it was the country's first four-wheel-drive car for the mass market. High energy prices and the appeal of a four-wheel-drive car drove sales in the 1970s and early 1980s. By 1986 Subaru achieved 12 straight years of record sales and profits.

The next year however a rising yen boosted Japanese car prices and sales dips fueled round after round of incentives. Profits tanked and Subaru responded by expanding trim levels and power train choices. The misstep confused shoppers and sales nose-dived.

Also in 1987 FHI and Isuzu teamed up to build an assembly plant (Subaru-Isuzu Automotive) in Indiana with other makers introduced minivans and sport utility vehicles. Focusing on cars Subaru missed the start of the SUV boom. Even the arrival

of the Legacy in 1989 failed to jumpstart sales. Lamm left Subaru in 1990 and two years later Subaru's US arm posted a record loss of $250 million.

Veteran CFO George Muller took over as president and COO of Subaru of America in 1993. Saddled with inventory plummeting sales and a poor brand image he promptly launched one of the greatest turnarounds in US automotive history.

Muller refined the niche Lamm carved out in the 1970s. He cut every product from the lineup that lacked all-wheel-drive. Enlisting the Legacy a car-SUV hybrid (Outback) was created in 1995 by lifting the body a few inches and adding beefy-looking body attachments.

Muller took aggressive steps at the corporate level to cut costs and build a culture of risk-taking initiative and speed. By 1999 profits were back to record levels. In Japan though trouble at parent FHI overshadowed Subaru's rejuvenation.

In 1998 revelations surfaced that FHI bribed legislator Yojiro Nakajima (a former official in Japan's defense agency and grandson of Chikuhei) to secure government contracts for a sea rescue aircraft. FHI had also illegally funneled cash to Nakajima to help his 1996 election bid. Nakajima along with FHI's chairman and several former executives was arrested. He later committed suicide and FHI was barred from bidding on defense contracts for one year.

GM bought 20% of FHI for $1.5 billion in 1999. The deal included the 4% held by FHI's largest investor Nissan. GM won access to FHI's all-wheel-drive technology and provided FHI resources to develop more-efficient fuel systems. Midway through 2000 Muller resigned from Subaru.

FHI struck a deal with Airbus in 2001 develop the company's new Airbus A380 airliner. Subaru and GM also unveiled plans to jointly produce an all-wheel-drive sport wagon to be built at the Subaru-Isuzu plant in the US.

FHI announced in 2002 that it would cease production of bus bodies and railway cars by March 2003. Later that year FHI bought Isuzu Motors' 49% stake in the companies' carmaking joint venture Subaru-Isuzu Automotive. FHI renamed the company Subaru of Indiana Automotive.

That same year FHI implemented sweeping changes in an effort to focus on its core business —building cars. The Fuji Dynamic Revolution-1 plan (FDR-1) aimed to increase sales by 35% by 2007 and to remake Subaru as a luxury brand. Part of the original plan was for the company to leverage its relationship with GM to reduce procurement and purchasing costs. GM however decided largely to terminate its relationship with FHI and has sold its 20% stake in the Japanese manufacturer about 9% of it going to Toyota Motor. It sold the remaining 11% through Fuji's open-market share-buyback program and through regular market sales.

In the first product tie-up since Toyota became FHI's largest shareholder the two companies announced in early 2006 that Toyota Camrys would be built at FHI's Subaru of Indiana plant. That production began the following year.

In 2006 FHI made a few adjustments to its FDR-1 plan. The company restructured its sales networks and laid off about 700 workers to meet its cost reduction goals. The notion of transforming into a luxury brand however was deemed to be infeasible from a cost standpoint. FDR-1's successes were mixed. FHI managed to increase sales but profits were hurt by poor sales at home in Japan and meager sales of higher-end Subaru models in the US which were likely slowed by high fuel prices.

In 2007 FHI established its Overseas Sales and Marketing Divisions I & II. The first overseas division is dedicated to centralizing control of manufacturing and sales activities in the US. The move aimed to bring refinement and sophistication to the Subaru brand in the US while capitalizing on its reputation of offering affordable compelling AWD vehicles.

EXECUTIVES

Deputy President, Jun Kondo
EVP, Naoto Muto
President and CEO, Yasuyuki Yoshinaga, age 40
EVP, Akira Mabuchi
EVP, Takeshi Tachimori
EVP, Hisashi Nagano
EVP and CFO, Mitsuru Takahashi
EVP, Masahiro Kasai
EVP, Shuzo Haimoto
Auditors: KPMG AZSA LLC

LOCATIONS

HQ: Fuji Heavy Industries Ltd
1-20-8 Ebisu, Shibuya-ku, Tokyo 150-8554
Phone: (81) 3 6447 8825   **Fax:** (81) 3 6447 8184
Web: www.fhi.co.jp

2016 Sales by Unit

	% of total
north America	65
Japan	19
Asia	7
Europe	4
Others	5
Total	**100**

PRODUCTS/OPERATIONS

2016 Sales

	% of total
Automobiles	93
Aerospace	5
Industrial products	1
Other	1
Total	**100**

Selected Products and Divisions

Aerospace
  AH-64D combat helicopter
  Center-wing section (Boeing B-777)
  Design and training simulators
  Fixed-wing aircraft
  T-1 Trainer
  Unmanned aircraft
Automobiles
  Dex
  Dias Wagon
  Exiga
  Forester
  Impreza (wagon sedan)
  Legacy (touring B4 Outback)
  Outback (sport wagon sedan)
  Sambar (van truck wagon)
  Stella (R1 R2 Pleo)
  Tribeca
Eco Technologies
  Clean Robot floor-cleaning system
  Intermediate refuse collection systems
  Maintenance and sanitation vehicles
  Refuse management systems
  Special purpose vehicles
  Sweepers and scrubbers
  Wind-power systems
Industrial Products
  Agricultural machinery
  Construction machinery
  Forestry machinery
  General-purpose engines (Robin)
  Other machine tools and their components

Selected Subsidiaries:

Fuji Heavy Industries U.S.A. Inc.
Fuji Machinery Co. Ltd. (Japan)
Subaru Canada Inc.
Subaru of China Ltd.
Subaru Europe N.V./S.A. (Belgium)
Subaru of America Inc. (US)
Subaru of Indiana Automotive Inc.

COMPETITORS

Daimler	Mitsubishi Heavy
FCA US	Industries
Ford Motor	Mitsubishi Motors
General Motors	Nissan
Honda	Sumitomo Heavy
Kawasaki Heavy	Industries
Industries	Suzuki Motor
MPM Technologies	Toyota
Mazda	Volvo Trucks

HISTORICAL FINANCIALS

Company Type: Public

Income Statement

FYE: March 31

	REVENUE ($ mil.)	NET INCOME ($ mil.)	NET PROFIT MARGIN	EMPLOYEES
03/16	28,783	3,888	13.5%	38,319
03/15	23,986	2,182	9.1%	36,822
03/14	23,330	2,001	8.6%	28,545
03/13	20,330	1,270	6.3%	27,509
03/12	18,494	468	2.5%	27,123
Annual Growth	**11.7%**	**69.7%**	**—**	**9.0%**

2016 Year-End Financials

Debt ratio: 0.0%
Return on equity: 36.8%
Cash ($ mil.): 4,519
Current ratio: 1.86
Long-term debt ($ mil.): 828

No. of shares (mil.): 780
Dividends
  Yield: 9.9%
  Payout: —
Market value ($ mil.): 55,095

	STOCK PRICE ($) FY Close	P/E High/Low		PER SHARE ($) Earnings	Dividends	Book Value
03/16	70.60	0	0	4.98	1.76	15.33
03/15	66.68	0	0	2.80	1.16	10.92
03/14	54.40	—	—	2.57	0.59	9.56
03/13	31.66	—	—	1.63	0.00	8.13
03/12	16.18	—	—	0.60	0.00	7.05
Annual Growth	**44.5%**			**— 69.7%**	**—**	**21.4%**

FUJIFILM Holdings Corp

FUJIFILM still has film in its name but FUJIDOCS or FUJI INFO might be more apt. The company's imaging unit is its smallest by far making photographic films and papers digital cameras photofinishing equipment and chemicals. FUJIFILM's main businesses about 85% of revenue together are document operations and information-related products and services. Its document business includes joint venture Fuji Xerox offering copy machines printers and production services. The information unit provides medical imaging large-scale printing recording media optical and flat panel display devices and components. Customers overseas account for about 60% sales.

Operations
The company's document solutions business generates 47% of revenue with information solutions accounting for 38%. The imaging unit provides 15% of revenue.

Document solutions includes the company's production services and global services office products and office printers.

Product groups in the information unit are medical and life sciences systems products and services for graphic arts applications flat panel displays in-

dustrial products and electronic materials and recording media and optical devices.

Imaging is a much smaller slice of FUJIFILM's pie now about 15% of sales though the company is still a major global force there. Photo imaging sells film paper chemicals photo finishing and lab services and electronic imaging consists of digital cameras.

Financial Performance
Revenue rose 2% in 2015 (ended March) from 2014. Sales increased for photo imaging medical systems electronic materials and the document business. That was almost balanced by decreases in sales in the optical devices electronic imaging and flat panel display materials.

Net income jumped 46% higher with help from reduced research and developed costs in 2015. Cash from continuing operations dropped from 2014 to 2015.

Strategy
FUJIFILM is making investments in three core markets: healthcare highly functional materials and document business. Particularly in health care the company is looking to build its pharmaceuticals business and regenerative medicine businesses and maintain stable profits from medical systems.

Mergers and Acquisitions
FUJIFILM acquired Cellular Dynamics International a developer and manufacturer of fully functioning human cells in industrial quantities to precise specifications in 2015. The purchase provide FUJIFILM's with more advanced capabilities in its bid to build its life sciences business. It continues a series of health and life science related acquisitions FUJIFILM has made in recent years.

HISTORY

Mokichi Morita president of Japan's leading celluloid maker (Dainippon Celluloid Company founded 1919) decided to start making motion picture film in the early 1930s. Movies were becoming popular in Japan but there was no domestic film supplier. Working with a grant from the government Dainippon Celluloid established Fuji Photo Film Co. an independent company in 1934 in Minami Ashigara Village near Mount Fuji.

At first the company had trouble gaining acceptance in Japan as a quality film producer. However German emulsion specialist Dr. Emill Mauerhoff helped Fuji overcome its product deficiencies producing black-and-white photographic film (1936) and the first Japanese-made color film (1948). In the meantime Fuji added 35mm photographic film 16mm motion picture film and X-ray film to its product line. By the early 1940s the company was operating four factories and a research laboratory in Japan. Its first overseas office opened in Brazil in 1955 was followed by offices in the US (1958) and Europe (1964).

Fuji continued to expand its product line adding magnetic tape in 1960. Two years later it formed Fuji Xerox a Japanese joint venture with Xerox to sell copiers in Japan and the Pacific Rim. It operated as a private-label film supplier in the US and did not market its products under its own brand name until 1972.

International marketing VP Minoru Ohnishi became Fuji's youngest president in 1980 at age 55. To decrease dependence on Japanese film sales he built sales in the US (agreeing to sponsor the 1984 Los Angeles Olympics after Eastman Kodak refused to was key) and pumped money into the production of videotapes floppy disks and medical diagnostic equipment. Fuji introduced Fujicolor Quicksnap the world's first 35mm disposable camera in 1986. It began establishing manufacturing operations in the US two years later.

The company created the FUJIFILM Micro-devices subsidiary to produce image-processing semiconductors in 1990. In 1992 Fuji scientists completed a crude artificial "eye" (a possible forerunner of more efficient eyes for robots). The following year it launched the Pictrostat instant print system which produces color prints in one minute from photos slides and objects.

Fuji was forced to temporarily raise US prices in 1994 after Kodak accused it of illegally dumping its photographic paper exported to the US. But Fuji skirted the problem in 1995 by making the paper at its US plant. That year Kodak asked for economic sanctions against Fuji and the Japanese government saying that the government encouraged Fuji to use exclusive contracts to control film distribution thus keeping Kodak from selling film in many stores. (The case was rejected by the World Trade Organization in 1997.)

The firm unveiled the Advanced Photo System (co-developed with Kodak and three other companies) in 1996 combining conventional photography with digital-image processing and printing technology. Also that year Fuji bought six off-site wholesale photofinishing plants from Wal-Mart (the largest US provider of photofinishing services) and won contracts to provide supplies to all of Wal-Mart's in-store one-hour photo labs.

In 1997 it chopped film prices in the US and began making film at its US plant. In 1999 Fuji introduced a high-quality image sensor for digital cameras (Super CCD) and Instax an instant picture camera. Fuji and Sony launched HiFD a floppy disk with 140 times the storage capacity of traditional disks in early 2000. Fuji later announced plans to develop more efficient low-cost ink jet printers through an alliance with Xerox and Sharp Corp.

In March 2001 Fuji acquired half of Xerox's 50% stake in the companies' Fuji Xerox joint venture. In 2002 the company acquired Japanese film processing company Jusphoto Co. and in 2003 purchased shares of Process Shizai Co. renaming it Fujifilm Graphic Systems Co. Ltd.

It bought Sericol from Saratoga Partners in 2005 for $230 million and Avecia Inkjet in 2006 for $260 million. Also that year the company adopted a new holding company structure and changed its name to FUJIFILM Holdings. Also that year the firm acquired US-based Problem Solving Concepts a manufacturer of medical imaging information systems for cardiology; TSR Holding S.A. a medical equipment service and maintenance supplier; and the remaining shares of Fuji Medical Systemes France S.A. a medical imaging products distributor.

In January 2008 FUJIFILM Holdings acquired Germany's IP Labs GmbH a developer of online photo service systems. The consolidation of Toyama Chemical into a consolidated subsidiary in March marked the holding company's entry into the pharmceutical business. In November it purchased Empiric Systems LLC a US-based maker of radiology information systems.

EXECUTIVES

Chairman and CEO, Shigetaka Komori
President and COO, Kenji Sukeno
Vice Chairman, Shigehiro Nakajima
Auditors: Ernst & Young ShinNihon LLC

LOCATIONS

HQ: FUJIFILM Holdings Corp
9-7-3 Akasaka, Minato-ku, Tokyo 107-0052
Phone: (81) 3 6271 1111
Web: www.fujifilmholdings.com

2015 Sales

	% of total
Domestic	41
Overseas	59
Total	100

PRODUCTS/OPERATIONS

2015 Sales

	% of total
Document	47
Information	38
Imaging	15
Total	100

2015 Sales

	% of total
Sales	86
Rentals	14
Total	100

Selected Products

Document
  Business process outsourcing
  Digital color printers
  Digital multifunction printer/copiers
  Digital photo printers
  On-demand publishing systems
Imaging
  Color photo printing paper and chemicals
  Digital cameras and accessories
  Electronic imaging systems
  Film processing services
  Motion picture films
  Photo lab equipment
  Photographic films
Information
  Data storage media
  LCD materials
  Medical imaging systems and films
  Nutraceuticals
  Pharmaceuticals
  Plate-making supplies films and chemicals
  Printer inks
  X-ray films

COMPETITORS

Agfa	Lexmark
Bayer AG	Mitsubishi Paper Mills
Brother Industries	NEC
Canon	Nikon
Datapulse Technology	Novartis
Eastman Kodak	Olympus
Electronics for	Panasonic Corp
Imaging	Pfizer
GlaxoSmithKline	Philips Electronics
HP	Ricoh Company
Hitachi	Samsung Electronics
IBM	Sharp Corp.
Imation	Sony
Konica Minolta	Toshiba
Kyocera	Xerox
Kyocera Document	
Solutions	

HISTORICAL FINANCIALS

Company Type: Public

Income Statement

FYE: March 31

	REVENUE ($ mil.)	NET INCOME ($ mil.)	NET PROFIT MARGIN	EMPLOYEES
03/16	22,187	1,098	4.9%	88,009
03/15	20,775	988	4.8%	88,662
03/14	23,638	784	3.3%	87,726
03/13	23,537	576	2.5%	89,324
03/12	26,762	533	2.0%	90,373
Annual Growth	(4.6%)	19.8%	—	(0.7%)

2016 Year-End Financials

Debt ratio: 0.1%
Return on equity: 5.7%
Cash ($ mil.): 5,600
Current ratio: 2.94
Long-term debt ($ mil.): 2,764
No. of shares (mil.): 450
Dividends
  Yield: 1.3%
  Payout: 25.3%
Market value ($ mil.): 17,750

	STOCK PRICE ($) FY Close	P/E High/Low		Earnings	PER SHARE ($) Dividends	Book Value
03/16	39.40	0	0	2.35	0.55	40.61
03/15	35.61	0	0	2.04	0.51	38.59
03/14	26.86	0	0	1.62	0.40	40.62
03/13	19.64	0	0	1.15	0.40	41.22
03/12	23.51	0	0	1.06	0.39	43.57
Annual Growth	13.8%	—	—	21.9%	8.7%	(1.7%)

Fujitsu Ltd.

Auditors: Ernst & Young ShinNihon LLC

LOCATIONS

HQ: Fujitsu Ltd.
Shiodome City Center, 1-5-2 Higashi-Shimbashi,
Minato-ku, Tokyo 105-7123
Phone: (81) 3 6252 2220
Web: www.fujitsu.com

HISTORICAL FINANCIALS

Company Type: Public

Income Statement

FYE: March 31

	REVENUE ($ mil.)	NET INCOME ($ mil.)	NET PROFIT MARGIN	EMPLOYEES
03/16	42,203	772	1.8%	173,722
03/15	39,616	1,167	2.9%	176,150
03/14	46,139	1,096	2.4%	179,859
03/13	46,568	(774)	—	168,733
03/12	54,462	520	1.0%	173,155
Annual Growth	(6.2%)	10.4%	—	0.1%

2016 Year-End Financials

Debt ratio: 0.1%
Return on equity: 11.0%
Cash ($ mil.): 2,089
Current ratio: 1.27
Long-term debt ($ mil.): 3,454
No. of shares (mil.): 2,068
Dividends
  Yield: 0.0%
  Payout: 94.3%
Market value ($ mil.): 38,331

	STOCK PRICE ($) FY Close	P/E High/Low		Earnings	PER SHARE ($) Dividends	Book Value
03/16	18.53	1	0	0.37	0.35	3.37
03/15	34.07	1	0	0.56	0.33	3.18
03/14	30.32	1	0	0.53	0.00	2.65
03/13	21.05	—	—	(0.37)	0.00	4.67
03/12	26.44	—	—	0.25	0.00	5.69
Annual Growth	(8.5%) (12.3%)	—	—	10.5%	—	—

Fukoku Mutual Life Insurance Co (Japan)

Fukoku Mutual Life Insurance Company is one of Japan's major life insurers. As part of its business it sells products through a network of nearly 10000 agents as well as through more than 60 branch locations and about 470 field offices. It operates primarily through half a dozen subsidiaries that extends its reach to London New York and Singapore. Fukoku Mutal sells both face-to-face in the field and through call centers offering life and non-life insurance products (such as medical and nursing care insurance) as well as a variety of financial products and services. Fukoku Mutual's typical clients include private individuals and business owners. Fukoku Mutual was founded in 1923.

Operations

In addition to selling life insurance Fukoku Mutual provides investment management services information systems development and maintenance services staffing services and research on its industry in Asia (through subsidiary Fukoku Life Research Singapore). Sales and MarketingThe company sells its policies through its own sales representatives and through financial institutions.

Financial Performance

In fiscal 2015 (ended March) net revenue grew 12% to ¥1 trillion (versus ¥936 billion in fiscal 2014). Net income also increased growing 34% to ¥70 billion. That gain was primarily due to a decrease in losses on disposal of fixed assets and higher surplus before income taxes.

Cash flow from operations increased 52% to ¥260 billion that year.

Strategy

Fukoku Mutual's traditional strategies —investing conservatively and targeting government agencies as customers —have earned it a reputation as one of the more stable insurers in an industry that has experienced heavy losses primarily stemming from the weak economy and slumping stock markets. The firm is looking to continue diversifying its practices in such areas as borrower and loan periods.

EXECUTIVES

Deputy President and Executive Officer, Katsumasa Furuya
President and CEO, Yoshiteru Yoneyama
Director and Managing Executive Officer, Hitoshi Sakai
Director and Managing Executive Officer, Toshihiro Hayashi
Director and Managing Executive Officer, Kenji Hirai
Director and Managing Executive Officer, Tadashi Akikawa
Chairman, Tomofumi Akiyama
Auditors: Kisaragi Audit Corp.

LOCATIONS

HQ: Fukoku Mutual Life Insurance Co (Japan)
2-2-2 Uchisaiwaisho, Chiyoda-ku, Tokyo, injike- 100-0011
Phone: (81) 3 3508 1101   **Fax:** (81) 3 3591 6446
Web: www.fukoku-life.co.jp

PRODUCTS/OPERATIONS

Selected Subsidiaries and Affiliates
Fukoku Capital Management Inc.
Fukoku Information Systems Co. Ltd.
Fukoku Life International (America) Inc.
Fukoku Life International (U.K.) Limited
Fukoku Shinyo Hosho Company Limited
Fukokushinrai Life Insurance Company

COMPETITORS

Asahi Mutual Life	Mitsui Life
Dai-ichi Life	Nippon Life Insurance
Daido Life	Sony Financial
Gibraltar Life	Sumitomo Life
Insurance	T&D Holdings
Meiji Yasuda Life	Taiyo Life

HISTORICAL FINANCIALS
Company Type: Public

Income Statement
FYE: March 31

	ASSETS ($ mil.)	NET INCOME ($ mil.)	INCOME AS % OF ASSETS	EMPLOYEES
03/15	69,400	0	—	12,677
03/14	75,738	0	—	12,999
03/13	80,122	0	—	13,488
03/12	85,745	0	—	13,502
03/11	80,553	0	—	13,702
Annual Growth	(3.7%)	—	—	(1.9%)

2015 Year-End Financials

Return on assets: —	Dividends
Return on equity: —	Yield: —
Long-term debt ($ mil.): —	Payout: —
No. of shares (mil.): —	Market value ($ mil.): —
Sales ($ mil): 8,728	

Galp Energia, SGPS, SA

Portugal's primary oil and gas group Galp Energia (formerly Petroleos de Portugal) produces transports refines distributes and sells crude oil natural gas and oil products. It operates mainly in Portugal and Spain but also has operations in a half-dozen former Portuguese colonies. Although Galp Energia is primarily a refining and marketing company with more than 1450 gas stations it is seeking to expand its exploration and production efforts. The company has significant exploration and production activities in Angola Brazil and Portugal and holds gas and power infrastructure assets in Portugal. Italian energy giant Eni and Portuguese investment firm Amorim Energia each own 33% of the company.

EXECUTIVES

Director, Carlos Nuno Gomes da Silva
CCO Corporate Service and New Energies, Carlos Costa Pina
CFO, Filipe Cris stomo Silva
COO, Thore E. Kristiansen
CCO and Head Supply Refining and Planning, Jose Carlos da Silva Costa
CCO and Head Gas and Power, Pedro Carmona de Oliveira Ricardo
CCO and Head Iberian and International Oil Marketing, Tiago C mara Pestana
Vice Chairman, Miguel Athayde Marques, age 61
Chairwoman, Paula Amorim
Auditors: PricewaterhouseCoopers & Associados

LOCATIONS

HQ: Galp Energia, SGPS, SA
Rua Tomas de Fonseca, Torre C, Lisbon 1600-209
Phone: (351) 21 240 866   **Fax:** (351) 21 242 965
Web: www.galpenergia.com

PRODUCTS/OPERATIONS

2013 Sales

	% of total
Refining & marketing	83
Gas & power	17
Total	100

Selected Subsidiaries
Galp Power (electricity generation and sales)

Galpgeste (management and operation of service stations)
GDP Gás de Portugal
Petróleos de Portugal (Petrogal; exploration and production refining transport distribution and sales of oil products)
Sacor Maritima (marine transport)
Sopor (51% distribution and sale of oil products)
Transgás Armazenagem (natural gas underground storage)

COMPETITORS

BP	Repsol
Endesa S.A.	Royal Dutch Shell
Exxon Mobil	TOTAL

HISTORICAL FINANCIALS
Company Type: Public

Income Statement
FYE: December 31

	REVENUE ($ mil.)	NET INCOME ($ mil.)	NET PROFIT MARGIN	EMPLOYEES
12/15	17,009	133	0.8%	6,792
12/14	22,032	(210)	—	6,855
12/13	27,210	259	1.0%	6,968
12/12	24,573	452	1.8%	7,241
12/11	21,972	559	2.5%	7,381
Annual Growth	(6.2%)	(30.1%)		(2.1%)

2015 Year-End Financials

Debt ratio: 30.2%	No. of shares (mil.): 829
Return on equity: 2.5%	Dividends
Cash ($ mil.): 1,231	Yield: 2.9%
Current ratio: 2.02	Payout: 101.3%
Long-term debt ($ mil.): 3,332	Market value ($ mil.): 4,835

	STOCK PRICE ($) FY Close	P/E High/Low		PER SHARE ($)		
			Earnings	Dividends	Book Value
12/15	5.83	45 29	0.16	0.17	6.27
12/14	5.02	— —	(0.26)	0.12	7.34
12/13	8.14	38 34	0.32	0.10	8.57
12/12	7.82	22 15	0.54	0.13	8.58
12/11	8.53	21 14	0.67	0.05	4.50
Annual Growth	(9.1%)	— —	(29.8%)	32.9%	8.6%

Gas Natural SDG, S.A.

Auditors: PricewaterhouseCoopers Auditores, S.L.

LOCATIONS

HQ: Gas Natural SDG, S.A.
Placa del Gas, 1, Barcelona 08003
Phone: (34) 93 219 9199   **Fax:** (34) 93 402 5870
Web: www.gasnatural.com

HISTORICAL FINANCIALS
Company Type: Public

Income Statement
FYE: December 31

	REVENUE ($ mil.)	NET INCOME ($ mil.)	NET PROFIT MARGIN	EMPLOYEES
12/15	28,335	1,636	5.8%	19,939
12/14	30,074	1,777	5.9%	21,961
12/13	34,375	1,989	5.8%	14,982
12/12	32,824	1,899	5.8%	15,959
12/11	27,260	1,713	6.3%	16,202
Annual Growth	1.0%	(1.2%)	—	5.3%

2015 Year-End Financials

Debt ratio: 40.8%
Return on equity: 10.5%
Cash ($ mil.): 2,603
Current ratio: 1.20
Long-term debt ($ mil.): 16,990

No. of shares (mil.): 1,000
Dividends
  Yield: 3.5%
  Payout: 8.0%
Market value ($ mil.): 4,093

	STOCK PRICE ($) FY Close	P/E High/Low		PER SHARE ($) Earnings	Dividends	Book Value
12/15	4.09	3	2	1.71	0.15	15.64
12/14	5.11	4	3	1.77	0.15	17.18
12/13	5.05	4	3	1.98	0.17	18.50
12/12	3.50	2	1	1.91	0.15	17.47
12/11	3.51	3	2	1.80	0.06	16.68
Annual Growth	3.9%	—	—	(1.2%)	25.2%	(1.6%)

Gazprom Neft PJSC

One of Russia's largest integrated oil companies and its third largest refiner Gazprom Neft explores for produces refines and markets petroleum products. Its retail operations include about 1750 gas stations. The company with proved reserves of 9.7 billion barrels of oil equivalent controls refineries in Moscow Mozyr Noyabrsk and Omsk that produce more than 45.7 million tonnes of petroleum products per year. It refines about 80% of the oil it produces a high ratio for Russia. Gazprom Neft also shares ownership of major natural gas project SeverEnergia with NOVATEK the country's largest independent gas producer. State-owned gas giant Gazprom controls Gazprom Neft.

HISTORY

In the aftermath of the fall of the Soviet Union in the early 1990s Sibneft was formed in 1995 as part of Russia's privatization of state industries. Sibneft included western Siberian oil producer Noyabrskneftegas and the Omsk oil refinery. The Russian government was to retain a 51% stake for three years while limiting foreign ownership to 15%. Finance Oil Company (FNK) controlled by business oligarch Boris Berezovsky the man reportedly behind Sibneft's formation gained a controlling stake in Sibneft. The new integrated oil company's prize asset was the Omsk refinery. Built in the mid-1980s it was Russia's largest and most modern refinery.

In 1997 Sibneft became the first Russian company to issue a Eurobond. Despite an economic crisis in 1998 Sibneft continued to service all of its financial obligations. That year Sibneft made plans to merge with rival oil company Yukos (controlled by oligarch Mikhail Khodorkovsky) but falling oil prices led the two firms to scuttle the proposed union.

Also in 1998 Sibneft published a corporate governance charter compiled by leading European experts to bring the company in line with international practices. This move was followed up with the appointment of three non-executives to the company's board of nine directors. A year later Sibneft became the first major Russian oil company to publish its financial accounts (audited by Arthur Andersen) according to US generally accepted accounting principles. In 1999 Sibneft also formed alliances with two Western oil services firms US-based Schlumberger and Canadian-based BJ Services to enhance its extraction of oil and gas.

During the 1999 Russian Duma elections reclusive oligarch Roman Abramovich (who had acquired a 12% stake in Sibneft in 1996) claimed to control Sibneft whereas Berezovsky (also elected

to the Duma) was said to have only a background role in Sibneft.

The company announced plans in 2000 to invest $52 million to modernize the Omsk refinery upgrading its capacity to produce lead-free gasoline. That year Sibneft also agreed to acquire majority stakes in two refined products retailers in the Urals region which together controlled 132 service stations and 20 storage sites.

Sibneft lost out in its bid to gain control of Onako another former state-owned oil company that was privatized in 2000. Sibneft had teamed up with two other oil companies Yukos and Stroitransgaz (a unit of Russian gas giant Gazprom) to bid for Onako but lost out to rival Tyumen Oil Co. (TNK). However Sibneft which had gained control of a 40% stake in Onako's main oil producing subsidiary Orenburgneft reportedly made an arrangement with TNK to swap its Orenburgneft shares for a minority stake in Onako. Also in 2000 Sibneft and other Russian oil companies were investigated by Russian authorities after allegations of tax evasion.

In 2001 the company announced plans to search for oil in the Chukotka autonomous district. (Abramovich is the governor of Chukotka). This unexplored area has a similar geological structure to Alaska's oil-rich North Slope. Later that year Sibneft acquired a 36% stake in a Moscow refinery from oil giant LUKOIL allowing the company to supply markets in European Russia.

In 2002 Sibneft opened its first gas station in Moscow.

Gazprom Neft (as Sibneft) was once controlled by UK-residing Chelsea soccer club-owning Russian oligarch Roman Abramovich through investment company Millhouse Capital. In 2005 Gazprom bought its majority stake in Sibneft from Millhouse Capital for $11 billion. The company changed its name to Gazprom Neft the next year and ENI acquired 20% of Gazprom Neft in 2007 following the bankruptcy of Yukos. Gazprom had the option to buy ENI's stake within two years and exercised that right in 2009 paying just more than $4 billion to ENI. Gazprom now directly owns or indirectly controls through subsidiaries about 95% of Gazprom Neft.

EXECUTIVES

Chairman and CEO, Alexander V. Dyukov, age 49
Deputy chairman and Deputy CEO for Logistics Processing and Sales, Anatoly Cherner, age 63
Deputy CEO Foreign Asset Management, Kirill Kravchenko, age 40
Deputy Chairman and First Deputy CEO, Vadim Yakovlev, age 46
Deputy Chairman and Deputy CEO Administration, Vitaliy Baranov
Deputy CEO International Business Development, Vladislav Baryshnikov
Deputy CEO Economics and Finance, Alexei Yankevich
Auditors: ZAO PricewaterhouseCoopers Audit

LOCATIONS

HQ: Gazprom Neft PJSC
3-5 Pochtamtskaya St., St. Petersburg 190000
Phone: (7) 812 363 31 52   **Fax:** (7) 812 363 31 51
Web: www.gazprom-neft.ru

PRODUCTS/OPERATIONS

2013 Sales

	% of total
Petroleum Products	81
Crude Oil	14
Gas	2
Other	3
Total	**100**

COMPETITORS

BP	Occidental Petroleum
Bashneft JOSC	Rosneft
Devon Energy	Royal Dutch Shell
Exxon Mobil	Surgutneftegas
JX Nippon Oil & Energy	TOTAL
LUKOIL	Tatneft
Mitsui	Transneft

HISTORICAL FINANCIALS

Company Type: Public

Income Statement

FYE: December 31

	REVENUE ($ mil.)	NET INCOME ($ mil.)	NET PROFIT MARGIN	EMPLOYEES
12/15	19,878	1,485	7.5%	0
12/14	23,925	2,074	8.7%	0
12/13	38,569	5,413	14.0%	0
12/12	40,415	5,791	14.3%	0
12/11	44,172	5,352	12.1%	0
Annual Growth	(18.1%)	(27.4%)	—	—

2015 Year-End Financials

Debt ratio: 0.4%
Return on equity: 9.8%
Cash ($ mil.): 1,546
Current ratio: 1.46
Long-term debt ($ mil.): 9,083

No. of shares (mil.): —
Dividends
  Yield: 5.9%
  Payout: 33.4%
Market value ($ mil.): —

	STOCK PRICE ($) FY Close	P/E High/Low		PER SHARE ($) Earnings	Dividends	Book Value
12/15	10.61	1	0	0.31	0.63	3.32
12/14	11.77	1	0	0.44	1.27	3.84
12/13	22.60	1	0	1.15	1.70	6.14
12/12	23.76	1	1	1.23	0.95	5.81
12/11	23.33	24	15	1.13	0.16	4.98
Annual Growth	(17.9%)	—	—	(27.4%)	41.0%	(9.6%)

GlaxoSmithKline Plc

GlaxoSmithKline (GSK) gives anxiety asthma and other ailments the ax. One of the top five pharmaceutical firms in the world GSK's bestsellers include respiratory neurological cardiovascular and dermatology drugs as well as vaccines and antivirals. Its top product is asthma medication Advair (aka Seretide) which combines two of its other asthma products Flovent and Serevent. Other bestsellers include epilepsy treatment Lamictal cholesterol medicine Lovaza and prostate enlargement treatment Avodart. GSK's consumer products include Tums dental care products Aquafresh and Sensodyne and smoking-cessation products Nico-Derm and Nicorette. In 2015 GSK bought Novartis' Vaccines and Consumer Health business and sold its cancer drugs business to the same company.

Operations

GSK operates through three primary segments - Pharmaceuticals Consumer Healthcare and Vaccines. Pharmaceuticals is the largest by far pulling in some 60% of revenue.

The Pharmaceuticals business develops and makes medicines that treat a wide variety of acute and chronic diseases. Respiratory drugs is its largest sales category primarily due to blockbuster Advair which brings in around £4 billion annually. Other respiratory products include Ventolin Relvar and Flixotide. GSK also has a strong presence in the HIV market (through majority-owned ViiV Healthcare) as well as the central nervous system treatment market alongside cardiovascular urogenital dermatology (through its Stiefel division) virology infectious disease and metabolism.

Consumer Healthcare products fall into the oral health wellness nutrition and skin health categories with top sellers including Sensodyne Panadol and Horlicks. The segment also makes key brands Theraflu Polident and Abreva. GSK sells these products in more than 150 countries around the world with around 40% of sales in emerging markets. In 2015 GSK combined its consumer health care operations with those of Novartis to create a global leader in the consumer health market.

The Vaccines business is a global leader with around 40 pediatric adolescent adult and travel vaccines on the market. Its Infanrix childhood vaccine for diptheria and tetanus leads the pack followed by products for the prevention of hepatitis pneumonia rotavirus and influenza with brands including Cervarix and Pediarix vaccines and antibiotic Augmentin. As part of the Novartis acquisition GSK gained two meningitis vaccines Menveo and Bexsero.

Geographic Reach

GSK has more than 80 manufacturing facilities in 36 countries. The group's major R&D centers are located in the UK the US Belgium and China. It has a presence in more than 115 countries.

The US and Europe pull in around 61% of revenue but the company's biggest chunk of revenue come from international markets. Japan is the largest international market and accounts for nearly 10%.

Sales and Marketing

The company markets its products directly to hospitals pharmacies doctors and other health care consumers; it also uses wholesale distributors in some markets and serves customers in more than 150 countries overall.

Financial Performance

Note: Growth rates may differ after conversion to US dollars.

Sales grew 6% to £23.9 billion in 2015 reflecting the contribution to sales of the acquired Vaccines and Consumer Health businesses from Novartis. Acquired products that aided growth include Voltaren and Otrivin in Consumer Health as well as the acquired Meningitis product portfolio. Pharmaceuticals the biggest segment by revenue at around 60% of total was down on prior year due to a decline in sales for big-selling Advair.

Growth rates in the US and Europe were affected by exchange rate effects. In real terms the US grew 11% and Europe 3% but at constant exchange rates Europe grew more strongly at 11%.

Net income rose to £8.3 billion from £2.8 in 2014. This 300% jump came from the net proceeds of the Novartis asset-swap.

Cash from operating activities fell to £2.5 billion from £5.2 in 2014 (which in turn was a fall from £7.2 in 2013). This fall was due to payments of non-core restructuring and integration costs and tax payments on the divested oncology business of £1 billion.

The company was also hit by a record fine of $490 million from Chinese authorities after the company was found to have bribed doctors to promote their products.

Strategy

GSK undertook a restructuring program in 2014-15 that included the divestment of the meningitis vaccine program and which brought savings across the business of £1 billion which exceeded expectations by £200 million. Part of these savings are to be funneled into R&D development across GSK's three business units.

In 2015 GSK completed a major asset swap with Novartis that reshaped its operations. It paid Novartis $7.8 billion for that company's vaccine business while collecting up to $16 billion for handing over its oncology line. The two companies are also combining their consumer products lines to create the world's top provider of over-the-counter (OTC) medicines. Altogether the three-part deal is expected to add £1.3 billion to GSK's bottom line and strengthen its core OTC and vaccine businesses.

The company divested its oncology division to focus on its core operations and the sale provides an immediate cash injection. In mid 2016 GSK sold its portfolio of anaesthetic drugs for £280 million to Aspen Pharmacare a South African pharma with which GSK has a long association. The sales comes as part of a drive to focus on core business.

As sales in the US GSK's largest market account for about a third of pharmaceutical sales maintaining a rich portfolio of US patent-protected products can make or break the company's future. For example cardiovascular drug Lovaza began facing generic competition in 2014 and fell 54% that year. Other established products that have experienced sales slumps due to patent losses include best-selling herpes drug Valtrex and anti-depressant Paroxetine (marketed as Seroxat and Paxil).

GSK is also working to pump potential new blockbusters into its pipeline by acquiring promising research firms and forming development agreements with other drug companies. The company is working with pharmaceutical firms Pfizer and Shionogi on HIV medications through ViiV Healthcare; many of the company's HIV and vaccine development programs aim to provide affordable disease preventions and treatments to developing countries.

In mid-2016 GSK went into partnership with Verily Google owner Alphabet's life science division to form Galvani Bioelectronics which will research develop and commercialize bioelectronic medicine. The two companies will invest a combined £540 million over five years and GSK will hold a 55% equity interest.

HISTORY

Company Background

Englishman Joseph Nathan started an import-export business in New Zealand in 1873. He obtained the rights to a process for drying milk and began making powdered milk in New Zealand selling it as baby food Glaxo.

Nathan's son Alec dispatched to London to oversee baby food sales in Britain increased Glaxo's name recognition by publishing the Glaxo Baby Book a guide to child care. After WWI the company began distribution in India and South America.

In the 1920s Glaxo launched vitamin D-fortified formulations. It entered the pharmaceutical business with its 1927 introduction of Ostelin a liquid vitamin D concentrate and continued to grow globally in the 1930s introducing Ostermilk (vitamin-fortified milk).

Glaxo began making penicillin and anesthetics during WWII; it went public in 1947. A steep drop in antibiotic prices in the mid-1950s led Glaxo to diversify; it bought veterinary medical instrument and drug distribution firms.

In the 1970s the British Monopolies Commission quashed both a hostile takeover attempt by Beecham and a proposed merger with retailer and drugmaker Boots. Glaxo launched US operations in 1978.

Glaxo shed nondrug operations in the 1980s to concentrate on pharmaceuticals. A 1981 market-

ing blitz launched antiulcer drug Zantac (to vie with SmithKline's Tagamet) in the US where Glaxo's sales had been small. The company boosted outreach by contracting to use Hoffmann-La Roche's sales staff. The Zantac sales assault gave Glaxo leadership in US antiulcer drug sales.

Under CEO Sir Richard Sykes Glaxo in 1995 made a surprise bid for UK rival Wellcome. Founded in 1880 by Americans Silas Burroughs and Henry Wellcome to sell McKesson-Robbins' products outside the US Burroughs Wellcome and Co. began making its own products two years later. By the 1990s the company which fostered Nobel Prize-winning researchers led the world in antiviral medicines. Its primary drug products were Zovirax (launched 1981) and Retrovir (1987).

Though an earlier bid by Glaxo had been rejected Sykes won the takeover with backing from Wellcome Trust Wellcome's largest shareholder.

In 1997 the company formed a new genetics division buying Spectra Biomedical and its gene variation technology. That year the company pulled diabetes drug Romozin (Rezulin in the US) from the UK market over concerns that it caused liver damage.

Glaxo in 1998 ended its joint venture with Warner-Lambert (begun 1993) selling its former partner the Canadian and US marketing rights to acid blocker Zantac 75.

In 1999 Glaxo trimmed its product line pulling hepatitis treatment Wellferon because of slow sales and selling the US rights to several anesthesia products. It also cut some 3400 jobs (half from the UK). Also that year Glaxo threatened to leave the UK after the National Health Service opted not to cover antiflu inhalant Relenza claiming the drug is not cost-effective.

The FDA in 2000 approved Glaxo's Lotronex for irritable bowel syndrome but several hospitalizations linked to the drug prompted the FDA to ask the company to withdraw it from the US market. Later that year Glaxo completed its merger with former UK rival SmithKline Beecham to create GlaxoSmithKline (GSK).

EXECUTIVES

CEO, Andrew Witty, age 52, $1,059,000 total compensation
President Consumer Healthcare Worldwide, Emma Walmsley
Chairman Global Vaccines, Moncef Slaoui, age 56, $1,180,000 total compensation
President Pharmaceuticals R&D, Patrick Vallance
President Global Pharmaceuticals, Abbas Hussain
CFO, Simon Dingemans, $699,000 total compensation
President Global Manufacturing & Supply, Roger Connor
CEO Viiv Healthcare JV, Domique Limet
CEO Viiv Healthcare JV, Deborah Waterhouse
Chairman, Philip Hampton, age 63
Auditors: PricewaterhouseCoopers LLP

LOCATIONS

HQ: GlaxoSmithKline Plc
980 Great West Road, Brentford, Middlesex TW8 9GS
Phone: (44) 20 8047 5000   **Fax:** (44) 20 8047 7807
Web: www.gsk.com

2015 Sales

	% of total
International	39
US	34
Europe	27
Total	**100**

PRODUCTS/OPERATIONS

2015 Sales

	% of total
Pharmaceuticals	60
Consumer healthcare	25
Vaccines	15
Total	**100**

Selected Products

Pharmaceuticals
 Respiratory
  Beconase (allergies)
  Becotide/Beclovent (asthma and chronic obstructive pulmonary disease)
  Flixonase/Flonase (allergies)
  Flixotide/Flovent (asthma and chronic obstructive pulmonary disease)
  Seretide/Advair (asthma and chronic obstructive pulmonary disease)
  Serevent (asthma and chronic obstructive pulmonary disease)
  Ventolin (asthma and chronic obstructive pulmonary disease)
  Veramyst/Avamys (rhinitis)
 Cardiovascular and urogenital
  Arixtra (deep vein thrombosis and pulmonary embolism)
  Avodart (prostatic hyperplasia)
  Benlysta (systemic lupus erychematosus with HGS)
  Coreg CR (heart failure and hypertension)
  Fraxiparine (deep vein thrombosis and pulmonary embolism)
  Levitra (erectile dysfunction with Bayer)
  Lovaza (coronary heart disease)
  Vesicare (overactive bladder)
  Volibris (pulmonary hypertension)
 Central nervous system disorders
  Horizant (post-herpetic neuralgia or restless leg syndrome)
  Imigran/Imitrex (migraines)
  Lamictal (epilepsy and bipolar disorder)
  Potiga/Trobalt (epilepsy and partial seizures)
  Requip (Parkinson's disease)
  Seroxat/Paxil (depression)
  Treximet (migraine)
  Wellbutrin SR (depression)
  ViiV Healthcare (HIV with Pfizer)
  Combivir/Biovir (reverse transcriptase inhibitor for HIV/AIDS)
  Epivir/3TC (reverse transcriptase inhibitor for HIV/AIDS)
  Epizicom/Kivexa (combination of Epivir and Ziagen for HIV/AIDS)
  Lexiva/Telzir (protease inhibitor for HIV/AIDS)
  Selzentry (HIV)
  Trizivir (three reverse transcriptase inhibitors for HIV/AIDS)
 Antibacterials
  Amoxil and Augmentin (antibiotics non-US only)
 Dermatology
  Bactroban (skin infections)
  Duac (acne vulgaris)
  Zovirax (herpes infections shingles chicken pox and cold sores)
 Antivirals
  Relenza (influenza)
  Hepsera (hepatitis B)
  Valtrex/Zelitrex (shingles and genital herpes)
  Zeffix/Septavir/Heptodin/Epivir HBV (hepatitis B)
Vaccines
 Cervarix (human papilloma virus)
 Fluarix (influenza)
 FluLaval (influenza)
 Infanrix/Pediarix (diphtheria tetanus pertussis polio and hepatitis B)
 Rotarix (rotavirus)
 Synflorix (pneumonia)
 Twinrix (hepatitis A and hepatitis B)
 Metabolic
  Avandia Avandamet (type 2 diabetes)
  Boniva/Bonviva (osteoporosis with Roche)
Consumer products
 Over-the-counter medicines
  Abreva (cold sores)
  alli (weight loss)
  Breathe Right (nasal strips)
  Citrucel (laxative)
  Commit (smoking-cessation)
  Contac (respiratory product)
  Nicabate/NicoDerm/NiQuitin CQ (smoking-cessation)
  Nicorette (smoking-cessation)
  Panadol (analgesic)
  Tums (antacid)
 Oral care
  Aquafresh (toothpaste and toothbrushes)
  Corega (denture care)
  Dr Best (toothbrushes)
  Macleans (toothpaste)
  Odol (toothpaste)
  Polident (denture cleaner)
  Poli-Grip (denture adhesive)
  Sensodyne (toothpaste)
 Nutritional health care
  Horlicks (milk-based malted food and chocolate drinks)
  Lucozade (glucose energy drink)
  Ribena (line of juice drinks rich in vitamin C)

COMPETITORS

Abbott Labs	Mylan
Amgen	Novartis
AstraZeneca	Novo Nordisk
Bayer AG	Pfizer
Biogen	Procter & Gamble
Bristol-Myers Squibb	Reckitt Benckiser
Colgate-Palmolive	Roche Holding
Dr. Reddy' s	Sanofi
Eli Lilly	Takeda Pharmaceutical
Gilead Sciences	Teva
Johnson & Johnson	UCB
Merck	

HISTORICAL FINANCIALS

Company Type: Public

Income Statement

FYE: December 31

	REVENUE ($ mil.)	NET INCOME ($ mil.)	NET PROFIT MARGIN	EMPLOYEES
12/15	35,452	12,480	35.2%	101,255
12/14	35,912	4,302	12.0%	97,921
12/13	43,801	8,983	20.5%	99,817
12/12	42,603	7,358	17.3%	98,681
12/11	42,308	8,127	19.2%	97,401
Annual Growth	(4.3%)	11.3%	—	1.0%

2015 Year-End Financials

Debt ratio: 46.1%	No. of shares (mil.): —
Return on equity: 179.6%	Dividends
Cash ($ mil.): 8,639	Yield: 6.0%
Current ratio: 1.24	Payout: 89.8%
Long-term debt ($ mil.): 22,709	Market value ($ mil.): —

	STOCK PRICE ($) FY Close	P/E High/Low		PER SHARE ($) Earnings	Dividends	Book Value
12/15	40.35	28	21	2.55	2.43	1.56
12/14	42.74	93	72	0.89	2.65	1.37
12/13	53.39	52	40	1.83	2.41	2.38
12/12	43.47	53	46	1.47	2.48	1.91
12/11	45.63	44	34	1.59	2.10	2.46
Annual Growth (3.0%) (10.8%)		—	—	12.5%	3.7%	

Glencore PLC

Glencore trades in the stuff of which stuff is made. The commodities trader (metals and minerals agricultural products and energy) and a diversified natural resources conglomerate has interests in companies involved in mining smelting refining and agriculture. In the energy sector it markets such products as coal crude oil jet fuel and gaso-line. Glencore's holdings include minority interests in Century Aluminum and French base metals refiner Recylex and majority control of Australian nickel miner Minara Resources. It also owns Canada-based grain giant Viterra. In 2016 Glencore and Qatar's sovereign wealth fund agreed to buy 19.5% of Rosneft from the Russian state for $11 billion.

Geographic Reach

Glencore has more than 90 offices in more than 50 countries worldwide.

Operations

The company is a major producer and marketer of more than 90 commodities and has more than 150 mining and metallurgical locations offshore oil production assets farms and agricultural facilities.

IPO

Glencore went public in an IPO of about 20% of its shares in 2011 freeing up cash to support an acquisition strategy.

Strategy

Glencore's long-term strategy is to move beyond trading by acquiring major mining companies and other commodity producers. Although extremely active in mergers and acquisitions the company tends to hold onto investments for the long term rather than looking for short-term gains.

Mergers and Acquisitions

In 2016 Russia agreed to sell 19.5% of Rosneft to Glencore and Qatar's sovereign wealth fund for $11 billion.

In one of its largest takeovers to date in 2013 the company paid $41 billion for the remaining stake in Xstrata. Xstrata exports coal from and produces ferrochrome and vanadium in Australia and South Africa mines and smelts zinc in Spain and Germany and mines copper throughout the Americas and the Asia/Pacific region. The deal made Glencore the world's fourth-largest diversified miner. In addition to garnering the support of at least 75% of their individual shareholders to complete the acquisition the deal also gained regulatory approval in various regions by such groups as the European Union China and the US. Glencore expects the merger to lead to annual savings of about $500 million.

In 2012 Glencore acquired Canada's largest grain company Viterra for $6.2 billion. The purchase gives Glencore entry into North American grain markets (Canada ranks as the world's third-largest wheat exporter and is also the top exporter of durum wheat which is used in making pasta). Glencore already had agricultural operations in Europe Russia and Australia. To get the deal greenlighted by Canadian authorities Glencore agreed to sell some of Viterra's assets to a couple of Canadian companies. Fertilizer producer Agrium agreed to pay $1.8 billion for about 90% of Viterra's retail stores. And Richardson International a top grain handler agreed to buy Viterra's 19 grain elevators some port-terminal assets and North America's largest oat-processing business for about $806 million.

Increasing its zinc and lead production footprint that year Glencore acquired 80.1% of Rosh Pinah a Namibian zinc and lead mining operation for $150 million. It also bought Vale's European manganese ferro alloys operations in France and Norway for a $190 million.

Financial Performance

Glencore's financial proforma combined revenues (post-Xstrata's acquisition by Glencore) for 2012 is estimated to be about $237 billion (marketing activities $190 billion; and industrial activities $47 billion). Revenues in 2012 jumped by 13% over 2011.

Pre-acquisiton Glencore's revenues grew by 15% in 2012 thanks to higher oil volumes handled (up more than 39%) partially offset by lower metals prices. The increase in revenues from agricultural products stemmed from higher grain and oilseed volumes (up more than 20% on 2011) in part due to the overall increase in non-US seaborne trade (thanks to a drought weakening US exports).

Metals and minerals revenues grew thanks to an increase in the marketing of Ferroalloys/Nickel/Cobalt/Iron ore partially offset by decline in industrial activities driven by lower average metal prices (aluminum copper nickel and zinc). Energy products revenues increased thanks to higher industrial demand and increased marketing and activities.

The growth in oil production volumes and strong profit margins from the Aseng oil field lifted Glencore's energy products' revenues in 2012.

However the company's net income dropped by 73% in 2012 thanks to higher costs of goods sold selling and administrative expenses loss on disposal of investments and net other expense. Net other expense in 2012 was $1.2 billion ($511 million in 2011). This amount included impairments of $1.7 billion $120 million in acquisition related expenses and $109 million of expense related to Glencore's public listing. These expenses were offset by a $497 million accounting gain mainly related to the revaluation of Glencore's initial stake in the Mutanda Congo copper mine (it acquired control of the asset in 2012).

Company Background
The company was founded in 1974.

EXECUTIVES

CEO, Ivan Glasenberg, age 59
CFO, Steven Kalmin
Chairman, Anthony B. (Tony) Hayward, age 59
Auditors: Deloitte LLP

LOCATIONS

HQ: Glencore PLC
Baarermattstrasse 3, P.O. Box 777, Baar CH-6341
Phone: (41) 41 709 2000   **Fax:** (41) 41 709 3000
Web: www.glencore.com

2015 Sales

	% of total
Asia	38
Europe	32
The Americas	19
Oceania	7
Africa	4
Total	100

PRODUCTS/OPERATIONS

2015 Sales

	$ mil.	% of total
Energy products	82,992	49
Metals and minerals	64,355	38
Agricultural products	23,146	13
Total	170,497	100

Selected Operations

Agricultural Products
  Barley
  Corn
  Meals
  Rice
  Sugar
  Wheat
Energy Products
  Coal
  Oil
Metals and Minerals
  Copper
  Ferroalloys
  Lead
  Nickel
  Zinc

COMPETITORS

ADM	Noble Group
Anglo American	Norsk Hydro ASA
BHP Billiton	Rio Tinto Limited

HISTORICAL FINANCIALS

Company Type: Public

Income Statement

FYE: December 31

	REVENUE ($ mil.)	NET INCOME ($ mil.)	NET PROFIT MARGIN	EMPLOYEES
12/15	170,497	(4,964)	—	156,468
12/14	221,073	2,308	1.0%	181,349
12/13	232,694	(7,402)	—	0
12/12	214,436	1,004	0.5%	0
12/11	186,152	4,048	2.2%	0
Annual Growth	(2.2%)	—	—	—

2015 Year-End Financials

Debt ratio: 34.2%
Return on equity: (-11.0%)
Cash ($ mil.): 2,707
Current ratio: 1.03
Long-term debt ($ mil.): 32,932
No. of shares (mil.): —
Dividends
  Yield: 13.6%
  Payout: —
Market value ($ mil.): —

	STOCK PRICE ($) FY Close	P/E High/Low	PER SHARE ($) Earnings	Dividends	Book Value
12/15	2.63	— —	(0.37)	0.36	2.90
12/14	9.23	71 48	0.18	0.31	3.74
12/13	10.42	— —	(0.67)	0.29	3.81
12/12	11.67	112 66	0.14	0.28	4.40
12/11	12.14	20 16	0.69	0.05	4.23
Annual Growth	(31.8%)	— —	—	63.6%	(9.0%)

Great Eastern Holdings Ltd. (Singapore)

Great Eastern Holdings Limited holds quite a few insurance companies in the far east and they all want to be great. The company through its subsidiaries has operations in Singapore and Malaysia where it is the largest and oldest insurer as well as in Brunei Indonesia China (via joint venture) and Vietnam. It offers asset management investment holding management services life insurance (through Great Eastern Life Assurance) and other financial services. Great Eastern Holdings' 20000 dedicated agents sell its products; representatives at major banks also offer its wares. The company which was incorporated in 1908 is owned by Oversea-Chinese Banking Corp.

Great Eastern Holdings which plans to eventually have branches across all of Asia operates in China through a joint venture with Chongqing Land Properties Group. The JV Great Eastern Life Assurance (China) has opened six offices and continues petitioning the Chinese government for permission to set up more.

The company opened its Vietnam office in Ho Chi Minh City in 2008. Shortly thereafter a second branch in Hanoi opened its doors.

Also in 2008 12-year CEO Tan Beng Lee retired and was replaced by insurance industry veteran Ng Keng Hooi. Ng was formerly the regional managing director of Asia for Prudential.

EXECUTIVES

Chief Executive Officer, Khor
Chief Finance Officer, Tony Cheong
Director & Chairman, Norman Ka Cheung Ip
Auditors: Ernst & Young LLP

LOCATIONS

HQ: Great Eastern Holdings Ltd. (Singapore)
1 Pickering Street #16-01, Great Eastern Centre, 048659
Phone: (65) 6248 2000   **Fax:** (65) 6438 3889
Web: www.greateasternlife.com

COMPETITORS

China Life Insurance	Guoco
China Pacific	Ping An Insurance
Insurance	Prudential plc
Edaran Otomobil	

HISTORICAL FINANCIALS

Company Type: Public

Income Statement

FYE: December 31

	ASSETS ($ mil.)	NET INCOME ($ mil.)	INCOME AS % OF ASSETS	EMPLOYEES
12/15	46,566	555	1.2%	0
12/14	49,711	665	1.3%	0
12/13	48,214	534	1.1%	0
12/12	48,811	972	2.0%	0
12/11	42,781	296	0.7%	0
Annual Growth	2.1%	17.0%	—	—

2015 Year-End Financials

Return on assets: 1.1%
Return on equity: 12.9%
Long-term debt ($ mil.): —
No. of shares (mil.): 473
Sales ($ mil): 698
Dividends
  Yield: —
  Payout: 33.1%
Market value ($ mil.): —

Great-West Life Assurance Co

Great-West Life Assurance has a great big array of insurance benefits and investment products for individuals and businesses large and small in Canada and Europe. Through its operating subsidiaries Canada Life and London Life the company provides group and individual life insurance supplemental health insurance disability and critical illness insurance and investment and retirement plans. Its European business is focused on the UK Ireland and Germany where it provides asset management individual insurance and reinsurance. Great-West Life Assurance is a subsidiary of Great-West Lifeco and part of the Power Financial group of companies.

While it has experienced organic growth the company has been acquisitive picking up businesses in both Canada and the UK. In 2009 the company acquired the Canadian group retirement and savings business of Fidelity Investments Canada. The acquisition gave Great-West Life Assurance about 100 plan sponsors nearly 500 retirement plans and about 100000 new members in Canada.

(For those wondering why the company's Canada Life operates in the UK but its London Life operates in Canada –the "London" in London Life refers to its hometown of London Ontario.)

Great-West Life Assurance's sister company Great-West Life & Annuity Insurance Company offers a more limited portfolio of products in the US including life insurance annuity and retirement products.

Founded in 1891 in Winnipeg Great-West Life Assurance is a leading provider of employee benefits programs in Canada and serves clients with large and small employee groups. The company is led by CEO D. Allen Loney who took over for Raymond McFeetors when he was named chairman of the board in 2008

EXECUTIVES

EVP General Counsel and Compliance, Andrew D. Brands
President and CEOThe Great-West Life Assurance CompanyGreat-West Lifeco Inc. London Life Insurance Company Canada Life Financial Corporation and The Canada Life Assurance Company, Paul A. Mahon
EVP Individual Customers, Gerry Hassett, age 51
SVP and Chief Actuary Capital Management, Arshil Jamal
EVP and Chief Investment Officer, Brian R. Allison
EVP and CFO, Garry MacNicholas
EVP Strategic Customer Marketing, Stephane Dubreuil
EVP Group Customers, Jeff Macoun
President Quebec Affairs, Monique Maynard
President and COO Canada, Stefan Kristjanson
EVP and Global Chief Information Officer, Philip Armstrong
EVP and Chief Risk Officer, Graham R. Bird
EVP and Chief Human Resources Office, Grace M. Palombo
EVP and Chief Actuary, Dervla M. Tomlin
Chairman, R. Jeffrey Orr
Auditors: Deloitte LLP

LOCATIONS

HQ: Great-West Life Assurance Co
100 Osborne Street North, Winnipeg, Manitoba R3C 1V3
Phone: 204 946-1190   **Fax:** 204 946-4139
Web: www.greatwestlife.com

COMPETITORS

AGF Management	Mackenzie Financial
Aviva	Manulife Financial
CPP Investment Board	RBC Insurance
Desjardins Financial Security	Sun Life
	Western Financial
ING	Group

HISTORICAL FINANCIALS

Company Type: Public

Income Statement   FYE: December 31

	ASSETS ($ mil.)	NET INCOME ($ mil.)	INCOME AS % OF ASSETS	EMPLOYEES
12/15	229,554	1,943	0.8%	0
12/14	249,304	2,246	0.9%	0
12/13	250,015	2,110	0.8%	0
12/12	202,090	1,754	0.9%	0
12/11	185,218	1,910	1.0%	0
Annual Growth	5.5%	0.4%	—	—

2015 Year-End Financials

Return on assets: 0.8%	Dividends
Return on equity: 13.2%	Yield: —
Long-term debt ($ mil.): —	Payout: —
No. of shares (mil.): 2	Market value ($ mil.): —
Sales ($ mil): 15,196	

Great-West Lifeco Inc

Great-West writes policies for the Great White North and beyond. Holding company Great-West Lifeco majority-owned by Power Financial is one of Canada's largest insurance organizations but its reach extends to the US and to Europe. Through subsidiaries (including Great-West Life Assurance in Canada and Great-West Life & Annuity in the US) the company offers a range of individual and group life and health insurance retirement savings and investment products reinsurance and services to financial institutions. Great-West Life Assurance's two major subsidiaries Canada Life and London Life Insurance provide individual insurance and wealth-management products in Canada Germany Ireland and the UK.
Operations
In the US Great-West Life & Annuity (GWL&A) provides retirement savings plans to employers. Great-West Lifeco's companies also provide reinsurance to niche markets in the US and Europe. Great-West Lifeco has more than $705 billion in assets under administration.
The company divides its business geographically: it offers financial services and asset management in the US its largest market individual and group insurance and wealth management services in Canada and insurance and annuities along with reinsurance in Europe. Its US asset management line of business brings in the largest part of revenue at 40%.
Financial Performance
A decline in European results balanced with increases in Canada and the US sales to result in flat revenue for 2012. Net income dropped due to higher commissions and general expenses.
Strategy
Going forward Great-West Lifeco intends to keep expanding geographically and across product lines. It believes multiple brands and distribution channels positions it well for growth. It continues to seek unique opportunities to support larger and more complex accounts especially in its wealth management business which is developing retirement income products as that segment of the population grows.
Mergers and Acquisitions
In 2013 Great-West Lifeco acquired Irish Life Group Limited for some euro 1.3 billion ($1.75 million) from the Irish government. The purchase gave Great-West a leading position in life insurance pension and investment management markets in Ireland. Following the transaction Great-West Lifeco moved its existing Irish subsidiary Canada Life (Ireland) into the Irish Life division.
Irish Life bought Irish health insurer Aviva Health and acquired the 49% of GloHealth it didn't already own in 2016. The unit will combine Aviva Health and GloHealth to create Irish Life Health; the moves provide the group with entry into that nation's health insurance market.

EXECUTIVES

President and CEO U.S., Robert L. Reynolds, age 64
EVP General Counsel and Compliance, Andrew D. Brands
President and CEO, Paul A. Mahon
EVP and CFO, Garry MacNicholas
President and COO Canada, J. Dave Johnston
EVP and Chief Investment Officer, S. Mark Corbett
EVP and Chief Human Resources Officer, Grace Palombo
President and COO Canada, Dave Johnston
Auditors: Deloitte LLP

LOCATIONS

HQ: Great-West Lifeco Inc
100 Osborne Street North, Winnipeg, Manitoba R3C 1V3
Phone: 204 946-1190   **Fax:** 204 946-4139
Web: www.greatwestlifeco.com

2012 Sales

	$ mil.	% of total
US		
Asset management	23	40
Financial services	6	10
Canada		
Wealth management	9	16
Group insurance	7	12
Individual insurance	3	7
Europe		
Insurance & annuities	5	8
Reinsurance	4	7
Total	**59**	**100**

PRODUCTS/OPERATIONS

Selected Subsidiaries & Affiliates

The Great-West Life Assurance Company
   Canada Life Financial Corporation
   The Canada Life Assurance Company
   Canada Life Capital Corporation Inc.
   The Canada Life Group (U.K.) Limited
   Canada Life International Re Limited
   Canada Life Irish Holding Company Limited
   Crown Life Insurance Company
   Laketon Investment Management Ltd.
   London Insurance Group
   London Life Insurance Company
   London Reinsurance Group Inc.
GWL&A Financial Inc. (US)
   Great-West Life & Annuity Insurance Company
   Advised Assets Group LLC
   FASCore LLC

COMPETITORS

AXA Financial
CIBC
Industrial Alliance Insurance and Financial Servic
John Hancock Financial Services
Liberty Mutual
Manulife Financial
Nationwide Financial
Prudential
RBC Financial Group
RBC Insurance
Sun Life

HISTORICAL FINANCIALS

Company Type: Public

Income Statement   FYE: December 31

	ASSETS ($ mil.)	NET INCOME ($ mil.)	INCOME AS % OF ASSETS	EMPLOYEES
12/15	287,948	2,079	0.7%	0
12/14	308,036	2,303	0.7%	0
12/13	306,494	2,264	0.7%	20,970
12/12	255,102	1,940	0.8%	17,870
12/11	234,062	2,076	0.9%	17,350
Annual Growth	5.3%	0.0%	—	—

2015 Year-End Financials

Return on assets: 0.7%	Dividends
Return on equity: 13.8%	Yield: 0.0%
Long-term debt ($ mil.): —	Payout: 47.1%
No. of shares (mil.): 993	Market value ($ mil.): 24,734
Sales ($ mil): 24,350	

STOCK PRICE ($) FY Close	P/E High/Low		PER SHARE ($) Earnings	Dividends	Book Value
12/15	24.90	10 8	1.99	0.94	16.27
12/14	29.02	11 10	2.20	1.06	16.68
12/13	30.70	13 10	2.16	1.16	16.60
12/12	24.42	13 11	1.91	1.24	15.95
12/11	20.04	13 9	2.07	1.21	14.32
Annual Growth	5.6%	— —	(0.9%)	(6.1%)	3.3%

Gree Electric Appliances Inc Of Zhuhai

Gree Electric Appliances finds it agreeable to keep things cool. The world's #1 maker of household air conditioners manufactures and distributes about a dozen different types of air conditioners — from small window units to large commercial systems. Gree Electric Appliances has manufacturing facilities in China Brazil and Pakistan capable of producing 10 million air conditioning units per year. The firm has been expanding its manufacturing facilities for several years and continues to explore new areas. Its appliances are sold in more than 180 countries. Company president Mingszhu Dong regularly makes Fortune magazine's list of the 50 most powerful women in business. Gree Group owns Gree Electric Appliances.

Geographic Reach
The company has about 10 production bases around the world seven in China (Zhuhai Chongqing Hefei Zhengzhou Wuhan Shijiazhuang and Wuhu) as well as in Brazil and Pakistan. Operations Gree Electric Appliances is an international air conditioning enterprise with integrated R&D manufacturing marketing and service. It has three brands —GREE TOSOT and KINGHOME — with a wide product range which includes residential air conditioners central air conditioners air source water heaters smart phones home appliances refrigerators etc. Sales and Marketing The company uses e-commerce to sell its products.

Financial Performance In fiscal 2015 Gree Electric Appliances' net sales decreased by RMB 40 billion due to lower sales from household appliance manufacturing. Sale of air conditioners saw a decrease of about RMB 35 billion. Net income dropped by RMB 1.6 billion due to decreased sales and lower income from investments. In fiscal 2015 net cash provided by the operating activities increased by 31% due to a change in refund of tax and levies. Strategy Gree Electric Appliances' is focused on increasing its investment in R&D sustaining innovation in products and improving product quality and competitiveness.

Mergers and Acquisitions
In 2016 Gree Electric Appliances suspended its planned acquisition of electric vehicle maker Zhuhai Yinlong New Energy Co. Zhuhai Yinlong's shareholders declined to sell the company. The acquisition would have established Gree Electric's entry into the electric vehicle market.

EXECUTIVES
President, Mingzhu Dong

LOCATIONS
HQ: Gree Electric Appliances Inc Of Zhuhai
Jinji West Road, Qianshan, Zhuhai, Guangdong Province 519070
Phone: (86) 756 8669232　　**Fax:** (86) 756 8622581
Web: www.gree.com.cn

2015 Sales
	% of total
Domestic	85
Overseas	15
Total	**100**

PRODUCTS/OPERATIONS

2015 Sales
	% of total
Household appliance manufacturing	90
Other businesses	10
Total	**100**

2015 Sales
	% of total
Air conditioners	85
Home appliances	2
Others	3
Other businesses	10
Total	**100**

COMPETITORS
Electrolux	Haier Group
Electrolux Home Appliances China	Samsung Group
GuangDong Midea	Whirlpool

HISTORICAL FINANCIALS
Company Type: Public

Income Statement
FYE: December 31

	REVENUE ($ mil.)	NET INCOME ($ mil.)	NET PROFIT MARGIN	EMPLOYEES
12/15	15,484	1,929	12.5%	0
12/14	22,558	2,280	10.1%	0
12/13	19,829	1,795	9.1%	72,150
12/12	16,058	1,183	7.4%	80,189
12/11	13,268	832	6.3%	72,671
Annual Growth	3.9%	23.4%	—	—

2015 Year-End Financials
Debt ratio: 0.8%
Return on equity: 27.3%
Cash ($ mil.): 13,676
Current ratio: 1.07
Long-term debt ($ mil.): —
No. of shares (mil.): —
Dividends
　Yield: —
　Payout: —
Market value ($ mil.): —

Groupama S.A. (France)

The feeling is definitely mutual. Groupama the second-largest mutual insurer in the world provides life health and property/casualty policies to some 13 million members in Europe and Asia. It specializes in agricultural coverage offering farmers' insurance as well as complementary packages. It utilizes a network of some 7700 sales representatives in France as well as multi-lane agents and brokers. The group operates under such names as Groupama Gan and Amaguiz (internet sales). Groupama is also engaged in financial services such as banking.

Geographic Reach

Groupama's largest market is France where it earns some 80% of its revenue.

The group is also active in other European markets (Bulgaria Greece Hungary Italy Portugal Romania and Slovakia) Tunisia Turkey and in Asia (China Hong Kong Vietnam).

Strategy
In 2016 Groupama introduced its new Prairies product which provides farmers with protection against weather risks.

EXECUTIVES
CFO, Christian Collin, age 63
Managing Director Insurance France, Thierry Martel, age 51
Managing Director IT Systems Logistics Management and Purchasing, Francis Thomine, age 54
Director Groupama National Federation, Maurice Faure, age 61
General Secretary Strategy and Human Resources, Philippe Carraud, age 62
Auditors: PricewaterhouseCoopers Audit

LOCATIONS
HQ: Groupama S.A. (France)
8-10, rue d' Astorg, Paris, Cedex 08 75383
Phone: (33) 1 44 56 77 77
Web: www.groupama.com

COMPETITORS
Allianz	Aspen Insurance
Allianz France	Atrium Underwriters
April Group	RSA Insurance

HISTORICAL FINANCIALS
Company Type: Public

Income Statement
FYE: December 31

	ASSETS ($ mil.)	NET INCOME ($ mil.)	INCOME AS % OF ASSETS	EMPLOYEES
12/15	108,207	144	0.1%	15,402
12/14	120,063	18	0.0%	15,675
12/13	125,829	185	0.1%	16,009
12/12	115,917	(819)	—	17,142
12/11	115,619	(2,343)	—	0
Annual Growth	(1.6%)	—	—	—

2015 Year-End Financials
Return on assets: 0.1%
Return on equity: 2.7%
Long-term debt ($ mil.): —
No. of shares (mil.): 329
Sales ($ mil): 13,582
Dividends
　Yield: —
　Payout: —
Market value ($ mil.): —

Grupo Financiero Banorte S.A. BDE C V

EXECUTIVES
Director General, Alejandro Valenzuela
Auditors: Galaz, Yamazaki, Ruiz Urquiza, S.C. (member of Deloitte & Touche Tohmatsu)

LOCATIONS

HQ: Grupo Financiero Banorte S.A. BDE C V
  Av. Prolongacion Reforma 1230, 14 piso, Col. Cruz
  Manca Santa Fe, Delegacion Cuajimalpa, Mexico City
  05349
Phone: (52) 55 1103 4000
Web: www.banorte.com

HISTORICAL FINANCIALS
Company Type: Public

Income Statement
FYE: December 31

	ASSETS ($ mil.)	NET INCOME ($ mil.)	INCOME AS % OF ASSETS	EMPLOYEES
12/15	68,987	984	1.4%	27,594
12/14	74,703	1,036	1.4%	27,943
12/13	76,883	1,031	1.3%	27,549
12/12	70,538	837	1.2%	26,212
12/11	59,365	609	1.0%	24,027
Annual Growth	3.8%	12.7%		3.5%

2015 Year-End Financials
Return on assets: 1.4%
Return on equity: 13.2%
Long-term debt ($ mil.): —
No. of shares (mil.): —
Sales ($ mil): 6,332
Dividends
  Yield: 1.0%
  Payout: —
  Market value ($ mil.): —

	STOCK PRICE ($) FY Close	P/E High/Low	Earnings	Dividends	Book Value
12/15	27.34	— —	0.36	0.28	2.83
12/14	27.62	— —	0.37	0.28	3.02
12/13	35.04	— —	0.41	0.39	2.94
12/12	32.51	— —	0.36	0.18	2.71
12/11	15.17	— —	0.27	0.00	2.19
Annual Growth	15.9%	— —	7.0%	—	6.6%

Gunma Bank, Ltd. (The) (Japan)

Gunma Bank hopes that you have more than just a yen for its services. Through more than 140 branches The Gunma Bank provides banking services in the Gunma prefecture and surrounding areas of Japan through some 150 branches. The Gunma Bank also operates a subsidiary in Hong Kong and a branch in New York City. As the company's name might imply the Gunma prefecture (known for its industry and agriculture-based economy) accounts for more than 80% of deposits. Besides deposits Gunma Bank's services include loans to companies individuals and the government securities insurance and exchange. The Gunma Bank was founded in 1932.

EXECUTIVES

President, KAZUO SAITO
Executive Vice President, Tetsuo Igarashi
Chairman, Takuji Tsuchikane
Auditors: Ernst & Young ShinNihon LLC

LOCATIONS

HQ: Gunma Bank, Ltd. (The) (Japan)
  194 Motosoja-machi, Maebashi, Gunma 371-8611
Phone: (81) 27 252 1111
Web: www.gunmabank.co.jp

COMPETITORS

77 Bank	Ito-Yokado
Hachijuni Bank	Japan Post

HISTORICAL FINANCIALS
Company Type: Public

Income Statement
FYE: March 31

	ASSETS ($ mil.)	NET INCOME ($ mil.)	INCOME AS % OF ASSETS	EMPLOYEES
03/16	67,958	254	0.4%	4,671
03/15	62,935	215	0.3%	4,641
03/14	69,189	192	0.3%	3,405
03/13	72,746	218	0.3%	3,405
03/12	78,760	228	0.3%	3,399
Annual Growth	(3.6%)	2.8%		8.3%

2016 Year-End Financials
Return on assets: 0.3%
Return on equity: 5.5%
Long-term debt ($ mil.): —
No. of shares (mil.): 448
Sales ($ mil): 1,200
Dividends
  Yield: —
  Payout: —
  Market value ($ mil.): —

	STOCK PRICE ($) FY Close	P/E High/Low	Earnings	Dividends	Book Value
03/16	0.00	— —	0.57	0.00	9.97
Annual Growth	—	— —	—	—	—

Hachijuni Bank, Ltd. (Japan)

Auditors: Deloitte Touche Tohmatsu LLC

LOCATIONS

HQ: Hachijuni Bank, Ltd. (Japan)
  178-8 Aza Okada, Oaza Nakagosho, Nagano 380-8682
Phone: (81) 26 227 1182
Web: www.82bank.co.jp

HISTORICAL FINANCIALS
Company Type: Public

Income Statement
FYE: March 31

	ASSETS ($ mil.)	NET INCOME ($ mil.)	INCOME AS % OF ASSETS	EMPLOYEES
03/16	72,775	268	0.4%	5,482
03/15	66,797	226	0.3%	5,520
03/14	73,510	256	0.3%	3,713
03/13	77,105	235	0.3%	3,756
03/12	80,473	211	0.3%	3,800
Annual Growth	(2.5%)	6.1%		9.6%

2016 Year-End Financials
Return on assets: 0.3%
Return on equity: 4.5%
Long-term debt ($ mil.): —
No. of shares (mil.): 506
Sales ($ mil): 1,613
Dividends
  Yield: 0.0%
  Payout: 264.5%
  Market value ($ mil.): 21,823

	STOCK PRICE ($) FY Close	P/E High/Low	Earnings	Dividends	Book Value
03/16	43.07	2 1	0.53	1.41	11.63
03/15	69.05	1 1	0.45	0.91	11.01
03/14	57.89	— —	0.51	0.00	11.37
03/13	59.46	— —	0.46	0.00	11.83
03/12	58.85	— —	0.41	0.00	11.75
Annual Growth	(7.5%)	— —	6.5%	—	(0.3%)

Haci Omer Sabanci Holding AS

Haci Ömer Sabanci is one of Turkey's largest industrial and financial conglomerates with interests in the energy banking retail cement textile and other industries. Its primary holding is a stake in Turkish banking firm Akbank which provides commercial retail and private banking as well as investment and foreign trade services. Other holdings include stakes in domestic energy company Enerjisa and supermarket operator Carrefoursa a joint venture with Carrefour. Sabanci's portfolio spans some 20 countries in Europe Africa Asia and the Americas. It also has several partnerships with multinationals such as Bridgestoneand Philip Morris. The wealthy Sabanci family owns 60% of the company.

HISTORY

Haci Ömer Sabanci's eponymous empire traces back to the 1930s. Sabanci left his native village Akcakaya at the age of 14 to become a laborer in a cotton plantation in the Adana region of Turkey in 1921. By 1932 he had become a shareholder in a cotton ginning plant. During the next decade he grabbed stakes in two vegetable oil plants: Türk Nebati Yaglar Fabrikasi (1943) and Marsa (1946; renamed in 1993 as Marsa KJS a joint venture with Kraft).

Quickly broadening his portfolio Sabanci along with more than 80 citizens of Adana and surrounding regions became a founding shareholder in Akbank (named for Sabanci's native village) in 1948. He further diversified with investments in Bossa a flour and cotton ginning mill in 1951. Sabanci's second financial holding the Aksigorta insurance business was formed in 1960 as a subsidiary of Akbank.

By the time Sabanci died in 1966 Akbank had opened its 100th branch office. Sabanci's five sons took the helm of their father's companies and moved the group's headquarters to the more cosmopolitan Istanbul in 1974 in accordance with Sabanci's growing stance as a global entity. Domestic operations continued to grow however; fabric producer Yünsa was founded in 1973 and the Çimsa unit began producing cement two years later.

The 1980s marked the Haci Ömer Sabanci group's emergence as a multinational and the beginnings of its signature business style: growth through partnerships with major players. In 1985 Akbank joined with Banque Nationale de Paris (now BNP Paribas) to create BNP-Ak Bank; leading German bank Dresdner joined the companies three years later to form BNP-Ak-Dresdner Bank. A joint venture with DuPont in 1987 created nylon yarn producer Dusa. The following year the company renamed its Lassa tire manufacturing concern Brisa after sealing a deal with Bridgestone of Japan. By the end of the decade the Sabanci family were billionaires.

The group continued developing powerful partnerships in the next decade. Two joint ventures with Philip Morris (1991 and 1994) involved Haci Ömer Sabanci in the manufacturing marketing and selling of the maker's cigarettes in Turkey. A trinational deal in 1997 with US conglomerate Koch Industries and Mexican billionaire Isaac Saba's Imasab created Sakosa a polyester tire cord and industrial yarn manufacturer. Another joint venture with DuPont in 1999 (DuPontsa BV) linked the companies' operations to create Europe's largest polyester producer.

An attempt to break into telecommunications stalled that year when the almost $3 billion price tag in Turkey's mobile phone license auction proved too steep for the Sabanci group. However the company was able to purchase Turk. Net Turkey's largest ISP for $25 million. By 2000 Haci Ömer Sabanci had ceased seeking out partnerships and ventures in disparate sectors planning instead to narrow its focus to select industries including energy the Internet and telecommunications.

In 2001 the company teamed up with DuPont to form global nylon industrial yarn and tire cord joint venture DUSA International. It also sold its stake in automotive joint venture Toyotasa to partner Toyota.

Chairman Sakip Sabanci's lifelong dream of creating a world-class museum in Turkey was realized in 2002 with the opening of the Sakip Sabanci Museum. Sabanci died two years later.

Also in 2004 Sabanci bought BNP Paribas and Dresdner Bank out of their BNP-Ak-Dresdner Bank venture.

Belgian partner Bekaert bought out Sabanci's share of their Beksa steel cord and metal fiber joint venture in 2008. Sabanci sold stakes in other holdings including its edible oils operations financial services companies and another joint venture with Toyota.

The group teamed up with Austria-based Verbund to own and operate a regional electricity distributor in Turkey in 2008. The landmark $1 billion deal was part of the Turkish government's plan to privatize and transform the country's power industry.

EXECUTIVES

CFO, Faruk Bilen, age 47
CEO; Board Member, Zafer Kurtul
President Energy, Selahattin Hakman, age 64
President Industry SBU, Mehmet N. Pekarun
President Cement, Mehmet Gocmen, age 59
President of Retailing and Insurance Unit, Haluk Dincer, age 54
Chief Information Officer, Gungor Kaymak
Vice Chairman, Erol Sabanci, age 78
Chairman and Managing Director, Guler Sabanci
Auditors: DRT BAGIMSIZ DENETIM VE SERBEST MUHASEBECI MALI M$AVIRLIK A.S.

LOCATIONS

HQ: Haci Omer Sabanci Holding AS
Sabanci Center 4, Levent, Istanbul 34330
Phone: (90) 212 385 80 80   **Fax:** (90) 212 385 88 88
Web: www.sabanci.com

PRODUCTS/OPERATIONS

Selected Investments
Cement
  Akçansa
  Çimsa

Energy
  Enerjisa
Financial services
  Akbank
  Aksigorta
Retail
  Carrefoursa
  Teknosa
Industrial
  Brisa
  Kordsa Global
  Temsa
  Sasa
  Yunsa
Other
  Bimsa
  Philip Morrissa
  Philsa
  Tursa

COMPETITORS

Alarko	Global Yatirim
Alfa Group	Ko§
Berkshire Hathaway	Yazicilar
Dogan Holding	

HISTORICAL FINANCIALS
Company Type: Public

Income Statement
FYE: December 31

	ASSETS ($ mil.)	NET INCOME ($ mil.)	INCOME AS % OF ASSETS	EMPLOYEES
12/15	90,896	765	0.8%	63,281
12/14	99,034	893	0.9%	60,170
12/13	96,571	809	0.8%	58,907
12/12	97,929	1,036	1.1%	57,556
12/11	80,059	994	1.2%	57,374
Annual Growth	3.2%	(6.3%)	—	2.5%

2015 Year-End Financials
Return on assets: 0.9%
Return on equity: 11.1%
Long-term debt ($ mil.): —
No. of shares (mil.): —
Sales ($ mil): 10,788
Dividends
Yield: 0.0%
Payout: 0.1%
Market value ($ mil.): —

	STOCK PRICE ($) FY Close	P/E High/Low		Earnings	PER SHARE ($) Dividends	Book Value
12/15	0.73	0	0	3.75	0.01	0.04
12/14	0.75	0	0	4.38	0.01	0.04
12/13	4.00	—	—	3.97	0.01	0.04
12/12	4.00	0	0	5.08	0.01	0.04
12/11	1.50	—	—	4.87	0.01	0.04
Annual Growth	(16.6%)	—	—	(6.3%)	(18.6%)	(0.7%)

Hang Seng Bank Ltd.

Auditors: PricewaterhouseCoopers

LOCATIONS

HQ: Hang Seng Bank Ltd.
83 Des Voeux Road Central,
Phone: (852) 2198 1111   **Fax:** (852) 2868 4047
Web: www.hangseng.com

HISTORICAL FINANCIALS
Company Type: Public

Income Statement
FYE: December 31

	ASSETS ($ mil.)	NET INCOME ($ mil.)	INCOME AS % OF ASSETS	EMPLOYEES
12/15	172,163	3,547	2.1%	10,141
12/14	162,986	1,951	1.2%	10,192
12/13	147,504	3,440	2.3%	9,856
12/12	138,949	2,506	1.8%	9,680
12/11	125,572	2,147	1.7%	9,834
Annual Growth	8.2%	13.4%	—	0.8%

2015 Year-End Financials
Return on assets: 2.1%
Return on equity: 19.5%
Long-term debt ($ mil.): —
No. of shares (mil.): 1,911
Sales ($ mil): 8,070
Dividends
Yield: 3.4%
Payout: —
Market value ($ mil.): 36,535

	STOCK PRICE ($) FY Close	P/E High/Low		Earnings	PER SHARE ($) Dividends	Book Value
12/15	19.11	145	114	0.02	0.65	9.58
12/14	16.56	2	2	1.02	0.64	9.39
12/13	16.28	1	1	1.80	0.61	7.27
12/12	15.49	2	1	1.31	0.72	6.23
12/11	11.80	2	1	1.12	0.60	5.30
Annual Growth	12.8%	—	—	(64.2%)	2.2%	15.9%

Hannover Rueckversicherung SE

Who insures insurance companies over and over? Hannover! Hannover Rück (Hannover Re) is the second-largest German reinsurance company (Munich Re is #1) and the fourth-largest such company in the world. Through more than 100 subsidiaries the company provides property and casualty (Hannover Re's largest segment) financial life and health reinsurance products in about 150 countries worldwide. Financial reinsurance is provided through Hannover Re Advanced Solutions a Dublin-based consortium managed jointly with HDI Reinsurance (Ireland); both Hannover Re and HDI Reinsurance (Ireland) are subsidiaries of HDI Haftpflichtverband der Deutschen Industrie.

Hannover Re is 50%-owned by German mutual insurance group Talanx AG part of HDI Haftpflichtverband der Deutschen Industrie.

Like nearly all other insurers Hannover Re saw its investment income for 2008 shrink significantly. But an uptick in demand for reinsurance in 2009 along with a decrease in catastrophe losses and a more than 300% increase in investment returns put group results back in line with pre-financial crisis levels. In the second quarter of 2010 however the company experienced higher-than-expected major losses with the sinking of the Deepwater Horizon oil rig operated by BP.

The property/casualty unit of the ever-diversifying Hannover Re accounts for more than 55% of all premiums and is geared toward markets in the US Germany and Japan. Its life/health business is marketed through subsidiary Hannover Life Re and focuses on treaty (groups of risks) rather than facultative (individual risk) policies.

To boost its presence in the US the company purchased a portfolio of life reinsurance from Scottish Re in 2009. The deal gave Hannover a business it attempted to buy from ING Groep in 2004 but lost out to Scottish Re. In 2011 Scottish Re offloaded another chunk of life reinsurance which Hannover Re readily purchased.

While Hannover Re's traditional brot und butter has been property and casualty reinsurance the firm has expanded its life and health lines which are contributing closer and closer to half of all premiums. Hannover Re has also adopted American accounting practices and become more transparent in order to remain a compelling stock in investors' eyes.

HISTORY

Hannover Re was founded in 1966 as the Aktiengesellschaft für Transport und Rückversicherung (ATR) by the Feuerschadenverband Rheinisch-Westfaelischer Zechen (FSV) a mutual insurer specializing in fire damage in the town of Bochum. Within five years ATR had expanded into international reinsurance markets. In 1970 FSV merged with another mutual HDI Haftpflichtverband der Deutschen Industrie which owned reinsurer Eisen und Stahl Rückversicherungs-AG. ATR's headquarters relocated to Hannover and six years later it was renamed Hannover Rückversicherungs-Gesellschaft.

Jointly managed by HDI Hannover Re and Eisen und Stahl operated separately until 1996: Hannover Re targeted international markets while Eisen und Stahl operated mostly within Germany.

Hannover Re maintained its foreign focus throughout the 1970s and 80s expanding in Europe and South Africa and making its first forays into the US. In 1990 the firm acquired US life insurer Reassurance Company of Hannover.

Hannover Re went public in 1994 selling 25% of its stock. Also that year the firm formed an Australian subsidiary. The next year Hannover Re acquired Eisen und Stahl (renamed E+S Ruck 1996) which then assumed total control of the company's domestic business.

In 1998 Hannover Re became the first reinsurer to securitize life insurance business (reinsurers often securitize non-life policies to protect against natural catastrophe risks) through an agreement with Interpolis an Irish reinsurance subsidiary of the Netherlands' Rabobank. Also that year the firm expanded its financial reinsurance business reorganizing the Irish consortium it formed with another subsidiary of HDI into Hannover Re Advanced Solutions.

As various natural disasters offset earnings in Hannover Re's property & casualty division in 1998 and 1999 its life and health segment boomed. To facilitate further growth the firm restructured these operations into a new subsidiary Hannover Life Re. Also in 1999 the firm acquired the Clarendon Insurance Group of New York. In 2001 Hannover Re joined Inreon an online reinsurance trading exchange set up by rivals Munich Re and Swiss Re. Also in 2001 the company established a Bermuda-based subsidiary focused on catastrophe business. The following year Hannover Re split its stock in order to stimulate demand and become a more widely held company.

Like many other insurers the company was hit hard by the attacks of September 11 2001 falling stock markets and in 2005 damages in the Gulf of Mexico caused by hurricanes Katrina and Rita.

Late in 2006 China loosened its regulation of a number of industries and insurance was one of them —Hannover Re was one of the first to gain permission to enter the Chinese market for life and health reinsurance.

At about the same time the company announced plans to cut down on its noncore business operations. The first move in this direction was the sale of its US-based Praetorian Group subsidiary to QBE's US-based subsidiary for a sum in excess of $800 million. Hannover Re used the proceeds to shore up its property/casualty and life/health reinsurance businesses.

EXECUTIVES

Executive Board Member Property and Casualty Treaty Reinsurance Germany Austria Switzerland and Italy; Credit Surety & Political Risk worldwide; Group Legal Services; Run Off Solutions, Michael Pickel, age 56
CFO, Roland Vogel
Executive Board Member Life and Health, Klaus Miller, age 56
Executive Board Member Property and Casualty Specialty Lines Worldwide, Sven Althoff
Executive Board Member Life and Health, Claude Chèvre
Executive Board Member Property and Casualty Coordination and Global Reinsurance, Jürgen Gräber
Deputy Chairman, Klaus Sturany, age 70
Chairman, Ulrich Wallin, age 55
Chairman, Herbert K. Haas
Auditors: KPMG AG Wirtschaftsprufungsgesellschaft

LOCATIONS

HQ: Hannover Rueckversicherung SE
Karl-Wiechert-Allee 50, Hannover D-30625
Phone: (49) 511 5604 0   **Fax:** (49) 511 5604 1188
Web: www.hannover-re.com

2013 Premiums Written

	% of total
Europe	
Germany	9
UK	19
France	4
Other countries	12
North America	
US	24
Other countries	5
Asia	12
Australia	6
Africa	3
Other regions	6
Total	**100**

COMPETITORS

Everest Re	Reinsurance Group of
General Re	America
Lloyd's	SCOR
Munich Re Group	Swiss Re
PartnerRe	XL Group plc

HISTORICAL FINANCIALS

Company Type: Public

Income Statement

FYE: December 31

	ASSETS ($ mil.)	NET INCOME ($ mil.)	INCOME AS % OF ASSETS	EMPLOYEES
12/15	68,854	1,253	1.8%	2,568
12/14	73,486	1,198	1.6%	2,534
12/13	74,227	1,232	1.7%	2,376
12/12	72,244	1,131	1.6%	2,263
12/11	64,500	783	1.2%	2,210
Annual Growth	**1.6%**	**12.5%**	**—**	**3.8%**

2015 Year-End Financials

Return on assets: 1.8%	Dividends
Return on equity: 14.7%	Yield: 3.0%
Long-term debt ($ mil.): —	Payout: 16.4%
No. of shares (mil.): 120	Market value ($ mil.): 6,916
Sales ($ mil) 17,709	

	STOCK PRICE ($) FY Close	P/E High/Low		PER SHARE ($) Earnings	Dividends	Book Value
12/15	57.35	6	4	10.39	1.75	72.87
12/14	45.55	6	4	9.93	1.32	76.10
12/13	43.22	6	5	10.23	1.43	67.22
12/12	38.93	6	3	9.38	0.98	66.19
12/11	24.82	6	4	6.49	1.06	53.31
Annual Growth	**23.3%**	**—**	**—**	**12.5%**	**13.4%**	**8.1%**

Hanwha Corp

LOCATIONS

HQ: Hanwha Corp
86 Cheonggyecheon-ro Jung-gu, Seoul 100-220
Phone: (82) 2 729 1881   **Fax:** (82) 2 729 1762
Web: www.hanwhacorp.co.kr

HISTORICAL FINANCIALS

Company Type: Public

Income Statement

FYE: December 31

	REVENUE ($ mil.)	NET INCOME ($ mil.)	NET PROFIT MARGIN	EMPLOYEES
12/15	35,167	(242)	—	5,387
12/14	34,235	(333)	—	5,202
12/13	36,823	123	0.3%	3,898
12/12	10,773	290	2.7%	3,840
12/11	10,516	116	1.1%	3,642
Annual Growth	**35.2%**	**—**		**10.3%**

2015 Year-End Financials

Debt ratio: 0.0%	No. of shares (mil.): 69
Return on equity: (-6.7%)	Dividends
Cash ($ mil.): 1,005	Yield: —
Current ratio: 0.88	Payout: —
Long-term debt ($ mil.): 4,724	Market value ($ mil.): —

Heineken Holding NV (Netherlands)

Auditors: Deloitte Accountants B.V.

LOCATIONS

HQ: Heineken Holding NV (Netherlands)
Tweede Weteringplantsoen 5, Amsterdam 1017 ZD
Phone: (31) 20 622 11 52   **Fax:** (31) 20 625 22 13
Web: www.heinekenholding.com

HISTORICAL FINANCIALS

Company Type: Public

Income Statement

FYE: December 31

	REVENUE ($ mil.)	NET INCOME ($ mil.)	NET PROFIT MARGIN	EMPLOYEES
12/15	22,340	1,042	4.7%	73,767
12/14	23,406	923	3.9%	76,136
12/13	26,437	940	3.6%	80,933
12/12	24,229	1,946	8.0%	76,191
12/11	22,147	927	4.2%	64,252
Annual Growth	**0.2%**	**3.0%**	**—**	**3.5%**

2015 Year-End Financials

Debt ratio: 36.3%
Return on equity: 14.8%
Cash ($ mil.): 897
Current ratio: 0.69
Long-term debt ($ mil.): 11,608

No. of shares (mil.): 288
Dividends
  Yield: 0.0%
  Payout: 14.4%
Market value ($ mil.): 11,351

	STOCK PRICE ($) FY Close	P/E High/Low		PER SHARE ($) Earnings	Dividends	Book Value
12/15	39.41	12	8	3.62	0.52	25.53
12/14	31.36	13	10	3.21	1.21	25.85
12/13	31.04	15	12	3.26	1.21	26.86
Annual Growth	12.7%	—	—	2.6%	(18.9%)	(1.3%)

Heineken N.V. (Netherlands)

EXECUTIVES

Director, Marcus Goumans
Auditors: KPMG Accountants N.V.

LOCATIONS

HQ: Heineken N.V. (Netherlands)
Tweede Weteringplantsoen 21, Amsterdam 1017 ZD
Phone: (31) 20 5239 239   **Fax:** (31) 20 627 9684
Web: www.theheinekencompany.com

HISTORICAL FINANCIALS

Company Type: Public

Income Statement

FYE: December 31

	REVENUE ($ mil.)	NET INCOME ($ mil.)	NET PROFIT MARGIN	EMPLOYEES
12/15	22,340	2,060	9.2%	73,767
12/14	23,406	1,842	7.9%	76,136
12/13	26,437	1,877	7.1%	80,933
12/12	24,229	3,886	16.0%	76,191
12/11	22,147	927	4.2%	64,252
Annual Growth	0.2%	22.1%	—	3.5%

2015 Year-End Financials

Debt ratio: 36.3%
Return on equity: 14.5%
Cash ($ mil.): 897
Current ratio: 0.69
Long-term debt ($ mil.): 11,608

No. of shares (mil.): 569
Dividends
  Yield: 1.2%
  Payout: 14.5%
Market value ($ mil.): 24,354

	STOCK PRICE ($) FY Close	P/E High/Low		PER SHARE ($) Earnings	Dividends	Book Value
12/15	42.75	14	9	3.59	0.53	25.88
12/14	35.33	15	10	3.20	0.47	26.25
12/13	33.76	17	14	3.26	0.48	27.30
12/12	33.57	7	6	6.75	0.00	53.50
Annual Growth	8.4% (16.6%)	—	—	(14.6%)	—	

Henkel AG & Co KGAA

Home and hearth are at the heart of Henkel. The company makes branded products for laundry and homecare (Persil Purex Pril) cosmetics and toiletries (Schwarzkopf Dial Syoss) and many adhe-

sives (Loctite Ceresit UniBond). Henkel's business is centered in Europe with a growing presence in developing economies such as Asia Africa and the Middle East and Latin America. It owns The Dial Corporation anchoring its US market. Henkel owns subsidiaries in some 75 countries with offices located nearly everywhere. Started in 1876 the company is owned by descendants of the founding Henkel family. In 2016 the company bought laundry care company Sun Products in a deal worth $3.6 billion.

Operations

Henkel's business is divided among three units: laundry and homecare which generates nearly 30% of sales; beauty care approximately 20% of sales; and adhesive technologies 50% of sales which includes industrial adhesives as well as those for consumers craftsmen and building. Each unit claims a large share of their market through established brands. All told the company's top 10-brands account for about 60% of sales. In beauty care 90% of sales are driven by the business unit's top-10 brands; in laundry and homecare more than 80%; and in adhesive technologies about 55%.

Geographic Reach

Laundry and homecare and beauty care are primarily sold in Europe and North America and certain developing regions. The company's adhesive technologies have gained a worldwide presence. Emerging markets (Eastern Europe Africa/Middle East Latin America and Asia excluding Japan) generate more than 40% of Henkel's sales.

Henkel manufactures products at 170 facilities dotting about 55 countries. Its largest plant located in Düsseldorf Germany makes detergents and household cleaning products as well as adhesives. The company's cosmetics and toiletries are produced at eight plants with the largest located in Wassertrüdingen Germany.

Financial Performance

Revenue at Henkel has been growing steadily since 2010. In 2014 it increased about 3% due to slight increases in laundry and home care as well as beauty care. Adhesives were unchanged. The company cited global unrest particularly in developing markets along with a lack of growth in the eurozone. However strong cost controls allowed the company to deliver 2% profit growth.

Strategy

A key component of Henkel's strategy is to simplify its operations. To that end it has integrated its systems and applications software in Europe and Asia converted nearly 50000 employees to digital work environments and combined its sourcing and supply chain activities into a global supply chain unit.

The company also uses acquisitions in new and established markets as a key part of its growth strategy. It made five purchases in 2014 in Europe and the US. Three of them were US professional hair care product manufacturers making Henkel number three in the market.

Mergers and Acquisitions

In 2016 the company acquired laundry care company Sun Products from Vestar Capital Partners for some $3.6 billion. The acquisition which includes Sun Products' Snuggle all and Wisk detergents and other brands positions Henkel as second in the laundry care market in North America behind Procter & Gamble.

The previous year Henkel purchased Colgate-Palmolive's entire line of laundry care products in Australia and New Zealand making it one of the largest detergent makers in those two countries.

In 2014 it picked up three US-based professional hair care product companies - Sexy Hair Alterna and Kenra. It also purchased France's Spotless Group which makes laundry and household care products and leads the market in France Italy

Spain and the UK. Later in the year Henkel acquired The Bergquist Company a US-based supplier of thermal management products to complement the adhesives product group. Lastly it bought Novamelt a German hotmelt adhesive maker.

HISTORY

Company Background

In 1876 Fritz Henkel a chemical plant worker started Henkel & Cie in Aachen Germany to make a universal detergent. He moved the business to Düsseldorf in 1878 and launched Henkel's Bleaching Soda one of Germany's first brand-name products. In the 1880s the company began making water glass an ingredient of its detergent which differs from soap in the way it emulsifies dirt. Henkel debuted Persil a detergent that eliminated the need for rubbing or bleaching clothes in 1907. Persil became a leading detergent in Germany.

Henkel set up an Austrian subsidiary in 1913. In response to a postwar adhesives shortage the company started making glue for its own packaging and soon became Europe's leading glue maker. Henkel began making cleansers with newly developed phosphates in the late 1920s.

When Fritz died in 1930 Henkel stock was divided among his three children. In the 1930s the company sponsored a whaling fleet that provided fats for its products and by 1939 the firm had 16 plants in Europe.

During WWII Henkel lost most of its foreign plants and made unbranded soap in Germany. After the war the company retooled its plants branched out into personal care products and competed with Unilever Procter & Gamble and Colgate-Palmolive for control of the German detergent market. (By 1968 Henkel dominated with close to a 50% share.)

In 1960 Henkel bought its first US company Standard Chemicals (renamed Henkel Corp. in 1971). Konrad Henkel who took over in 1961 modernized the company's image by making changes in management structure and marketing techniques. Henkel patented a substitute for environmentally harmful phosphates acquired 15% of Clorox in 1974 and bought General Mills' chemical business in 1977.

Henkel owned at the time by 66 family members went public with nonvoting shares in 1985. It bought US companies Nopco (specialty chemicals) and Parker Chemical (metal surface pretreatment) in 1987 and Emery the #1 US oleochemicals maker in 1989.

Henkel reorganized its product lines in 1991 by selling several noncore businesses. That year Henkel formed a partnership with Ecolab (of which it owned 24% –later expanded to 50%); acquired interests in Hungary Poland Russia and Slovenia; and introduced Persil in Spain and Portugal. In 1994 Henkel expanded into China and bought 25% of a Brazilian detergent maker.

The company's 1995 acquisition of Hans Schwarzkopf GmbH made Henkel the #1 hair-coloring manufacturer in Germany. The company bought Novamax Technologies a US-based maker of metal-surface treatments in 1996. The next year Henkel paid $1.3 billion for US adhesive giant Loctite its biggest purchase to date. In 1998 it bought Ohio-based adhesive maker Manco to combine its US and Canadian consumer adhesive businesses (parts of Loctite and LePage respectively) under Manco. Henkel pushed into the US toiletries market in 1998 by paying $93 million for DEP and creating a new subsidiary Schwarzkopf & DEP Inc.

In 1999 Henkel created chemicals unit Cognis to focus primarily on palm kernel- and coconut oil-based products. To strengthen Cognis Henkel bought Laboratoires Serobiologiques a French producer of ingredients for the cosmetic and food industries and divested specialty-paper chemicals operations. Henkel also formed a joint venture with soap maker Dial (Dial/Henkel LLC); the joint venture later bought the Custom Cleaner home dry cleaning business from Creative Products Resource.

Henkel picked up Yamahatsu Sangyo a Japanese maker of hair colorants in 2000. The company sold its Substral unit (fertilizer and plant care) to Scotts Company (now Scotts Miracle-Gro). In 2001 Henkel bought TOTAL's metal-treatment chemicals business. In addition the company sold its Cognis specialty chemicals unit to private equity funds Schroeder Ventures and Goldman Sachs Capital Partners for about $2.2 billion. Also in 2001 Henkel said it would cut 2500-3000 jobs (about 5% of its workforce) over the next two years.

In 2003 Henkel purchased a majority stake in La Luz S.A. a Central American manufacturer and marketer of detergents and household cleaners. (Henkel entered the Latin American detergents market via Mexico in 2000.)

Henkel strengthened its adhesives business in Russia and North Central and Eastern Europe when it acquired Makroflex from YIT Construction Ltd. in July 2003. Makroflex located in Finland and Estonia developed and made old sealants and insulation materials for the construction industry.

In 2004 Henkel acquired Alberto-Culver's Indola European professional hair care business which had logged about $55 million in recent annual sales. That year Henkel and US bleach giant Clorox agreed to a deal (in the form of an asset swap) that dissolved Henkel's nearly 30% stake in Clorox. The $2.8 billion transaction involved Henkel's purchase of Clorox's 20% stake in Henkel Iberica a joint venture between the two in Portugal and Spain. Henkel also bought Clorox's stake in a pesticide company as part of the transaction and added Combat insecticides and Soft Scrub bathroom cleaner to its brand portfolio.

Henkel acquired Advanced Research Laboratories in 2004 and folded the company into its existing Schwarzkopf & Dep subsidiary based in California. The deal boosted the company's share of the US hairstyling market. Henkel bought US-based Dial Corporation (Dial soap Purex laundry products Renuzit air fresheners) in 2004 for $2.9 billion in cash.

Also in 2004 Henkel bought 70% of Coventry's Chemtek an independent firm that specializes in formulating and manufacturing liquid cleaners. The balance of the share is owned by Chartered-brands of Edinburgh.

To strengthen its foothold in the electronics market in China Henkel in late 2005 bought a majority stake in Huawei Electronics Co. Ltd. a maker of epoxy molding compounds for semiconductors.

EXECUTIVES

SVP Information Technology, Peter Wroblowski
CEO, Hans Van Bylen, age 55
SVP Adhesive Technologies; President Asia-Pacific, Jan-Dirk Auris, age 48
EVP Finance and Purchasing and Integrated Business Solutions, Carsten Knobel, age 48
EVP Laundry and Home Care, Bruno Piacenza, age 51
EVP Human Resources and Infrastructure Services, Kathrin Menges, age 52
EVP Beauty Care, Pascal Houdayer, age 47
Vice Chairman Supervisory Board, Winfried Zander, age 62
Chairman Supervisory Board, Simone Bagel-Trah, age 48
Auditors: KPMG AG

LOCATIONS

HQ: Henkel AG & Co KGAA
Henkelstrasse 67, Duesseldorf D-40191
Phone: (49) 211 797 0   **Fax:** (49) 211 798 4040
Web: www.henkel.com

2015 Sales

	% of total
Western Europe	34
North America	20
Asia Pacific	17
Eastern Europe	15
Africa/Middle East	7
Latin America	6
Corporate	1
Total	**100**

PRODUCTS/OPERATIONS

2015 Sales

	% of total
Adhesive Technologies	50
Laundry & Home Care	28
Beauty Care	21
Corporate	1
Total	**100**

Selected Brands

Adhesives technologies
 Ariasana
 Ceresit
 Elch
 Fster
 LePage
 Loctite
 Metylan
 Pattex
 Ponal
 Pritt
 Rubson
 Sellotape
 Sista
 Solvite
 Tangit
 Technomelt
 Teroson
 Thomsit
 UniBond
Cosmetics and toiletries
 Antica Erboristeria
 Aok
 Bac
 Barnängen
 Citre Shine
 Clynol viton
 Coast
 Denivit
 Dep
 Diadermine
 Dial
 Dry Idea
 Fa
 Indola Professional
 L.A. Looks
 La Toja
 Licor del Polo
 Mon Saint Michel
 Natural & Easy
 Neutromed
 Right Guard
 Schwarzkoph
 Seborin
 Smooth ' N Shine
 Soft & Dri
 Syoss
 Theramed
 Thicker Fuller Hair
 Tone
 Vademecum
 Zero Frizz
Laundry and homecare
 Bref
 Dixan
 Mir
 Persil
 Perwoll
 Pril
 Pur

Purex
Sil
Soft Scrub
Somat
Spee
Vernel

COMPETITORS

3M	Estee Lauder
Alticor	H.B. Fuller
Avon	Johnson & Johnson
BASF SE	Kimberly-Clark
Bayer AG	L' Oreal
Beiersdorf	Procter & Gamble
Church & Dwight	Reckitt Benckiser
Clorox	S.C. Johnson
Colgate-Palmolive	Shiseido
Dow Chemical	Unilever
DuPont	

HISTORICAL FINANCIALS

Company Type: Public

Income Statement

FYE: December 31

	REVENUE ($ mil.)	NET INCOME ($ mil.)	NET PROFIT MARGIN	EMPLOYEES
12/15	19,702	2,092	10.6%	49,450
12/14	19,968	1,978	9.9%	49,750
12/13	22,516	2,187	9.7%	46,850
12/12	21,761	1,990	9.1%	46,610
12/11	20,184	1,620	8.0%	47,753
Annual Growth	(0.6%)	6.6%		0.9%

2015 Year-End Financials

Debt ratio: 4.3%
Return on equity: 15.2%
Cash ($ mil.): 1,280
Current ratio: 1.09
Long-term debt ($ mil.): 4

No. of shares (mil.): 259
Dividends
 Yield: 0.9%
 Payout: —
Market value ($ mil.): 28,952

	STOCK PRICE ($) FY Close	P/E High/Low	PER SHARE ($) Earnings	Dividends	Book Value
12/15	111.44	28 22	4.81	1.00	57.27
12/14	106.78	29 24	4.55	1.21	53.84
12/13	116.68	32 23	5.03	0.89	53.23
12/12	82.38	25 17	4.57	0.75	47.57
12/11	57.91	23 17	3.71	0.00	43.02
Annual Growth	17.8%	— —	6.7%	—	7.4%

Hennes & Mauritz AB

Auditors: Ernst & Young AB

LOCATIONS

HQ: Hennes & Mauritz AB
Master Samuelsgatan 46A, Stockholm SE-106 38
Phone: (46) 8 796 55 00   **Fax:** (46) 8 796 55 44
Web: www.hm.com

HISTORICAL FINANCIALS

Company Type: Public

Income Statement

FYE: November 30

	REVENUE ($ mil.)	NET INCOME ($ mil.)	NET PROFIT MARGIN	EMPLOYEES
11/15	20,777	2,400	11.6%	104,634
11/14	20,419	2,693	13.2%	93,351
11/13	19,646	2,621	13.3%	81,099
11/12	18,170	2,537	14.0%	72,276
11/11	15,988	2,299	14.4%	64,874
Annual Growth	6.8%	1.1%	—	12.7%

2015 Year-End Financials

Debt ratio: —
Return on equity: 38.1%
Cash ($ mil.): 1,487
Current ratio: 1.99
Long-term debt ($ mil.): —

No. of shares (mil.): 1,655
Dividends
  Yield: 3.2%
  Payout: 15.5%
Market value ($ mil.): 12,181

	STOCK PRICE ($) FY Close	P/E High/Low		PER SHARE ($) Earnings	Dividends	Book Value
11/15	7.36	1	1	1.45	0.24	4.03
11/14	8.53	1	1	1.63	0.25	4.20
11/13	8.45	1	1	1.58	0.29	4.18
11/12	6.42	1	1	1.53	0.27	3.98
11/11	6.25	1	1	1.39	0.31	3.87
Annual Growth	**4.2%**	**—**	**—**	**1.1%**	**(6.2%)**	**1.0%**

Hindalco Industries Ltd.

LOCATIONS

HQ: Hindalco Industries Ltd.
Century Bhavan, 3rd Floor, Dr. Annie Besant Road,
Worli, Mumbai 400 030
Phone: (91) 22 6662 6666   **Fax:** (91) 22 2422 7586
Web: www.hindalco.com

HISTORICAL FINANCIALS

Company Type: Public

Income Statement

FYE: March 31

	REVENUE ($ mil.)	NET INCOME ($ mil.)	NET PROFIT MARGIN	EMPLOYEES
03/15	16,867	136	0.8%	0
03/14	14,882	362	2.4%	0
03/13	14,997	557	3.7%	0
03/12	16,178	667	4.1%	0
03/11	16,332	550	3.4%	19,341
Annual Growth	**0.8%**	**(29.4%)**		

2015 Year-End Financials

Debt ratio: 0.7%
Return on equity: 2.1%
Cash ($ mil.): 848
Current ratio: 1.27
Long-term debt ($ mil.): 8,855

No. of shares (mil.): —
Dividends
  Yield: 0.0%
  Payout: 23.9%
Market value ($ mil.): —

	STOCK PRICE ($) FY Close	P/E High/Low		PER SHARE ($) Earnings	Dividends	Book Value
03/15	0.00	1	0	0.07	0.02	(0.00)
03/14	1.81	3	0	0.18	0.02	(0.00)
03/13	1.71	0	0	0.29	0.03	(0.00)
03/12	2.60	0	0	0.35	0.02	(0.00)
Annual Growth	**—**	**—**	**—**	**(34.0%)**	**(10.7%)**	**—**

Hindustan Petroleum Corp., Ltd. (India)

Hindustan Petroleum is one of India's top oil refiners (along with Indian Oil and Bharat Petroleum) and accounts for 10% of the country's total refining requirements. The company has two major refineries —one in Mumbai the other in the southern Indian city of Vishakhapatnam —and produces lubricants aviation fuel liquefied petroleum gas and light diesel oil. Hindustan Petroleum also holds a 17% stake in a refinery at Mangalore. Other businesses include pipelines a lube refinery (with a 40% share of the lube oil market) and more than 13800 retail outlets nationwide. The Indian government owns 51% of the company.

Operations

Hindustan Petroleum has two business segments: Downstream (refining marketing and transportation of petroleum products) and Upstream (Oil and gas exploration and production).

The company has a refining capacity of more than 17 million metric tons per year. Its refineries produce a wide variety of petroleum fuels and specialty products. Its supply and distribution infrastructure includes terminals pipeline networks aviation service stations LPG bottling plants inland relay depots and retail outlets lube and LPG distributorships.

Hindustan Petroleum has 46 LPG bottling plants and seven lube blending plants.

The company has the second largest share of product pipelines in India with a pipeline network of more than 3015 km.

Geographic Reach

The company's marketing network consists of 13 zonal offices in major cities and 106 regional offices. It has a major refinery in Mumbai on India's west coast and in Vishakhapatnam on the east coast and 17% of Mangalore Refinery & Petrochemicals Limited in the south of India and a joint venture refinery in the Punjab in the north.

Sales and Marketing The company's marketing infrastructure includes a network 73 depots more than 13800 retail outlets 37 aviation service fueling stations 1640 SKO/LDO dealers and 4280 LPG distributors. Lubes business line caters to Lubricant and Greases requirement of industrial customers in power plants chemical units fertilizer companies railways state transport units army etc.

Financial Performance

Lower commodity prices helped to depress the company's revenues of $24.8 billion of fiscal 2015 (March year end) which declined by 11% over the previous year.

Net income grew by 32.7% in fiscal 2015 to $239 million due to lower net sales higher stock adjustment costs and higher other expenses.

Strategy

The company expects that demand for oil in India will rise to about 330 million tons by the year 2030 and 450 million tons by 2040 with about 260 million new passenger vehicles on the roads of India.

It is also projected that LPG increasingly will substitute kerosene and fuel wood as the cooking fuel in Indian households.

As a result of these trends Hindustan Petroleum plans increase its refining capacity and has planned significant investments over the next five years. Major projects planned include expansion of the Visakh and Mumbai refineries; expanding the existing Visakh-Vijayawada-Secunderabad and Mundra-Delhi pipelines with associated terminal facilities; and adding new POL Depots LPG Plants and Lube Blending plants.

Some major projects in progress in different parts of India are Visakh Refinery Modernization Project (VRMP); Rewari Kanpur Pipe Line (RKPL); Uran-Chakan/Shikrapur LPG Pipeline Project; Mangalore-Hassan-Mysore LPG Pipeline; Diesel Hydro Treating (DHT) at Mumbai & Visakhapatnam refineries and LPG bottling plant at Narsinngarh District Rajgarh (MP).

Strengthening its market position in north central and eastern India in fiscal 2016 the company opened the 443 km long Rewari- Kanpur pipeline commissioned a new terminal at Kanpur in Uttar Pradesh and a new depot at Bokaro in Jharkhand. Further consolidating its LPG infrastructure Hindustan Petroleum commissioned a new LPG Plant at Solapur in Maharashtra and an LPG mounded storage facility at MLIF Mangalore. New aviation service facilities were also initiated at Chandigarh and at Dharamshala in Himachal Pradesh.

EXECUTIVES

Director Finance, J. Ramaswamy
Director Refineries, B. K. Namdeo
Chairman and Managing Director, Mukesh K. Surana, age 54

LOCATIONS

HQ: Hindustan Petroleum Corp., Ltd. (India)
Petroleum House, 17, Jamshedji Tata Road, Mumbai 400020
Phone:
Web: www.hindustanpetroleum.com

COMPETITORS

Bharat Petroleum
Essar Group
Exxon Mobil
Indian Oil

HISTORICAL FINANCIALS

Company Type: Public

Income Statement

FYE: March 31

	REVENUE ($ mil.)	NET INCOME ($ mil.)	NET PROFIT MARGIN	EMPLOYEES
03/15	34,928	239	0.7%	0
03/14	39,248	179	0.5%	0
03/13	40,012	92	0.2%	11,027
03/12	36,620	34	0.1%	11,226
03/11	31,397	382	1.2%	11,248
Annual Growth	**2.7%**	**(11.0%)**	**—**	**—**

2015 Year-End Financials

Debt ratio: 0.6%
Return on equity: 10.7%
Cash ($ mil.): 357
Current ratio: 1.09
Long-term debt ($ mil.): 4,562

No. of shares (mil.): —
Dividends
  Yield: —
  Payout: —
Market value ($ mil.): —

Hino Motors, Ltd.

Hino Motors introduced Japan's first truck in 1918 long before Godzilla was throwing vehicles all over Tokyo. These days the company not only manufactures medium- and heavy-duty diesel trucks but it also makes buses special-purpose vehicles and industrial diesel engines. Hino Motors dominates Japan's domestic truck market beating out such competitors as Mitsubishi Motors and Isuzu Motors and manufactures 150000 Hino-brand trucks and buses each year. Toyota Motor owns more than 50% of the company.

Geographic Reach

In Japan Hino Motors produces vehicles engines and components at four plants. Its manufacturing operations in other nations include plants for producing trucks buses and components in Thailand Indonesia Vietnam China Pakistan Colombia and the US. It generates nearly 65% of its total sales from Japan and 27% from other countries in Asia.

Sales and Marketing

Manufacturing vehicles and service parts for Toyota Motor represents more than 26% of the company's salesFinancial PerformanceThe company's revenue increased by 17% in 2013 primarily due to additional sales derived from Japan Asia and as well from other countries. The demand in the truck (heavy light and medium-duty) and bus market in Japan was healthy due to reconstruction demand and an eco-car tax reduction/subsidy measure which increased the overall sales in Japan.As for overseas markets Hino Motors experienced favorable sales in the Asian countries of Indonesia and Thailand. The company was also aided by the 2012 launch of the small model Hino 300 Series which increased the sales volume of trucks and buses outside Japan in 2013.

Strategy

The company has a strong brand in Southeast Asia and it has strengthened its presence in the region by dividing the sales and production functions at its Thailand and Indonesian operations into separate companies. Meanwhile it has grown its presence in Africa which it expects will become an important Hino market along with Southeast Asia Oceania and Latin America.

HISTORY

Hino Motors was founded in 1910 as a unit of the Tokyo Gas Industry Company. It was established to build trucks for the emerging Japanese industrial economy. By 1918 the company was mass-producing the A-Type truck. The pace of industrialization increased in Japan in the early 1930s. To survive automotive companies had to maximize economies of scale. Finding safety in numbers many merged their operations.

In 1937 Tokyo Gas combined its auto unit with Automobile Industry Company and Kyodo Kokusan. The new enterprise was called Tokyo Automobile Industry Company.

Japan's occupation of China during the late 1930s had opened new markets but it also brought a trade embargo from the US in 1941. Japan did not back down however. Instead the Japanese government continued a program of military buildup that greatly benefited companies such as Tokyo Automobile. Later in 1941 the company changed its name to Diesel Motor Industry Company.

By 1942 Japan was at war with the US and Britain and Diesel Motor was split into two companies. The larger company retained the Diesel Motor name (eventually it became Isuzu Motors) and the smaller one became Hino Heavy Industry Company.

Most of Hino's Tokyo facilities escaped damage during the war until an American bomb hit a Hino factory in 1945. After the war the factory was converted into a barracks for occupying forces. A year after the end of the war Hino introduced a new truck the massive T10-20 that found immediate popularity. In 1947 the company launched a bus based on the T10-20 frame —the 96-passenger T11-B-25. Hino was listed on the Tokyo Stock Exchange in 1949.

Demand for trucks by United Nations forces during the Korean War prompted Hino to open an additional production line. Taking notice of Japan's demand for foreign passenger cars Hino began to look for a manufacturing partner and eventually decided on Renault. Hino began producing Renault 4CV cars in Japan in 1953.

Struck by the fact that much of Japan was being rebuilt with pricey foreign dump trucks Hino resolved to build a similar truck to compete with imports. Hino introduced the 13.5 ton ZG and it soon became Japan's leading dump truck. In 1959 the company changed its name to Hino Motors Ltd.

Hino introduced its own car the Contessa 900 in 1961. However the company was not yet ready

to ride solo. In 1966 Hino linked its carmaking operations with those of Toyota and began making Toyotas on a large scale.

By the mid-1970s Hino was ready to embark on an aggressive export campaign. It set up a sales network in Southeast Asia and opened parts depots in Latin America and Europe. Hino's products were a hit overseas and in 1980 the company opened a new factory to meet demand. During the 1980s Hino established offices in Pakistan and an assembly plant in Taiwan. Hino entered the US market in 1984 with the introduction of a cab-over engine (COE) medium duty truck.

With the US and Japanese economies in recession the early 1990s were tough for Hino although the company managed to continue to expand into new markets. It entered a joint venture to produce buses in China (1993) and teamed with the Vietnamese government to make trucks and buses in Vietnam (1996). Toyota turned its manufacturing of two-ton-sized trucks over to Hino and increased its stake in the company from 11% to 16% in 1997 and to 20% the next year.

In 1999 Hino made plans to combine its busmaking operations with those of Isuzu by 2002 in hopes of capturing 50% of the Japanese market (these plans were later postponed due to the worldwide drop in truck demand). Toyota increased its stake to 34% in 2000. Toyota Motor further increased its stake in Hino to more than 50% in 2001.

EXECUTIVES

President, Yasuhiko Ichihashi, age 64
EVP, Koichi Ojima
EVP, Hiroshi Kokaji
EVP, Kenji Suzuki
President Canada, Yumiko Kawamura
Chairman, Masakazu Ichikawa
Auditors: PricewaterhouseCoopers Aarata

LOCATIONS

HQ: Hino Motors, Ltd.
  3-1-1 Hinodai, Hino, Tokyo 191-8660
Phone: (81) 42 586 5111
Web: www.hino.co.jp

2016 Sales

	% of total
Japan	66
Asia	21
Other	13
Total	**100**

PRODUCTS/OPERATIONS

2016 Sales

	% of total
Trucks and buses	53
Total	**20**
Service parts	6
Other	21
Total	**100**

Selected Overseas Subsidiaries and Affiliates

Hino Motor Sales Australia Pty. Ltd.
Hino Motor Sales U.S.A. Inc.
Hino Motors (Malaysia) Sdn. Bhd.
Hino Motors Sales (Thailand) Ltd.
Hinopak Motors Ltd. (Pakistan)
Shenyang Shenfei Hino Automobile Manufacturing Co. Ltd. (China)

COMPETITORS

Ashok Leyland	Navistar International
China Yuchai	PACCAR
Cummins	Renault
Daimler	Scania
General Motors	UD Trucks

Isuzu
Mitsubishi Fuso Truck & Bus
Volvo

HISTORICAL FINANCIALS

Company Type: Public

Income Statement

FYE: March 31

	REVENUE ($ mil.)	NET INCOME ($ mil.)	NET PROFIT MARGIN	EMPLOYEES
03/16	15,543	579	3.7%	52,025
03/15	14,046	620	4.4%	29,864
03/14	16,465	863	5.2%	28,998
03/13	16,381	506	3.1%	27,705
03/12	16,025	198	1.2%	25,820
Annual Growth	**(0.8%)**	**30.7%**	**—**	**19.1%**

2016 Year-End Financials

Debt ratio: 0.1%
Return on equity: 15.3%
Cash ($ mil.): 308
Current ratio: 1.12
Long-term debt ($ mil.): 401

No. of shares (mil.): 573
Dividends
  Yield: 0.0%
  Payout: 363.5%
Market value ($ mil.): 62,950

	STOCK PRICE ($) FY Close	P/E High/Low		PER SHARE ($) Earnings	Dividends	Book Value
03/16	109.82	1	1	1.01	3.67	6.67
03/15	144.53	1	1	1.08	3.18	(0.00)
03/14	147.90	—	—	1.51	3.29	6.43
03/13	110.00	—	—	0.89	0.00	5.56
03/12	70.28	—	—	0.35	0.00	5.02
Annual Growth	**11.8%**	**—**	**—**	**30.5%**	**—**	**7.4%**

Hiroshima Bank, Ltd. (The) (Japan)

Few banks have deeper roots in the Hiroshima Prefecture than the Hiroshima Bank. Established in 1878 the bank serves Japan's Chugoku and Shikoku regions through more than 175 offices and 830 ATMs. Hiroshima organizes its business approach into three distinct areas: financial intermediation risk management assistance and information provision. It offers the traditional array of financial services including investment and private banking products real estate appraisal banking software venture capital support and assistance with corporate restructuring.

EXECUTIVES

President, KOJI IKEDA
Auditors: KPMG AZSA LLC

LOCATIONS

HQ: Hiroshima Bank, Ltd. (The) (Japan)
  1-3-8 Kamiya-cho, Naka-ku, Hiroshima 730-0031
Phone: (81) 82 247 5151   **Fax:** (81) 82 247 5234
Web: www.hirogin.co.jp

COMPETITORS

Aozora Bank	Miyazaki Bank
Chugoku Bank	Shizuoka Bank
Higo Bank	
Mitsubishi UFJ Financial Group	

HISTORICAL FINANCIALS
Company Type: Public

Income Statement
FYE: March 31

	ASSETS ($ mil.)	NET INCOME ($ mil.)	INCOME AS % OF ASSETS	EMPLOYEES
03/16	73,028	279	0.4%	4,517
03/15	65,986	221	0.3%	4,465
03/14	69,808	221	0.3%	3,187
03/13	75,050	184	0.2%	3,207
03/12	81,075	168	0.2%	3,274
Annual Growth	(2.6%)	13.4%	—	8.4%

2016 Year-End Financials
Return on assets: 0.3%
Return on equity: 7.0%
Long-term debt ($ mil.): —
No. of shares (mil.): 622
Sales ($ mil): 1,196

Dividends
Yield: —
Payout: —
Market value ($ mil.): —

Hitachi, Ltd.

Auditors: Ernst & Young ShinNihon LLC

LOCATIONS

HQ: Hitachi, Ltd.
1-6-6 Marunouchi, Chiyoda-ku, Tokyo 100-8280
Phone: (81) 3 3258 1111
Web: www.hitachi.co.jp

HISTORICAL FINANCIALS
Company Type: Public

Income Statement
FYE: March 31

	REVENUE ($ mil.)	NET INCOME ($ mil.)	NET PROFIT MARGIN	EMPLOYEES
03/16	89,355	1,533	1.7%	380,355
03/15	81,471	1,812	2.2%	385,262
03/14	93,162	2,567	2.8%	369,116
03/13	96,087	1,863	1.9%	374,775
03/12	117,833	4,232	3.6%	369,722
Annual Growth	(6.7%)	(22.4%)	—	0.7%

2016 Year-End Financials
Debt ratio: 0.2%
Return on equity: 6.0%
Cash ($ mil.): 6,227
Current ratio: 1.18
Long-term debt ($ mil.): 18,535

No. of shares (mil.): —
Dividends
Yield: 2.0%
Payout: 14.4%
Market value ($ mil.): —

	STOCK PRICE ($) FY Close	P/E High/Low		PER SHARE ($) Earnings	Dividends	Book Value
03/16	4.55	0	0	0.74	0.97	5.04
03/15	6.80	0	0	0.84	1.05	5.08
03/14	7.35	0	0	0.53	0.98	5.32
03/13	5.87	0	0	0.39	0.11	4.58
03/12	6.46	0	0	0.88	0.10	4.66
Annual Growth	(8.4%)	—	—	(4.1%)	77.5%	2.0%

Hochtief AG

HOCHTIEF is a giant in Germany and beyond. In addition to doing business throughout Europe the construction-related services provider operates in the Americas and the Asia/Pacific region and is among the world's largest general builders. US subsidiaries Turner and Flatiron provide building and infrastructure construction. CIMIC (formerly Leighton Holdings) based in Australia provides engineering and construction services for the infrastructure and mining industries. The group also operates in such European countries as the Czech Republic Poland Russia and the UK. All of HOCHTIEF's businesses focus on the Americas Asia Pacific Europe and concessions.

Spanish construction group Actividades de Construccions y Servicios (ACS) is HOCHTIEF's largest shareholder controlling more than 65% of its capital (and more than 50% voting rights). (A Qatar sovereign wealth fund sold its 10% stake in 2015; about half of that went to ACS. ACS has been building up its ownership for several years.

HOCHTIEF aims to provide services that span the lifecycle of a construction project. The company is known for building private projects such as warehouses and retail complexes. But its growing concessions and public-private partnership (PPP) division works on major federal state and municipal projects such as power plants toll roads tunnels and water treatment facilities. HOCHTIEF is continually growing and has its sights set on areas of growth especially in places where the PPP market is expanding as it is in North America. Other growth areas include the wind power market. Geographically HOCTIEF plans to expand into India.

Through its concessions division the group also is active in airport projects and it runs public buildings such as schools hospitals and prisons. HOCHTIEF AirPort has grown to become one of the world's largest independent airport managers. The division also takes ownership stakes in projects; its portfolio encompasses principal airports in Athens; Budapest Hungary; Düsseldorf and Hamburg Germany; Sydney; and Tirana Albania. HOCHTIEF in 2013 agreed however to sell its airport portfolio to Public Sector Pension Investment Board of Canada. The deal values the business at 1.5 billion Euros ($2 billion) giving HOCHTIEF about 1.1 billion Euros after its other business partners are paid. Also in 2011 HOCHTIEF sold several of its Leighton mining assets in Australia as a way to boost profit.

The company's former real estate and services divisions merged into the Europe division in 2011. The restructuring helped streamline business and save the company money. The Europe division includes HOCHTIEF Solutions which plans develops and markets large real estate properties such as hotels office buildings and retail and residential projects in Europe.

In addition to building and developing properties HOCHTIEF also makes sure those properties stay running. Its services division includes facility management and energy management providers. The division specializes in servicing the automotive industry chemical and pharmaceutical plants financial services facilities airports and health care and event facilities.

HISTORY

Brothers Philipp and Balthasar Helfmann mill and farm workers from Kelsterbach Germany started construction company Fa. Gebr. Helfmann Bauunternehmer in Frankfurt am Main in 1875.

The firm primarily built houses until 1878 when it was contracted to build the university at Giessen.

In 1884 the company was made a general partnership. Projects of this era included Frankfurt's Hotel Continental and Wiesbaden's Hotel Kaiserhof. When Balthasar died in 1896 Philipp converted the business to a joint stock company and renamed it Actien-Gesellschaft für Hoch- und Tiefbauten. Three years later with new capital for expansion the company won its first contract abroad —construction of a pneumatic conveyer-equipped granary in the harbor at Genoa (its first reinforced-concrete project).

Philipp Helfmann died in 1899 but the company continued operating. The battlefields of WWI took away most of the workforce and construction slowed to a near halt. But in the years following the war the company grew. In 1921 German industrialist Hugo Stinnes began buying stakes in the company and was its major shareholder by 1923. The company decided in 1922 to relocate to Essen closer to the Stinnes Group's operations and in 1923 it was renamed HOCHTIEF Aktiengesellschaft für Hoch- und Tiefbauten vorm. Gebr. Helfmann.

Stinnes died in 1924 and two years later his empire collapsed. But German banks helped keep HOCHTIEF alive and operating as an independent company. That year Rheinisch-Westfälische-Elektrizitätswerke AG (RWE) the electric utility that Stinnes helped create became the main shareholder in HOCHTIEF with a 31% stake.

Many of RWE's facilities were damaged during WWII including its Essen headquarters and the RWE staff used the HOCHTIEF building until 1961. Postwar reconstruction kept the company active including Germany's first nuclear reactor built by HOCHTIEF and commissioned in 1966. After the war RWE began increasing its stake in HOCHTIEF until it became the majority shareholder (56%) in 1989.

As a division of the RWE Group HOCHTIEF began acquiring former state-owned companies throughout Germany. By 1996 it had added financing and operation of major projects to its services. That year it led a consortium to build and operate an international airport in Athens. In 1997 it teamed with Ireland's Aer Rianta to build new terminals and manage the airport in Düsseldorf Germany. The next year HOCHTIEF won a bid to build and operate Berlin's new airport but a rival's allegations of bidding irregularities led to a raid by prosecutors on HOCHTIEF's headquarters. Charges were dismissed but the company was disqualified from the project.

The company sought to expand internationally with an agreement to take a 49% stake in the US holdings of its main rival Philipp Holzmann (1997). But when these plans failed and HOCHTIEF was blocked by regulators from increasing its 20% stake in the competitor (held since 1981) it lost interest and relinquished its shares.

HOCHTIEF like many of its competitors expanded abroad in 1999 by helping engineer Canadian firm Armbro's takeover of rival BFC (and then grabbing a 49% share in the merged firm now Aecon Group) and by acquiring US construction giant Turner. The company suffered a $75 million operating loss in 2000 because of a slowdown in the German construction industry and expenses related to acquisitions.

It secured a contract to build a rail tunnel under the River Thames in London in 2001. Also that year it merged its building and civil units into HOCHTIEF Construction and made plans to join former rival IVG Immobilien to bid on building Berlin's new airport Berlin-Brandenburg. HOCHTIEF reorganized in 2001 to reflect its increasingly international operations.

By 2002 Philipp Holzmann was in insolvency and HOCHTIEF initially made plans to bid on its former rival's technical services group HSG. However after reviewing the unit's prospectus HOCHTIEF withdrew from the bidding.

Longtime shareholder and German energy giant RWE sold its 56% stake in HOCHTIEF in 2004 to European and US institutional investors. It was the largest such transaction involving a German stock.

HOCHTIEF subsidiary Leighton and joint venture partner Downer EDI won a euro 100 million contract to build a four-lane highway in New Zealand in 2006. The project is expected to be finished in 2010.

In 2007 the company acquired the energy contracting business of Vattenfall Europe adding to its existing service portfolio of energy contracting and management operations. Also that year HOCHTIEF acquired Flatiron Construction from Royal BAM Group. That deal provided the group with entry into infrastructure PPP markets in the US and Canada.

EXECUTIVES

President and CEO Turner Construction, Peter J. Davoren, age 61

CEO Flatiron Construction, John A. DiCiurcio, age 61

CFO and Member Executive Board, Peter Sassenfeld, age 51

Chief Executive Officer CEO, Rainer Eichholz, age 61

CEO Leighton Holdings Limited, Hamish G. Tyrwhitt, age 53

CEO HOCHTIEF Solutions, Nikolaus Graf von Matuschka, age 53

COO HOCHTIEF AG and HOCHTIEF Solutions., Jose Ignacio Legorburo, age 51

Auditors: Deloitte & Touche GmbH Wirtschaftspraefungsgesellschaft

LOCATIONS

HQ: Hochtief AG
Opernplatz 2, Essen D-45128
Phone: (49) 201 824 0   **Fax:** (49) 201 824 2777
Web: www.hochtief.com

2013 Sales

	% of total
Australia	47
Americas	32
Asia	10
Germany	8
Rest of Europe	3
Total	**100**

PRODUCTS/OPERATIONS

2013 Sales

	% of totoal
HOCHTIEF Asia Pacific	57
HOCHTIEF Americas	32
HOCHTIEF Europe	11
Total	**100**

Selected Subsidiaries and Associates

Airport
  HOCHTIEF AirPort Capital Verwaltungs GmbH & Co. KG
  HOCHTIEF AirPort GmbH
Construction Services Americas
  Flatiron Construction Corp. (US)
  HOCHTIEF Americas GmbH
  HOCHTIEF do Brasil S.A. (92%)
  The Turner Corporation (US)
Construction Services Asia Pacific
  HOCHTIEF Asia Pacific GmbH
Construction Services Europe
  DURST-BAU GmbH (Austria)
  HOCHTIEF Construction AG

Development
  Deutsche Bau-und Siedlungs-Gesellschaft mbH
  HOCHTIEF Aurestis Beteiligungsgesellschaft mbH

COMPETITORS

Acciona	Heathrow Airport
Avionic Services	Holdings
International	KBR Building Group
Bechtel	PCL Employees Holdings
Bilfinger	Parsons Corporation
Bouygues	Peter Kiewit Sons'
Cheung Kong	STRABAG SE
Infrastructure	Skanska
Dragados	Tutor Perini
Fluor	VINCI

HISTORICAL FINANCIALS

Company Type: Public

Income Statement

FYE: December 31

	REVENUE ($ mil.)	NET INCOME ($ mil.)	NET PROFIT MARGIN	EMPLOYEES
12/15	22,998	226	1.0%	47,129
12/14	26,824	305	1.1%	68,426
12/13	35,265	235	0.7%	80,912
12/12	33,767	208	0.6%	79,987
12/11	29,928	(207)	—	75,449
Annual Growth	(6.4%)	—	—	(11.1%)

2015 Year-End Financials

Debt ratio: 21.7%
Return on equity: 9.6%
Cash ($ mil.): 3,059
Current ratio: 1.33
Long-term debt ($ mil.): 2,551

No. of shares (mil.): 65
Dividends
  Yield: 0.0%
  Payout: 8.0%
Market value ($ mil.): 1,173

	STOCK PRICE ($) FY Close	P/E High/Low		PER SHARE ($) Earnings	Dividends	Book Value
12/15	18.00	6	5	3.39	0.27	35.82
12/14	13.90	4	4	4.42	0.24	38.67
12/13	18.24	8	5	3.26	0.18	40.51
12/12	11.73	6	6	2.83	0.00	45.20
12/11	11.39	—	—	(2.82)	0.00	43.65
Annual Growth	12.1%	—	—	—	—	(4.8%)

Hokuhoku Financial Group Inc

Short on cash and passing through the Hokuriku or Hokkaido districts of Japan? You might want to check in with this group. The Hokuhoku Financial Group's core business is banking primarily through its chief subsidiaries: The Hokuriku Bank and The Hokkaido Bank. Through both banks' approximately 325 branches the financial services group targets the Toyama Ishikawa and Fukui Prefectures. In addition to banking Hokuhoku Financial Group provides credit cards leasing services venture capital and financing products. Hokuriku Bank (founded in 1877) merged with Hokkaido Bank in 2004 to form Hokuhoku Financial Group which today operates in the Hokuriku and Hokkaido district and Tokyo Osaka and Nagoya.

EXECUTIVES

President, EISHIN IHORI
Auditors: Deloitte Touche Tohmatsu LLC

LOCATIONS

HQ: Hokuhoku Financial Group Inc
1-2-26 Tsutsumicho-dori, Toyama 930-8637
Phone: (81) 76 423 7331
Web: www.hokuhoku-fg.co.jp

PRODUCTS/OPERATIONS

Selected Subsidiaries and Affiliated Companies

Hokugin Lease Co. Ltd.
Hokugin Software Co. Ltd.
Hokuriku Capital Co. Ltd.
Hokuriku Card Co. Ltd.
Hokuriku Hosho Services Co. Ltd.
Nihonkai Services Co. Ltd.
The Hokkaido Bank Ltd.
  Dogin Business Service Ltd.
  Dogin Card Co. Ltd.
The Hokuriku Bank Ltd.
  Hokugin Business Services Co. Ltd.
  Hokugin Corporate Co. Ltd.
  Hokugin Office Services Co. Ltd.
  Hokugin Real Estate Services Co. Ltd.
  Hokugin Shisankanri Co. Ltd.
  Hokuriku International Cayman Limited

COMPETITORS

Bank of Nagoya	Mitsubishi UFJ
Hachijuni Bank	Financial Group
Hokkoku Bank	Sapporo Hokuyo
Hyakujushi Bank	

HISTORICAL FINANCIALS

Company Type: Public

Income Statement

FYE: March 31

	ASSETS ($ mil.)	NET INCOME ($ mil.)	INCOME AS % OF ASSETS	EMPLOYEES
03/16	103,567	256	0.2%	8,755
03/15	97,375	235	0.2%	8,851
03/14	107,681	264	0.2%	5,510
03/13	116,686	192	0.2%	5,569
03/12	129,578	172	0.1%	5,573
Annual Growth	(5.4%)	10.5%	—	12.0%

2016 Year-End Financials

Return on assets: 0.2%
Return on equity: 5.0%
Long-term debt ($ mil.): —
No. of shares (mil.): 1,340
Sales ($ mil): 1,721

Dividends
  Yield: —
  Payout: —
Market value ($ mil.): —

	STOCK PRICE ($) FY Close	P/E High/Low		PER SHARE ($) Earnings	Dividends	Book Value
03/16	0.00	—	—	0.18	0.00	3.75
Annual Growth	—	—	—	—	—	—

Holding CMA-CGM (France)

LOCATIONS

HQ: Holding CMA-CGM (France)
  4, Quai d' Arenc, Marseille 13002
Phone: (33) 4 88 91 90 00   **Fax:** (33) 4 88 91 90 95
Web: www.cma-cgm.com

HISTORICAL FINANCIALS

Company Type: Public

Income Statement

FYE: December 31

	REVENUE ($ mil.)	NET INCOME ($ mil.)	NET PROFIT MARGIN	EMPLOYEES
12/15	15,674	566	3.6%	20,411
12/14	16,739	583	3.5%	18,249
12/13	15,901	407	2.6%	16,842
12/12	15,923	332	2.1%	16,239
Annual Growth	(0.5%)	19.5%	—	7.9%

2015 Year-End Financials

Debt ratio: 36.0%
Return on equity: 10.9%
Cash ($ mil.): 1,224
Current ratio: 1.21
Long-term debt ($ mil.): 4,414

No. of shares (mil.): 10
Dividends
  Yield: —
  Payout: —
Market value ($ mil.): —

	STOCK PRICE ($) FY Close	P/E High/Low		PER SHARE ($) Earnings	Dividends	Book Value
12/15	0.00	—	—	37.50	0.00	506.39
Annual Growth						

Hon Hai Precision Industry Co Ltd

Hon Hai Precision Industry has a big hand in making the devices you hold in your hand. The company known by its trade name Foxconn is the world's largest contract electronics manufacturer. It manufactures mobile phones as well as computers servers and TVs. Other products it makes include components such as connectors cable assemblies enclosures flat-panel displays game consoles and motherboards. Hon Hai also provides design engineering and mechanical tooling services. The global company's customers include Apple Cisco Dell Nokia and Sony. Chairman Terry Gou founded Hon Hai in 1974 to make plastic switches for TVs. In 2016 Hon Hai bought Japanese electronics company Sharp.

Geographic Reach

Most of Hon Hai's factories are in Taiwan where the company is headquartered. It also runs factories in China. The company was to build a plant in India for making Apple products.

A third of Hon Hai's revenue comes from the US with 30% originating in Ireland. Customers in China Singapore Japan and Taiwan team up to account for 22% of the company's revenue with other countries generating 6%.

Financial Performance

In 2015 revenue rose 6% from 2014. Sales to customers in the US Ireland and Taiwan increased 18% 9% and 51% respectively. Sales fell to customers in China Singapore and Japan.

Hon Hai reported a profit gain of 13% in 2015 over 2014 on the higher revenue an increase in other income and lower selling expenses.

Cash flow from operations surged 27% in 2015 from 2014.

Strategy

Hon Hai gets about 53% of it revenue in making iPhones and iPads for Apple. It added more work from Apple when it acquired Sharp Corp. which makes displays for Apple products. That's fine when Apple products are selling like well Apple products. But when iPhone sales fell in early 2016 the impact was felt by Hon Hai. The company is working to diversity its customer base within the Internet-Computing-Telecommunications world and developing manufacturing capablities in nanotechnology heat transfer wireless connectivity material sciences and green manufacturing.

In 2016 the company completed its $3.8 billion deal to buy electronics maker Sharp Corp. which moves Hon Hai higher up the value chain. Hon Hai is expected to cut costs at Sharp and try to rejuvenate Sharp as a maker and seller of top-flight TVs.

Also in 2016 Hon Hai joined Nvidia the maker of graphics chips and Quanta Computer to develop servers with artificial intelligence capabilities. That's in line with Hon Hai's focus on the Internet of Things as one of its strategic focuses.

EXECUTIVES

Chairman and CEO, Terry T.M. Gou
Director and President, Lu Fang-ming
Director and President, Chien Yi-bin
Auditors: PricewaterhouseCoopers Taiwan

LOCATIONS

HQ: Hon Hai Precision Industry Co Ltd
  No. 66, Zhongshan Road, Tucheng Industrial Zone,
  Tucheng District, New Taipei 236
Phone: (886) 2 2268 3466
Web: www.foxconn.com

PRODUCTS/OPERATIONS

2015 Sales

	% of total
U.S.A.	33
Ireland	30
Singapore	9
China	7
Japan	5
Taiwan	1
Others	15
Total	**100**

Selected Products

Cable assemblies
CD-ROMs
Connectors
E-book readers
Enclosures
Flat-panel displays
Game consoles
Handsets
Keyboards
LCD (liquid-crystal display) TVs
Mobile phones
Motherboards
Personal computers
Servers
Smartphones
Switches
Tablets
Thermal products

HISTORICAL FINANCIALS

Company Type: Public

Income Statement

FYE: December 31

	REVENUE ($ mil.)	NET INCOME ($ mil.)	NET PROFIT MARGIN	EMPLOYEES
12/15	136,401	4,469	3.3%	830,174
12/14	133,055	4,122	3.1%	900,758
12/13	132,534	3,577	2.7%	0
12/12	134,567	3,261	2.4%	1,290,000
12/11	113,912	2,703	2.4%	961,000
Annual Growth	4.6%	13.4%	—	(3.6%)

2015 Year-End Financials

Debt ratio: 0.3%
Return on equity: 15.1%
Cash ($ mil.): 19,998
Current ratio: 1.69
Long-term debt ($ mil.): 5,327

No. of shares (mil.): —
Dividends
  Yield: 3.1%
  Payout: 60.6%
Market value ($ mil.): —

	STOCK PRICE ($) FY Close	P/E High/Low		PER SHARE ($) Earnings	Dividends	Book Value
12/15	4.96	1	1	0.26	0.14	1.78
12/14	5.45	1	1	0.24	0.06	1.72
12/13	5.10	1	1	0.21	0.04	1.51
12/12	5.82	1	1	0.19	0.04	1.32
12/11	5.27	—	—	0.16	0.00	1.21
Annual Growth	(1.5%)	—	—	13.0%	—	10.1%

Honda Motor Co., Ltd.(Honda Giken Kogyo Kabushiki Kaisha) (Japan)

According to Honda you might want to do your Civic duty and get Fit. Honda Motor is Japan's #2 automaker (after Toyota) and the world's largest motorcycle producer. The company's car models include the Accord CR-V Civic Element and Fit; gasoline-electric hybrid versions of the Civic and Accord; and seven models of the luxury Acura line. Honda's line of motorcycles includes everything from scooters to superbikes. The company also makes a line of ATVs and personal watercraft. Honda's power products division makes commercial and residential machinery (lawn mowers snow blowers and tillers); portable generators; and outboard motors. Almost 75% of Honda Motor sales come from outside Japan.

Geographic Reach

The company's major geographic areas are concentrated in North America (the US Canada and

Mexico); Europe (the UK Germany France Belgium and Russia); and Asia (Thailand Indonesia China India and Vietnam). It also has a major presence in Brazil and Australia. Japan accounts for 24% of net sales while North America generates 45%. Asia brings in 21% and Europe 4%.

Operations

Honda's operations are divided across the segments of automobile (73% of net sales) motorcycle (14%) financial services (12%) and power product and other (2%).

Financial PerformanceHonda's revenue increased 7% from 2014 to 2015 due to increased sales across all its segments. Its net income however decreased 16% in 2015 due to additional selling general and administrative expenses resulting from increased product warranty expenses related to airbag inflators. (Note: growth rates may differ after conversion to the US dollar.)

Motorcycle segment sales grew 9% in 2015 largely due to a spike in sales in India and Vietnam. Financial services revenue grew 17% as a result of a rise in operating lease revenues and the positive effects of foreign currency translations. Automobile sales surged by 5% primarily due to the launch of new automobile models in Indonesia and India. In addition power product and other segment sales increased by 3% in 2015 resulting from positive foreign currency translation effects.

StrategyHonda is enjoying brisk motorcycle sales particularly in Asia where motorcycles are a popular mode of transportation. Motorcycle sales account for almost 15% of revenues. The company is beefing up production capacity in India to keep up with demand. Indonesia is the world's third-largest market for motorcycles (after China and India). To meet demand in 2014 Honda opened a second factory in Indonesia.

Throughout 2015 the company expanded its sales of the HondaJet for the first time to South America. With the expansion into Brazil the HondaJet dealer network spans three continents and includes 11 territories spanning North America Europe and South America.

HISTORY

Company Background

Soichiro Honda spent six years as an apprentice at Tokyo service station Art Shokai before opening his own branch of the repair shop in Hamamatsu in 1928. He also raced cars and in 1931 received a patent for metal spokes that replaced wood in wheels.

Honda started a piston ring company in 1937. During WWII the company produced metal propellers for Japanese bombers. When bombs and an earthquake destroyed most of his factory Honda sold it to Toyota in 1945.

In 1946 Honda began motorizing bicycles with war-surplus engines. When this proved popular Honda began making engines. The company was renamed Honda Motor Co. in 1948 and began producing motorcycles. Soichiro Honda hired Takeo Fujisawa in 1949 to manage the company so Honda could focus on engineering. Honda's innovative overhead valve design made its early 1950s Dream model a runaway success. In 1952 the smaller Cub sold through bicycle dealers accounted for 70% of Japan's motorcycle production.

Funded by a 1954 public offering and Mitsubishi Bank Honda expanded capacity and began exporting. American Honda Motor Company was formed in Los Angeles in 1959 accompanied by the slogan "You meet the nicest people on a Honda" in a campaign crafted to counter the stereotypical biker image. Honda added overseas factories in the 1960s and began producing lightweight trucks sports cars and minicars.

The company began selling its tiny 600 model in the US in 1970 but it was the Civic introduced in 1973 that first scored with the US car market. Three years later Honda introduced the Accord which featured an innovative frame adaptable for many models. In 1982 Accord production started at the company's Ohio plant.

EXECUTIVES

EVP; President Honda North America, Tetsuo Iwamura, age 65
Operating Officer; President and Director Honda Manufacturing of Alabama LLC, Takashi Yamamoto
Managing Officer; President Honda Motor Europe, Manabu Nishimae
Managing Officer; President Asian Honda Motor, Hiroshi Kobayashi, age 62
Senior Managing Officer, Sho Minekawa, age 62
Managing Officer General Manager Suzuka Factory Production Operations, Hidenobu Iwata
Operating Officer; President and CEO Honda Engineering, Hiroshi Sasamoto
Managing Executive Officer; President Honda South America, Masahiro Takedagawa
Managing Officer; President Honda Motor India, Yoshiyuki Matsumoto
Operating Officer; President Honda Motor (China) Investment, Seiji Kuraishi, age 58
Managing Operating Officer European Operations, Toshiaki Mikoshiba
Operating Officer; President Honda Aircraft, Michimasa Fujino
Operating Officer; President Honda R&D Europe (U.K.), Soichiro Takizawa
Operating Officer; COO Motorcycle Operations, Shinji Aoyama
President and CEO, Takahiro Hachigo, age 57
President and CEO Honda Cars India, Yoichiro Ueno
Chairman, Fumihiko Ike, age 64
Auditors: KPMG AZSA LLC

LOCATIONS

HQ: Honda Motor Co., Ltd.(Honda Giken Kogyo Kabushiki Kaisha) (Japan)
1-1, Minami-Aoyama 2-chome, Minato-ku, Tokyo 107-8556
Phone: (81) 3 3423 1111   **Fax:** (81) 3 5412 1515
Web: www.honda.co.jp

2014 Sales

	% of total
North America	40
Japan	28
Asia	19
Europe	5
Other region	8
Total	**100**

PRODUCTS/OPERATIONS

2014 Sales

	% of total
Automobiles	78
Motorcycles	14
Financial services	5
Power products & other	3
Total	**100**

Selected Acura Models

CSX (Canada)
MDX
RDX
RL
TL
TSX
ZDX

Selected Honda Car and Truck ModelsPassenger cars

CBR600RR
CBR1000RR
Elite (scooter)
Fury
Gold Wing
Interstate
NT700V
Nighthawk
PCX (scooter)
Ruckus (scooter)
Sabre
SH150i (scooter)
Shadow RS
Silver Wing (scooter)
Stateline
ST1300
VFR1200F

Selected ATVs

Utility ATVs
  FourTrax Foreman 4x4
  FourTrax Rancher
  FourTrax Rancher AT
  FourTrax Recon
  FourTrax Rincon
Multipurpose Utility Vehicles
  Big Red

Selected Personal Watercraft

AquaTrax F-15
AquaTrax F-15X

Selected Power Products

Cogeneration Units
Commercial mowers
Engines
Lawn mowers
Marine motors
Portable generators
Pumps
Snowblowers
Tillers

COMPETITORS

BMW	Kia Motors
Briggs & Stratton	Land Rover
Brunswick Corp.	Mahindra Renault
Caterpillar	Mazda
Daihatsu	Mitsubishi Motors
Daimler	Nissan
Deere	Peugeot
Exmark Manufacturing	Renault
FCA US	Suzuki Motor
Fiat Chrysler	Tata Motors
Ford Motor	Textron
Fuji Heavy Industries	Toro Company
General Motors	Toyota
Harley-Davidson	Triumph Motorcycles
Hyundai Motor	Viper Motorcycle
Indian Motorcycle	Volkswagen
Isuzu	Volvo
Kawasaki Heavy Industries	Yamaha Motor

HISTORICAL FINANCIALS

Company Type: Public

Income Statement

FYE: March 31

	REVENUE ($ mil.)	NET INCOME ($ mil.)	NET PROFIT MARGIN	EMPLOYEES
03/16	130,022	3,068	2.4%	208,399
03/15	111,086	4,246	3.8%	204,730
03/14	114,730	5,562	4.8%	198,561
03/13	104,981	3,902	3.7%	190,338
03/12	96,892	2,578	2.7%	187,094
Annual Growth	**7.6%**	**4.4%**	**—**	**2.7%**

2016 Year-End Financials

Debt ratio: —	No. of shares (mil.): 1,802
Return on equity: 4.9%	Dividends
Cash ($ mil.): 15,650	Yield: 2.6%
Current ratio: 1.14	Payout: 46.0%
Long-term debt ($ mil.): —	Market value ($ mil.): 49,274

	STOCK PRICE ($) FY Close	P/E High/Low		PER SHARE ($) Earnings	Dividends	Book Value
03/16	27.34	0	0	1.70	0.73	33.41
03/15	32.76	0	0	2.36	0.80	32.87
03/14	35.34	0	0	3.09	0.99	31.82
03/13	38.26	0	0	2.17	0.76	29.71
03/12	38.43	0	0	1.43	0.73	29.78
Annual Growth	(8.2%)	—	—	4.4%	(0.0%)	2.9%

Hong Leong Bank Berhad

One of Malaysia's largest banks Hong Leong Bank operates about 200 branches in its home country. It offers loans deposits credit cards investments and insurance to retail customers. The bank's offerings for corporate and commercial clients include loans trade financing economic research and debt capital markets services. Hong Leong Bank also provides Syariah-compliant banking services and Takaful (insurance) to Islamic customers. Its Singapore branch focuses on private banking investment banking Islamic banking treasury and asset management. The bank also has an office in Hong Kong. Started in 1905 as Kwong Lee Mortgage and Remittance Hong Leong Bank is a subsidiary of Hong Leong Group.

Hong Leong Bank has been expanding throughout Southeast Asia. In late 2008 the company established commercial banking operations in Vietnam and it created a consumer lending joint venture in China the following year; it's the first Malaysian bank to have operations in each country. Hong Leong offered nearly $1.5 billion to acquire smaller Malaysian banking company EON Capital in 2010. After initially rejecting the bid EON's board eventually accepted the buyout deal. The merger also was held up by a lawsuit filed by one of Eon Capital's largest shareholders who argued that the deal was illegal. However the lawsuit was dismissed and the deal was completed in 2011.

Auditors: PricewaterhouseCoopers

LOCATIONS

HQ: Hong Leong Bank Berhad
Level 8, Wisma Hong Leong, 18 Jalan Perak, Kuala Lumpur 50450
Phone: (60) 3 2164 8228   **Fax:** (60) 3 2164 2503
Web: www.hlb.com.my

COMPETITORS

AmBank Group	Edaran Otomobil
Bank Muamalat	Hang Seng Bank
Bank of China	Maybank
Berjaya Group	Norinchukin Bank
CIMB Group	Sime Darby

HISTORICAL FINANCIALS

Company Type: Public

Income Statement

FYE: June 30

	ASSETS ($ mil.)	NET INCOME ($ mil.)	INCOME AS % OF ASSETS	EMPLOYEES
06/16	47,604	477	1.0%	0
06/15	48,796	592	1.2%	0
06/14	53,048	654	1.2%	0
06/13	51,775	587	1.1%	0
06/12	49,668	518	1.0%	0
Annual Growth	(1.1%)	(2.1%)	—	—

2016 Year-End Financials

Return on assets: 1.0%	Dividends
Return on equity: 10.0%	Yield: —
Long-term debt ($ mil.): —	Payout: —
No. of shares (mil.): 2,086	Market value ($ mil.): —
Sales ($ mil): 2,046	

HSBC Bank Canada

Boasting around $70 billion in assets HSBC Bank Canada is one of the largest foreign-owned banks in Canada. Through more than 150 bank branches across the country it provides a range of commercial and retail financial services including deposit accounts loans and mortgages import and export financing equipment leasing and investment capital financing. Through subsidiaries the bank also offers brokerage services insurance mutual funds merchant banking trust services and portfolio management and investment counseling. HSBC Bank Canada is controlled by one of the largest banks on the planet UK-based financial services heavyweight HSBC Holdings.

Operations HSBC Bank Canada operates three business segments: Retail banking and Wealth management which offers banking services to 800000 retail and high-net-worth clients; Commercial Banking which serves small and mid-sized businesses and multi-national companies; and Global Banking and Markets which consists of its markets capital financing and investment banking divisions.

The bank made 68% of its total revenue from interest income during 2015 with 80% of that being loan interest. Another 30% came from fee income with about half of that coming from credit facilities and funds under management fees and the rest coming from various service fees involving account services credit card corporate finance remittance brokerage commissions insurance and trustee fees among others. Geographic ReachThe Vancouver-based bank operates branches across Canada.

Financial Performance

Note: Growth rates may differ after conversion to US dollars. This analysis uses financials from the company's annual report. HSBC Bank Canada's annual revenues and profits have been in decline in recent years mostly as it's struggled to grow its loan business and as interest margins have been shrinking in the low-interest environment. The bank's revenue slipped 9% to C$2.5 billion ($1.8 billion) during 2015 with all three segments reporting lower revenue due to the tough Canadian economy and the sharp decline in oil prices.

Revenue declines low interest margins and higher loan loss provisions stemming from more non-performing energy loans in 2015 caused HSBC Bank Canada's net income to fall more than

30% to C$447 million ($322.4 million). The bank's operating cash levels climbed sharply to C$3.65 billion ($2.63 billion) for the year (operations used C$546 million in 2014) despite the drop in earnings mostly thanks to favorable working capital changes related to changes in operating liabilities. StrategyHSBC Canada continued to follow its four strategic initiatives in early 2016 which included: leveraging its distinct geographic network which connects developed and fast-growing regions; connecting its clients to global growth opportunities; continuing to leverage its wide variety of financial products to benefit from global trends; and boost collaboration with other global businesses to better serve international clients.

Company Background

In 2012 as part of parent HSBC's restructuring efforts to create a leaner group HSBC Bank Canada announced plans to wind down the Consumer Finance segment which provided products including mortgages loans specialty insurance and credit cards through subsidiary HSBC Financial. The closure followed the 2011 sale of the full-service investment advisory business of HSBC Securities (Canada) to National Bank of Canada. Both divestitures reflected the group's strategy to focus on commercial banking retail banking and wealth management.

EXECUTIVES

President & Board Member, Caleb Y.M. Chan
President & Board Member, Lindsay Gordon
Auditors: PricewaterhouseCoopers LLP

LOCATIONS

HQ: HSBC Bank Canada
885 West Georgia Street, Vancouver, British Columbia V6C 3E8
Phone: 604 685-1000   **Fax:** 604 641-3098
Web: www.hsbc.ca

PRODUCTS/OPERATIONS

2015 sales

	%
Interest income	66
Fee income	25
Net trading income	5
Gains less losses from financial investments	2
Other operating income	2
Total	**100**

Selected Products

Banking
Chequing accounts
Credit cards
eSwitch
Foreign currency accounts
Savings accounts
Tax-Free Savings Accounts (TFSA)
Travel insurance

Selected Subsidiaries

Household Trust Company
HSBC Capital (Canada) Inc.
HSBC Financial Corporation Limited
HSBC Global Asset Management (Canada) Limited
HSBC Investment Funds (Canada) Inc.
HSBC Loan Corporation (Canada)
HSBC Mortgage Corporation (Canada)
HSBC Securities (Canada) Inc.
HSBC South Point Investments (Barbados) LLP
HSBC Trust Company (Canada)

COMPETITORS

BMO Financial Group	National Bank of
CIBC	Canada
Canadian Western Bank	RBC Financial Group
IGM Financial	Scotiabank
Laurentian Bank	TD Bank

HISTORICAL FINANCIALS

Company Type: Public

Income Statement

FYE: December 31

	ASSETS ($ mil.)	NET INCOME ($ mil.)	INCOME AS % OF ASSETS	EMPLOYEES
12/15	67,696	298	0.4%	6,060
12/14	76,168	529	0.7%	6,150
12/13	79,241	579	0.7%	6,050
12/12	81,154	693	0.9%	0
12/11	78,418	620	0.8%	7,900
Annual Growth	(3.6%)	(16.7%)	—	(6.4%)

2015 Year-End Financials

Return on assets: 0.4%
Return on equity: 8.1%
Long-term debt ($ mil.): —
No. of shares (mil.): 498
Sales ($ mil): 1,921

Dividends
Yield: 5.0%
Payout: —
Market value ($ mil.): 9,044

	STOCK PRICE ($) FY Close	P/E High/Low	PER SHARE ($) Earnings	Dividends	Book Value
12/15	18.14	22 21	0.60	0.98	7.76
12/14	21.88	18 18	1.06	1.15	8.31
12/13	23.75	20 19	1.17	1.23	9.21
12/12	25.96	19 18	1.39	1.28	10.35
12/11	25.21	20 18	1.24	1.23	9.78
Annual Growth	(7.9%)	— —	(16.8%)	(5.3%)	(5.6%)

HSBC Holdings Plc

HSBC would be a real alphabet soup if the company's name reflected its geographic diversity. One of the world's largest banking groups by assets (and the leader in customer deposits with more than $1 trillion) HSBC Holdings owns subsidiaries throughout Europe Hong Kong and the rest of the Asia/Pacific region the Middle East and Africa and the Americas. All told the company has some 6000 locations in more than 70 countries. Its activities include consumer and commercial banking credit cards private banking investment banking and leasing. Its North American operations include HSBC USA HSBC Bank Canada HSBC Bank Bermuda and Grupo Financiero HSBC in Mexico.

Operations

HSBC operates four core business segments. Its Retail Banking and Wealth Management (RBWM) division which accounted for 43% of the firm's total revenue in 2015 provides traditional banking products and services to retail customers as well as insurance investment products global asset management and financial planning services to mass affluent individuals. Commercial Banking (CMB) which brought in another 21% of total revenue provides credit and lending international trade and receivables finance commercial insurance and investments and treasury and cash management-related services to small and medium-sized enterprises (SMEs) as well as mid-market enterprises and corporations.

HSBC's Global Banking and Markets (GB&M) division generated 23% of its total revenue in 2015 and offers financing advisory and transaction services for major government corporate and institutional clients and private investors around the globe. Its Global Private Banking (GPB) division (3% of revenue) provides investment services to high-net-worth individuals and families.

The bank has always had a bent toward international expansion even from its inception. Founded in Hong Kong in 1865 HSBC owns all or parts of HSBC Bank plc in the UK The Hongkong and Shanghai Banking Corporation HSBC France The Saudi British Bank and Hong Kong's Hang Seng Bank. The company was also one of the first foreign banks to receive regulatory approval to incorporate in China. It owns about 20% of Bank of Communications one of the largest commercial banks in the country.

Geographic Reach

HSBC operates in more than 70 countries. It generated 35% of its revenue from its business in Europe during 2015 while business in Asia brought in another 31%. The bank's other largest markets are in North America (23% of revenue) Latin America (5%) and the Middle East and North Africa or MENA (6%).

Sales and Marketing

HSBC served more than 47 million customers at the end of 2015 ranging from individuals to large corporations.

Financial Performance

HSBC's revenues and profits have been trending lower in recent years mostly due to fee income declines and shrinking interest margins on loans amidst the low-interest environment.

The bank's revenue fell 6% to $91.62 billion during 2015 mainly as unfavorable currency exchange rates (especially in Latin America and Europe) hurt both its interest and fee income. Excluding FX rates the group's loan interest income was mostly unchanged with declines in Europe (mostly on lower mortgage yields in the UK) and North America (from the run-off of its CML portfolio) being offset by increases in Asia (on loan growth in Hong Kong and China) and Latin America (mostly from loan growth in Argentina). Excluding FX on its non-interest sources HSBC's RBWM and GB&M segment fee income fell in Europe largely as UK consumers wisened up on overdraft fees. Its fee income rose however in its Asia RBWM business and its North America GB&M business.

Revenue declines in 2015 caused HSBC's net income to dip 1% to $13.52 billion despite a $130 million reduction in loan impairment and credit risk provisions as its loan portfolio's creditworthiness improved. HSBC's operations used $1.12 billion or one-twentieth the amount of cash used in 2014 due to favorable working capital changes mostly related to the change in net trading securities and net derivatives and loans and advances to customers.

Strategy

HSBC maintained in 2016 that it would continue making moves toward emerging markets in Asia Latin America and the MENA region for long-term growth. The company believes the global economy will shift toward those markets over the next few decades —expecting those markets in particular to grow by "four-fold" by 2050 —and plans to be in place to provide them with cross-border trade and capital flow services.

Struggling to grow in the meantime HSBC has been making big cuts in under-performing global markets in recent years to free up resources for stronger investments elsewhere. HSBC in 2015 stated that it planned to reduce its risk-weighted assets by $290 billion (or 25%) while cutting up to 25000 jobs worldwide aiming to save between $4.5 billion to $5 billion by the end of 2017. In initiating its second sweeping restructuring in four years the bank in 2016 sold its Brazilian operations to Banco Bradesco for $15.2 billion not long after deciding to restructure its unprofitable Turkish unit in February 2016. In June 2014 the bank sold its UK pensions business to ReAssure Limited part of Admin Re Group and Swiss Re Group. In 2013 the company sold off its 15.6% stake in Chinese

insurer Ping An to Thailand's CP Group for $9.4 billion.

Company Background

In Asia HSBC sold its private banking operations in Japan to Credit Suisse in 2012. It also shut down its retail banking operations in Japan though it continues to offer corporate banking there. HSBC sold its US credit card portfolio worth some $30 billion to Capital One in 2012 and sold 195 US bank branches mainly in upstate New York to First Niagara Financial Group for £613 million ($1 billion).

HISTORY

Company BackgroundScotsman Thomas Sutherland and other businessmen in 1865 opened the doors to Hongkong & Shanghai Bank financing and promoting British imperial trade in opium silk and tea in East Asia. It soon established a London office and created an international branch network emphasizing China and East Asia. It claims to have been the first bank in Thailand (1888).

War repeatedly disrupted but never demolished the bank's operations. During WWII the headquarters were temporarily moved to London. (They moved back on a permanent basis in 1991.) The bank's chief prewar manager Sir Vandeleur Grayborn died in a Japanese POW camp. After the Communists took power in China in 1949 the bank gradually withdrew; by 1955 only its Shanghai office remained and it was later closed. The bank played a key role in Hong Kong's postwar growth by financing industrialists who fled there from China.

In the late 1950s Hongkong & Shanghai Bank's acquisitions included the British Bank of the Middle East (founded 1889; now The Saudi British Bank) and Mercantile Bank (with offices in India and Southeast Asia). In 1965 the company bought 62% of Hang Seng Hong Kong's #2 bank. It also added new subsidiaries including Wayfoong (mortgage and small-business finance 1960) and Wardley (investment banking Hong Kong 1972).

In the late 1970s and into the 1980s China began opening to foreign business. The bank added operations in North America to capitalize on business between China and the US and Canada. Acquisitions included Marine Midland Bank (US 1980) Hongkong Bank of Canada (1981) 51% of treasury securities dealer Carroll McEntee & McGinley (US 1983) most of the assets and liabilities of the Bank of British Columbia (1986) and Lloyds Bank Canada (1990).

Following the 1984 agreement to return Hong Kong to China Hongkong & Shanghai Bank began beefing up in the UK buying London securities dealer James Capel & Co. (1986) and the UK's #3 bank Midland plc (1992). In 1993 the company formed London-based HSBC Holdings and divested assets most notably its interest in Hong Kong-based Cathay Pacific Airways.

HSBC then began expanding in Asia again particularly in Malaysia where its Hongkong Bank Malaysia became the country's first locally incorporated foreign bank. The company returned to China with offices in Beijing and Guangzhou. It also added new European branches.

Latin American banks acquired in 1997 were among the non-Asian operations that cushioned HSBC from the worst of 1998's economic crises. Nonetheless The Hong Kong Monetary Authority took a stake in the bank to shore up the stock exchange and foil short-sellers.

In 1999 China's government made HSBC a loan for mainland expansion. That year the company was foiled in its attempt to buy South Korea's government-owned Seoulbank but did buy the late Edmond Safra's Republic New York Corporation and his international bank holding company Safra Republic Holdings (it negotiated a $450 million discount on the $10 billion deal after a Japanese probe of Republic's securities division caused delays).

The company unveiled several online initiatives in 2000 including Internet ventures with CK Hutchison Holdings and Merrill Lynch and bought CCF (then called Credit Commercial de France now HSBC France). However HSBC's plans to buy a controlling stake in Bangkok Metropolitan Bank fell through before the year's end.

In 2001 HSBC agreed to pick up Barclays Bank's fund management operations in Greece. Later in response to the slowing economy it froze the salaries of 14000 employees. Argentina's 2001 peso devaluation cost the company half a billion dollars in currency conversion losses alone. Total charges pertaining to Argentina equaled more than $1 billion that year.

HSBC expanded its consumer finance operations with the purchase of US-based Household International (now HSBC Finance) in 2003.

The next year HSBC acquired The Bank of Bermuda as well as Marks and Spencer Financial Services (aka M&S Money) one of the UK's leading credit card issuers. It bought US credit card company Metris the following year.

HSBC's Latin American operations at this point were primarily in Argentina Brazil and Mexico. The company expanded its presence in Central America and the Caribbean with the 2006 purchase of Panama-based Banistmo a banking group with offices in the Bahamas Colombia Costa Rica El Salvador Honduras and Nicaragua.

HSBC asold its regional banking operations in France to Banque Populaire in 2008. The deal included eight banks with around 400 branches. Also that year the company canceled its proposed $6 billion acquisition of Lone Star's 51% stake in Korea Exchange Bank a deal that had been held up for months by an investigation by the South Korean government. HSBC cited weakened asset values in the global financial markets for the cancellation.

Beset by mortgage defaults the group closed its Decision One US-based wholesale subprime lending unit in 2007. In 2009 it shuttered its North American consumer lending business placing related portfolios (excluding credit cards) in run-off. To further reduce its exposure to consumer credit it sold a $4 billion car loan portfolio and servicing platform to an affiliate of Santander USA.

The company acquired a majority stake in Indonesian lender Bank Ekonomi in 2009 doubling its presence in the nation.

In 2010 HSBC sold HSBC Insurance Brokers to Marsh & McLennan in a £135 million ($218 million) cash-and-stock deal. As part of the transaction the companies entered into a strategic partnership under which Marsh markets insurance and risk management services to HSBC's corporate and private clients ahead of other providers.

In late 2011 the Financial Services Authority (the UK regulator of financial services providers) fined HSBC £10.3 million after it was found that salespeople at its NHFA Limited subsidiary had sold inappropriate and unsuitable five-year bonds to nearly 3000 elderly customers. HSBC which had alerted the FSA once it was made aware of the issue closed NHFA to new business that year.

EXECUTIVES

President and CEO HSBC North America Holdings Inc., Patrick J. (Pat) Burke, age 54
Group Chief Executive, Stuart T. Gulliver, age 56, $800,000 total compensation
Chief Executive Global Banking and Markets, Samir Assaf, age 56
Chief ExecutiveThe Hong Kong and Shanghai Banking Corporation, Peter T. S. Wong, age 65
Group CIO, Darryl West
Chief Executive Global Private Banking, Peter W. Boyles, age 60
Executive Director and Chief Risk Officer, Marc Moses, age 58
Group Director Finance, Iain J. Mackay, age 54
Chief Executive Global Asset Management, John Flint, age 47
Group COO, Andy Maguire, age 49
CEO HSBC Latin America and Executive Chairman HSBC Mexico, Paulo Maia, age 57
CEO UK and Continental Europe, Antonio Simoes, age 40
CEO Asset Management India, Ravi Menon
Head Asset Management Southeast Asia, Puneet Chaddha
Deputy Chairman and Chief Executive HSBC Bank Middle East Limited, Mohammad Al Tuwaijri
CEO HSBC Middle East and North Africa (MENA), Georges Elhedery
Chief Executive Global Commercial Banking, Noel Quinn
Chairman, Douglas J. Flint, age 61
Auditors: KPMG Audit Plc

LOCATIONS

HQ: HSBC Holdings Plc
8 Canada Square, London E14 5HQ
Phone: (44) 20 7991 8888   **Fax:** (44) 20 7992 4880
Web: www.hsbc.com

2015 Income

	% of total
Asia	31
Europe	35
North America	23
Latin America	5
MENA	6
Total	**100**

PRODUCTS/OPERATIONS

2015 Sales

	% of total
Interest	51
Fees	20
Net earned insurance premiums	11
Net trading income	10
Other	8
Total	**100**

2015 Sales by Segment

	% of total
Retail banking & wealth management	43
Global banking & markets	23
Commercial banking	21
Global private banking	3
Other	10
Total	**100**

Selected Subsidiaries

Hang Seng Bank Limited (62% Hong Kong)
The Hong Kong and Shanghai Banking Corporation Limited
HSBC Asset Finance (UK) Ltd.
HSBC Bank Argentina S.A. (99.9%)
HSBC Bank A.S. (Turkey)
HSBC Bank Australia Limited
HSBC Bank Bermuda Limited
HSBC Bank Brasil S.A. - Banco Múltiplo
HSBC Bank Canada
HSBC Bank (China) Company Limited
HSBC Bank Egypt S.A.E. (95%)
HSBC Bank International Limited (Jersey)
HSBC Bank Malaysia Berhad
HSBC Bank Malta p.l.c. (70%)
HSBC Bank Middle East Limited
HSBC Bank (Panama) S.A.
HSBC Bank plc
HSBC Bank USA N.A.
HSBC Finance Corporation (US)
HSBC France
HSBC Mexico S.A. Institución de Banca Múltiplo Grupo Financiero HSBC (99.9%)
HSBC Private Banking Holdings (Suisse) S.A. (Switzerland)
HSBC Securities (USA) Inc.
HSBC Trinkaus & Burkhardt AG (80% Germany)
Marks and Spencer Retail Financial Services Holdings Limited

COMPETITORS

BBVA	Lloyds Banking Group
Bank of America	Mitsubishi UFJ
Bank of China	Financial Group
Barclays	Mizuho Financial
CIBC	Prudential plc
Citigroup	RBC Financial Group
Credit Suisse	Royal Bank of Scotland
Deutsche Bank	Standard Chartered
Intesa Sanpaolo	UBS
JPMorgan Chase	

HISTORICAL FINANCIALS

Company Type: Public

Income Statement

FYE: December 31

	ASSETS ($ mil.)	NET INCOME ($ mil.)	INCOME AS % OF ASSETS	EMPLOYEES
12/15	2,409,656	13,522	0.6%	264,000
12/14	2,634,139	13,688	0.5%	266,000
12/13	2,671,318	16,204	0.6%	263,000
12/12	2,692,538	14,027	0.5%	284,186
12/11	2,555,579	16,797	0.7%	305,984
Annual Growth	**(1.5%)**	**(5.3%)**	**—**	**(3.6%)**

2015 Year-End Financials

Return on assets: 0.5%
Return on equity: 7.1%
Long-term debt ($ mil.): —
No. of shares (mil.): —
Sales ($ mil): 91,617

Dividends
  Yield: 6.3%
  Payout: 390.6%
Market value ($ mil.): —

	STOCK PRICE ($) FY Close	P/E High/Low		PER SHARE ($) Earnings	Dividends	Book Value
12/15	39.47	77	57	0.64	2.50	9.57
12/14	47.23	81	67	0.69	2.45	9.91
12/13	55.13	70	60	0.84	2.40	9.66
12/12	53.07	72	52	0.74	2.50	9.48
12/11	38.10	64	39	0.91	1.95	8.88
Annual Growth	**0.9%**		**—**	**(8.4%)**	**6.4%**	**1.9%**

Hua Nan Commercial Bank, Ltd.

EXECUTIVES

President, Teng Chen Liu
Auditors: Deloitte & Touche

LOCATIONS

HQ: Hua Nan Commercial Bank, Ltd.
No. 123, Songren Road, Xinyi District, Taipei
Phone: (886) 2 23713111   **Fax:** (886) 2 23316741
Web: www.hncb.com.tw

HISTORICAL FINANCIALS

Company Type: Public

Income Statement

FYE: December 31

	ASSETS ($ mil.)	NET INCOME ($ mil.)	INCOME AS % OF ASSETS	EMPLOYEES
12/15	70,012	402	0.6%	7,025
12/14	69,827	392	0.6%	7,034
12/13	71,012	320	0.5%	7,196
12/12	69,718	300	0.4%	7,109
12/11	63,883	276	0.4%	7,163
Annual Growth	2.3%	9.9%	—	(0.5%)

2015 Year-End Financials

Return on assets: 0.5%
Return on equity: 9.0%
Long-term debt ($ mil.): —
No. of shares (mil.): —
Sales ($ mil): 1,464

Dividends
Yield: —
Payout: —
Market value ($ mil.): —

Huaneng Power International, Inc.

Huaneng Power International is one of China's largest independent power producers. Its nearly 50 power plants in about 20 provinces have a capacity of more than 66700 MW; nearly all of the company's power is produced from coal. Huaneng Power International which is always expanding also owns Singapore's electricity retailer Tuas Power. Huaneng Power International sells power to local utilities primarily in China's coastal provinces. Huaneng International Power Development Corporation a subsidiary of the China Huaneng Group owns 36% of Huaneng Power International; China Huaneng Group 16%. Huaneng Power International was formed in 1994.

Huaneng Power International has been steadily increasing power generation through the acquisition on new power plants and in response to rapid increases in power consumption in the regions where the company operates.

In 2008 the company acquired SinoSing Power from parent China Huaneng Group. It also acquired 40% of Huating Coal Mining Group the largest coal producer in northwestern China's Gansu province.

Expanding its renewable sources in 2009 it agreed to acquire a 65% stake in Qidong Windpower.

EXECUTIVES

Chairman, Peixi Cao, age 61
President, Guoyue Liu, age 53
Chief Engineer, Yong He
VP and Chief Accountant, Hui Zhou, age 53
Vice Chairman, Guo Junming, age 51
Chaiman, Xiangdong Ye, age 49
Auditors: KPMG Huazhen LLP

LOCATIONS

HQ: Huaneng Power International, Inc.
 Huaneng Building, 6 Fuxingmennei Street, Xicheng District, Beijing 100031
Phone: (86) 10 6322 6999   **Fax:** (86) 10 6322 6888
Web: www.hpi.com.cn

2013 Sales

	% of total
PRC power	89
Singapore	11
Total	**100**

COMPETITORS

AES	Hong Kong and China
CLP Holdings	Gas
China Power	Huadian Power
China Resources Power	Korea Electric Power
Datang Power	Power Assets

HISTORICAL FINANCIALS

Company Type: Public

Income Statement

FYE: December 31

	REVENUE ($ mil.)	NET INCOME ($ mil.)	NET PROFIT MARGIN	EMPLOYEES
12/15	19,848	2,102	10.6%	42,039
12/14	20,206	1,733	8.6%	37,737
12/13	22,106	1,722	7.8%	37,729
12/12	21,488	884	4.1%	36,326
12/11	21,196	187	0.9%	35,903
Annual Growth	(1.6%)	83.0%	—	4.0%

2015 Year-End Financials

Debt ratio: 8.5%
Return on equity: 17.7%
Cash ($ mil.): 1,160
Current ratio: 0.27
Long-term debt ($ mil.): 12,039

No. of shares (mil.): —
Dividends
Yield: 6.4%
Payout: 1,451.9%
Market value ($ mil.): —

	STOCK PRICE ($) FY Close	P/E High/Low		PER SHARE ($) Earnings	Dividends	Book Value
12/15	34.30	62	35	0.14	2.20	0.85
12/14	54.17	74	41	0.12	2.21	0.78
12/13	36.25	68	46	0.12	1.19	0.73
12/12	37.15	95	55	0.06	0.26	0.64
12/11	21.02	310	199	0.01	1.12	0.58
Annual Growth	13.0%	—	—	83.7%	18.5%	10.3%

Hyakugo Bank Ltd. (Japan)

Serving its primary business base in the Mie Prefecture Hyakugo Bank is a Japanese regional bank offering traditional banking services such as electronic corporate and consumer banking as well as international and securities offerings. Hyakugo Bank serves its products through more than 100 branches and 26 sub-branches and also owns foreign offices in Singapore and Shanghai. Listed subsidiaries include Hyakugo Business Service Company Hyakugo Staff Service Company and Hyakugo Property Research Company. The bank goes all the way back to 1878 when it was established as The 105th National Chartered Bank.

EXECUTIVES

President, TOSHIYASU ITO
Auditors: KPMG AZSA LLC

LOCATIONS

HQ: Hyakugo Bank Ltd. (Japan)
 21-27 Iwata, Tsu, Mie 514-8666
Phone: (81) 59 227 2151   **Fax:** (81) 59 228 2010
Web: www.hyakugo.co.jp

COMPETITORS

Aozora Bank	Mitsubishi UFJ
Iyo Bank	Financial Group
Mie Bank	Shizuoka Bank

HISTORICAL FINANCIALS

Company Type: Public

Income Statement

FYE: March 31

	ASSETS ($ mil.)	NET INCOME ($ mil.)	INCOME AS % OF ASSETS	EMPLOYEES
03/16	47,505	121	0.3%	4,282
03/15	44,462	88	0.2%	4,259
03/14	49,139	111	0.2%	2,917
03/13	50,855	100	0.2%	2,925
03/12	55,017	94	0.2%	2,923
Annual Growth	(3.6%)	6.4%	—	10.0%

2016 Year-End Financials

Return on assets: 0.2%
Return on equity: 4.0%
Long-term debt ($ mil.): —
No. of shares (mil.): 253
Sales ($ mil): 773

Dividends
Yield: —
Payout: —
Market value ($ mil.): 1,218

	STOCK PRICE ($) FY Close	P/E High/Low		PER SHARE ($) Earnings	Dividends	Book Value
03/16	4.80	0	0	0.48	0.00	11.48
03/15	4.12	0	0	0.35	0.00	11.47
03/14	4.23	—	—	0.44	0.00	11.35
03/13	4.23	—	—	0.39	0.00	11.80
03/12	3.80	—	—	0.37	0.00	11.88
Annual Growth	6.0%	—	—	6.5%	—	(0.9%)

Hyakujushi Bank, Ltd.

Businesses and individuals who say “Hi” to Hyakujushi Bank might find themselves saying “Hai” (yes) to the institution's banking and financial services offerings. One of Japan's regional banks Hyakujushi Bank serves the Kagawa prefecture and about 10 other nearby prefectures through some 120 banking offices and a network of about 300 ATMs. (Most of the bank's loans originate outside its home base.) Hyakujushi Bank also has operations in Tokyo and Osaka. Hyakujushi Bank offers a variety of traditional banking services including deposit banking and lending.

EXECUTIVES

President, TOMOKI WATANABE
Executive Vice President, Kazuo Yamamoto
Auditors: Ernst & Young ShinNihon LLC

LOCATIONS

HQ: Hyakujushi Bank, Ltd.
 5-1 Kamei-cho, Takamatsu, Kagawa 760-8574
Phone: (81) 87 831 0114
Web: www.114bank.co.jp

COMPETITORS

Awa Bank	Mizuho Financial
Chugoku Bank	Norinchukin Bank
Hiroshima Bank	Resona
Mitsubishi UFJ	Sumitomo Mitsui
Financial Group	

HISTORICAL FINANCIALS
Company Type: Public

Income Statement
FYE: March 31

	ASSETS ($ mil.)	NET INCOME ($ mil.)	INCOME AS % OF ASSETS	EMPLOYEES
03/16	42,028	103	0.2%	3,242
03/15	38,465	74	0.2%	3,235
03/14	43,530	0	—	2,457
03/13	43,939	0	—	2,531
03/12	48,992	0	—	2,551
Annual Growth	(3.8%)	—	—	6.2%

2016 Year-End Financials
Return on assets: 0.2%
Return on equity: 4.2%
Long-term debt ($ mil.): —
No. of shares (mil.): 296
Sales ($ mil): 725

Dividends
Yield: —
Payout: —
Market value ($ mil.): —

Hyundai Engineering & Construction Co., Ltd. (South Korea)

Hyundai Engineering & Construction (HDEC) is one of South Korea's largest construction and civil engineering companies. The company provides services for a wide variety of projects including harbors and terminals bridges and highways dams nuclear and other power plants petrochemical plants commercial buildings and high-rise apartments. The firm has built industrial infrastructure commercial hospitality and multifamily residential projects (under the Hillstate brand) in approximately 50 countries. HDEC was the former parent of Hyundai Group Korea's largest chaebol (or conglomerate) which was broken up under government orders.

Looking to strengthen its international business it maintains operations in about 20 countries primarily in Asia and the Middle East. Key recent projects include a $2.1 billion construction contract for the Ras Laffan IWPP power plant in Qatar and the Colombo Port Expansion in Sri Lanka.

HDEC was founded as Hyundai Civil Works Company in 1947. South Korea president Lee Myung-bak served as the company's chairman from 1998 to 2002.

EXECUTIVES
President, Soo Hyun Jung

LOCATIONS
HQ: Hyundai Engineering & Construction Co., Ltd. (South Korea)
75 Yulgok-ro Jongno-gu, Seoul 110-801
Phone: (82) 2 746 1114   **Fax:** (82) 2 746 4846
Web: www.hdec.co.kr

COMPETITORS

Acciona	Mitsubishi Heavy
Bechtel	Industries
Bilfinger	Obayashi
Bouygues	Sembcorp
Chiyoda Corp.	Shimizu
Daelim Industrial	Skanska

EIFFAGE	Sumitomo Mitsui
Ferrovial	Construction
Fluor	Technip
HOCHTIEF	VINCI

HISTORICAL FINANCIALS
Company Type: Public

Income Statement
FYE: December 31

	REVENUE ($ mil.)	NET INCOME ($ mil.)	NET PROFIT MARGIN	EMPLOYEES
12/15	16,252	312	1.9%	7,131
12/14	15,891	383	2.4%	7,226
12/13	13,253	478	3.6%	7,468
12/12	12,479	477	3.8%	7,335
12/11	10,287	548	5.3%	4,211
Annual Growth	12.1%	(13.1%)	—	14.1%

2015 Year-End Financials
Debt ratio: 0.0%
Return on equity: 6.5%
Cash ($ mil.): 1,697
Current ratio: 1.67
Long-term debt ($ mil.): 1,866

No. of shares (mil.): 111
Dividends
Yield: —
Payout: —
Market value ($ mil.): —

Hyundai Heavy Industries Co., Ltd.

Not afraid to play the heavy Hyundai Heavy Industries (HHI) is the world's largest shipbuilder and among the top five manufacturers in heavy industries. Started in 1972 HHI's shipbuilding division builds containerships tankers bulk/petrochemical carriers drill ships and specialty vessels. HHI also offers offshore construction and exploration services and it has expanded into robotic systems and large industrial pumps and presses. Additionally HHI makes diesel engines and engine parts for industrial and marine applications. Other HHI offerings include electric systems (circuit breakers switchgear transformers) and construction equipment (excavators forklifts and loaders).

Operations

HHI operates through several business divisions: Construction Equipment Electro Electric System Engine and Machinery Green Energy Industrial Plant and Engineering Offshore and Engineering Financial Services Oil Refining and its bread and butter Shipbuilding.

The Construction Equipment segment is capitalizing on China's infrastructure market flooded with government stimulus funding. HHI's excavators claim more than a 10% share of China's excavator market. The company operates manufacturing plants in China as well as India that position HHI to capture an increasing share of the countries' construction equipment growth.

The Offshore and Engineering business operates a 292-acre offshore yard and fabrication shop for engineering and construction of offshore oil and gas facility projects. The Industrial Plant and Engineering business works on industrial plant projects for power generation desalination and oil and gas processing and capitalizes on burgeoning work in the Middle East and South America. Despite a drop in marine engine and power engine demand pressured by the slow economy the Engine and Machinery business continues to benefit from HHI's move into China India and other developing markets.

Another small business of HHI is its Electro Electric Systems segment which manufactures and installs electrical systems in power plants locomotives subways and marine vessels. The business' performance is buoyed by the increase in replacement electrical equipment for renovating and upgrading power transformers and other facilities in North America as well as building new facilities in the Middle East and other rapidly modernizing regions.

Financial Performance

Research and development is also bolstering HHI's reach into profitable niche markets related to its established presence. Shipbuilding HHI's largest business represents roughly 35% of sales and revenues. In fiscal 2013 its net sales decreased 1% compared to 2012. The primary cause of the marginal dip in sales was a decrease in sales from its Oil Refining and Offshore and Engineering segments.

EXECUTIVES
Chairman and CEO, Choi Kil-Seon
Vice Chairman and CEO, Kwon Oh-gab
COO Hyundai Construction Equipment, Ki Young Kong
Auditors: Samjong Accounting Corporation (A Member Firm of KPMG)

LOCATIONS
HQ: Hyundai Heavy Industries Co., Ltd.
1000, Bangeojinsunhwando-ro Dong-gu, Ulsan 682-792
Phone: (82) 52 202 2114   **Fax:** (82) 52 202 3432
Web: www.hhi.co.kr

2014 Sales

	% of total
Korea	86
Asia	12
North America	1
Europe	1
Total	**100**

PRODUCTS/OPERATIONS

2014 Sales

	% of total
Shipbuilding	34
Oil Refining	15
Financial Services	10
Construction Equipment	5
Offshore and Engineering	4
Engine and Machinery	3
Electro Electric Systems	3
Industrial Plant and Engineering	2
Green Energy	1
Others	23
Total	**100**

Selected Divisions Products and Services
Construction Equipment
  Excavators
  Forklifts
  Skid loaders
  Wheel loaders
Electro Electric Systems
  Low- and Medium-voltage circuit breakers
  Power electronics and control systems
  Rotating machinery
  Transformers gas insulated switchgear switchgear
Engine and Machinery
  Diesel and gas power plant engines
  Industrial and marine pumps industrial robots side thrusters
  Propellers and crankshafts
  Presses conveyor systems steel strip process lines
  Steam turbines and turbochargers
  Two-stroke diesel engines four-stroke (HiMSEN) engines
Green Energy
Industrial Plant and Engineering
  Plant equipment
  Power plants
  Process plants

Offshore and Engineering
Floating units
Fix platforms
Land-based modules
Offshore installations
Pipelines and subsea facilities

Shipbuilding
Containerships bulk carriers OBO carriers
Drillships
LNG carriers LPG carriers
Ro-pax ships ro-ro ships pure car carriers
tankers/VLCCs
Submarines destroyers frigates
VLCCs tankers product carriers chemical tankers

COMPETITORS

ALSTOM
Aker Solutions
BWX Technologies
Baltija Shipbuilding
Bechtel
Bharat Heavy Electricals
Caterpillar
China State Shipbuilding
China Yuchai
Crown Equipment
DSME
Doosan Infracore
Ebara
Evergreen Marine
General Dynamics
Gulf Island Fabrication
Hanjin Heavy Industries & Construction
Harbison-Fischer
Hitachi Zosen
Huntington Ingalls
KBR
Kawasaki Heavy Industries
Komatsu
McDermott
Mitsubishi Heavy Industries
Mitsui Engineering & Shipbuilding
NASSCO
Oceaneering International
Samsung Heavy Industries
Siemens Industry Automation
Stolt-Nielsen
Sumitomo Heavy Industries
Technip USA

HISTORICAL FINANCIALS
Company Type: Public

Income Statement
FYE: December 31

	REVENUE ($ mil.)	NET INCOME ($ mil.)	NET PROFIT MARGIN	EMPLOYEES
12/15	39,294	(1,147)	—	27,409
12/14	48,059	(1,617)	—	28,291
12/13	51,526	265	0.5%	27,246
12/12	51,487	921	1.8%	26,255
12/11	46,355	2,208	4.8%	24,948
Annual Growth	(4.0%)	—	—	2.4%

2015 Year-End Financials
Debt ratio: 0.0%
Return on equity: (-9.3%)
Cash ($ mil.): 2,639
Current ratio: 1.18
Long-term debt ($ mil.): 7,824
No. of shares (mil.): 65
Dividends
  Yield: —
  Payout: —
Market value ($ mil.): —

Hyundai Mobis Co Ltd (South Korea)

South Korean auto parts giant Hyundai Mobis keeps drivers mobile with automotive modules and systems including chassis brakes air bags telematics and electronic devices. Established as a container manufacturer in 1977 the Hyundai (HMC) affiliate has since reinvented itself as a leading auto parts manufacturer supplying components in all Hyundai and Kia vehicles; other customers include BMW GM and Chrysler. The company has taken aggressive steps toward expanding beyond its Korean borders with forays into Japan China and Eastern Europe. Mobis markets its products in North America Australia Southeast Asia the Middle East and Europe.

Geographic Reach
Hyundai Mobis' main markets are Korea and China which collectively account for 70% of its total annual revenue. The US generates around 15% while the continent of Europe accounts for roughly 10%.

Operations
Hyundai Mobis has two reportable segments: auto parts (80% of total sales) and after sales services (20%).

Financial Performance
The company's net revenues increased 19% from 2010 to 2011 while its profits jumped by 11% over that same period. It was helped by a 16% surge in demand for its auto parts in Korea and a 19% increase in China.

Ownership
Kia Motors owns nearly 17% of Hyundai Mobis.

EXECUTIVES

EVP Hyundai Motor International Plant Support Division, Lim Young-deuk
Auditors: Samjong Accounting Corporation (A Member Firm of KPMG)

LOCATIONS

HQ: Hyundai Mobis Co Ltd (South Korea)
140-2 Gangnam-gu, Seoul 135-916
Phone: (82) 2 2018 5114   **Fax:** (82) 2 2018 6000
Web: www.mobis.co.kr

2015 sales

	% of total
Korea	36
China	25
America	22
Europe	12
Other regions	5
Total	**100**

PRODUCTS/OPERATIONS

2015 sales

	% of total
Auto parts	82
After-sales	18
Total	**100**

Selected Products
Airbags
Brake systems
Chassis modules
Cockpit modules
Wheel and deck assemblies

COMPETITORS

Autoliv	Johnson Controls
Dana	Robert Bosch
Delphi Automotive Systems	Visteon
	ZF TRW Automotive

HISTORICAL FINANCIALS
Company Type: Public

Income Statement
FYE: December 31

	REVENUE ($ mil.)	NET INCOME ($ mil.)	NET PROFIT MARGIN	EMPLOYEES
12/15	30,614	2,596	8.5%	8,569
12/14	33,072	3,128	9.5%	8,068
12/13	32,519	3,253	10.0%	7,615
12/12	28,836	3,332	11.6%	7,085
12/11	22,693	2,608	11.5%	6,663
Annual Growth	7.8%	(0.1%)	—	6.5%

2015 Year-End Financials
Debt ratio: 0.0%
Return on equity: 12.5%
Cash ($ mil.): 2,123
Current ratio: 1.92
Long-term debt ($ mil.): 1,109
No. of shares (mil.): 94
Dividends
  Yield: —
  Payout: —
Market value ($ mil.): —

Hyundai Motor Co., Ltd.

Hyundai vehicles run the gamut from budget cars to luxury sedans to commercial trucks. South Korea's leading carmaker Hyundai Motor produces compact and luxury cars SUVs minivans trucks buses and other commercial vehicles. Its cars are sold in 180 countries through some 6000 dealerships. Hyundai generates about half of its sales in South Korea but its vehicles are also popular in emerging markets such as China and India. The company operates a dozen manufacturing plants in China the Czech Republic India Russia South Korea Turkey and the US. It sold 3.6 million passenger cars in 2010 but only 500000 in the US where it does business as Hyundai Motor America. Hyundai also owns a 34% stake in Kia Motors.

Although South Korea accounts for half of Hyundai's sales and vehicle production capabilities the company is focused on growth in other markets. China's two plants now account for about 20% of production and construction on a third plant began in 2011. The plant a 50/50 joint venture with Beijing Automotive Industry Holding Co. Ltd. will be the company's largest in China capable of producing 400000 small and mid-size vehicles specifically designed for the Chinese market. (Hyundai's other two plants can make 300000 cars per year each). When the plant opens in 2012 Hyundai will be manufacturing 1 million cars a year in China.

Hyundai also established a second 50/50 joint venture in spring 2011 to begin making commercial trucks and buses in China. Both Hyundai and Sichuan Nanjun Automobile are investing about $275 million each to build Sichuan Hyundai a plant with an annual production capacity of 160000 units (150000 trucks and 10000 buses) starting in 2013. Sichuan Hyundai will make two types of trucks —value models sold under the Nanjun brand and higher-priced models sold under the Hyundai brand. Still the market for commercial vehicles in China is very tight and Hyundai only expects to sell 160000 trucks and buses per year by 2015 for a market share of 3%. A previous joint venture with Baotou Bei Ben Heavy-Duty Truck signed in late 2009 fell through.

To keep pace with markets in Europe Hyundai has manufacturing plants in the Czech Republic Russia and Turkey. The Russian plant opened in early 2011 and can manufacture 150000 Solaris sedans a model specifically designed to withstand Russia's cold climate. Hyundai exports another 10 models to Russia including the Elantra sedan the Sonata sedan and the Santa Fe SUV. Together the company's plants in the Czech Republic and Turkey produce about 7% of Hyundai's vehicles while all of Europe accounts for about 15% of sales.

The company is also setting up shop in Brazil to target the fast-growing Latin American market. Construction on a $600 million manufacturing plant began in early 2011 with the government providing Hyundai with free land and tax breaks. The plant will first produce a small hatchback specifically designed for the market with a goal of manufacturing 150000 ethanol flex-fuel cars per year. Currently top models for the Brazilian market include the compact i30 the Azera and Sonata sedans and the Veracruz and ix35 SUVs.

Hyundai is a leading brand in India as well trailing domestic players Maruti Suzuki India and Tata Motors. India accounts for more than 15% of the company's total production and is the company's international base for economy vehicles. Its newest compact vehicle for India the Eon launched in October 2011.

HISTORY

Hyundai Motor Company was established in 1967 and it initially began manufacturing cars and light trucks through a technology collaboration with Ford's UK operations. By the early 1970s Hyundai was ready to build cars under its own nameplate. The company debuted the subcompact Hyundai Pony in 1974 at Italy's annual Turin Motor Show.

The Pony was an instant domestic success and soon propelled Hyundai to the top spot among South Korea's carmakers. During the mid-1970s the company began exporting the Pony to El Salvador and Guatemala.

By the 1980s Hyundai was ready to shift into high gear and begin high-volume production in anticipation of penetrating more overseas markets. The company began exporting to Canada in 1983.

Hyundai introduced the Hyundai Excel in 1985. That year the company established its US subsidiary Hyundai Motor America. By 1986 Hyundai was exporting Excels for sale in the US. Sales of the Excel soared the next year so Hyundai decided to build a factory in Bromont Quebec.

But by the time the factory was finished in 1989 consumers were tiring of the aging compact car and the quality problems that came with it. Hyundai closed the plant after just four years of operation.

The company introduced its first sports car the Scoupe in 1990. The following year it developed the first Hyundai-designed engine called the Alpha. Two years later the carmaker unveiled its second-generation proprietary engine the Beta.

By 1998 Hyundai was beginning to feel the pinch of the Asian economic crisis as domestic demand dropped drastically. However the decrease in Korean demand was largely offset by exports. That year Hyundai took a controlling stake in Korean competitor Kia Motors.

In hopes of increasing its share of the Asian automotive market Daimler AG took a 10% stake in Hyundai in 2000 (sold 2004). The deal included the establishment of a joint venture to manufacture commercial vehicles as well as an agreement among Hyundai Daimler and Mitsubishi Motors to develop small cars for the global market.

In 2001 Hyundai decreased its stake in Kia Motors to about 46%.

The following year Daimler announced it would exercise its option to take a 50% stake in Hyundai's heavy truck business.

In 2004 Hyundai CEO Kim Dong-Jin was indicted in South Korea on charges that he violated campaign finance laws and engaged in managerial negligence. The charges stemmed from a general crackdown on campaign finance violations during which more than a dozen members of South Korea's parliament were either indicted or detained. Later in 2004 Kim was convicted of the charges against him and sentenced to a suspended two-year prison term.

To increase its presence in the US Hyundai completed construction of a new manufacturing plant Hyundai Motor Manufacturing Alabama in 2005. The plant's annual production was about 300000 cars.

In 2006 Hyundai's legal woes persisted when two executives were arrested as part of a Korean bribery investigation. The pair were accused of creating a slush fund that was allegedly used to fund a lobbyist who sought favors for Hyundai from the South Korean government. Officials were also investigating whether the slush fund was created at the behest of Hyundai chairman Chung Mong-Koo.

Chung then was indicted and arrested on charges that he embezzled Hyundai company cash to finance bribes for Korean government officials in exchange for corporate favors. After two months of incarceration Chung was released from jail on $1 million bail.

He was convicted early in 2007. Under Korean law Chung faced a potential life sentence but received only a three-year prison term as the judge in the case said Chung contributed hugely to the development of the Korean economy. During his trial Chung admitted some wrongdoing when he said "I admit to my guilt to some extent." However Chung appealed the conviction. Three other Hyundai officials were also convicted but they received suspended sentences. Chung's son Kia Motors boss Chung Eui-Sun also was under investigation but prosecutors did not indict him.

Later in 2007 Chung's three-year prison sentence was suspended by an appeals court with a three-judge panel citing his importance to Korea's economy. The appellate judges however required the Hyundai executive to maintain a clean record for five years to avoid prison and to fulfill a promise he made to donate $1.1 billion of his personal assets to society.

EXECUTIVES

President Ulsan Plant, Yoon Gap Han
President and CEO, Lee Won Hee
Chairman, Chung Mong-Koo, age 68
Vice Chairman, Chung Eui-Sun, age 45
Auditors: Anjin & Co. (A Member Firm of Deloitte Touche Tohmatsu)

LOCATIONS

HQ: Hyundai Motor Co., Ltd.
12, Heolleung-ro Seocho-gu, Seoul 137-938
Phone: (82) 2 3464 1114   **Fax:** (82) 2 3463 3484
Web: www.hyundai-motor.com

2015 Sales

	% of total
Korea	44
North America	32
Europe	14
Asia	8
Other regions	2
Total	**100**

PRODUCTS/OPERATIONS

2015 Sales

	% of total
Vehicle	79
Finance	14
Others	7
Total	**100**

Selected Models
Commercial vehicles
  Aero (large city bus)
  Aero Town (medium bus)
  County (small bus)
  e-Mighty (light commercial truck)
  Super Aero City (bus)
  Universe (large coach bus)
Passenger cars
  Accent (compact coupe)
  Atos Prime (subcompact)
  Avante XD
  Azera (sedan)
  Elantra (sedan)
  Entourage (minivan)
  Equus/Centennial (premium sedan)
  Genesis (premium coupe)
  Getz (compact sedan)
  Santa Fe (SUV)
  Sonata (sedan)
  Tiburon (coupe)
  Tucson (SUV)
  Trajet (SUV)
  Veracruz (SUV)

COMPETITORS

BYD	Honda
Chery Automobile	Isuzu
Daihatsu	Maruti Suzuki
Daimler	Mazda
Dongfeng Motor	Nissan
FCA US	Peugeot
Fiat Chrysler	Renault
Ford Motor	Ssangyong Motor
GM Korea	Tata Motors
General Motors	Toyota
Hindustan Motors	Volkswagen

HISTORICAL FINANCIALS

Company Type: Public

Income Statement

FYE: December 31

	REVENUE ($ mil.)	NET INCOME ($ mil.)	NET PROFIT MARGIN	EMPLOYEES
12/15	78,160	5,454	7.0%	66,404
12/14	81,579	6,714	8.2%	64,956
12/13	83,019	8,122	9.8%	63,099
12/12	79,113	8,018	10.1%	59,831
12/11	67,142	6,607	9.8%	57,105
Annual Growth	**3.9%**	**(4.7%)**	**—**	**3.8%**

2015 Year-End Financials

Debt ratio: 0.0%
Return on equity: 10.7%
Cash ($ mil.): 6,231
Current ratio: 1.64
Long-term debt ($ mil.): 38,043
No. of shares (mil.): 207
Dividends
  Yield: 4.2%
  Payout: 8.4%
Market value ($ mil.): 8,935

	STOCK PRICE ($) FY Close	P/E High/Low		PER SHARE ($) Earnings	Dividends	Book Value
12/15	43.15	0	0	20.28	1.81	254.59
12/14	56.75	0	0	24.71	0.96	252.56
12/13	58.00	0	0	29.90	0.86	235.97
12/12	30.15	0	0	29.52	0.85	197.10
12/11	25.25	0	0	24.34	0.67	153.06
Annual Growth	**14.3%**		**—**	**(4.5%)**	**28.1%**	**13.6%**

Iberdrola SA

EXECUTIVES

Authorised Signing Officer, Fernando Julio Arias Coterillo
Auditors: Ernst & Young, S.L.

LOCATIONS

HQ: Iberdrola SA
Tomas Redondo, 1, Madrid 28033
Phone: (34) 91 784 2742   **Fax:** (34) 91 784 2977
Web: www.iberdrola.es

HISTORICAL FINANCIALS

Company Type: Public

Income Statement   FYE: December 31

	REVENUE ($ mil.)	NET INCOME ($ mil.)	NET PROFIT MARGIN	EMPLOYEES
12/15	34,221	2,637	7.7%	27,169
12/14	36,504	2,827	7.7%	28,021
12/13	45,167	3,540	7.8%	30,678
12/12	45,078	3,744	8.3%	31,338
12/11	40,935	3,627	8.9%	31,885
Annual Growth	(4.4%)	(7.7%)	—	(3.9%)

2015 Year-End Financials

Debt ratio: 31.8%
Return on equity: 6.6%
Cash ($ mil.): 1,256
Current ratio: 0.74
Long-term debt ($ mil.): 27,120
No. of shares (mil.): —
Dividends
Yield: 3.3%
Payout: —
Market value ($ mil.): —

	STOCK PRICE ($) FY Close	P/E High/Low		PER SHARE ($) Earnings	Dividends	Book Value
12/15	28.32	76	63	0.41	0.96	6.48
12/14	26.91	78	60	0.44	1.58	6.84
12/13	25.55	64	48	0.56	1.22	7.80
12/12	21.32	55	30	0.60	0.99	7.25
12/11	24.10	70	48	0.62	0.00	7.23
Annual Growth	4.1%	—	—	(9.7%)	—	(2.7%)

ICICI Bank Ltd (India)

You see ICICI Bank is India's #2 bank (after State Bank of India) and its largest private bank boasting over $130 billion in assets. The bank has some 4000 branches nationwide as well as locations in about 20 other countries. The Retail banking group offers lending and deposit services to small businesses and individuals while Wholesale Banking does the same for corporate clients in India and abroad. The rural and government banking unit offers micro-loans and agricultural banking. Its International Banking unit deals with the bank's foreign operations and international trade finance-related service. The bank also offers life and property/casualty insurance through subsidiaries.

OperationsServing some 52 million customers the bank operates three core business segments: Retail Banking (30% of revenue); Wholesale Banking (30% of revenue) which serves corporate customers in India and overseas in providing working capital finance export finance trade transaction and commercial banking and foreign currency term loans; and Treasury (40% of revenue) which manages the bank's investment portfolio and includes the Proprietary Trading Group Markets Group and Asset Liability Management Group.

Key subsidiaries include ICICI Prudential Life Insurance (the largest private sector life insurer in the country) ICICI Lombard General Insurance (property/casualty coverage) ICICI Prudential Asset Management (mutual funds) ICICI Securities (investment banking and brokerage) and ICICI Venture Funds Management (venture capital).

Geographic ReachWhile it operates in 17 countries ICICI generates more than 90% of its total revenue in its home country. The bank has an international presence through its ICICI Bank UK and ICICI Bank Canada subsidiaries in the UK and Canada respectively. It also has branches in the US China Singapore Hong Kong Dubai Sri Lanka Bahrain South Africa Bangladesh Malaysia and Indonesia.

Financial Performance

Note: Growth rates may differ after conversion to US dollars. This analysis uses the company-provided financials from its 2015 Annual Report.

ICICI Bank's revenues and profits have been steadily rising over the past few years mostly as its overall loan business (particularly loans to its Retail customers) has continued to grow with aggressive domestic branch expansion.

The bank's revenue rose by 12% to R$613 billion ($10 billion) in fiscal 2015 (ended March) mostly thanks to double-digit interest income growth as its Retail and Wholesale loan assets grew by 10% and as interest margins ticked up slightly during the year. ICICI's fee income rose by 7% on higher transaction banking fees third-party referral fees and commercial banking fees. The bank's Treasury segment grew by 12% thanks to higher gains on government securities and other fixed income securities exchange gains on overseas operations dividend income from subsidiaries and gains on its equity and mutual fund investment portfolio.

Higher revenue in FY2015 drove ICICI's net income higher by 13% to R$111 billion (nearly $2 billion) for the year. The bank's operating cash levels fell sharply during the year with operations using R$48.2 billion ($769 million) after unfavorable changes in working capital related to its investments advances deposits and other assets liabilities and provisions.

Strategy

ICICI Bank has continued to move toward digital banking channels that are quickly taking the industry by storm allowing the bank to slow expensive branch-expansion plans and cut operating costs significantly while giving customers faster access to banking services. As India's first bank to offer mobile banking (its iMobile app) and its first bank to offer money transfer via Twitter (and the second Globally) pioneering ICICI Bank had more than 100 electronic Touch Banking branches across 33 Indian cities in 2015 which allowed customers to have full 24/7 bank access without the need for a physical branch. During FY2015 it also launched its "Pockets" digital mobile wallet app which offered customers a full suite of bank and e-commerce services; as well as its "Tap n Pay" solution that enabled customers to tap their cards for fast payment transactions.

But that doesn't mean it's done growing its physical branch network. Already boasting a vast network of more than 4050 domestic branches ICICI in 2015 continued to expand what is the largest branch network among private sector banks in India. It's also been expanding abroad opening its first branch in China in 2015.

The company is spinning off part of its stake in ICICI Prudential Life Insurance in an offering that is expected to be India's largest IPO in five years. The insurer plans to raise as much as 60.6 billion rupees.

Ownership
Deutsche Bank Trust owned 29% of ICICI Bank at the FY2015.

EXECUTIVES

Managing Director and CEO, Chanda D. Kochhar, age 55
Executive Director, N. S. Kannan, age 51
Executive Director, Krishnaswamy Ramkumar, age 55
President, Zarin Daruwala
Executive Director, Rajiv Sabharwal
President, Vijay Chandok
CFO, Rakesh Jha
Chairman, Mahendra Kumar Sharma, age 69
Auditors: B S R & Co. LLP

LOCATIONS

HQ: ICICI Bank Ltd (India)
ICICI Towers, Bandra-Kurla Complex, Mumbai 400 051
Phone: (91) 22 33667777   **Fax:** (91) 22 26531122
Web: www.icicibank.com

PRODUCTS/OPERATIONS

2015 Sales by Segment

	% of total
Treasury	39
Wholesale Banking	30
Retail Banking	30
Other Banking	1
Total	**100**

COMPETITORS

BNP Paribas	ING
Bank of Baroda	Industrial Development
Bank of India	Bank of India
Canara Bank	Punjab National Bank
Citigroup	Standard Chartered
GE Money India	State Bank of India
HDFC Bank	UCO Bank
HSBC	

HISTORICAL FINANCIALS

Company Type: Public

Income Statement   FYE: March 31

	ASSETS ($ mil.)	NET INCOME ($ mil.)	INCOME AS % OF ASSETS	EMPLOYEES
03/16	138,929	1,539	1.1%	97,132
03/15	132,079	1,958	1.5%	90,486
03/14	124,533	1,838	1.5%	94,204
03/13	0	1,769	—	85,217
03/12	118,759	1,502	1.3%	81,254
Annual Growth	4.0%	0.6%	—	4.6%

2016 Year-End Financials

Return on assets: 1.1%
Return on equity: 11.3%
Long-term debt ($ mil.): —
No. of shares (mil.): —
Sales ($ mil): 15,332
Dividends
Yield: 4.3%
Payout: 57.5%
Market value ($ mil.): —

	STOCK PRICE ($) FY Close	P/E High/Low		PER SHARE ($) Earnings	Dividends	Book Value
03/16	7.16	1	0	0.26	0.31	2.45
03/15	10.36	3	0	0.33	0.15	2.34
03/14	43.80	2	1	0.32	0.13	2.20
03/13	42.90	3	2	0.31	0.12	(0.00)
03/12	34.87			0.26	0.00	2.09
Annual Growth	(32.7%)	—	—	0.3%	—	4.0%

Idemitsu Kosan Co Ltd

As long as Japanese drive Toyotas there will be a role for Idemitsu Kosan. The company is the #2 oil refiner in Japan (behind Nippon Oil). At its four refineries in Japan (processing 640000 barrels per day) Idemitsu Kosan produces petroleum products such as gasoline and other fuels kerosene and lubricants. It markets its fuel products through a network of 4600 service stations. Idemitsu Kosan sells heavy oil and jet fuels to industries and kerosene and liquefied petroleum gas to the residential sector. The company also has interests in oil exploration and production as well as coal and uranium. In 2016 it agreed to buy a 31.3% stake in Showa Shell Sekiyu from Royal Dutch Shell for $1.35 billion. OperationsIdemitsu Kosan has three reportable segments: Its petroleum products business includes fuel oil and petrochemical products. Its petrochemical products operations consist of the basic chemicals business which jointly operates an ethylene complex with Mitsui Chemicals and the functional materials business which develops functional flexible polypropylene. The company's resources businesses is engaged in exploration activities to expand its oil reserves.

In addition to its oil and gas businesses the company has a number of New Growth activities including agro-business (pesticides) and green energy (wind solar and geothermal). Idemitsu Kosan is also developing electronic materials (organic light-emitting diode luminous materials with Sony Corporation) and lithium battery development.

Geographic Reach

Idemitsu Kosan has offices in Africa Asia (East South East and South West) Australia Europe (including Russia) the Middle East and North and South America.

Financial Performance

In 2012 the company's revenues increased by 18% due to increases in the prices of crude oil and naphtha significant rises in coal prices and an increase in the volume of products sold. Japan accounted for 84% of the company's revenues that year.

Net income increased by 6% in 2012 thanks to higher revenues and the result of progress in streamlining activities in production sales and distribution as well as improved product margins for petrochemical products despite a contraction of margins for petroleum products.

StrategyTo meet increased demand Idemitsu Kosan is enhancing its petroleum products business in the growing overseas markets centered on the Pacific Rim. As part of this process in 2012 it acquired Freedom an independent Australian petroleum products distributor that sells petroleum products wholesale and operates about 40 gas stations on Australia's east coast.

That year it also opened an office in China formed a joint venture in Taiwan and set up a lubricant manufacturing and sales company in Vietnam.

Idemitsu Kosan unified its ethylene production with Mitsui Chemicals in 2010 to promote efficiency.

Company Background

Pooling their LPG resources and expertise in 2006 Idemitsu Kosan merged its LPG operations with those of Mitsubishi to form Astomos Energy.

EXECUTIVES

CEO, Takashi Tsukioka
EVP, Yoshihisa Matsumoto
EVP, Daisuke Seki
EVP, Hiroshi Seki
Auditors: Deloitte Touche Tohmatsu LLC

LOCATIONS

HQ: Idemitsu Kosan Co Ltd
  3-1-1 Marunouchi, Chiyoda-ku, Tokyo 100-8321
Phone: (81) 3 3213 3150
Web: www.idemitsu.co.jp

2016 Sales

	% of total
Japan	75
Asia and Oceania	16
North America	6
Europe	2
Other	1
Total	**100**

PRODUCTS/OPERATIONS

2016 Sales

	% of total
Petroleum products	77
Petrochemical products	15
Resources	6
Others	2
Total	**100**

Products & Services
Agri-Bio
Electronic Materials
Lubricants
Packing Materials Logistics Plastics
Petrochemicals
Petroleum Transportation
Refinery & Plant
Renewable Energy
Research & Development
Resource Development
SUBSIDIARIES
AltaGas Idemitsu Joint Venture Limited Partnership
Apolloretailing Co.Ltd.
Astomos Energy Corp.
Formosa Idemitsu Petrochemicals Corporation
Idemitsu Apollo Corporation
Idemitsu Australia Resources Pty Ltd
Idemitsu Canada Corporation
Idemitsu Canada Resouces Ltd.
Idemitsu Credit Co. Ltd.
Idemitsu Engineering Co. Ltd.
Idemitsu Insurance Service Co.Ltd.
Idemitsu International (Asia) Pte.Ltd.
Idemitsu Oita Geothermal Co.Ltd.
Idemitsu Petroleum Norge AS
Idemitsu Petroleum UK Ltd.
Idemitsu Retail Marketing Co. Ltd.
Idemitsu SM (Malaysia) Sdn.Bhd.
Idemitsu Tanker Co. Ltd.
Idemitsu Unitech Co. Ltd.
Nghi Son Refinery and Petrochemical LLC
Prime Polymer Co. Ltd.
PS Japan Corp.
SDS Biotech K.K.

COMPETITORS

Cosmo Oil	JX Nippon Oil & Energy
JX Holdings	SK Innovation
JX Nippon Mining & Metals	Showa Shell Sekiyu

HISTORICAL FINANCIALS
Company Type: Public

Income Statement
FYE: March 31

	REVENUE ($ mil.)	NET INCOME ($ mil.)	NET PROFIT MARGIN	EMPLOYEES
03/16	31,792	(320)	—	9,203
03/15	38,587	(1,149)	—	8,829
03/14	48,779	351	0.7%	8,749
03/13	46,493	533	1.1%	8,684
03/12	52,545	784	1.5%	8,243
Annual Growth	(11.8%)	—	—	2.8%

2016 Year-End Financials

Debt ratio: 0.3%
Return on equity: (-6.6%)
Cash ($ mil.): 1,078
Current ratio: 0.92
Long-term debt ($ mil.): 5,482
No. of shares (mil.): 159
Dividends
  Yield: 0.0%
  Payout: —
Market value ($ mil.): 1,368

	STOCK PRICE ($) FY Close	P/E High/Low	Earnings	Dividends	Book Value
03/16	8.55	— —	(2.00)	0.22	27.87
03/15	8.97	— —	(7.19)	0.21	30.60
03/14	10.54	— —	2.20	0.00	45.05
03/13	21.97	— —	3.33	0.00	45.71
03/12	26.72	— —	4.91	0.00	46.83
Annual Growth	(24.8%)	— —	—	—	(12.2%)

Imperial Brands PLC

Auditors: PricewaterhouseCoopers LLP

LOCATIONS

HQ: Imperial Brands PLC
  121 Winterstoke Road, Bristol BS3 2LL
Phone: (44) 117 963 6636
Web: www.imperial-tobacco.com

HISTORICAL FINANCIALS
Company Type: Public

Income Statement
FYE: September 30

	REVENUE ($ mil.)	NET INCOME ($ mil.)	NET PROFIT MARGIN	EMPLOYEES
09/16	35,803	817	2.3%	33,900
09/15	38,383	2,566	6.7%	36,000
09/14	43,088	2,301	5.3%	33,900
09/13	45,631	1,512	3.3%	35,300
09/12	46,277	1,098	2.4%	37,200
Annual Growth	(6.2%)	(7.1%)	—	(2.3%)

2016 Year-End Financials

Debt ratio: 55.1%
Return on equity: 11.8%
Cash ($ mil.): 1,650
Current ratio: 0.74
Long-term debt ($ mil.): 16,057
No. of shares (mil.): 958
Dividends
  Yield: 2.7%
  Payout: 147.7%
Market value ($ mil.): 49,345

	STOCK PRICE ($) FY Close	P/E High/Low	Earnings	Dividends	Book Value
09/16	51.47	162 76	0.86	1.42	7.18
09/15	103.50	60 43	2.69	4.04	8.45
09/14	86.77	61 48	2.40	4.00	8.56
09/13	74.15	85 71	1.55	3.38	9.31
09/12	74.04	124 101	1.10	1.63	9.87
Annual Growth	(8.7%)	— —	(6.1%)	(3.4%)	(7.7%)

Imperial Oil Ltd

Imperial Oil Canada's second-largest oil integrated company behind Suncor Energy holds sway over a vast empire of oil and gas resources. Imperial is one of Canada's top natural gas producers a leading refiner and marketer of petroleum products and a major supplier of petrochemicals. It sells petroleum products including gasoline heating oil and diesel fuel under the Esso name and other brand names. The company reported proved reserves in 2013 of 3.6 billion barrels of oil-equivalent including 62 million barrels of liquids 678 billion cu. ft. of natural gas 579 million barrels of synthetic oil and 2.9 billion barrels of bitumen. Exxon Mobil owns about 70% of Imperial.

Geographic Reach

Most of the company's production comes from fields in Alberta and the Northwest Territories.

Operations

Imperial has three main segments: Upstream Downstream and Chemical. Upstream operations include the exploration for and production of crude oil natural gas synthetic oil and bitumen; Downstream operations consist of the transportation and refining of crude oil blending of refined products and the distribution and marketing of those products; and its Chemical operations consist of the manufacturing and marketing of various petrochemicals such as ethylene benzene aromatic and aliphatic solvents plasticizer intermediates and polyethylene resin.

In addition to its conventional upstream operations Imperial owns 25% of Syncrude Canada which operates the world's largest oil sands development with synthetic oil and bitumen/heavy oil end products.

The Downstream segment owns and operates three refineries. The Strathcona and Sarnia refineries process Canadian crude oil and the Nanticoke refinery processes a combination of Canadian and foreign crude oil. The Strathcona refinery operates lubricating oil production facilities. The company maintains a nationwide distribution system including 22 primary terminals to handle bulk and packaged petroleum products moving from refineries to market by pipeline tanker rail and road transport. It also owns and operates natural gas liquids and products pipelines in Alberta Manitoba and Ontario and has interests in the capital stock of one crude oil and two products pipeline companies.

Sales and Marketing

The company sells gasoline to motorists at more than 1700 primarily Esso-branded gas stations across Canada.

It markets more than 550 petroleum products throughout Canada to all types of customers. It also serves the Canadian agriculture residential heating and small commercial markets through 28 branded resellers and sells petroleum products to large industrial and commercial accounts as well as to other refiners and marketers.

Financial Performance

Imperial's revenues grew by 6% in 2013 primarily due to increased Upstream sales partially offset by lower Downstream and Chemical sales.

Upstream segment revenue growth was fueled by higher production of both conventional crude oil and natural gas (as the result of the Celtic acquisition and the Horn River pilot which more than offset normal field decline) as well as priced. The improvement was partially offset by lower production of Cold Lake bitumen.

Downstream segment revenues declined due to reduced refinery throughput of 426000 barrels per day in 2013 (compared to 435000 barrels per day in 2012) as well as the closing of its Dartmouth refinery. This was partially offset by increased production higher product sales and reduced maintenance activities.

The chemical segment revenue decline was due to a lower volume of petrochemical sales in 2013.

Imperial's net income declined by 25% in 2013 due to significantly lower industry refining margins higher Kearl bitumen project costs (as production

contribution was more than offset by start-up and operating costs) lower volumes at Syncrude and a lower contribution from Cold Lake as well as an after-tax charge associated with the conversion of the Dartmouth refinery to a terminal.

Cash flow generated from operating activities decreased by $1.4 billion in 2013 primarily due to lower net income and working capital effects.

Strategy

Seeking to focus on its expanding oil sands and refining businesses in 2016 Imperial Oil agreed to sell 497 Esso-brand retail gas stations to five fuel distributors for $2.8-billion.

Reorganizing its portfolio in 2014 Imperial sold its interests in assets located in Boundary Lake Cynthia/West Pembina and Rocky Mountain House in Western Canada to Whitecap Resources Inc. for C$855 million (US$785 million).

In 2013 the company converted its underperforming Dartmouth refinery to a fuels terminal. That year Imperial invested about $8 billion in capital and exploration expenditures primarily in the Upstream segment related to Celtic and Clyden acquisitions and post-acquisition investments and the advancement of the Kearl expansion and Nabiye projects. In 2012 the company entered into a $2 billion expansion of the company's Cold Lake operation in northeastern Alberta. The expansion called Nabiye will bring on additional commercial bitumen production of more than 40000 barrels per day at Cold Lake. The project (which has access to 280 million barrels of recoverable reserves) is expected to start up by the end of 2014.

In 2013 the company's research expenditures were $199 million and were mainly targeted on developing technologies to reduce the environmental impact and improve bitumen recovery in the upstream segment and for supporting environmental and process improvements in the refineries as well as accessing Exxon Mobil's data worldwide.

Mergers and Acquisitions

In 2013 following the acquisition of Celtic Exploration by ExxonMobil Canada Imperial acquired 50% of Celtic from ExxonMobil Canada for $1.6 billion. A general partnership was formed to hold and operate the assets of Celtic under the name of XTO Energy Canada.

That year Imperial and ExxonMobil Canada also acquired ConocoPhillips' interest in the Clyden oil sands lease.

HISTORY

London Ontario boomed from the discovery of oil in the 1860s and 1870s but when the market for Canadian kerosene became saturated in 1880 16 refiners banded together to form the Imperial Oil Company.

The company refined sulfurous Canadian oil nicknamed "skunk oil" for its powerful smell. Imperial faced tough competition from America's Standard Oil which marketed kerosene made from lighter less-odorous Pennsylvania crude. Guided by American expatriate Jacob Englehart Imperial built a better refinery and hired a chemist to develop a process to clean sulfur from the crude.

By the mid-1890s Imperial had expanded from coast to Canadian coast. Cash-starved from its expansion the company turned to old nemesis Standard Oil which bought a controlling interest in Imperial in 1898. That interest is today held by Exxon Mobil.

After the turn of the century Imperial began producing gasoline to serve the new automobiles. The horseless carriages were spooking the workhorses at the warehouse where fuel was sold so an Imperial manager in Vancouver opened the first Canadian service station in 1907. The company marketed its gas under the Esso banner borrowed from Standard Oil.

An Imperial crew discovered oil in 1920 at Norman Wells in the remote Northwest Territories. In 1924 a subsidiary sparked a new boom with a gas well discovery in the Turner Valley area northeast of Edmonton. But soon Imperial's luck ran as dry as the holes it was drilling; it came away empty from the next 133 consecutive wells. That string ended in 1947 when it struck oil in Alberta at the Leduc No. 1. To get the oil to market Imperial invested in the Interprovincial Pipe Line from Alberta to Superior Wisconsin.

The company began research in 1964 to extract bitumen from the oil sands in Cold Lake Alberta. During the 1970s oil crisis Imperial continued to search for oil in northern Canada. It found crude on land near the Beaufort Sea (1970) and in its icy waters (1972). The company formed its Esso Resources Canadian Ltd. subsidiary in 1978 to oversee natural resources production.

In 1989 Texaco (acquired by Chevron in 2001) still reeling from a court battle with Pennzoil sold Texaco Canada to Imperial. To diminish debt and comply with regulators Imperial agreed to sell some of Texaco Canada's refining and marketing assets in Atlantic Canada its interests in Interhome Energy and oil and gas properties in western Canada.

Imperial reorganized in 1992 centralizing several units and in 1993 closed its refinery at Port Moody British Columbia. It sold most of its fertilizer business in 1994 disposed of 339 unprofitable gas stations in 1995 and the next year closed down Canada's northernmost oil refinery at Norman Wells.

In 1997 Imperial announced an ambitious program to expand Syncrude's oil sands bitumen upgrading plant. In 1998 Exxon agreed to buy Mobil which had substantial Canadian oil assets. In 1999 Canada preapproved the potential merger of Imperial Oil and Mobil Canada. Later that year Exxon completed its purchase of Mobil to form Exxon Mobil.

Expanding its exploration and production assets in 2007 Imperial and ExxonMobil Canada acquired exploration rights for a development parcel in the Beaufort Sea and in 2008 in the Horn River area of northeastern British Columbia.

EXECUTIVES

Chairman President and CEO, R. M. (Rich) Kruger, $4,837,802 total compensation
SVP Finance and Administration and Treasurer, Paul J. Masschelin, age 62, $499,694 total compensation
SVP Upstream, B.P. (Bart) Cahir
VP and General Counsel, W.J. (Bill) Hartnett, $434,333 total compensation
Treasurer, David Bailey
VP Fuels Lubricants and Specialties Marketing, B.G. Merkel, $424,333 total compensation
Auditors: PricewaterhouseCoopers LLP

LOCATIONS

HQ: Imperial Oil Ltd
505 Quarry Park Boulevard S.E., Calgary, Alberta T2C 5N1
Phone: 587 476-3950   **Fax:** 587 476-1166
Web: www.imperialoil.ca

PRODUCTS/OPERATIONS

2015 Sales

	% of total
Downstream	74
Upstream	22
Chemical	4
Total	**100**

COMPETITORS

Abraxas Petroleum	Marathon Oil
Ashland Inc.	Murphy Oil
BHP Billiton	Occidental Petroleum
BP	PEMEX
Barnwell Industries	PETROBRAS
Canadian Natural	Petríeos de
ConocoPhillips	Venezuela
Devon Energy	Pioneer Natural
Dominion Resources	Resources
DuPont	Repsol Oil & Gas
Encana	Royal Dutch Shell
Eni	Suncor
Hunting	Sunoco
Husky Energy	TOTAL
Koch Industries Inc.	

HISTORICAL FINANCIALS

Company Type: Public

Income Statement

FYE: December 31

	REVENUE ($ mil.)	NET INCOME ($ mil.)	NET PROFIT MARGIN	EMPLOYEES
12/15	19,359	807	4.2%	5,700
12/14	31,922	3,268	10.2%	5,500
12/13	30,967	2,659	8.6%	5,300
12/12	31,358	3,786	12.1%	5,100
12/11	30,108	3,304	11.0%	5,085
Annual Growth	(10.5%)	(29.7%)	—	2.9%

2015 Year-End Financials

Debt ratio: 14.2%
Return on equity: —
Cash ($ mil.): 146
Current ratio: 0.68
Long-term debt ($ mil.): 4,726

No. of shares (mil.): 847
Dividends
Yield: 1.6%
Payout: 56.8%
Market value ($ mil.): 27,564

	STOCK PRICE ($) FY Close	P/E High/Low		PER SHARE ($) Earnings	Dividends	Book Value
12/15	32.52	31	22	0.95	0.42	19.90
12/14	43.03	11	9	3.84	0.47	22.95
12/13	44.23	13	11	3.12	0.47	21.66
12/12	43.00	11	9	4.44	0.48	19.43
12/11	44.48	13	9	3.87	0.43	15.41
Annual Growth	(7.5%)	—	—	(29.6%)	(0.8%)	6.6%

Indian Oil Corp., Ltd. (India)

LOCATIONS

HQ: Indian Oil Corp., Ltd. (India)
3079/3, Sadiq Nagar, J.B. Tito Marg, New Delhi 110049
Phone: (91) 11 26260000
Web: www.iocl.com

HISTORICAL FINANCIALS

Company Type: Public

Income Statement

FYE: March 31

	REVENUE ($ mil.)	NET INCOME ($ mil.)	NET PROFIT MARGIN	EMPLOYEES
03/15	72,542	785	1.1%	0
03/14	81,907	1,180	1.4%	0
03/13	85,711	819	1.0%	34,084
03/12	81,004	830	1.0%	34,233
03/11	70,257	1,756	2.5%	34,105
Annual Growth	0.8%	(18.2%)	—	—

2015 Year-End Financials

Debt ratio: 0.4%
Return on equity: 7.1%
Cash ($ mil.): 195
Current ratio: 0.97
Long-term debt ($ mil.): 5,883

No. of shares (mil.): —
Dividends
Yield: —
Payout: —
Market value ($ mil.): —

Industria De Diseno Textil (Inditex) SA

Industria de Diseño Textil (Inditex) makes disposable chic fashions that are here today and gone tomorrow. The Spanish designer-cum-retailer uses technology and an armada of designers to master cheap chic. Inditex sells on a global scale with more than 7000 shops in upwards of 75 countries under eight different banners: Zara Oysho Massimo Dutti Pull&Bear Bershka Stradivarius Zara Home and Uterqüe. Located mostly in Europe the firm's stores answer to popular trends by telling designers in Spain what customers are asking for locally. Inditex responds in about two weeks with new designs. Amancio Ortega Gaona one of the world's wealthiest men founded Zara in 1975 and later created Inditex as a holding company.

Operations

Zara is Inditex's primary brand and brings in around 65% of the company's revenue. It makes trendy clothing for young adults at a mid price point. With an army of 600 designers pumping out 20000 pieces a year Zara is both a supplier (of itself) and retailer enabling it to respond with great speed to changes in taste and fashion. Its omnichannel offering consists of over 2100 stores and an e-commerce website. As well as clothing Zara also offers homewear.

Berska is Inditex's second-biggest earner bringing in 9% of revenue. It targets a younger demographic at a lower price point.

Its other brands Massimo Dutti (upscale fashion) Oysho (lingerie) Pull&Bear (urban youth 14-28) Uterque (high-end women's fashion) and Stradivarius account for 9% of revenue combined.

Geographic Reach

The company makes around 20% of revenue in Spain where it has more than 1900 stores. It has stores across the world but its footprint in the US is small in comparison with its massive European presence.

Sales and Marketing

Inditex records minimal marketing spending relying on word-of-mouth to promote Zara.

Financial Performance

Note: Growth rates may differ after conversion to US Dollars.

Inditex is big and growing recording revenue growth of 15% in 2015 to euro 20.9 billion. A like-for-like sales increase of 8.5% and 330 store openings in the year both contributed. Growth was seen in all brands with Zara leading with pack with 18% revenue growth to euro 13.6 billion by itself.

Net income also increased 15% to euro 2.9 billion tracking the increase in net sales. The company's cash position strengthened further with cash from operations increasing 39% to euro 4.5 billion.

Strategy

Inditex continues to expand rapidly. In 2015 the company opened 330 new stores in 56 markets and has fleshed out its online offering in Taiwan

Hong Kong Macau and Australia. The company invested euro 1.5 billion in its logistics and export activities.

HISTORY

Holding company Industria de Diseño Textil (Inditex) got its start as Confecciones Goa in 1963 making women's lingerie and housecoats in La Coruña Spain.

Founder Amancio Ortega learned the rag trade as a boy when at age 13 he made deliveries for a shirtmaker. Managing a tailor shop when he was a young man Ortega spied an expensive negligee for sale and he thought he could make copies and sell them for half the price. From there he made nightshirts and pajamas before he opened the first Zara store in La Coruña in 1975 where Ortega began expanding his offerings for women.

Ortega formed Inditex as a holding company for his growing operations in 1985. Inditex ran nearly 100 Zara stores before venturing out of the country to Portugal in 1988. New York City and Paris stores opened in 1989.

The company created the Pull & Bear clothing chain in 1991. About that time Inditex purchased a 65% stake in the Massimo Dutti group. (Inditex owns it all now.) The group continued to open stores around the globe: Mexico in 1992 Greece in 1993 Belgium and Sweden in 1994 Malta and Cyprus in 1996 and Israel and Norway in 1997.

In 1998 Inditex opened the Berksha chain to lure young females. The company further expanded that year into Argentina Japan Lebanon the UK and Venezuela.

Inditex then acquired 90% of Stradivarius a young women's chain with about 80 stores mostly in Spain. Meanwhile that year Inditex moved into nine more countries: Bahrain Brazil Canada Chile Germany the Netherlands Poland Saudi Arabia and Uruguay.

In 2000 the company announced it would open 150 new stores in the next two years including perhaps 40 in the US. Later in the year however the company said it would hold off on US expansion to concentrate on European growth. To fuel the growth of its Zara chain Inditex floated 26% of the company in a public offering in May 2001.

Over the course of 2001 Inditex entered six new markets: the Czech Republic Iceland Ireland Jordan Luxembourg and Puerto Rico.

In 2003 the first Zara Home stores opened and Inditex entered new markets in Malaysia Russia Slovakia and Slovenia. The following year the group surpassed the 2000 store count and entered Estonia Hungary Latvia Lithuania Morocco Panama and Romania.

Early in 2005 Inditex stopped selling fur items in all of its stores worldwide. In June Pablo Isla Alvarez de Tejera succeeded Jose Maria Castellano Rios as chief executive of the Spanish fashion giant. Castellano remained a non-executive vice chairman of the company until September when he resigned unexpectedly following a disagreement with Inditex's chairman Amancio Ortega over his failed bid for Fenosa a Spanish utility company. Castellano's departure ended a 31-year partnership between the two men.

Overall Inditex opened about 450 stores in 2005 and in the process became Europe's largest apparel retailer ahead of Sweden's H&M Hennes & Mauritz.

In February 2006 the first Zara store opened its doors in Shanghai the first Inditex shop in China.

In 2007 80% of new stores opened were located outside of Spain. Overall the group added 560 stores in some 50 countries. Also in 2007 the group's Kiddy's Class business segment combined operations with Zara Childrenswear. In October Zara Home launched an online shopping site. The online portal is a first for Inditex which has focused on the international expansion of its fashion chains.

In 2009 Inditex signed a joint venture with the Tata Group to open stores in India beginning in 2010. Also in 2009 the firm opened its first stores in Syria.

EXECUTIVES

Chairman and CEO, Pablo Isla
Auditors: DELOITTE, S.L.

LOCATIONS

HQ: Industria De Diseno Textil (Inditex) SA
Avda. de la Diputacion s/n, Edificio INDITEX, La Coruna, Arteixo 15142
Phone: (34) 98 118 5400
Web: www.inditex.es

2010 Sales

	% of total
Europe	
Spain	32
Other countries	46
America	10
Asia & other regions	12
Total	**100**

2010 Stores

	No.
Europe	
Spain	1,916
Other countries	2,006
Americas	390
Asia & other regions	595
Total	**4,907**

PRODUCTS/OPERATIONS

2015 Stores

	No.
Zara	2,162
Bershka	1,044
Pull & Bear	936
Stradivarius	950
Massimo Dutti	740
Oysho	607
Zara Home	502
Uterqüe	72
Total	**7,013**

2015 Sales

	% of total
Zara	65
Bershka	9
Massimo Dutti	7
Pull & Bear	7
Stradivarius	6
Zara Home	3
Oysho	2
Uterqüe	1
Total	**100**

COMPETITORS

Adolfo Domnguez	H&M
Arcadia	IKEA
Benetton	Kering
Carrefour	L Brands
Cortefiel	LVMH
Diesel SpA	NEXT plc
El Corte Ingles	Prada
Fast Retailing	Selfridges
French Connection	The Gap

HISTORICAL FINANCIALS

Company Type: Public

Income Statement

FYE: January 31

	REVENUE ($ mil.)	NET INCOME ($ mil.)	NET PROFIT MARGIN	EMPLOYEES
01/16	22,821	3,138	13.8%	152,854
01/15	20,563	2,838	13.8%	137,054
01/14	22,657	3,220	14.2%	128,313
01/13	21,613	3,199	14.8%	120,314
01/12	18,180	2,546	14.0%	109,512
Annual Growth	**5.8%**	**5.4%**	**—**	**8.7%**

2016 Year-End Financials

Debt ratio: 0.0%	No. of shares (mil.): —
Return on equity: 26.3%	Dividends
Cash ($ mil.): 4,613	Yield: 0.0%
Current ratio: 1.81	Payout: 20.0%
Long-term debt ($ mil.): 0	Market value ($ mil.): —

	STOCK PRICE ($) FY Close	P/E High/Low	PER SHARE ($) Earnings	Dividends	Book Value
01/16	16.42	20 15	1.01	0.20	4.00
01/15	14.70	32 14	0.91	0.21	3.80
01/14	29.79	43 33	1.03	0.44	4.02
01/13	27.90	39 23	1.03	0.35	3.67
01/12	17.45	30 22	0.82	0.35	3.14
Annual Growth	**(1.5%)**	**— —**	**5.4%**	**(12.8%)**	**6.3%**

Industrial and Commercial Bank of China (Asia) Limited

EXECUTIVES

Chief Executive Officer, Aiping Chen
Auditors: KPMG

LOCATIONS

HQ: Industrial and Commercial Bank of China (Asia) Limited
33/F., ICBC Tower, 3 Garden Road, Central,
Phone: (852) 2588 1188   **Fax:** (852) 2805 1166
Web: www.icbcasia.com

HISTORICAL FINANCIALS

Company Type: Public

Income Statement

FYE: December 31

	ASSETS ($ mil.)	NET INCOME ($ mil.)	INCOME AS % OF ASSETS	EMPLOYEES
12/15	94,640	875	0.9%	2,475
12/14	87,762	821	0.9%	2,395
12/13	73,480	677	0.9%	2,317
12/12	54,914	517	0.9%	1,845
12/11	52,131	405	0.8%	0
Annual Growth	**16.1%**	**21.2%**	**—**	**—**

2015 Year-End Financials

Return on assets: 0.9%	Dividends
Return on equity: 11.1%	Yield: —
Long-term debt ($ mil.): —	Payout: —
No. of shares (mil.): —	Market value ($ mil.): —
Sales ($ mil): 2,816	

Industrial and Commercial Bank of China Ltd

Boasting assets of roughly $3.35 trillion Industrial and Commercial Bank of China (ICBC) is one of China's biggest banks —and one of the largest in the world. The bank provides corporate retail and investment banking as well as asset management trust financial leasing insurance and other financial services to more than 5 million corporate clients and some 465 million individuals through 17000-plus branches across China and nearly 400 overseas branches and offices in more than 40 countries in six continents. The Chinese government controls about 70% of ICBC.

OperationsICBC operates three business segments. Corporate Banking which brings in nearly 50% of the bank's total operating income provides traditional banking products institutional and international banking settlement and cash management services trade finance investment banking underwriting asset trading and various other financial services to corporations. Its Personal Banking division makes up around 40% of the bank's total revenue and provides deposit and loan products as well as private banking services to individuals. Its Treasury operations (nearly 10% of total revenues) manage the bank's money market and investment securities.

In addition to these divisions the bank also provides wealth management asset custody and pension services and has a Metal business Franchise Treasury business and Asset Securitization business. ICBC owns most of Bank Halim Indonesia a majority stake in South Africa-based Standard Bank Group and an approximately 80% stake in ICBC (Macau). The company also has an 80% stake in Bank of East Asia's Canadian unit —now ICBC (Canada).Altogether the bank made 84% of its total revenue from interest income in 2014 (mostly from loans and advances followed by investment interest) while 14% came from fee and commission income.

Geographic Reach

The bank generates roughly 95% of its revenues from China while the remainder comes from 40 other countries.

Sales and Marketing

The bank reaches its large customer base through its massive branch network and more than 2000 correspondent banks worldwide. It also offers its services through its E-Banking network via internet and telephone banking and self-service banking centers.

Financial Performance

Note: Growth rates may differ after conversion to US dollars.

ICBC's revenues and profits have risen at a healthy clip over the past few years mostly thanks to its fast-growing client base double-digit loan business growth and the doubling of its net fee and commission income from other services since 2010. The bank's revenue jumped by 11% to C¥1015.4 billion (around $165 billion) in 2014 thanks mostly to higher interest income on double-digit growth of its loan and advances asset balances. The banks interest income on investments also increased thanks to a high-yield bond investment opportunity while fee and commission income grew thanks to the bank's growing card private banking and wealth management businesses. The boost in revenue coupled with strong cost controls also pushed the bank's net income higher by 5% to C¥276 billion ($44.8 billion). The bank's operating cash rose sharply to C¥201 billion ($32.7 billion) thanks to higher cash earnings mostly after adjusting for a $18 billion increase in non-cash impairment losses on loans and advances to customers.

Strategy

ICBC reiterated in 2015 its core plans for growth which included: focusing on product innovation and bolstering its service lines; diversifying its operations; continuing its aggressive global expansion plans; and continuing to invest in IT-based banking developments. Although it doesn't have the international presence of fellow Chinese group Bank of China ICBC has had its eyes on growth abroad over the past few years. In 2015 the bank's acquisitions expanded its business into Turkey as well as in several new locations in the UK US Japan and the UAE. And during 2014 the bank expanded its global reach in opening its businesses in New Zealand opening new branches in Kuwait and London and obtaining regulatory approval for its Yangon branch and Mexico subsidiary.

Mergers and Acquisitions

In May 2015 expanding its operations into Turkey for the first time ICBC bought a 75.5% stake in Tekstilbank from GSD Holding AS making it the first business institution operating in Turkey by a Chinese Bank.

In February 2015 with its eye on global expansion ICBC purchased a controlling 60% stake in Standard Bank PLC from Standard Bank Group Limited for $690 million. The joint-venture deal boasted operations in London New York Singapore Dubai Tokyo Hong Kong and Shanghai and would provide trading services in commodities foreign exchange interest rates credit and equities to clients worldwide.

In 2012 ICBC purchased a majority of the Bank of East Asia's US operations including more than a dozen bank branches in New York and California. The deal marked the first time that a US retail bank was acquired by a Chinese company.

Company Background

ICBC ventured into the US broker-dealer business in 2010 when it acquired the Prime Dealer Services unit of Fortis Securities from BNP Paribas.

EXECUTIVES

Chief Risk Officer, Wei Guoxiong, age 61
SEVP, Zhang Hongli
Chairman Board of Supervisors, Qian Wenhui
SEVP, Wang Xiquan
SEVP, Zheng Wanchun, age 52
SEVP, Gu Shu
SEVP, Wang Jingdong
CIO, Lin Xiaoxuan
Chairman and Executive Director, Yi Huiman, age 52
Auditors: KPMG Huazhen LLP

LOCATIONS

HQ: Industrial and Commercial Bank of China Ltd
No. 55 Fuxingmennei Avenue, Xicheng District, Beijing 100140
Phone: (86) 10 66106114   **Fax:** (86) 10 66107571
Web: www.icbc.com.cn

2014 Sales

	% of total
Mainland China	94
Overseas and other	6
Total	**100**

PRODUCTS/OPERATIONS

2014 Sales

	% of total
Interest	84
Noninterest	
Fees & commissions	14
Other	2
Total	**100**

2014 Sales by Segment

	% of total
Corporate banking	49
Personal banking	37
Treasury operations	13
Other	1
Total	**100**

Selected ServicesBank card services　Credit Card Instalments　Credit Card SMS Banking　Limited Hours Card Opening Services　Peony Credit Card VIP Services　Verified by Visa Services Corporate banking services　Assets

COMPETITORS

Agricultural Bank of China	China Construction Bank
Bank of China	China Merchants Bank
Bank of Communications	HSBC
CITIC International Financial	Hua Xia Bank

HISTORICAL FINANCIALS
Company Type: Public

Income Statement
FYE: December 31

	ASSETS ($ mil.)	NET INCOME ($ mil.)	INCOME AS % OF ASSETS	EMPLOYEES
12/15	3,419,761	42,671	1.2%	466,346
12/14	3,320,774	44,439	1.3%	462,282
12/13	3,124,889	43,385	1.4%	441,902
12/12	2,813,847	38,261	1.4%	427,356
12/11	2,458,831	33,087	1.3%	408,859
Annual Growth	8.6%	6.6%	—	3.3%

2015 Year-End Financials

Return on assets: 1.2%	Dividends
Return on equity: 16.6%	Yield: 5.8%
Long-term debt ($ mil.): —	Payout: 566.1%
No. of shares (mil.): —	Market value ($ mil.): —
Sales ($ mill): 162,175	

	STOCK PRICE ($) FY Close	P/E High/Low	PER SHARE ($) Earnings	Dividends	Book Value
12/15	11.96	22 14	0.12	0.70	0.77
12/14	14.60	19 14	0.13	0.71	0.70
12/13	13.58	21 15	0.12	0.65	0.60
12/12	14.48	22 15	0.11	0.53	0.52
12/11	11.92	30 15	0.09	0.47	0.44
Annual Growth	0.1%	— —	6.1%	10.3%	15.4%

Industrial Bank Co., Ltd.

There's nothing average about Industrial Bank. Founded in 1988 Industrial Bank is one of China's first joint stock commercial banks. Through some 95 branches and more than 815 sub-branches across China Industrial Bank offers standard deposit loan wealth management credit card and e-banking products and services to personal and commercial banking customers. Fujian Finance Department a government institution controls nearly a fifth of Industrial Bank while Hong Kong's Hang Seng Bank owns more than 10%.

EXECUTIVES

Director and President, Li Renjie, age 61
Chairman, Gao Jianping
Chairman Supervisory Board, Kang Kang
Auditors: Fujian Huaxing Certified Public Accountants Ltd.

LOCATIONS

HQ: Industrial Bank Co., Ltd.
154 Hudong Road, Fuzhou, Fujian Province 350003
Phone: (86) 591 87824863   **Fax:** (86) 591 87842633
Web: www.cib.com.cn

PRODUCTS/OPERATIONS

2015 Sales

	% of total
Head office	36
Fujian	11
Northeast and other regions	10
Western China	10
Central China	9
Guangdong	6
Beijing	5
Shanghai	5
Zhejiang	4
Jiangsu	4
Total	**100**

2015 Sales

	% of total
Net Interest Income	78
Net non-interest income	22
Total	**100**

Selected Products and Services

Credit cards
Corporate banking
Electronic banking
Financial markets
Personal banking
Private banking

COMPETITORS

Bank of China	China Merchants Bank
Bank of East Asia	China Minsheng Banking
Bank of Shanghai	Shanghai Pudong
China Construction Bank	Development Bank

HISTORICAL FINANCIALS
Company Type: Public

Income Statement
FYE: December 31

	ASSETS ($ mil.)	NET INCOME ($ mil.)	INCOME AS % OF ASSETS	EMPLOYEES
12/15	815,897	7,730	0.9%	0
12/14	709,980	7,595	1.1%	0
12/13	607,449	6,807	1.1%	0
12/12	521,470	5,568	1.1%	0
12/11	382,689	4,052	1.1%	0
Annual Growth	20.8%	17.5%	—	—

2015 Year-End Financials

Return on assets: 1.0%	Dividends
Return on equity: 17.5%	Yield: —
Long-term debt ($ mil.): —	Payout: —
No. of shares (mil.): —	Market value ($ mil.): —
Sales ($ mill): 23,779	

ING Groep NV

ING Groep is a Dutch hybrid of banking insuring and asset-managing services. One of the world's largest banking and financial services companies its operations are focused on its home Benelux market as well as the rest of Europe; it also has operations in the Americas and Asia. Its banking operations include commercial and retail banking mortgage lending and online retail banking (ING Direct). Key insurance products include life insurance pensions and retirement services. ING provides asset management for individuals and institutions through both its insurance and banking units. The firm sold off insurance operations as well as some banking and investment businesses to repay government bailout loans.

Operations

Amid the global financial crisis of 2008 ING accepted a euro 10 billion (about $13 billion) bailout loan from the Dutch government to shore up its capital position and reassure wary investors. Since then ING has been focused on enacting strategic measures to further offset losses including layoffs and asset sales. Under requirements for the bailout funds ING has also been working to separate its banking and insurance operations through the sale of the insurance assets (as well as some banking assets). In late 2014 it completed paying off the debt.

The company is focused on its European banking operations —including divisions in the Netherlands Belgium and Germany —which provide a full range of services including savings and investment products. Due to the restructuring efforts banking operations now account for 60% of revenues (insurance was previously the core business).

ING's retail banking operations are primarily delivered online which reduces overhead and offers potential savings to customers.

Geographic Reach

ING operates in more than 40 countries in Europe North America Latin America Asia and the Asia/Pacific region. The Netherlands is its largest single market accounting for about 30% of its total interest income followed by Belgium (some 20%). The rest of Europe represents nearly 40% of total interest. (North America was previously the largest segment but the company sold its US retail bank in 2014 as well as insurance operations on both sides of the Atlantic as it continues to streamline operations.)

Sales and Marketing

ING uses a multi-channel distribution model to reach customers including individuals families small business entities large corporations government agencies and institutions. Marketing and sales methods include Internet banking mobile banking call centers mailings and branch and outbound sales representative efforts. ING has more than 33 million private corporate and institutional customers.

In 2014 the company spent euro 405 million on advertising and public relations (slightly up from euro 404 million spent in 2013).

Financial Performance

ING's revenues have seen a steady decline over the past five years largely due to asset disposal efforts. In 2014 revenue fell 9% to euro 51.7 billion due to declines in its commercial banking operations and investment income. Net income which has fluctuated in recent years fell 78% to euro 1.1 billion as values on non-trading derivatives declined.

After ING reported an euro 8 billion cash outflow in 2013 cash flow from operations rose to euro 12 billion in 2014 as the group generated funds due from banks and trading liabilities.

Strategy

ING has been divesting many of its holdings to create a stronger more streamlined operation with a renewed focus on banking in the Netherlands Belgium and Germany. Its restructuring plan which is nearly complete encompasses the sale or spin-off of all of its insurance operations which have included life insurance and non-life insurance businesses in Europe the Americas and the Asia/Pacific. In early 2014 the company raised $1.18 billion by selling off a majority stake in its US insurance unit. The plan also includes the divestiture of the company's insurance-related investment management operations as well as select non-core banking operations. The company is now focused on building strong domestic retail and commercial banking units as well as strong banking positions in other Central and Eastern European markets.

The company has made more than 50 divestitures over the past five years. Some of its largest sales have included banking firms ING Direct USA ING Direct Canada and ING Direct UK; it sold its investment management business in South Korea as well as insurance assets in China Hong Kong Macau and Thailand. In 2014 it agreed to sell its Taiwanese asset management business to Nomura Asset Management. Also that year it exited its equity investment business in the Middle East and North Africa as well as its insurance business in Brazil. In India the company exited the Vysya insurance business; in 2015 its ING Vysya bank merged with Kotak Mahindra Bank with ING retaining a small stake in the combined entity.

Some of ING's divestitures are being conducted through public offerings. ING U.S. (since renamed Voya Financial) went public in 2013 raising some $1.3 billion. ING retained a 75% stake in ING U.S. which holds ING's remaining US-based life insurance retirement and investment management operations. The company divested its holding in Voya Financial in early 2015.

ING conducted an IPO to sell part of its stake in NN Group its European life insurance and investment management operations in 2014. The group's insurance segment was eliminated after the IPO as those businesses were classified as discontinued operations. ING further reduced its holdings in NN Group in 2015 and completed the divestiture in 2016.

Also in 2016 the company announced plans to cut some 7000 jobs (about 12% of its workforce) as it looks to invest in its own technology platform. It plans to invests around euro 800 million towards its digital overhaul over the next five years.

Company Background

Prior to the economic meltdown ING took aim at becoming a financial services player in all four corners of the world and made acquisitions accordingly. Along with much of the insurance industry it shifted its base from traditional life insurance products to investment-backed products which favor companies that can sell through banks. ING utilized its owns banks to distribute such products. The company also targeted expansion in growing economies such as South Korea Turkey and Thailand to meet anticipated consumer demand for new banking and retirement options. In more mature markets like North America and Europe the company had the aging population in its sights and placed retirement planning and pensions as sources of future growth.

HISTORY

HCING Groep's roots go back to 1845 when its earliest predecessor the Netherlands Insurance Co. was founded. The firm began expanding geographically; in 1903 it added life insurance. In 1963 it merged with the century-old Nationale Life Insurance Bank to form Nationale-Nederland (NN). Over the next three decades the company grew primarily through acquisitions in Europe North America and Australia. In 1986 NN became the first European life insurance company to be licensed in Japan.

Another predecessor the Rijkspostspaarbank was founded in 1881 to provide Dutch citizens with simple post office savings accounts. In 1918 the Postcheque-en Girondienst (giro) system was established to allow people to use vouchers drawn on their savings accounts to pay bills. This system became the main method of settling accounts (instead of bank checking accounts).

Rijkspostspaarbank and Postcheque merged in 1986 to become Postbank. Postbank merged in 1989 with the Nederlandse Middenstandsbank (founded 1927) to become NMB Postbank. The vast amounts of cash tied up in the post office savings and giro systems fueled NMB's business.

In 1991 as the European economic union became a reality and barriers between banking and insurance began to fall NN merged with NMB Postbank to form Internationale Nederland Groep (ING). ING began cutting costs shedding redundant offices and unprofitable operations in both its segments. In the US where insurance and banking were legally divided the company "debanked" itself in order to keep its more lucrative insurance operations (but retained the right to provide banking services to those operations).

ING sought to increase its investment banking and finance operations in the 1990s. In 1995 it took over UK-based Barings Bank (personal banker to the Queen of England) after Nicholas Leeson a trader in Barings' Singapore office lost huge sums of money in derivatives trading. The acquisition gave the firm a higher profile but cost more than anticipated and left it embroiled in lingering legal actions.

In 1996 ING bought Poland's Bank Slaski (the company had first entered Poland in 1994). The next year it expanded its securities business by acquiring investment bank Furman Selz doubled its US life insurance operations by purchasing Equitable of Iowa and listed on the NYSE. In 1998 ING's acquisition strategy again involved Europe and North America: It bought Belgium's Banque Bruxelles Lambert and Canadian life insurer Guardian Insurance Co. (from Guardian Royal Exchange now part of AXA UK).

ING turned eastward in 1999 kicking off asset management operations in India and buying a minority stake in South Korea's HC&B (formerly Housing & Commercial Bank). In 2000 the company bulked up its North American operations with the purchase of 40% of Savia SA a Mexican insurance concern. It also bought US firm ReliaStar Financial in a $6 billion deal and Charterhouse Securities from CCF (then called Credit Commercial de France).

In 2004 ING realigned its management structure dividing the company's operations into six business lines: Insurance Americas Insurance Europe Insurance Asia-Pacific Wholesale Banking Retail Banking and ING Direct. ING boosted its North American insurance operations with the acquisition of Allianz's Canadian property and casualty operations.

The company struggled with investment banking arm ING Barings. The unit was reorganized and streamlined for cost-savings purposes but ultimately was put on the block. Its Asian equities operations were sold to Macquarie Bank in 2004. Barings Private Equity Partners unit was sold to its management. The Barings investment management operations were sold to MassMutual in 2005 while Northern Trust bought up its fund administration trust and custody operations.

ING sold most of ING BHF-Bank to Sal. Oppenheim during 2004. The next year ING turned over its US life reinsurance operations to Scottish Re and sold subsidiary Life Insurance Company of Georgia to Jackson National Life.

During 2005 ING acquired a 20% stake in the Bank of Beijing as part of a strategic alliance. In 2006 the company sold off its UK brokerage business Williams de Broë to The Evolution Group.

In 2008 the company acquired CitiStreet a leading US administrator of defined-contribution retirement savings pension health and other plans; it paid about $900 million for the firm.

After the global financial crisis hit in 2008 ING accepted a euro 10 billion (more than $13 billion) bailout loan from the Dutch government. The bailout was intended to shore up the company's capital position and reassure wary investors. Strategic measures to further offset losses and repay debt were enacted in 2009 including layoffs and asset sales. CEO Michael Tilmant stepped down and was replaced by former chairman Jan Hommen. By the end of 2009 job cuts totaled about 10% of its workforce. The company also outlined plans to split the company in half by separating its insurance and banking operations.

Prior to the bailout ING has already been working to simplify and streamline its operations through a "Back to Basics" strategy. Restructuring measures under the strategy include the refocusing of ING's banking operations on (mostly Central) Europe and the reduction of the company's US financial product offerings.

In early 2009 the company sold its ING Canada property/casualty business which was then renamed Intact Financial. ING sold its life insurance joint venture stake in Australia and New Zealand to partner ANZ and offloaded its noncore annuity and mortgage businesses in Chile to life insurer Corp Group Vida Chile in late 2009. The company also sold its Taiwanese life insurance business to Fubon Financial Holding in a deal worth euro 447 million ($600 million) in mid-2009. ING gained a 5% stake in Fubon through the deal which it sold the following year for another euro 395 million ($522 million).

In early 2010 ING completed sales of the company's Swiss Private Banking unit to Julius Baer for $506 million and its Asian Private Banking unit (operating in Hong Kong the Philippines and Singapore) to OCBC Bank for nearly $1.5 billion. In addition the company sold its North American reinsurance operations to RGA and most of its US insurance brokerage operations to Lightyear Capital in early 2010. ING has also agreed to sell its stake in one of its Chinese life insurance ventures (Pacific Antai with China Pacific Insurance) to China Construction Bank.

In 2011 ING sold its Asian and European real estate investment management (REIM) operations as well as select US REIM assets for about $940 million to broker CBRE Group (formerly CB Richard Ellis Group). The firm sold its remaining US REIM assets to Lightyear Capital for some $100 million. Also that year the firm agreed to sell its Australian investment management business to UBS for an undisclosed sum.

Farther south in 2011 the company sold its Latin American insurance operations to Columbian insurer GrupoSura for $3.7 billion. The sale included insurance savings and investment management operations in Chile Colombia Mexico Uruguay and Peru. It also sold ING Car Least to BMW.

EXECUTIVES

Chairman Executive Board and CEO, R.A.J.G. (Ralph) Hamers
CFO, P.G. (Patrick) Flynn
Chief Risk Officer, W.F. (Wilfred) Nagel
Chairman Supervisory Board, Jeroen van der Veer
Auditors: Ernst & Young Accountants LLP

LOCATIONS

HQ: ING Groep NV
  Bijlmerplein 888, Amsterdam 1102 MG
Phone: (31) 20 563 6710
Web: www.ing.com

2014 Total Income

	% of total
Europe	
The Netherlands	29
Belgium	21
Other countries	37
North America	3
Asia	4
Australia	3
Other	3
Total	**100**

PRODUCTS/OPERATIONS

2014 Interest Income

	% of total
Commercial banking	60
Retail Netherlands	15
Retail Belgium	5
Retail Germany	7
Retail rest of world	9
Corporate line banking	4
Total	**100**

2014 Sales

	% of total
Interest income banking operations	93
Commission income	4
Investment income	1
Result on disposals of group companies	1
Net trading income	1
Share of result from associates & joint ventures	-
Other income	-
Total	**100**

COMPETITORS

ABN AMRO Group	Delta Lloyd
AEGON	Deutsche Bank
Achmea	Deutsche Bundesbank
Ageas Insurance	HSBC
International	KBC
Barclays	Rabobank Group
Citigroup	UBS
Credit Suisse	

HISTORICAL FINANCIALS

Company Type: Public

Income Statement

FYE: December 31

	ASSETS ($ mil.)	NET INCOME ($ mil.)	INCOME AS % OF ASSETS	EMPLOYEES
12/15	912,600	5,365	0.6%	57,553
12/14	1,200,561	1,170	0.1%	68,431
12/13	1,482,196	6,301	0.4%	83,690
12/12	1,531,742	4,295	0.3%	92,572
12/11	1,647,314	6,130	0.4%	104,419
Annual Growth	**(13.7%)**	**(3.3%)**	**—**	**(13.8%)**

2015 Year-End Financials

Return on assets: 0.5%
Return on equity: 10.7%
Long-term debt ($ mil.): —
No. of shares (mil.): —
Sales ($ mil): 56,268

Dividends
  Yield: 2.5%
  Payout: 24.5%
Market value ($ mil.): —

	STOCK PRICE ($) FY Close	P/E High/Low		PER SHARE ($) Earnings	Dividends	Book Value
12/15	13.46	14	9	1.38	0.35	12.66
12/14	12.97	237	193	0.07	0.15	14.69
12/13	14.01	13	7	1.46	0.00	15.77
12/12	9.49	14	9	0.91	0.00	17.95
12/11	7.17	14	7	1.10	0.00	15.18
Annual Growth	**17.1%**	**—**	**—**	**5.9%**	**—**	**(4.4%)**

International Consolidated Airlines Group SA

Auditors: Ernst & Young, S.L.

LOCATIONS

HQ: International Consolidated Airlines Group SA
  El Caserio, Iberia Zona Industrial no 2, Camino de La Munoza, Madrid 28042
Phone: (44) 20 8564 2800
Web: www.iairgroup.com

HISTORICAL FINANCIALS

Company Type: Public

Income Statement

FYE: December 31

	REVENUE ($ mil.)	NET INCOME ($ mil.)	NET PROFIT MARGIN	EMPLOYEES
12/15	24,897	1,628	6.5%	60,862
12/14	24,516	1,193	4.9%	59,484
12/13	25,564	167	0.7%	60,089
12/12	23,879	(1,242)	—	59,574
12/11	20,828	726	3.5%	56,791
Annual Growth	**4.6%**	**22.3%**	**—**	**1.7%**

2015 Year-End Financials

Debt ratio: 33.3%
Return on equity: 34.3%
Cash ($ mil.): 6,378
Current ratio: 0.80
Long-term debt ($ mil.): 8,166
No. of shares (mil.): 2,040
Dividends
  Yield: 2.4%
  Payout: 58.7%
Market value ($ mil.): 91,294

	STOCK PRICE ($) FY Close	P/E High/Low		PER SHARE ($) Earnings	Dividends	Book Value
12/15	44.75	65	44	0.77	0.44	2.79
12/14	37.02	78	50	0.56	0.00	2.08
12/13	33.55	524	252	0.09	0.00	2.65
12/12	15.45	—	—	(0.67)	0.00	3.38
12/11	11.38	76	32	0.38	0.00	3.75
Annual Growth	**40.8%**	**—**	**—**	**18.9%**	**—**	**(7.2%)**

Intesa Sanpaolo S.P.A.

Intesa Sanpaolo provides retail and commercial banking services in Italy through its Banca dei Territori division. The company serves 11.1 million customers from 4500 branches throughout Italy and an additional 1400 locations in Central and Eastern Europe as well as North African areas. Intesa Sanpaolo also provides investment banking corporate finance public and infrastructure finance factoring and trade financing services. The company offers life property and casualty insurance through Fideuram Vita and other insurance subsidiaries. Asset management is handled by Eurizon Capital while Banca Fideuram arm provides financial planning services.

OperationsBanca dei Territori is the company's flagship brand generating more than 60% of total revenue. It boasts more than 4000 branches that provide traditional banking and loan products. More than 80% of the group's loan portfolio is made up of commercial banking loans half of which are mortgages with the other half being current accounts and advances and other loans. Nonperforming loans make up roughly 10% of the overall loan portfolio. The division's affiliates include the company's small to medium enterprises (SME) finance hub Mediocredito Italiana non-profit organization lender Banca Prossima and payment systems provider Setefi. Corporate and Investment Banking makes up nearly 20% of total revenue and offers investment banking and capital market services through Banca IMI via a network of more than 40 branches in Italy. The International Subsidiary Banks division bring in another roughly 10% of revenue. This division serves more than 8 million customers in 11 countries through more than 1100 branches in select countries in Central-Eastern Europe and the Middle East and North Africa region. The other divisions include Private Banking (under the Banca Fideuram brand) which offers wealth management services to high net worth individuals; the Asset Management division (under the Eurizon Capital brand) which manages more than euro 200 billion in assets under management for the individuals as well as institutional clientele; and the Insurance division (under Intensa Sanpaolo Vita Fideuram Vita and Intesa Sanpaolo Assicura brands) which boasts more than euro 25 billion in premiums and more than euro 110 billion in technical reserves. Capital Light Bank a noncore segment manages non-performing loans and repossessed assets (including those of Pravex-Bank in Ukraine). Geographic ReachIntesa Sanpaolo and its subsidiary banks boasts nearly 4500 branches across Italy more than 1200 branches in select countries in Central and Eastern Europe. It also has more than 150 branches in Africa and the Middle East and a handful of branches and representative offices in America and Asia. Nearly 80% of revenue comes from business in Italy while Europe makes up more than 15%.

Sales and Marketing

The banking group serves individuals (including households in financial difficulty) small to mid-size enterprises (SMEs) startup and large businesses consumer associations public entities and industrial associations. In all the group serves more than 19 million customers with the average customer holding an account for more than 12 years.

The company spent euro 160 million on advertising and promotional expenses in 2014 up from euro 154 million spent in 2013.

Financial Performance

Note: Growth rates may differ after conversion to US dollars.

Intesa Sanpaolo's financial performance has been volatile in recent years as the bank has been grappling with recession in Italy and as it has been working to de-risk its portfolio in the years following the financial crisis. Revenue in 2014 rose by double digits to euro 16.9 billion ($20.5 billion) mostly thanks to a combination of higher net fee and commission income and increased income from the insurance business. Net fee and commission income grew thanks to higher collections and payment services fees higher guarantee fees and higher credit and debit card fees. The insurance business grew by 16% thanks to strong investment performance. Higher revenue and lower operating

costs in 2014 pushed Intesa Sanpaolo back into profitability as net income jumped to euro 1.31 billion (roughly $1.6 billion) compared to a net loss of euro 4.55 billion ($6.3 billion) in 2013. Cash from operations rose thanks to higher cash earnings.

Strategy

Intesa Sanpaolo is working to strengthen its retail banking operations and maintain a diversified presence in international markets. For now its focus is on its flagship Banca dei Territori division which handles domestic commercial banking and is responsible for retail customers individual customers and small businesses. Leaning on its Banca dei Territori business in 2014 the company introduced its growth-oriented Banca 5 project designed to cross sell its banking customers on the group's insurance and investing products and services from its other divisions.

Intesa Sanpaolo has also formed strategic partnerships with other financial companies to extend into new financial markets. In 2015 for example the company partnered with GSO Capital Partners (the credit investment arm of Blackstone) to provide alternative funding to Italian middle market businesses which have faced a tight private credit market for the past several years.

Company Background

Intesa Sanpaolo is the result of the 2007 megamerger between Banca Intesa and Sanpaolo IMI. After the merger the company reshuffled its assets and sold off some branches in order to comply with antitrust orders and raise capital.

HISTORY

Company BackgroundIn Italy charity begins at home and often heads to the financial institutions. In 1563 Turin citizens founded Compagnia di San Paolo a foundation that provided education and dowries to orphaned girls and aid to impoverished nobility. In 1579 the organization began a pawn shop the Monte di Pieta or Mountain of Mercy (founded in 1519 and reopened by the Compagnia). The foundation grew over the next 200 years fattened by bequests and inheritances from wealthy Piedmontese families.

The French Republican government in Piedmonte gradually took control of the foundation's operations and closed it in 1802. The Monte di Pieta was reopened in 1804 and under the French influence became more bank-like. In 1848 the charitable and financial operations were formally divided.

Industrialization came slowly to Italy after its unification in the 1860s (the country remained largely agricultural until after WWII) and the organization survived a banking crisis from 1887 to 1894 by operating conservatively. It contributed to the WWI effort by purchasing government bonds. In 1928 the foundation separated Monte di Pieta's credit and pawn operations and adopted the name Istituto di San Paolo di Torino - Beneficenza e Credito (San Paolo).Specialized institutions were founded in the 1920s to finance utilities and transportation; one of them La Centrale Societa per il Finanziamento di Imprese Elettriche e Telefoniche was formed in 1925 to help finance Italy's energy and telecommunications industries. In 1965 this entity enlarged its focus and changed its name to La Centrale Finanziaria Generale a forerunner of Banca Intesa.

La Centrale's interests in energy were transferred to ENEL the state holding company in 1985 leaving it with banking finance and insurance holdings. That year the bank merged with Nuovo Banco Ambrosiano formerly Banco Ambrosiano.

Banco Ambrosiano was founded in 1896 by Guiseppi Tovino whose good works and sturdy faith made him a saint (he was beatified in 1998).

Betraying his legacy in 1981 chairman Roberto Calvi was found hanging under the Blackfriars Bridge in London. Calvi called "God's Banker" for his connections to the Vatican left behind a tangle of debt phony holding companies and fraud that implicated the Catholic Church brought down an archbishop and involved a secretive Masonic lodge. Banco Ambrosiano was taken over by a group of creditor banks and its name was changed to Nuovo Banco Ambrosiano.

In 1989 Nuovo Banco Ambrosiano merged with its subsidiary Banco Cattolica del Veneto and became known as Banco Ambroveneto. It bought La Cassa di Risparmio delle Provincie Lombarde (Cariplo) Italy's biggest savings bank in 1997; they merged to form Banca Intesa the following year. Cariplo was founded by the Austro-Hungarian government in 1823 when the region was still recovering from Napoleon's depredations. Count Giovanni Pietro Porro wanted to allow artisans and day laborers to set aside money and the company remained true to that mission throughout Italy's unification and two world wars.

Italy began its race toward privatization in 1990 to counter the growing interest of foreign banks in the Italian market and help the nation meet the criteria for joining the European Union. In 1992 San Paolo was one of the first banks to sell a 20% stake in itself (it sold another 20% in 1997). The bank bought several regional and national banks over the next few years and in 1998 merged with investment bank Istituto Mobiliare Italiano or IMI (founded 1931) to form Sanpaolo IMI.

Banca Intesa was the product of a combination of the staid Cassa di Risparmio delle Provincie Lombarde (Cariplo) and the somewhat more colorful Banco Ambroveneto whose history helped inspire the plot of The Godfather Part III . It took over Banca Commerciale Italiana (BCI or Comit) in 2000 creating one of Italy's largest banks. Banca Intesa integrated BCI to form IntesaBci the following year and then in late 2002 rebranded as Banca Intesa.

Banca Intesa and Sanpaolo IMI merged in 2007. After the deal antitrust authorities ordred the company to sell some 200 branches to France-based Credit Agricole. In late 2008 the Italian banking group sold 36 branches to Veneto Banca for euro 274 million ($401 million).A good portion of its branches were acquired in 2007 when Intesa Sanpaolo increased its stake in Banca CR Firenze to some 60% in preparation for taking over the bank outright. Banca CR Firenze added about 550 locations in Tuscany and surrounding regions to Intesa Sanpaolo's network.

The next year the bank upped its stake in Cassa dei Risparmi di Forli e della Romagna to about 70% increasing its influence in northern Italy. During more reshuffling of assets Intesa Sanpaolo sold a 30% stake in Cassa di Risparmio di Fano to Credito Valtellinese in 2009.

EXECUTIVES

Chief Risk Officer, Bruno Picca, age 67
Head of Planning and Control, Carlo Messina, age 55
Head of Italian and International Subsidiary Banks Divisions, Giovanni Boccolini, age 63
Chief Economist, Gregorio de Felice
Chief Lending Officer, Eugenio Rossetti, age 61
CFO, Stefano Del Punta
Head Corporate and Investment Banking Division, Gaetano Micciche
COO, Eliano Omar Lodesani
Chairman Management Board; President Intesa Sanpaolo Bank, Gian Maria Gros-Pietro
Chairman Supervisory Board, Giovanni Bazoli, age 84

Deputy Chairman Supervisory Board, Mario Bertolissi, age 68
Senior Deputy Chairman Management Board, Marcello Sala
Auditors: KPMG S.p.A.

LOCATIONS

HQ: Intesa Sanpaolo S.P.A.
Piazza San Carlo, 156, Torino 10121
Phone: (39) 11 5551
Web: www.intesasanpaolo.com

2014 Sales

	% of total
Italy	79
Europe	17
Rest of the world	4
Total	**100**

PRODUCTS/OPERATIONS

2014 Sales

	% of total
Net interest income	50
Net fee and commission income	40
Profits on tradings	5
Income from insurance business	5
Total	**100**

Selected Subsidiaries

Banca CR Firenze
Banca dell' Adriatico
Banca di Credito Sardo
Banca di Trento e Bolzano
Banca Fideuram
Banca IMI
Banca Intesa
Banca Intesa Beograd
Banca Monte Parma
Banca Prossima
Banco di Napoli
Bank of Alexandria
Banka Koper
Cassa dei Risparmi di Forlì e della Romagna
Cassa di Risparmio del Friuli Venezia Giulia
Cassa di Risparmio del Veneto
Cassa di Risparmio della Provincia di Viterbo (CARIVIT)
Cassa di Risparmio di Civitavecchia
Cassa di Risparmio di Pistoia e della Lucchesia
Cassa di Risparmio di Rieti (CARIRI)
Cassa di Risparmio di Venezia
Cassa di Risparmio in Bologna
Casse di Risparmio dell' Umbria
CIB Bank
Epsilon Associati SGR
Equiter
Eurizon A.I. SGR
Eurizon Capital
IMI Fondi Chiusi SGR
IMI Investimenti
Infogroup

COMPETITORS

BBVA	Dexia
BNL bc	Mediobanca
Banca Popolare di Milano	Monte dei Paschi di Siena
Banco Popolare	UniCredit

HISTORICAL FINANCIALS

Company Type: Public

Income Statement

FYE: December 31

	ASSETS ($ mil.)	NET INCOME ($ mil.)	INCOME AS % OF ASSETS	EMPLOYEES
12/15	736,846	2,983	0.4%	90,807
12/14	785,735	1,520	0.2%	89,486
12/13	862,226	(6,264)	—	93,945
12/12	887,669	2,115	0.2%	96,170
12/11	826,801	(10,593)	—	100,118
Annual Growth	(2.8%)	—	—	(2.4%)

2015 Year-End Financials

Return on assets: 0.4%	Dividends
Return on equity: 5.9%	Yield: 1.6%
Long-term debt ($ mil.): —	Payout: 175.7%
No. of shares (mil.): —	Market value ($ mil.): —
Sales ($ mil): 41,708	

	STOCK PRICE ($) FY Close	P/E High/Low	Earnings	PER SHARE ($) Dividends	Book Value
12/15	19.99	147 92	0.17	0.32	3.28
12/14	17.32	238163	0.10	0.31	3.43
12/13	14.95	— —	(0.39)	0.57	3.96
12/12	10.64	125 68	0.13	0.28	4.22
12/11	9.94	— —	(0.72)	1.10	3.93
Annual Growth	19.1%	— —	—(26.7%)	(4.4%)	

Investec Ltd

Auditors: Ernst & Young Inc.

LOCATIONS

HQ: Investec Ltd
100 Grayston Drive, Sandown, Sandton 2196
Phone: (27) 11 286 7000   **Fax:** (27) 11 286 7966
Web: www.investec.com

HISTORICAL FINANCIALS

Company Type: Public

Income Statement

FYE: March 31

	ASSETS ($ mil.)	NET INCOME ($ mil.)	INCOME AS % OF ASSETS	EMPLOYEES
03/16	65,280	530	0.8%	8,966
03/15	38,812	366	0.9%	3,707
03/14	40,520	351	0.9%	3,564
03/13	41,756	350	0.8%	3,577
03/12	45,347	353	0.8%	3,519
Annual Growth	9.5%	10.7%	—	26.3%

2016 Year-End Financials

Return on assets: 0.1%	Dividends
Return on equity: 2.2%	Yield: 0.0%
Long-term debt ($ mil.): —	Payout: 80.4%
No. of shares (mil.): 267	Market value ($ mil.): 3,679
Sales ($ mil.): 4,596	

	STOCK PRICE ($) FY Close	P/E High/Low	Earnings	PER SHARE ($) Dividends	Book Value
03/16	13.77	46 33	0.53	0.42	18.24
03/15	17.60	— —	(0.00)	0.43	9.09
03/14	14.87	— —	(0.00)	0.40	9.46
03/13	14.01	— —	(0.00)	0.48	9.59
03/12	12.70	— —	(0.00)	0.45	10.39
Annual Growth	2.0%	— —	—	(1.6%)15.1%

Israel Discount Bank Ltd.

Who doesn't love a discount? Israel Discount Bank the third-largest bank in Israel has about 150 locations across the country. The bank offers standard consumer services like deposits loans and credit cards in addition to private banking international trade and commercial banking activities. Is-

rael Discount Bank oversees four subsidiaries — Discount Mortgage Bank Mercantile Discount Bank (which has about 75 branches) Israel Discount Bank of New York and IDB (Swiss) Bank Ltd. It also owns a 26% stake in First International Bank of Israel the country's fifth-largest bank. In 2015 IDB sold Uruguay-based subsidiary Discount Bank Latin America to Bank of Nova Scotia in a deal worth $65 million.

Company BackgroundIn 2010 Israel Discount Bank announced it was selling off Tachlit Investment House its portfolio management subsidiary that has about $3 billion in assets under management.
Auditors: Ziv Haft

LOCATIONS

HQ: Israel Discount Bank Ltd.
23 Yehuda Halevi Street, Tel-Aviv 65136
Phone: (972) 3 514 5555   **Fax:** (972) 3 514 5346
Web: www.discountbank.net

COMPETITORS

Bank Hapoalim	Mizrahi Tefahot
Bank Leumi le-Israel	
First International Bank of Israel	

HISTORICAL FINANCIALS

Company Type: Public

Income Statement

FYE: December 31

	ASSETS ($ mil.)	NET INCOME ($ mil.)	INCOME AS % OF ASSETS	EMPLOYEES
12/15	52,477	191	0.4%	6,034
12/14	53,256	153	0.3%	9,215
12/13	57,783	251	0.4%	9,877
12/12	53,893	215	0.4%	9,942
12/11	52,966	244	0.5%	10,211
Annual Growth	(0.2%)	(5.9%)	—	(12.3%)

2015 Year-End Financials

Return on assets: 0.3%	Dividends
Return on equity: 5.6%	Yield: —
Long-term debt ($ mil.): —	Payout: —
No. of shares (mil.): 105	Market value ($ mil.): 191
Sales ($ mil): 2,127	

	STOCK PRICE ($) FY Close	P/E High/Low	Earnings	PER SHARE ($) Dividends	Book Value
12/15	1.81	— —	0.18	0.00	32.24
12/14	1.81	3 3	0.15	0.00	32.34
12/13	1.50	2 2	0.24	0.00	33.45
12/12	0.96	2 1	0.20	0.00	30.14
12/11	1.42	2 2	0.21	0.00	26.67
Annual Growth	6.2%	— —	(3.8%)		4.9%

Isuzu Motors, Ltd. (Japan)

Isuzu Motors has been trucking along since 1916 as one of Japan's first automobile makers. The company is one of the world's top commercial truck manufacturers boasting heavy- medium- and light-duty models. Isuzu is also a leading diesel engine maker for such companies as Adam Opel and GM; its engines are used in automotive as well as industrial and marine applications. Other vehicle products include sightseeing and private buses passenger pickup trucks and SUVs. Its D-MAX pickup is particularly popular in Thailand and South America. Isuzu Motors which sells its products in more than 100 countries through a worldwide distributor network has stopped selling passenger vehicles in the US.

The company once a pioneer in the American SUV market announced it would stop selling its pickups and SUVs in the US in early 2009 after an eight-year slide in US sales. Longtime partner GM produced the Ascender SUV and the i-Series pickups Isuzu had been selling in the US but it struggled against automakers with stronger brands and dealer networks. (GM had gradually sold off its holding in Isuzu; Mitsubishi currently holds 9% and Toyota 6%.) Isuzu said it would continue to provide parts and service for those vehicles in the US and would continue to sell its two main products —commercial vehicles and diesel engines —in an effort to gain market share in the US and around the world.

Commercial truck and bus demand is forecast to grow in developing markets specifically China Russia and India (where Isuzu has established a production facility via a joint venture with Sumitomo Corp. and local companies). In 2010 Isuzu set up a truck sales joint venture in China with Qingling Motors. The venture builds on a manufacturing tie-up started in 1985 which fostered co-production of trucks sport utility vehicles and diesel engines and sales on behalf of Isuzu by Qingling Motors. Through the sales venture Isuzu took the wheel in setting prices and selecting models with the hope of building China into its largest market. It plans to double its annual capacity of trucks in China to 200000 units by around 2015. The company is also building new sales facilities in South America and a plant in Saudi Arabia to build medium-duty trucks.

At home it is maintaining a strong domestic market position especially with its N Series light-duty line of trucks. Isuzu is also attempting to hold on to if not surpass its spot as the world's #4 manufacturer of diesel engines (by production volume) by continuing to invest in research and development of advanced diesel technology. The sluggish economy in Japan has hampered any real growth though.

Like the rest of the automotive industry Isuzu has been buffeted by the global recession. Sales peaked in 2008 but have declined since as demand plummeted. The company did manage to turn around its $273 million net income loss from 2009 to show positive $90 million net income in 2010 by increasing sales through pushing into new markets and streamlining operations. It plans to more than double net income for fiscal 2011.

HISTORY

After collaborating on car and truck production for 21 years Tokyo Ishikawajima Shipbuilding and Engineering and Tokyo Gas and Electric Industrial formed Tokyo Motors Inc. in 1937. The partners began producing the A truck (1918) and the A9 car (1922) under licenses from Wolseley (UK).

Tokyo Motors made its first truck under the Isuzu nameplate in 1938. It spun off Hino Heavy Industries in 1942. By 1943 the company was selling trucks powered by its own diesel engines mostly to the Japanese military.

By 1948 the company was Japan's premier maker of diesel engines. It was renamed Isuzu (Japanese for "50 bells") in 1949. With generous public- and private-sector financing and truck orders from the US Army during the Korean War Isuzu survived and refined its engine- and truck-making prowess. A pact with the Rootes Group

(UK) enabled Isuzu to enter automaking. Beginning in 1953 Isuzu built Rootes' Hillman Minx in Japan.

Despite its strong reputation as a truck builder Isuzu suffered financially and by the late 1960s its bankers were shopping the company around to more stable competitors. GM after witnessing rapid Japanese progress in US and Asian auto markets bought about 34% of Isuzu in 1971. During the 1970s Isuzu launched the popular Gemini car and gained rapid entry to the US through GM exporting such vehicles as the Chevy Luv truck and the Buick Opel.

As exports to GM waned Isuzu set up its own dealer network in the US in 1981. That year GM CEO Roger Smith told a stunned Isuzu chairman Toshio Okamoto that Isuzu lacked the global scale GM was seeking. Smith asked Okamoto for help in buying a piece of Honda. After Honda declined and GM settled for 5% of Suzuki Isuzu extended its GM ties building the Geo Storm and establishing joint production facilities in the UK and Australia.

Despite a high-profile advertising campaign featuring Joe Isuzu the company suffered in the 1980s in its efforts to gain any kind of significant share of the US passenger car market. Post-1985 yen appreciation hurt exports. Subaru-Isuzu Automotive a joint venture with Fuji Heavy Industries initiated production of Rodeos in Lafayette Indiana in 1989.

After Isuzu lost nearly $500 million in 1991 and 1992 it called on GM for help. GM responded by sending Donald Sullivan a strategic business planning expert to become Isuzu's #2 operations executive.

Isuzu signed a joint venture with Jiangxi Automobile Factory and ITOCHU in 1993 to build light-duty trucks in China. In 1994 Nissan and Isuzu agreed to cross-supply vehicles.

Isuzu weathered a public relations storm in 1996 when Consumer Reports magazine claimed that the top-selling Trooper sport utility vehicle was prone to tip over at relatively low speeds. Isuzu dismissed the report as unscientific and the National Highway Traffic Safety Administration sided with the automaker. In 1997 the company sued the magazine for defamation. (Isuzu lost the case in 2000.) Also in 1997 Isuzu agreed to develop GM's diesel engines and began constructing a plant in Poland to supply engines to GM's Germany-based subsidiary Opel AG.

The next year GM and Isuzu announced a joint venture to make diesel engines in the US. Also in 1998 Isuzu announced restructuring plans that included cutting 4000 jobs and reducing the number of its domestic marketing subsidiaries. In 1999 the plant in Poland opened and GM boosted its stake in Isuzu to 49%. Isuzu also agreed to form a joint venture with Toyota to manufacture buses.

Amid mounting losses and pressure from GM Isuzu announced a management shake-up in 2001 that included naming GM chairman John Smith Jr. as special advisor and installing Randall Schwarz (GM truck group) as VP. Days later Isuzu announced its "Isuzu V plan" its sweeping cost-savings scheme that included job cuts and the closure of one factory.

The Isuzu V plan was revised in 2002 when the company announced GM would write off its entire stake while infusing Isuzu with about $84 million. Near the close of 2002 Isuzu agreed to sell its 49% stake in carmaking joint venture Subaru-Isuzu Automotive Inc. to Fuji Heavy Industries (FHI). When the deal was completed in January 2003 FHI renamed the company Subaru of Indiana Automotive Inc.

Isuzu had some rocky going in the early part of the 21st century. The company asked its creditor banks to forgive 100 billion yen (about $750 mil-

lion) in debt in exchange for stakes in the company. As part of the plan GM wrote off its entire stake in Isuzu and reinfused the ailing carmaker with $84 million. The deal resulted in a recapitalized Isuzu and reduced GM's stake to 8%. Early in 2006 GM sold its 8% stake in Isuzu to entities including Mitsubishi Corporation ITOCHU Corporation and Mizuho Corporate Bank.

As 2006 wound near its close Toyota Motor picked up a 6% stake in Isuzu Motors from Mitsubishi and ITOCHU. The two companies agreed to cooperate on engine technologies with Isuzu focusing on small diesel engines and diesel emission controls and Toyota concentrating on environmental improvements to gasoline engines and alternative fuels.

EXECUTIVES

President, Masanori Katayama, age 61
Managing Executive Officer and Director, Kazuhiko Ito
Managing Executive Officer and Director, Yoshifumi Komura
Managing Executive Officer and Director, Makoto Kawahara
Managing Executive Officer Director and Chairman Isuzu Motors India (IMI), Hiroshi Nakagawa, age 62
EVP and Director, Takao Shiomi
Managing Executive Officer and Director, Kuniharu Nakagawa
Managing Executive Officer, Toru Nakata
Chairman, Susumu Hosoi
Auditors: Ernst & Young ShinNihon LLC

LOCATIONS

HQ: Isuzu Motors, Ltd. (Japan)
6-26-1 Minami-Oi, Shinagawa-ku, Tokyo 140-8722
Phone: (81) 3 5471 1141
Web: www.isuzu.co.jp

2016 Sales

	% of total
Japan	36
Thailand	18
Other	46
Total	**100**

PRODUCTS/OPERATIONS

2016 Sales

	% of total
Vehicles	72
Engines & components	5
Parts of overseas production	4
Other	19
Total	**0**

Selected Vehicles and Brands

Buses
  Erga heavy-duty bus
  Erga Mio medium-duty bus
Commercial vehicles
  C&E Series heavy-duty trucks & tractors
  F Series medium-duty trucks
  N Series light-duty trucks
Diesel engines
  Automotive
  Industrial
  Marine
Pickup trucks & SUVs
  D-MAX
  MU-7 (Thailand)
  Panther (Indonesia)

Selected Subsidiaries and Affiliates

Anadolu Isuzu Otomotiv Sanayi Ve Ticaret AS (Turkey)
DMAX Ltd. (US)
Isuzu Australia Limited
Isuzu Motors Europe N.V. (Belgium)
Isuzu (China) Holding Co. Ltd.
Isuzu Commercial Truck of America Inc.

Isuzu Commercial Truck of Canada Inc.
Isuzu Motors America LLC
Isuzu Motors Asia Ltd. (Singapore)
Isuzu Motors Co. (Thailand) Ltd.
Isuzu Motors Germany GmbH
Isuzu Motors Polska Sp. zo. o. (Poland)
Isuzu Philippines Corporation
Isuzu Truck (UK) Ltd.
P.T. Isuzu Astra Motor Indonesia
Qingling Motors Co. Ltd. (China)

COMPETITORS

Ashok Leyland	MAN
China Yuchai	Mitsubishi Fuso
Cummins	Navistar International
Daimler	PACCAR
Daimler Trucks North	Renault
America	Scania
Ford Motor	UD Trucks
General Motors	Volkswagen
Hino Motors	Volvo

HISTORICAL FINANCIALS
Company Type: Public

Income Statement
FYE: March 31

	REVENUE ($ mil.)	NET INCOME ($ mil.)	NET PROFIT MARGIN	EMPLOYEES
03/16	17,159	1,021	6.0%	42,049
03/15	15,664	975	6.2%	39,758
03/14	17,059	1,155	6.8%	29,430
03/13	17,595	1,025	5.8%	26,102
03/12	17,067	1,112	6.5%	24,656
Annual Growth	0.1%	(2.1%)	—	14.3%

2016 Year-End Financials
Debt ratio: 0.1%
Return on equity: 15.1%
Cash ($ mil.): 2,544
Current ratio: 1.64
Long-term debt ($ mil.): 1,665
No. of shares (mil.): 788
Dividends
Yield: 2.5%
Payout: —
Market value ($ mil.): 8,103

	STOCK PRICE ($) FY Close	P/E High/Low		PER SHARE ($) Earnings	Dividends	Book Value
03/16	10.28	0	0	1.23	0.26	8.49
03/15	13.24	0	0	1.16	0.71	7.55
03/14	57.55	—	—	1.36	1.18	8.79
03/13	60.33	—	—	1.21	0.00	7.79
03/12	58.66	—	—	1.31	0.00	6.91
Annual Growth	(35.3%)			(1.6%)	—	5.3%

Itau Unibanco Holding S.A.

Itau Unibanco is one way of saying "really big bank." The Brazilian bank offers a variety of standard retail and commercial banking services as well as consumer credit financial management leasing foreign exchange and trade financing. It is one of Brazil's largest credit card issuers. It also provides investment banking securities brokerage and insurance services. Besides its network of more than 3900 Brazilian branches the firm boasts operations in other South America countries and in North America the Caribbean Asia and Europe. It leverages acquisitions such as its 2013 Credicard purchase to boost its presence. Banco Itau merged with Unibanco in 2009 to become Itau Unibanco.

The deal to combine the two Brazilian megabanks established the largest private financial conglomerate in South America. Itau Unibanco is now better equipped to compete on an international level as it expands its global presence. The merger also allowed the bank to expand credit and increase its range of products and services. Since joining forces the group has more than doubled its earnings.

In 2012 the bank agreed to buy the 49.99% it doesn't already own in card payment processing firm Redecard for some R11.8 billion (approximately $6.8 billion). The deal will help boost earnings from credit and debit card usage; it should also help Redecard compete in the growing payment-processing sector.

Itau Unibanco is controlled by holding company IUPAR itself controlled by the Egydio de Souza Aranha family. The Moreira Salles family which previously controlled Unibanco holds a stake of about 25% of the bank. Together the families have board representation with five company directors (including president and CEO Egydio Setubal).

EXECUTIVES

EVP and Investor Relations, Alfredo Egydio Setubal, age 61
CEO, Candido Botelho Bracher, age 57
CFO and EVP, Caio Ibrahim David, age 47
EVP Wholesale Banking, Eduardo Vassimon
Head Retail Banking, Marcio Schettini
Chairman, Pedro Moreira Salles, age 57
Vice Chairman, Alfredo Egydio Arruda Villela Filho, age 46
Auditors: PricewaterhouseCoopers Auditores Independentes

LOCATIONS

HQ: Itau Unibanco Holding S.A.
Praca Alfredo Egydio de Souza Aranha, 100, Sao Paulo 04344-902
Phone: (55) 11 5019 1267
Web: www.itau-unibanco.com

PRODUCTS/OPERATIONS

2015 Sales

	% of total
Interest and similar income	73
Banking service fees	15
Income related to insurance and private pension	11
Other income	1
Total	**100**

COMPETITORS

Banco Bradesco	Banco do Brasil
Banco Frances	Caixa Econômica
Banco Santander	Federal

HISTORICAL FINANCIALS
Company Type: Public

Income Statement
FYE: December 31

	ASSETS ($ mil.)	NET INCOME ($ mil.)	INCOME AS % OF ASSETS	EMPLOYEES
12/15	322,276	6,498	2.0%	90,320
12/14	424,191	8,111	1.9%	93,175
12/13	434,889	6,952	1.6%	95,696
12/12	468,153	6,179	1.3%	96,977
12/11	438,678	7,419	1.7%	104,542
Annual Growth	(7.4%)	(3.3%)	—	(3.6%)

2015 Year-End Financials
Return on assets: 2.1%
Return on equity: 24.3%
Long-term debt ($ mil.): —
No. of shares (mil.): —
Sales ($ mil): 47,703
Dividends
Yield: 5.9%
Payout: 25.8%
Market value ($ mil.): —

	STOCK PRICE ($) FY Close	P/E High/Low		PER SHARE ($) Earnings	Dividends	Book Value
12/15	6.51	2	1	1.08	0.35	4.79
12/14	13.01	4	3	1.48	0.34	6.83
12/13	13.57	5	3	1.40	0.28	13.99
12/12	16.46	7	5	1.36	0.35	16.22
12/11	18.56	7	4	1.64	0.40	17.32
Annual Growth	(23.0%) (27.5%)	—	—	(9.8%)	(3.3%)	

ITOCHU Corp. (Japan)

Itochu Enex is totally immersed in Japan's oil and gas markets. The company operates more than 20 subsidiaries. The home life segment supplies liquefied petroleum gas (LPG) to more than 1 million homes and businesses throughout Japan. The company's car life and industrial materials divisions operate full service gas stations and sells gasoline kerosene and oil to service stations. Additionally they cater to the manufacturing trucking and shipping industries selling them oil LPG and coal as well as secondary energy like electricity and heat and industrial materials such as asphalt and cement. The energy trade division engages in global oil product trading and logistics.

EXECUTIVES

President and CEO, Kenji Okada, age 65
Senior Managing Officer and Chief Compliance Officer, Masaaki Itoyama, age 66
Senior Managing Officer, Tatsunosuke Nagao, age 64
Senior Managing Officer, Masahiko Takasaka, age 59
CFO and CIO, Masayasu Tanaka, age 61
President Itochu Enex Home-Life Kanto, Masanori Toyoshima
Auditors: Deloitte Touche Tohmatsu LLC

LOCATIONS

HQ: ITOCHU Corp. (Japan)
3-1-3 Umeda, Kita-ku, Osaka 530-8448
Phone: (81) 6 7638 2121
Web: www.itochu.co.jp

PRODUCTS/OPERATIONS

2014 Sales

	% of total
Energy Trade	25
Car-Life	59
Total	**13**
Power and Utility	3
Other	.
Total	**100**

COMPETITORS

Marubeni	TonenGeneral
Showa Shell Sekiyu	

HISTORICAL FINANCIALS
Company Type: Public

Income Statement
FYE: March 31

	REVENUE ($ mil.)	NET INCOME ($ mil.)	NET PROFIT MARGIN	EMPLOYEES
03/16	45,268	2,140	4.7%	135,026
03/15	46,603	2,505	5.4%	142,178
03/14	54,132	2,376	4.4%	134,010
03/13	48,673	2,978	6.1%	98,272
03/12	52,066	3,663	7.0%	94,366
Annual Growth	(3.4%)	(12.6%)	—	9.4%

2016 Year-End Financials

Debt ratio: 0.3%
Return on equity: 10.3%
Cash ($ mil.): 5,635
Current ratio: 1.48
Long-term debt ($ mil.): 24,660

No. of shares (mil.): 1,581
Dividends
Yield: 3.1%
Payout: 62.6%
Market value ($ mil.): 38,847

	STOCK PRICE ($) FY Close	P/E High/Low		Earnings	Dividends	Book Value
03/16	24.56	0	0	1.35	0.78	12.35
03/15	21.74	0	0	1.56	0.88	12.86
03/14	23.38	0	0	1.50	0.81	12.56
03/13	24.49	0	0	1.88	1.01	11.89
03/12	21.85	0	0	2.32	0.62	10.54
Annual Growth	3.0%	—	—	(12.6%)	6.0%	4.0%

Iyo Bank, Ltd. (Japan)

With 15-plus branches and about a dozen subsidiaries The Iyo Bank targets customers across the four prefectures of Shikoku and the seven prefectures surrounding the Seto Inland Sea. The institution which has grown to become Japan's #1 regional bank offers retail products including deposits leasing services trusts and pension products and mergers and acquisitions support services. The Iyo Bank also operates a securities brokerage business arm. Its Corporate Consulting Division helps companies galvanize their operations and capital. Established in 1941 the bank owns and operates branch offices in Hong Kong Shanghai and New York. It boasts alliances with banks in China Thailand Indonesia and India.

EXECUTIVES
President, IWAO OTSUKA
Chairman, Gizo Mizuki
Auditors: KPMG AZSA LLC

LOCATIONS
HQ: Iyo Bank, Ltd. (Japan)
1 Minami-Horibatacho, Matsuyama, Ehime 790-8514
Phone: (81) 89 941 1141 **Fax:** 212 688-6420
Web: www.iyobank.co.jp

Selected Branch Locations
Head Offic
Aichi
Fukuoka
Hiroshima
Hyogo
Kagawa
Kochi
Oita
Okayama
Osaka
Tokushima
Tokyo
Yamaguchi

PRODUCTS/OPERATIONS

Selected Subsidiaries
Computer Services Inc. Iyogin
Iyogin Business Service Co. Ltd.
Iyogin Capital Co. Ltd.
Iyogin guarantee Ltd.
Iyogin Leasing Co. Ltd.
Iyogin Securities Co. Ltd.
Ltd. Iyo silver Regional Center for Economic Research
Ltd. Iyogin Dee Sea card

COMPETITORS
Aozora Bank
Miyazaki Bank
Shizuoka Bank
Toho Bank

HISTORICAL FINANCIALS
Company Type: Public

Income Statement
FYE: March 31

	ASSETS ($ mil.)	NET INCOME ($ mil.)	INCOME AS % OF ASSETS	EMPLOYEES
03/16	57,972	217	0.4%	4,511
03/15	54,804	225	0.4%	4,483
03/14	59,337	253	0.4%	2,937
03/13	63,817	195	0.3%	2,872
03/12	69,151	224	0.3%	2,857
Annual Growth	(4.3%)	(0.8%)	—	12.1%

2016 Year-End Financials

Return on assets: 0.3%
Return on equity: 4.2%
Long-term debt ($ mil.): —
No. of shares (mil.): 316
Sales ($ mil): 1,066

Dividends
Yield: —
Payout: —
Market value ($ mil.): —

	STOCK PRICE ($) FY Close	P/E High/Low		Earnings	Dividends	Book Value
03/16	0.00	—	—	0.69	0.00	15.96
03/15	0.00	0	0	0.71	0.00	15.22
03/14	7.92	—	—	0.80	0.00	15.56
Annual Growth	—	—	—	(3.7%)	—	0.6%

J Sainsbury PLC

J Sainsbury's trolley is filled with more than groceries. The UK's second-largest food retailer (after Tesco) operates the Sainsbury's Supermarkets chain of some 600 stores throughout the UK. Its Sainsbury's online home delivery shopping service covers more than 90% of the UK population. In addition to supermarkets it operates a fast-growing convenience store business with over 770 shops under the Sainsbury's Local banner. The firm also owns half of Sainsbury's Bank (in a 50-50 joint venture with Lloyds Banking Group) and a pair of property joint ventures. Sainsbury also sells apparel and home goods including cookware and bedding in its supermarkets and online. The company acquired Home Retail Group for $1.9 billion in September 2016.

Operations

The Group divides it operations into three segments: Retailing (supermarkets and convenience) Financial Services and Property Investment. Retail sales account for 99% of revenue. Sainsbury's supermarkets sell a wide range of consumer products including clothing (under the Tu clothing brand); general merchandise including homeware cookware and domestic appliances; entertainment prod-

ucts; and pharmacy products alongside its core food operation. Sainsbury's financial services operation (through Sainsbury's Bank) hold 1.7 million customer accounts and Sainsbury's Entertainment offers music eBook and magazine downloads.

Convenience stores bring in around 10% of revenue.

Sainsbury's has a well-established omnichannel offering with a home delivery operation and click-and-collect facilities in 101 of its stores.

Geographic Reach

Based in London Sainsbury's has a presence across the UK.

Sales and Marketing

The company has 23 distribution centers and sells via online and stores. Its Nectar Card loyalty cardholders number 15 million.

Financial Performance

Note: Growth rates may differ after conversion to US Dollars.

In fiscal 2016 revenue declined 1% on prior year to £23.5 billion amid a decrease in like-for-like sales as competition from discount retailers increases.

However net income leaped 384% in fiscal 2016 to £637 million as a result of an onerous impairment charge in 2015. Cash from operating activities was down 57% on 2015.

Strategy

In 2016 J Sainsbury's acquired Home Retail Group plc in order to strengthen its non-food offering. Home Retail Group owns Argos a high street retailer of general home merchandise and Habitat a household furnishing retailer. The acquisition is hoped to enable fast delivery networks.

In terms of products Sainsbury's is emphasizing quality in design and speed of brand renewal.

Mergers and Acquisitions In February 2016 Sainsbury's acquired Home Retail Group for £1.3 billion (around $1.9 billion). The combined company makes Sainsbury's one of the UK largest food and non-food retailers with over 90000 products 2000 stores.

HISTORY

Newlyweds John James and Mary Ann Sainsbury established a small dairy shop in their London home in 1869. Customers flocked to the clean and efficient store a far cry from most cluttered and dirty London shops. They opened a second store in 1876. By 1914 115 stores had been opened and the couple's sons had entered the business.

During WWI the company's stores established grocery departments to meet demand for preserved products such as meat and jams which were sold under the Sainsbury's label.

Mary Ann died in 1927 and John James the next year. Son John Benjamin wholly devoted to the family business took charge. (He is reported to have said on his deathbed "Keep the stores well lit.") In the 1930s he engineered the company's first acquisition the Thoroughgood stores.

Sales dropped by 50% during WWII and some shops were destroyed by German bombing. Under third-generation leader Alan John Sainsbury the company opened its first self-service store in 1950 in Croydon. The 75000-sq.-ft. store opened in 1955 in Lewisham was considered to be the largest supermarket in Europe.

J Sainsbury went public in 1973. It established a joint venture with British Home Stores in 1975 forming the Savacentre hypermarkets (the company bought out its partner in 1989).

Sainsbury partnered with Grand Bazaar Innovation Bon Marche of Belgium in 1979 to establish Homebase a do-it-yourself chain. (It bought the remaining 25% in 1996 and then sold the company in 2001 retaining only 18%.)

By 1983 most of Sainsbury's 229 stores were clustered in the south of England. A mature market and stiff competition forced the company to look elsewhere —both overseas and close to home. It began buying out US-based Shaw's Supermarkets in New England and in 1984 opened its first Scottish hypermarket. By 1987 the grocer owned 100% of Shaw's which had 60 stores in Massachusetts Maine and New Hampshire.

In 1991 Sainsbury came under competitive pressure from Tesco and the Argyll Group (later renamed Safeway plc) which also began building superstores. It responded with an expansion drive of its own including opening its first Scottish supermarket (in Glasgow) the next year.

In 1994 the company purchased a $325 million stake in Maryland-based Giant Food. Sainsbury bought home improvement retailer Texas Homecare from UK leisure concern Ladbroke in 1995 and integrated it into its Homebase unit. The following year it bought 12 supermarkets in Connecticut from Dutch retailer Ahold Delhaize (the purchase lowered its profits for the year) and entered Northern Ireland.

A year later the company opened Sainsbury's Bank. Royal Ahold bought Giant Food including Sainsbury's 20% stake in 1998. David Sainsbury —a great-grandson of the founders —retired as chairman in 1998 to pursue politics marking the first time a Sainsbury had not headed up the company in its more-than-a-century history.

As a cost-cutting effort in 1999 Sainsbury cut 2200 jobs more than half in management. It also launched its convenience store concept called Sainsbury's Local. Also that year Sainsbury bought the 53-store Star Markets chain of Massachusetts merging it into its Shaw's operations. In March 2000 Sir Peter Davis took over as CEO of Sainsbury's Supermarkets replacing David Bremner.

In 2001 Sainsbury acquired 19 Grand Union stores in the US (17 of which were converted to the Shaw's banner) and opened 25 new stores in the UK. The company also exited the Egyptian market and sold its home-and-garden chain Homebase to private equity firm Permira.

In 2002 Shaw's Supermarkets bought control of 18 stores in New England from bankrupt discounter Ames.

In November 2003 Sainsbury reached a £2 million out-of-court settlement with designer Jeff Banks over termination of his contract to revamp its clothing line in a bid to emulate rival ASDA's success with its George line of apparel.

In January 2004 the grocery chain acquired Swan Infrastructure (an Accenture affiliate) the company that ran its information technology systems for about $1 billion. The move brought the grocers information technology operations which were outsourced in 2000 back in-house.

In February 2004 Sainsbury acquired 54 Bells convenience stores. (Bells Stores was founded in 1968 by Les Bell and was owned by the Bell family until its acquisition.) Justin King (formerly of Marks & Spencer) joined Sainsbury as its CEO in March 2004 succeeding Sir Peter Davis who became chairman of the board. In April Sainsbury sold JS USA Holdings which operated 203 Shaw's and Star Markets stores in New England to US grocery chain Albertson's in a deal worth about $2.4 billion. The retailer also disposed of JS Developments its property development operation in fiscal 2004. Davis stepped down as chairman of Sainsbury on July 1 2004 one year ahead of schedule and following a prolonged dispute with investors that culminated in a fight over his compensation.

Philip Hampton (former finance director of Lloyds TSB (now Lloyds Banking Group) BT Group and BG Group) joined Sainsbury as its new chairman on July 19 2004. Hampton's appoint-

ment and experience with mergers and acquisitions fueled speculation that the struggling grocery chain may become a takeover target. In August Sainsbury acquired Jacksons Stores Ltd. and its wholly owned subsidiary Jacksons Stores 2002 Ltd. for about £100 million. In September Sainsbury agreed to pay ex-chairman Davis £2.6 million despite shareholder protests in July that forced the grocery retailer to withdraw a similar offer. At that time Lord Levene of Portsoken and Keith Butler-Wheelhouse both nonexecutive directors of the company and members of the remuneration committee resigned from the board.

In October 2004 Sainsbury said it was writing off £140 million against information technology systems and an another £120 million linked to ineffective supply-chain equipment as a result of a huge infrastructure investment program instituted by ex-chairman Davis that failed. In November the company acquired JB Beaumont a convenience store chain with six stores in the East Midlands. In 2005 the grocery chain acquired the five-store SL Shaw chain in southeastern England. Sainsbury renamed the shops Sainsbury's Local. The acquisitions pushed Sainsbury's convenience store count to nearly 300 outlets throughout the UK giving the company a 2% share of the convenience market.

The company sold 5% of its majority stake in Sainsbury's Bank in February 2007 to its joint venture partner HBOS for about £21 million ($40 million). As a result the bank became a 50-50 joint venture between the two firms. Also in 2007 the company shutdown its online entertainment division Sainsbury's Entertain You which offered books CDs DVDs videos computer games and a DVD rental service citing stiff competition in the online arena. The company removed hydrogenated fats from its branded products in 2007.

In mid-2008 Qatar Holding-backed real estate investment group Delta Two increased its stake in Sainsbury to about 25% fueling speculation that it may attempt to take over the British grocer. (In 2007 Delta Two made a bid to buy the remainder of the company but withdrew the offering in November amid turmoil in the credit markets.) Delta Two was the second suitor to leave the grocery chain at the altar. The company and key shareholders from the founding Sainsbury family rebuffed a group of private equity investors led by CVC Capital earlier in the year.

In mid-2009 the grocery chain launched online sales of some 8000 nonfood items such as kitchenware and furniture. It also extended its online home grocery delivery service to an additional 200 stores. The company welcomed David Tyler formerly chairman of Logica as its new chairman in November 2009. Tyler succeeded Sir Philip Hampton.

In November 2010 the company launched Sainsbury's Entertainment a digital download service that provides customers with access to more than 150000 books DVDs Blu-rays CDs and games to purchase online.

EXECUTIVES

CFO, Kevin O'Byrne, age 51
CEO Sainsbury's Bank, Peter L. Griffiths, age 57
CEO Sainsbury's Argos, John Rogers
CEO, Mike Coupe
Digital and Technology Director, Jon Rudoe
Chairman, David A. Tyler, age 63
Auditors: Ernst & Young LLP

LOCATIONS

HQ: J Sainsbury PLC
33 Holborn, London EC1N 2HT
Phone: (44) 20 7921 6000
Web: www.j-sainsbury.co.uk

PRODUCTS/OPERATIONS

2016 segment

	%
Retailing	99
Financial services	1
Property investments	0
Total	**100**

2016 Stores

	No.
Sainsbury's Supermarkets	601
Convenience stores	773
Total	**1,374**

PRODUCTS
Summer
Fruit & veg
Meat & fish
Dairy eggs & chilled
Bakery
Frozen
Food cupboard
Drinks
Health & beauty
Baby
Household
Pet
Home
Cook event

COMPETITORS

ALDI	Musgrave Retail
ASDA	Partners
Co-operative Group	SNAX 24
Costcutter	SPAR (UK)
Supermarkets	Tesco
Iceland Foods	Waitrose
Lidl	Wm Morrison
METRO AG	Supermarkets
Marks & Spencer	

HISTORICAL FINANCIALS

Company Type: Public

Income Statement

FYE: March 12

	REVENUE ($ mil.)	NET INCOME ($ mil.)	NET PROFIT MARGIN	EMPLOYEES
03/16	33,615	673	2.0%	162,700
03/15	35,195	(245)	—	161,100
03/14	39,747	1,188	3.0%	160,500
03/13	35,322	930	2.6%	157,000
03/12	35,079	940	2.7%	152,000
Annual Growth	**(1.1%)**	**(8.0%)**	**—**	**1.7%**

2016 Year-End Financials

Debt ratio: 20.3%	No. of shares (mil.): 1,924
Return on equity: 7.9%	Dividends
Cash ($ mil.): 1,634	Yield: 0.0%
Current ratio: 0.66	Payout: 199.6%
Long-term debt ($ mil.): 3,131	Market value ($ mil.): 30,069

	STOCK PRICE ($) FY Close	P/E High/Low		PER SHARE ($) Earnings	Dividends	Book Value
03/16	15.63	69	54	0.32	0.64	4.73
03/15	15.39	—	—	(0.13)	1.02	4.27
03/14	21.14	74	54	0.61	1.12	5.22
03/13	21.84	67	52	0.49	0.98	4.59
03/12	19.10	71	51	0.50	0.95	4.70
Annual Growth	**(4.9%)**	—	—	**(10.2%)**	**(9.4%)**	**0.1%**

Japan Tobacco Inc.

Japan Tobacco (JT) has plenty to puff about. The company secures about 55% of the Japanese cigarette market —the fourth largest worldwide. It holds eight of the country's top 10 brands including Mild Seven Seven Stars and Caster. Globally JT is the #3 tobacco maker trailing Philip Morris International and BAT. Driving growth its JT International arm which owns Britain's Gallaher Group makes and markets Camel Salem and Winston brands outside the US (once made by Reynolds American's RJR Tobacco) and others. JT also has holdings in the food and pharmaceutical industries. In 1985 the company shifted from a state monopoly to a public company; some 50% of JT is held by Japan's Minister of Finance.

Operations

Japan Tobacco operates six cigarette manufacturing plants and four factories that make tobacco related products across Japan. Outside its home country it operates 28 factories that make cigarettes and other tobacco and tobacco-related products. Foreign subsidiaries of the company include UK-based Gallaher Ltd. (acquired in 2007) and Liggett-Ducat in Russia. Beyond tobacco which accounts for more than 90% of the company's sales the company is engaged in the production of processed foods and beverages through its JT Beverage and TableMark Co. subsidiaries. Japan Beverage makes canned coffee drinks (under the Roots brand) and operates beverage vending machines. TableMark which makes and sells frozen and other processed foods is exiting the processed fishery products business. The company is also active in the research and development of new drugs through a pharmaceutical arm Torii Pharmaceutical Co. Ltd.

Geographic Reach

Japan accounts for more than 50% of the company's sales. International markets include Africa Brazil Europe Malaysia North America and Russia. Japan Tobacco's total tobacco sales volume at home and abroad comes to about 534 billion cigarettes per year representing nearly 9% of the global market.

Financial Performance

Japan Tobacco saw its adjusted net fiscal 2012 (ends March) sales decline at home by more than 3% vs. the prior year while international sales increased less than 1% over the same period. In Japan sales volume declined as a result of the contracting adult population stricter anti-smoking laws higher taxes and the impact of the massive earthquake that struck eastern Japan in March 2011. Still profits increased at home due to price increases. Indeed the company shipped 534 billion cigarettes in fiscal 2012 compared with 563 billion in 2011. The company's pharmaceutical business posted a nearly 8% gain in 2012 sales while the food and beverage sales declined for the third consecutive year.

Mergers and Acquisitions

In late 2015 the company said it would pay Reynolds American $5 billion for the non-US rights to its Natural American Spirit tobacco brand. The brand is popular with younger smokers and should help Japan Tobacco as it looks for growth outside its stagnant home market.

Faced with a contracting market at home Japan Tobacco is looking to Africa Asia Eastern Europe and Russia for growth. To that end in late-2011 it paid $450 million to acquire the Haggar Cigarette & Tobacco Factory of Sudan and South Sudan. Haggar produces the Bringi brand of cigarettes and boasts more than 80% market share in Sudan. Its sales volume in 2010 was reportedly more than

4.5 billion cigarettes. Indeed the international business is the profit growth engine for the group. Through additional acquisitions on ongoing investment in foreign markets Japan Tobacco hopes to grow its market share in many key markets. Among other threats to its tobacco business JT faces volatile prices for various crops which cause leaf tobacco costs to stay high. The company has moved to increase its control over both the price and quality of its tobacco leaf supply through a series of acquisitions and alliances. In 2009 the company acquired UK-based Tribac Leaf and two Brazilian firms in a deal valued at about $230 million. Tribac Leaf has growing operations in Malawi Zambia China and India and the Brazilian units operate in their home country. Separately JT formed a new tobacco sourcing company —called JTI Leaf Services –with US leaf suppliers Hail & Cotton and J.E.B. International.

HISTORY

In 1898 roughly 325 years after tobacco was introduced in Japan the nation's Ministry of Finance formed a bureau to monopolize its production to fund military and industrial expansion.

During WWII Japan's tobacco leaf imports from North and South America grew scarce and led to cigarette rationing. In 1949 the government began operating the tobacco production bureau as a business: the Japan Tobacco and Salt Public Corporation (in 1905 the bureau also became responsible for a salt monopoly).

The company launched Hope the first Japanese-made filter cigarette in 1957 and it became the world's best seller a decade later. In 1972 it began printing mild packaging "warnings": "Be careful not to smoke excessively for your health."

Japan Tobacco and Salt began selling Marlboro cigarettes licensed from Philip Morris in 1973. The Mild Seven brand (its current best-seller) went on sale in 1977; it became the world's #1 cigarette in 1981 but dropped to #2 (behind Marlboro) in 1993.

When its tobacco monopoly ended in 1985 the government established the firm as Japan Tobacco (a government-owned joint stock company). As competition from foreign imports increased the firm came up with new means of making yen. It formed Japan Tobacco International (cigarette exports mainly to the US and Southeast Asia) moved into agribusiness and real estate operations and in 1986 created JT Pharmaceutical. In 1987 cigarette import tariffs ended and importers lowered prices to match the company's; its sales and market share subsequently declined. During the late 1980s it introduced HALF TIME beverages and its first low-tar cigarettes (Mild Seven Lights is now the world's #1 light cigarette).

In 1992 Japan Tobacco bought its first overseas production facility Manchester Tobacco (closed in 2001). Former Ministry of Finance official Masaru Mizuno became CEO that year —and soon took up smoking. Also in 1992 the company and Agouron Pharmaceuticals agreed to jointly develop immune system drugs; in 1994 they added antiviral drugs. The government sold about 20% of the firm's stock to the public in 1994 and 13% in 1996. The firm began operating Burger King restaurants in Japan in 1996. Japan Tobacco bought Pillsbury Japan in 1998.

Japan Tobacco in 1999 paid nearly $8 billion for R.J. Reynolds International the international tobacco unit of what was then RJR Nabisco. The company then renamed the unit which has operations in 70 countries worldwide JT International. It also bought the food products division of Asahi Chemical Torii Pharmaceutical from Asahi Breweries and the Unimat vending machine company.

Slowing sales prompted Japan Tobacco to announce in 2000 that it would reduce its workforce by 6100 by 2005. Company exec Katsuhiko Honda became CEO that year (Mizuno remained as chairman) and said he'd push the government to sell its stake. Honda retired in 2006. In February 2001 the company announced plans to sell parts of its OTC drugs and health care businesses to Nichiiko Pharmaceutical to concentrate on prescription drugs. It also intends to sell all 25 of its Burger King outlets. In May Mizuno stepped down as chairman and was replaced by Takashi Ogawa.

In December 2001 Japan's Ministry of Finance recommended that it cut its holdings in the company from 66% to 50%; it would also allow the company to sell additional shares which could further dilute the government's stake to as little as 33%. In 2002 Japan Tobacco completed the sale of its 25 Burger King outlets and its OTC drug business.

In January 2004 the company unveiled six new brands: Mild Seven One Menthol Box Bitter Valley Fuji Renaissance Fuji Renaissance 100's Hi-Lite Menthol and BB Slugger. An added brand Hope Menthol currently being tested in the marketplace also will see expanded availability. Japan Tobacco's Canadian subsidiary filed for bankruptcy protection in August 2004 following a billion-dollar smuggling claim by the Canadian government. Canada said that the company owed $1.4 billion in Canadian back taxes for allegedly smuggling cigarettes in 1998 and 1999.

Japan Tobacco in 2005 ended its agreement with Philip Morris to make and sell Marlboro cigarettes. The company closed 13 of its 25 manufacturing plants and six of its 30 sales branches by early 2006 as part of an effort to increase profits. These reductions slashed as many as 4000 jobs from company payrolls as demand for cigarettes partly depressed by higher taxes continues to decline. Japan Tobacco is also using its own line of premium smokes to fill the gap left in the product line by the absence of Marlboro cigarettes. The company's deal with Philip Morris to sell Marlboro lapsed in 2005.

In April 2007 JT acquired Britain's Gallaher Group for about $15 billion. The purchase which added Silk Cut and Benson & Hedges cigarette brands to its products portfolio was the largest foreign acquisition by a Japanese company.

In January 2008 the company acquired a majority stake in Katokichi Co. for about $900 million. It then sold a 49% stake in the business to Nissin Foods forming a joint venture. In April JT entered the seasonings business acquiring a controlling stake in Fuji Foods.

At the end of 2008 Japan Tobacco placed Hans Group its Australia-based chilled foods venture and its subsidiaries into administration under the care of KordaMetha.

In 2009 Japan Tobacco acquired the UK's Tribac Leaf and Brazil-based leaf suppliers Kannenberg & Cia and Kannenberg Barker Hail & Cotton Tabacos.

EXECUTIVES

President and CEO, Thomas A. (Tom) McCoy
Regional President The Americas, Michel Poirier
Regional President Asia Pacific, Stefan Fitz, age 50
EVP Business Development Corporate Affairs and Corporate Communications, Eddy Pirard, age 54
Regional President Middle East Near East Africa Turkey and Worldwide Duty Free, Fadoul Pekhazis
Deputy CEO; EVP Emerging Products and Corporate Strategy, Masamichi Terabatake
SVP Information Technology and CFO, Roland Kostantos
Regional President Central Europe, Jorge da Motta
SVP Global Leaf, Paul Neumann

Regional President CIS+, Kevin Tomlinson
Regional President Western Europe, Vassilis Vovos
Chairman, Yasutake Tango
Auditors: Deloitte Touche Tohmatsu LLC

LOCATIONS

HQ: Japan Tobacco Inc.
2-2-1 Toranomon, Minato-ku, Tokyo 105-8422
Phone: (81) 3 3582 3111   **Fax:** (81) 3 5572 1441
Web: www.jti.co.jp

2015 Sales

	% of total
Japan	40
Overseas	60
Total	**100**

PRODUCTS/OPERATIONS

2015 Sales

	% of total
International Tobacco	59
Domestic Tobacco	30
Processed Food	7
Pharmaceuticals	3
Other	1
Total	**100**

SELECTED BRANDS
Camel
LD
MEVIUS
Winston

COMPETITORS

Ajinomoto	Nisshin Seifun Group
Altadis	Philip Morris
Asahi Breweries	International
British American	Reemtsma
Tobacco	Cigarettenfabriken
Coca-Cola	Suntory Holdings
Imperial Brands	Unilever
Mitsubishi Chemical	Vector Group
Nestle	

HISTORICAL FINANCIALS

Company Type: Public

Income Statement

FYE: December 31

	REVENUE ($ mil.)	NET INCOME ($ mil.)	NET PROFIT MARGIN	EMPLOYEES
12/15	18,714	4,034	21.6%	52,343
12/14*	18,053	3,041	16.8%	60,041
03/14	23,249	4,146	17.8%	60,693
03/13	22,533	3,651	16.2%	58,820
03/12	24,793	3,911	15.8%	59,231
Annual Growth	(6.8%)	0.8%	—	(3.0%)

*Fiscal year change

2015 Year-End Financials

Debt ratio: 0.0%
Return on equity: 19.4%
Cash ($ mil.): 4,375
Current ratio: 1.42
Long-term debt ($ mil.): 1,793

No. of shares (mil.): 1,790
Dividends
  Yield: 2.3%
  Payout: 19.2%
Market value ($ mil.): 33,263

	STOCK PRICE ($) FY Close	P/E High/Low		PER SHARE ($) Earnings	Dividends	Book Value
12/15	18.58	0	0	2.25	0.43	11.37
12/14*	13.73	0	0	1.67	0.00	11.70
Annual Growth	35.3%	—	—	7.6%	—	(0.7%)

*Fiscal year change

Jardine Cycle & Carriage Ltd

Jardine Cycle & Carriage is a driving force in Singapore. The company known as JC&C distributes and retails a range of vehicles including Toyota Honda Kia Peugeot Daihatsu BMW and Mercedes-Benz cars and commercial vehicles in southeast Asia. In addition to subsidiaries operating under the Cycle & Carriage banner in Singapore and Malaysia JC&C owns more than 50% of diversified Indonesian auto group Astra International and about 44% of Indonesian vehicle retailer Tunas Ridean. It also has auto stakes in Vietnam and Myanmar. Founded in 1899 JC&C is majority owned by sister companies Jardine Strategic Holdings and Jardine Matheson Holdings.

EXECUTIVES

President Director PT Astra International Tbk (Indonesia), Prijono Sugiarto
Director Operations Cycle & Carriage Bintang Berhad (Malaysia), Ramasamy Devaraju
Group Managing Director, Alexander Newbigging
Group Finance Director, Adrian Teng
Managing Director Singapore Motor Operations, Eric Chan
President Director PT Tunas Ridean Tbk (Indonesia), Rico Setiawan
Chairman Truong Hai Auto Corporation (Vietnam), Tran Ba Duong
Chairman Refrigeration Electrical Engineering Corporation (Vietnam), Thi Mai Thanh Nguyen
Chairman Siam City Cement Public Company Limited (Thailand), Veraphan Teepsuwan
General Manager Myanmar Operations, Kee Min Chin
Auditors: PricewaterhouseCoopers LLP

LOCATIONS

HQ: Jardine Cycle & Carriage Ltd
239 Alexandra Road, 159930
Phone: (65) 6473 3122   **Fax:** (65) 6475 7088
Web: www.jcclgroup.com

PRODUCTS/OPERATIONS

2015 Sales

	% of total
Sale of goods	72
Rendering of services	21
Financial services	7
Total	**100**

2015 Sales

	% of total
Indonesia	87
Others	13
Total	**100**

2015 Sales

	% of total
Astra	87
Direct motor interest	13
Total	**100**

Selected Operations
Astra International (50.1% Indonesia conglomerate with auto finance industrial agriculture infrastructure logistics and technology holdings)
Cycle & Carriage Automobile Myanmar (60% vehicle repair)
Cycle & Carriage Bintang (59% Malaysia vehicle retail and distribution)

Singapore Motors (retail and distribution)
Truong Hai Auto Corporation (32% Vietnam)
Tunas Ridean (44% Indonesia vehicle retailer)

COMPETITORS

Borneo Motors	Toyota Motor Thailand

HISTORICAL FINANCIALS

Company Type: Public

Income Statement

FYE: December 31

	REVENUE ($ mil.)	NET INCOME ($ mil.)	NET PROFIT MARGIN	EMPLOYEES
12/15	15,718	688	4.4%	250,000
12/14	18,675	820	4.4%	245,000
12/13	19,787	915	4.6%	214,000
12/12	21,541	987	4.6%	201,000
12/11	20,083	1,030	5.1%	182,000
Annual Growth	(5.9%)	(9.6%)	—	8.3%

2015 Year-End Financials

Debt ratio: 25.6%
Return on equity: 13.9%
Cash ($ mil.): 2,175
Current ratio: 1.39
Long-term debt ($ mil.): 2,497

No. of shares (mil.): 395
Dividends
  Yield: 0.0%
  Payout: 143.0%
Market value ($ mil.): 19,394

	STOCK PRICE ($) FY Close	P/E High/Low		PER SHARE ($) Earnings	Dividends	Book Value
12/15	49.07	35	21	1.82	2.60	13.33
12/14	62.88	33	23	2.31	2.08	13.00
12/13	56.76	34	20	2.57	2.38	11.98
12/12	79.83	30	24	2.77	2.38	13.04
12/11	69.05	28	17	2.90	1.91	12.39
Annual Growth	(8.2%)	—	—	(11.0%)	8.1%	1.8%

Jardine Matheson Holdings Ltd.

EXECUTIVES

Presidente, Benjamin William Keswick
Presidente Junta Directiva, Henry Keswick
Auditors: PricewaterhouseCoopers LLP

LOCATIONS

HQ: Jardine Matheson Holdings Ltd.
4th Floor, Jardine House, 33-35 Reid Street, Hamilton HM 12
Phone: (441) 292 0515   **Fax:** (441) 292 4072
Web: www.jardines.com

HISTORICAL FINANCIALS

Company Type: Public

Income Statement

FYE: December 31

	REVENUE ($ mil.)	NET INCOME ($ mil.)	NET PROFIT MARGIN	EMPLOYEES
12/15	37,007	1,797	4.9%	440,000
12/14	39,921	1,710	4.3%	430,000
12/13	39,465	1,566	4.0%	390,000
12/12	39,593	1,688	4.3%	0
12/11	37,967	3,449	9.1%	0
Annual Growth	(0.6%)	(15.0%)	—	—

2015 Year-End Financials

Debt ratio: 16.4%	No. of shares (mil.): 306
Return on equity: 9.1%	Dividends
Cash ($ mil.): 4,782	Yield: 2.8%
Current ratio: 1.33	Payout: 28.1%
Long-term debt ($ mil.): 6,995	Market value ($ mil.): 14,774

	STOCK PRICE ($) FY Close	P/E High/Low		PER SHARE ($) Earnings	Dividends	Book Value
12/15	48.28	14	9	4.81	1.35	65.19
12/14	60.70	14	11	4.61	1.32	63.17
12/13	52.81	16	12	4.25	1.29	60.68
12/12	62.23	14	10	4.62	1.19	59.34
12/11	47.51	6	5	9.46	1.10	54.89
Annual Growth	0.4%	—	—	(15.6%)	5.4%	4.4%

Jardine Strategic Holdings Ltd (Bermuda)

Jardine Strategic Holdings (JSH) has a garden of multinationals. Primary interests include Dairy Farm International with 5800 locations hotel group Mandarin Oriental with 45 hotels holding company Jardine Cycle & Carriage (the largest engine manufacturer in Indonesia) financial services firm Rothchilds Continuation and real estate developer Hongkong Land. JSH and its Hong Kong-based affiliate Jardine Matheson Holdings share these interests and are operated together in a complex ownership structure. Jardine Matheson provides services to JSH owns about 80% of its stock. Formed after the breakup of the East India Company's tea monopoly in 1832 JSH was instrumental in the formation of Hong Kong.

The company was originally formed in the wake of the breakup of the East India Company's tea trade monopoly in 1832. Following Jardines' founding it was a key company that promoted the founding of Hong Kong.

EXECUTIVES

Chairman and Managing Director, Ben Keswick
Deputy Chairman and Deputy Managing Director, Y. K. Pang
Group Finance Director, John R. Witt
Chairman, Henry Keswick
Auditors: PricewaterhouseCoopers LLP

LOCATIONS

HQ: Jardine Strategic Holdings Ltd (Bermuda)
Jardine House, 33-35 Reid Street, Hamilton
Phone:
Web: www.jardines.com

PRODUCTS/OPERATIONS

2015 Sales

	% of total
Astra	47
Dairy Farm	38
Hong-Kong Land	6
Jardine Cycle & Carriage	7
Mandarin Oriental	2
Intersegment transaction	0
Total	**100**

2015 Sales

	% of total
Motor Vehicles	31

	% of total
Retail	38
Mining	10
Property and hotels	9
Engineering and Construction	3
Agribusiness	3
Financial Services	4
Logistics and IT Services	2
Resturants	0
Total	**100**

2015 Sales

	% of total
Southeast Asia	72
Greater China	27
United Kingdom	0
Rest of World	1
Total	**100**

Subsidiaries
Astra International
Dairy Farm
Hongkong Land
Jardine Cycle & Carriage
Jardine Lloyd Thompson
Jardine Matheson
Jardine Motors
Jardine Pacific
Mandarin Oriental

COMPETITORS

Accor	Hopewell Holdings
Ahold Delhaize	Hyatt
China Resources Beer	ITOCHU
Continental Automotive Group	Marriott
	Marubeni
Daiei	McDonald's
HSBC	Swire Pacific

HISTORICAL FINANCIALS

Company Type: Public

Income Statement

FYE: December 31

	REVENUE ($ mil.)	NET INCOME ($ mil.)	NET PROFIT MARGIN	EMPLOYEES
12/15	29,391	1,953	6.6%	0
12/14	32,236	1,832	5.7%	0
12/13	32,666	1,700	5.2%	0
12/12	33,098	1,839	5.6%	0
12/11	31,049	3,943	12.7%	0
Annual Growth	(1.4%)	(16.1%)	—	—

2015 Year-End Financials

Debt ratio: 15.7%	No. of shares (mil.): 189
Return on equity: 8.2%	Dividends
Cash ($ mil.): 4,575	Yield: 0.8%
Current ratio: 1.37	Payout: 3.7%
Long-term debt ($ mil.): 6,684	Market value ($ mil.): 2,571

	STOCK PRICE ($) FY Close	P/E High/Low		PER SHARE ($) Earnings	Dividends	Book Value
12/15	13.61	6	4	3.25	0.12	126.95
12/14	17.08	6	5	3.02	0.12	118.33
12/13	16.01	7	6	2.79	0.11	112.39
12/12	17.76	23	5	2.99	0.42	106.72
12/11	54.92	11	8	6.34	0.10	98.26
Annual Growth	(29.5%)	—	—	(15.4%)	5.7%	6.6%

JBS SA

Auditors: BDO RCS Auditores Independentes SS

LOCATIONS

HQ: JBS SA
Avenida Marginal Direita do Tiete, 500, Sao Paulo, SP 05118-100
Phone: (55) 11 3144 4000   **Fax:** (55) 11 3144 4279
Web: www.jbs.com.br

HISTORICAL FINANCIALS

Company Type: Public

Income Statement

FYE: December 31

	REVENUE ($ mil.)	NET INCOME ($ mil.)	NET PROFIT MARGIN	EMPLOYEES
12/15	41,133	1,171	2.8%	230,000
12/14	45,335	766	1.7%	216,000
12/13	39,328	392	1.0%	185,000
12/12	37,024	351	0.9%	0
12/11	33,134	(40)	—	0
Annual Growth	5.6%	—	—	—

2015 Year-End Financials

Debt ratio: 13.6%	No. of shares (mil.): —
Return on equity: 17.9%	Dividends
Cash ($ mil.): 4,757	Yield: 1.5%
Current ratio: 1.25	Payout: 18.6%
Long-term debt ($ mil.): 11,355	Market value ($ mil.): —

	STOCK PRICE ($) FY Close	P/E High/Low		PER SHARE ($) Earnings	Dividends	Book Value
12/15	6.20	6	3	0.40	0.10	2.45
12/14	8.48	13	8	0.27	0.05	3.11
12/13	7.34	2	1	1.37	0.05	3.24
12/12	6.00	3	2	1.22	0.00	3.54
12/11	6.31	—	—	(0.15)	0.00	3.74
Annual Growth	(0.4%)	—	—	—	(10.0%)	—

JCR Pharmaceuticals Co Ltd

Pharmaceutical preparations

EXECUTIVES

President, Shin Ashida
Auditors: Deloitte Touche Tohmatsu LLC

LOCATIONS

HQ: JCR Pharmaceuticals Co Ltd
3-19 Kasuga-cho, Ashiya, Hyogo 659-0021
Phone: (81) 797 32 8591
Web: www.jcrpharm.co.jp

HISTORICAL FINANCIALS

Company Type: Public

Income Statement

FYE: March 31

	REVENUE ($ mil.)	NET INCOME ($ mil.)	NET PROFIT MARGIN	EMPLOYEES
03/16	155,288	15,935	10.3%	526
03/15	140,488	14,022	10.0%	501
03/14	152	12	8.3%	472
03/13	149	7	5.2%	437
03/12	156	7	4.9%	424
Annual Growth	461.2%	573.8%	—	5.5%

2016 Year-End Financials

Debt ratio: 0.0%	No. of shares (mil.): 31
Return on equity: 6.6%	Dividends
Cash ($ mil.): 17,352	Yield: —
Current ratio: 3.03	Payout: —
Long-term debt ($ mil.): 5,759	Market value ($ mil.): —

JD.com, Inc.

Auditors: PricewaterhouseCoopers Zhong Tian LLP

LOCATIONS

HQ: JD.com, Inc.
20th Floor, Building A, No. 18 Kechuang 11 Street,
Daxing District, Beijing 101111
Phone: (86) 10 8911 8888
Web: www.jd.com

HISTORICAL FINANCIALS

Company Type: Public

Income Statement
FYE: December 31

	REVENUE ($ mil.)	NET INCOME ($ mil.)	NET PROFIT MARGIN	EMPLOYEES
12/15	27,913	(1,443)	—	105,963
12/14	18,529	(805)	—	68,109
12/13	11,453	(8)	—	62,051
12/12	6,637	(277)	—	27,952
12/11	3,356	(203)	—	20,153
Annual Growth	69.8%	—		51.4%

2015 Year-End Financials

Debt ratio: 1.1%	No. of shares (mil.): —
Return on equity: (-27.5%)	Dividends
Cash ($ mil.): 3,076	Yield: —
Current ratio: 1.19	Payout: —
Long-term debt ($ mil.): 424	Market value ($ mil.): —

	STOCK PRICE ($) FY Close	P/E High/Low	Earnings	PER SHARE ($) Dividends	Book Value
12/15	32.27	— —	(0.53)	0.00	1.72
12/14	23.14	— —	(0.86)	0.00	2.21
Annual Growth	39.4%	— —			(6.2%)

JFE Holdings Inc

JFE Holdings has an iron will unmatched in Japan and much of the rest of the world. The "J" in JFE stands for Japan; "F" is for Fe the chemical symbol for iron; and "E" stands for engineering. JFE Holdings' steel business unit JFE Steel accounts for about 85% of total sales and manufactures steel products such as bars pipes steel frames tubes and stainless steel for the automotive construction and petroleum industries. JFE is among the world's largest steel companies ranking behind ArcelorMittal Japan's Nippon Steel & Sumitomo Metal and China's Hebei Iron and Steel and Baosteel.

Geographic Reach

While most of its steel production facilities are in Japan JFE's reach is global and it has offices in 12 other countries.

Operations

JFE's engineering unit makes designs and builds facilities such as gasifying and melting furnaces water purification plants steelworks plants and equipment and steel structures used in the energy environmental and steel structural sectors. Its shipbuilding unit constructs both merchant and military vessels in several Japanese ports including Kyoto and Yokahama. JFE's urban development unit develops large-scale condominium complexes using large plots of undeveloped land while its microelectronics (LSI) division includes Kawasaki Microelectronics which produces integrated circuits for digital cameras.

Financial Performance

The company's revenues decreased by a marginal 1% (in local currency) in fiscal year 2012 to a decrease in sales in the steel urban development and LSI segments due to a decline in demand which was partially offset by an increase in sales in the engineering and shipbuilding segments.

However its net income decreased by 163% in local currency in fiscal year 2012 due to a drop in operating income and ordinary income and a loss on the valuation of overseas investments.

Strategy

The company buys and sell steel companies and other assets as it seeks to deliver the best returns for its shareholders.

In 2012 JFE Steel agreed to acquire threading business and related assets of US-based Benoit Machine LLC through holding company Benoit Holding jointly owned by JFE Steel and Kanematsu USA a subsidiary of Kanematsu. The deal will enable JFE Steel and Kanematsu to establish a total supply chain for the manufacture threading and distribution of oilfield tubing and downhole accessories and thereby meet diversified needs in the oil and gas industry and capture growing demand for oilfield tubing going

On the other side of the ledger in 2012 JFE Steel sold part of its stake in South Korean steelmaker Hyundai Hysco to the Hyundai Group for an undisclosed amont. The stake was cut to below 8%. JFE Steel supplies hot-rolled steel sheet to Hyundai Hysco for the construction and automobile industries but Hyundai has stepped up its steel production and reduced the need for imports.

In 2010 JFE Steel acquired all shares of Toyohira Steel it did not already own taking full control of the company. Toyohira a Sapporo-based electronic furnace steelmaker is a wholly owned subsidiary of JFE Steel.

That same year JFE Steel acquired a 24% stake in Pancheng Yihong Pipe Co. a China-based maker of seamless pipes for oilfields in a stock-purchase deal. Following the investment JFE jointly owns the company along with China's Chengdu Steel & Vanadium Co. (51%) and another Japanese company Marubeni-Itochu Steel (25%).

EXECUTIVES

President JFE Engineering, Sumiyuki Kishimoto
Director and SVP Corporate Planning and Controller, Eiji Hayashida
President and CEO JFE Shoji Trade Corporation, Tsutomu Yajima
SVP Finance and Investor Relations, Shinichi Okada
Auditors: Ernst & Young ShinNihon LLC

LOCATIONS

HQ: JFE Holdings Inc
2-2-3 Uchisaiwai-cho, Chiyoda-ku, Tokyo 100-0011
Phone: (81) 3 3597 4321
Web: www.jfe-holdings.co.jp

PRODUCTS/OPERATIONS

2015 Sales

	% of total
Steel	53
Engineering	38
Trading	9
Adjustment	-
Total	**100**

Selected Products

Electrical Steel
Energy
Environment
Iron Powders
Pipes and Tubes
Plates
Shapes
Sheets
Slag
Stainless
Steel Bars and Wire Rods
Steel Structure
Titanium

COMPETITORS

ArcelorMittal
Baosteel
BlueScope Steel
Kobe Steel
Nippon Steel & Sumitomo Metal Corporation
Nippon Yakin
Nisshin Steel
Severstal
Shougang Corp.
United States Steel

HISTORICAL FINANCIALS

Company Type: Public

Income Statement
FYE: March 31

	REVENUE ($ mil.)	NET INCOME ($ mil.)	NET PROFIT MARGIN	EMPLOYEES
03/16	30,559	299	1.0%	59,460
03/15	32,091	1,161	3.6%	58,856
03/14	35,524	991	2.8%	57,210
03/13	33,894	420	1.2%	57,044
03/12	38,601	(446)	—	54,133
Annual Growth	(5.7%)	—		2.4%

2016 Year-End Financials

Debt ratio: 0.2%	No. of shares (mil.): 576
Return on equity: 1.7%	Dividends
Cash ($ mil.): 575	Yield: —
Current ratio: 1.47	Payout: —
Long-term debt ($ mil.): 8,637	Market value ($ mil.): 8,191

	STOCK PRICE ($) FY Close	P/E High/Low	Earnings	PER SHARE ($) Dividends	Book Value
03/16	14.21	0 0	0.52	0.00	27.87
03/15	23.03	0 0	2.01	0.00	28.03
03/14	19.75	— —	1.72	0.00	29.33
03/13	20.15	— —	0.76	0.00	29.41
03/12	22.05	— —	(0.84)	0.00	32.97
Annual Growth	(10.4%)	— —			(4.1%)

Jiangxi Copper Co., Ltd.

EXECUTIVES

Chairman, Baomin Li
Auditors: Deloitte Touche Tohmatsu Certified Public Accountants LLP

LOCATIONS

HQ: Jiangxi Copper Co., Ltd.
7666 Changdong Avenue, High and New Technology
Development Zone, Nanchang, Jiangxi Province
330096
Phone: (86) 791 82710117   **Fax:** (86) 791 82710114
Web: www.jxcc.com

HISTORICAL FINANCIALS

Company Type: Public

Income Statement

FYE: December 31

	REVENUE ($ mil.)	NET INCOME ($ mil.)	NET PROFIT MARGIN	EMPLOYEES
12/15	28,520	106	0.4%	20,873
12/14	31,945	467	1.5%	21,366
12/13	28,955	587	2.0%	22,425
12/12	25,344	829	3.3%	22,596
12/11	18,606	1,046	5.6%	22,500
Annual Growth	11.3%	(43.6%)	—	(1.9%)

2015 Year-End Financials

Debt ratio: 4.0%	No. of shares (mil.): —
Return on equity: 1.5%	Dividends
Cash ($ mil.): 2,572	Yield: 0.0%
Current ratio: 1.48	Payout: 3,589.9%
Long-term debt ($ mil.): 53	Market value ($ mil.): —

	STOCK PRICE ($) FY Close	P/E High/Low	PER SHARE ($) Earnings	Dividends	Book Value
12/15	46.55	424209	0.03	1.11	2.04
12/14	68.62	93 72	0.14	2.90	2.13
12/13	70.71	113 60	0.17	2.94	2.12
12/12	108.25	75 55	0.24	3.95	1.98
12/11	86.01	78 32	0.30	2.25	1.80
Annual Growth	(14.2%)	— —	(43.5%)	(16.3%)	3.1%

Johnson Controls International plc

Auditors: PricewaterhouseCoopers LLP

LOCATIONS

HQ: Johnson Controls International plc
One Albert Quay, Cork
Phone: (353) 21 423 5000
Web: www.johnsoncontrols.com

HISTORICAL FINANCIALS

Company Type: Public

Income Statement

FYE: September 30

	REVENUE ($ mil.)	NET INCOME ($ mil.)	NET PROFIT MARGIN	EMPLOYEES
09/16	37,674	(868)	—	209,000
09/15	9,902	551	5.6%	57,000
09/14	10,340	1,838	17.8%	57,000
09/13	10,647	536	5.0%	70,000
09/12	10,403	472	4.5%	70,000
Annual Growth	37.9%	—	—	31.5%

2016 Year-End Financials

Debt ratio: 25.8%	No. of shares (mil.): 935
Return on equity: (-6.0%)	Dividends
Cash ($ mil.): 2,718	Yield: 0.0%
Current ratio: 1.05	Payout: —
Long-term debt ($ mil.): 14,606	Market value ($ mil.): 43,543

	STOCK PRICE ($) FY Close	P/E High/Low	PER SHARE ($) Earnings	Dividends	Book Value
09/16	46.53	— —	(1.30)	1.16	25.77
09/15	34.47	33 25	1.35	0.81	10.02
09/14	44.23	11 8	4.16	0.71	11.40
09/13	34.95	47 22	1.19	0.00	11.52
09/12	56.26	54 37	1.07	0.94	11.31
Annual Growth	(4.6%)	— —	—	5.3%	22.9%

Johnson Matthey Plc (United Kingdom)

Johnson Matthey is truly a golden oldie. The company founded in 1817 is a leader in the refining and distribution of gold silver and platinum group metals (about 60% of sales). It is the sole marketing arm for Anglo American Platinum through its Precious Metal Products division. Johnson Matthey's Emission Control Technologies division produces emission control products fuel cells and process catalysts; and Process Technologies division is a global supplier of catalysts and licensing technologies. Its Fine Chemicals division makes base and precious metals catalysts and chemicals as well as active pharmaceutical ingredients (API) sold to pharmaceuticals manufacturers.

Geographic Reach

Johnson Matthey operates in 30 countries on six continents. Europe accounted 50% of its revenue in 2015 of which 24% was contributed by the UK. The US accounted for 25% and Asia 20%.

Operations

Johnson Matthey operates through global divisions: Precious Metal Products (56% of sales) is organized into its services businesses (the management distribution refining and recycling of precious metals) and manufacturing (the fabrication of products using precious metals or related materials platinum group metal catalysts and platinum group metal chemicals).

Emission Control Technologies (33%) is a global manufacturer of catalysts and catalyst systems which reduce emissions vehicles and industrial machines and improve air quality. Process Technologies (6%) is a global supplier of catalysts licensing technologies and other services to the syngas oleo/biochemical petrochemical oil refining and gas processing industries. Fine Chemicals (4%) is a global supplier of active pharmaceutical ingredients fine chemicals and other specialty chemical products and services to a wide range of pharmaceutical and chemical industry customers and industrial and academic research organizations. The New Businesses segment focuses on areas adjacent to its current interests that build on its core technology competences. It comprises its Battery Technologies and Fuel Cells businesses together with its new business development programs.

Sales and Marketing The company is targeting industries such as environmental automotive chemical pharmaceutical/medical and recycling.

Financial Performance

Johnson Matthey's revenues decreased by 10% in 2015 due to a 21% decline in Precious Metal Products impacted by the change in its contracts with Anglo American Platinum which reduced sales by 12% as a result of decline in commission income and also due to lower average precious metal prices and weakness in some of its manu-

facturing businesses' markets such as China. All other segments reported growth in revenue except fine chemicals which had flat revenues. Net income increased by 26% due to profit on the sale of its precious metal products' gold and silver refining business to Asahi Holdings. The company's operating cash flow decreased by 74% as the result of an increase in cash used in inventories due to higher inventories.

Strategy The company's 3C Strategy stands for Collaborate Customer Focus and Create Value.

Johnson Matthey is also focused on maintaining differentiation through technology by investing in R&D and it aims to deliver superior growth in existing and new markets. Developing a larger presence in oil and gas markets is a key part of its overall strategy. The company is targeting opportunities with sales potential of around £200 million per annum in ten years. Alongside organic development Johnson Matthey also focuses on growth through acquisitions. In pursuit of its strategy to focus on value adding sustainable technologies the company has made a number of bolt-on acquisitions this year including two in our new business area of battery technologies.

Active worldwide the company has been concentrating on expanding its business in China and India. In the former Johnson Matthey focuses on catalysts that will control nitrogen oxide emissions from China's massive coal industry. The company has set a long-term strategy of focusing on leading-edge catalysts using technology as a differentiator keeping platinum group metals (PGMs) as a major part of its operations and concentrating on organic growth.

In 2015 the company sold its Precious Metal Products' Gold and Silver Refining business to Asahi Holdings a collector refiner and recycler of precious and rare metals from waste materials for £124.3 million. This is in line with the group's long term strategy to focus on areas where it can use its expertise in chemistry and its applications to deliver high technology solutions or that provide a strategic service to the rest of the group.

Mergers and Acquisitions

In 2015 Johnson Matthey acquired Stepac L.A. Ltd. and its subsidiaries plus related assets for £20.3 million. Stepac is a provider of modified atmosphere packaging. It also bought the Pharmorphix solid form research business from Sigma-Aldrich which added material science capabilities to Johnson Matthey's expanding European API and clinical supply services. In 2015 the company purchased the battery materials business of Clariant AG. Two other acquisitions were completed during the year were the business and assets of Catacel Corporation a supplier of novel technology centered on the use of metal foil coated catalysts and sorbents which will allow the group to offer an enhanced range of market leading catalyst technologies for hydrogen or syngas manufacture and the purchase of Illumink Limited a printed liquid crystal laser technology company which gives the group access to a newly developed on surface anti-counterfeiting solution which could be a tracer solution for the oil and gas reservoir sector.

In 2014 Johnson Matthey acquired a cathode material manufacturing facility and related business from A123 Systems LLC .

HISTORY

Company Background

Percival Johnson set up an assayer's shop in London in 1817. Using chemical and physical tests he determined the amount of gold in a given bar and guaranteed his results by offering to buy the bars he assayed. Johnson then set up a gold refinery in the early 1830s and developed a method for extracting platinum group metals. As part of that process he produced vitreous colors for pottery and glass refined nickel and silver nitrate for medical use and later for photographic uses.

George Matthey joined the company in 1838 and championed the platinum business securing a steady supply of platinum from Russia. The company thrived on business generated by gold rushes in California (1849) and Australia (1851). It built a silver refinery to melt down European coinage and extract component metals and in 1870 it bought a company that produced magnesium antimony vanadium and aluminum. In 1891 the company became Johnson Matthey & Co. Limited. Around the turn of the century it bought rolling mills and began forming metals into sheet tube and wire to better serve jewelers.

During WWI Johnson Matthey & Co. provided platinum catalysts and magnesium powder for explosives and in WWII the company was appointed the government's agent for controlling platinum stocks. Johnson Matthey & Co. expanded its international operations rapidly during the post-war boom adding holdings in Australia India North America and South Africa. It established subsidiaries in France and the Netherlands (1956) Italy (1959) Sweden (1960) Belgium (1961) and Austria (1962). The company also began conducting research on automotive catalytic converters to reduce pollution. It formed Johnson Matthey Bankers (JMB) to carry out its banking and trading activities.

A foray into the US jewelry business led to big losses in 1980 and the company pressed JMB to make higher-risk loans. JMB's contribution to profits went from less than 25% in 1981 (the year the company took its present name) to more than 60% in 1983. The bank ended up with so many bad loans that the Bank of England had to arrange a bailout in 1984. Gene Anderson who became CEO in 1985 cut 3000 jobs and reduced the number of divisions from 78 to 4. Profits rebounded but Anderson resigned in 1989 after failing to persuade the board to diversify away from platinum.

During the 1990s the company invested heavily in its electronics division which had been doing well since the 1989 acquisition of Cominco Electronic Materials (ultra-pure metals for microchips). By 1995 the division was responsible for about a third of Johnson Matthey's profits. In 1998 it bought Cookson Group's 50% share of its ceramics joint venture.

In 1998 Johnson Matthey shifted its focus to three core businesses: catalysts colors and coatings and precious metals. The next year it sold its electronic materials business Johnson Matthey Electronics to US-based AlliedSignal (now Honeywell International) and began looking for takeover opportunities in its core markets. In 2001 the company acquired pharmaceuticals manufacturers Meconic (now Macfarlan Smith; it's the UK's only maker of medical opiates –cocaine and heroin) and Pharm-Eco then used these acquisitions as the basis for a fourth division: Pharmaceutical Materials (now a part of its Fine Chemicals and Catalysts Division).

In 2002 the company acquired Cascade Biochem Limited to strengthen its Pharmaceutical Materials division and metal catalyst company Synetix. CEO Chris Clark retired in 2003. He was succeeded by Neil Carson former executive director of the precious metals and catalysts operations.

Following the sale of its Pigments & Dispersions unit to Rockwood Pigments in 2004 Johnson Matthey restructured its Colours and Coatings division by closing several of its manufacturing sites and transferring some operations to its Precious Metal Products division. The moves created what became the Ceramics division

the 2007 sale of which was the last in the dismantling of the Colours and Coatings division.

At the beginning of 2008 the company acquired the Argillon Group which manufactured catalysts and advanced ceramic materials from Ceramics Luxembourg (owned by KKR). Later that year Johnson Matthey sold the acquired ceramic insulators alumina business for about $40 million.

In 2010 a Johnson Matthey subsidiary formed a joint venture with Aoxing Pharmaceutical to manufacture ingredients for narcotics and neurological drugs for the Chinese market. That same year Johnson Matthey acquired Intercat a supplier of fluid catalytic cracking services for the petroleum refining industry for $56 million. It became part of Johnson Matthey's Process Technologies division's Ammonia Methanol Oil and Gas unit.

EXECUTIVES

Executive Director Environmental Technologies Division and Director, Larry C. Pentz, age 61, $295,000 total compensation
Director Technology Centre, B. A. Murrer
Chief Executive, Robert MacLeod, age 52, $294,000 total compensation
Division Director Catalysts Chemicals and Refining, G. P. Otterman
Executive Director Precious Metal Products, W. F. (Bill) Sandford, $209,000 total compensation
President Catalysts Environmental Catalysts and Technologies North America, J. B. Fowler
Managing Director Emission Control Technologies Europe, J. F. Walker
General Manager Noble Metals Europe, C. C. Howlett
General Manager Noble Metals North America, J. D. Malanga
Managing Director Tracerco and Vertec, A. C. Hurst
President Global Research Chemicals, B. C. Singelais
President Davy Process Technology, D. J. Tomlinson
General Manager Gold North America, A. J. McCullough
Managing Director Emission Control Technologies Asia, J. V. Zubrickas
Managing Director Colour Technologies, R. L. P. J. van der Heijden
Managing Director Refineries and Gas Processing, J.K. Dunleavy
Managing Director Syngas and Gas to Products, A. Wright
Group Finance Director, Den Jones
Chairman, Tim E. P. Stevenson, age 67
Auditors: KPMG LLP

LOCATIONS

HQ: Johnson Matthey Plc (United Kingdom)
5th Floor, 25 Farringdon Street, London EC4A 4AB
Phone: (44) 20 7269 8400   **Fax:** (44) 20 7269 8433
Web: www.matthey.com

2015 Sales

	%
Europe	
UK	24
Germany	12
Rest of Europe	11
USA	25
Rest of North America	2
China (including Hong Kong)	11
Rest of Asia	10
Rest of World	5
Total	**100**

PRODUCTS/OPERATIONS

2015 Sales

	% of total
Precious Metals	56
Emission Control Technologies	33
Process Technologies	6
Fine Chemicals	4
New Businesses	1
Total	**100**

Businesses
Emission Control Technologies Division
Emission Control Technologies website
Stationary Emissions Control website
Process Technologies Division
Process Technologies website
Chemical Catalysts website
Johnson Matthey Formox website
Johnson Matthey Davy Technologies website
Tracerco website
Precious Metal Products Division
Services Businesses
Precious Metals Management
Global Precious Metal Refining website
Scavenging Technologies
PGM Database
Johnson Matthey & Brandenberger website
Manufacturing Businesses
Noble Metals website
Medical Device Components website
Metal Joining website
USA Jewellery Products
Advanced Glass Technologies website
Silver and Coating Technologies website
Chemical Products website
Piezoproducts website
Fine Chemicals Division
API Manufacturing
Johnnson Matthey Macfarlan Smith website
Johnson Matthey Pharmaceutical Materials - USA website
Johnson Matthey Pharma Services website

COMPETITORS

BASF Catalysts	Metalor USA Refining
GEA Group	Mitsui Mining and
Heraeus Holding	Smelting
Heraeus Precious	Showa Denko
Metals	Umicore
IBIDEN	Vectra
Impala Platinum	Vesuvius
Kyocera	

HISTORICAL FINANCIALS

Company Type: Public

Income Statement

FYE: March 31

	REVENUE ($ mil.)	NET INCOME ($ mil.)	NET PROFIT MARGIN	EMPLOYEES
03/16	15,421	479	3.1%	12,325
03/15	14,867	633	4.3%	12,266
03/14	18,571	566	3.0%	11,556
03/13	16,303	420	2.6%	10,995
03/12	19,266	506	2.6%	10,058
Annual Growth	**(5.4%)**	**(1.3%)**	**—**	**5.2%**

2016 Year-End Financials

Debt ratio: 35.3%   No. of shares (mil.): 193
Return on equity: 18.1%   Dividends
Cash ($ mil.): 438   Yield: 0.0%
Current ratio: 1.69   Payout: 200.3%
Long-term debt ($ mil.): 1,203   Market value ($ mil.): 15,533

	STOCK PRICE ($) FY Close	P/E High/Low		PER SHARE ($) Earnings	Dividends	Book Value
03/16	80.26	61	38	2.39	4.78	13.78
03/15	100.40	48	38	3.11	0.00	13.06
03/14	109.17	68	45	2.78	0.00	12.67
03/13	69.85	59	47	2.03	0.00	10.34
03/12	73.17	52	33	2.35	0.00	11.43
Annual Growth	**2.3%**	**—**	**—**	**0.4%**	**—**	**4.8%**

JSC VTB Bank

Auditors: Ernst & Young LLC

LOCATIONS

HQ: JSC VTB Bank
29, Bolshaya Morskaya Street, St. Petersburg 190000
Phone: (7) 495 739 77 99   **Fax:** (7) 495 258 47 81
Web: www.vtb.ru

HISTORICAL FINANCIALS

Company Type: Public

Income Statement

FYE: December 31

	REVENUE ($ mil.)	NET INCOME ($ mil.)	NET PROFIT MARGIN	EMPLOYEES
12/15	15,722	144	0.9%	92,882
12/14	15,338	69	0.5%	101,072
12/13	23,063	3,088	13.4%	103,808
12/12	23,468	2,818	12.0%	80,860
12/11	15,176	2,769	18.2%	67,912
Annual Growth	0.9%	(52.2%)	—	8.1%

2015 Year-End Financials

Debt ratio: —
Return on equity: 0.8%
Cash ($ mil.): 8,687
Current ratio: —
Long-term debt ($ mil.): —

No. of shares (mil.): —
Dividends
  Yield: —
  Payout: 585,918.1%
Market value ($ mil.): —

Juroku Bank, Ltd.

The Juroku Bank is industriously working to serve its customers in the prefectures of Gifu and Aichi both part of the industrial region of Chubu. The regional bank has about 150 offices in its primary service areas as well as offices in Osaka and Tokyo and overseas offices in Hong Kong and Shanghai. In addition to traditional deposit banking products and services The Juroku Bank and its subsidiaries do business in such areas as credit cards credit guarantees investments and leasing. The bank joined with five other regional banks to form the Tokai-Kinki PFI Financial Network which is intended to help its member strengthen their abilities related to private finance initiatives.

In 2005 the bank fell prey to an ATM scam in 2005 the same year Juroku Bank signed on to use Hitachi's finger-vein authentication system to verify identification at its cash machines.

EXECUTIVES

President, YUKIO MURASE
Auditors: Deloitte Touche Tohmatsu LLC

LOCATIONS

HQ: Juroku Bank, Ltd.
8-26 Kanda-machi, Gifu 500-8516
Phone: (81) 58 265 2111
Web: www.juroku.co.jp

COMPETITORS

Mie Bank
Mitsubishi UFJ Financial Group

Mizuho Financial
Resona
Sumitomo Mitsui

HISTORICAL FINANCIALS

Company Type: Public

Income Statement

FYE: March 31

	ASSETS ($ mil.)	NET INCOME ($ mil.)	INCOME AS % OF ASSETS	EMPLOYEES
03/16	55,297	119	0.2%	4,382
03/15	50,746	190	0.4%	4,417
03/14	55,667	163	0.3%	3,497
03/13	60,236	246	0.4%	3,565
03/12	66,902	145	0.2%	3,689
Annual Growth	(4.7%)	(4.9%)	—	4.4%

2016 Year-End Financials

Return on assets: 0.2%
Return on equity: 3.9%
Long-term debt ($ mil.): —
No. of shares (mil.): 373
Sales ($ mil.): 1,020

Dividends
  Yield: —
  Payout: —
Market value ($ mil.): —

JX Holdings, Inc.

Japan's JX Holdings is an integrated energy holding company that combines the businesses of two of the country's top oil refiners Nippon Oil and Nippon Mining Holdings which merged to become a powerhouse with diverse operations in petroleum refining and marketing oil and natural gas exploration and production and metals (mainly copper). JX Holdings produces 128000 barrels of oil equivalent from its exploration and production asserts. Its refineries have the capacity to process roughly 1.7 million barrels of crude oil per day representing more than a quarter of the total amount of crude oil processed per day in Japan. In 2015 JX Holdings agreed to merge with TonenGeneral Sekiyu.

Geographic Reach
The company markets refined products across Japan; is engaged in exploration development and production of oil and gas in 14 countries around the world; and has stake in a copper mine in Chile.

Operations
JX Holding operates through three major subsidiaries: JX Nippon Oil & Energy; JX Nippon Oil & Gas Exploration; and JX Nippon Mining & Metals.

The company's petroleum refining and marketing business accounted for 87% of total revenues in fiscal 2014. Among its refined petroleum products are gasoline and gas oil for automobiles and trains; jet fuel for aircraft; kerosene for heating homes; lubricant oil for machinery and engines; naphtha for production of petrochemicals; petrochemicals for manufacturing synthetic fibers paints and plastics; and fuel oils and other heavy oils for heating buildings and operating heavy machinery.

Its energy business consists of petroleum refining and marketing basic chemical products lubricants specialty and performance chemicals coal electricity gas and new energy and oil and natural gas exploration development and production.

Its Metals segment includes non-ferrous metal resources development and mining copper gold silver sulfuric acid copper foils materials for rolling and processing thin film materials non-ferrous metal recycling and industrial waste treatment transportation by ships of products including metal business products and titanium.

Other businesses include asphalt paving civil engineering work construction work electric wires land transportation real estate leasing business

and common JX Group activities including fund procurement.

JX Holdings has a nearly 40% market share in Japan of both fuel oil marketing and lubricating oil marketing.

Financial Performance
The company has reported an increase in net revenues over the last four years.

In fiscal 2014 net sales increased by 10.6%.

In the Oil and Natural Gas E&P business sales volume declined due primarily to the spontaneous reduction of production volume. Nonetheless as a result of the depreciation of the yen cash flow increased and ordinary income was up year on year.

In the Metals business the copper price was low but the depreciation of the yen had a positive effect on ordinary income and results were about the same level as in the previous year.

The company has seen it net income decline trend over the last four years.

In fiscal 2014 JX Holdings' net income declined by 33% due to an increase in impairment losses expenses on suspended mines a growth in deferred taxes and an increase in cost of sales.

Cash from operating activities grew by 15% thanks to income before income taxes and minority interests of ¥220.3 billion and depreciation and amortization of ¥183.6 billion outpace the decline in cash from operating activities from a decrease in notes and accounts payable-trade of ¥84.2 billion.

Strategy
JX Holdings allocates profits and cash reserves from its Japan-based petroleum refining and marketing operations and from other existing businesses to the development of petroleum natural gas and mineral resources as well as new energy businesses. In the near future it plans to formulate a new long-term vision for 2030.

In the meantime JX Holdings is working to strengthen its sales network by opening new service stations and converting others to self service. It is also reevaluating its card strategy and expanding the number of service stations that offer the Dr. Drive car care service. The group is aiming to increase its production volume of 200000 barrels per day.

Company Background
The merger of Nippon Oil and Nippon Mining in 2010 was spurred on by changes in the Japanese oil industry including excess refining capacity due to the continued decline in domestic demand for refined petroleum products a growing consumer awareness of environmental issues and alternative energy options and a sluggish Japanese economy. Such trends prompted the two to consider restructuring and integrating their businesses to strengthen competitiveness. Following the merger JX Nippon set up upstream oil business JX Nippon Oil & Gas Exploration and metals unit JX Nippon Mining and Metals as operating subsidiaries.

Petroleum refining and marketing will continue to be a core segment that JX Holdings plans to expand further throughout Asia and arpund the world. However it may also look for future opportunities to engage in new energy markets such as fuel cells and photovoltaic power generation to keep up with the growing green trend.

In 2012 the company's wholly owned subsidiary JX Nippon Exploration and Production (U.K.) Limited signed sale and purchase agreements to acquire an extensive portfolio of non-operated oil and gas assets in the UK Continental Shelf from ENI. The assets give JX a substantial long-term oil and gas production base in the UK.

EXECUTIVES

President, Isao Matsushita, age 69

Executive Officer, Yuji Nakajima
Executive Officer, Satoru Uchida
Executive Officer, Susumu Hara
Executive Officer, Ichiro Yamamoto
Chairman, Yasushi Kimura, age 69
Auditors: Ernst & Young ShinNihon LLC

LOCATIONS

HQ: JX Holdings, Inc.
1-2 Otemachi 1-chome, Chiyoda-ku, Tokyo 100-8161
Phone: (81) 3 6275 5009
Web: www.hd.jx-group.co.jp

2014 Sales

	% of total
Japan	74
China	19
Other countries	7
Total	**100**

PRODUCTS/OPERATIONS

2014 Sales

	% of total
Energy	87
Metals	8
Oil & natural gas exploration & production	2
Other	3
Total	**100**

COMPETITORS

Cosmo Oil	Mitsui Mining and
Exxon Mobil	Smelting
Honeywell	SK Innovation
International	Showa Shell Sekiyu
Idemitsu Kosan	Singapore Petroleum
Mitsubishi Electric	Sumitomo Metal Mining

HISTORICAL FINANCIALS

Company Type: Public

Income Statement

FYE: March 31

	REVENUE ($ mil.)	NET INCOME ($ mil.)	NET PROFIT MARGIN	EMPLOYEES
03/16	77,810	(2,480)	—	37,860
03/15	90,702	(2,310)	—	39,174
03/14	120,248	1,037	0.9%	26,616
03/13	119,239	1,694	1.4%	25,569
03/12	130,730	2,079	1.6%	24,236
Annual Growth	(12.2%)	—	—	11.8%

2016 Year-End Financials

Debt ratio: 0.3%
Return on equity: (-16.1%)
Cash ($ mil.): 4,387
Current ratio: 0.96
Long-term debt ($ mil.): 13,542

No. of shares (mil.): —
Dividends
Yield: 0.0%
Payout: —
Market value ($ mil.): —

	STOCK PRICE ($) FY Close	P/E High/Low	Earnings	Dividends	Book Value
03/16	3.95	— —	(1.00)	0.21	5.36
03/15	3.84	— —	(0.93)	0.07	6.51
03/14	5.12	— —	0.42	0.00	10.26
03/13	5.69	— —	0.68	0.00	9.93
03/12	5.60	— —	0.84	0.00	10.02
Annual Growth	(8.4%) (14.5%)	— —	—	—	—

Jyske Bank A/S

Jyske Bank is a leading independent Danish bank offering a variety of financial services to private customers and small and medium-sized businesses. The shareholder-owned bank operates a decentralized network of around 110 domestic branches that operate separately under a guiding set of policies and goals. Securities and currency transactions asset management investment services and leasing are among Jyske Bank's primary offerings. The bank was established in 1967 as the result of a merger of four Danish banks. It has international branch operations in Switzerland Gibraltar Germany France and the Netherlands.

EXECUTIVES

Chief Executive Officer, Anders Christian Dam
Auditors: Deloitte Statsautoriseret
Revisionsaktieseiskab

LOCATIONS

HQ: Jyske Bank A/S
Vestergade 8-16, Silkeborg DK-8600
Phone: (45) 89 89 89 89   Fax: (45) 89 89 19 99
Web: www.jyskebank.dk

COMPETITORS

Danske Bank	Sydbank
Nordea Bank	

HISTORICAL FINANCIALS

Company Type: Public

Income Statement

FYE: December 31

	ASSETS ($ mil.)	NET INCOME ($ mil.)	INCOME AS % OF ASSETS	EMPLOYEES
12/15	79,313	361	0.5%	4,021
12/14	88,431	504	0.6%	4,191
12/13	48,355	333	0.7%	3,774
12/12	45,625	104	0.2%	3,728
12/11	47,014	85	0.2%	3,802
Annual Growth	14.0%	43.5%	—	1.4%

2015 Year-End Financials

Return on assets: 0.4%
Return on equity: 8.6%
Long-term debt ($ mil.): —
No. of shares (mil.): 94
Sales ($ mil): 2,419

Dividends
Yield: —
Payout: —
Market value ($ mil.): —

	STOCK PRICE ($) FY Close	P/E High/Low	Earnings	Dividends	Book Value
12/15	0.00	— —	3.81	0.00	46.32
12/14	6.27	— —	5.73	0.00	47.34
12/13	6.27	0 0	4.68	0.00	45.17
12/12	7.20	1 1	1.50	0.00	38.68
Annual Growth	—	— —	26.2%	—	4.6%

Kajima Corp. (Japan)

As one of the world's leading construction firms Kajima was among the first skyscraper builders in Japan and continues to develop earthquake-resistant technologies. The group operates as a general contractor-developer providing a full array of engineering design development and construction services. It builds skyscrapers bridges highways and railways nuclear power plants and other commercial and civil projects. Projects have included the Suez Canal Bridge in Egypt and the Nukui Dam in Hiroshima. Kajima has a presence in more than 20 countries in Africa Asia Europe the Middle East and North America.

OperationsKajima Corporation generated 45% of its total revenue from its building construction business in FY2015 (ended March 31) with its Civil Engineering business making up another 20%. Its domestic subsidiary and affiliate companies made up 17% of total revenues while its overseas subsidiaries and affiliates made up 15%. The remainder of revenues came from its real estate development business. The company's Kajima USA subsidiary runs the North American arm of the business.

Geographic ReachKajima gets more than 80% of its revenues from its projects in Japan while another more than 15% of revenues are split between Asia and North America. Its offices in Japan are located in the cities of Hokkaido Tohoku Kanto Yokohama Hokuriku Chubu Kansai Shikoku Chugoku and Kyushu. Its international offices are in Taiwan Singapore Indonesia Vietnam Myanmar and Tanzania.

Financial Performance
Kajima Corporation's revenues have been slowly growing in recent years thanks to a strengthening Japanese construction market and the company's ability to secure more contract awards. Meanwhile Kajima's profits have struggled to consistently grow as it hasn't been able to control its operating expenses. The builder's revenue grew by 11% to ¥1694 billion ($14.16 billion) in fiscal 2015 (ended March 31) with growth across its Civil Engineering Real Estate Development Domestic affiliates and overseas affiliates. A 7.5% decline in the company's building construction business offset some of this revenue growth however as its profits on certain construction projects deteriorated during the year. Despite higher revenue in 2014 the builder's net income declined by 27% to ¥15.14 billion ($126.5 million) as its operating expenses nearly doubled during the year. Its operating cash climbed by nearly 80% to ¥59.21 billion ($494.9 million) despite lower earnings.

Mergers and Acquisitions
In March 2015 Kajima acquired a majority stake in the mid-tier builder Icon Co to expand its exposure to the Australian construction market. The deal came at a time when the country's biggest-ever housing boom was about to take off and when Icon had some $850 million worth of major contracts in the pipeline in Victoria NSW and Queensland.

Company Background
Founded in 1840 Kajima has had an illustrious and venerable history. It began earthquake remediation work in the early 1920s and built railroads and the first Western-style buildings in Japan.

EXECUTIVES

EVP, Naoki Atsumi
President, Mitsuyoshi Nakamura
Managing Director, Hiroshi Kaneko
Managing Executive Officer, Atsushi Hattori
EVP, Takashi Hinago
Managing Executive Officer, Tamiharu Tashiro
Auditors: Deloitte Touche Tohmatsu LLC

LOCATIONS

HQ: Kajima Corp. (Japan)
1-3-1 Motoakasaka, Minato-ku, Tokyo 107-8388
Phone: (81) 3 5544 1111
Web: www.kajima.co.jp

2013 Sales

	% of total
Asia	
Japan	85
Other countries	7
North America	6
Europe	1
Other regions	-
Total	**0**

PRODUCTS/OPERATIONS

2013 Sales

	% of total
Construction	88
Real Estate & others	12
Total	**100**

2013 Sales

	% of total
Building construction	50
Civil Engineering	18
Real estate development and others	4
Others	28
Total	**100**

Selected Subsidiaries

Act Technical Support Inc. (sales and services)
Azuma Kanko Kaihatsu Co. Ltd. (hotels and leisure)
Chung-Lu Construction Co. Ltd. (Taiwan)
East Real Estate Co. Ltd.
Green Materials Recycle Corporation (sales and services)
Hawaiian Dredging Construction Company Inc. (US)
Ilya Corporation (design and consulting)
Kajima Kress Co. Ltd. (procurement and construction)
Kajima Real Estate Investment Advisors Inc.
Kajima Tatemono Sogo Kanri Co. Ltd. (real estate
  development and management)
Public Relations Officer Corporation (sales and services)
Shinrinkohen Golf Club Co. Ltd.
Taiko Trading Co. Ltd. (procurement and construction)
Yaesu Book Center Co. Ltd. (culture)

COMPETITORS

Bechtel	Shimizu
CSCEC	Sumitomo Mitsui
Fluor	Construction
Hazama	TOA
Kumagai Gumi	Taisei
Mitsubishi Heavy	Takenaka
Industries	Tokyu Construction
Obayashi	

HISTORICAL FINANCIALS

Company Type: Public

Income Statement

FYE: March 31

	REVENUE ($ mil.)	NET INCOME ($ mil.)	NET PROFIT MARGIN	EMPLOYEES
03/16	15,518	644	4.2%	19,084
03/15	14,116	126	0.9%	18,587
03/14	14,737	201	1.4%	15,391
03/13	15,782	249	1.6%	15,468
03/12	17,770	46	0.3%	15,149
Annual Growth	**(3.3%)**	**92.7%**	**—**	**5.9%**

2016 Year-End Financials

Debt ratio: 0.1%
Return on equity: 15.9%
Cash ($ mil.): 2,154
Current ratio: 1.11
Long-term debt ($ mil.): 1,724

No. of shares (mil.): 1,039
Dividends
  Yield: 0.0%
  Payout: —
Market value ($ mil.): 67,712

	STOCK PRICE ($) FY Close	P/E High/Low		PER SHARE ($) Earnings	Dividends	Book Value
03/16	65.12	1	1	0.62	0.48	4.04
03/15	46.72	3	2	0.12	0.41	3.49
03/14	35.27	—	—	0.19	0.49	3.39
03/13	27.70	—	—	0.24	0.00	3.25
03/12	30.85	—	—	0.04	0.00	3.01
Annual Growth	**20.5%**	**—**	**—**	**92.7%**	**—**	**7.6%**

Kansai Electric Power Co., Inc. (Kansai Denryoku K. K.) (Japan)

Japan's #2 electric utility (behind Tokyo Electric) the Kansai Electric Power Company (KEPCO) provides electricity to 12.7 million customers in Japan's Kansai region. The utility has a generating capacity of 36573 MW which is produced at hydroelectric fossil-fueled and nuclear power plants. As deregulation takes effect KEPCO is moving into new business arenas including retail natural gas sales in Japan. Additionally KEPCO is engaged in information technology telecommunications construction and engineering services environmental services home security real estate transportation leasing and other energy-related operations. It has about 60 main affiliated companies primarily in Japan.

Operations
KEPCO's reportable segments consist of electrical power (85% of sales) IT/communication and other.

The company's power plant portfolio includes more than 150 hydroelectric plants about a dozen fossil-fired plants and three nuclear plants. It has 131480 km of overhead distribution lines and 6245 km of underground lines. It also more than 18730 km of overheads transmission lines and 4413 km of underground transmission lines.

Geographic Reach
KEPCO's supply area includes all of Osaka Hyogo Kyoto Nara Shiga and Wakayama prefectures and portions of Fukui Gifu and Mie prefectures.

Financial Performance
Note: Growth rates may differ after conversion to US Dollars.

The company's revenues decreased in fiscal year 2016 (March year end) from ¥3406 billion to ¥3246 billion due to a 5% decline in electricity sales as the result of warmer than usual winter weather crimping demand.

KEPCO's reported net income was ¥140.8 billion in fiscal 2016 (compared to a net loss of ¥148.3 billion a year earlier) thanks to lower operating expenses higher interest and dividend income and a major gain from sales of property plant and equipment.

Strategy
The company is looking to take advantage of the shake up of the Japanese electric power industry since the Great East Japan Earthquake Disaster in 2011 that prompted Japan to shut down vulnerable nuclear plants and re-examine its reliance on nuclear power. As a result both the retail electricity and gas retail markets are being liberalized.

In this context KEPCO is taking steps to increase safety at its nuclear plants while boosting its interests in thermal power hydropower and renewable energy in order to become a comprehensive energy supplier. It is also eyeing expansion into markets outside of Japan.

Company Background
The company was established in 1951.

KEPCO has a longstanding relationship with Australia's North West Shelf liquefied natural gas (LNG) joint venture. One of the venture's first customers in 1989 the company in 2009 signed a new deal guaranteeing the Japanese utility some 3.3 million metric tons a year in LNG supply.

EXECUTIVES

Managing Director, Masao Ikoma
EVP, Hideki Toyomatsu
EVP, Jiro Kagawa
President, Shigeki Iwane, age 63
Chairman, Makoto Yagi, age 67
Auditors: Deloitte Touche Tohmatsu LLC

LOCATIONS

HQ: Kansai Electric Power Co., Inc. (Kansai Denryoku K. K.) (Japan)
3-6-16 Nakanoshima, Kita-ku, Osaka 530-8270
Phone: (81) 6 6441 8821
Web: www.kepco.co.jp

PRODUCTS/OPERATIONS

2016 Sales

	% of total
Electric power	86
IT/Communications	5
Other	9
Total	**100**

Selected Subsidiaries

Kanden Energy Solution Co. Inc
SAKAI LNG Corp
ECHIZEN ENELINE CO. INC
Osaka Bioenergy Co. Ltd
K-Opticom Corp
Kanden System Solutions Co. Inc
Kanden Realty & Development Co. Ltd.
Clearpass Co. Ltd
KANDEN AMENIX Corp
Kanden Community Co. Ltd
Kanden CS Forum Inc.
Kanden Oce Work Co. Inc
Kanden Power-Tech Corp
Kanden Business Support Corp.
San Roque Power Corporation
LNG EBISU Shipping Corporation
KPIC Netherlands B.V.

COMPETITORS

Chubu Electric Power
Chugoku Electric Power
Hokkaido Electric Power
Hokuriku Electric Power
Internet Initiative Japan
KDDI
Kobe Steel
Kyushu Electric Power
NTT
Nippon Steel & Sumitomo Metal Corporation
Osaka Gas
SOFTBANK MOBILE
Shikoku Electric
Tohoku Electric Power
Tokyo Electric
Tokyo Gas

HISTORICAL FINANCIALS

Company Type: Public

Income Statement

FYE: March 31

	REVENUE ($ mil.)	NET INCOME ($ mil.)	NET PROFIT MARGIN	EMPLOYEES
03/16	28,904	1,253	4.3%	45,647
03/15	28,388	(1,236)	—	45,458
03/14	32,237	(943)	—	33,657
03/13	30,385	(2,587)	—	33,537
03/12	34,273	(2,953)	—	32,961
Annual Growth	(4.2%)	—	—	8.5%

2016 Year-End Financials

Debt ratio: 0.4%
Return on equity: 12.6%
Cash ($ mil.): 1,140
Current ratio: 0.52
Long-term debt ($ mil.): 27,889
No. of shares (mil.): 892
Dividends
 Yield: —
 Payout: —
Market value ($ mil.): 3,848

	STOCK PRICE ($) FY Close	P/E High/Low		PER SHARE ($) Earnings	Dividends	Book Value
03/16	4.31	0	0	1.40	0.00	11.76
03/15	4.57	—	—	(1.38)	0.00	9.21
03/14	5.37	—	—	(1.06)	0.00	13.16
03/13	4.55	—	—	(2.90)	0.00	15.21
03/12	7.65	—	—	(3.31)	0.00	20.88
Annual Growth	(13.4%)	—	—	—	—	(13.4%)

KB Financial Group, Inc.

KB Financial Group holding company for Kookmin Bank provides commercial and consumer banking services in South Korea. It offers asset management and life insurance through alliances with Netherlands-based ING Groep. The bank's lending activities mainly entail residential mortgages home equity loans consumer loans and corporate loans. Kookmin Bank has more than 1200 branches in its home country where it claims some 26 million customers or about half of the population of South Korea. The bank provides corporate services such as foreign exchange and securities trading from offices at home and abroad in New York London Hong Kong Tokyo and Auckland New Zealand.

KB Financial became a bank holding company in 2008 and made no bones about its ambitions to stretch its wings with acquisitions. It has been eyeing brokerage firms as well as other financial services companies.

It is reportedly interested in acquiring troubled Korea Exchange Bank. This is the second time KB Financial has wanted to buy KEB; in 2006 its $7 billion offer was stymied by KEB's parent US-based private equity firm Lone Star Funds. In 2008 the South Korean government blocked HSBC's acquisition of KEB putting the bank in play once more.

A proposed KEB acquisition is just one part of KB Financial's strategy. Seeking strategic opportunities in emerging markets the bank has opened representative offices in Kazakhstan the Ukraine and Vietnam and is mulling moves into other Central and Southeast Asian nations. In 2008 it bought a 30% stake in Kazakhstan bank JSC Bank CenterCredit; it eventually intends to build up to a controlling stake of that bank.

In the meantime the company sold its nearly 14% stake in PT Bank International Indonesia to Malayan Banking Berhad for some $309 million.

Kookmin Bank spun off its credit card business in 2011 and KB Financial took it over. The new company KB Kookmin Card Co. will focus on credit card/telecommunications services and include a mobile credit card. Other services include consumer financing and insurance.

In 2006 erstwhile Kookmin Bank CEO Kim Jung-tae resigned in the face of disciplinary sanctions imposed by financial regulators after he was accused of accounting irregularities. Some South Korean newspapers speculated that a disciplinary warning issued by the Financial Supervisory Commission was retaliation for Kim's opposition to government-led bailouts of financially troubled companies.

Citigroup owns around 17% of KB Financial.

EXECUTIVES

Chairman and CEO, Jong Kyoo Yoon
Auditors: Samil Accounting Corporation (A Member Firm of PircewaterhouseCoopers)

LOCATIONS

HQ: KB Financial Group, Inc.
 84 Namdaemun-ro Jung-gu, Seoul 100-703
Phone: (82) 2 2073 2844   **Fax:** (82) 2 2073 2848
Web: www.kbfng.com

PRODUCTS/OPERATIONS

Selected Subsidiaries

KB Asset Management Co. Ltd. (80%)
KB Credit Information Co. Ltd. (99.7%)
KB Data Systems Co. Ltd. (99.99%)
KB Futures Co. Ltd. (99.98%)
KB Investment Co. Ltd. (99.99%)
KB Real Estate Trust Co. Ltd. (99.99%)
Kookmin Bank
Kookmin Bank Hong Kong Ltd.
Kookmin Bank International Ltd.

COMPETITORS

Busan Bank	Korea Exchange Bank
Citigroup	Samsung Life Insurance
Daegu Bank	Shinhan Financial
Hana Bank	Woori
Industrial Bank of Korea	

HISTORICAL FINANCIALS

Company Type: Public

Income Statement

FYE: December 31

	ASSETS ($ mil.)	NET INCOME ($ mil.)	INCOME AS % OF ASSETS	EMPLOYEES
12/15	279,689	1,443	0.5%	181
12/14	281,834	1,280	0.5%	168
12/13	277,505	1,198	0.4%	151
12/12	264,124	1,594	0.6%	157
12/11	239,580	2,048	0.9%	148
Annual Growth	3.9%	(8.4%)	—	5.2%

2015 Year-End Financials

Return on assets: 0.5%
Return on equity: 6.0%
Long-term debt ($ mil.): —
No. of shares (mil.): 386
Sales ($ mil): 11,822
Dividends
 Yield: 2.5%
 Payout: 17.4%
Market value ($ mil.): 10,768

	STOCK PRICE ($) FY Close	P/E High/Low		PER SHARE ($) Earnings	Dividends	Book Value
12/15	27.87	0	0	3.72	0.71	63.10
12/14	32.62	0	0	3.30	0.48	64.62
12/13	40.51	0	0	3.09	0.53	63.14
12/12	35.90	0	0	4.12	0.64	59.42
12/11	31.34	0	0	5.56	0.10	51.19
Annual Growth	(2.9%)	—	—	(9.6%)	61.5%	5.4%

KBC Group NV

Holding companies nec nsk
Auditors: Ernst & Young Bedrijfsrevisoren BCVBA

LOCATIONS

HQ: KBC Group NV
 Havenlaan 2, Brussels 1080
Phone: (32) 2 429 49 16   **Fax:** (32) 2 429 44 16
Web: www.kbc.com

HISTORICAL FINANCIALS

Company Type: Public

Income Statement

FYE: December 31

	ASSETS ($ mil.)	NET INCOME ($ mil.)	INCOME AS % OF ASSETS	EMPLOYEES
12/15	274,868	2,874	1.0%	36,411
12/14	298,010	2,141	0.7%	36,187
12/13	332,214	1,397	0.4%	38,167
12/12	338,588	806	0.2%	48,026
12/11	369,127	16	0.0%	51,127
Annual Growth	(7.1%)	261.6%	—	(8.1%)

2015 Year-End Financials

Return on assets: 1.0%
Return on equity: 16.3%
Long-term debt ($ mil.): —
No. of shares (mil.): 418
Sales ($ mil): 11,663
Dividends
 Yield: 2.5%
 Payout: 18.5%
Market value ($ mil.): 13,023

	STOCK PRICE ($) FY Close	P/E High/Low		PER SHARE ($) Earnings	Dividends	Book Value
12/15	31.15	9	6	4.14	0.79	41.19
12/14	27.93	9	7	4.04	0.00	48.08
12/13	28.37	28	17	1.42	0.43	46.71
12/12	17.83	—	—	(1.44)	0.00	49.31
12/11	6.10	—	—	(2.50)	0.32	61.01
Annual Growth	50.3%	—	—	—	25.7%	(9.4%)

KDDI Corp

Auditors: Kyoto Audit Corp.

LOCATIONS

HQ: KDDI Corp
 3-10-10 Iidabashi, Chiyoda-ku, Tokyo 102-8460
Phone: (81) 3 6678 0712
Web: www.kddi.com

HISTORICAL FINANCIALS
Company Type: Public

Income Statement
FYE: March 31

	REVENUE ($ mil.)	NET INCOME ($ mil.)	NET PROFIT MARGIN	EMPLOYEES
03/16	39,816	4,403	11.1%	65,972
03/15	35,631	3,298	9.3%	61,782
03/14	41,984	3,119	7.4%	27,073
03/13	38,922	2,566	6.6%	20,238
03/12	43,546	2,908	6.7%	19,680
Annual Growth	(2.2%)	10.9%	—	35.3%

2016 Year-End Financials

Debt ratio: 0.1%	No. of shares (mil.): —
Return on equity: 15.4%	Dividends
Cash ($ mil.): 1,711	Yield: 1.9%
Current ratio: 1.81	Payout: 16.2%
Long-term debt ($ mil.): 8,520	Market value ($ mil.): —

	STOCK PRICE ($) FY Close	P/E High/Low		PER SHARE ($) Earnings	Dividends	Book Value
03/16	13.34	0	0	1.76	0.26	11.83
03/15	16.98	0	0	1.32	0.34	10.20
03/14	14.52	—	—	1.29	0.39	11.28
03/13	20.80	—	—	1.02	0.00	10.77
03/12	16.24	—	—	1.15	0.00	11.32
Annual Growth	(4.8%)	—	—	11.2%	—	1.1%

Keiyo Bank, Ltd. (The) (Japan)

Keiyo Bank aims to be chief in Chiba. Founded in 1943 the regional bank operates mainly in the urban areas in and surrounding Chiba Prefecture Japan. Among its commercial banking services are ATM consumer loans and foreign currency deposits. Keiyo operates via some 262 locations including a Tokyo branch and 114 in Chiba proper. Japan Trustee Services Bank claims a 5.37% stake in the bank alongside Nipponkoa Insurance (4.33%) and The Chiba Bank (4.19%).

EXECUTIVES
President, TOSHIYUKI KUMAGAI
Auditors: Ernst & Young ShinNihon LLC

LOCATIONS
HQ: Keiyo Bank, Ltd. (The) (Japan)
1-11-11 Fujimi, Chuo-ku, Chiba 260-0015
Phone: (81) 43 222 2121
Web: www.keiyobank.co.jp

COMPETITORS
Chiba Bank   Chiba Kogyo Bank

HISTORICAL FINANCIALS
Company Type: Public

Income Statement
FYE: March 31

	ASSETS ($ mil.)	NET INCOME ($ mil.)	INCOME AS % OF ASSETS	EMPLOYEES
03/16	40,016	135	0.3%	3,111
03/15	36,259	124	0.3%	3,044
03/14	39,938	148	0.4%	2,000
03/13	41,842	160	0.4%	1,989
03/12	46,078	145	0.3%	1,993
Annual Growth	(3.5%)	(1.9%)	—	11.8%

2016 Year-End Financials

Return on assets: 0.3%	Dividends
Return on equity: 5.4%	Yield: —
Long-term debt ($ mil.): —	Payout: —
No. of shares (mil.): 266	Market value ($ mil.): —
Sales ($ mil): 623	

Kia Motors Corp. (South Korea)

South Korea's #2 carmaker (behind Hyundai Motor) Kia Motors produces about 3 million vehicles a year at 10 manufacturing and assembly plants in five countries which are then sold through a network of distributors and dealers covering 150 countries. Its compact Kia picanto is the second-best selling car in South Korea. Other popular models include the Forte the Sorento and the Soul. Kia also makes a number of commercial vehicles. Its high-capacity plants outside Korea are in the US Slovakia and China. After Korea Kia's second-largest market is the US. Part of the Hyundai Kia Automotive Group Kia operates as an affiliate of Hyundai Motor.

Geographic Reach
Kia has established manufacturing plants in key regions two in China (set up as joint partnerships with Yueda and Dongfeng Motor) a Slovakia assembly plant in Eastern Europe (that also produces Hyundai vehicles) and one in the US (in Georgia). In 2014 it invested $1 billion to launch a new manufacturing plant in Monterrey Mexico.

Strategy
Kia is focused on edging out the competition with its stylish design that doesn't come with a European price tag. By strengthening its platform to smaller lighter cars Kia aims to rapidly respond to changes in consumer demand. The company markets its value in design esthetics and fuel efficiency. None of its vehicles are gas guzzlers and its Optima sedan came with a hybrid engine option. Most of its vehicles have a gasoline direct injection (GDI) engine that results in better fuel economy.

HISTORY
Kia's conglomerate ownership is also fundamental to its operation. Favoring its founding family former president of Kia Hyundai Motors vice chairman Chung Eui-sun is the son of Hyundai Kia Automotive Group chairman Chung Mong-koo. The elder Chung is the son of Hyundai's founder and controls the car company through a series of cross-holdings involving auto-parts maker Hyundai Mobis and steelmaker Hyundai Steel. In 2010 he stepped down from Kia Motors' board. To fill his vacancy the role of CEO was jointly held by Kia

vice chairman Chung Sung-eun and Kia president Seo Young-jong until late 2010 when Chung Sung-eun resigned amidst the recall of some 100000 automobiles. President and COO Lee Hyoung-keun was named as Chung's replacement.

Leadership has had other rough patches as well. A court found then-chairman Chung guilty of embezzlement and fraud in a slush fund scandal that passed corporate control and wealth from father to son hurting shareholders' value. An appeals court suspended the chairman's prison sentence to community service citing the executive's irreplaceable role in the company and country's economic well-being. He was subsequently pardoned by the South Korean president.

EXECUTIVES
Vice Chairman and Co-CEO, Hyoung-Keun (Hank) Lee
Co-CEO, Han-Woo Park
EVP and CFO, Han Chun-Soo
Chairman, Chung Mong-Koo, age 68
Auditors: Samjong Accounting Corporation (A Member Firm of KPMG)

LOCATIONS
HQ: Kia Motors Corp. (South Korea)
12 Heolleung-ro Seocho-gu, Seoul 137-130
Phone: (82) 2 3464 1114   **Fax:** (82) 2 3464 6813
Web: www.kia.co.kr

2015 Sales

	% of total
Domestic	38
North America	38
Europe	22
Other regions	2
Total	**100**

PRODUCTS/OPERATIONS

Selected Models
Commercial vehicles
  K2700/Strong/3000s/2500TCI
  K4000G
Passenger cars
  Cadenza
  cee' d
  cee' d_sw
  Cerato/Forte
  Cerato/Forte Koup
  Optima
  Picanto
  pro_cee' d
  Rio
  Soul
SUV & MPV
  Borrego/Mohave
  Carens/Rondo
  Carnival/Sedona
  Sorento
  Sportage
  Venga

COMPETITORS

BYD	Isuzu
Chery Automobile	Mazda
China FAW	Nissan
Daimler	Peugeot
FCA US	Renault
Fiat Chrysler	Shanghai Automotive
Ford Motor	Ssangyong Motor
Fuji Heavy Industries	Suzuki Motor
GM Korea	Toyota
General Motors	Volkswagen
Honda	

HISTORICAL FINANCIALS

Company Type: Public

Income Statement

FYE: December 31

	REVENUE ($ mil.)	NET INCOME ($ mil.)	NET PROFIT MARGIN	EMPLOYEES
12/15	42,090	2,235	5.3%	34,121
12/14	43,046	2,736	6.4%	34,112
12/13	45,260	3,629	8.0%	33,576
12/12	44,247	3,619	8.2%	32,756
12/11	37,275	2,947	7.9%	32,411
Annual Growth	3.1%	(6.7%)	—	1.3%

2015 Year-End Financials

Debt ratio: 0.0%
Return on equity: 11.2%
Cash ($ mil.): 939
Current ratio: 1.26
Long-term debt ($ mil.): 3,001

No. of shares (mil.): 400
Dividends
  Yield: —
  Payout: —
Market value ($ mil.): —

Kirin Holdings Co Ltd

You might say this company makes good-luck beer. Named for a unicorn which is a Japanese symbol of good fortune Kirin Holdings is a top beer maker in Japan through its Kirin Brewery Co. In addition to its domestic Kirin-branded beers the company owns brewers that serve overseas markets such as Australia's Lion and Philippines-based San Miguel Brewery. The beer brewer also makes soft drinks (coffee tea drinks and mineral water) the alcoholic fruit drink chu-hi and owns Japanese wine producer Mercian Corporation. Beyond beverages Kirin also has operations in health and dairy foods and pharmaceuticals-manufacturing sectors.

Geographic Reach

Outside Japan Kirin has established local operations in Australia China Germany the Philippines Singapore South Korea Taiwan the UK the US and Vietnam. In the US it owns soft-drink bottler Coca-Cola Bottling Company of Northern New England and bourbon maker Four Roses Distillery in Kentucky.

Strategy

Kirin is looking to expand outside Japan because of the country's unfavorable demographics (i.e. a declining birth rate). Indeed Japan's beer market has shrunk by about 15% in terms of shipment volumes over the past decade. One focus of expansion for Kirin is the Asia-Oceania region where it aims to build on recent acquisitions. Kirin took 100% control of Lion Nathan paying A$3.5 billion (about $3.2 billion) to acquire the 54% of Australia's #2 brewer that it did not already own. Australia presents Kirin with a stable customer base and was one of the few countries that avoided the recessionary conditions that rocked the global economy in 2009.

China is another attractive market for Kirin. The company has a joint venture with China Resources Beer —producer of China's top-selling Snow beer brand —that makes and distributes nonalcoholic beverages including bottled water and soft drinks in China. Kirin plans to invest about $400 million in the joint venture and will transfer ownership of four local subsidiaries in Shanghai and Beijing to the partnership.

HISTORY

American William Copeland went to Yokohama Japan in 1864 and five years later established the Spring Valley Brewery the first in Japan to provide beer for foreign nationals. Lacking funds to continue the brewery Copeland closed it in 1884. The next year a group of foreign and Japanese businessmen reopened it as Japan Brewery. The business created the Kirin label in 1888 and was soon profitable.

The operation was run primarily by Americans and Europeans at first but by 1907 Japanese workers had filled the ranks and adopted the Kirin Brewery Company name. Sales plummeted during WWII when the government limited brewing output. After the war the US occupation forces inadvertently assisted Kirin when they split Dai Nippon Brewery (Kirin's main competitor) into two companies (Asahi and Sapporo Breweries) while leaving Kirin intact. The company became Japan's leading brewer during the 1950s.

During the 1970s Kirin introduced several soft drinks and in 1972 branched into hard liquor through a joint venture with Seagram (Kirin-Seagram).

The firm bought several Coca-Cola bottling operations in New England and Japan in the 1980s. Kirin also entered the pharmaceuticals business in part through a joint venture with US-based Amgen. In 1988 the brewer signed an agreement with Molson to produce Kirin beer for the North American market. In 1989 Kirin bought Napa Valley's Raymond Vineyards.

In 1991 Kirin formed a partnership to market Tropicana drinks in Japan. It also entered an alliance with Sankyo (Japan's #2 drug company) in 1991 to market Kirin's medication for anemia which it had developed with Amgen.

Chairman Hideyo Motoyama resigned in 1993 after four company executives were arrested for allegedly paying a group of racketeers who had threatened to disrupt Kirin's annual meeting. Joint venture Kirin-Amgen won the rights to make thrombopoietin (TPO) a blood platelet growth stimulator in 1995.

Yasuhiro Satoh became president of Kirin in 1996. The brewer moved into China that year through an agreement with China Resources (Shenyang) Snowflake Brewery. To brew its beers in the US the company formed Kirin Brewery of America also in 1996.

In response to losing market share to Asahi Kirin cut its workforce in 1998 and introduced Tanrei a cheaper low-malt beer that quickly captured half its market. Building on its presence in China Kirin bought 46% of brewer Lion Nathan (based in Australia and New Zealand) for $742.5 million that year. It became a licensed brewer of Anheuser-Busch in 1999.

Like other Japanese brewers Kirin struggled against dwindling demand for its most expensive brews in 2000. Koichiro Aramaki was named president of the company the following year and began to expand and diversify Kirin's operations to overcome slow growth domestically. In 2002 the company bought 15% of Philippine food and drink giant San Miguel for about $530 million. It also boosted ties with beverage giant Pernod Ricard by purchasing 32% of SIFA a French food services firm for an estimated $155 million. In 2002 Kirin also formed Flower Season Ltd. a joint venture with Dole Food Company to sell flowers to Japanese retailers. Also in 2002 Kirin launched its new Pure Blue brand of "shochu" distilled liquor.

In 2006 Aramaki stepped down as president (he remained chairman) and turned the reins over to former managing director Kazuyasu Kato. The following year Kirin reorganized as a holding company.

The company added to its international dairy holdings with its 2007 acquisition of Australian milk and cheese producer National Foods. The following year National Foods acquired Australian dairy company Australian Co-operative Foods Limited (dba Dairy Farmers) for about $763 million. With some 2000 members Dairy Farmers is one of the biggest dairy product makers in Australia. These acquisitions made Kirin a top player in the Oceania dairy sector which is part of the company's larger strategy to focus and grow in the Asian and Oceania markets.

In 2009 Kirin acquired a 100% interest in San Miguel Brewery of the Philippines. Following Kirin's successful tender offer to acquire the remainder of Lion Nathan's shares later that year Lion Nathan and National Foods were consolidated under Kirin's Australian holding company which was renamed Lion Nathan National Foods.

Early in 2010 company veteran Senji Miyake was named president and CEO of the Japanese brewer (among other top management changes). Miyake joined Kirin Brewery Company in 1970. In December Kirin made Mercian Corp. a wholly owned subsidiary following a scandal at Mercian's fish feedstuffs division.

EXECUTIVES

Managing Director, Hirotake Kobayashi
EVP and Director, Senji Miyake
Managing Director, Hajime Nakajima
CFO, Masahito Suzuki
Managing Director, Toru Suzuki
Managing Executive Officer, Kazuyasu Kato, age 72
Auditors: KPMG AZSA LLC

LOCATIONS

HQ: Kirin Holdings Co Ltd
4-10-2 Nakano, Nakano-ku, Tokyo 164-0001
Phone: (81) 3 6837 7015
Web: www.kirinholdings.co.jp

2013 Sales

	% of total
Japan	65
Asia/Oceania	22
Others	13
Total	**100**

PRODUCTS/OPERATIONS

2013 sales

	% of total
Japan integrated beverages	45
Overseas integrated beverages	35
Pharmaceuticals and bio-chemicals	17
Others	3
Total	**100**

COMPETITORS

Anheuser-Busch InBev	Megmilk Snow Brand
Asahi Breweries	Mercian
Asia Pacific Breweries	Molson Coors
Carlsberg	Nippon Beet Sugar
Chugai	Novartis
Coca-Cola	Pabst
Diageo	PepsiCo
E. & J. Gallo	Red Bull
FEMSA	SABMiller
Fonterra	Sapporo
Heineken	Suntory Holdings
ITOCHU	Taiwan Tobacco & Wine
Kokubu	Takara
LVMH	Tsingtao

HISTORICAL FINANCIALS

Company Type: Public

Income Statement

FYE: December 31

	REVENUE ($ mil.)	NET INCOME ($ mil.)	NET PROFIT MARGIN	EMPLOYEES
12/15	18,249	(393)	—	39,888
12/14	18,403	271	1.5%	39,894
12/13	21,478	816	3.8%	39,922
12/12	25,382	652	2.6%	41,246
12/11	26,771	95	0.4%	40,348
Annual Growth	(9.1%)	—	—	(0.3%)

2015 Year-End Financials

Debt ratio: 0.2%
Return on equity: (-5.3%)
Cash ($ mil.): 552
Current ratio: 1.17
Long-term debt ($ mil.): 4,975

No. of shares (mil.): 912
Dividends
  Yield: 2.3%
  Payout: —
Market value ($ mil.): 12,374

	STOCK PRICE ($) FY Close	P/E High/Low		Earnings	PER SHARE ($) Dividends	Book Value
12/15	13.56	—	—	(0.43)	0.32	8.54
12/14	12.40	—	—	0.30	0.36	12.27
12/13	14.40	—	—	0.86	0.52	13.33
12/12	11.73	—	—	0.67	0.34	13.93
12/11	12.00	—	—	0.09	0.00	14.08
Annual Growth	3.1% (11.8%)	—	—	—	—	—

Kobe Steel Ltd (Japan)

One of Japan's leading steel companies Kobe Steel (aka Kobelco) makes more than enough wire and rod to cage its markets. A diversified manufacturer Kobe Steel also makes aluminum copper and titanium products and it produces welding products such as welding robots and industrial machinery including compressors and crushers. The company also provides wholesale power supply operating two power plants in Kobe. Kobe Steel's real estate division rents manages and sells properties. Kobe Steel's joint venture with United States Steel —PRO-TEC Coating Company —produces hot-dipped galvanized steel sheet.

Operations

Kobe Steel's operations are vast. Indeed the firm lists more than 210 subsidiaries and more than 55 affiliated companies. Its foundation and largest business segment is iron and steel production representing more than 35% of its sales; construction machinery and aluminum and copper production each account for about 20% of sales. The firm's natural resources and engineering business offers engineering products and services to the energy oil refining and chemical industries. Kobe Steel's environmental business Kobelco Eco-Solutions is active in waste water treatment waste disposal and recycling. Kobelco Construction Machinery specializes in hydraulic excavators and is active in fast-growing markets including China India and Southeast Asia. The company also makes cranes.

Geographic Reach

Japan accounts for nearly two-thirds of Kobe Steel's sales. However its international business is growing quickly: tripling its percentage contribution to Kobe's total sales over the past few years. China is a major foreign market accounting for nearly 10% of sales. The company's US arm Kobe Steel USA is located in New York and Michigan.

Kobe Steel also has offices in Singapore and Thailand.

Financial Performance

Note: Growth rates may differ after conversion to US Dollars.

Kobe Steel's fiscal 2016 (ended March) sales dropped by 3.5% to ¥1823 billion despite similar levels of sales volume to 2015 due to a decline in steel sales price as the result of lower primary raw material prices.

Net income plunged. The company reported a net loss of ¥21.6 billion in fiscal 2016 compared to net income of ¥86.6 billion in fiscal 2015 due to lower revenue and higher costs and charges. It was primarily due to lower demand for copper products in China and the rapid decline of the construction machinery segment in that country (causing the company to post extraordinary losses of ¥39.5 billion).

Cash flow from operating activities dropped by ¥55.2 billion to ¥97.9 billion due to higher costs brought on by weaker market conditions.

Strategy

Japan's long-suffering economy has Kobe Steel looking abroad for growth particularly to emerging markets (including China India Thailand and Vietnam) where infrastructure improvements are driving demand for iron and steel other metals and heavy construction machinery.

Long term Kobe Steel is looking to grow its business around three core segments —Materials Machinery and Electric Power.

In 2016 Kobe Steel opened a steel wire venture in Mexico broke ground on a US-based aluminum extrusion plant and set up a joint venture in Japan to treat radioactive waste.

Streamlining its business portfolio in 2016 the company created the Electric Power segment to take over the electric supply business operated by the Iron & Steel business at Kobe Works and two power generation projects (Moka Tochigi Prefecture and Kobe Hyogo Prefecture).

That year it created the Construction Machinery segment by merging subsidiaries Kobelco Construction Machinery Co. Ltd. and Kobelco Cranes Co. Ltd. The company also boosted the Engineering segment with the inclusion of the Kobelco Eco-Solutions unit.

EXECUTIVES

EVP, Tetsu Takahashi
Officer Head Office and Technical Development Group, Jun Tanaka
EVP, Hiroaki Fujiwara
EVP, Ikuhiro Yamaguchi
Senior Managing Director, Tsuyoshi Kasuya
President and CEO, Hiroya Kawasaki
Senior Managing Director, Kazuhide Naraki
Chairman, Hiroshi Sato, age 71
Auditors: KPMG AZSA LLC

LOCATIONS

HQ: Kobe Steel Ltd (Japan)
2-2-4 Wakinohama-Kaigandori, Chuo-ku, Kobe, Hyogo 651-8585
Phone: (81) 78 261 5198   **Fax:** (81) 78 261 4123
Web: www.kobelco.co.jp

2016 sales

	% of total
Japan	64
China	8
Other countries	28
Total	100

PRODUCTS/OPERATIONS

2016 Sales

	% of total
Iron & Steel	35
Construction Machinery	18
Aluminum & Copper	18
Machinery	9
Welding	5
Electric power	4
Cranes	
Engineering	7
Other	4
Total	100

Selected Products

Iron and Steel
  Steel bars
  Steel sheet
  Titanium
  Wire rod
Aluminum and Copper
  Automotive aluminum
  Copper strip
  Copper tubes
Infrastructure and Plant Engineering
  Engineering services (planning and executing large-scale projects)
Land Development
  Land development projects (private and public)
Machinery
  Compressors
  Crushers
Welding
  Electrodes
  Flux-cored wires
  Metallic flux-cored wire
  Solid wires
  Welding fluxes

COMPETITORS

AK Steel Holding Corporation
ArcelorMittal
Baosteel
JFE Holdings
Nippon Steel & Sumitomo Metal Corporation
Nisshin Steel
POSCO
ThyssenKrupp Steel
United States Steel
Yamato Kogyo

HISTORICAL FINANCIALS

Company Type: Public

Income Statement

FYE: March 31

	REVENUE ($ mil.)	NET INCOME ($ mil.)	NET PROFIT MARGIN	EMPLOYEES
03/16	16,232	(191)	—	42,635
03/15	15,726	721	4.6%	42,600
03/14	17,677	680	3.8%	36,019
03/13	17,913	(286)	—	36,018
03/12	22,731	(173)	—	35,496
Annual Growth	(8.1%)	—	—	4.7%

2016 Year-End Financials

Debt ratio: 0.3%
Return on equity: (-2.9%)
Cash ($ mil.): 1,380
Current ratio: 1.29
Long-term debt ($ mil.): 4,956

No. of shares (mil.): —
Dividends
  Yield: 3.6%
  Payout: —
Market value ($ mil.): —

	STOCK PRICE ($) FY Close	P/E High/Low		Earnings	PER SHARE ($) Dividends	Book Value
03/16	4.45	—	—	(0.05)	0.16	1.70
03/15	9.36	0	0	0.20	0.28	1.78
03/14	6.53	—	—	0.22	0.00	1.96
03/13	5.84	—	—	(0.10)	0.00	2.02
03/12	8.24	—	—	(0.06)	0.00	2.32
Annual Growth	(14.3%)	—	—	—	—	(7.5%)

Koc Holdings AS

In Turkey Koc (pronounced "coach") class equals first class. Led by its energy businesses Koc Holding is Turkey's dominant industrial conglomerate. The company's Tofas unit an alliance with Fiat is Turkey's champion carmaker; Koc's joint venture with Ford Motor sells imported Ford models. Other businesses include consumer goods such as large household appliances (Arcelik teaming up with LG Electronics) and energy (distribution of liquefied petroleum gas). Subsidiaries engage in food production construction international trading and hospitality and tourism. Koc also operates banking securities brokerage and insurance businesses. The Koc family one of the wealthiest in Turkey controls the company.

OperationsKoc's business activities include the acquisition disposal and exchanging of shares of domestic and foreign corporations and limited liability companies for all types of commercial industrial agricultural and financial activities.

Koc and Royal Dutch Shell together continue to drive a 51% stake in oil refiner T PRAS. T PRAS the 8th largest refining company in Europe controls 40% ownership in the fuel distribution company Opet Petrolc l k.

The company's finance segment includes three main groups; banking insurance and consumer finance. Leasing factoring portfolio management custody and brokerage services are included in the banking sector.

Financial Performance

Koc's revenues increased by 41% in 2011 thanks to a growth in revenues from all of its segments. Higher revenues fueled the company's net income growth of 23% that year.

Strategy

Koc is reaching far across the Bosporus while simultaneously refocusing its efforts in consumer goods automotive finance and energy markets. The company's strategy is to buy and sell assets to achieve portfolio diversification to minimize sector and regional risks. It is also focusing on expanding its operations in developing markets through acquisitions and joint ventures.

In 2011 its Arcelik subsidiary acquired the South Africa-based Defy which is engaged in the production of refrigerators freezers dryers ovens cooking appliances and the selling and marketing of all kinds of durable home appliances across Southern Africa.

That year Koc established a shipping subsidiary Sariyer Tankercilik. To raise cash it also agreed to sell Koc.Net Haberlesme Teknolojileri ve Iletisim Hizmetleri A.S. (Kocnet) to Vodafone.

Expanding its role in power production and responding to the Turkish government's plan to privatize power generation in Turkey in 2010 Koc formed a joint venture with energy powerhouse AES to develop new power plants. AES-Entek aims to become one of the top five independent power producers in Turkey by 2015.

Ownership

With a combined stake of more than 69% members of the Koc family direct the operations of Koc Holding.

HISTORY

In 1917 16-year-old Vehbi Koc and his father opened a small grocery store in Ankara Turkey. With the fall of the Ottoman Empire after WWI Turkey's capital was moved to Ankara which was then only a village. The Kocs recognized an opportunity and expanded into construction and building supplies winning a contract to repair the roof of the Turkish parliament building. By age 26 Koc was a millionaire.

Ford Motor made Koc its Turkish agent in 1928. In 1931 Mobil Oil and Koc entered an exclusive agreement to search for oil in Turkey. The company incorporated in 1938 as Koc Ticaret Corporation the first Turkish joint stock company with an employee stock-ownership program.

Despite Turkey's neutrality in WWII the fighting disrupted Koc's business. The nation became isolationist after the war and restricted foreign concerns to selling through local agents; Koc benefited by importing foreign products.

General Electric and Koc entered a joint venture in 1946 to build Turkey's first lightbulb factory. In 1955 Koc set up Arcelik the first Turkish producer of refrigerators washing machines and water heaters; T rk Demir D k m the first Turkish producer of radiators and later auto castings; and Turkay the country's first private producer of matches. In 1959 Koc constructed Turkey's first truck assembly plant (Otosan).

Other firsts followed in the 1960s as the company leveraged its size and government influence to attract more ventures. These included a tire factory (with Uniroyal) a cable factory (with Siemens) production of electric motors and compressors (with GE) and the production of Anadol the first car to be made entirely in Turkey (by Otosan under license from Ford). In 1974 Koc expanded into retailing with the purchase of Migros Turkey's largest chain of supermarkets.

The Turkish military imposed martial law in 1980 and restricted foreign exchange payments forcing Koc to limit its operations. In 1986 a year after foreign companies were allowed to export products directly to Turkey Koc and American Express started Koc-Amerikan Bank (which Koc bought out and renamed Kocbank in 1992). In the late 1980s Vehbi's only son Rahmi took over the company's leadership. Vehbi Koc died in 1996.

Auto sales fell sharply in 1996 as buyers awaited the country's entry into the European Union's customs union. In an effort to offset market risks Koc forged a number of alliances in 1997. It participated in a British-Canadian-Turkish consortium that was building a large power plant in central Turkey.

Reflecting a greater willingness to open the company to foreign investors Koc announced plans to offer $250 million in shares in a public offering in 1998 but it soon canceled the offering because of market volatility. A year later the company completed an auto plant in Samarkand Uzbekistan to build Otoyol-Iveco buses and trucks.

Koc entered into a joint venture –Koc Finansal Hizmetler –with Unicredito Italiano in 2002 in an effort to further consolidate its financial holdings.

Significant company moves in 2008 included selling its Otomotiv Lastikleri Tevzi (Oltas) to Germany's Continental AG. Oltas had distributed Continental tires and related products since 2003. The company's interest in supermarkets dwindled to less than 50% with the sale of its stake in Migros. Its sway however in the IT data processing business of KocNet Haberlesme Teknolojileri ve Iletisim Hizmetleri A.S. increased to almost 100%. The company picked up military aero and marine tech simulator Kaletron an arm of Kale Group too.

In 2009 the global recession curtailed industrial output and demand and hurt the company's revenues. However its diversified portfolio and cost saving measures enabled it to post a modest improvement in net income.

EXECUTIVES

President Tourism Food and Retailing Group, Tamer Hasimoglu

President Energy Group, Erol Memio lu, age 62

CFO, Ahmet Ashabolu

President Defense Industry Other Automotive and IT Group, Kudret Onen

President Automotive Group, Cenk Cimen

President Banking and Insurance Group, Faik Acikalin

CEO, Levent akiroglu

Chairman, Mehmet O. Koc

Vice Chairman, Yildirim A. Koc

Auditors: Guney Bagimsiz Denetim ve Serbest Muhasebeci Mali Musavirlik Anonim Sirketi

LOCATIONS

HQ: Koc Holdings AS
Nakkastepe, Azizbey Sokak No. 1, Istanbul, Kuzguncuk 34674
Phone: (90) 216 531 0000   Fax: (90) 216 531 0099
Web: www.koc.com.tr

PRODUCTS/OPERATIONS

2011 Sales

	% of total
Energy	63
Automotive	13
Consumer durables	11
Finance	8
Other	5
Total	**100**

Core Businesses
Automotive
Construction and mining
Durable goods
Food/Beverage/Tobacco
Energy
Financial services
Information technology
International trade
Marinas
New business development
Tourism and services

COMPETITORS

Adam Opel	Renault
Caterpillar	Robert Bosch
Electrolux	Sabanci
Hellenic Petroleum	Siemens AG
Honda	Yazicilar
International Power	

HISTORICAL FINANCIALS

Company Type: Public

Income Statement

FYE: December 31

	REVENUE ($ mil.)	NET INCOME ($ mil.)	NET PROFIT MARGIN	EMPLOYEES
12/15	23,789	1,221	5.1%	91,304
12/14	29,480	1,164	3.9%	85,517
12/13	30,940	1,252	4.0%	80,996
12/12	47,364	1,292	2.7%	82,158
12/11	40,127	1,125	2.8%	80,987
Annual Growth	(12.3%)	2.1%	—	3.0%

2015 Year-End Financials

Debt ratio: 11.5%	No. of shares (mil.): —
Return on equity: 16.4%	Dividends
Cash ($ mil.): 3,612	Yield: 1.5%
Current ratio: 1.43	Payout: 52.0%
Long-term debt ($ mil.): 5,874	Market value ($ mil.): —

	STOCK PRICE ($) FY Close	P/E High/Low	PER SHARE ($) Earnings	Dividends	Book Value
12/15	18.84	17 13	0.48	0.28	0.03
12/14	26.39	25 15	0.46	0.29	0.03
12/13	20.61	26 18	0.49	0.41	0.03
12/12	26.16	29 17	0.51	0.27	0.04
12/11	14.88	25 16	0.47	0.50	0.03
Annual Growth	6.1%	—	— 0.8%	(13.4%)	0.6%

Komatsu, Ltd.

Auditors: KPMG AZSA LLC

LOCATIONS

HQ: Komatsu, Ltd.
2-3-6 Akasaka, Minato-ku, Tokyo 107-8414
Phone: (81) 3 5561 2604   **Fax:** (81) 3 3505 9662
Web: www.komatsu.co.jp

HISTORICAL FINANCIALS

Company Type: Public

Income Statement

	REVENUE ($ mil.)	NET INCOME ($ mil.)	NET PROFIT MARGIN	EMPLOYEES
03/16	16,518	1,223	7.4%	50,496
03/15	16,491	1,283	7.8%	51,222
03/14	18,927	1,545	8.2%	51,973
03/13	20,033	1,342	6.7%	46,730
03/12	24,158	2,036	8.4%	44,206
Annual Growth	(9.1%)	(12.0%)	—	3.4%

FYE: March 31

2016 Year-End Financials

Debt ratio: 0.1%
Return on equity: 9.0%
Cash ($ mil.): 965
Current ratio: 1.98
Long-term debt ($ mil.): 1,893

No. of shares (mil.): 942
Dividends
  Yield: 2.7%
  Payout: 39.3%
Market value ($ mil.): 16,086

	STOCK PRICE ($) FY Close	P/E High/Low		PER SHARE ($)	
			Earnings	Dividends	Book Value
03/16	17.07	0 0	1.30	0.47	14.34
03/15	19.60	0 0	1.35	0.53	13.53
03/14	20.73	0 0	1.62	0.53	14.00
03/13	23.76	0 0	1.41	0.48	13.31
03/12	28.75	0 0	2.11	0.50	12.93
Annual Growth	(12.2%)	— —	(11.5%)	(1.6%)	2.6%

Kommunalbanken A/S (Norway)

Auditors: Ernst & Young AS

LOCATIONS

HQ: Kommunalbanken A/S (Norway)
Haakon VIIs gate 5B, Oslo N-0110
Phone: (47) 21 50 20 00   **Fax:** (47) 21 50 20 01
Web: www.kbn.org

HISTORICAL FINANCIALS

Company Type: Public

Income Statement

	ASSETS ($ mil.)	NET INCOME ($ mil.)	INCOME AS % OF ASSETS	EMPLOYEES
12/15	50,987	210	0.4%	72
12/14	61,382	66	0.1%	56
12/13	59,561	178	0.3%	56
12/12	62,385	335	0.5%	54
12/11	61,022	120	0.2%	50
Annual Growth	(4.4%)	15.0%	—	9.5%

FYE: December 31

2015 Year-End Financials

Return on assets: 0.4%
Return on equity: 18.1%
Long-term debt ($ mil.): —
No. of shares (mil.): 3
Sales ($ mil.): 747

Dividends
  Yield: —
  Payout: —
Market value ($ mil.): —

Koninklijke Ahold Delhaize NV

Koninklijke Ahold Delhaize (formerly Royal Ahold) has a super market presence in the US and Europe. The retail company owns or has an interest in more than 6500 supermarkets and specialty stores in two dozen US states and across Europe. Formed in 2016 from the merger of Royal Ahold and Delhaize Group the company ranks as a leading supermarket operator along the East Coast of the US under the Giant Food Stop & Shop Food Lion and other banners. The company also operates Albert Heijn (the #1 food retailer in The Netherlands) as well as stores in Germany Belgium and the Czech Republic. Other interests include the US online grocery ordering and delivery service Peapod as well as Gall & Gall liquor stores. The company owns some 35 retail brands.

HISTORY

Albert Heijn and his wife took over his father's grocery store in Ootzaan Netherlands in 1887. By the end of WWI the company had 50 Albert Heijn grocery stores in Holland and at WWII's end it had almost 250 stores. In 1948 the company went public.

It opened its first self-service store in 1952 and its first supermarket in 1955. Growing into the #1 grocer in the Netherlands Albert Heijn opened liquor and cosmetic stores in 1973. (It changed its name to Ahold that year to better reflect its range of businesses.) Ahold expanded outside the Netherlands in 1976 when it founded supermarket chain Cadadia in Spain (sold 1985).

Ahold entered the US in 1977 by purchasing BI-LO and furthered its expansion in 1981 by adding Pennsylvania-based Giant Food Stores. In 1987 in honor of its 100th anniversary Ahold was granted the title Koninklijke (Dutch for "royal"). In 1988 it bought a majority stake in Dutch food wholesaler Schuitema.

The company added New York-based TOPS Markets in 1991. That year Royal Ahold founded food retailer and distributor Euronova (now called Ahold Czech Republic) and in 1992 it acquired 49% of Portuguese food retailer Jeronimo Martins Retail. In 1993 Cees van der Hoeven was promoted to chief executive and Royal Ahold was listed on the NYSE.

Other acquisitions included New England grocery giant The Stop & Shop Companies in 1996. That year saw the beginning of several Asian joint ventures that gave Royal Ahold stores in Singapore Malaysia and Thailand. It also formed a joint venture in 1998 with Argentina's Velox Retail Holdings (owner of about 90% of supermarket operators DISCO and Santa Isabel) and Royal Ahold added Maryland-based grocer Giant Food Inc. (unrelated to Royal Ahold's Giant Food Stores).

Royal Ahold's moves in 1999 included the acquisition of several Spanish supermarket chains (with a total of about 200 stores) the purchase of

Dutch institutional food wholesaler Gastronoom and the acquisition of 50% of Sweden's top food seller ICA AB. In Central America it acquired half of La Fragua an operator of supermarkets and discount stores. However North American expansion plans hit a snag when Royal Ahold backed out of a deal to buy Pathmark Stores.

In 2000 Royal Ahold acquired Spanish food retailer Kampio+ #2 and #4 foodservice distributors U.S. Foodservice and PYA/Monarch US convenience store chains Sugar Creek and Golden Gallon and all of the voting stock of Brazilian retailer Bompreço. In June the firm bought a 51% stake in online grocer Peapod. Royal Ahold took over food retailer Superdiplo which runs more than 300 stores in Spain (including the Canary Islands) in late 2000.

In March 2001 Royal Ahold began buying the remaining outstanding shares of Bompreço with the intention of delisting the company from the Brazilian Luxembourg and New York stock exchanges (which it did in late December). Chicago-based Peapod became a wholly owned Royal Ahold subsidiary in 2001. The retailer also expanded its bricks-and-mortar US presence in 2001 by purchasing Alliant Exchange parent of Alliant Foodservice which distributes food to more than 100000 customers and Bruno's Supermarkets which operates more than 180 stores in the Southeast. In December Ahold also agreed to buy the 32-store G. Barbosa supermarket chain which would add to its holdings in Brazil.

Royal Ahold reported its first net loss in nearly 30 years in the second quarter of 2002. In August 2002 Royal Ahold assumed full control of Disco Ahold International Holdings its former joint venture company with Velox Retail Holdings. Soon after the company increased its ownership stake in Chilean grocery chain Santa Isabel from 70% to 97% in a tender offer. In October the company integrated its Polish Czech and Slovak operations under the umbrella of Ahold Central Europe (ACE). ACE will manage more than 400 Albert supermarkets and Hypernova hypermarkets in Central Europe. In late 2002 subsidiary U.S. Foodservice agreed to buy Allen Foods a major independent foodservice distributor in the Central Plains region.

In February 2003 CEO Cees van der Hoeven and CFO Michiel Meurs resigned following an announcement that the grocery giant would restate its financial results by at least $500 million because of accounting irregularities at U.S. Foodservice. (van der Hoeven is facing charges by Dutch prosecutors in connection with the scandal at U.S. Foodservice.) Chairman Henny de Ruiter became acting CEO of the company and Dudley Eustace a British national who serves as a director of several Dutch companies was named interim CFO in March. In May 2003 IKEA veteran Anders Moberg became acting CEO; de Ruiter remained chairman. Soon after Ahold said it would restate earnings downward by $880 million (much more than the original $500 million projection) because of the accounting scandal at U.S. Foodservice. Further accounting investigations uncovered about $29 million in irregularities at the company's TOPS Markets US subsidiary.

In May Ahold completed the sale of its De Tuinen natural product stores to NBTY's British subsidiary Holland & Barrett Europe. In June it sold its Jamin chain of candy stores to Jamin management. The Santa Isabel chain in Chile was sold in July to Cencosud for about $95 million far less than the $150 million originally discussed. Adding to its woes in July the public prosecutor in Amsterdam launched a criminal investigation into possible falsification of accounts by the company. Soon after Ahold completed the sale of 22 stores in Indonesia to PT Hero Supermarket as well as its Malaysian retail business. In September the board of directors of Royal Ahold approved the appointment of Moberg and Ryöppönen as CEO and CFO respectively. Later in the month the global grocer sold its operations in Paraguay (Supermercados Stock S.A.) to A.J. Vierci for about $4 million.

In October 2003 Royal Ahold published its long-awaited 2002 results revealing a $1.27 billion loss which the retailer attributed to special charges related to overstated profits at U.S. Foodservice. That month the company completed the sale of its 138-store Golden Gallon convenience chain to The Pantry for about $187 million and de Ruiter resigned and was succeeded by Karel Vuursteen previously a board member. In November Royal Ahold sold two hypermarkets in Poland to Carrefour Poland as part of its overall strategy to restructure its retail portfolio. In December the Peruvian operations of its Santa Isabel chain were sold to Grupo Interbank and other investors led by Nexus Group.

In March 2004 Royal Ahold sold its 118-store Bompreço chain in Brazil to Wal-Mart Stores and its credit card business (Hipercard) there to Unibanco S.A. for a combined price of about $500 million. Also in March the Dutch chain sold its stake in CRC Ahold operating in Thailand to its partner the Central Food Retail Co. completing the company's withdrawal from Asia. At a shareholders meeting in March Ahold placed the blame for the accounting scandal which nearly bankrupted the company in 2003 squarely on the shoulders of Jim Miller the former CEO of U.S. Foodservice. (Later Miller and Ahold agreed in late 2007 to settle litigation related to the matter with Miller paying Ahold $8 million.) In August Karel Vuursteen resigned as chairman of the supervisory board for personal reasons as was succeeded by Rene Dahan. In September Ahold reached a settlement with the Dutch public prosecutor in which the company agreed to pay euro 8 million. In return the Dutch prosecutor agreed not to undertake proceedings against Royal Ahold. In October the company reached a settlement with the US Securities and Exchange Commission that imposed no fines on Royal Ahold due in part to its "extensive co-operation" with the investigation. The company also finalized a deal to increase its stake in its Scandinavian retail joint venture ICA AB. It paid its euro 811 million for a 20% stake in the partnership sold by Canica. In December Ahold completed the sale of its retail activities in Spain and the Canary Islands (nearly 600 stores) to the Permira Funds.

In January 2005 the grocery giant sold its BI-LO and Bruno's chains in the southeastern US to an affiliate of Lone Star Funds for some $660 million. In February the Dutch retailer completed the sale of a dozen Hypernova hypermarkets in Poland to rival Carrefour followed by the sale of a single large hypermarket to a local Polish firm two months later. Also in April Royal Ahold completed its exit from Brazil with the sale of 32 G. Barbosa hypermarkets there to ACON Investments a US-based investment firm. In May the company announced completion of the sale of its 50% stake in Spanish winery Bodegas Williams & Humbert (formerly known as Luis Paez) to its joint venture partner Jose Medina y Cia SA for an undisclosed sum. In June Ahold completed the sale of its chain of 198 Wilson Farms and Sugarcreek convenience stores part of its TOPS Markets subsidiary in the US to WFI Acquisition for an undisclosed sum. In September Ahold sold its Deli XL foodservice operation in Belgium and the Netherlands to a subsidiary of South Africa-based The Bidvest Group for about euro 140 million.

CFO Hannu Ryöppönen resigned at the end of August 2005 to join Stora Enso an integrated paper packaging and forest products company. In October Royal Ahold completed the acquisition of 56 stores in the Czech Republic from Julius Meinl a.s. In November the company settled a US class action lawsuit by paying $1.1 billion to shareholders who purchased stock between July 3 1999 and February 23 2003; just before the 2003 accounting scandal broke. Concurrently the company reached an agreement to settle litigation with the Dutch Shareholders' Association.

The grocery chain also sold 13 large Hypernova hypermarkets in Poland to Carrefour and a local operator in early 2005. The company also moved its corporate headquarters from Zaandam to Amsterdam later in the year.

In 2006 the company sold three shopping centers in Poland and the Czech Republic for about euro 108 million. In April Jose Alvarez was named president and CEO of the combined Stop & Shop/Giant-Landover organization succeeding Marc Smith who retired. In September Royal Ahold was reported to be in talks with its Belgian counterpart Delhaize regarding a possible merger. However negotiations were later suspended. In November the Dutch grocer completed the acquisition of 27 Konmar stores in the Netherlands from Laurus B.V. for about $130 million.

More than three years after teetering on the brink of bankruptcy as a result of one of Europe's largest financial scandals a Dutch court found former CEO Cees van der Hoeven and former CFO Michael Meurs guilty of fraud. Van der Hoeven and Meurs were accused of improperly booking sales from four subsidiaries in Scandinavia Argentina and Brazil. Both men were fined and given suspended sentences. Former executive board member Jan Andreae who headed Ahold's European operations was sentenced to four months in jail suspended for two years and fined.

CEO Anders Moberg left the company in July 2007. Also in July U.S. Foodservice was finally sold to a consortium of Clayton Dubilier & Rice and Kohlberg Kravis Roberts & Co. for about $7.1 billion. In November John Rishton Ahold's CFO who had been serving as interim chief executive since Moberg's departure was named to the post permanently. In December Royal Ahold sold its underperforming TOPS Markets chain to Morgan Stanley Private Equity for about $310 million.

In June 2008 the company completed sold its 73% stake in Schuitema N.V. to private equity firm CVC Capital Partners in return for cash and the transfer of 50-plus Schuitema stores to Ahold.

In 2009 Royal Ahold's Albert/Hypernova business in the Czech Republic and Slovakia closed 23 underperforming stores and downsized a dozen hypermarkets. It also finished converting its Hypernova stores to the Albert brand in the Czech Republic.

In February 2010 Ahold acquired 25 Ukrop's Super Market stores inventory equipment and leases in a $140 million transaction. The Ukrop's chain became part of Ahold USA's Giant-Carlisle division.

In March 2013 the company sold its 60% stake in the Sweden's largest food retailer ICA AB to Sweden's Hakon Invest for SEK 21.2 billion ($3.3 billion) in cash to better stick to its strategy of focusing on businesses it controls.

EXECUTIVES

CEO, A. Dick Boer, age 59, $625,000 total compensation
COO Europe, Sander van der Laan, age 47
CFO, Jeff Carr, age 56
COO Ahold USA, James McCann, age 47
Vice Chairman, Tom de Swaan, age 71
Chairman, Rene Dahan, age 75
Auditors: PricewaterhouseCoopers Accountants N.V.

LOCATIONS

HQ: Koninklijke Ahold Delhaize NV
Provincialeweg 11, Zaandam 1506 MA
Phone: (31) 88 659 5100
Web: www.ahold.com

PRODUCTS/OPERATIONS

Selected Operations
Retail
Europe
Albert (supermarkets Czech Republic and Slovakia)
Albert Heijn (supermarkets convenience stores)
Alfa-Beta (supermarkets)
Delhaize (supermarkets)
Etos (drugstores online shopping)
Gall & Gall (liquor stores)
MAXI (supermarkets)
Mega Image (supermarkets)
Shop & Go (convenience stores)
US
Food Lion (supermarkets)
Giant-Carlisle (supermarkets & superstores)
Giant-Landover (supermarkets)
Stop & Go (convenience stores)
Stop & Shop (supermarkets)

COMPETITORS

A&P	METRO AG
ALDI	NorgesGruppen
BJ' s Wholesale Club	Safeway
Big Y Foods	Shaw' s
Carrefour	Target Corporation
Costco Wholesale	Tesco
Golub	Wal-Mart
Kooperativa F‖bundet	Wegmans
Kroger	Whole Foods
Lidl	

HISTORICAL FINANCIALS

Company Type: Public

Income Statement
FYE: January 3

	REVENUE ($ mil.)	NET INCOME ($ mil.)	NET PROFIT MARGIN	EMPLOYEES
01/16*	41,484	925	2.2%	236,000
12/14	39,945	723	1.8%	227,000
12/13	45,217	3,517	7.8%	222,000
12/12	43,286	1,090	2.5%	225,000
01/12	39,154	1,315	3.4%	218,000
Annual Growth	1.5%	(8.4%)	—	2.0%

*Fiscal year change

2016 Year-End Financials

Debt ratio: 23.9%	No. of shares (mil.): 770
Return on equity: 16.0%	Dividends
Cash ($ mil.): 1,982	Yield: 0.0%
Current ratio: 1.05	Payout: 50.9%
Long-term debt ($ mil.): 3,593	Market value ($ mil.): 16,281

	STOCK PRICE ($) FY Close	P/E High/Low		PER SHARE ($) Earnings	Dividends	Book Value
01/16*	21.14	20	14	1.18	0.60	7.93
12/14	17.87	25	20	0.87	0.62	7.63
12/13	18.21	7	5	3.52	0.69	9.78
12/12	13.33	17	14	1.09	0.00	8.08
01/12	13.45	14	10	1.22	0.00	7.62
Annual Growth	12.0%	—	—	(1.0%)	—	1.0%

*Fiscal year change

Koninklijke Philips NV

Auditors: KPMG Accountants N.V.

LOCATIONS

HQ: Koninklijke Philips NV
 Philips Center, Amstelplein 2, Amsterdam 1096 BC
Phone: (31) 20 59 77 777
Web: www.philips.com

HISTORICAL FINANCIALS

Company Type: Public

Income Statement

FYE: December 31

	REVENUE ($ mil.)	NET INCOME ($ mil.)	NET PROFIT MARGIN	EMPLOYEES
12/15	26,406	702	2.7%	112,959
12/14	26,000	504	1.9%	113,678
12/13	32,117	1,609	5.0%	116,681
12/12	32,671	297	0.9%	118,087
12/11	29,204	(1,675)	—	125,241
Annual Growth	(2.5%)	—	—	(2.5%)

2015 Year-End Financials

Debt ratio: 20.2%
Return on equity: 5.7%
Cash ($ mil.): 1,923
Current ratio: 1.26
Long-term debt ($ mil.): 4,460

No. of shares (mil.): 917
Dividends
 Yield: 2.9%
 Payout: 114.2%
Market value ($ mil.): 23,340

	STOCK PRICE ($) FY Close	P/E High/Low		PER SHARE ($) Earnings	Dividends	Book Value
12/15	25.45	43	32	0.76	0.76	13.85
12/14	29.00	76	56	0.55	0.93	14.45
12/13	36.97	29	22	1.75	0.83	16.90
12/12	26.54	107	72	0.32	0.80	16.05
12/11	20.95	—	—	(1.76)	0.00	17.26
Annual Growth	5.0%	—	—	—	—	(5.3%)

Korea Electric Power Corp

Auditors: Samjong Accounting Corporation (A Member Firm of KPMG)

LOCATIONS

HQ: Korea Electric Power Corp
 512 Yeongdong-daero Gangnam-gu, Seoul 135-882
Phone: (82) 2 3456 3114   **Fax:** (82) 2 3456 4298
Web: www.kepco.co.kr

HISTORICAL FINANCIALS

Company Type: Public

Income Statement

FYE: December 31

	REVENUE ($ mil.)	NET INCOME ($ mil.)	NET PROFIT MARGIN	EMPLOYEES
12/15	50,111	11,295	22.5%	20,603
12/14	52,531	2,455	4.7%	20,223
12/13	51,384	57	0.1%	20,000
12/12	46,287	(2,965)	—	19,568
12/11	37,570	(2,908)	—	19,579
Annual Growth	7.5%	—	—	1.3%

2015 Year-End Financials

Debt ratio: 0.0%
Return on equity: 22.1%
Cash ($ mil.): 3,215
Current ratio: 0.97
Long-term debt ($ mil.): 43,400

No. of shares (mil.): 641
Dividends
 Yield: 1.0%
 Payout: 1.2%
Market value ($ mil.): 13,590

	STOCK PRICE ($) FY Close	P/E High/Low		PER SHARE ($) Earnings	Dividends	Book Value
12/15	21.17	0	0	17.59	0.23	88.22
12/14	19.36	0	0	3.92	0.04	76.31
12/13	16.61	0	0	0.09	0.00	76.71
12/12	13.97	—	—	(4.76)	0.00	75.00
12/11	10.98	—	—	(4.67)	0.00	73.79
Annual Growth	17.8%	—	—	—	—	4.6%

Korea Gas Corp. (South Korea)

As the world's largest importer of liquefied natural gas (LNG) KOGAS single-handedly helps South Koreans stay warm and chill out. The company is the sole provider of LNG to the country (about 25 million tons imported annually) operating three terminals and a nationwide pipeline network. KOGAS supplies LNG to power plants and utility companies throughout South Korea and produces and supplies LNG products to domestic and overseas markets. It imports come around the world including from Indonesia Malaysia Myanmar Oman Qatar and Russia. KOGAS development initiatives include natural gas vehicles LNG chiller/heater systems for homes and fuel cells.

Geographic Reach

The company is headquartered in Taegu South Korea. The company has presence in Korea Mexico Australia Canada Iraq Russia Mozambique Timor and Cyprus.

Operations

KOGAS operates four LNG terminals (Pyeongtaek Incheon Tongyeong and Samcheok) and a nationwide pipeline network spanning over 4240 km. The company imports LNG and distributes it to consumers across South Korea. It has storage capacity of 9.46 million in 63 facilities. Ten power generation companies (17 power generation plants) supply the gas to end users within their respective regions.

It major business lines include: Construction and Operation of LNG Terminals and Natural Gas Distribution Network; Exploration and Import/Export of Natural Gas and LNG; Production and Distribution of Natural Gas (including Purification and Sales of By-products); and Research and Technical Development.

Sales and Marketing KOGAS safely delivers natural gas supplied from LNG regasification terminals to pipelines of city gas companies. As a public enterprise KOGAS is in charge of wholesale of natural gas in the domestic market while 30 private city gas companies are granted with exclusive retail sales rights within their respective regions.

Financial Performance

In 2014 the company's net revenues (in local currency) decreased by 2%.

Net income saw a strong improvement from previous year's loss mainly due to the benefit from income tax.

KOGAS' cash from operating activities increased by 34% due to the changes in trade accounts receivable and other receivables.

Strategy

It has expanded its research and development's core competencies in upstream businesses new energy and future growth engines and is expanding its network by adding domestic and overseas energy research and development institutes.

KOGAS plans to increase its LNG storage ratio to 21% by 2027 to stabilize supply and demand. It continues to conduct overseas resource development projects to secure a stable gas supply in Korea and enhance national energy security. In this regard in 2015 it teamed up with Exxon Mobil and the Korea Institute of Energy Technology Evaluation and Planning to hold discussions concerning natural gas technologies and new energy technologies. KOGAS aims to secure the oil and gas resources of 400 million tons (10% of the energy demand forecast of Korea in 2020) and the annual production volume is expected to reach 10 million tons (25% of Korea'sl energy consumption). It also plans further stabilize the supply and demand by increasing storage facilities securing storage capacity and exporting its gas technologies.

Company Background

KOGAS was incorporated by the Korean government in 1983.

In 2006 KOGAS acquired an 8% interest in China Gas Holdings as a strategic partner. The deal paved the way for further expansion in China's gas distribution market. KOGAS additionally acquired four LNG tankers in a joint venture with three other South Korean companies. The move pointed to a broadening of its overall LNG business.

In 2011 KOGAS signed on to an LNG joint development project in Indonesia and in 2010 it secured development and production rights in the oil and gas fields in Zubair and Badra in Iraq and an equity partnership in Australia's Gladstone LNG project.

The Korean government owns about 26% of the company KEPCO 20.5%.

EXECUTIVES

CEO, Kangsoo Choo
Auditors: Samil Accounting Corporation (A Member Firm of PircewaterhouseCoopers)

LOCATIONS

HQ: Korea Gas Corp. (South Korea)
 171, Dolma-ro Bundang-gu, Seongnam-si, Gyeonggi-do 463-754
Phone: (82) 31 710 0114   **Fax:** (82) 31 710 0399
Web: www.kogas.or.kr

COMPETITORS

BP	JX Nippon Oil & Energy
Exxon Mobil	SK Innovation
GS Caltex	

HISTORICAL FINANCIALS

Company Type: Public

Income Statement

FYE: December 31

	REVENUE ($ mil.)	NET INCOME ($ mil.)	NET PROFIT MARGIN	EMPLOYEES
12/15	22,143	271	1.2%	3,412
12/14	34,078	408	1.2%	3,349
12/13	36,193	(190)	—	3,202
12/12	32,809	343	1.0%	2,999
12/11	24,591	156	0.6%	2,815
Annual Growth	(2.6%)	14.7%	—	4.9%

Kreditanstalt Fuer Wiederaufbau (Germany, Fed. Rep.)

KfW (formerly KfW Bankengruppe) is a state-owned development bank designed to assist developing countries and the German economy. The bank lends to small and midsized enterprises (SMEs) and buys securitized SME loan portfolios from German banks to keep that area of lending robust. It also provides funds for housing infrastructure environmental protection and venture capital. Additionally KfW finances telecommunications transportation energy infrastructure and industrial projects worldwide. The bank receives funds from the federal budget as well as through investments in the domestic and international capital markets. The German government owns 80% of KfW; the Länder or German states own the rest.

OperationsKfW Mittelstandsbank is KfW's lending business lending and investment arm while KfW Privatkundenbank and KfW Kommunalbank provide housing environmental education and infrastructure funding. The group's main operating subsidiaries include KfW IPEX-Bank which provides project and export financing and DEG a unit focused on promoting the private sector in developing and industrializing countries. The company's KfW Entwicklungsbank funds projects to fight hunger and poverty.

Geographic Reach

KfW operates a network of 80 offices in more than 70 cities around the world with its main offices in the German cities of Berlin Bonn and Frankfurt. Its DEG subsidiary is headquartered in Cologne Germany. Beyond having presences in developed countries in North America and Western Europe the bank also has branches in several emerging and developing locations in Africa Eastern Asia and South America as well as in Russia India and China. KfW relies on a network of commercial banks throughout the nation to process applications and service loans.About 60% of the company's revenue is generated in Germany with another 15% coming from the rest of Europe.

Sales and Marketing

KfW serves more than one million customers; private customers public institutions and corporations are its primary targets.

Financial Performance

KfW's revenue was down for a second straight year falling 17% to euro 3.43 billion (about $16.45 billion) in fiscal 2013 as the bank collected less income from net interest hedge accounting and other financial instruments. The bank's net interest income in 2012 was significantly higher thanks to extraordinary events involving an irregular interest rate structure.

Net income dropped 47% to euro 1.27 billion ($1.75 billion) in 2013 with falling revenues playing a role along with an increase in administrative expenses as the bank spent more on investments designed to modernize its personnel and equipment. Cash levels fell significantly as well. Operations used euro 4.44 billion (about $6.11 billion) in fiscal 2013 –a stark difference from the euro 4.8 billion (about $6.35 billion) that operations provided in 2012 –mostly because the bank generated lower earnings and spent more paying down its certified liabilities (which consist of bonds notes and money-market instruments) and debt to other banks. StrategyTo grow its lending business and to capitalize on the long-term trends of climate change and the environment as well as globalization and technical progress KfW will provide special financing to promote innovative technology companies that are working toward energy efficiency or renewable energy production.

In 2014 KfW dedicated around 35% of its new loan commitments to climate and environmental protection funding. In late 2014 it partnered with the Republic of Chile and the Chilean development bank CORFO to lend euro 100 million (about $122 million) for the expansion of solar energy in Chile with part of the funds going to Latin America's first solar power plant for generating electricity on a commercial scale. Also in late 2014 as part of its energy and infrastructure financing strategy the bank invested euro 1 billion (about $1.22 billion) on behalf of the Federal Ministry for Economic Cooperation and Development for new power lines in India. The deal included a euro 500 million (about $608 million) loan agreement with Indian power transmission company Powergrid for the powerlines themselves with another portion of the loan going toward "green corridors" or transmission lines that will take renewable energy and feed it into the public electricity network. Beyond these initiatives KfW has been focused on domestic financing of high-business-volume startups and small and mid-sized enterprises (SMEs). In 2014 for example the bank set aside 47% of its planned financing for SMEs. The bank also said it will lend to private customers looking to "invest in their future" through education and training loans as well as through loans to refurbish their homes with energy-efficient upgrades.

HISTORY

Company BackgroundThe Kreditanstalt für Wiederaufbau (KfW) began operations in 1948 to distribute Marshall Plan funds from the Allies. Formed by the British and American military governments that occupied West Germany following WWII the Frankfurt-based company (whose name translates as "reconstruction loan corporation") spent its first five years channeling about half of its financing directly to West German firms and the rest to banks that doled out loans. Concentrating on the highly industrialized Ruhr Valley it mainly funded rebuilding projects and industries relating to raw materials energy generation steel farming and food.

By 1954 the bank had largely achieved its original goals. But the West German government to which the company reported realized the political advantages of an entity with expertise in economic development and set up the European Recovery Program an extension of Marshall Plan funds. KfW shifted its focus to financing projects in such weak regions of West Germany as areas bordering East Germany and Saarland which joined the republic after French occupation ended in 1957.

During the second half of the 1950s the bank began its metamorphosis from a distribution agency for postwar reconstruction aid to a financial institution that had a role in driving the West German economy. It entered into export financing providing funds for middle- and long-term West German export risks like power plants and machinery. The company also began to offer loans to West German firms that contracted with domestic suppliers.

As the Berlin Wall was being constructed in 1961 the bank started providing financing to foreign countries with an emphasis on development aid projects. Among its initial programs was a partnership with the International Development Organization to finance the construction of the Rosieres Dam in Sudan. Also that year spurred by a meeting between West German chancellor Konrad Adenauer and Israeli Prime Minister David Ben-Gurion the company began to surreptitiously provide loans to Israel in a project known as "Operation Business Partner" which continued until 1965 when Israel began to officially receive aid.

In the 1970s KfW started floating bonds on the domestic capital market to raise funds. Using this money it initiated programs that granted low-interest loans to small to midsized domestic businesses that traditionally did not have access to international capital markets. The bank also financed major West German companies that were involved in such prominent international projects as the Channel Tunnel which would connect the UK to continental Europe.

In 1975 the company subsidized the migration of ethnic Germans from Poland into West Germany.

The bank received permission from the US Securities and Exchange Commission to become the first German financial institution to issue bonds on the US capital markets in 1986. Two years later it formed US-based subsidiary KfW International Finance.

After the fall of the Berlin Wall in 1989 KfW concentrated its efforts on reconstruction efforts in East Germany. By 1990 approximately two-thirds of its loans were being funneled into the eastern Länder (German states). Its largest deal though was a program to construct some 45000 homes in the USSR for Russian soldiers being transferred from East Germany. The company merged with Staatsbank Berlin the central bank of the former East Germany in 1994.

EXECUTIVES

Member Executive Board, Norbert Kloppenburg, age 60
Member Executive Board, Edeltraud Leibrock, age 52
CEO, Ulrich Schroder, age 64
Member Executive Board, Ingrid Hengster
Member Executive Board, Bernd Loewen
Chairman, Gunther Braunig, age 61

LOCATIONS

HQ: Kreditanstalt Fuer Wiederaufbau (Germany, Fed. Rep.)
Palmengartenstrasse 5-9, Frankfurt am Main D-60325
Phone: (49) 69 7431 0   **Fax:** (49) 69 7431 2944
Web: www.kfw.de

Selected Subsidiaries

KfW IPEX-Bank GmbH Frankfurt am Main (KfW IPEX-Bank)
DEG - Deutsche Investitions- und Entwicklungsgesellschaft mbH Cologne (DEG)
KfW IPEX-Beteiligungsholding GmbH Frankfurt am Main
KfW Beteiligungsholding GmbH Bonn
tbg Technologie-Beteiligungs-Gesellschaft mbH Bonn (tbg)
Finanzierungs- und Beratungsgesellschaft mbH Berlin (FuB)

PRODUCTS/OPERATIONS

Selected Markets
Energy infrastructure

Industrial projects
Telecommunications
Transportation

COMPETITORS

BayernLB	Landesbank
Citigroup	Baden-Wrttemberg
Commerzbank	Landesbank Berlin
Deutsche Bank	UniCredit Bank AG
Deutsche Postbank	WestLB
HSBC	

HISTORICAL FINANCIALS
Company Type: Public

Income Statement   FYE: December 31

	ASSETS ($ mil.)	NET INCOME ($ mil.)	INCOME AS % OF ASSETS	EMPLOYEES
12/15	547,843	2,364	0.4%	5,807
12/14	594,469	1,840	0.3%	5,518
12/13	639,844	1,752	0.3%	5,374
12/12	674,343	3,142	0.5%	5,190
12/11	640,023	2,674	0.4%	4,765
Annual Growth	(3.8%)	(3.0%)	—	5.1%

2015 Year-End Financials

Return on assets: 0.4%
Return on equity: 9.2%
Long-term debt ($ mil.): —
No. of shares (mil.): —
Sales ($ mil): 11,605

Dividends
  Yield: —
  Payout: —
Market value ($ mil.): —

Krung Thai Bank Public Co. Ltd.

One of Thailand's largest financial institutions Krung Thai Bank provides banking and financial services to consumers and corporate clients throughout the country. It offers deposit accounts credit and debit cards loans mortgages and leasing as well as life insurance commercial insurance wealth management and access to investments such as securities and mutual funds. In addition to approximately 1160 domestic locations Krung Thai Bank also operates a fleet of some 90 mobile vans that provide on-the-go banking services in remote areas and at tourist destinations and festival sites. Founded in 1966 Krung Thai Bank listed on the Stock Exchange of Thailand in 1989.
Auditors: Office of the Auditor General of Thailand

LOCATIONS

HQ: Krung Thai Bank Public Co. Ltd.
  35 Sukhumvit Road, Klong Toey Nua Subdistrict,
  Wattana District, Bangkok 10110
Phone: (66) 2 255 2222   **Fax:** (66) 2 255 9391
Web: www.ktb.co.th

COMPETITORS

Bangkok Bank	KASIKORNBANK
Bank of Ayudhya	Thanachart Capital

HISTORICAL FINANCIALS
Company Type: Public

Income Statement   FYE: December 31

	ASSETS ($ mil.)	NET INCOME ($ mil.)	INCOME AS % OF ASSETS	EMPLOYEES
12/15	78,138	790	1.0%	0
12/14	83,313	1,009	1.2%	23,014
12/13	76,815	1,036	1.3%	20,770
12/12	73,652	768	1.0%	20,121
12/11	62,440	541	0.9%	18,428
Annual Growth	5.8%	10.0%	—	—

2015 Year-End Financials

Return on assets: 1.0%
Return on equity: 11.9%
Long-term debt ($ mil.): —
No. of shares (mil.): —
Sales ($ mil): 4,750

Dividends
  Yield: 4.6%
  Payout: 684.2%
Market value ($ mil.): —

	STOCK PRICE ($) FY Close	P/E High/Low		Earnings	PER SHARE ($) Dividends	Book Value
12/15	9.20	6	4	0.06	0.43	0.49
12/14	13.55	7	4	0.07	0.43	0.51
12/13	11.00	7	4	0.07	0.22	0.45
12/12	13.04	7	6	0.07	0.00	0.42
Annual Growth	(11.0%)	—	—	(3.5%)	—	3.7%

KT Corp (Korea)

Auditors: Samil Accounting Corporation (A Member Firm of PircewaterhouseCoopers)

LOCATIONS

HQ: KT Corp (Korea)
  90 Buljeong-ro Bundang-gu, Sungnam-si, Gyeonggi-do 463-711
Phone: (82) 31 727 0850   **Fax:** (82) 31 727 0949
Web: www.kt.co.kr

HISTORICAL FINANCIALS
Company Type: Public

Income Statement   FYE: December 31

	REVENUE ($ mil.)	NET INCOME ($ mil.)	NET PROFIT MARGIN	EMPLOYEES
12/15	18,937	469	2.5%	23,531
12/14	21,407	(964)	—	23,371
12/13	22,641	(154)	—	32,451
12/12	22,281	990	4.4%	32,186
12/11	18,978	1,248	6.6%	31,981
Annual Growth	(0.1%)	(21.7%)	—	(7.4%)

2015 Year-End Financials

Debt ratio: 0.0%
Return on equity: 5.2%
Cash ($ mil.): 2,175
Current ratio: 0.99
Long-term debt ($ mil.): 5,952

No. of shares (mil.): 244
Dividends
  Yield: —
  Payout: —
Market value ($ mil.): 2,916

	STOCK PRICE ($) FY Close	P/E High/Low		Earnings	PER SHARE ($) Dividends	Book Value
12/15	11.91	0	0	1.92	0.00	37.65
12/14	14.12	—	—	(3.94)	0.38	38.60
12/13	14.87	—	—	(0.63)	0.88	45.83
12/12	16.74	0	0	4.06	0.88	47.30
12/11	15.64	0	0	5.13	1.04	41.52
Annual Growth	(6.6%)	—	—	(21.8%)	—	(2.4%)

Kuehne & Nagel International AG

Pass it on –Kuehne + Nagel International is one of the world's top freight forwarding and logistics groups. Kuehne + Nagel (pronounced "KOO-nuh and NAH-gel") provides sea freight and airfreight forwarding arranges the transportation of goods by road and rail and offers customs brokerage services. The company's contract logistics unit offers warehousing and distribution services and it manages more than 7 million sq. meters of warehouse space. Overall Kuehne + Nagel operates from over 900 locations in more than 100 countries worldwide. Executive chairman Klaus-Michael Kuehne grandson of the company's co-founder owns a controlling stake in Kuehne + Nagel.

Operations in Europe account for about two-thirds of the company's sales. Understandably continued growth in Europe is one of the chief destinations on Kuehne + Nagel's roadmap for success. In 2011 it moved to bolster its road and rail operations outside of its primary target (southern and eastern Europe) by making good on its acquisition strategy. It plans to take over Brazil trucking company Grupo Eichenberg for $52 million. The deal follows Kuehne + Nagel's acquisitions of Translago in Columbia and UK-based RH Freight (Rennies Investment). The latter transaction (for an undisclosed sum) extends Kuehne + Nagel's overland network with 17 hubs in the UK and two in Finland as well as its sea- and airfreight and contract logistics capacity.

In 2010 the company opened new distribution centers in France Germany Spain and Latvia. Other stops along the way include Asia and the Middle East; Kuehne + Nagel added 18 new shipping routes to Asia in late 2010 and relocated the hub for its Middle East operations from Istanbul to Dubai. In early 2009 the company acquired France-based Alloin Group a logistics aggregator operating more than 50 cross-docking terminals. The group manages 20000 shipments per day.

The company's US arm Kuehne + Nagel Inc. specializes in contract logistics services. Kuehne + Nagel has gained revenue in the US and Canada as customers based elsewhere have expanded their operations in North America. Kuehne + Nagel agreed to pay a $9.87 million fine in late 2010 to settle charges that the Sherman Act was violated when the logistics company established surcharges for international freight forwarding services to the US.

As it works to gain market share Kuehne + Nagel transitioned its leadership team in early 2009 when CEO Klaus Herms retired after more than 40 years with the company. Deputy CEO Reinhard Lange a veteran of Kuehne + Nagel's freight forwarding business replaced him.

HISTORY

Kuehne + Nagel (also K hne + Nagel) was founded in 1890 in Bremen Germany by shipping veterans August Kuehne and Friedrich Nagel. The forwarding and commissioning agency's initial contracts were for glassware and cotton. Kuehne + Nagel convinced Hamburg sugar refiners to use its services to transport sugar by rail to the ice-free port of Bremen when the refiners' major export route the Weser River was frozen. By 1902 Kuehne + Nagel had an office in Hamburg. Nagel died in 1907.

Rebuilding after WWI Kuehne + Nagel acquired the Weber & Freund import company in the early 1920s and expanded into Austria Czechoslovakia Switzerland and the Balkans. In 1932 when August Kuehne died sons Alfred and Werner became sole owners of Kuehne + Nagel. (Werner left the company in 1951.)

Kuehne + Nagel's headquarters in Bremen was destroyed in WWII. As postwar German trade recovered Kuehne + Nagel grew rapidly opening a subsidiary in Canada in 1953 and setting up branches across Germany including Frankfurt (1949) Bonn and Hanover (1950) Wuppertal (1961) and Nuremberg (1963).

After the European Economic Community was founded Kuehne + Nagel established a network of forwarding agents and subsidiaries across Europe including offices in Antwerp Belgium and Rotterdam the Netherlands in 1954 and offices in Basel and Zurich Switzerland in 1963. Kuehne + Nagel took control of Greek forwarder Proodos in 1963 and set up an Italian subsidiary a year later.

Alfred Kuehne died in 1981. Heavy losses resulting from the expansion of the shipping fleet of Kuehne + Nagel prompted it to sell half of the company to British conglomerate Lonrho (renamed Lonmin in 1999). Alfred's son Klaus-Michael Kuehne and Lonrho's Roland "Tiny" Rowland were appointed as joint chief executives.

In 1985 Kuehne + Nagel began expanding its transportation warehousing and distribution network by acquiring stakes in leading freight companies including Domenichelli (Italy) Hollis Transportation (UK) and Van Vliet (the Netherlands). The Kuehne family expanded Kuehne + Nagel's presence in Switzerland (seen as a pan-European center) during the 1970s and 1980s and in 1992 Kuehne + Nagel moved its global headquarters to Schindellegi near Zurich.

In the early 1990s after German reunification and the fall of the Soviet Union Kuehne + Nagel acquired former East German state-owned forwarder VEB Deutrans. It also signed deals with local freight-forwarding operators in Russia and across Eastern Europe.

In 1992 Klaus-Michael Kuehne bought out Lonrho's stake and later sold a 33% stake to German conglomerate VIAG (later part of E.ON) which sold it back to Kuehne + Nagel in 1999. In 1994 Kuehne + Nagel went public.

To expand its rail network the company in 1997 acquired a 51% stake in Swiss rail forwarder Ferroviasped a major player in freight services for national railroads in Denmark France Spain and Switzerland.

To stay competitive in a rapidly consolidating industry Kuehne + Nagel formed an alliance in 1999 with French freight forwarder GEFCO a subsidiary of Peugeot S.A. A year later Kuehne + Nagel formed an alliance with Singapore-based SembCorp Logistics which later acquired a 20% stake in Kuehne + Nagel. In return Kuehne + Nagel bought 5% of SembCorp Logistics.

In 2000 Kuehne + Nagel also made plans to expand operations in the US. The company followed through the next year when it bought Connecticut-based USCO Logistics for $300 million. USCO Logistics was renamed Kuehne + Nagel Logistics in 2004.

Also in 2004 Kuehne + Nagel and SembCorp Logistics terminated their alliance in order to proceed independently.

Kuehne + Nagel expanded its operations in Europe by acquiring ACR Logistics in January 2006. Later that year the company bought HSBC Export Services a UK-based provider of sea freight and road freight forwarding and export documentation and credit management services.

EXECUTIVES

CFO, Gerard van Kesteren, age 67
CEO, Reinhard Lange, age 67
COO Road and Rail Logistics, Xavier Urbain, age 58
CIO, Martin Kolbe, age 55
Managing Director Kuehne + Nagel KG; Regional Manager Central Europe, Hans-Georg Brinkmann
EVP Sea and Air Logistics, Peter Ulber, age 55
Managing Director Poland, Tobias Jerschke
Chairman, Klaus-Michael Kuehne, age 79
Vice Chairman, Bernd Wrede, age 73
Auditors: Ernst & Young Ltd

LOCATIONS

HQ: Kuehne & Nagel International AG
  Kuehne & Nagel House, P.O. Box 67, Schindellegi CH-8834
Phone: (41) 44 786 95 11   **Fax:** (41) 44 786 95 95
Web: www.kuehne-nagel.com

PRODUCTS/OPERATIONS

480855501

COMPETITORS

APL Logistics	Geodis
Agility Public Warehousing	Hellmann Worldwide Logistics
Bollore	Menlo Worldwide
C.H. Robinson Worldwide	Nippon Express
	Panalpina
CEVA Logistics	Ryder System
DB Mobility Logistics	Sinotrans
Damco	UPS Supply Chain Solutions
Expeditors	Wincanton
GEFCO	

HISTORICAL FINANCIALS

Company Type: Public

Income Statement

FYE: December 31

	REVENUE ($ mil.)	NET INCOME ($ mil.)	NET PROFIT MARGIN	EMPLOYEES
12/15	16,847	680	4.0%	67,236
12/14	17,692	639	3.6%	63,448
12/13	19,278	669	3.5%	62,744
12/12	18,675	529	2.8%	63,248
12/11	17,238	638	3.7%	63,110
Annual Growth	(0.6%)	1.6%	—	1.6%

2015 Year-End Financials

Debt ratio: 0.3%
Return on equity: 29.5%
Cash ($ mil.): 846
Current ratio: 1.15
Long-term debt ($ mil.): 11
No. of shares (mil.): 119
Dividends
  Yield: 0.0%
  Payout: 15.1%
Market value ($ mil.): 3,356

STOCK PRICE ($) FY Close	P/E High/Low		PER SHARE ($) Earnings	Dividends	Book Value
12/15	28.00	5	4	5.67	0.86	17.82
12/14	27.20	5	4	5.34	0.85	20.63
12/13	26.25	6	5	5.59	0.42	23.74
12/12	24.33	7	5	4.43	0.48	21.83
12/11	22.35	5	4	5.35	0.00	21.22
Annual Growth	5.8%	—	—	1.5%	—	(4.3%)

Kyushu Electric Power Co Inc

Kyushu Electric Power generates transmits and distributes electricity on Japan's southernmost island. The company serves more than 8 million residential and business customers in the Kyushu region which includes the cities of Nagasaki and Fukuoka providing nuclear thermal and hydroelectric power generation. The company's other operations include telecommunications information technology facility construction and maintenance liquefied natural gas (LNG) real estate and recycling and environmental services. It also sells wholesale electricity and has international power production and consulting operations primarily in Asia. Kyushu Electric was established in 1951.

Operations Kyushu Electric's segments are Electric power; Energy related businesses; Information technology and telecommunications; and Other.

Electric Power (more than 90% of the company's total revenue) has more than 10700 kilometers of transmission line more than 140300 kilometers of distribution line and almost 600 electric substations. The Energy related businesses segment is engaged in obtaining storing gasifying supplying and selling LNG. It also operates renewable energy activities and other businesses related to energy. Information technology and telecommunications is primarily engaged in providing telecommunications and related services.

The Other segment consists of environment and recycling lifestyle-oriented services and other activities. Geographic Reach Kyushu Electric has operations in Japan the Ukraine Tanzania Cape Verde Nigeria Indonesia Singapore Philippines Vietnam Mexico China and Taiwan. Sales and Marketing

The company supplies electricity to residential and business customers through transmission and distribution lines.

Financial Performance

Note: Growth rates may differ after conversion to US Dollars.

Kyushu Electric saw its revenue drop from ¥1874 billion in fiscal 2015 (March year end) to ¥1836 billion in fiscal 2016. In the electric power business lighting and power revenue declined due to an adjustment in fuel costs which caused unit charges to decrease. Volume of sales also declined.

However operating expenses decreased by 10.5% as the result of a company-wide effort to cut costs a sharp fall in fuel prices and the restart of the Sendai Nuclear Power Station Units 1 and 2 among other factors reducing fuel costs. As a result of this and lower income taxes and investment gains Kyushu Electric's net income improved from a net loss of ¥114.7 billion in 2015 to net income of ¥73.5 billion in 2016.

Cash flow from operating activities improved from ¥88.7 billion to ¥329.5 billion in 2016 largely thanks to a decrease in thermal power fuel costs.

Strategy

Like other nuclear power providers in Japan in response to the major accident at the Fukushima Daiichi Nuclear Power Station in 2011 Kyushu Electric suspended operations at all its nuclear power stations. However in 2015 Kyushu Electric resumed operations at its Sendai nuclear power stations with units 1 and 2 brought back online.

As a result the company saved on thermal fuel costs and (in conjunction with other cost-saving measures) improved its financial condition in fiscal 2016.

That year compliance tests under new regulations were continuing at Units 3 and 4 of the Genkai Nuclear Power Station.

With full-scale liberalization of the Japanese retail power sector starting in 2016 the company was facing a period of challenging competition for its retail power services. To serve its customers better and improve its operational efficiency Kyushu Electric Power has introduced call centers companywide.

EXECUTIVES

President, Michiaki Uriu
EVP, Tomoyuki Aramaki
EVP, Naofumi Satou
EVP, Kazuhiro Izaki
EVP, Yuuzou Sasaki
Senior Managing Executive Officer, Hideomi Yakushinji
Senior Managing Executive Officer, Yoshiro Watanabe
Senior Managing Executive Officer, Takashi Yamasaki
Senior Managing Executive Officer, Akira Nakamura
Senior Managing Executive Officer, Narumi Nagao
Chairman, Masayoshi Nuki
Auditors: Deloitte Touche Tohmatsu LLC

LOCATIONS

HQ: Kyushu Electric Power Co Inc
2-1-82 Watanabe-dori, Chuo-ku, Fukuoka 810-8720
Phone: (81) 92 761 3031   **Fax:** (81) 92 713 8449
Web: www.kyuden.co.jp

PRODUCTS/OPERATIONS

2016 Sales

	% of total
Electric power	92
IT and Telecommunication	4
Energy related Business	3
Others	1
Total	**100**

COMPETITORS

Chubu Electric Power	KEPCO
Chugoku Electric Power	Shikoku Electric
Hokkaido Electric Power	Tohoku Electric Power
Hokuriku Electric Power	Tokyo Electric
	Tokyo Gas

HISTORICAL FINANCIALS

Company Type: Public

Income Statement

FYE: March 31

	REVENUE ($ mil.)	NET INCOME ($ mil.)	NET PROFIT MARGIN	EMPLOYEES
03/16	16,346	654	4.0%	20,929
03/15	15,614	(955)	—	20,753
03/14	17,352	(930)	—	20,870
03/13	16,429	(3,533)	—	20,853
03/12	18,384	(2,028)	—	20,865
Annual Growth	**(2.9%)**	**—**	**—**	**0.1%**

2016 Year-End Financials

Debt ratio: 0.6%
Return on equity: 16.0%
Cash ($ mil.): 3,743
Current ratio: 0.88
Long-term debt ($ mil.): 24,366

No. of shares (mil.): 473
Dividends
　Yield: —
　Payout: —
Market value ($ mil.): 5,811

	STOCK PRICE ($) FY Close	P/E High/Low		PER SHARE ($) Earnings	Dividends	Book Value
03/16	12.26	0	0	1.38	0.00	9.02
03/15	9.19	—	—	(2.02)	0.00	7.60
03/14	22.55	—	—	(1.97)	0.00	10.13
03/13	22.55	—	—	(7.47)	0.00	12.56
03/12	22.55	—	—	(4.29)	0.00	22.94
Annual Growth (14.1%)	**(20.8%)**	**—**	**—**	**—**	**—**	**—**

L'Air Liquide S.A. (France)

Auditors: ERNST & YOUNG et Autres

LOCATIONS

HQ: L' Air Liquide S.A. (France)
75, quai d' Orsay, Paris, Cedex 07 75321
Phone: (33) 1 40 62 55 55
Web: www.airliquide.com

HISTORICAL FINANCIALS

Company Type: Public

Income Statement

FYE: December 31

	REVENUE ($ mil.)	NET INCOME ($ mil.)	NET PROFIT MARGIN	EMPLOYEES
12/15	18,051	1,913	10.6%	51,500
12/14	18,945	2,023	10.7%	50,300
12/13	21,221	2,258	10.6%	50,250
12/12	20,378	2,121	10.4%	49,500
12/11	18,879	1,985	10.5%	46,200
Annual Growth	**(1.1%)**	**(0.9%)**	**—**	**2.8%**

2015 Year-End Financials

Debt ratio: 30.8%
Return on equity: 14.6%
Cash ($ mil.): 1,051
Current ratio: 0.96
Long-term debt ($ mil.): 6,851

No. of shares (mil.): 342
Dividends
　Yield: 2.5%
　Payout: 9.8%
Market value ($ mil.): 7,692

	STOCK PRICE ($) FY Close	P/E High/Low		PER SHARE ($) Earnings	Dividends	Book Value
12/15	22.43	5	4	5.55	0.57	39.40
12/14	24.65	5	5	5.80	0.63	40.81
12/13	28.37	6	5	6.65	0.59	42.55
12/12	25.45	6	5	6.16	0.53	39.21
12/11	24.60	6	5	5.77	0.49	36.81
Annual Growth	**(2.3%)**	**—**	**—**	**(0.9%)**	**3.7%**	**1.7%**

L'Oreal S.A. (France)

Auditors: Deloitte & Associés

LOCATIONS

HQ: L' Oreal S.A. (France)
14, rue Royale, Paris 75008
Phone: ( )   **Fax:** (33) 1 47 56 86 42
Web: www.loreal.com

HISTORICAL FINANCIALS

Company Type: Public

Income Statement

FYE: December 31

	REVENUE ($ mil.)	NET INCOME ($ mil.)	NET PROFIT MARGIN	EMPLOYEES
12/15	27,510	3,591	13.1%	82,881
12/14	27,387	5,968	21.8%	78,611
12/13	31,632	4,072	12.9%	77,452
12/12	29,606	3,779	12.8%	72,637
12/11	26,312	3,153	12.0%	68,886
Annual Growth	**1.1%**	**3.3%**	**—**	**4.7%**

2015 Year-End Financials

Debt ratio: 2.5%
Return on equity: 15.0%
Cash ($ mil.): 1,524
Current ratio: 1.13
Long-term debt ($ mil.): 44

No. of shares (mil.): 559
Dividends
　Yield: 1.7%
　Payout: 9.2%
Market value ($ mil.): 18,900

	STOCK PRICE ($) FY Close	P/E High/Low		PER SHARE ($) Earnings	Dividends	Book Value
12/15	33.75	7	5	6.36	0.60	45.93
12/14	33.33	4	3	10.20	0.69	44.27
12/13	35.15	8	6	6.70	0.60	51.96
12/12	27.98	6	4	6.25	0.52	46.11
12/11	20.83	6	4	5.28	0.47	38.37
Annual Growth 12.8%		**—**	**—**	**4.8%**	**6.3%**	**4.6%**

LafargeHolcim Ltd

What do you use to build a modern colossus? Cement of course. LafargeHolcim (formerly Holcim) is the world's largest cement maker with an annual production capacity of nearly 400 million tons. The company operates in some 90 countries around the world providing cement concrete asphalt and aggregates for use in housing infrastructure and oil & gas wells among other projects. It also offers research import/export trading consulting and management services for the construction industry. The company was created in 2015 with the merger of rivals Holcim based in Switzerland and Lafarge based in France.

Operations

The company has more than 2500 plants including more than 1600 concrete some 600 aggregates about 180 cement and 70 grinding plants.

Geographic Reach

LafargeHolcim has production sites in around 90 countries and boasts a market presence on every continent making the firm more geographically diversified than its rivals.

Strategy

Holcim in 2014 agreed to merge with Lafarge in a deal that created the world's biggest cement company with annual sales in excess of $40 billion. The combined business took the name LafargeHolcim.

In addition to growing key relationships with its homebuilding commercial construction and infrastructure clients the company is focused on innovation amid a rapidly changing industry. With the environment in mind LafargeHolcim is developing sustainable construction services and products and implementing changes in its logistics processes to reduce its energy footprint. In addition the company is investigating new business opportunities in waste collection handling and management.

To cut costs in 2016 the company agreed to divest its interest in Lafarge India for about $1.4 billion.

HISTORY

Cement company Aargauische Portlandcementfabrik Holderbank-Wildegg was founded near Zurich in 1912. Two years later Ernst Schmidheiny bought a stake in the company. His son and namesake later expanded the company beyond Switzerland then grouped its interests under holding company "Holderbank" Financière Glaris Ltd. in 1930. By WWII Holderbank had operations in Belgium Egypt Greece Lebanon and South Africa.

After the war Holderbank expanded into the Americas. It purchased Canada-based St. Lawrence Cement in 1953 and was listed on the Zurich stock exchange in 1958.

In 1970 the company swapped some assets with rival Swiss Cement-Industrie-Gesellschaft in a deal that increased Holderbank's presence in Costa Rica Lebanon Mexico and West Germany. The company also converted several of its minority stakes into majority shareholdings. Thomas Schmidheiny became chairman of Holderbank's executive committee in 1978 and chairman of the board in 1984 upon his father's (Ernst's brother Max) retirement.

During a late-1980s market slump Holderbank bought stakes in several US cement companies. It became the #1 US cement maker by purchasing Ideal Basic Industries in 1986. As the decade closed Holderbank consolidated in Europe and in 1990 placed many of its US operations under holding company Holnam.

Holderbank then pushed into Central and Eastern Europe where it gained production capacity in Hungary among other countries. The company bought a 51% stake in Morocco-based Les Ciments de l'Oriental (CIOR) in 1993. Geographic diversity helped Holderbank weather depressed periods in regional markets such as in Mexico where profits dropped 83% from 1994 to 1995 during an economic crisis there.

The company picked up major acquisitions in Malaysia the Philippines Sri Lanka and Thailand during a crippled economic period in Asia in the late 1990s. It also added capacity in the booming US market. Holderbank sought to invest in India in 1999 but the fragmented market there prevented it from finding a sizable company. Mean-

while Holderbank continued searching for investments in China to expand its presence there. The following year the company became the majority shareholder of Indonesian cement company PT Semen Cibinong (now PT Holcim Indonesia). Its joint bid (with Portugal's Secil) for CIMPOR the largest Portuguese cement manufacturer got stuck in regulatory issues however.

Holderbank changed its name to Holcim Ltd. in 2001. The name is derived from "Holderbank" (where it was founded) and "ciment" (French for cement). In 2002 Holcim's Thai subsidiary Siam City Cement acquired a controlling stake in TPI Polene beating out rival CEMEX for the deal. Holcim acquired Spain-based Cementos de Hispania and disposed of Eternit AG business in 2003.

That year when operations in Europe and North America showed little growth the company looked toward emerging markets in Africa Asia and Latin America. Holcim tightened its hold on Holcim Apasco in Mexico by increasing its stake in the company from 69% to 93% in 2004; it later took full ownership.

In 2005 Holcim acquired UK-based construction products provider Aggregate Industries. The deal gave the group more than 140 quarries in the UK and US. It followed that up the following year with the purchases of aggregates producer Foster Yeoman in the UK and ready-mix concrete maker Meyer Material in the US.

In 2007 Holcim acquired control of Ambuja Cements in India; took a majority stake in the Croatian Plovanija Kamen cement plant and stone quarry; and bought building materials supplier Jurong Cement in Singapore.

The company acquired Tarmac Iberia from Anglo American for some euro 148 million ($228 million) in 2008. The deal added about 50 ready-mixed concrete plants in Spain.

EXECUTIVES

Group CFO, Ron H. Wirahadiraksa, age 56
CEO, Eric C. Olsen, age 52
Region Head Europe, Roland K ␣hler, age 63
Area Manager North America and UK, Alain Bourguignon
Area Manager East Asia Pacific and Holcim Trading, Ian Thackwray, age 59
Area Manager Middle-East Africa, Sa␣d Sebbar
Chairman, Beat W. Hess, age 67
Auditors: Ernst & Young Ltd.

LOCATIONS

HQ: LafargeHolcim Ltd
Zuercherstrasse 156, Jona 8645
Phone: (41) 58 858 86 00   **Fax:** (41) 55 222 87 19
Web: www.lafargeholcim.com

COMPETITORS

Boral	Martin Marietta
CEMEX	Materials
CRH	Sumitomo Osaka Cement
Dyckerhoff	Taiheiyo Cement
Franz Haniel	Tarmac
HeidelbergCement	Titan Cement
Italcementi	Vicat

HISTORICAL FINANCIALS

Company Type: Public

Income Statement

FYE: December 31

	REVENUE ($ mil.)	NET INCOME ($ mil.)	NET PROFIT MARGIN	EMPLOYEES
12/15	23,747	(1,479)	—	100,956
12/14	19,318	1,301	6.7%	67,584
12/13	22,129	1,427	6.5%	70,857
12/12	23,501	678	2.9%	78,103
12/11	22,049	292	1.3%	80,967
Annual Growth	1.9%	—		5.7%

2015 Year-End Financials

Debt ratio: 20.5%
Return on equity: (-6.0%)
Cash ($ mil.): 4,423
Current ratio: 0.90
Long-term debt ($ mil.): 15,028
No. of shares (mil.): 605
Dividends
  Yield: 2.2%
  Payout: —
Market value ($ mil.): 6,140

	STOCK PRICE ($) FY Close	P/E High/Low		Earnings	Dividends	Book Value
12/15	10.14	—	—	(3.13)	0.23	52.15
12/14	14.19	4	3	3.80	0.26	51.50
12/13	15.02	5	4	4.18	0.21	53.20
12/12	14.59	8	6	1.99	0.19	54.12
12/11	10.60	20	11	0.87	0.27	53.27
Annual Growth	(1.1%)	—	—	—	(4.2%)	(0.5%)

Landesbank Hessen-Thueringen Girozentrale (Helaba) (Germany, Fed. Rep.)

Savings institutions except federal nsk

EXECUTIVES

Chief Executive Officer, Hans-Dieter Brenner
Auditors: PricewaterhouseCoopers Aktiengesellschaft Wirtschaftprufungsgesellschaft

LOCATIONS

HQ: Landesbank Hessen-Thueringen Girozentrale (Helaba) (Germany, Fed. Rep.)
Neue Mainzer Strasse 52-58, Frankfurt am Main D-60311
Phone: (49) 69 91 32 01   **Fax:** (49) 69 29 15 17
Web: www.helaba.de

HISTORICAL FINANCIALS

Company Type: Public

Income Statement

FYE: December 31

	ASSETS ($ mil.)	NET INCOME ($ mil.)	INCOME AS % OF ASSETS	EMPLOYEES
12/15	187,623	465	0.2%	6,200
12/14	218,169	487	0.2%	6,274
12/13	245,173	484	0.2%	6,293
12/12	262,688	417	0.2%	6,284
12/11	212,106	513	0.2%	5,748
Annual Growth	(3.0%)	(2.4%)	—	1.9%

2015 Year-End Financials

Return on assets: 0.2%
Return on equity: 5.6%
Long-term debt ($ mil.): —
No. of shares (mil.): —
Sales ($ mil): 6,119

Dividends
Yield: —
Payout: —
Market value ($ mil.): —

Landwirtschaftliche Rentenbank (Germany, Fed. Rep.)

EXECUTIVES

Vorstandsmitglied, Hans Bernhardt
Auditors: KPMG AG Wirtschaftsprüfungsgesellschaft

LOCATIONS

HQ: Landwirtschaftliche Rentenbank (Germany, Fed. Rep.)
Hochstrasse 2, Frankfurt am Main D-60313
Phone: (49) 69 2107 0   **Fax:** (49) 69 2107 6444
Web: www.rentenbank.de

HISTORICAL FINANCIALS

Company Type: Public

Income Statement

FYE: December 31

	ASSETS ($ mil.)	NET INCOME ($ mil.)	INCOME AS % OF ASSETS	EMPLOYEES
12/15	101,615	482	0.5%	269
12/14	107,992	73	0.1%	269
12/13	112,799	633	0.6%	257
12/12	116,512	321	0.3%	250
12/11	114,958	(89)	—	239
Annual Growth	(3.0%)	—	—	3.0%

2015 Year-End Financials

Return on assets: 0.4%
Return on equity: 12.6%
Long-term debt ($ mil.): —
No. of shares (mil.): —
Sales ($ mil): 4,286

Dividends
Yield: —
Payout: —
Market value ($ mil.): —

Legal & General Group PLC (United Kingdom)

Legal & General Group is one of the UK's biggest life insurers. The holding company operates six divisions covering annuities lifetime mortgages investment activities savings and de-risking in the US. The investment management arm generates more than 50% of revenues as the UK's largest pension fund manager serving institutional and retail investors. Legal & General's risk businesses provide groups and individuals with life insurance annuities and homeowners insurance. Personal savings products include unit trusts investment bonds and savings accounts. The firm operates in the US as Banner Life Insurance Company and William Penn Life Insurance Company of New York.

Operations

Legal & General's six business segments are Legal & General Retirement (LGR) Legal & General Investment Management (LGIM) Legal & General Capital (LGC) Insurance Savings and Legal & General America (LGA).

Geographic Reach

The company is headquartered in London and has offices in Hove Cardiff and in Suffolk.

Sales and Marketing

As part of its distribution network Legal & General's Mortgage Club serves as a marketplace for mortgage advisors to shop for lenders and other services.

The company serves more than 7 million individual corporate and institutional customers. It mainly distributes its insurance products in the UK through retail independent financial advisers (IFAs) and employee benefit consultants which make up a majority of its distribution mix. Banks and building societies including Sainsbury's Bank and Barclays also distribute its products.

Financial Performance

Note: Growth rates may differ after conversion to US Dollars.

In 2015 Legal & General saw its net revenue decrease 75% to £12.7 billion amid a contraction in investment return and premiums earned. Net income increased 9% however to £1.1 billion due to changes in provisions for investment contract liabilities and a decrease in claims and a change in insurance liabilities. Cash flow from operating activities in 2015 was an outflow of £820 million (down from an inflow of £5.5 billion) as a result of changes in working capital.

Strategy

Legal & General's strategy has developed in response to several big picture changes to its operating environment. The 2008 financial crisis prompted a move to place asset management at the core of Legal & General's activities and assets under management grew from £264 billion in 2009 to £746 billion at the end of 2015; it is now a top-15 global asset manager. Further changes to the UK's pension regulations have triggered an advancement in geographic diversification particularly towards the US. The company launched a lifetime mortgage business to help over 65s make use of the £1.4 trillion tied up in equity in their homes.

Recent investments include in clean energy via windpower company NTW Wind Management Limited. It also entered Japan Korea and Taiwan in 2015.

The company sold off Suffolk Life and Legal & General Holdings (France) to Curtis Banks Group and APICIL Prevoyance while acquiring New Life Home Finance (Newlife). Newlife is a UK-based lifetime mortgage provider.

Mergers and Acquisitions

In 2015 Legal & General acquired New Life Home Finance (Newlife) a UK-based lifetime mortgage provider for £5 million which provides the company with further direct investment assets to back its annuity liabilities.

HISTORY

The Legal in Legal & General's name comes from its founding mission —to provide life insurance to members of the legal profession. The company was started in 1836 by six lawyers as the Legal & General Life Assurance Society; its first customer solicitor Thomas Smith ill-manneredly died four years later after paying less than 200 pounds on a 1000-pound policy.

Throughout that century and into the next the company made loans to individuals and corporations; it also moved into real estate. After struggling under claims during WWI and the 1918 flu pandemic it moved into fire and accident coverage in 1920. It opened membership to nonlawyers in 1929. The company took over the UK operations of the US firm Metropolitan Life (MetLife) in 1933.

In 1934 Legal & General bought Gresham Life Assurance and Gresham Fire and Accident to gain a presence in Australia. During WWII the company was hit hard by German air attacks both physically (it had to relocate away from London for a time) and at the bottom line.

The postwar years were a time of expansion as the company moved into South Africa and also broadened its operations at home. In 1949 it moved into marine insurance and in 1956 inaugurated life insurance in Australia.

The company began expanding its product offerings in the 1970s with managed pension funds and retail unit trusts. It established a direct sales force for life and pensions in 1977. The company also formed alliances with several European insurance companies and sold its Gresham life subsidiary. In 1979 it formed Legal & General Group Limited as a holding company for its now-separate insurance international and investment management operations.

In 1981 Legal & General bought US auto insurer GEICO's two-thirds interest in Government Employees Life Insurance Company changing the subsidiary's name to Banner Life. Three years later it bought the Dutch operations of Unilife Assurance and created a subsidiary in the Netherlands. Despite all this activity however the company's performance during the 1980s was poor and it brought in David Prosser (who became CEO in 1991) to goose its asset management operations.

In 1989 the company bought William Penn Life Insurance from Continental Corp. and opened its first real estate agency —just in time for the real estate market crash. Legal & General and other mortgage guarantee insurers were also squeezed by the resulting increase in mortgage default rates as homebuyers were caught between high interest rates and high unemployment.

The company formed a joint venture with Woolwich Building Society to provide Woolwich customers with insurance products in 1995. The next year it followed the insurance industry trend by establishing a bank of its own.

With each succeeding merger of its rivals Legal & General became the target of rumors about its own fate. The company has remained adamantly independent with Prosser claiming that Legal & General could instead benefit by picking up business left behind by the new entities.

In 1998 the British insurance industry was stung by scandalous revelations regarding improper pension sales in the late 1980s and early 1990s. Legal & General set aside about $1 billion to compensate victims; it also sold its Australian operations. In 1999 banking company National Westminster and Legal & General talked takeover but the deal fell through. (NatWest was eventually bought by Royal Bank of Scotland.)

In 2001 Legal & General announced a deal with UK-based Barclays to provide the bank's customers with life insurance and pension products. In 2002 Legal & General extended its marketing agreement with UK financial services company Alliance & Leicester.

The company then discontinued its health insurance offerings and reduced its venture capital investment operations. In 2005 the company sold its Gresham Insurance subsidiary to Barclays Bank.

EXECUTIVES

Managing Director Legal & General Insurance, Duncan Finch
CFO, Stephen Halliwell
CEO Legal & General Investment Management, Mark Zinkula
CEO Legal & General Investment Management America, Robert J. Moore
Interim President and CEO Legal & General America, Gene Gilbertson
Group CEO, Nigel Wilson
Managing Director Legal & General Retirement, Kerrigan Procter
Managing Director Legal & General Capital, Paul Stanworth
Managing Director Mature Savings, Jackie Noakes
Chairman, John Kingman
Auditors: PricewaterhouseCoopers LLP

LOCATIONS

HQ: Legal & General Group PLC (United Kingdom)
One Coleman Street, London EC2R 5AA
Phone: (44) 20 3124 2000   **Fax:** (44) 20 3124 2500
Web: www.legalandgeneralgroup.com

PRODUCTS/OPERATIONS

2015 Sales

	% of total
Investment return	47
Net premiums earned	37
Fees from fund management and investment contracts	9
Operational income	7
Total	**100**

Selected Acquisitions

COMPETITORS

AEGON	MetLife
AXA	Prudential
Allianz	Prudential plc
Aviva	Royal London Mutual
ING	Standard Life
Lloyds Banking Group	Zurich Insurance Group

HISTORICAL FINANCIALS

Company Type: Public

Income Statement

FYE: December 31

	ASSETS ($ mil.)	NET INCOME ($ mil.)	INCOME AS % OF ASSETS	EMPLOYEES
12/15	588,034	1,593	0.3%	10,148
12/14	623,711	1,537	0.2%	11,038
12/13	600,157	1,475	0.2%	11,163
12/12	558,191	1,310	0.2%	9,864
12/11	504,733	1,121	0.2%	9,138
Annual Growth	3.9%	9.2%	—	2.7%

2015 Year-End Financials

Return on assets: 0.2%	Dividends
Return on equity: 17.2%	Yield: 4.2%
Long-term debt ($ mil.): —	Payout: 313.3%
No. of shares (mil.): —	Market value ($ mil.): —
Sales ($ mil): 18,822	

	STOCK PRICE ($) FY Close	P/E High/Low		PER SHARE ($) Earnings	Dividends	Book Value
12/15	20.13	122	95	0.27	0.86	1.60
12/14	19.27	117	97	0.26	0.77	1.59
12/13	18.45	123	81	0.25	0.59	1.58
12/12	12.42	87	60	0.22	0.49	1.49
12/11	7.95	77	54	0.19	0.35	1.37
Annual Growth	26.1%	—	—	9.0%	24.9%	4.0%

Lenovo Group Ltd

Lenovo Group not only tops the worldwide PC market ahead of #2 HP and #3 Dell but it operates competitive phone and server businesses. Through a series of acquisitions the Hong Kong-based company has assembled a device-driven product lineup that competes in various technology markets around the world. Lenovo has resurrected the Motorola brand in smartphones and unleashed IBM's former low-end server entity into a fast-growing business. Besides ThinkPad-branded commercial PCs Lenovos turns out tablets ultrabooks software and accessories. Its sales are fairly evenly sourced from the major world markets of China North America and Europe.

Operations

Lenovo's personal computer business racks up two-thirds of the company's sales followed by the mobile phone segment which supplies about 20% of revenue and the enterprise group with about 10%.

The company makes many of its own products but outsources some manufacturing as well.

Geographic Reach

Hong Kong-based Lenovo serves customers in more than 160 countries. Its three biggest markets the Americas China and Europe together for about 85% of sales. The Asia/Pacific region generates the rest.

Lenovo has operations in more than 60 countries across the globe. It has operational hubs in Beijing Paris and North Carolina and a marketing hub in Bangalore India. It also has major research centers in Yokohama Japan and in China in Beijing Shanghai and Shenzhen. It makes products at plants in China Singapore India Japan Brazil Switzerland and the US.

Sales and Marketing

Lenovo rebranded itself under the tag line "Never Stand Still" marking its expansion in size and scope. The rebranding rollout included the company's first conference Lenovo Tech World held in Beijing where it brought users and developers together and touted new products.

Financial Performance

Lenovo's growing stable of products and geographic expansion pushed revenue higher for six years until 2016 (ended March). The company reported a 3% revenue decline to about $45 billion in 2016 from 2015. Lenovo blamed currency fluctuations reduced PC demand and smartphone development for the drop. The company said revenue would have increased 3% without the currency impact. The worldwide slowing of the PC market hit Lenovo's biggest business with an 11 revenue drop. Its 6% decline in shipments bettered the industry wide 12% drop and the company also fattened its No. 1 market share. Sales in the mobile business rose 7% even as Lenovo integrated its Motorola Mobility acquisition into its existing phone operations. Enterprise sales just 10% revenue jumped a whopping 70% in 2016. Geographically sales fell in China and North America while growing in EMEA Latin America and Asia/Pacific.

A 20% increase in operating expenses wiped out Lenovo's profit and plunged it to a loss of about $130 million in 2016. Costs were higher for usual expenses - sales and administration selling and research and development - in 2016. The company also reported costs stemming from the acquisitions of IBM's server business and Motorola Mobility. Then there were costs associated from a restructuring and realignment of the company's businesses.

Even with the loss Lenovo's cash from operations increased to more than $290 million in 2016 from about $240 million in 2015.

Strategy

Lenovo has been adept at building a $45 billion revenue company from parts that other companies didn't want. It bought its world-leading PC business from IBM in 2005 and added IBM's x86 server business in 2014 as Big Blue de-emphasized hardware. Lenovo in 2014 bought the Motorola Mobility phone business from Google which at that time couldn't find the right touch for the phone business.

With those assets Lenovo has established itself as the market leader in the shrinking but still huge PC market; as developer of competitive smartphones; and a fast-growing provider of servers for data centers. The company realigned its corporate structure n 2016 to better exploit those businesses. The PC and Smart Device Business Group handles PCs as well as tablets detachables gaming and other smart devices. The Mobile Business Group handles smartphones with sub-units focusing on China and emerging markets. The Data Center Group develops high performance servers for the converged/hyperconverged cloud and hyperscale markets. A fourth unit Lenovo Capital and incubator Group funds startups and explores new technologies.

The company's emphasis on servers comes at time when the market might be right for relatively new play to step up. Competitors have dealt with mega-merger (Dell Technologies which swallowed EMC) and super splits (Hewlett Packard Enterprise which resulted from the breakup of Hewlett-Packard. Lenovo competes with HP Inc. in the PC business). That could leave an opening for a single-minded provider such as Lenovo. The company has also leveraged relationship with companies like Nutanix SAP Microsoft Juniper Networks and others to develop applications and gain a faster path of customers.

In phones the Motorola acquisition and a good amount of development work (as well as draining inventory of old models) propelled the business to account for more than 20% of Lenovo's revenue. The competition however is stiff throughout the world but particularly in China. Telecom equipment maker Huawei has emerged as the dominant player in the world's largest phone market. Other top smartphone sellers in China are Oppo Xiaomi and Apple. That might be why Lenovo has set its sights on other emerging markets such as Latin America and the Asia/Pacific region. The 83% revenue growth for smartphones in the EMEA region in 2016 was largely driven by sales in Eastern Europe the Middle East and Africa.

Lenovo is developing more products such as digital assistants and virtual reality hardware.

Mergers and Acquisitions

In the last two years Lenovo has made acquisitions to beef up its hardware offerings and support expansion in select markets. In 2014 it paid more than $5 billion to acquire two new major product lines. First it bought IBM's low-end x86 server business for $2.3 billion.

Also in 2014 Lenovo spent some $2.9 billion for Motorola Mobility from Google. As part of the deal Lenovo owns the brands Moto X Moto G and the DROID Ultra series while Google retained the patent portfolio.

HISTORY

Liu Chuanzhi an engineer at the Chinese Academy of Sciences who wrote industry research reports established Legend Group Holdings Co. in 1984 in Beijing. Backed by a modest investment from the academy Liu who went on to become something of an entrepreneurial hero in China and

10 other engineers were given a green light to form a retail business. They first bought and sold items ranging from TVs to roller skates but later focused on distributing computer products and eventually moved into manufacturing PCs for AST Research. Legend introduced its first proprietary product a Chinese character system for PCs in 1985.

In 1988 the company formed Legend Holdings Limited which was originally a Hong Kong-based PC distributor. The following year the parent company began designing and manufacturing motherboards and added systems integration services to its offerings. In 1990 China reduced import tariffs a move that opened the trade door for companies such as IBM and Compaq. That year Legend Group Holdings began making its own brand of PCs.

Legend Holdings went public in 1994 and the following year began absorbing operations from its parent company which retained approximately 60% ownership in the subsidiary. By 1996 it was tied with IBM for PC market share in China; it became the country's top brand the following year.

In 1998 parent company Legend Group Holdings transferred Beijing Legend Group to its Hong Kong-based subsidiary. The following year Microsoft looking to extend its operating system dominance into China teamed up with Legend Holdings to create set-top boxes. In 2000 the company partnered with Pacific Century CyberWorks to provide broadband Internet services. The following year Legend spun off its distribution business Digital China as a separate public company. In 2001 Yang Yuanqing was named CEO of the company.

In 2002 Legend Holdings changed its English company name to Legend Group Limited. The company launched a corporate brand Lenovo the following year and in 2004 it officially adopted Lenovo as its English name. It also sold its non-telecom IT services business to AsiaInfo Holdings renamed AsiaInfo-Linkage in 2004.

Lenovo acquired IBM's worldwide PC operations for approximately $1.75 billion in 2005. IBM executive Stephen Ward was named CEO of Lenovo at the time of the merger but he was replaced by William Amelio before year's end. Amelio headed Dell's Asia/Pacific operations before joining Lenovo. In 2006 Lenovo launched a unit called Lenovo Services.

In 2007 Lenovo stopped using the IBM PC brand to which it still held the rights and began offering only Lenovo-branded machines. The following year it sponsored and supported the Olympic Summer Games in Beijing providing more than 30000 pieces of equipment and 600 engineers.

Looking to focus on its core PC operations Lenovo sold its mobile phone business Lenovo Mobile Communications to Hony Capital in 2008. Hony the private equity arm of Legend Holdings paid $100 million for the unit.

A year later Lenovo bought back the mobile communications business for about $200 million in cash and stock. The company cited the growth of the mobile Internet market and the increasing convergence between the PC and wireless handset sectors for the about-face in product strategy. Lenovo's move came as Dell introduced a mobile phone for the Chinese market.

Citing a flagging economy Lenovo announced a restructuring plan in 2009 that included a workforce reduction of 11% executive pay cuts and the consolidation of its China and the Asia/Pacific units. The company also initiated a management shakeup including its chairman taking over as CEO. The change may in part have reflected a strategy shift for Lenovo. With corporate spending flagging particularly in the US the company

planned to focus on China and other emerging markets with an emphasis on consumers.

EXECUTIVES

SVP and Chief Marketing Officer, David A. Roman
Chairman and CEO, Yang Yuanqing, age 53, $894,000 total compensation
SVP Centralized Services, Wang Xiaoyan, age 55
Assistant President; Head of Sales Commercial Department, Chen Xudong
President and COO and President PC and Smart Devices, Gianfranco Lanci, age 61
COO Asia Pacific and Chairman Lenovo India, Amar Babu
EVP and CFO, Wong Wai Ming, age 58
SVP Co-President Mobile Business Group and Chairman and President Motorola Mobility, Aymar de Lencquesaing
SVP and CIO, Zhou Qingtong
Managing Director Lenovo India, Rahul Agarwal
SVP Lenovo Capital and Incubator Group and Acting CTO, He (George) Zhiqiang
Auditors: PricewaterhouseCoopers

LOCATIONS

HQ: Lenovo Group Ltd
23rd Floor, Lincoln House, Taikoo Place, 979 King's Road, Quarry Bay,
Phone: (852) 2590 0228   **Fax:** (852) 2516 5384
Web: www.lenovo.com

2016 Sales

	$ mil.	% of total
Americas (AG)	13,604	30
China	12,358	28
Europe Middle east & Africa (EMEA)	11,794	26
Asia Pacific (AP)	7,154	16
Total	**44,912**	**100**

PRODUCTS/OPERATIONS

2016 Sales

	$ mil.	% of total
PC Business Group	29,646	66
Mobile Business Group	9,779	22
Enterprise Business Group	4,553	10
Others	933	2
Total	**44,912**	**100**

Product Categories
Laptops
Desktops & All-in-Ones
Smartphones
Tablet PCs
Network Storage
Workstations
Accessories & Upgrades

COMPETITORS

ASUSTeK	Huawei Technologies
Acer	IBM
Apple Inc.	LG Electronics
BlackBerry	Microsoft
Dell	NEC
Digital China	Nokia
Founder Holdings	Panasonic Corp
Fujitsu	Positivo Informtica
Great Wall Technology	Samsung Electronics
HP	Siemens AG
HTC Corporation	Sony
Hedy Holding	Toshiba
Hitachi	Wipro

HISTORICAL FINANCIALS

Company Type: Public

Income Statement

FYE: March 31

	REVENUE ($ mil.)	NET INCOME ($ mil.)	NET PROFIT MARGIN	EMPLOYEES
03/16	44,912	(128)	—	60,000
03/15	46,295	828	1.8%	60,000
03/14	38,707	817	2.1%	54,000
03/13	33,873	635	1.9%	35,026
03/12	29,574	472	1.6%	27,000
Annual Growth	**11.0%**	**—**	**—**	**22.1%**

2016 Year-End Financials

Debt ratio: 13.0%
Return on equity: (-3.8%)
Cash ($ mil.): 1,926
Current ratio: 0.82
Long-term debt ($ mil.): 2,505

No. of shares (mil.): —
Dividends
Yield: 4.1%
Payout: 5,549.0%
Market value ($ mil.): —

	STOCK PRICE ($) FY Close	P/E High/Low		PER SHARE ($) Earnings	Dividends	Book Value
03/16	15.54	3069	1344	0.01	0.64	0.25
03/15	29.15	423	280	0.08	0.58	0.35
03/14	22.09	354	211	0.08	0.48	0.27
03/13	20.10	377	225	0.06	0.33	0.24
03/12	17.98	398	229	0.05	0.19	0.23
Annual Growth	**(3.6%)**	**—**	**—**	**(29.0%)**	**36.3%**	**2.4%**

LG Chem Ltd (New)

LG Chem got there first. Founded in 1947 it was Korea's first chemical company. The company produces a variety of products including cosmetics personal care products petrochemicals pharmaceuticals and specialty chemicals. It's divided into two segments. The Petrochemicals unit makes basic chemicals like ethylene propylene and their derivatives as well as PVC acrylates and engineering plastics. The company's Information and Electronic Materials segment produces rechargeable batteries and display materials. It boasts 12 manufacturing subsidiaries and 20-plus marketing subsidiaries. Formerly the chemical division of the LG Group the company went public in 2001 while LG still owns a third of LG Chem.

After the global recession of 2008 LG Chem saw a significant rise in profitability in 2009 with growth in its petrochemical business due to a booming Chinese economy and improvements in its information and electronic materials business due to a general rise in worldwide demand. Overall LG Chem's sale grew about 8% in 2009 while its net income jumped more than 55%.

In 2009 the company spun off its Industrial Materials unit saying that the business was sufficiently different from LG Chem's core operations that it made more sense to operate it separately. The new company called LG Hausys manufactures window frames flooring materials and other construction-industry products.

The company gets about half of its sales domestically but China accounts for a rapidly growing percentage of its foreign sales around 25%. (Domestic sales accounted for less than half of 2008's total sales marking the first time that has happened for the company.) LG Chem is looking to grow its already strong position in the Chinese PVC market.

Further expanding it geographic assets in 2011 the company announced that a joint venture would invest $4 billion to build a petrochemical complex in Kazakhstan.

EXECUTIVES

Vice Chairman and CEO, Park Jin Soo Jin-Soo
CFO and Director, Jeong Ho-Young
Auditors: Samil Accounting Corporation (A Member Firm of PircewaterhouseCoopers)

LOCATIONS

HQ: LG Chem Ltd (New)
LG Twin Towers, 128 Yeouido-dong, Youngdeungpo-gu, Seoul 150-721
Phone: (82) 2 3777 1114   **Fax:** (82) 2 3773 7813
Web: www.lgchem.com

2015 Sales

	% of total
China	33
Korea	32
America	6
Southeast Asia	20
Western Europe	8
Other	1
Total	**100**

PRODUCTS/OPERATIONS

2015 Sales

	% of total
Basic materials and chemicals	71
Information Technology & Electronic Materials	11
Energy Solution	16
Advance Material	2
Total	**100**

COMPETITORS

Mitsubishi Chemical   Sumitomo Chemical
OCI Company

HISTORICAL FINANCIALS

Company Type: Public

Income Statement

FYE: December 31

	REVENUE ($ mil.)	NET INCOME ($ mil.)	NET PROFIT MARGIN	EMPLOYEES
12/15	17,174	979	5.7%	14,280
12/14	20,635	793	3.8%	13,623
12/13	22,007	1,203	5.5%	12,617
12/12	21,787	1,399	6.4%	11,683
12/11	19,569	1,845	9.4%	10,722
Annual Growth	(3.2%)	(14.6%)	—	7.4%

2015 Year-End Financials

Debt ratio: 0.0%
Return on equity: 9.1%
Cash ($ mil.): 1,449
Current ratio: 1.80
Long-term debt ($ mil.): 431

No. of shares (mil.): 65
Dividends
  Yield: —
  Payout: —
Market value ($ mil.): —

LG Display Co Ltd

The world is truly flat for LG Display —as in flat-panel displays. The company is one of the world's top producers of TFT-LCDs (thin-film transistor liquid-crystal displays) the svelte screens that go into laptop and notebook computers desktop PC monitors TV sets wireless handsets and a variety of applications in automotive navigation avionics consumer electronics instrumentation and medical equipment. LG Electronics and Philips merged their LCD businesses in 1999. Philips no longer holds any equity in LG Display. The company gets about 70% of its sales from customers in the Asia/Pacific region.

The global economic downturn had little effect on LG Display's sales which rose by 23% in 2009 and by 13% in 2008. Driven by demand for larger and wider screens the increase in unit sales for large-size panels —particularly those for televisions and desktop monitors —more than offset the decrease in average selling prices for the years. The company's profitability remained relatively strong as well; its net income for 2009 was $954 million about a 20% increase over 2008 but around 17% lower than reported in 2007. The lower profits for 2008 and 2009 were due in part to higher raw material costs and higher salary and bonus expenses related to growth in sales and employees. In addition 2008 and 2009 included payments related an antitrust-related settlement. In 2008 LG Display pleaded guilty to fixing prices on LCD panels under charges brought by the US Department of Justice and paid a fine of $424 million.

The company has a limited number of end-brand customers with its top three customers —LG Electronics Philips and Hewlett-Packard —accounting for more than 40% of sales. HP became a significant customer after LG Display agreed to supply panels to HP in 2005 in a three-year deal worth $5 billion. The contract was renewed for another three years in 2008. The flat panels are installed in HP notebook computers and PC monitors.

The flat-panel display industry has grown rapidly but is also highly cyclical and subject to rapid price declines. LG Display counters these declines by carefully allocating its production and development capacity. It also shifts its product mix towards large panels which fetch premium prices. In 2009 the company focused on large-size wide-format panels for desktop monitors notebook computers and televisions. Panels for LCD TVs account for close to half of the company's sales.

LG Display also makes small to midsized panels which are primarily used in handheld applications such as mobile phones GPS units digital photo frames and e-book readers. The average selling price for the panels is significantly lower that other panels and the market is extremely competitive though global demand for products that use the panels continues to grow.

The company must also contend with shifts in display technologies as advanced techniques for making displays challenge the mainstream LCD trade. In 2008 LG Display acquired the active-matrix organic light-emitting diode (AMOLED) business of LG Electronics for nearly $5 million in cash. AMOLEDs are an advanced type of display; OLED displays which are starting to show up in TV sets and other consumer electronics products don't require a backlight like LCDs do and they can offer superior images. The company had worked on AMOLED technology with Eastman Kodak (where the OLED was originally invented) and produced a flexible AMOLED monotone display in 2008 that can function as an "e-newspaper" after introducing a flexible color e-book display in 2007. In 2009 LG Display and its affiliates formed a joint venture company —Global OLED Technology LLC —that acquired Kodak's OLED business. LG Display holds 49% of the JV.

A bright spot for South Korean LCD flat-panel makers came in December 2009 when the South Korean government gave approval for LG Display and Samsung Electronics to export their TFT-LCD technology to China allowing the companies to move forward with plans to build plants there. LG Display has announced it will set up a joint venture to build a $4 billion 8th generation LCD plant in China giving the company expanded access to the rapidly growing Chinese LCD TV market.

Most of LG Display's production and assembly facilities are located in South Korea and China. In order to better serve its customers in the European market LG Display invested $533 million in building and expanding an LCD component factory in Poland which began mass production in 2007.

Philips gradually sold off its equity stake in LG Display. In 2007 Philips reduced its stake in LG Display from 33% to around 20% selling 46.4 million shares for about $2.2 billion. The following year Philips sold another 24 million shares cutting its stake by nearly 7%. The company got slightly more than $1 billion for those shares. In 2009 the Dutch giant sold its last remaining shares in LG Display for about $803 million.

In light of Philips selling its interests in the company shareholders voted in 2008 to change the name of the company from LG.

Philips LCD to LG Display. LG Electronics continues to own about 38% of LG Display.

EXECUTIVES

President and Chief Marketing Officer, Sang-Deog (Eddie) Yeo, age 61
Vice Chairman and CEO, Sang-Beom Han
SVP and CFO, Sang-Don Kim
EVP; Head TV Business Unit, Yong-Kee Hwang
EVP; Head Information Technology Business Unit, Kyong-Deuk Jeong
EVP; Head Mobile Business Unit, Hyung-Seok Choi
EVP and Chief Production Officer, Sang-Mun Shin
SVP and CTO, In-Byeong Kang
Chairman, Yu Sig Kang
Auditors: Samjong Accounting Corporation (A Member Firm of KPMG)

LOCATIONS

HQ: LG Display Co Ltd
12th Floor, 128 LG Twin Tower, Youngdengpo-gu, 128 Yeoi-dearo, Seoul 150-875
Phone: (82) 2 3777 5114   **Fax:** (82) 2 3777 0797
Web: www.lgdisplay.com

2014 Sales

	% of total
Asia/Pacific	
China	60
Other countries	11
Europe	6
Americas	8
Poland	5
Total	**100**

PRODUCTS/OPERATIONS

2014 Sales

	% of total
TFT-LCD televisions	39
Desktop monitors	18
Tablet products	13
Notebook computers	10
Mobile and others	20
Total	**100**

Products Selected
TV Display
Commercial Display
Monitor Display
Notebook Display
Mobile Display
Auto Display
IPS
AIT
Transparent flexible display
3D

COMPETITORS

AU Optronics   NEC Display Solutions

Amax
BOE Technology
Chimei Innolux
Chunghwa Picture Tubes
Delta Electronics
 Thailand
HannStar Display
JDI
Mitsubishi Electric

SVA Group
Samsung Electronics
Sharp Electronics
Sony
Truly International
Varitronix
ViewSonic
Wintek

HISTORICAL FINANCIALS

Company Type: Public

Income Statement

FYE: December 31

	REVENUE ($ mil.)	NET INCOME ($ mil.)	NET PROFIT MARGIN	EMPLOYEES
12/15	24,124	821	3.4%	32,603
12/14	24,180	826	3.4%	32,434
12/13	25,705	405	1.6%	33,643
12/12	27,563	218	0.8%	34,657
12/11	20,964	(665)	—	34,803
Annual Growth	3.6%	—	—	(1.6%)

2015 Year-End Financials

Debt ratio: 0.0%
Return on equity: 8.1%
Cash ($ mil.): 2,145
Current ratio: 1.44
Long-term debt ($ mil.): 2,386

No. of shares (mil.): 357
Dividends
 Yield: 2.1%
 Payout: 9.2%
Market value ($ mil.): 3,736

	STOCK PRICE ($) FY Close	P/E High/Low		PER SHARE ($) Earnings	Dividends	Book Value
12/15	10.44	0	0	2.30	0.23	28.96
12/14	15.15	0	0	2.31	0.00	29.20
12/13	12.14	0	0	1.13	0.00	28.20
12/12	14.48	0	0	0.61	0.00	26.72
12/11	10.53	—	—	(1.86)	0.22	24.40
Annual Growth	(0.2%)	—	—	—	1.4%	4.4%

LG Electronics Inc

LG Electronics (LGE) makes the products that have tech-savvy consumers chomping at the bit in the kitchen in the media room and on the go. A leader in consumer electronics mobile communications and home appliances LGE operates through more than 100 subsidiaries worldwide that design and make flat panel TVs audio and video products mobile handsets air conditioners washing machines refrigerators and more. Asia and North America are its two largest markets each contributing about a quarter of LGE's sales. LGE owns Zenith Electronics (acquired in 1995) and LG Display. Founded in 1958 as Goldstar LGE established a North American headquarters in 2004. South Korea's LG Corp. owns about one-third of LGE.

 Geographic Reach
 Seoul-based LG Electronics (LGE) rings up nearly 15% of its sales at home in South Korea. North America accounts for nearly a quarter of its total sales. Other important markets for geographically-diversified LGE include Central and South America (15%) and Europe. About 15% of the company's sales come from emerging markets including India China and Russia. The Middle East and Africa accounts for about 10%. The company controls 114 local subsidiaries across the globe.
 Operations
 Home entertainment including OLED and Ultra HD TVs and other video and audio products is

LGE's largest business accounting for a 45% of sales. Home appliances and mobile communications products each represent about 20% of sales.
 Financial Performance
 The consumer electronics giant rang up $53.1 billion in sales and a net profit of $203.7 million in 2013 marking an improvement over 2012 results. LGE's operating profit increased modestly in 2013 to nearly $1.2 billion up from $1.1 billion in 2012. The company's mobile communications business posted a 29% jump in annual sales with help from stronger smartphone sales including its G2 and Nexus 5 models. Smartphone shipments rose 54% year over year. LGE's air conditioning and home appliance businesses also posted annual sales gains of 8% and 5% respectively. The laggard was home entertainment which suffered a 5% decline in annual sales despite higher demand for LCD TVs in North America Asia and the CIS countries.
 Strategy
 LGE is focusing on boosting its mobile communication handset business and enhancing its share of the LCD TV market. Indeed the company is looking to sell about 20% more cell phones. To that end LGE will enter the world's largest 4G mobile market — China —with the introduction of its LG-E985T smartphone through China Mobile (the world's largest mobile operator with nearly 750 million subscribers). The company is also going after the premium kitchen appliance market with the establishment in 2013 of a new division focused exclusively on high-end kitchen packages. The new division will initially focus on the US and Korean markets. The Korean company has formed a strategic relationship with GE to share patents on kitchenware and refrigerators. LGE also has alliances with other companies including Prada (phones) Siemens (air conditioners) and Hitachi (optical storage).
 LGE is continuing to invest heavily in marketing to boost its position as one of the world's top consumer electronics brands up there with rivals Sony Samsung and Panasonic. The company is also focused on boosting sales of its commercial air conditioners drum washing machines and side-by-side (aka French door) refrigerators. LGE and US rival Whirlpool have been trading patent infringement claims over refrigerator technology.
 Mergers and Acquisitions
 In February 2013 LGE acquired the webOS operating system technology from Hewlett-Packard to support its next-generation Smart TV technology. LGE acquired the source code and other assets associated with webOS. The purchase will allow LGE to offer an intuitive user experience and Internet services across a range of consumer electronics devices.
 To bolster production of large-scale air conditioning systems both in South Korea and abroad LGE acquired the A/C business of industrial machinery manufacturer LS Mtron for $134 million in early 2011. The deal included a factory in Jeonju South Korea as well as a research and development team. LS Mtron operated as part of LG Group until 2003 when its operations were spun off.

EXECUTIVES

President and CEO Home Entertainment Company, Bong-Suk Kwon
President Business to Business Sector, Lee Sang-bong
President and CEO Vehicle Components, Lee Woo-Jong
Auditors: Samil Accounting Corporation (A Member Firm of PircewaterhouseCoopers)

LOCATIONS

HQ: LG Electronics Inc
 LG Twin Towers, 128 Yeouido-dong, Yeongdeungpo-gu, Seoul 150-721
Phone: (82) 2 3777 1114   **Fax:** (82) 2 3777 3428
Web: www.lge.com

2015 Sales

	% of total
North America	29
Korea	25
Asia	11
Europe	10
South America	8
Middle East & Africa	8
China	6
Other	3
Total	**100**

PRODUCTS/OPERATIONS

2015 Sales

	% of total
Home entertainment	30
Home appliance	28
Mobile communications	25
Innotek	11
Vehicle components	3
Other	3
Total	**100**

Selected Major Products & Services

Home Entertainment (LCD TVs plasma TVs audio video & optical storage)
Mobile Communication (mobile handsets mobile accessory)
Home Appliance (washing machines refrigerators cooking appliances vacuum cleaners built-in appliances)
Air Conditioning (residential air conditioners commercial air conditioners home solution compressors)
Business Solutions (monitors commercial displays car infotainment security business)

COMPETITORS

Apple Inc.
BSH Home Appliances
Electrolux
GE Appliances & Lighting
Haier Group
Panasonic Corp

Philips Electronics
SANYO
Samsung Electronics
Sony
Technicolor
Toshiba
Whirlpool

HISTORICAL FINANCIALS

Company Type: Public

Income Statement

FYE: December 31

	REVENUE ($ mil.)	NET INCOME ($ mil.)	NET PROFIT MARGIN	EMPLOYEES
12/15	48,029	105	0.2%	37,902
12/14	53,962	365	0.7%	37,835
12/13	55,285	168	0.3%	38,363
12/12	47,728	62	0.1%	36,376
12/11	46,825	(405)	—	35,286
Annual Growth	0.6%	—	—	1.8%

2015 Year-End Financials

Debt ratio: 0.0%
Return on equity: 1.0%
Cash ($ mil.): 2,377
Current ratio: 1.11
Long-term debt ($ mil.): 5,525

No. of shares (mil.): 162
Dividends
 Yield: —
 Payout: —
Market value ($ mil.): —

Li & Fung Ltd.

A global provider of supply chain management services Li & Fung helps retailers including Wal-Mart and Target keep their shelves filled with consumer goods from far-flung factories. The company concentrates on the design sourcing production and delivery of soft goods (mainly clothing); it also designs and sources hard goods such as handicrafts home furnishings shoes sporting goods and toys. Li & Fung's 240 offices and distribution centers source from more than 15000 suppliers and serve 40 countries with a concentration in China. Items destined for the US account for more than 65% of sales. The company is part of global logistics firm Li & Fung Group which was founded in 1906.

Looking to bolster its presence in the lucrative markets of the US Europe and Asia the company has been on a buying spree. Five purchases in mid-2011 brought about $660 million in sales to the fold. They included an apparel sourcing and development firm (Loyaltex Apparel) a UK cosmetics company (Collection 2000) an IKEA-esque furniture producer (Exim Designs) and two distributors (TV Mania and Hampshire Designs). At the end of the spree Li & Fung said it would focus on organic growth and digesting its purchases for the next three years. Then it hedged and said it would still be open to opportunities in Japan.

In 2010 the company spent about $1.1 billion on a handful of purchases. The largest was US-based Jimlar Corporation a designer and manufacturer of footwear for Coach and Calvin Klein. Jimlar's 2010 revenue was about $540 million; its brands include Frye Mountrek and RJ Colt. The other large purchase was Integrated Distribution which added an extensive distribution network in China and gave Li & Fung's an entrance into mainland China.

EXECUTIVES

Group CEO, Spencer T. Fung, age 43
President LF Products, Henry Chan
Executive Director and President LF Sourcing, Marc Compagnon
CFO, Ed Lam
President LF Fashion, Wai Ping Leung
President LF Private Label, Stephen Lister
President LF Logistics, Joseph Phi
President LF Beauty and LF Asia, Gerard Raymond
Group CTO, Manuel Fernandez
Group Chairman, William Fung, age 68
Auditors: PricewaterhouseCoopers

LOCATIONS

HQ: Li & Fung Ltd.
11th Floor, LiFung Tower, 888 Cheung Sha Wan Road, Kowloon,
Phone: (852) 2300 2300   **Fax:** (852) 2300 2020
Web: www.lifung.com

2015 Sales

	% of total
US	62
Europe	16
Asia	15
Rest of the world	7
Total	**100**

PRODUCTS/OPERATIONS

2015 Sales

	% of total
Soft goods	59
Hard Tools	36
Logistics	5
Total	**100**

2015 Sales

	$ of total
Trading Network	95
Logistics Network	5
Total	**100**

COMPETITORS

APL Logistics	Geodis
CEVA Logistics	Global Sources
Connor & Associates	Kurt Salmon Associates

HISTORICAL FINANCIALS

Company Type: Public

Income Statement

FYE: December 31

	REVENUE ($ mil.)	NET INCOME ($ mil.)	NET PROFIT MARGIN	EMPLOYEES
12/15	18,830	421	2.2%	25,320
12/14	19,288	441	2.3%	25,781
12/13	20,745	725	3.5%	28,210
12/12	20,221	617	3.1%	28,465
12/11	20,030	681	3.4%	29,624
Annual Growth	(1.5%)	(11.3%)	—	(3.8%)

2015 Year-End Financials

Debt ratio: 17.0%
Return on equity: 13.7%
Cash ($ mil.): 342
Current ratio: 1.00
Long-term debt ($ mil.): 1,253
No. of shares (mil.): —
Dividends
  Yield: 7.6%
  Payout: 197.3%
Market value ($ mil.): —

	STOCK PRICE ($) FY Close	P/E High/Low	PER SHARE ($) Earnings	Dividends	Book Value
12/15	1.30	41 23	0.05	0.10	0.36
12/14	1.82	60 34	0.05	0.50	0.37
12/13	2.55	44 27	0.09	0.07	0.66
12/12	3.58	69 39	0.07	0.10	0.61
12/11	3.67	79 36	0.08	0.09	0.49
Annual Growth	(22.9%)	— —	(12.1%)	1.7%	(7.4%)

Liberty Global plc

Liberty Global provides cable-based TV phone and Internet access to about 27 million users both residential and commercial mostly in Europe (but growing in Latin America). Its core market is Western Europe where it does business through UPC and Virgin; in Germany through Unitymedia; in Switzerland through Cablecom; and in Belgium through a stake in Telenet. In the Americas Liberty Global serves Puerto Rico through Liberty Cablevision and Chile via an 80% stake in VTR Global Com. The company also offers satellite TV service. After acquiring Virgin in 2013 the holding company changed from Liberty Global Inc. to Liberty Global plc and made the UK its headquarters. In 2015 Liberty Global acquired Cable & Wireless and its operations in the Caribbean and Panama.

OperationsLiberty Global makes 80% of its revenue from residential cable services. That breaks down to 36% from video 26% from broadband Internet and 18% from fixed-line telephones. Just 6% of sales come from mobile telephone subscriptions and business accounts account for 8%. Overall the company has 56 million revenue generating units —set-top boxes and other devices.

Geographic Reach

Germany Switzerland and the Netherlands combine to represent almost 31% of Liberty Global's sales. Altogether Liberty Global operates in more than a dozen countries including Chile as well at the US territory Puerto Rico. The $5.3 billion acquisition of Cable & Wireless extended Liberty Global's reach in the Americas to include several nations in the Caribbean Panama and the Seychelle islands in the Indian Ocean.

The company is the largest cable network operator in most of its markets; it is the second-largest in Germany the Netherlands and Romania.

Sales and Marketing

Liberty Global spent some $35 million on sales and marketing in 2014 a 5.3% increase from 2014. The company reported higher costs for ad campaigns in the UK Germany the Netherlands and Switzerland. It also paid higher third-party sales commissions and advertising costs related to Chile's cable operations.

Financial Performance

Liberty Global dialed up a 26% revenue increase in 2014 to $18.2 billion buoyed by performance in the UK and Germany. The addition of Virgin's operations boosted UK revenue and in Germany FX charged revenue.

The revenue jump helped reduce Liberty Global's net loss to $695 million an improvement by $269 million from 2013. Besides revenue gains on investment helped reduce the loss. Higher operating costs some of them related to the Virgin acquisition still resulted in the overall loss.

Liberty Global reported cash flow from operations of $5.6 billion at the end of 2014 compared to $4 billion in 2013.

Mergers and Acquisitions

Liberty agreed to buy Cable & Wireless Communications a telecom services provider in the Caribbean and Central America. The deal announced in late 2015 adds to Liberty's already extensive Latin America holdings.

That late-in-the-year deal culminated a busy acquisition schedule for Liberty Global. Other 2015 transactions included the Telenet Group subsidiary's acquisition of BASE Company the third-largest mobile network operator in Belgium and the conclusion of the acquisition of Puerto Rico Cable Acquisition Company Inc. (Choice Cable) the second largest cable and broadband services provider in Puerto Rico.

In a milestone announcement that sent shockwaves across the cable industry Liberty Global acquired Virgin Media in a stock and cash merger valued at roughly $23.3 billion in 2013. The mega deal created the world's leading broadband communications company and covers 47 million homes and serves 25 million customers spanning 14 countries.

On the other side of acquisitions Liberty Global said goodbye to Chellomedia a programming network in the UK and the Netherlands selling it for about $1 billion.

Ownership

Chairman John Malone controls more than 35% of the company's voting power.

HISTORY

Liberty Global was formed through the 2005 merger of cable operators Liberty Media International (LMI) and UnitedGlobalCom (UGC) each of which was previously spun off from TV programming behemoth Liberty Media Corporation.

The company had a busy first fiscal year as it tweaked its holdings through divestitures and acquisitions. It unloaded its Norwegian and Belgian cable businesses (UPC Norge AS and UPC Belgium respectively) in 2005; the former was sold to a European private equity firm for about $540 million and the latter went to Belgian cable operator Telenet Group Holding for $245 million. LGI also sold its French cable subsidiary UPC France to

Cinven in a 2006 deal valued at more than $1.5 billion.

The company's 2005 acquisitions included Swiss cable firm Cablecom ($2.2 billion) and Romanian telecommunications provider Astral Telecom. It also bought out Walt Disney's stake in IPS Multicanal which operated seven television channels in Spain and Portugal.

LGI expanded in Japan during 2008 when subsidiary J:COM acquired cable TV and Internet services provider Mediatti. The company was also active in Belgium where its Telenet subsidiary acquired cable TV assets from a handful of municipalities around the country.

EXECUTIVES

Vice Chairman President and CEO, Michael T. (Mike) Fries, age 53, $2,115,000 total compensation

EVP and Co-CFO, Charles H. R. (Charlie) Bracken, age 50, $1,037,303 total compensation

CEO Central Europe Group, Eric J. Tveter, age 57

EVP General Counsel and Secretary, Bryan H. Hall, age 53

CEO Unitymedia, Lutz Schüler, age 48

EVP and CTO, Balan Nair, age 49, $1,057,500 total compensation

CEO Ziggo BV, Baptiest Coopmans, age 51

EVP and Chief Commercial Officer, Diederik Karsten, age 59, $889,402 total compensation

Managing Director and CIO, Veenod Kurup, age 52

CEO Virgin Media, Tom Mockridge

President and COO Latin American and Caribbean Operations, Betzalel Kenigsztein

CEO Telenet Group Holding NV, John Porter

Chairman, John C. Malone, age 75

Auditors: KPMG LLP

LOCATIONS

HQ: Liberty Global plc
Griffin House, 161 Hammersmith Rd, London 80112
Phone: (44) 208 483 6449
Web: www.lgi.com

2014 Sales

	$ mil.	% of total
Europe operation divisions		
U.K	6,941	38
Germany	2,711	15
Belgium	2,279	12
Switzerland	1,414	8
The Netherlands	1,498	8
Ireland	468	3
Poland	469	3
Austria	431	2
Hungary	310	2
The Czech Republic	221	1
Romania	173	1
Slovakia	74	0
Other	3	0
Chile	898	5
Puerto Rico	306	2
Adjustments	45	0
Total	**18,248**	**100**

PRODUCTS/OPERATIONS

2014 Sales

	% of total
Subscription	
Video	36
Broadband Internet	26
Telephony	18
Mobile subscription revenue	6
B2B revenue	8
Other revenue	6
Total	**100**

COMPETITORS

AAPT	Orange
BBC	PCCW Ltd.
BT	PrimaCom
CANAL+	SES Group
Cableuropa	Sky Network Television
Central European Media	Sky plc
DNA Ltd.	Spark New Zealand
Deutsche Telekom	Swisscom
Elisa Corporation	TF1
Eutelsat	Tele2
ITV	Telecomunicaciones de
KPN	Chile
Kabel Deutschland	Telefnica
M6	Telekom Austria
Net Servi§os de	Telenor
Comunica§e	TeliaSonera
Optus	

HISTORICAL FINANCIALS
Company Type: Public

Income Statement
FYE: December 31

	REVENUE ($ mil.)	NET INCOME ($ mil.)	NET PROFIT MARGIN	EMPLOYEES
12/15	18,280	(1,152)	—	37,000
12/14	18,248	(695)	—	38,000
12/13	14,474	(963)	—	35,000
12/12	10,310	322	3.1%	22,000
12/11	9,510	(772)	—	22,000
Annual Growth	**17.7%**	**—**		**13.9%**

2015 Year-End Financials

Debt ratio: 69.3%	No. of shares (mil.): 891
Return on equity: (-9.0%)	Dividends
Cash ($ mil.): 982	Yield: —
Current ratio: 0.37	Payout: —
Long-term debt ($ mil.): 44,519	Market value ($ mil.): 36,335

	STOCK PRICE ($) FY Close	P/E High/Low	PER SHARE ($) Earnings	Dividends	Book Value
12/15	40.77	— —	(1.32)	0.00	11.95
12/14	48.31	— —	(0.87)	0.00	16.50
12/13	84.32	— —	(1.44)	0.00	15.25
12/12	58.75	98 67	0.61	0.00	4.27
12/11	39.52	— —	(1.47)	0.00	5.10
Annual Growth	**0.8%**	**— —**	**—**	**—**	**23.7%**

Linde AG (Germany, Fed. Rep.)

Linde's business is lighter than air. With operations in more than 100 countries Linde is one of the leading gases and engineering companies in the world. The company runs two core operating segments: Gases which maintains four product areas of Bulk Cylinder On-site and Healthcare gases; and Engineering. The latter builds process plants for companies in the petrochemical pharmaceutical and gas manufacturing industries. Founded by fridge magnate Carl von Linde in 1895 the company bears his name. In late 2016 the company agreed to be acquired by US-based rival Praxair for $35.1 billion.

Operations

Gases is by far the larger of the two core units racking up some 85% of revenue. It is divided into three regional segments: EMEA (Europe Middle East and Africa) the Asia-Pacific region and the Americas. The segment produces compressed and liquefied gases for use in a number of industries including energy steel chemical food glass and electronics. Its Heathcare business which is growing strongly globally works in fields such as MRI imaging to which Linde supplies essential liquid helium and cryogenics.

Engineering (14% of revenue) focuses on sectors like natural gas plants hydrogen plants air separation and synthesis gas plants.

A small third division (1% of sales) the logistics services company Gist provides logistics and supply chain services to a broad range of commercial and industrial sectors including electronics grocery retail and gas.

Geographic Reach

The Gases segment has five cross-regional Global Governance Centers which establish and enforce best practice across the company's many regions and operations. The Gases segment's largest region is EMEA at 39% of revenue. The Americas and Asia/Pacific bring in 34% and 27% respectively but as a share of revenue the Americas region is growing the fastest. In 2015 Linde rolled out its Voice of the Customer platform which is a customer-engagement program to fifteen countries around the world (with more in the pipeline).

Financial Performance

Linde recorded steady 5% revenue growth to euro 17944 million in 2015 despite difficult external conditions much in line with recent trends (growth is lower but still positive after taking unfavorable exchange rate effects into account). The Gases segment recorded year-on-year growth of 8% to euro 15168 million although growth was weighted almost entirely towards the Americas region which saw a 20% increase in sales thanks to a strong performance in the Healthcare gases sector. Growth of 1% in the Asia-Pacific region was mostly due to the acquisition of Wesfarmers Kleenheat Gas in February 2015 which contributed euro 86 million to the headline take. Revenue growth in EMEA the largest region by revenue at 39% was flat.

The Engineering segment bore the brunt of the oil-price crash in 2015 and a sharp fall in demand for new oil and gas plants saw revenue for the year drop 16.5% to euro 2594 million (from euro 3106 million in 2014). The sharpest fall came in the Asia-Pacific region which saw revenue fall nearly 60% from euro 1131 million to euro 459 million on prior year. This was counterbalanced to an extent by a 20% rise in North American revenue to euro 998 million.

Net income after tax rose modestly in 2015 from euro 1102 million to euro 1149 million. This 4% rise is attributable to the rise in total revenue.

Cash flow from operating activities jumped 20% to euro 3593 million in 2015 outpacing the rise in net income. Part of this was due to an exceptional cost of euro 300 million in 2014 but even accounting for this the increase was notable.

Strategy

Linde's growth strategy is multi-faceted. Dealing with the sudden change in the fortunes of the oil industry has been perhaps Linde's biggest difficulty in 2014-16. It views the oil price crash as a mixed blessing: it could lower prices for secondary industries and stimulate economic growth or a sustained low could trigger bankruptcies. So far the Engineering segment has felt the negative effects more strongly than Gases. Linde is aiming to limit damage by making use of the advantages of a low oil price by improving execution processes in preparation for the next upswing whenever it may arrive.

The company is embracing the move towards green energy solutions and plays a leading role in the development of hydrogen technologies. It participates in the H2 Mobility Initiative a joint venture with five other partners that aims to build 400 hydrogen filling stations in Germany by 2023.

Linde is also working on processes that convert energy from renewables into gas so it can be stored more easily - a big hurdle in the way of green uptake is the difficulty in storing energy generated by renewable means.

The company also sees Healthcare as an opportunity for growth as witnessed in the jump in revenue in Linde's Healthcare gases division in 2015.

Linde views joint enterprises and the acquisition of small and medium-sized businesses as a means to achieve greater closeness to its target markets. To this end it acquired American HomePatient a respiratory therapy specialist and spent a total of euro 120 million on acquisitions and financial assets in 2015.

Mergers and Acquisitions

Linde acquired American HomePatient in January 2016 to expand its medical gas business in the US; Linde is looking to capitalize on the strong growth in this area in 2015. HomePatient is a specialist in respiratory therapy and owns 220 branches in 38 US states and operates mostly on the east coast. It generated euro 260 million in 2015.

It also acquired the LPG business of Wesfarmers Kleenheat Gas an Australian gas producer in a deal worth euro 53 million with a view to expand its LPG business on the east coast of Australia.

HISTORY

German engineer Karl von Linde perfected the ammonia-compression refrigeration machine in 1876. For the first time ice could be produced commercially instead of being cut in blocks from lakes. In 1879 Gesellschaft fur Linde's Eismaschinen was founded to sell the machines. Its first customers were brewers who wanted to make beer in the summer; the company later designed a refrigerator for the home.

Von Linde granted technology licenses to foreign firms but many licensees couldn't create working systems. Von Linde bought his patents back and in 1885 he set up his first affiliate outside of Germany the Linde British Refrigeration Company which built a London ice factory.

A decade later Von Linde a pioneer in cryogenics patented a process for the liquefaction of air — he had discovered the means to mass produce liquid oxygen. At the same time a similar process was developed by a Frenchman George Claude. To beat his rival Von Linde built an oxygen factory near Munich in 1902 and set up Linde Air Products (now Praxair) in the US in 1907.

After Germany's defeat in WWI the overseas businesses were seized. In the 1920s Linde's Eismaschinen bought German engine manufacturers including Guldner-Motoren-Gesellschaftin (1929). Von Linde died in 1934 at the age of 92. Then came WWII and in the aftermath the company again lost its industrial rights and investments overseas. (In the US Air Products had supplied oxygen to Allied fighter pilots.)

The recovering company launched Hydrocar the first platform truck with a hydrostatic drive in 1955. In 1958 Guldner began making forklift trucks and hydraulic equipment.

Renamed Linde AG in 1965 the firm won its first industrial construction contract to build a petrochemical plant. Switching gears Linde sold its home appliances business to AEG in 1967 and in 1969 Guldner stopped building tractors and diesel engines in favor of materials handling equipment and hydraulics. The forklift operations expanded further with the acquisition of SE Fahrzeugwerke (now STILL) in 1973.

Linde established branches to make industrial gases in Brazil and Australia (1974) and bought forklift manufacturers: Fenwick in France (1984); UK firm Lansing (1989); and a 51% stake in Italy's FIAT OM Carrelli Elevatori (1992). In 1992 it also increased its holding in Hoek's Machine-en Zuurstoffabriek (aka Hoek Loos) the Netherland's largest industrial gases supplier to 60%. Other major acquisitions followed including Italian supplier Caracciolossigeno (1994) Czech gases firm Technoplyn (1995) and US engineering firm ProQuip (1996).

The company also built up its lines of refrigerated cases. It had taken a stake in CRIOSBANC an Italian manufacturer in 1992 (buying the rest in 1998). Linde acquired UK supplier Radford Retail Systems in 1997 and the next year gained controlling stakes in Brazilian supplier Seral do Brasil and in European distributor Chief Group.

In 1998 Linde also bought Thyssen Krupp Stahl's air separation plants in Duisburg-Ruhrort. A year later Linde reorganized its gases division as a separate operating company (Linde Technische Gase) and in 2000 it acquired Swedish industrial gases giant AGA in a deal that made Linde the world's #4 gas supplier. That year after abandoning plans to take over rival Messer Griesheim's gas operations Linde inked a deal with Japan's Komatsu Forklift for global collaboration. The demise of the Messer Griesheim merger led Linde to restructure its gas and engineering business segment and its refrigeration operations in 2001.

In 2004 Linde sold its refrigeration equipment and cooling systems business to Carrier (a subsidiary of United Technologies Corporation) for $400 million.

Linde became the world's largest gas manufacturer ahead of France's L'Air Liquide in the mid-2000s after it acquired UK gas producer BOC Group. Following the BOC acquisition Linde separated its material handling division and sold it to Kohlberg Kravis Roberts and Goldman Sachs Capital Partners for about $5 billion.

EXECUTIVES

CEO, Aldo Belloni, age 66, $720,000 total compensation

Member Executive Board, Sanjiv Lamba, age 53

Member Executive Board; CFO, Georg Denoke, age 51, $564,000 total compensation

Member Executive Board, Thomas Blades

Second Deputy Chairman, Michael Diekmann, age 62

Deputy Chairman, Hans-Dieter Katte

Chairman, Wolfgang Reitzle

Auditors: KPMG AG

LOCATIONS

HQ: Linde AG (Germany, Fed. Rep.)
Klosterhofstrasse 1, Munich, Bavaria 80331
Phone: (49) 89 35757 01   Fax: (49) 89 35757 1398
Web: www.linde.com

PRODUCTS/OPERATIONS

2015 Sales

	% of total
Gases	
EMEA	33
Americas	29
Asia-Pacific	23
Engineering	14
Other	1
Total	**100**

COMPETITORS

Air Products	L'Air Liquide
Fluor	Praxair
GEA Group	

HISTORICAL FINANCIALS

Company Type: Public

Income Statement

FYE: December 31

	REVENUE ($ mil.)	NET INCOME ($ mil.)	NET PROFIT MARGIN	EMPLOYEES
12/15	19,544	1,251	6.4%	64,538
12/14	20,720	1,339	6.5%	65,591
12/13	22,929	1,813	7.9%	63,487
12/12	20,139	1,647	8.2%	61,965
12/11	17,832	1,518	8.5%	50,417
Annual Growth	2.3%	(4.7%)	—	6.4%

2015 Year-End Financials

Debt ratio: 29.2%	No. of shares (mil.): 185
Return on equity: 8.2%	Dividends
Cash ($ mil.): 1,543	Yield: 1.6%
Current ratio: 0.96	Payout: 3.5%
Long-term debt ($ mil.): 9,214	Market value ($ mil.): 2,678

	STOCK PRICE ($) FY Close	P/E High/Low		PER SHARE ($) Earnings	Dividends	Book Value
12/15	14.43	3	2	6.73	0.24	85.53
12/14	18.46	3	3	7.18	0.28	87.78
12/13	21.00	3	3	9.75	0.24	94.70
12/12	17.69	3	2	9.19	0.22	93.19
12/11	14.91	2	2	8.82	0.19	87.74
Annual Growth	(0.8%)	—	—	(6.5%)	6.4%	(0.6%)

Lixil Group Corp

When opportunity knocks in Japan it's probably knocking on a LIXIL door. The company is a leading supplier of housing and building materials in Japan. Through about 10 subsidiaries it provides such products as doors housing sashes storm shutters ceramic siding bathroom units and tile and insulated panels as well as security systems. It also supplies storefronts for commercial buildings as well as skylights steel doors and customized store facades and shutters. LIXIL Group works with distributors and has sales offices throughout Japan. Other operations include a real estate brokerage franchise a chain of do-it-yourself stores and home services including inspections and warranties.

Operations

LIXIL manufactures and sells a wide range of products related to housing living and towns from windows and interior/exterior building materials tiles and entrance doors to kitchens bathrooms restrooms and other plumbing equipment. It also supplies fabrics and other interior products to office buildings commercial facilities stations and other public facilities and spaces.

Financial Performance

LIXIL experienced a 3% bump in revenues from 2014 to 2015 primarily due to increased sales from its distribution and retail business. It also generated additional revenue from Asia and from a previous acquisition it made.

Mergers and Acquisitions

The company has achieved revenue growth through the help of acquisitions. In 2013 LIXIL purchased SD Americas Holding Corp. the parent company of American Standard Brands (ASB) for $542 million. ASB is a leading North American manufacturer of a wide range of high quality kitchen and bath products. The deal enhanced LIXIL's core offerings and significantly improved its position in the North American market.

EXECUTIVES

President and CEO, Yoshiaki Fujimori, age 65
COO, Kinya Seto, age 56
EVP, Takashi Tsutsui
EVP, Yosuke Yagi
EVP, Sachio Matsumoto
Chairman, Yoichiro Ushioda
Auditors: Deloitte Touche Tohmatsu LLC

LOCATIONS

HQ: Lixil Group Corp
2-1-1 Ojima, Koto-ku, Tokyo 136-8535
Phone: (81) 3 3638 9300
Web: www.lixil-group.co.jp

2015 Sales

	% of total
Domestic	76
Overseas	
North America	9
Greater China	5
Europe	3
Middle East	2
Vietnam	1
Korea	1
Thailand	1
Other Asian countries	1
Others	1
Total	**100**

PRODUCTS/OPERATIONS

2015 Sales

	% of total
Overseas	23
Home center sales	12
Housing sashes and related products	12
Exterior	7
Building sashes and shutters	7
Sanitary ware	6
Kitchens	6
Bathroom units	5
Wooden interior furnishing materials	3
Washstand cabinet units	2
Exterior wall materials for houses	2
Tiles	2
Interior fabric	2
Housing structures and precut woods	2
Other	9
Total	**100**

Selected Subsidiaries

CLASSIS Corporation (real estate)
HIVIC (wood manufacturing and distribution)
JIO Corporation (home insurance)
Kawashima Selkon Textiles (fabric manufacturer)
LIXIL ERA Japan (brokerage)
LIXIL Group Finance (financial services)
LIXIL Housing Research Institute (homebuilding franchise chain)
LIXIL Realty (real estate services)
LIXIL Viva (operates Viva Home and Super Viva Home retail chains)

COMPETITORS

Andersen Corporation	Sanwa Shutter
Installux	YKK
Nippon Sheet Glass	

HISTORICAL FINANCIALS

Company Type: Public

Income Statement

FYE: March 31

	REVENUE ($ mil.)	NET INCOME ($ mil.)	NET PROFIT MARGIN	EMPLOYEES
03/16	16,834	(228)	—	73,580
03/15	14,214	257	1.8%	66,807
03/14	15,778	433	2.7%	51,419
03/13	15,265	226	1.5%	45,602
03/12	15,742	22	0.1%	48,163
Annual Growth	1.7%	—	—	11.2%

2016 Year-End Financials

Debt ratio: 0.3%
Return on equity: (-4.6%)
Cash ($ mil.): 1,154
Current ratio: 1.03
Long-term debt ($ mil.): 4,464

No. of shares (mil.): 286
Dividends
  Yield: 2.3%
  Payout: —
Market value ($ mil.): 11,719

	STOCK PRICE ($) FY Close	P/E High/Low	PER SHARE ($) Earnings	Dividends	Book Value
03/16	40.85	— —	(0.80)	0.98	16.29
03/15	47.52	0 0	0.87	1.09	15.54
03/14	55.07	— —	1.48	0.89	20.86
03/13	39.89	— —	0.78	0.00	20.71
03/12	42.06	— —	0.08	0.00	22.60
Annual Growth	(0.7%)	— —	—	—	(7.9%)

Lloyds Bank plc

LOCATIONS

HQ: Lloyds Bank plc
25 Gresham Street, London EC2V 7HN
Phone:
Web: www.lloydsbankinggroup.com

HISTORICAL FINANCIALS

Company Type: Public

Income Statement

FYE: December 31

	REVENUE ($ mil.)	NET INCOME ($ mil.)	NET PROFIT MARGIN	EMPLOYEES
12/15	37,496	982	2.6%	85,703
12/14	42,565	2,778	6.5%	95,088
Annual Growth	(11.9%)	(64.6%)	—	(9.9%)

2015 Year-End Financials

Debt ratio: —
Return on equity: 1.3%
Cash ($ mil.): 87,603
Current ratio: —
Long-term debt ($ mil.): —

No. of shares (mil.): 1,574
Dividends
  Yield: —
  Payout: —
Market value ($ mil.): —

	STOCK PRICE ($) FY Close	P/E High/Low	PER SHARE ($) Earnings	Dividends	Book Value
12/15	0.00	— —	(0.00)	0.00	44.21
12/14	0.00	— —	(0.00)	0.00	48.37
/0.00	—	—	(0.00)	0.00	(0.00)
Annual Growth	—	— —	—	—	—

Lloyds Banking Group Plc

Auditors: PricewaterhouseCoopers LLP

LOCATIONS

HQ: Lloyds Banking Group Plc
25 Gresham Street, 5th Floor, London EC2V 7HN
Phone: (44) 20 7356 1274   **Fax:** (44) 20 7356 1808
Web: www.lloydsbankinggroup.com

HISTORICAL FINANCIALS

Company Type: Public

Income Statement

FYE: December 31

	ASSETS ($ mil.)	NET INCOME ($ mil.)	INCOME AS % OF ASSETS	EMPLOYEES
12/15	1,195,467	1,274	0.1%	75,306
12/14	1,334,512	2,204	0.2%	84,490
12/13	1,399,784	(1,384)	—	97,869
12/12	1,490,254	(2,300)	—	113,617
12/11	1,499,351	(696)	—	120,449
Annual Growth	(5.5%)	—	—	(11.1%)

2015 Year-End Financials

Return on assets: 0.1%
Return on equity: 1.8%
Long-term debt ($ mil.): —
No. of shares (mil.): —
Sales ($ mil.): 45,775

Dividends
  Yield: 2.1%
  Payout: 505.6%
Market value ($ mil.): —

	STOCK PRICE ($) FY Close	P/E High/Low	PER SHARE ($) Earnings	Dividends	Book Value
12/15	4.36	667521	0.01	0.09	0.97
12/14	4.64	322264	0.02	0.06	1.06
12/13	5.32	— —	(0.02)	0.07	0.90
12/12	3.20	— —	(0.03)	0.06	1.01
12/11	1.57	— —	(0.01)	0.00	1.03
Annual Growth	29.1%	— —	—	—	(1.6%)

Loblaw Companies Ltd

Auditors: KPMG LLP

LOCATIONS

HQ: Loblaw Companies Ltd
22 St. Clair Avenue East, Toronto, Ontario M4T 2S7
Phone: 416 490-2699   **Fax:** 416 490-2771
Web: www.loblaw.ca

HISTORICAL FINANCIALS

Company Type: Public

Income Statement

FYE: January 2

	REVENUE ($ mil.)	NET INCOME ($ mil.)	NET PROFIT MARGIN	EMPLOYEES
01/16	32,765	449	1.4%	196,000
01/15*	36,528	45	0.1%	195,000
12/13	30,394	591	1.9%	138,000
12/12	31,776	653	2.1%	134,000
12/11	30,634	753	2.5%	135,000
Annual Growth	1.7%	(12.1%)	—	9.8%

*Fiscal year change

2016 Year-End Financials

Debt ratio: 24.8%
Return on equity: 4.8%
Cash ($ mil.): 734
Current ratio: 1.36
Long-term debt ($ mil.): 7,227

No. of shares (mil.): 409
Dividends
  Yield: 0.0%
  Payout: 65.8%
Market value ($ mil.): 19,343

	STOCK PRICE ($) FY Close	P/E High/Low	PER SHARE ($) Earnings	Dividends	Book Value
01/16	47.18	35 28	1.09	0.72	23.15
01/15*	53.87	384254	0.12	0.84	26.56
12/13	39.43	21 16	2.08	0.88	23.34
12/12	41.20	18 14	2.29	0.85	22.91
12/11	37.82	15 13	2.66	0.82	20.93
Annual Growth	5.7%	—	(20.0%)	(3.4%)	2.6%

*Fiscal year change

Lotte Shopping Co Ltd

Lotte Shopping's department stores offer more than the usual shopping experience. The company is a leading retailer in South Korea with some 30 department and discount stores across the nation. It owns one of the largest retail chains in the country with facilities that are part of vast retail complexes that often include cinemas shopping malls hotels theme parks and wedding halls. It also has a store in Moscow (opened in 2007). In China where Lotte Shopping is looking to grow its 2009 purchase of Times Ltd. an operator of 65 hypermarkets and supermarkets in east China boosted its retail presence there to about 75 stores. Lotte Shopping which was established in 1979 is looking to grow overseas.

To bolster its position in South Korea's retail arena Lotteshopping in February 2010 agreed to acquire three department stores more than a dozen large discout stores from its smaller rival GS Retail (owned by GS Holdings) for about $1.15 billion. Also the company plans to open another department store in South Korea in 2010 and a second department store in China in 2011. Lotteshopping in fall 2009 agreed to buy grocer Times Ltd. in a deal worth about $629 million thereby substantially expanding its retail footprint in China. Previous foreign acquisitions for the South Korea company include Makro Indonesia which operates about 20 outlets there.

EXECUTIVES

CEO, Lee Won Joon
Auditors: Samjong Accounting Corporation (A Member Firm of KPMG)

LOCATIONS

HQ: Lotte Shopping Co Ltd
  81 Namdaemun-ro Jung-gu, Seoul 100-721
Phone: (82) 2 771 2500 **Fax:** (82) 2 2118 2028
Web: www.lotteshopping.com

2015 Sales

	% of total
Domestic	91
China	5
Vietnam	1
Indonesia	3
Total	**100**

PRODUCTS/OPERATIONS

2015 Sales

	% of total
Department stores	28
Discount stores	28
Consumer electronics retail	13
Convenience stores	11
Finance business	6
Others	14
Total	**100**

2015 Sales

	% of total
Sales of merchandise	83
Revenue of card business	5
Other operating revenue	12
Total	**100**

COMPETITORS

Bailian Group	Tesco
Costco Wholesale	WuMart
GS Holdings	

HISTORICAL FINANCIALS

Company Type: Public

Income Statement FYE: December 31

	REVENUE ($ mil.)	NET INCOME ($ mil.)	NET PROFIT MARGIN	EMPLOYEES
12/15	24,757	(325)	—	26,030
12/14	25,682	481	1.9%	27,880
12/13	26,826	749	2.8%	26,943
12/12	23,455	1,011	4.3%	24,976
12/11	19,205	804	4.2%	24,801
Annual Growth	6.6%	—	—	1.2%

2015 Year-End Financials

Debt ratio: 0.0%
Return on equity: (-2.3%)
Cash ($ mil.): 1,488
Current ratio: 1.34
Long-term debt ($ mil.): 8,343
No. of shares (mil.): 29
Dividends
  Yield: —
  Payout: —
Market value ($ mil.): —

LVMH Moet Hennessy Louis Vuitton

LVMH Moët Hennessy Louis Vuitton is the world's largest luxury goods company with brands that are bywords for the good life and everything showy. LVMH makes wines and spirits (Dom Perignon Moët & Chandon Veuve Clicquot and Hennessy) perfumes (Christian Dior Guerlain and Givenchy) cosmetics (Nude Fresh and Benefit) fashion and leather goods (Donna Karan Givenchy Kenzo and Louis Vuitton) and watches and jewelry (TAG Heuer Bulgari). LVMH's selective retail division includes Sephora cosmetics stores Le Bon Marche Paris department stores and 61% of DFS Group (duty-free shops). Chairman Bernard Arnault the richest man in France and his family own about 46% of LVMH through Groupe Arnault. In 2016 the company agreed to sell its majority stake in Donna Karan International to G-III Apparel Group.

Operations
LVMH operates through six groups: Fashion & Leather Goods Wine & Spirits Perfumes & Cosmetics Watches & Jewelry Selective Retailing and other activities. Fashion & Leather Goods is the largest segment accounting for some 35% of revenue. Selective Retailing and other activities together generate 30%.

Geographic Reach
The Paris-based luxury powerhouse operates more than 3800 stores across Asia Europe and North America with recent growth in store numbers focused mainly in Asia. While more than a third of its stores are in Europe Asia is the company's single largest market accounting for more than 35% of sales. LVMH rings up about 30% of its sales in Europe (including France with 10%). The US represents more than a quarter of revenue.

Financial Performance
Note: Growth rates may differ after conversion to US Dollars.

After a period of relatively flat sales during the global financial crisis LVMH has experienced six consecutive years of revenue growth. Indeed sales hit euro 35.7 billion in 2015 a 16% increase in revenue versus 2014 and an all-time record for the luxury goods company. Net profits fell year on year in 2015 largely due to an exceptional gain in 2014 to euro 3.6 billion in 2015 down 37%. Like its customers the company is cash rich reporting euro 3.7 billion in free cash flow from operations in 2015.

Organic revenue growth was 6% that year with an additional 10% increase a result of favorable currency exchange rates. The five main business groups all saw significant improvements on prior year. The largest chunk of revenue growth was in the Selective Retailing business which expanded by euro 1.7 billion to euro 11.2 billion due to among other things impressive performance in the Middle East and North America. Fashion & Leather Goods the largest business by revenue at euro 12.4 billion in 2015 also grew strongly while Watches & Jewelry recorded the organization's fastest growth at 19%.

Regionally while slowing growth in the Chinese middle class has seen Asia fall as a percentage of total revenue it remains the company's largest market at more than 35% ahead of the United States at 26%.

Strategy
With the market for luxury goods in shaping up well LVMH is flush with cash for acquisitions and organic growth. Indeed the company is growing its stores base in all of its markets bar Japan where the number of stores fell from 412 in 2014 to 407 in 2015; in total LVMH added 152 stores in 2015. China is a huge emerging market for luxury goods including wines & spirits and a pillar of growth for the French company.

The company has been focusing on controlling as much of its distribution across its 70 brands as possible. LVMH has more than 3800 retail outlets (more than 85% are outside France). Nearly half belong to its Selective Retailing business which consists primarily of Sephora cosmetics stores. About 40% are fashion and leather goods shops led by Louis Vuitton and also include Fendi boutiques and hundreds of other shops under the Celine Givenchy Donna Karan Thomas Pink Pucci and Marc Jacobs brands among others. LVMH's namesake Louis Vuitton brand as well as Fendi and Bulgari have strengthened despite adverse global economic conditions.

LVMH has put innovation in digital at the forefront of its strategy and recognizes the need to create a digital experience that can match that of its luxurious stores. It is also tightening the link between the physical and digital spheres with its Sephora subsidiary leading the way with mobile terminals and other features.

Mergers and Acquisitions
LVMH has agreed to acquire Germany luxury luggage brand Rimowa for around euro 640 million. Bernard Arnault's son Alexandre will become co-chief director. The acquisition increases LVHM's exposure to the growing tourism market.

HISTORY

Woodworker Louis Vuitton started his Paris career packing dresses for French Empress Eugenie. He later designed new types of luggage and in 1854 he opened a store to sell his designs. In 1896 Vuitton introduced the LV monogram fabric that the company still uses. By 1900 Louis Vuitton had stores in the US and England and by WWI Louis' son Georges had the world's largest retail store for travel goods.

Henry Racamier a former steel executive who had married into the Vuitton family took charge in 1977 repositioning the company's goods from esoteric status symbols to designer must-haves. Sales soared from $20 million to nearly $2.5 billion within a decade. Concerned about being a takeover target Racamier merged Louis Vuitton in 1987 with Moët Hennessy (which made wines spirits and fragrances) and adopted the name LVMH Moët Hennessy Louis Vuitton.

Moët Hennessy had been formed through the 1971 merger of Moët et Chandon (the world's #1 champagne maker) and the Hennessy Cognac company (founded by Irish mercenary Richard Hennessy in 1765). Moët Hennessy acquired rights to Christian Dior fragrances in 1971.

Racamier tried to reverse the merger when disagreements with chairman Alain Chevalier arose. Racamier invited outside investor Bernard Arnault to increase his interest in the company. Arnault gained control of 43% of LVMH and became chairman in 1989. Chevalier stepped down but Racamier fought for control for another 18 months and then set up Orcofi a partner of cosmetics rival L'Oreal.

LVMH increased its fashion holdings with the purchases of the Givenchy Couture Group (1988) Christian Lacroix (1993) and Kenzo (1993). The company also acquired 55% of French media firm Desfosses International (1993) Celine fashions (1996) the Château d'Yquem winery (1996) and duty-free retailer DFS Group (1996). Next LVMH bought perfume chains Sephora (1997) and Marie-Jeanne Godard (1998). In 1998 LVMH integrated the Paris department store Le Bon Marche which was controlled by Arnault.

LVMH accumulated a 34% stake in Italian luxury goods maker Gucci in early 1999 and planned to buy all of it. Fellow French conglomerate Pinault-Printemps-Redoute (PPR) later thwarted LVMH by purchasing 42% of Gucci.

Through its LV Capital unit in 1999 LVMH began acquiring stakes in a host of luxury companies including a joint venture with fashion company Prada to buy 51% of design house Fendi (LVMH bought Prada's 25.5% stake for $265 million in November 2001). It has since upped its Fendi stake to about 70%. LVMH later added the Ebel Chaumet and TAG Heuer brands to its new watch division.

In early 2000 LVMH bought Miami Cruiseline Services which operates duty-free shops on cruise ships auction house L'Etude Tajan and 67% of Italian fashion house Emilio Pucci. The company later purchased 35% of French video game retailer Micromania and 51% of department store Samaritaine. In late 2000 LVMH acquired Gabrielle Studio which owns all Donna Karan licenses. In 2001 the company bought Donna Karan International.

LVMH bought in 2001 the Newton and MountAdam vineyards for about $45 million. It then began marketing De Beers diamond jewelry in a 50-50 joint venture with the diamond powerhouse. In March LVMH prompted the investigation of a Dutch court into the PPR-Gucci alliance. The company sold its stake in Gucci to PPR for $806.5 million in October.

In October 2002 LVMH ceased trading on the Brussels and Nasdaq exchanges to concentrate on its Euronext investors. In October 2003 the company sold Canard-Duchene to the Alain Thienot Group. LVMH shed several of the less productive of its 50 brands in 2003 including auction house Phillips de Pury & Luxemborg and fashion brand Michael Kors.

LVMH opened its biggest store —a four-story emporium on New York's Fifth Avenue —in Feb-ruary 2004. A few months later the company added whisky-maker Glenmorangie PLC to its subsidiary roster. LVMH also made its debut in the South African market in October 2004 opening its first sub-Saharan boutique in Johannesburg. Also during the year Bliss spas was sold off.

In early 2004 LVMH won a landmark lawsuit against Morgan Stanley alleging that the firm had used biased research in misstatements about the financial health of LVMH that caused damage to the company's image. The presiding Parisian court ordered Morgan Stanley to pay 100 million euros (about $38 million) in damages. Morgan Stanley appealed the ruling later that year.

In late 2005 LVMH opened its largest store to date on the Champs-Elysees in Paris and the De Beers brand was introduced in the US with stores in New York and Los Angeles. Also that year LVMH was the winning bidder for whisky maker Glenmorangie PLC for which it paid £300 million. On the sell side LVMH divested fashion design house Christian Lacroix SNC.

In May 2007 LVMH acquired a 55% stake in Chinese distillery Wenjun for an undisclosed amount. (Jiannanchun the distillery's previous owner retained a 45% stake in Wenjun.) In December 2007 the luxury goods firm acquired the French newspaper Les Echos from publisher Pearson. LVMH controls Les Echos' rival the financial daily La Tribune but has agreed to sell it. Group Les Echos deal includes the newspaper Web site business magazine Enjeux and other financial information services.

In late 2008 Sephora SA acquired a 45% stake in the Russian perfume and cosmetics chain Ile de Beaute. (The agreement which gave Sephora the option to become a majority shareholder allowed LVMH to up its share to 65% in mid-2011.) The firm acquired the luxury yacht-maker Royal Van Lent.

In August 2009 LVMH acquired 50% stakes in two French wine makers: privately-held Cheval Blanc; and La Tour du Pin owner of the Chateau Quinault l'Enclose estate.

In early 2010 LVMH acquired a 40% stake in Dondup an Italian apparel and denim brand for more than $43 million (or 30 million euros). Its plans are to expand Dondup's business internationally. Later in 2010 the company purchased a 70% stake in the Brazilian fragrance and cosmetics retailer Sack's. The acquisition estimated to be worth R$250 million is a move on LVMH's part to expand its Sephora beauty chain in Brazil one of the fastest-growing beauty markets in the world.

Adding to its vast portfolio of luxury brands in February 2011 LVMH acquired Ole Henriksen a leading luxury botanical skincare company founded and owned by its namesake. Later that same week LVMH bought a 70% stake in Nude Brands skin care as the company continues to acquire niche brands. The four-year-old line - described as "biocompatible luxury skin care" - was founded by Bryan Meehan and Ali Hewson wife of U2 front man Bono. In March LVMH fired Dior star designer John Galliano amid charges of anti-Semitism. In September LVMH completed its tender offer from Rome-based Bulgari acquiring about 98% of the shares.

EXECUTIVES

Chairman and CEO, Bernard Arnault, age 67
Group Managing Director, Antonio (Toni) Belloni, age 62
Director Strategy, Jean-Baptiste Voisin, age 49
Managing Director Groupe Arnault, Nicolas Bazire, age 59
Chairman and CEO Louis Vuitton, Michael Burke, age 59

Group EVP Human Resources and Synergies, Chantal Gaemperle
CFO, Jean-Jacques Guiony, age 55
CEO Sephora, Chris de Lapuente, age 51
CEO Moet Hennessy, Christophe Navarre
Chairman LVMH Investment Funds, Daniel Piette, age 71
Chairman and CEO LVMH Fashion Group, Pierre-Yves Roussel
Chairman and CEO DFS Group, Philippe Schaus, age 53
Vice Chairman, Pierre Gode, age 72
Auditors: ERNST & YOUNG et Autres

LOCATIONS

HQ: LVMH Moet Hennessy Louis Vuitton
  22, avenue Montaigne, Paris 75008
Phone: (33) 1 44 13 22 22   **Fax:** (33) 1 44 13 21 19
Web: www.lvmh.com

2015 Stores

	No.
Europe	
France	482
Other countries	1,012
Asia	
Japan	407
Other countries	951
US	732
Other regions	276
Total	**3,860**

2015 Sales

	% of total
Europe	
France	10
Other countries	18
Asia	
Japan	7
Other countries	27
US	26
Other regions	12
Total	**100**

PRODUCTS/OPERATIONS

2015 Sales

	% of total
Fashion & leather goods	35
Selective retailing	30
Wines & spirits	13
Perfumes & cosmetics	13
Watches & jewelry	9
Total	**100**

Selected Brands and Operations

Fashion and leather goods
  Berluti
  Celine
  Donna Karan
  Emilio Pucci
  Fendi
  Gabrielle Studio (Donna Karan label)
  Givenchy
  Kenzo
  Loewe
  Loro Piana
  Louis Vuitton
  Marc Jacobs
  Thomas Pink
Retailing
  DFS Group
  La Samaritaine
  Le Bon Marché
  Miami Cruiseline Services (duty-free shops)
  Sephora
Fragrances and cosmetics
  Aqua di Parma
  BeneFit
  Bliss
  Fresh
  Guerlain
  Kenzo Parfums
  Make Up For Ever
  Marc Jacobs Fragrances
  Nude skin care

Ole Henriksen
Parfums Christian Dior
Parfums Givenchy
Spirits and wines
  10 Cane
  Belvedere
  Canard-Duchêne
  Chandon Estates
  Château d' Yquem
  Dom Pérignon
  Hennessy
  Krug
  Mercier
  Moët & Chandon
  MountAdam
  Newton
  Ruinart
  Veuve Clicquot
Watches and jewelry
  Bulgari
  Chaumet
  De Beers
  Ebel
  Fred
  Omas
  TAG Heuer
  Zenith
Media (Desfosses International Group)
  Investir
  La Tribune
  Les Echos
  Radio Classique
Other
  Royal van Lent (luxury yachts)

COMPETITORS

Armani	Kirin Holdings Company
Asprey	L' Oreal
Avon	MacAndrews & Forbes
Bacardi	Oscar de la Renta
Brown-Forman	Patek Philippe
Calvin Klein	Prada
Chanel	Puig
Douglas Holding	Ralph Lauren
E. & J. Gallo	Richemont
Escada	Rolex
Estee Lauder	Remy Cointreau
Galeries Lafayette	Shiseido
Gianni Versace	Swatch
Harry Winston	Taittinger
Hermès	Tiffany & Co.
Hugo Boss	Unilever
Inditex	Vera Wang
Kering	

HISTORICAL FINANCIALS
Company Type: Public

Income Statement
FYE: December 31

	REVENUE ($ mil.)	NET INCOME ($ mil.)	NET PROFIT MARGIN	EMPLOYEES
12/15	38,831	3,891	10.0%	125,346
12/14	37,234	6,865	18.4%	121,289
12/13	40,130	4,730	11.8%	114,635
12/12	37,041	4,513	12.2%	106,348
12/11	30,601	3,964	13.0%	97,559
Annual Growth	6.1%	(0.5%)	—	6.5%

2015 Year-End Financials

Debt ratio: 15.6%
Return on equity: 15.5%
Cash ($ mil.): 3,914
Current ratio: 1.49
Long-term debt ($ mil.): 4,913
No. of shares (mil.): 502
Dividends
  Yield: 12.9%
  Payout: 50.4%
Market value ($ mil.): 15,836

	STOCK PRICE ($) FY Close	P/E High/Low		PER SHARE ($) Earnings	Dividends	Book Value
12/15	31.50	5	4	7.71	4.08	52.73
12/14	34.44	3	3	13.63	0.83	52.71
12/13	36.60	6	5	9.40	0.79	73.44
12/12	37.69	5	4	8.99	0.76	64.75
12/11	28.10	5	4	8.06	0.58	58.29
Annual Growth	2.9%	—	—	(1.1%)	63.1%	(2.5%)

LyondellBasell Industries NV

Auditors: PricewaterhouseCoopers LLP

LOCATIONS

HQ: LyondellBasell Industries NV
  Delftseplein 27E, Rotterdam 3013 AA
Phone: (31) 10 275 5500
Web: www.lyondellbasell.com

HISTORICAL FINANCIALS
Company Type: Public

Income Statement
FYE: December 31

	REVENUE ($ mil.)	NET INCOME ($ mil.)	NET PROFIT MARGIN	EMPLOYEES
12/16	29,183	3,836	13.1%	13,000
12/15	32,735	4,476	13.7%	13,000
12/14	45,608	4,174	9.2%	13,100
12/13	44,062	3,857	8.8%	13,300
12/12	45,352	2,848	6.3%	13,500
Annual Growth	(10.4%)	7.7%	—	(0.9%)

2016 Year-End Financials

Debt ratio: 38.3%
Return on equity: 60.7%
Cash ($ mil.): 875
Current ratio: 2.11
Long-term debt ($ mil.): 8,385
No. of shares (mil.): 404
Dividends
  Yield: 0.0%
  Payout: 36.4%
Market value ($ mil.): 34,659

	STOCK PRICE ($) FY Close	P/E High/Low		PER SHARE ($) Earnings	Dividends	Book Value
12/16	85.78	10	8	9.13	3.33	14.97
12/15	86.90	11	8	9.59	3.04	14.88
12/14	79.39	14	9	7.99	2.70	17.07
12/13	80.28	12	8	6.75	2.00	22.74
12/12	57.09	11	7	4.92	4.20	19.47
Annual Growth	10.7%	—	—	16.7%	(5.6%)	(6.4%)

Macquarie Group Ltd

One of the few domestically owned investment banks in the Land Down Under Macquarie Group does business at home in Australia and beyond. Boasting assets of nearly A$190 billion ($145 billion) the holding company for Macquarie Bank and other subsidiaries operates an investment banking practice that performs financing trading strategic advisory equities research and other serv-ices for corporate and government clients. Other operations include asset management retail banking and lending and wealth management. Through its Macquarie Energy arm the company participates in the international private-equity market focusing on the energy sector. Founded in 1969 Macquarie Group has offices in nearly 30 countries.

OperationsMacquarie Group operates six divisions. This includes three "annuity style" businesses (that generated nearly 70% of overall profit in fiscal 2015 ended March): Macquarie Asset Management (35% of profit) or MAM which offers infrastructure and real asset management securities investment management and other fund and equity investment services; Corporate and Asset Finance (27% of profit) or CAF which provides specialty asset finance for corporations and and real estate credit lending; and Banking and Financial Services (7% of profit) or BFS which provides personal and business banking and wealth management services. The other three "capital markets facing" business divisions include: the Macquarie Securities Group (1% of profit) which covers sales research equity capital markets execution and derivatives trading; Macquarie Capital (10% of profit) which provides corporate finance services such as M&A equity and debt capital markets and principal investments across six key industry groups and Commodities and Financial Markets (20% of profit) or CFM which provides risk and capital solutions across physical and financial markets.

The bank enjoys a diversified revenue base. It generated 41% of its revenue from interest and similar income during 2015 (ended March 31) while fees and commission income made up another 39%. The rest was made from non-recurring income sources such as net trading income (14% of revenue) and other operating income and charges (6%). It had a staff of more than 14000 at the end of FY2015.

Geographic Reach

The Sydney-based group generates over 35% of its operating income from customers in the Americas while Australia contributes another 30%. Macquarie generates the rest of its operating income from the Europe Middle East and Africa region (22%) and the Asia Pacific region (12%).

Financial Performance

Note: Growth rates may differ after conversion to US dollars. This analysis uses financials from the company's annual report.

Macquarie Group's revenues and profits have been rising each year since 2013. The company's revenue rose 22% to $A12.2 billion ($9.4 billion) in fiscal 2015 (ended March 31) mostly driven by 33% growth in its annuity-style businesses as MAM enjoyed an increase in base and performance fee income CAF's loan and lease volumes grew and as BFS' grew its Australian mortgage business lending and deposits volumes. The groups capital markets facing businesses grew 19% with Macquarie Capital generating higher fee income across all product classes (mostly M&A and debt capital markets) and increased investment sale gains and with CFM generating higher performance from its commodities business increased income across interest rates and foreign exchange platforms and increased fee income and debt capital markets activity in the US.

Higher revenue during FY2015 drove Macquarie Group's net income higher by 27% to A$1.6 billion ($1.2 billion). Its operating cash levels declined during the year with operations using A$2.4 billion ($1.9 billion) mostly due to unfavorable working capital changes mostly related to its net payments on trading portfolio assets and other financial assets/liabilities. StrategyMacquarie Group outlined its medium-term strategy in 2015 which listed several goals including: building its annuity-style businesses (such as asset and wealth management specialty financing and investment and retail banking services) and capital markets-facing businesses in a diversified way that produces steady returns in a range of market conditions; diversifying its businesses across different locations and with different service offerings to limit risk and create steady returns; continuing to leverage the group's deep expertise in its target sectors; acquire or grow into business lines that complement existing ones; promoting ideas and innovation for growth; and maintaining a strong balance sheet with capital levels above ordinary requirements. As part of its goals toward growing into complementary business lines Macquarie in August 2015 entered the US ETF market-making business adding to its market-making service lines already offered for ETFs domiciled in Asia and Europe.

The company in 2015 continued to boast its "deep knowledge of Asia-Pacific financial markets" and "deep expertise" that has led to market-leading positions in the resources and commodities energy financial institutions infrastructure and real estate sectors. Mergers and Acquisitions

In 2015 a subsidiary of Macquarie Bank Limited agreed to purchase an aircraft operating lease portfolio of 90 modern current-generation commercial passenger aircraft leased to 40 airlines from AWAS Aviation Capital Limited. The deal helped to grow its Corporate and Asset Finance (CAF) division specifically its Macquarie Aviation leasing business.

HISTORY

Company BackgroundMacquarie has made a slew of acquisitions in its past. It acquired several North America-based financial services companies including investment bank Fox-Pitt Kelton Cochran Caronia Waller. In 2010 Macquarie expanded upon its individual and institutional asset management business when it acquired US-based Delaware Investments. It also bought the Canadian investment dealing business of Blackmont Capital and rebranded it as Macquarie Private Wealth.

Two more US acquisitions were designed to enhance Macquarie Capital's advisory business. In 2010 Macquarie bought US-based specialist Presidio Partners which performs real estate advisory and capital raising advisory services. Macquarie also bought Los Angeles-based investment bank Regal Capital Advisors a specialist in strategic and financial advice for the gaming lodging and leisure industries. Overseas Macquarie acquired the cash equities sales and research business of German private bank Sal. Oppenheim Jr. & Cie. in 2010. The acquisition broadened Macquarie's European business bolstering its presence in several key markets. Macquarie is looking to buy trading and investment banking businesses in Europe.

The company has also used acquisitions to bolster its position in the energy and other non-traditional banking markets.

In 2009 it acquired Canadian boutique investment bank Tristone Capital which served the oil and gas industry. Macquarie also acquired the downstream natural gas trading operations of Constellation Energy. The company then combined that business with its Macquarie Cook Energy business to form Macquarie Energy a larger North American wholesale gas company. In 2010 Macquarie Energy acquired the wholesale electric marketing and trading portfolio of Integrys Energy Services in a deal that more than doubled Macquarie Energy's customer base and strengthened its position in key North American power markets. Also that year subsidiary Macquarie Aerospace agreed to purchase a portfolio of 53 aircraft from AIG unit International Lease Finance Corporation.

HISTORICAL FINANCIALS

Company Type: Public

Income Statement

FYE: March 31

	ASSETS ($ mil.)	NET INCOME ($ mil.)	INCOME AS % OF ASSETS	EMPLOYEES
03/16	151,431	1,587	1.0%	14,372
03/15	142,854	1,218	0.9%	14,085
03/14	142,035	1,167	0.8%	13,913
03/13	157,029	886	0.6%	13,663
03/12	159,857	759	0.5%	14,202
Annual Growth	(1.3%)	20.2%	—	0.3%

	STOCK PRICE ($) FY Close	P/E High/Low		PER SHARE ($) Earnings	Dividends	Book Value
03/16	49.69	11	7	4.62	2.64	36.33
03/15	58.79	12	8	3.68	2.54	34.07
03/14	53.40	14	9	3.41	0.00	32.82
03/13	38.72	16	10	2.56	0.00	34.96
03/12	30.22	18	10	2.11	0.00	33.44
Annual Growth	13.2%	—	—	21.7%	—	2.1%

Magna International Inc.

Through its various subsidiaries and divisions Magna International makes just about everything needed to put together a motor vehicle. Magna Steyr its largest division offers vehicle engineering and assembly. Magna's interior and exterior systems division makes trim lighting sealing systems instrument and door panels and sound insulation. Cosma International makes body and chassis systems. Magna Powertrain offers transaxles transmission systems and engine parts while Magna Mirrors makes mirrors and driver assistance products. Other Magna operations include Seating E-Car Systems Electronics Roof and Closures. Its geographic markets include North America Europe Africa and Asia.

OperationsThe company based in Ontario Canada operates segments along geographic lines to be more responsive to customers' needs. Its segments include North America (which generated 53% of Magna's total revenue in 2014) Europe (40% of revenue) Asia (5% of revenue) and Rest of World (2% of revenue). The "Rest of World" markets include developing regions such as Africa Asia Eastern Europe and South America. Magna boasts almost 320 manufacturing facilities and roughly 85 product development engineering and sales centers in nearly 30 countries. Magna follows a decentralized mode of operation meaning its businesses operate independently.

By product exterior and interior system sales generated 35% of Magna International's total revenue in 2014 while body systems and chassis system sales contributed another 22% to sales. The rest of its total revenue came from powertrain system sales (14% of total sales); complete vehicle assembly sales (8%); tooling engineering and other services (8%); vision and electronic system sales (7%) and closure system sales (6%).

Sales and Marketing

BMW Daimler Fiat/Chrysler Ford GM and VW accounted for approximately 83% of Magna's total sales in 2014.

Financial Performance

Magna has enjoyed sizable revenue and profit growth since 2009 as demand for new cars continues to strengthen around the world. The company's sales rose 5% to a record $36.6 billion during 2014 mostly thanks to business growth in North America with the launch of new programs and as light vehicle production in North America grew by 5% to 17 million units. Total sales were also helped by 18% sales growth in Asia driven by new program launches with Magna content (particularly in China) and higher light vehicle production in Asia. Revenue growth in 2014 drove Magna International's net income higher by 21% to a record $1.88 billion for the year. The company's operating cash levels climbed 9% to $2.79 billion during the year thanks to higher cash earnings.

Strategy

Magna International ranked as the world's second-largest parts supplier behind Robert Bosch GmbH and ahead of ZF as of mid-2015. To satisfy automakers' demand for more of a one-stop-shop in auto part manufacturing the company regularly expands its product lines and expertise through acquisitions of auto parts manufacturers.

That said it's also been selective on what auto part manufacturing businesses it wants to be in favoring more profitable business lines and "key areas" of the vehicle. In August 2015 for example Magna sold its interiors operations business including some 36 manufacturing facilities and 12000 employees to Grupo Antolin for $525 million. Magna International often uses strategic partnerships to grow or complement its product lines and extend its reach into new geographic markets. In 2015 subsidiary body and chassis maker Cosma International effectively expanded Magna's reach and product offerings to customers in fast-growing China after it formed a joint venture with Chongqing Xingqiaorui. Also in 2015 Magna International partnered with Argus Cyber Security to offer automotive electronic systems that featured Argus' intrusion prevention system service and cloud-based monitoring service designed to prevent cyber-attacks. In 2014 Magna formed a 50/50 joint venture with Tata AutoComp Systems to provide seating systems to the Indian commercial vehicle industry. Mergers and AcquisitionsIn July 2015 Magna International purchased German transmission manufacturer Getrag for $1.9 billion as part of its continued plan to expand its service and product lines for auto makers.

Company BackgroundMagna International has historically expanded its product lines through acquisitions of other auto parts manufacturers. In early 2011 Magna Seating acquired Germany-based Vogelsitze GmbH which made seats for buses and passenger trains. In 2012 Magna obtained Verwaltungs GmbH a maker of automotive vacuum engine and transmission pumps with two facilities in Germany and one in each of China and Bulgaria. Also in 2012 to strengthen its automotive pump operations Magna purchased the remaining 50% interest it didn't already own of STT Technologies which made transmission and engine related pumps for the North American market.

HISTORY

Company BackgroundMagna International is rooted in a tool and die shop founded by Frank Stronach and friend Tony Czapka in Ontario Canada in 1957. Austrian-born Stronach immigrated to Canada in 1954. By the end of 1957 the business called Multimatic had 10 employees. Multimatic delved into car parts when it landed a contract in 1960 to make sun visor brackets for a General Motors division in Canada.

To go public Multimatic underwent a reverse merger in 1969 with Magna Electronics a publicly traded maker of components for aerospace defense and industrial markets. (Stronach retained control of the company.) Annual sales reached $10 million that year. The company expanded its automotive operations during the early 1970s by adding more stamped and electronic components. Magna was renamed Magna International in 1973.

With sales increasing steadily among its auto parts businesses Magna sold its aerospace and defense business (now part of Heroux-Devtek) in 1981. The new Magna consisted of five distinct automotive divisions that made seat tracks door latches electronic components and other auto parts. During the 1980s the company expanded by adding factories and product lines. It also capitalized on car makers' penchant for outsourcing labor and bypassing unions. By 1987 when sales reached $1 billion the company was producing systems for every area of the automobile. Stronach didn't spend all his time on cars however; he owned race horses and restaurants. He had opened restaurants tried various publishing ventures (which failed) and even made an unsuccessful run for a Canadian parliament seat in 1988.

Aggressive expansion during the 1980s eventually caught up with the company and in 1989 Magna began to restructure selling assets to pay off its debt. The company also was bailed out in part by two of its principal customers –General Motors and Chrysler. Having recovered somewhat Magna began acquiring small auto parts companies in Europe in 1992.

Magna expanded its European presence with the purchase of Austria-based Steyr-Daimler-Puch in 1998 adding about $1 billion in annual sales. The deal steered Magna into the auto assembly business. Stronach also added Santa Anita Park to his holdings that year. In late 1999 the company's racetrack interests were spun off as Magna Entertainment with Magna retaining a 78% stake. Stronach's horse Red Bullet won the 2000 Preakness. Later that year Magna sold its 50% stake in Webasto Sunroofs to privately-owned German auto parts maker Webasto.

Early in 2001 Stronach's daughter Belinda was named vice chairman and CEO. The company then prepared to spin off Magna Steyr and Intier (now Magna's interiors and seating divisions) as public companies; Intier was spun off later in 2001.

Magna acquired rival automotive mirror maker Donnelly in 2002 in a stock-and-debt deal worth $320 million. The company divested its stake in Magna Entertainment in 2003.

Belinda Stronach stepped down as president CEO and director in order to make a bid for the leadership of Canada's new Conservative Party. Her father assumed the role of interim president in early 2004. Ms. Stronach's bid for the leadership of the Conservative Party was not successful. Mr. Stronach ran the company until 2005 when Magna adopted a co-CEO management structure with Donald Walker and Siegfried Wolf at the helm.

Magna and Daimler announced in 2004 that Magna would buy Daimler's drivetrain manufacturing subsidiary New Venture Gear for about $435 million. After approval by the European Commission New Venture Gear was acquired by a newly created joint venture called New Process Gear with Magna holding an 80% interest; Daimler held 20% until 2007 when Magna bought out its stake.

Russian conglomerate Basic Element led by Russian aluminum magnate Oleg Deripaska spent about $1.5 billion to purchase 20% of Magna in 2007. The transaction gave Magna entry to the Russian market but late in 2008 Deripaska's bank BNP Paribas made a margin call that forced the businessman to give up his shares. In 2008 Magna International acquired Technoplast a Russia-based manufacturer of plastic automotive interior and exterior parts which bolstered its capacity in Eastern Europe and Russia.

On the heels of the General Motors bankruptcy filing in 2009 the German government selected Magna International as a partner for Adam Opel and agreed to provide about euro 1.5 billion (around $2 billion) in bridge loans while GM and Magna finalized the contract. A trusteeship for Opel was arranged to keep European operations separate from the Chapter 11 proceedings of GM.

Magna teamed up with Russian banking firm Sberbank to purchase a 55% interest in Opel and its UK-based Vauxhall unit. While GM initially agreed to the sale in September 2009 it backed out in November. The GM board decided to restructure Opel and its European operations instead because business conditions were improving and the Opel brand was important to its global strategy. In Europe the decision was met with demands by the German government that its euro 1.5 billion in bridge loans be returned as well as protests and planned work stoppages by the German labor union.

The GM bankruptcy was brought on by the economic crisis of 2008 and 2009. Magna responded by implementing cost cutting measures which included reducing its headcount by approximately 11500 representing a 14% cutback between 2007 and 2009. It also sold off some of its non-core assets.

Founder and chairman Frank Stronach stepped down in 2010 citing the trend toward more regulatory limitations on company management as one of the reasons. He gave up his controlling share in the company and with it his voting control. The company purchased and cancelled all of its Class B shares held by the Stronach Group and issued Class A Common shares. This capital transaction ended the company's dual class stock structure. The former premier of Ontario Mike Harris took Stronach's place. Co-CEO Siegfried ("Sigi") Wolf also resigned which made co-CEO Donald Walker the sole CEO of Magna International as of mid-2011.

In early 2011 Magna Seating acquired Germany-based Vogelsitze GmbH which made seats for buses and passenger trains. In 2012 Magna obtained Verwaltungs GmbH a maker of automotive vacuum engine and transmission pumps with two facilities in Germany and one in each of China and Bulgaria.

EXECUTIVES

Chief Executive Officer; Director, Donald J. Walker, age 59

Executive Vice-President and Chief Financial Officer, Vincent J. Galifi, $110,500 total compensation

EVP of Global Human Resources, Marc J. Neeb

COO, Tom Skudutis, $110,500 total compensation

EVP and Chief Strategy Officer, Herbert Demel, age 63

EVP, Alon Ossip

President Magna Europe, Guenther Apfalter

Chief Marketing Officer and President Magna Asia, James J. (Jim) Tobin

CTO, Burkhard Goeschel, age 69

Executive Vice-President Corporate Engineering & R&D, Seetarama Kotagiri

Chairman of the Board, William L. Young, age 60

Auditors: Deloitte LLP

LOCATIONS

HQ: Magna International Inc.
337 Magna Drive, Aurora, Ontario L4G 7K1
Phone: 905 726-2462 **Fax:** 905 726-2603
Web: www.magna.com

PRODUCTS/OPERATIONS

2014 Sales

	$ mil.	% of total
Exterior & interior systems	12,840	35
Body systems & chassis systems	8,079	22
Powertrain systems	4,954	14
Complete vehicle assembly	3,067	8
Tooling engineering & other	2,971	8
Vision & electronic systems	2,644	7
Closure systems	2,086	6
Total	**36,641**	**100**

2014 Sales

	$ mil.	% of total
North America	19,603	53
Europe	14,494	40
Asia	1,837	5
Rest of world	694	2
Corporate & Other	13	-
Total	**36,641**	**100**

Selected Operations Products and Services

Cosma International Inc. - body and chassis systems
  Body systems
  Chassis systems
  Design and engineering
  Finishing
  Metal forming technologies
  Stampings
Decoma International - exterior and interior systems
  Body side systems
  Bumper systems (front and rear)
  Cargo management
  Carpet and loadspace
  Cockpit systems
  Engineered glass
  Exterior trim
  Greenhouse systems
  Lighting systems
  Plastic body panels
  Polymeric glazing systems
  Sealing systems
  Vehicle enhancement packages
Magna Car Top Systems - roof systems
  Soft tops
  Removable roof systems
  Retractable hard tops
  Sliding roof systems
Magna Closures - closure systems
  Door modules
  Driver controls
  Handle assemblies
  Power closures and latching systems
  Window systems
Magna E-Car Systems
  Battery cells and packs
  Hybrid and electric vehicle development and
  production
Magna Electronics - electronic systems
  Body electronics
  Driver assistance and safety systems
  Engine electronics
  Intelligent power systems
  Lighting systems
  Liquid sensors
Magna Mirrors - vision systems
  Actuators
  Electronic vision systems
  Exterior and interior mirrors
Magna Powertrain - powertrain systems
  Automatic overdrives
  Die castings
  Differentials
  Engine systems
  Fluid pressure and controls
  Power take-offs
  Stampings
  Transaxles
  Transfer cases
  Transmission systems
Magna Seating - seating systems

Seat mechanism systems
Seating systems
Magna Steyr - complete vehicle manufacturing and OEM
  engineering
Energy storing systems
Fuel systems

COMPETITORS

A.G. Simpson	Hella
Aisin Seiki	Johnson Controls
American Axle &	KUO
Manufacturing	Lacks Enterprises
Benteler Automotive	Lear Corp
BorgWarner	Linamar Corp.
Calsonic Kansei	Meritor
Commercial Vehicle	Plastic Omnium
DENSO	Prodrive
DURA Automotive	Robert Bosch
Dana	Tenneco
Delphi Automotive	Textron
Systems	Torotrak
Faurecia	Tower International
Ficosa	Toyota Auto Body
GKN	Valeo
Gentex	Visteon
Haldex	ZF Friedrichshafen

HISTORICAL FINANCIALS

Company Type: Public

Income Statement

FYE: December 31

	REVENUE ($ mil.)	NET INCOME ($ mil.)	NET PROFIT MARGIN	EMPLOYEES
12/15	32,134	2,013	6.3%	129,000
12/14	36,641	1,882	5.1%	131,000
12/13	34,835	1,561	4.5%	125,000
12/12	30,837	1,433	4.6%	119,000
12/11	28,748	1,018	3.5%	108,275
Annual Growth	**2.8%**	**18.6%**	**—**	**4.5%**

2015 Year-End Financials

Debt ratio: 13.1%
Return on equity: 22.8%
Cash ($ mil.): 2,863
Current ratio: 1.53
Long-term debt ($ mil.): 2,346
No. of shares (mil.): 402
Dividends
  Yield: 2.1%
  Payout: 18.0%
Market value ($ mil.): 16,317

	STOCK PRICE ($) FY Close	P/E High/Low		PER SHARE ($) Earnings	Dividends	Book Value
12/15	40.56	22	8	4.88	0.88	22.29
12/14	108.69	26	18	4.35	0.76	21.10
12/13	82.06	25	15	3.38	0.64	21.76
12/12	50.02	16	11	3.05	0.55	20.22
12/11	33.31	29	15	2.10	0.50	17.52
Annual Growth	**5.0%**	**—**	**—**	**23.5%**	**15.2%**	**6.2%**

Magnit PJSC

Auditors: Ernst & Young LLC

LOCATIONS

HQ: Magnit PJSC
15/2, Solnechnaya street, Krasnodar 350 072
Phone: (7) 861 210 98 10
Web: www.magnit-info.ru

HISTORICAL FINANCIALS

Company Type: Public

Income Statement

FYE: December 31

	REVENUE ($ mil.)	NET INCOME ($ mil.)	NET PROFIT MARGIN	EMPLOYEES
12/15	15,594	968	6.2%	0
12/14	19,872	1,241	6.2%	207,853
12/13	18,201	1,118	6.1%	175,720
12/12	14,429	807	5.6%	0
12/11	11,423	418	3.7%	123,506
Annual Growth	**8.1%**	**23.3%**	**—**	**—**

2015 Year-End Financials

Debt ratio: 25.7%
Return on equity: 40.2%
Cash ($ mil.): 115
Current ratio: 0.79
Long-term debt ($ mil.): 815
No. of shares (mil.): 94
Dividends
  Yield: —
  Payout: —
Market value ($ mil.): —

Malayan Banking Berhad

Malayan Banking Berhad (better known as Maybank) is Malaysia's largest financial services group. Boasting assets of RM640 billion ($145 billion) the firm and its subsidiaries provide deposit services mortgages credit cards and other loan products to businesses and individuals through some 400 branches in Malaysia nearly 430 branches in Indonesia over 20 branches in Singapore and 30-plus branches across Southeast Asia. The firm also offers investment banking asset management on-line banking brokerage insurance unit trusts and other investments and corporate finance services through 2400 offices in 20 countries. Amanah Raya a trust company controlled by the Malaysian government owns over 45% of Maybank.

OperationsMaybank also in 2014 ranked as South East Asia's fourth-largest bank the largest Islamic financing bank in Malaysia and the third-largest Islamic financing bank globally by assets. As Malaysia's largest bank it controlled an 18.4% market share of the loans advances and financing market in Malaysia as well as a 27.6% share of the savings deposit market and 21.1% share of the checking account market.

The bank categorizes its financial services under three key business pillars. Its Community Financial Services (which generated 35% of the company's net operating income or NOI in 2014) includes consumer banking SME and business banking services. The Global Banking pillar includes corporate banking (12% of NOI) investment banking (7%) global markets (8%) transaction banking and asset management. The Insurance & Takaful (8% of NOI) pillar offers insurance and Islamic services and also consists of Maybank's international business operations (28% NOI). Islamic financial services are also offered across all of its business units.

Broadly speaking Maybank generates about half of its operating income from net interest income (mostly from loans and advances including from Islamic Banking Scheme operations). Around 20% of its operating income comes from net earned insurance premiums. The company had 46000 employees at the end of 2014.

Geographic Reach
Maybank's home markets are in Malaysia Singapore and Indonesia; which contributed nearly

89% of the group's profit before tax (PBT) in fiscal 2014. About 60% of its loans and 71% of its PBT were originated in Malaysia alone during the fiscal year. Singapore made up about 14% of its PBT. Outside of these markets Maybank operates in 20 countries (including 10 ASEAN countries) in major financial centers such as Hong Kong Shanghai London New York and Bahrain. It also has associates in Pakistan (MCB Bank's 1242 branches) and Vietnam (An Binh Bank's 145 branches). Sales and MarketingThe firm serves more than 22 million individuals organizations and businesses (including those of Muslim faith).

Financial Performance
Note: Growth rates may differ after conversion to US dollars. This analysis uses financials from the company's annual report. Maybank's revenues and profits have risen more than 30% since 2011 thanks largely to strong loan business growth.

The company's revenue rose by 7% to RM35.7 billion ($10.2 billion) in 2014 mostly thanks to higher interest income as its loan advances and financing assets grew by 13% driven by a 47.5% jump in international loan growth and buoyed by better-than-industry loan growth in Malaysia and Singapore. Its financial investment portfolio assets also grew 8% during the year which boosted interest income further. Higher revenue in 2014 drove Maybank's net income up 3% to a record RM6.7 billion ($1.91 billion) for the year. The company's operating cash levels fell by 39% to RM5.27 billion ($1.5 billion) despite higher earnings due to unfavorable working capital changes mostly related to financial assets purchased under resale agreements and because it used more cash toward loans advances and financing. Strategy

Maybank's strategic objectives over the past five years (2010 through 2015) have included: being Malaysia's no. 1 retail financial services provider in 2015; be the leading ASEAN Wholesale bank expanding into the Middle East China and India; be Malaysia's leading Insurance and Takaful provider and an emerging regional player in the field as well; become a "truly regional organization" with around 40% of pre-tax profit coming from international operations by 2015; and becoming a global leader in Islamic Finance.Some of Maybank's fastest growing businesses include Islamic financing and Takaful (insurance) services that adhere to Islamic law which prohibits the collection of interest but allows profit-sharing and the sale and buy-back of homes (instead of the origination of mortgages). Serving Muslim individuals organizations and businesses the company is opening branches at home and abroad that offer such services. Indeed Islamic Financing grew by 25% during 2014 which increased its proportion of total Malaysia loans to 43.8% at the end of 2014 (from 38.9% at the end of 2013). The growth also solidified Maybank as the largest Islamic bank in Malaysia and the third-largest globally by assets.

Maybank also continues to expand its global reach beyond its home markets. During 2014 it opened its first branch in Myanmar and its third branch in Kunming China. That year it also launched its Etiqa Insurance and Private Wealth businesses in Singapore.

Company Background
Maybank has made several acquisitions in the past to boost its international presence. In 2011 the company acquired 100% of Singapore brokerage Kim Eng Holdings. The addition boosted Maybank's international profile and expanded its distribution capabilities. In 2008 the bank completed its acquisition of the 250-branch Bank International Indonesia (BII). The deal had stalled when banking regulator Bank Negara Malaysia prohibited the transaction but that decision was reversed and the acquisition was ultimately allowed. Also in 2008 the bank acquired minority stakes in Pak-

istan's MCB Bank and Vietnam's An Binh Bank (ABBank) as well as Kookmin Bank's minority stake in PT Bank International Indonesia.
Auditors: Ernst & Young

LOCATIONS

HQ: Malayan Banking Berhad
14th Floor, Menara Maybank, 100, Jalan Tun Perak, Kuala Lumpur 50050
Phone: (60) 3 2070 8833   **Fax:** (60) 3 2032 4775
Web: www.maybank.com

PRODUCTS/OPERATIONS

2013 Sales

	% of total
Interest income	65
Income from islamic banking scheme operations	11
Non-interest income	24
Total	**100**

Selected Subsidiaries

BinaFikir Sdn. Bhd.
Etiqa Insurance Berhad
Etiqa Life International (L) Ltd.
Etiqa Takaful Berhad
Maybank (PNG) Limited2
Maybank Ageas Holding Berhad (formerly known as Maybank Fortis Holdings Berhad)
Maybank Allied Credit & Leasing Sdn. Bhd.
Maybank International (L) Ltd.
Maybank Investment Bank Berhad
Maybank Islamic Berhad
Maybank Philippines Incorporated1
Maysec Sdn. Bhd.
PT Bank Internasional Indonesia TBK1
PT Bank Maybank Syariah Indonesia1
PT BII Finance Centre1
PT Wahana Ottomitra Multiartha TBK1

COMPETITORS

AmBank Group	Malaysian Industrial
Bank Muamalat	Development Finance
Bank of China	OCBC Bank
Bank of East Asia	Public Bank
CIMB Group	RHB Capital
Hang Seng Bank	Standard Chartered
Hong Leong Bank	

HISTORICAL FINANCIALS
Company Type: Public

Income Statement
FYE: December 31

	ASSETS ($ mil.)	NET INCOME ($ mil.)	INCOME AS % OF ASSETS	EMPLOYEES
12/15	164,540	1,587	1.0%	45,000
12/14	183,112	1,920	1.0%	47,000
12/13	171,082	2,000	1.2%	47,771
12/12	161,627	1,876	1.2%	47,233
12/11	142,407	815	0.6%	45,000
Annual Growth	3.7%	18.1%	—	0.0%

2015 Year-End Financials

Return on assets: 1.0%	Dividends
Return on equity: 11.9%	Yield: 6.4%
Long-term debt ($ mil.): —	Payout: 135.3%
No. of shares (mil.): —	Market value ($ mil.): —
Sales ($ mil): 7,877	

	STOCK PRICE ($) FY Close	P/E High/Low		PER SHARE ($) Earnings	Dividends	Book Value
12/15	3.97	6	5	0.17	0.26	1.47
12/14	5.15	8	6	0.21	0.30	1.63
12/13	6.00	9	7	0.23	0.31	1.58
12/12	6.11	11	6	0.24	0.42	1.63
12/11	5.65	23	9	0.11	0.25	1.38
Annual Growth	(8.4%)	—	—	11.4%	0.5%	1.5%

Mangalore Refinery & Petrochemicals Ltd. (India)

Mangalore Refinery and Petrochemicals (MRPL) produces a variety of oil and petrochemical products. A 72%-owned subsidiary of Oil & Natural Gas Corporation MRPL processes 15 million metric tons of oil annually at its Mangalore refinery. It is the country's only refinery to boast two facilities producing premium diesel and high-octane unleaded petrol. Its products include petrochemical and fertilizer-grade naphtha automobile gasoline liquefied petroleum gas and aviation turbine fuel. Other operations include an asphalt production plant a power plant pipelines and a port facility. MRPL was established in 1988 and was acquired by Oil & Natural Gas Corporation in 2003.

EXECUTIVES

Managing Director, Shri H. Kumar
Director (Refinery), Shri M. Venkatesh
Director (Finance), Shri A. K. Sahoo
Chairman, Shri D. K. Sarraf

LOCATIONS

HQ: Mangalore Refinery & Petrochemicals Ltd. (India)
Mudapadav, Kuthethoor, P.O. Via Katipalla, Mangalore, Karnataka 575 030
Phone: (91) 824 2270 400   **Fax:** (91) 824 2270 028
Web: www.mrpl.co.in

2014 Sales

	% of total
Domestic	51
Export	49
Total	**100**

COMPETITORS

Bharat Petroleum	Hindustan Petroleum
Essar Group	Indian Oil
Exxon Mobil	Reliance Industries

HISTORICAL FINANCIALS
Company Type: Public

Income Statement
FYE: March 31

	REVENUE ($ mil.)	NET INCOME ($ mil.)	NET PROFIT MARGIN	EMPLOYEES
03/15	92,601	(2,883)	—	0
03/14	95,760	807	0.8%	0
03/13	0	0	—	0
03/12	0	0	—	0
03/11	0	0	—	0
Annual Growth	—	—	—	—

2015 Year-End Financials

Debt ratio: 0.5%	No. of shares (mil.): —
Return on equity: (-33.0%)	Dividends
Cash ($ mil.): 16,479	Yield: —
Current ratio: 0.74	Payout: —
Long-term debt ($ mil.): 18,785	Market value ($ mil.): —

Manulife Financial Corp.

Manulife the holding company for The Manufacturers Life Insurance Company and John Hancock Financial Services has gone mano a mano with its competitors. Manulife provides individual life insurance group life and health group pension products variable annuities wealth management and financial products in nearly two dozen countries and territories worldwide. North America and Asia make up its largest operations. Manulife's reinsurance division provides life health and accident reinsurance and was one of North America's top life retrocessionaires (firms that reinsure reinsurers) until it sold that division in 2011. The company also provides investment management real estate and lending services.

Operations

Along with its John Hancock subsidiary Manulife is one of the top five life insurers in North America and is a top 10 global life insurer based on market capitalization. North American financial products are offered primarily under the John Hancock brand while life insurance is offered through Manufacturers Life. Other brands and subsidiaries include Portland Investment Counsel (mutual funds retail investment funds) and Pottruff & Smith (travel insurance).

Geographic Reach

Sales in the US still make up about a third of Manulife's annual revenue (though the market there has shrunk in response to the flagging economy); Canada and Asia each account for about 30% of Manulife's premium income. Its efforts to grow in China through partnerships have paid off with the company's sales there challenging those in Canada (formerly its second-largest market after the US).

Strategy

Besides building up its more successful offerings and divesting those with higher risks Manulife's strategy for growth includes maintaining a diversified mix and hedging its in-force public equity and interest rate risks over time. The company's objective is to increase its earnings to $4 billion by 2015.

Manulife also grows through collaborations such as its partnership with Edward Jones which helped the company expand its sales network in the US and add agents to increase its distribution presence in Asia. Its Manulife-Sinochem (MSL) partnership with Sinochem has also allowed the company to deepen its reach in China. With operations in 50 Chinese cities MSL has the broadest geographic footprint of any foreign invested joint venture firm in that country. Manulife also has a 49% interest in ABN AMRO TEDA Fund Management in China. The Manulife-TEDA partnership allows the company to expand in China's wealth management market.

Further expansion in China is in the company's plans as is increasing sales of wealth management products. In 2012 for example Manulife Asset Management procured licensure to provide institutional asset management services in Korea's fast-growing market.

Mergers and Acquisitions

The firm's future growth strategy is focused on individual and group life health and group pensions. Towards those ends it has agreed to buy the Hong Kong pension business of Standard Chartered. The deal also includes a 15-year exclusive distribution deal with the UK bank's Hong Kong customers.

Manulife's mutual fund business is an area the company is making great effort to grow. It purchased Wellington West Financial Services from National Bank Financial Group in 2012 for an undisclosed price adding about 40 advisors and some $900 in assets under management to its Canadian investment unit (Manulife Securities) in the deal.

In 2013 Manulife expanded in Canada's mortgage creditor insurance market through the purchase of Benesure Canada. Benesure provides distribution and third-party administration of life and disability creditor policies to mortgage brokerage entities.

Company Background

Manulife acquired US financial services giant John Hancock in a $10 billion deal in 2004 bringing Manulife into the top ranks of US and global life insurers. Manulife subsequently rebranded its US financial products with the more-recognizable John Hancock name and logo. Manulife also consolidated John Hancock's Canadian subsidiary Maritime Life Assurance Company into its flagship subsidiary The Manufacturers Life Insurance Company.

EXECUTIVES

President and CEO, Donald A. Guloien, $774,835 total compensation
SVP Investments, Warren A. Thomson
EVP Global Head of Wealth and Asset Management; President and CEO Manulife Asset Management, Kai R. Sotorp
Chief Actuary, Steven (Steve) Finch
President and CEO Manulife Canada; SEVP and General Manager Canadian Division, Marianne Harrison
President John Hancock Financial Services; SEVP and General Manager US Division, Craig R. Bromley
EVP General Account Investments, Scott S. Hartz
EVP Human Resources, Stephani E. Kingsmill
EVP and Chief Actuary, Cindy L. Forbes
EVP and Chief Risk Officer, Rahim Hirji
SEVP and CFO, Stephen B. (Steve) Roder
EVP and General Counsel, Stephen P. Sigurdson
EVP and CIO, Greg Framke
SEVP and General Manager Asia; President and CEO Manulife Asia, Roy Gori
EVP and Chief Innovation Officer, Timothy W. Ramza
COO, Linda Mantia
President and CEO Quebec, Richard Payette
Chairman, Richard B. DeWolfe
Auditors: Ernst & Young LLP

LOCATIONS

HQ: Manulife Financial Corp.
200 Bloor Street East, North Tower 10, Toronto, Ontario M4W 1E5
Phone: 416 926-3000   **Fax:** 416 926-5454
Web: www.manulife.com

2015 Revenues

	% of total
Asia	41
Canada	29
US	29
Other	1
Total	**100**

PRODUCTS/OPERATIONS

2015 Revenues

	% of total
Premiums	46
Investment income	25
Other	29
Total	**100**

Selected Subsidiaries & Affiliates

Elliott & Page Limited
FNA Financial Inc.
John Hancock Financial Network Inc. (US)
John Hancock Financial Services Inc. (US)
John Hancock Investment Management Services LLC (US)
John Hancock Life Insurance Company (U.S.A.)
John Hancock Life Insurance Company of New York
Manulife International Holdings Limited (Bermuda)
Manulife (Singapore) Pte. Ltd.
Manulife (Vietnam) Limited
Manulife Bank of Canada
Manulife Life Insurance Company (Japan)
Manulife Sinochem Life Insurance Co. Ltd. (China)
NAL Resources Management Limited
P.T. Asuransi Jiwa Manulife Indonesia
The Manufacturers Investment Corporation (US)
The Manufacturers Life Insurance Co. (Philippines) Inc.
The Manufacturers Life Insurance Company

COMPETITORS

AEGON
AIG
Allianz
Canada Life
China Life Insurance
Dai-ichi Life
Fairfax Financial Holdings
Generali
Great-West Lifeco
ING
Industrial Alliance Insurance and Financial Servic
Liberty Mutual
Meiji Yasuda Life
MetLife
Nationwide
New York Life
Nippon Life Insurance
Power Financial
Principal Financial
Prudential
Sun Life
Swiss Re
T&D Holdings
The Hartford
Tokio Marine

HISTORICAL FINANCIALS

Company Type: Public

Income Statement

FYE: December 31

	ASSETS ($ mil.)	NET INCOME ($ mil.)	INCOME AS % OF ASSETS	EMPLOYEES
12/15	507,335	1,577	0.3%	33,000
12/14	500,346	3,023	0.6%	0
12/13	483,036	2,943	0.6%	0
12/12	488,707	1,745	0.4%	28,000
12/11	452,995	126	0.0%	26,000
Annual Growth	**2.9%**	**87.9%**	**—**	**6.1%**

2015 Year-End Financials

Return on assets: 0.3%
Return on equity: 5.8%
Long-term debt ($ mil.): —
No. of shares (mil.): 1,972
Sales ($ mil): 24,789

Dividends
Yield: 4.4%
Payout: 87.9%
Market value ($ mil.): 29,541

	STOCK PRICE ($) FY Close	P/E High/Low		PER SHARE ($) Earnings	Dividends	Book Value
12/15	14.98	16	13	0.76	0.52	15.10
12/14	19.09	11	9	1.55	0.52	15.50
12/13	19.73	12	8	1.52	0.51	14.58
12/12	13.59	16	11	0.88	0.52	14.08
12/11	10.62	938500		0.02	0.51	13.32
Annual Growth	**9.0%**	**—**		**—149.2%**	**0.6%**	**3.2%**

Mapfre SA

Auditors: KPMG Auditores S.L.

LOCATIONS

HQ: Mapfre SA
Paseo de Recoletos, 25, Madrid 28004
Phone: (34) 91 581 1100   **Fax:** (34) 91 581 1143
Web: www.mapfre.es

HISTORICAL FINANCIALS

Company Type: Public

Income Statement

FYE: December 31

	ASSETS ($ mil.)	NET INCOME ($ mil.)	INCOME AS % OF ASSETS	EMPLOYEES
12/15	69,153	772	1.1%	38,405
12/14	81,720	1,027	1.3%	35,871
12/13	78,234	1,088	1.4%	36,280
12/12	75,106	877	1.2%	34,962
12/11	70,953	1,245	1.8%	32,798
Annual Growth	(0.6%)	(11.3%)	—	4.0%

Marks & Spencer Group PLC

The sun never sets on Marks and Spencer (M&S). The British retail icon operates about 345 M&S department stores and some 500 Simply Food shops throughout the UK. Beyond Britain it boasts about 480 locations mostly franchises in about 60 countries including China India Indonesia Russia and South Korea. Its department stores sell mid-priced apparel food and household items under the company's private label brands including Autograph Classic per una and Portfolio. About 90% of the company's sales are made in its home country where it is the #1 provider of womenswear lingerie and menswear. The retailer also sells goods online. M&S has been in business for more than 125 years.

Operations

Marks & Spencer divides its operations into Food which accounts for just over half of revenue and General Merchandise. The company has more than 504 small Simply Food outlets around the UK located mainly on high streets or within railway stations and airports.

Geographic Reach

The company has 345 M&S stores and more than 500 Simply Food shops in the UK as well as another nearly 500 locations in 60 countries including growth markets China India Indonesia Russia and South Korea. It rings up about 90% of its sales in the UK.

Financial Performance

Marks & Spencer has reported growing sales every year since 2011 and 2015 was no exception as the company reported 1% growth. Higher foods sales at home drove the gain tempered by lower sales overseas. After several years of falling profit the number rebounded in 2014 but was down again in 2015 by 5% due to higher taxes.

Strategy

The retailer has been relying heavily on its Simply Food stores and there's no let up in sight; it plans to open about 60 new locations per year. Other strategic initiatives include continued focus on overseas growth mostly through franchises and updating both its infrastructure and its flagship stores. In 2014 it updated flagship M&S stores in The Hague (Netherlands) Hong Kong and Shanghai and opened new locations in Belgium Macau and Kuwait.

HISTORY

Fleeing anti-Semitic persecution in Russian Poland 19-year-old Michael Marks immigrated to England in 1882. Eventually settling in Leeds Marks eked out a meager existence as a traveling peddler until he opened a small stall at the town market in 1884. Because he spoke little English Marks laid out all of his merchandise and hung a sign that read "Don't Ask the Price It's a Penny" unaware at the time that self-service would eventually become the retailing standard. His methods were so successful that he had penny bazaars in five cities by 1890.

Finding himself unable to run the growing operation alone Marks established an equal partnership with Englishman Tom Spencer a cashier for a local distributor forming Marks and Spencer in 1894. By the turn of the century the company had 36 branches. Following the deaths of Spencer (1905) and Marks (1907) management of the company did not return to family hands until 1916 when Marks' 28-year-old son Simon became chairman.

Marks and Spencer broke with time-honored British retailing tradition in 1924 by eliminating wholesalers and establishing direct links with manufacturers. In 1926 the firm went public and two years later it launched its now famous St Michael brand. The company turned its attention to pruning unprofitable departments to concentrate on goods that had a rapid turnover. In 1931 the Marks & Spencer stores (M&S) introduced a food department that sold produce and canned goods.

The company sustained severe losses during WWII when bombing damaged approximately half of its stores. Marks and Spencer rebuilt and in 1964 Simon's brother-in-law Israel Sieff became chairman. The company expanded to North America a decade later by buying three Canadian chains: Peoples (general merchandise sold 1992) D'Allaird's (women's clothing sold 1996) and Walker's (clothing shops converted to M&S). Sieff's son Marcus Sieff became chairman in 1972. It opened its first store in Paris in 1975.

Derek Rayner replaced Marcus Sieff as chairman in 1984 becoming the first chairman hired from outside the Marks family since 1916. Under Rayner Marks and Spencer moved into financial services by launching a charge card in 1985. The company purchased US-based Kings Super Markets and Brooks Brothers (upscale clothing stores) in 1988. Rayner retired in 1991 and CEO Richard Greenbury became chairman. During the 1990s M&S opened new stores in Germany Hong Kong Hungary Spain and Turkey.

In 1997 it paid Littlewoods $323 million for 19 UK stores which it converted to M&S. Greenbury facing criticism that the company was too slow to expand and embrace new ideas was succeeded in 1999 as CEO by handpicked heir Peter Salsbury. That year continued poor sales led Marks and Spencer to cut 700 jobs close its 38 M&S stores in Canada and part ways with its clothing supplier of 30 years William Baird. In early 2000 Marks and Spencer dodged a takeover attempt by investor Philip Green. Chairman Luc Vandevelde took over as CEO in September when Salsbury resigned.

In spring 2001 Marks and Spencer announced a recovery plan to salvage its struggling M&S chain by selling off many of its global operations including its profitable US businesses (Brooks Brothers and Kings Super Markets). Unhappy with the company's direction and its departure from older values Marks and Spencer board members Sir David Sieff (the last remaining founder member) Sir Ralph Robins and Sir Michael Perry left the board in July 2001. Marks and Spencer sold Brooks Brothers to Retail Brand Alliance for $225 million (a loss from the $750 million the company paid for it in 1988) in November 2001 and nearly managed to sell its Kings Super Markets business to New York supermarket operator D'Agostino in July 2002 but the deal fell through later in the year due to a lack of financing.

Also in July 2002 Vandevelde –who is credited with masterminding the M&S turnaround —announced he would give up his role as CEO and hand the reins to managing director Roger Holmes. Vandevelde became the company's part-time chairman in January 2003.

In May 2004 both Vandevelde and Holmes left M&S. Stuart Rose formerly head of Arcadia was named CEO; non-executive board member Paul Myners was named interim chairman of the company. Prior to the shift in management billionaire entrepreneur Philip Green (who owns Arcadia and Bhs in the UK) confirmed that he would mount a takeover bid for the retail group. Ultimately Green's final proposal (the third he made for the retailer in a five week period) was rejected by the M&S board in July 2004. In October M&S bought the Per Una brand from designer George Davies for about £126 million and moved its head office from the old Baker Street location to Waterside House by the Grand Union Canal in London. In November Rose ousted more than a handful of company executives including Maurice Helfgott Mark McKeon Laurel Powers-Freeling Jean Tomlin Jack Paterson and 20-year veteran Alison Reed who stepped down as CFO in April 2005.

M&S relaunched its Home catalogue in early 2005. In February of that year the company announced the sale of its former Baker Street headquarters Michael House to real estate company London & Regional Properties for £115 million. M&S which is in a profit squeeze said it plans to used the proceeds for "general corporate purposes." In August M&S sold its Lifestore in Gateshead to Active Asset Investment Management for £43 million. In December M&S won a ruling by the European Court of Justice that resulted in the company receiving a £30 million tax windfall from the Treasury.

In April 2006 M&S completed the sale of its 26-store Kings Super Markets chain in the US for about $61.5 million. Lord Burns a former chairman of Abbey National took up the post of chairman in July 2006 after joining Marks and Spencer as deputy chairman in 2005. Burns succeeded interim chairman Paul Myners.

In 2007 M&S opened three stores in Taiwan. (Marks & Spencer Taiwan is 60%-owned by the British retailer and 40% by President Chain Store.) The following year M&S opened its first store on the mainland in Shanghai.

In June 2008 Lord Burns stepped down as chairman of the company and was succeeded by CEO Stuart Rose who became executive chairman. David Michels was appointed deputy chairman as well. Rose stepped down as CEO in May 2010 to make way for Marc Bolland thus decoupling the roles of chairman and chief executive at the firm.

EXECUTIVES

Executive Director Marketing & Business Development, Patrick Bousquet-Chavanne, age 58
CFO, Helen A. Weir, age 54

Executive Director Multi-Channel E-Commerce, Laura Wade-Gery, age 51
CEO, Steve Rowe
Director Property, Clem Constantine
Director Information Technology and Logistics, Darrell Stein
Director e-Commerce, John Dixon
Director General Merchandise Presentation, Nayna McIntosh, age 52
Director International, Jan Heere
Director Supply Chain, Dirk Lembregts
Director Retail, Sacha Berendji
Chairman, Robert Swannell, age 65
Auditors: Deloitte LLP

LOCATIONS

HQ: Marks & Spencer Group PLC
Waterside House, 35 North Wharf Road, London W2 1NW
Phone: (44) 20 7935 4422
Web: www.marksandspencer.com

2015 Sales

	% of total
UK	89
International	11
Total	**100**

PRODUCTS/OPERATIONS

2015 Sales

	% of total
UK	
Food	51
General merchandise	39
International	10
Total	**100**

COMPETITORS

ASDA	J Sainsbury
Arcadia	John Lewis
Benetton	Kingfisher
Berwin & Berwin	Mothercare
Burberry	NEXT plc
Carrefour	New Look
Co-operative Group	Pret A Manger
Debenhams	Primark
Fortnum & Mason	Shop Direct
Gap UK	T.K. Maxx
H&M	Tesco
Harrods	Topshop
Harvey Nichols	Zara
House of Fraser	

HISTORICAL FINANCIALS

Company Type: Public

Income Statement

FYE: April 2

	REVENUE ($ mil.)	NET INCOME ($ mil.)	NET PROFIT MARGIN	EMPLOYEES
04/16*	15,102	582	3.9%	82,948
03/15	15,366	725	4.7%	83,069
03/14	17,163	873	5.1%	85,813
03/13	15,236	709	4.7%	81,734
03/12	15,918	822	5.2%	81,208
Annual Growth	**(1.3%)**	**(8.3%)**	**—**	**0.5%**

*Fiscal year change

2016 Year-End Financials

Debt ratio: 34.9%	No. of shares (mil.): 1,622
Return on equity: 12.0%	Dividends
Cash ($ mil.): 354	Yield: 0.0%
Current ratio: 0.69	Payout: 137.6%
Long-term debt ($ mil.): 2,539	Market value ($ mil.): 19,119

	STOCK PRICE ($)	P/E	PER SHARE ($)		
	FY Close	High/Low	Earnings	Dividends	Book Value
04/16*	11.78	68 45	0.35	0.49	3.04
03/15	15.73	54 38	0.44	0.48	2.89
03/14	15.06	53 38	0.54	0.49	2.76
03/13	11.83	42 32	0.44	0.48	2.36
03/12	12.06	40 29	0.52	0.50	2.78
Annual Growth	**(0.6%)**	— —	**(8.9%)**	**(0.6%)**	**2.2%**

*Fiscal year change

Marubeni Corp.

Marubeni's name combines the Japanese words for "circle" and "red" and Marubeni hopes the comprehensive range of products manufactured and traded by its circle of operating units will keep the company out of the red. One of Japan's largest sogo shosha (general trading companies) Marubeni has a broad range of operating segments: Chemicals; Energy; Finance Logistics & IT Business; Food; Forest Products; Lifestyle; Metals & Mineral Resources; Real Estate Development; Plant & Industrial Machinery; Power Projects & Infrastructure; and Transportation Machinery.

In 2011 the trading company simplified its reporting structure into four broad segments: Machinery (Plant & Industrial Machinery Power Projects & Infrastructure and Transportation Machinery); Resources (Energy and Metals & Mineral Resources); Materials (Chemicals Forest Products and General Merchandise); and Consumer Products (Finance Logistics & IT Business Food Lifestyle and Real Estate Development.)

Marubeni has hundreds of operating companies in 70 countries.

A recovering economy and a robust growth in commodity prices lifted Marubeni's revenues and income in 2012. In fiscal 2012 the company reported a 19% increase in revenues driven by a 17% jump in the volume of Marubeni's trading transactions especially from higher oil prices. Energy accounted for 29% of total trading volume in 2012 and was 22% greater in actual volume than in 2011. Marubeni's higher overall revenues in 2012 outpaced increased expenses enabling the trading house to post a 26% jump in net income.

The group has been particularly active in Asia where its diversity has enabled it to develop local industries and to help build utility and industrial infrastructures such as telephone systems power plants and water systems. The company has championed international expansion since the mid-1990s but Japan's credit crunch and the Asian economic crisis have hurt the company's production and processing operations across Southeast Asia. Marubeni has been reducing debt controlling operating costs and investing in commodity trading natural resources projects and international power generation schemes.

Growing its commodity business in 2012 the company agreed to acquire US-based grain fertilizer and energy commodities distribution and natural gas network Gavilon for $3.6 billion.

Taking advantage of BP's need to raise cash in the wake of its Gulf of Mexico oil disaster in 2011 Marubeni bought four mature producing deepwater oil and gas fields in Gulf from BP for $650 million. In 2013 it also agreed to acquire a 49% stake in Williams Partners' floating production platform project for Tubular Bells Field in the Gulf of Mexico.

In 2011 Marubeni formed a joint venture with Supreme Energy and International Power to develop the Rantau Dedap geothermal project located in Sumatra. The 220 MW geothermal plant is part of the Indonesian government's long-term plan meet its country's needs with renewable power.

It also entered a new market that year airplane leasing with a deal with Deucalion Limited to set up a company in Singapore to invest into aircraft assets.

In 2011 the company announced a medium-term growth plan focusing on natural resources (primarily copper) infrastructure environmental products (especially water businesses) and essential living commodities (building up its grain position in China).

HISTORY

Marubeni's origins are closely linked to those of another leading Japanese trading company. ITOCHU founder Chubei Itoh set up Marubeni Shoten K. K. in 1858 as an outlet in Osaka for his textile trading business (originally C. Itoh & Co.). The symbol for the store was a circle (maru) drawn around the Japanese word for red (beni). As C. Itoh's global operations expanded the Marubeni store served as headquarters.

Marubeni was split off from C. Itoh in 1921 to trade textiles although it soon expanded its operations to include industrial and consumer goods. To mobilize for WWII the Japanese government reunited Marubeni and C. Itoh in 1941 merging them with another trading company Kishimoto into a new entity Sanko Kabushiki Kaisha. In 1944 Sanko Daido Boeki and Kureha Spinning were ordered to consolidate into a larger entity to be called the Daiken Co. but the war ended before all operations were fully integrated.

Spun off from Daiken in 1949 Marubeni began trading internationally. It opened a New York office in 1951 and diversified into food metals and machinery. During the Korean War Marubeni benefited from the UN's use of Japan as a supply base.

In 1955 Marubeni merged with Iida & Company and changed its name to Marubeni-Iida. It received a government concession to supply silicon steel and iron sheets critical to the growing Japanese auto and appliance industries. The company expanded into engineering —building factories aircraft and a nuclear reactor for the Japan Atomic Energy Research Institute —and into petrochemicals fertilizers and rubber products.

Marubeni-Iida was behind the Fuyo keiretsu formed in the early 1960s. Fuyo (another word for Mt. Fuji) is a powerful assemblage of some 150 companies including Canon Hitachi and Nissan that form joint ventures and develop think tanks.

The firm became Marubeni Corp. in 1972 and a year later it bought Nanyo Bussan another trading company. In 1973 Marubeni's image was tarnished by allegations that it had hoarded rice for sale on the Japanese black market.

In the 1990s Marubeni won several major construction contracts. Among them Marubeni formed a venture in 1998 with John Laing and Turkey's Alarko Alsim to rebuild three airports in Uzbekistan.

Marubeni had begun offering Internet access in 1995 and two years later it launched an Internet-based long-distance telephone service. In 1999 the trading house formed two ventures with US firm Global Crossing one to start operating Pacific Crossing One (the Japan-US cable) and another to lay a cable network in Japan.

That year Marubeni tied up with fellow trading company ITOCHU to integrate their steel processing subsidiaries in China to try to keep their Chinese businesses afloat. In 2000 ITOCHU and

Marubeni formed an online steel trading joint venture with US-based e-commerce company MetalSite. The two companies also integrated their entire steel divisions in 2001 forming the Marubeni-Itochu Steel joint venture among the largest steel companies in Japan.

Taking responsibility for the sharp downturn in Marubeni's financial performance chairman Iwao Toriumi announced in 2001 that he would step down. The company launched a major restructuring effort the next year that was designed to give more autonomy to the managers of individual business units.

In 2005 Marubeni launched a large power and water project in Abu Dhabi.

In 2007 Marubeni entered into the finance leasing industry in the US launching subsidiary CoActiv Capital Partners.

In 2008 Marubeni acquired US-based The PIC Group Inc. an independent global provider of services and programs focused on power generation and other industrial facilities and services. In 2009 it acquired 49% of Invenergy Thermal Financing LLC which owns three natural-gas fired power plants (with 1014 MW of generating capcity) in the US.

In 2009 the company completed the Laffan Refinery in Qatar which began commercial operations that year. It also signed a $2 billion deal to build the Shuweihat S2 Independent Water and Power Producer project in the United Arab Emirates.

EXECUTIVES

President and CEO, Fumiya Kokubu
SEVP, Shigeru Yamazoe
SEVP, Mitsuru Akiyoshi
Managing Executive Officer, Nobuhiro Yabe
Managing Executive Officer, Hikaru Minami
Chairman, Teruo Asada
Auditors: Ernst & Young ShinNihon LLC

LOCATIONS

HQ: Marubeni Corp.
1-4-2 Ohtemachi, Chiyoda-ku, Tokyo 100-8088
Phone: (81) 3 3282 2111   **Fax:** (81) 3 3282 4241
Web: www.marubeni.co.jp

2016 Sales

	% of total
Japan	53
US	33
Singapore	4
Other countries	10
Total	**100**

PRODUCTS/OPERATIONS

2016 Sales

	% of total
Food & Consumer Products	46
Energy & Metals	23
Chemical & Forest products	19
Transportation & Industrial Machinery	8
Power projects & Plant	4
Total	**100**

2016 Sales

	% of total
Goods	97
Commission on service & trading margins	3
Total	**100**

COMPETITORS

ITOCHU	Samsung Group
Jardine Matheson	Seika
Kanematsu	Showa Denko
LG Group	Sime Darby
Largo Vista	Sojitz

Mitsubishi Corp.	Sojitz Corporation of
Mitsubishi	America
International	Sumitomo
Mitsui	Sumitomo Heavy
Nissan Chemical	Industries
Rio Tinto plc	

HISTORICAL FINANCIALS
Company Type: Public

Income Statement

				FYE: March 31
	REVENUE ($ mil.)	NET INCOME ($ mil.)	NET PROFIT MARGIN	EMPLOYEES
03/16	65,008	554	0.9%	47,887
03/15	65,297	880	1.3%	47,925
03/14	68,356	2,043	3.0%	49,996
03/13	51,665	2,186	4.2%	42,937
03/12	53,521	2,098	3.9%	41,503
Annual Growth	5.0%	(28.3%)	—	3.6%

2016 Year-End Financials

Debt ratio: 0.4%	No. of shares (mil.): 1,735
Return on equity: 4.3%	Dividends
Cash ($ mil.): 5,350	Yield: 3.7%
Current ratio: 1.22	Payout: 646.9%
Long-term debt ($ mil.): 24,326	Market value ($ mil.): 88,097

	STOCK PRICE ($) FY Close	P/E High/Low		PER SHARE ($) Earnings	Dividends	Book Value
03/16	50.76	2	1	0.32	1.89	6.76
03/15	58.17	1	1	0.51	2.31	7.29
03/14	67.80	1	1	1.18	2.40	7.73
03/13	76.48	1	0	1.26	2.36	6.93
03/12	72.50	1	0	1.21	1.99	5.98
Annual Growth	(8.5%)	—	—	(28.3%)	(1.3%)	3.1%

Mazda Motor Corp. (Japan)

Mazda and its Zoom-Zoom spirit races alongside the top automakers in Japan. Selling more than 1.2 million vehicles annually Mazda makes passenger cars commercial vehicles and crossover SUVs. It comprises more than 50 subsidiaries including sales companies: Mazda Motor of America Europe and Australia. The company manufactures in Japan China and Thailand. Models include the Mazda 2 3 6 and 8 passenger vehicles; MX-5 (Miata) RX-8 sports cars; E-series commercial vehicles; and B-Series pickup trucks. Mazda added crossover SUVs to its lineup with the Tribute Mazda5 (Premacy) Verisa Biante CX-7 and CX-9. Ford Motor holds a 3.5% stake in Mazda.

Just as the automotive industry was getting back on course natural catastrophe in the form of the Great Tohoku Kanto Earthquake and subsequent tsunamis struck Japan in March 2011. Many industries ground to a halt temporarily including Mazda's manufacturing facilities in Hiroshima and Hofu —limited production continued through the end of the month picking up to full production in April. Compounding factors to this event include political unrest in various regions of the world and rising oil prices. Still the company experienced sales increases in certain regions particularly in North America (10% increase) as well as emerging markets such as Russia China and other Asian countries. Mazda realized a 7% increase in overall

sales for 2011 but this total was offset by sluggish sales in Japan and European countries as well as a strong yen. Before the fiscal year ended the earthquake struck and Mazda felt the aftershock to its 2011 bottom line posting an almost 60% loss over 2010.

Mazda had started on the road to recovery after the economic crisis in 2009. It weathered the worst of the downturn by implementing cost-saving measures —its workforce was reduced temporary workers' contracts were not renewed and inventory adjustments were made to match demand. Additionally Mazda executives agreed to take a 20% salary cut.

As a result of the recession Mazda's business plan revised target numbers and put an emphasis on brand and technology. Both areas are being served through new models and features. With an added emphasis on innovative technologies Mazda introduced its SKYACTIV technologies in 2011 with the claim that it will improve the fuel efficiency of its vehicles 30% by 2015. The SKYACTIV vision includes the redesign of Mazda's transmissions bodies and chassis for inclusion in its upcoming models. The SKYACTIV-G is a direct-injection gas engine that can achieve 30% fuel economy without the use of an electric motor; it is scheduled for release in Australia in 2011. The Demio (Mazda2) sporting the new engine was released in Japan early in 2011. Prior technology releases included Mazda's Smart Idle Stop System (iStop) which automatically shuts down the engine when the vehicle is stationary. The Mazda Premacy Hydrogen RE (Rotary Engine) Hybrid vehicle is the first of its kind to be made available through leasing; the RX-8 Hydrogen RE was introduced to Norway in 2009.

Ford once held a majority stake in Mazda but it cut its 33% interest to 13% in 2008 because it needed cash. As of 2011 Ford held only 3.5% of Mazda. Following the independence from Ford Takashi Yamanouchi took over as president and CEO of Mazda in 2008 assuming the responsibility of shoring up tumbling profits caused by an unstable yen and a decrease in demand. Former president Hisakazu Imaki continues serving as chairman but plans to retire in the near future; insiders report that Yamanouchi will assume the chairmanship. The management shakeup means Yamanouchi who is a proponent of expanding into the Chinese automobile market may speed up the process of the company's independent development strategy in China.

HISTORY

Ingiro Matsuda founded cork producer Toyo Cork Kogyo in Hiroshima in 1920. The company changed its name to Toyo Kogyo in 1927 and began making machine tools. Impressed by Ford trucks used in 1923 earthquake-relief efforts Matsuda had the company make a three-wheel motorcycle/truck hybrid in 1931.

During the 1930s the company supplied products to the Sumitomo industrial conglomerate. The Sumitomo Bank became a major shareholder of Toyo Kogyo.

The second Sino-Japanese War forced Toyo Kogyo to make rifles and cut back on its truck production. Although the company built a prototype passenger car in 1940 the outbreak of WWII refocused it on weapons. The August 1945 bombing of Hiroshima killed more than 400 Toyo Kogyo workers but the company persevered producing 10 trucks that December. By 1949 it was turning out 800 per month.

The company launched the first Mazda a twoseat minicar in 1960. The next year Toyo Kogyo licensed AUDI's new rotary engine technology. After releasing a string of models the company became Japan's #3 automaker in 1964. Toyo Kogyo introduced the first Mazda powered by a rotary engine Cosmo/110S in 1967 followed by the Familia in 1968.

The company grew rapidly and began exporting to the US in 1970. However recession high gas prices and concern over the inefficiency of rotary engines halted growth in the mid-1970s. Sumitomo Bank bailed out Toyo Kogyo. The company shifted emphasis back to piston engines but managed to launch the rotary engine RX-7 in 1978.

Ford's need for small-car expertise and Sumitomo's desire for a large partner for its client led to Ford's purchase of 25% of Toyo Kogyo in 1979. The company's early 1980s GLC/323 and 626 models were sold as Fords in Asia Latin America and the Middle East.

Toyo Kogyo changed its name to Mazda Motor Corporation in 1984. ("Mazda" is loosely derived from Matsuda's name but the carmaker has never discouraged an association with the Zoroastrian god of light Ahura Mazda.) The company opened a US plant in 1985 but a strong yen expensive increases in production capacity and a growing number of models led to increased overhead soaring debt and shrinking margins. By 1988 Mazda had begun to focus on sporty niche cars launching the hot-selling Miata in 1989.

The company faced more problems with the early 1990s recession. In 1992 Mazda introduced a new 626 model. That year Mazda also sold half its interest in its Flat Rock Michigan plant to Ford. As the yen development costs and prices for its cars in the US all rose sales in the US fell. In 1993 Mazda reorganized subsidiary Mazda of America by cutting staff.

Ford sank $481 million into Mazda in 1996 increasing its stake to 33%. That year the Ford-appointed former EVP of Mazda Henry Wallace became Mazda's president making history as the first non-Japanese to head a major Japanese corporation. In 1997 Wallace resigned to become CFO of Ford's European operations and former Ford executive James Miller replaced him. That year Mazda consolidated four US operations into Mazda North American Operations.

Restructuring continued in 1998 as Mazda consolidated some European operations and closed a plant in Thailand. In 1999 Mazda sold its credit division to Ford and its Naldec auto parts unit to Ford's Visteon unit. It announced plans to sell its stake in South Korean carmaker Kia Motors. Later in the year another American Ford's Mark Fields took over as president.

In 2000 Mazda recalled 30000 of that year's MPV minivans to fix a powertrain control module and asked owners of all 2000 MPVs to bring in their vehicles for front-bumper reinforcement. Mazda also announced plans to close about 40% of its North American dealership outlets over the next three years. The following year Mazda completed a program to assume direct control over distribution in some European markets including France Italy Spain and the UK.

In 2007 Mazda opened a new vehicle assembly plant in Nanjing China and also began building its passenger vehicle plant in Thailand. To strengthen its sales in Japan the company introduced the Mazda Advantage Loan in 2007 in cooperation with PRIMUS Financial Services. Mazda acquired a 40% stake in PRIMUS in March 2008 to strengthen its auto financing business.

Ford's 33% stake in the company was reduced to about 13% in 2008 after the cash-strapped company sold off approximately 20% of its holdings. A consortium of Hiroshima Bank Panasonic (both Mazda business partners) and Mazda itself paid a combined sum of about $540 million to bring control of the company back to Japan.

EXECUTIVES

EVP, Akira Marumoto
Senior Managing Executive Officer China Operations Domestic and Fleet Sales, Nobuhide Inamoto
Executive Officer Strategic Review Project, Jeffrey H. Guyton
President and CEO, Masamichi Kogai
Senior Managing Executive Officer; COO Europe Asia & Oceania Middle East Africa and New and Emerging Markets, Yuji Nakamine
Senior Managing Executive Officer, Yuji Harada
Senior Managing Executive Officer R&D and MDI, Kiyoshi Fujiwara
Senior Managing Executive Officer Quality Brand Enhancement Production and Business Logistics, Kiyotaka Shobuda
Managing Executive Officer, Masahiro Moro
Senior Managing Executive Officer Corporate Planning Profit Control Global IT and MDI, Akira Koga
Managing Executive Officer Domestic Sales and Fleet Sales and President Mazda Chuhan Co. Ltd., Kazuyuki Fukuhara
Chairman, Seita Kanai
Auditors: KPMG AZSA LLC

LOCATIONS

HQ: Mazda Motor Corp. (Japan)
3-1 Shinchi, Fuchu-cho, Aki-gun, Hiroshima 730-8670
Phone: (81) 82 282 1111
Web: www.mazda.co.jp

2016 Sales

	% of total
Japan	51
North America	26
Europe	12
Other regions	11
Total	**100**

PRODUCTS/OPERATIONS

Selected Models
B-Series (pickup)
E-Series (vans and commercial vehicles)
CX-7 (crossover SUV)
CX-9 (crossover SUV)
Mazda 2 (Demio)
Mazda 3 (Axela hatchback sedan)
Mazda 5 (Premacy minivan)
Mazda 6 (sport sedan)
Mazda 8 (MPV)
Mazda Biante (minivan)
Mazda Tribute
MX-5 Miata (roadster)
RX-8 (sports car)
Tribute (SUV)

Selected Subsidiaries and Affiliates
Mazda Australia Pty. Ltd.
Mazda Motor Logistics Europe NV (Belgium)
Mazda Motor of America Inc.

COMPETITORS

BMW	Isuzu
Daimler	Kia Motors
FCA US	Nissan
Fiat Chrysler	Peugeot
Ford Motor	Renault
Fuji Heavy Industries	Suzuki Motor
General Motors	Toyota
Honda	Volkswagen

HISTORICAL FINANCIALS
Company Type: Public

Income Statement

FYE: March 31

	REVENUE ($ mil.)	NET INCOME ($ mil.)	NET PROFIT MARGIN	EMPLOYEES
03/16	30,335	1,197	3.9%	46,398
03/15	25,286	1,323	5.2%	44,035
03/14	26,082	1,314	5.0%	40,892
03/13	23,437	364	1.6%	37,745
03/12	24,784	(1,313)	—	37,617
Annual Growth	**5.2%**	**—**		**5.4%**

2016 Year-End Financials

Debt ratio: 0.2%
Return on equity: 14.7%
Cash ($ mil.): 4,075
Current ratio: 1.38
Long-term debt ($ mil.): 3,149

No. of shares (mil.): 597
Dividends
  Yield: 1.3%
  Payout: —
Market value ($ mil.): 4,675

	STOCK PRICE ($) FY Close	P/E High/Low		PER SHARE ($) Earnings	Dividends	Book Value
03/16	7.82	0	0	2.00	0.10	14.21
03/15	10.15	0	0	2.21	0.02	12.08
03/14	44.50	—	—	2.20	0.00	10.97
03/13	29.99	—	—	0.61	0.00	9.12
03/12	17.50	—	—	(3.52)	0.00	9.67
Annual Growth	**(18.2%)**	**—**	**—**	**—**	**—**	**10.1%**

Mediobanca Banca Di Credito Finanziario SpA

There's not much room for mediocrity at Mediobanca. A leading Italian investment bank the firm offers underwriting M&A support wholesale banking and financial advisory to corporate clients worldwide. It also offers retail banking private banking factoring credit management and leasing services. Despite being known as a top investment bank nearly 50% of Mediobanca's revenue comes from its Retail and Consumer Banking businesses which include Compass Futuro Compass RE Creditech and CheBanca! About 40% of its revenue comes from its Corporate and Investment Banking division. Mediobanca's international offices are in Frankfurt Istanbul London Madrid Mexico City New York and Paris.

Operations

Mediobanca operates four divisions. The bank's Retail and Consumer Banking (RCB) business (which made up 48% of its total revenue during fiscal 2015 ended June 30 2015) counts its consumer credit and retail banking business which includes Compass Futuro Compass RE Creditech and CheBanca! Mediobanca's Corporate and Investment Banking (CIB) division (37% of revenue) consists of the Wholesale Banking (WSB) unit which includes lending structured finance and investment banking; as well as the Private Banking (PB) unit which counts Compagnie Monegasque de Banque Spafid and Prudentia and 50% of Banca Esperia pro rata. The Principal Investing (PI) division (12% of revenue) mostly counts the bank's 13% equity stake in Assicurazioni Generali. The Corporate division (3% of revenue) houses other businesses including the leasing business.

Broadly speaking about 75% of Mediobanca's revenue came from interest and similar income (about three-fourths of which came from retail loans) in FY2015 while about 15% came from fee and commission income. Around 47% of its euro 30 billion loan book was tied to RCB loans while about 44% was tied to CIB loans.

Geographic Reach

Mediobanca generates most of its business in Italy though it operates international branches and subsidiary offices in Frankfurt Istanbul London Madrid Mexico City New York and Paris. About 80% of its banking revenue came from Italy during FY2015 while 20% came from other parts of Europe. Around 55% of its wholesale banking revenue came from Italy that year while 24% came from the UK and another 16% was split between Germany France and Spain.

Sales and Marketing

About 48% of Mediobanca's revenue came from consumer finance and retail clients in FY2015 while 31% came from wholesale banking clients and 12% came from principal investing clients.

Financial Performance

Note: Growth rates may differ after conversion to US dollars. This analysis uses financials from the company's annual report.

Mediobanca's annual revenues and profits have been growing over the past few years with revenue growing more than 25% since fiscal 2013 (ended June). The bank's revenue jumped 12% to euro 2.05 billion ($2.27 billion) during FY2015 while net profit rose 27% to euro 590 million ($654.57 million).

Strategy

Mediobanca plans to continue building its capital-light fee-generating businesses to boost its overall profitability. Indeed during FY2015 the bank generated 47% of its before-tax profit from its Corporate and Investment Banking (CIB) division despite it making up 37% of its revenue. By comparison Mediobanca's interest-focused Retail and Consumer Banking (RCB) division generated nearly half of the group's revenue but only 17% of its profit. Mergers and AcquisitionsIn August 2015 Mediobanca agreed to buy a 51% majority interest in London-based credit asset manager and advisory firm Cairn Capital Group. The move would continue to build on Mediobanca's international Alternative Asset Management business which involves strategic partnerships with asset managers with strong track records "high quality" management teams and scalable platforms.

HISTORY

Company BackgroundIn 1946 the three Italian "banks of national interest" Banca Commerciale Italiana (Comit) Credito Italiano (now Unicredito Italiano) and Banco di Roma (now part of Banca di Roma) founded Mediobanca to offer medium-term credit a market they were barred from.

Enrico Cuccia was with Comit at the time Mediobanca was formed and moved over to head the new institution. In 1955 he created the shareholder structure that later caused a twin uproar in Italian banking and politics: Although the state owned well more than half of the bank's shares a group of wealthy shareholders who together owned less than 10% of the bank wielded the power.

Over the next several decades Cuccia and Mediobanca operated on the behalf of these powerful shareholders and their family businesses devising deals on terms that other companies could not get. Mediobanca also created a web of cross-holdings in other banks which made money for the bank by selling its funds and other services.

In the 1960s and 1970s the bank was at the center of a number of deals not all of which were stellar successes. The bank engineered a merger between Pirelli and Dunlop which fizzled and also

pushed the merger of chemical companies Montecatini and Edison into Montedison which took a beating in the marketplace.

In 1982 Cuccia ostensibly retired taking the title of honorary chairman. However his influence never waned and the 1980s brought a war for the soul of Italian business. In 1985 Romano Prodi head of IRI the state-run organization (liquidated in 2000) that owned nearly 60% of the bank planned to privatize the bank. Instead the noble wing came up with its own privatization plan: The private shareholders requested that the state bring its stake in Mediobanca to below 50% by selling some of its shares to the Mediobanca cabal. In 1988 the privatization went through but as part of the pact it was stipulated that the new shareholders would share decision-making powers with the Ala Nobile.

If the 1980s were wild the 1990s were out of control. Italy's banking industry hampered by red tape and old alliances was left behind the rest of Europe. Many of Italy's banks became stock companies when banking laws changed and many merged to compete in the European Union. Many of those deals threatened Mediobanca's hegemony so it tried to block them. The bank nixed Unicredito's 1998 bid for Comit (which instead merged with Banca Intesa) as well as Sanpaolo IMI's 1999 offer for Banca di Roma.

In 2000 the bank still keeping a grip on the wheels of finance orchestrated investment firm Compart's buyout of Montedison (the merged entity took the Montedison name). That year the company launched an online private banking joint venture with Banca Mediolanum.

Also in 2000 its 46-year relationship with Lazard ended when the international investment banker announced plans to sell back to Mediobanca its 4% stake in the company along with its nearly 5% stake in Assicurazioni Generali.

After Cuccia's death in 2000 successor Vincenzo Maranghi battled such controlling shareholders as the Agnelli and Pirelli families and Deutsche Bank over the bank's future. These shareholders wanted to bring Mediobanca into the modern world by possibly merging it with another top Italian bank or even separating its investment management operations from its investment banking which generates a large majority of Mediobanca's profits.

However in a bid to stick to the old ways Maranghi arranged for backing (in exchange for a small stake in Mediobanca) from Swiss Life. Maranghi was blamed in part for the bank's decline: He forced out some of the investment banking division's top talent in the late 1990s and eventually resigned in 2003

Despite efforts to become more open some of the mystery surrounding Mediobanca remains. The shareholder dispute erupted after the death of Cuccia (whose body was subsequently robbed from its grave and later found).

Maranghi's replacement Gabriele Galateri di Genola had his work cut out for him repairing cracks in Mediobanca's image but he saw profits rise considerably. Under his watch the group has made its first foray into operations abroad opening an office in Paris. By 2004 the company posted improved financial results for a second consecutive year including a 20% increase in investment banking fees.

Galateri di Genola resigned from Mediobanca in 2007 after he lost the support of the supervisory board. He was succeeded by Alberto Nagel the company's general manager.

EXECUTIVES

President Titolare, RENATO PAGLIARO
Amministratore Delegato, ALBERTO NAGEL
Vice Presidente, MARCO TRONCHETTI PROVERA
Vice Presidente, MAURIZIA ANGELO COMNENO
Consigliere, GILBERTO BENETTON
Consigliere, MARINA NATALE
Consigliere, ALEXANDRA YOUNG
Consigliere, MARIE CANDICE GAELLE BOLLORE'
Consigliere, MAURIZIO COSTA
Consigliere, VANESSA FRANCOISE MARIE LABERENNE
Auditors: PricewaterhouseCoopers S.p.A.

LOCATIONS

HQ: Mediobanca Banca Di Credito Finanziario SpA
Piazzetta Enrico Cuccia 1, Milan 20121
Phone: (39) 02 8829 1   Fax: (39) 02 882 9367
Web: www.mediobanca.it

PRODUCTS/OPERATIONS

2015 Sales

	% of total
Retail and consumer banking	50
Corporate and private banking	32
Principal investing	15
Corporate center	3
Total	**100**

COMPETITORS

Banca Carige	Goldman Sachs
Banca Popolare di	Interbanca
Milano	Intesa Sanpaolo
Banco di Desio	Lazard
CREDEM	Morgan Stanley
Credit Suisse	UBS Investment Bank
Deutsche Bank	UniCredit
Gemina	Vontobel

HISTORICAL FINANCIALS

Company Type: Public

Income Statement

FYE: June 30

	ASSETS ($ mil.)	NET INCOME ($ mil.)	INCOME AS % OF ASSETS	EMPLOYEES
06/16	77,542	671	0.9%	4,036
06/15	79,005	658	0.8%	3,790
06/14	96,213	634	0.7%	3,688
06/13	95,201	(235)	—	3,673
06/12	99,026	101	0.1%	3,652
Annual Growth	**(5.9%)**	**60.3%**	**—**	**2.5%**

2016 Year-End Financials

Return on assets: 0.8%
Return on equity: 6.7%
Long-term debt ($ mil.): —
No. of shares (mil.): 855
Sales ($ mil): 3,176

Dividends
Yield: 2.9%
Payout: 23.0%
Market value ($ mil.): 5,046

	STOCK PRICE ($) FY Close	P/E High/Low		PER SHARE ($) Earnings	Dividends	Book Value
06/16	5.90	16	7	0.78	0.17	11.59
06/15	7.71	11	11	0.75	0.11	11.42
06/14	5.31	—	—	0.72	0.00	12.83
06/13	5.31	—	—	(0.26)	0.04	10.76
06/12	3.50	58	36	0.11	0.00	9.85
Annual Growth	**13.9%**	—	—	**61.9%**	**—**	**4.1%**

Medipal Holdings Corp

In Japan Medipal Holdings keeps drug and household products retailers well-stocked. Its primary business is the wholesale distribution of prescription and OTC pharmaceuticals medical supplies cosmetics and personal sundries. In addition to supplying some 300000 Japanese pharmacies and retail stores Medipal distributes to hospitals and provides information technology support to its customers through its numerous subsidiaries and affiliates including Mediceo Everlth Atol and Paltac. Its MP Agro subsidiary distributes animal health products.

Operations

Medipal's Animal Health Products Wholesale business sells animal health products raw materials for processing food and food additives.

Geographic Reach

The company operates from more than 300 bases in Japan.

Sales and Marketing

Medipal has more than 4000 sales representatives working nationwide.

Financial Performance

Medipal has experienced rising revenues over the past few years but saw a 3% decline in revenue to ¥2.9 trillion in fiscal 2015 (ended March) as all segments —Prescription Pharmaceutical Wholesale; Cosmetics Daily Necessities and OTC Pharmaceutical Wholesale; and Animal Health Products Wholesale —slipped. Net income decreased 7% to ¥23 billion due to the lower revenue and lower non-operating income such as research fee earnings.

However the company reported an operating cash inflow of ¥80 billion in fiscal 2015 (versus an outflow in 2014) due to changes in notes and accounts receivable.

Strategy

Medipal is focused on marketing of new prescription products as well as niche prescription offerings including subsidized vaccines and lifestyle disease drugs. In addition it is investing in R&D firms to contribute to the development of new pharmaceuticals with the condition that it receives an option to exclusively market the drugs if they gain regulatory approval. The company is also adding new services for retail cosmetic and OTC outlets such as point-of-sale marketing tools.

The company is also investing in its distribution infrastructure including in the area of disaster readiness so that stock-outs are prevented.

Company Background

Medipal was formed when Mediceo Holdings took over household products distributor Paltac in 2005. Paltac brought with it a distribution network and logistical prowess which allowed the new firm to move further into the OTC and non-drugs business. Previously Mediceo Holdings become Japan's largest drug wholesaler in 2004 when it was formed through the merger of three smaller drug wholesalers (Kuraya Pharmaceuticals Sanseido and Tokyo Iyakuhin).

EXECUTIVES

Director and General Manager Sales Division; President and Chief Executive Director KURAYA SANSEIDO, Shuichi Watanabe
Managing Executive Officer, Toshio Hirasawa
Director, Takuro Hasegawa
Director, Kazushi Takao
Executive Officer; Deputy Chief Director of System, Kazuki Kakutani
President of Subsidiary; Director, Koji Orime
Executive Officer; Deputy Chief Director of Business Development, Kuniaki Imagawa
Executive Officer, Masanori Kawara
President of Subsidiary; Director, Yasuhiro Chofuku
Auditors: KPMG AZSA LLC

LOCATIONS

HQ: Medipal Holdings Corp
2-7-15 Yaesu, Chuo-ku, Tokyo 104-8461
Phone: (81) 3 3517 5800   **Fax:** (81) 3 3517 5811
Web: www.medipal.co.jp

PRODUCTS/OPERATIONS

2015 Sales
% of toal

Prescription Pharmaceutical Wholesale	71
Cosmetics Daily Necessities and OTC Pharmaceutical Wholesale	28
Animal Health Products Wholesale	1
Total	0 100

Selected Divisions and Brands
Atol Co.
Butsuryu 24
Everlth Co.
Kuraya (USA)
Mediceo
M.I.C. (Medical Information College)
MM Corporation
MP Agro
Paltac
Tokimo Co.
Trim Co.

COMPETITORS

Alfresa   Toho Pharmaceutical
Suzuken

HISTORICAL FINANCIALS
Company Type: Public

Income Statement
FYE: March 31

	REVENUE ($ mil.)	NET INCOME ($ mil.)	NET PROFIT MARGIN	EMPLOYEES
03/16	26,966	274	1.0%	20,473
03/15	23,945	197	0.8%	20,398
03/14	28,558	246	0.9%	10,930
03/13	29,874	198	0.7%	11,115
03/12	33,527	142	0.4%	11,194
Annual Growth	(5.3%)	17.9%	—	16.3%

2016 Year-End Financials
Debt ratio: 0.0%
Return on equity: 7.6%
Cash ($ mil.): 1,499
Current ratio: 1.17
Long-term debt ($ mil.): 108
No. of shares (mil.): 226
Dividends
 Yield: 0.0%
 Payout: —
Market value ($ mil.): 3,628

	STOCK PRICE ($) FY Close	P/E High/Low	Earnings	PER SHARE ($) Dividends	Book Value
03/16	16.02	0 0	1.21	0.22	16.32
03/15	11.23	0 0	0.87	0.20	14.37
03/14	14.94	— —	1.09	0.00	17.47
03/13	12.21	— —	0.87	0.00	18.01
03/12	12.43	— —	0.60	0.00	18.51
Annual Growth	6.5%	— —	18.9%	—	(3.1%)

Medtronic PLC

Auditors: PricewaterhouseCoopers LLP

LOCATIONS

HQ: Medtronic PLC
20 On Hatch, Lower Hatch Street, Dublin 55432
Phone: (353) 1 438 1700
Web: www.medtronic.com

HISTORICAL FINANCIALS
Company Type: Public

Income Statement
FYE: April 29

	REVENUE ($ mil.)	NET INCOME ($ mil.)	NET PROFIT MARGIN	EMPLOYEES
04/16	28,833	3,538	12.3%	88,000
04/15	20,261	2,675	13.2%	92,000
04/14	17,005	3,065	18.0%	49,247
04/13	16,590	3,467	20.9%	46,659
04/12	16,184	3,617	22.3%	44,944
Annual Growth	15.5%	(0.6%)	—	18.3%

2016 Year-End Financials
Debt ratio: 31.3%
Return on equity: 6.6%
Cash ($ mil.): 2,876
Current ratio: 3.29
Long-term debt ($ mil.): 30,247
No. of shares (mil.): 1,399
Dividends
 Yield: 1.9%
 Payout: 106.2%
Market value ($ mil.): 110,732

	STOCK PRICE ($) FY Close	P/E High/Low	Earnings	PER SHARE ($) Dividends	Book Value
04/16	79.15	32 26	2.48	1.52	37.21
04/15	77.61	32 24	2.41	0.31	37.44
04/14	58.21	20 15	3.02	1.12	19.46
04/13	46.36	14 11	3.37	1.04	18.38
04/12	37.69	13 9	3.41	0.97	16.50
Annual Growth	20.4%	— —	(7.7%)	11.9%	22.5%

Mega International Commercial Bank Co Ltd

Commercial banks not chartered

EXECUTIVES

President, Yu Tsai Tsai
Auditors: PricewaterhouseCoopers, Taiwan

LOCATIONS

HQ: Mega International Commercial Bank Co Ltd
 No. 100, Chi-lin Road, Taipei 10424
Phone: (886) 2 2563 3156   **Fax:** (886) 2 2356 8936
Web: www.megabank.com.tw

HISTORICAL FINANCIALS
Company Type: Public

Income Statement
FYE: December 31

	ASSETS ($ mil.)	NET INCOME ($ mil.)	INCOME AS % OF ASSETS	EMPLOYEES
12/15	93,997	782	0.8%	5,647
12/14	93,953	820	0.9%	5,600
12/13	94,550	630	0.7%	5,542
12/12	84,186	654	0.8%	5,471
12/11	76,711	495	0.6%	5,803
Annual Growth	5.2%	12.1%	—	(0.7%)

2015 Year-End Financials
Return on assets: 0.8%
Return on equity: 10.8%
Long-term debt ($ mil.): —
No. of shares (mil.): —
Sales ($ mil): 2,071
Dividends
 Yield: —
 Payout: —
Market value ($ mil.): —

Meiji Yasuda Life Insurance Co.

Meiji Yasuda Life Insurance knows the value of life. The company one of Japan's largest life insurers offers individual life and annuities group life and pensions and investment products. It also has some general insurance health care and investment and financial services operations. Meiji Yasuda provides its products to a range of customers including individuals small businesses and corporations. The company has about ¥204 billion of life insurance policies in force and some 6.6 million policy holders. While most of its operations are in Japan Meiji Yasuda operates in Asia Europe and North America.

Operations

The company's operating segments include Individual Insurance Marketing Group Insurance Marketing General Agent Marketing and Asset Management.

Geographic Reach

Meiji Yasuda is headquartered in Tokyo. It also has about 75 regional offices 20 marketing centers and some 1000 agency locations. It has international affiliate locations in 10 global cities: Beijing Frankfurt Hong Kong Honolulu London Los Angeles New York Seoul Shanghai and Warsaw.

Sales and Marketing

The company sells its products through an internal sales force of about 30000 personnel. It makes some sales to banks and other financial institutions through general agents.

Financial Performance

Meiji Yasuda reported a 1% revenue increase to ¥4781 billion (about $46 billion) in 2013 due to higher interest and dividends on investment securities as well as gains on securities sold and redeemed. Net income increase 2% to ¥240 billion that year as a result of the higher earnings and lower claims paid.

Cash flow from operations slipped 11% to ¥1138 billion in 2013 due to changes in non-investment assets and an increase in reinsurance accounts payable.

Strategy

Meiji Yasuda is especially focused on growth in international markets. Through a partnership with Talanx for instance the company is investing in the German insurance market. It has also expanded its operations in countries including Poland Indonesia and China through partnerships and by investing in minority ownership of global insurance entities. In the US the company acquired StanCorp Financial Group (parent of Standard Insurance) for $5 billion in 2016. That company is now Meiji Yasuda's primary US unit.

In addition Meiji Yasuda works to expand its domestic life insurance business as well as on entering other health related markets in Japan such as the nursing home business. In 2013 the company introduced an educational endowment insurance product to help customers prepare for educational expenses; it also launched bicycle insurance and medical insurance for child dependents (including hospitalization coverage).

Also in 2013 Meiji Yasuda introduced its Meister Mobile tablet terminals designed to make the application process easier and faster.

Other strategies include increasing risk management efforts across the company's operations to strengthen its finances and its capital base.

Mergers and Acquisitions

To take advantage of the growing Indonesian life insurance market Meiji Yasuda bumped up its stake in Indonesian partner PT Avrist Assurance from 23% to nearly 30% in 2013.

Company Background

Tracing its roots back to 1881 Meiji Yasuda in its current incarnation was formed through the merger of Meiji Life Insurance and Yasuda Mutual Life in 2004. Prior to their merger Meiji Life and Yasuda Mutual Life were part of the Mitsubishi Group and Mizuho Financial Group respectively.

EXECUTIVES

President, Akio Negishi
Senior Managing Executive Officers, Yasushi Wada
Chief General Manager Tokyo Marketing Headquarters, Katsunari Maeda
Senior Managing Executive Officers, Hiroshi Tokuoka
Chief Executive Investment, Toshihiko Yamashita
Chief Executive Individual Insurance Marketing, Takashi Ito
Chief Executive General Agent Marketing, Tatsuo Ogoshi
Managing Executive Officers, Hiromasa Suzuki
Managing Executive Officers, Masahiro Ifuku
Managing Executive Officers, Kikuo Asano
Chief Executive Group Marketing, Akio Sakai
Managing Executive Officers, Masahiko Sagara
Managing Executive Officers, Shigeru Kawamoto
Chief General Manager Nagoya Marketing Headquarters, Kazuhito Nakakuma
Managing Executive Officers, Tadashi Onishi
General Manager Product Development Department, Shinya Makino
General Manager Agency Department, Takashi Tsunematsu
General Manager Corporate Market Development Department, Tetsuo Maejima
Chief General Manager Osaka Marketing Headquarters, Takashi Kikugawa
General Manager General Agent Channel Department, Yasuyuki Ayai
General Manager International Business Department, Kazunori Yamauchi
Chairman of the Board, Nobuya Suzuki

LOCATIONS

HQ: Meiji Yasuda Life Insurance Co.
2-1-1 Marunouchi, Chiyoda-ku, Tokyo 100-0005
Phone: (81) 3 3283 8293   **Fax:** (81) 3 3215 8123
Web: www.meijiyasuda.co.jp

PRODUCTS/OPERATIONS

Selected Subsidiaries
Meiji Yasuda America Incorporated
Meiji Yasuda Asia Limited
Meiji Yasuda Europe Limited
Meiji Yasuda Realty USA Incorporated
Pacific Guardian Life Insurance Company Limited
Pacific Guardian Life Insurance Company Limited

COMPETITORS

AXA Life Insurance	Mitsui Life
American Life Insurance	Nippon Life Insurance
Asahi Mutual Life	Prudential
Dai-ichi Life	Samsung Life Insurance
Daido Life	Sumitomo Life
Fukoku Mutual	T&D Holdings
Gibraltar Life Insurance	Taiyo Life
	Tokio Marine

HISTORICAL FINANCIALS
Company Type: Public

Income Statement
FYE: March 31

	REVENUE ($ mil.)	NET INCOME ($ mil.)	NET PROFIT MARGIN	EMPLOYEES
03/15	37,189	2,212	5.9%	40,793
03/14	44,758	2,331	5.2%	37,129
03/13	48,296	2,515	5.2%	0
03/12	71,958	2,105	2.9%	0
03/11	55,968	1,586	2.8%	0
Annual Growth	(9.7%)	8.7%		

2015 Year-End Financials

Debt ratio: —
Return on equity: 7.5%
Cash ($ mil.): 2,000
Current ratio: 1,033.07
Long-term debt ($ mil.): —
No. of shares (mil.): —
Dividends
Yield: —
Payout: —
Market value ($ mil.): —

Metallurgical Corp China Ltd

Engineering services nsk

EXECUTIVES

Chairman, Heting Shen
Auditors: PricewaterhouseCoopers Zhong Tian CPAs Limited Company

LOCATIONS

HQ: Metallurgical Corp China Ltd
MCC Tower, 28 Shuguang Xili, Chaoyang District, Beijing 100028
Phone: (86) 10 59868666   **Fax:** (86) 10 59868999
Web: www.mccchina.com

HISTORICAL FINANCIALS
Company Type: Public

Income Statement
FYE: December 31

	REVENUE ($ mil.)	NET INCOME ($ mil.)	NET PROFIT MARGIN	EMPLOYEES
12/15	33,462	739	2.2%	0
12/14	34,768	638	1.8%	0
12/13	33,480	492	1.5%	0
12/12	35,468	(1,115)	—	0
12/11	36,496	674	1.8%	127,746
Annual Growth	(2.1%)	2.3%		

2015 Year-End Financials

Debt ratio: 3.6%
Return on equity: 8.9%
Cash ($ mil.): 5,193
Current ratio: 1.17
Long-term debt ($ mil.): 4,655
No. of shares (mil.): —
Dividends
Yield: —
Payout: —
Market value ($ mil.): —

	STOCK PRICE ($) FY Close	P/E High/Low	PER SHARE ($) Earnings	Dividends	Book Value
12/15	3.39	— —	0.04	0.12	(0.00)
12/14	3.39	16 16	0.03	0.16	(0.00)
12/13	3.36	— —	0.03	0.00	(0.00)
12/12	3.36	— —	(0.06)	0.00	(0.00)
12/11	4.79	44 22	0.03	0.00	0.40
Annual Growth	(8.3%)	— —	1.4%	—	—

Metro AG

A ride on this METRO could be a shopper's delight. Germany's über retailer the company ranks fourth in the world (behind Wal-Mart Carrefour and Tesco). METRO owns and operates more than 2200 wholesale stores supermarkets hypermarkets department stores and the fast-growing Media Markt and Saturn consumer electronics chains. More than 930 of its shops are in Germany but METRO also has stores in about 30 other countries including China Egypt France India Russia and Vietnam. Store banners include METRO and Makro Cash & Carry wholesale outlets Real hypermarkets and Galeria Kaufhof department stores. METRO is also launching e-commerce platforms for each of its retail businesses.

Operations

The German retail group comprises five units: Metro Cash & Carry self-service wholesale stores (about half of revenue); Media Markt Saturn and Redcoon consumer electronics stores; Real hypermarkets; Galeria Kaufhof department stores in Germany and Belgium; and METRO Properties the group's international real estate arm with properties in about 30 countries. METRO Cash & Carry and Makro wholesale outlets which sell food and other grocery and non-grocery items to businesses and institutional customers account for nearly 50% of group sales while Media-Saturn is Europe's #1 seller of consumer electronics with about 985 locations in 15 countries. With about 140 department stores Galeria Kaufhof is a leading Germany department store chain. Real operates about 425 hypermarkets mostly in Germany but also in Eastern Europe including Poland and Romania.

Geographic Reach

Germany is METRO AG's largest market accounting for about a quarter of sales. About 25 other countries in Western and Eastern Europe account for another quarter while Asia and Africa (4%) and a blanket International category (37%) make up the rest.

Financial Performance

Euro zone currency and debt woes have negatively impacted METRO AG's operations over the years causing fluctuations in revenue and net income. In fiscal 2014 revenue was euro 63 billion or about 4% lower than the previous year. A "very negative" currency environment the disposal of some assets and generally lower sales all contributed to the result. A decrease in selling and in interest expenses lead to a euro 162 gain in net income from a net loss the previous year.

Strategy

METRO AG is focused on growth - of products number of stores and the bottom line. To that end it has been working to streamline its organization and use technology to introduce new products and services. The company is also interested in expanding outside its home market particularly by opening new stores in locations where it already has a foothold namely Brazil Russia India and China. In 2014 it invested more than euro 1200 million in modernizing and refurbishing stores as well as purchasing real estate for its Galeria Kaufhof unit.

HISTORY

Company Background

Otto Beisheim founded METRO SB-Grossmarkte in the German town of Mulheim in 1964. A wholesale business serving commercial customers it operated under the name METRO Cash & Carry. Three years later Beisheim received backing from the owners of Franz Haniel & Cie (an industrial company founded in 1756) and members of the Schmidt-Ruthenbeck family (also in wholesaling). This allowed METRO to expand rapidly in Germany and in 1968 into the Netherlands under the name Makro Cash & Carry via a partnership with Steenkolen Handelsvereeniging (SHV). During the 1970s the company expanded its wholesaling operations within Europe and moved into retailing.

METRO's foray into retailing was aided during the next decade by the acquisition of department store chain Kaufhof AG. By the 1980s the rise of specialty stores had many department stores on the defensive and Kaufhof's owners sold it to METRO and its investment partner Union Bank of Switzerland.

As METRO's ownership interest in Kaufhof rose above 50% the chain began converting some of its stores from department stores into fashion and sporting goods sellers. Kaufhof began acquiring a stake in computer manufacturer and retailer Vobis in 1989. In 1993 METRO now operating as METRO Holding AG acquired a majority interest in supermarket company Asko Deutsche Kaufhaus which owned the Praktiker building materials chain. The reclusive Beisheim retired from active management the following year.

To cut costs and prepare for expansion into Asia in 1996 METRO Holding merged its German retail holdings —Kaufhof; Asko; another grocery operation Deutsche SB Kauf; and its German cash-and-carry operations —into one holding company METRO AG.

EXECUTIVES

Chairman, Olaf Koch, age 46
CFO, Mark Frese, age 52
Vice Chairman, Werner Klockhaus, age 56
Chairman, Franz M. Haniel, age 61
Auditors: KPMG AG

LOCATIONS

HQ: Metro AG
  Metro-Strafe 1, Duesseldorf 40235
Phone: (49) 211 6886 0   **Fax:** (49) 211 68 86 20 00
Web: www.metrogroup.de

2014 Sales

	% of total
International	37
Germany	25
Western Europe(excl. Germany	19
Europe	15
Asia & Africa	4
Consolidation	-
Total	**100**

2014 Stores

	No.
Western Europe	
Germany	951
Other countries	620
Eastern Europe	498
Asia & Africa	131
Total	**2,200**

PRODUCTS/OPERATIONS

2014 Sales

	% of total
Cash & carry	48
Media-Saturn	33
Real	14
Galeria Kaufhof	5
Other	-
Total	**100**

2014 Stores

	No.
Media Markt & Saturn	986
METRO Cash & Carry	766
Real	311
Galeria Kaufhof	137
Total	**2,200**

Selected Operations

Wholesale Stores
  Makro
  Metro Cash & Carry (wholesale stores)
Food
  Extra (supermarkets)
  Real (hypermarkets)
Nonfood Specialty Stores
  Media Markt (consumer electronics)
  Saturn (consumer electronics)
Department Store
  Galeria Kaufhof
Other Operations
  Dinea Gastronomie (restaurants/catering)
  METRO MGE Einkauf (purchasing)
  METRO MGI Informatik (IT services)
  METRO Real Estate Management (construction services)
  METRO Werbegesellschaft (advertising)
  METRO Online AG (Internet retailer)
  MGB METRO Buying Group Hong Kong Ltd.
    (purchasing Asia and Non-European Union countries)

COMPETITORS

ALDI	Marktkauf
Ahold Delhaize	Maxeda
Best Buy	REWE
Carrefour	Tengelmann
Casino Guichard	Tesco
Edeka Zentrale	Wal-Mart
Lidl	

HISTORICAL FINANCIALS

Company Type: Public

Income Statement

	REVENUE ($ mil.)	NET INCOME ($ mil.)	NET PROFIT MARGIN	EMPLOYEES
09/15	66,393	753	1.1%	233,962
09/14	79,352	159	0.2%	264,142
09/13*	62,520	(95)	—	278,594
12/12	87,965	3	0.0%	288,107
12/11	86,275	816	0.9%	280,856
Annual Growth	**(6.3%)**	**(2.0%)**	**—**	**(4.5%)**

*Fiscal year change

2015 Year-End Financials

Debt ratio: 29.8%
Return on equity: 13.2%
Cash ($ mil.): 4,949
Current ratio: 0.92
Long-term debt ($ mil.): 5,304

No. of shares (mil.): 324
Dividends
  Yield: 2.4%
  Payout: 5.6%
Market value ($ mil.): 1,766

	STOCK PRICE ($) FY Close	P/E High/Low		Earnings	Dividends	Book Value
09/15	5.45	4	2	2.31	0.13	17.92
09/14	6.48	24	16	0.49	0.00	19.37
09/13*	7.98	—	—	(0.30)	0.17	21.57
12/12	5.60	832547		0.01	0.23	24.50
12/11	7.81	8	4	2.50	0.22	25.40
Annual Growth	**(8.6%)**	**—**	**—**	**(1.9%)**	**(12.3%)**	**(8.4%)**

*Fiscal year change

Mitsubishi Chemical Holdings Corp

Mitsubishi Chemical Holdings is the largest chemical manufacturer in Japan. Subsidiary Mitsubishi Chemical Corporation produces a wide variety of petrochemicals specialty chemicals and the like. Another unit Mitsubishi Plastics manufactures plastics and films data storage devices such as CDs and DVDs as well as chemicals for semiconductor manufacturing. Mitsubishi Tanabe Pharma makes pharmaceutical products for central nervous system cardiovascular and gastrointestinal disorders in addition to OTC and anti-inflammatory drugs. Mitsubishi Rayon as its fourth business unit.

Mitsubishi Chemical Holdings serves customers in the performance products health care and industrial material markets. Its major products include optical recording media polymer films plastics pharmaceuticals purified terephthalic acid synthetic fibers and a range of polymers. It has more than 340 consolidated subsidiaries and more than 60 affiliated companies.

The company has major operations in Australia India North Asia Southeast Asia Europe and the US.

In Fiscal 2012 Mitsubishi Chemical Holdings reported a 1% drop in revenues (in local currency) as the company's growth in production was offset by weak economic conditions in Japan (still recovering from the major earthquake in 2011) the appreciation of the yen Europe's economic slowdown and the industrial disruption caused by floods in Thailand. However it posted a 36% drop in net income (in local currency) largely due to higher current and deferred taxes.

In 2010 Mitsubishi Chemical Holdings spent $2.4 billion to purchase Mitsubishi Rayon a manufacturer of monomers and polymers which became the holding company's fourth line of business. It is also the world's #1 maker of methyl methacrylate (a common and versatile plastic also known as MMA) through its 2008 acquisition of Lucite.

Earlier the company merged the former Mitsubishi Pharma with the former Tanabe Seiyaku to form Mitsubishi Tanabe of which it owns about half. In 2008 the company split off its Performance Products segment into a separate operating subsidiary.

Mitsubishi Chemical Holdings was formed in 2005 as the parent of Mitsubishi Chemical Corporation. The company is a subsidiary of Mitsubishi Corporation.

EXECUTIVES

Senior Managing Corporate Executive Officer, Noriyoshi Ohira

Senior Managing Corporate Executive Officer, Masanori Karatsu

President and CEO, Hitoshi Ochi

Senior Managing Corporate Executive Officer, Kenkichi Kosakai

Managing Corporate Executive Officer, Steve P. Yurich

Vice Chairman, Takumi Ubagai

Chairman, Yoshimitsu Kobayashi

Vice Chairman, Hiroaki Ishizuka

Auditors: Ernst & Young ShinNihon LLC

LOCATIONS

HQ: Mitsubishi Chemical Holdings Corp
1-1-1 Marunouchi, Chiyoda-ku, Tokyo 100-8251
Phone: (81) 3 6748 7115
Web: www.mitsubishichem-hd.co.jp

2014 Sales

	% of total
Japan	69
Other countries	31
Total	**100**

PRODUCTS/OPERATIONS

2014 Sales

	% of total
Chemicals	26
Polymers	25
Designed Materials	23
Health Care	15
Electronics	4
Other	7
Total	**100**

COMPETITORS

Asahi Kasei	Mitsui Chemicals
Astellas	Nissan Chemical
BASF SE	SABIC Innovative
Bayer AG	Plastics
Chugai	Sinopec Group
Daicel Chemical	Sumitomo Chemical
Daiichi Sankyo	Sumitomo Dainippon
DuPont	Pharma
Evonik Degussa	Takeda Pharmaceutical
Hitachi Chemical	Tokai Carbon
Kyowa Hakko Kirin	Tokuyama

HISTORICAL FINANCIALS

Company Type: Public

Income Statement

FYE: March 31

	REVENUE ($ mil.)	NET INCOME ($ mil.)	NET PROFIT MARGIN	EMPLOYEES
03/16	34,044	413	1.2%	75,955
03/15	30,474	507	1.7%	74,364
03/14	33,897	312	0.9%	56,031
03/13	32,825	197	0.6%	55,131
03/12	39,109	432	1.1%	53,979
Annual Growth	**(3.4%)**	**(1.1%)**	**—**	**8.9%**

2016 Year-End Financials

Debt ratio: 0.3%
Return on equity: 4.8%
Cash ($ mil.): 2,803
Current ratio: 1.35
Long-term debt ($ mil.): 7,681

No. of shares (mil.): 1,464
Dividends
  Yield: 0.0%
  Payout: 219.9%
Market value ($ mil.): 39,054

	STOCK PRICE ($) FY Close	P/E High/Low		PER SHARE ($) Earnings	Dividends	Book Value
03/16	26.67	1	1	0.28	0.62	5.67
03/15	30.42	1	0	0.34	0.50	5.59
03/14	20.81	—	—	0.21	0.00	8.70
03/13	23.85	—	—	0.13	0.00	8.67
03/12	26.99	—	—	0.28	0.00	9.46
Annual Growth (12.0%)	**(0.3%)**	**—**	**—**	**0.5%**		

Mitsubishi Corp

In Japanese mitsubishi means "three diamonds" and Mitsubishi Corporation is one of Japan's crown jewels. The sogo shosha or trading company operates through six main business groups: living essentials (agricultural products food and beverages textiles and construction materials); metals; machinery (power generation equipment electrical systems automobiles); energy (liquefied natural gas crude oil); and chemicals (petrochemicals fertilizers plastics). Its other main business group is industrial finance which handles banking asset management construction and logistics. The company generated most of its fiscal 2012 gross

profit from living essentials (42%) metals (24%) and machinery (16%).

Mitsubishi Corporation is part of the Mitsubishi keiretsu a network of affiliated companies that has no official status as a group but within which there is some cross-ownership and considerable business activity. Other affiliates include Mitsubishi Heavy Industries The Bank of Tokyo-Mitsubishi Mitsubishi Electric Mitsubishi Motors and Nikon.

Mitsubishi operates a network of more than 500 group companies in about 90 countries.

Buoyed by higher energy commodity prices and earlier investments in its chemicals segment the company posted an 8% rise in revenues in fiscal 2012. However lower metals income (due in part to a strike which disrupted coal operations in Australia) and lower automobile manufacturing production (due to flooding in Thailand) dragged down Mitsubishi's net income by 2%.

The Sendai earthquake and tsunami in 2011 severely disrupted the Japanese economy and affected Mitsubishi's operations and domestic revenues and net income that year (limited as it occurred late in the fiscal year). Nevertheless Mitsubishi was able to post an overall growth in revenues and net income thanks to a stronger global economy and an increase in demand for steel products and higher oil prices among other factors.

Mitsubishi has set about strengthening its financial position and devised a strategic growth plan that involves focusing on new operational initiatives including new energy sources and on environment and financial services.

Energy plans include the development of biofuels solar and wind energy technologies as industrial emissions-reducing technologies. It is also looking to ramp up its holdings in the global water business to meet growing water infrastructure demand from emerging economies.

On the financial front Mitsubishi is leveraging the group's financial assets and sheer size to facilitate the financing of its own as well as other companies' growth efforts. With its financial services operations the group is targeting real estate development aircraft and other industrial leasing services and it is considering strategic acquisitions of additional financial services assets.

Growing its metals assets in 2011 Mitsubishi acquired nearly 25% of Anglo American Sur a Chile-based copper mining and smelting company owned by Anglo American plc. Anglo American Sur's copper assets include the Los Bronces mine El Soldado mine and Chagres smelter. The purchase is expected to boost Mitsubishi's attributable copper production to 250000 metric tons per year.

To further expand its metals operations Mitsubishi agreed in 2012 to invest about $95 million to acquire a 25% stake in Stillwater Mining's Marathon PGM (platinum group metals) project in Ontario Canada. The project is expected to produce about 200000 ounces of PGMs and 17000 metric tons of copper per year for about 11 1/2 years. Mitsubishi also has the option to purchase up to 100% of the PGM production. PGMs are used in applications such as automobile catalysts electronic devices and fuel cells.

In 2012 Mitsubishi along with Indian fertilizer company Zuari Industries acquired a 30% stake in Fasfatos del Pacifico (FOSPAC) from a Peruvian cement manufacturer Cementos Pacasmayo. Pacasmayo explores for and produces rock phosphate in Peru and the investment will allow the companies to acquire FOSPAC's rock phosphate production (after fulfillment of local demand) for 20 years. The initial production capacity is expected to be about 2.5 million metric tons per year.

That year the company entered the Indonesian geothermal power market through the acquisition of 20% of Star Energy Geothermal Pte Ltd. Mitsubishi is looking to become further involved in geothermal power generation in countries that possess promising geothermal resources including Japan.

Growing another segment in 2013 the company agreed to buy Kirin's Food Science Business.

To raise cash in 2011 Mitsubishi sold its subsidiary Jicoux Datasystems Inc. to NEC Corp. Jicoux offers a fleet management service for commercial vehicles that includes automatic creation of daily reports based on speed route and distance data collected from in-vehicle devices over the internet. NEC plans to absorb the Jicoux's employees and operations and liquidate the company.

Along with the rest of the Mitsubishi companies Mitsubishi Corporation has been hurt by Japan's persistent economic stagnation. The company has restructured and reduced its workforce in the past decade and it has divided the operations of its former information technology and electronics business among its other groups.

HISTORY

Yataro Iwasaki's close ties to the Japanese government (along with subsidies and monopoly rights) ensured the success of his shipping and trading company Mitsubishi. Founded in 1870 Mitsubishi diversified into mining (1873) banking (1885) and shipbuilding (1887); it began to withdraw from shipping in the 1880s. During the next decade it invested in Japanese railroads and property.

In 1918 the Mitsubishi zaibatsu (conglomerate) spun off its central management arm Mitsubishi Trading (the forerunner of Mitsubishi Corporation). By WWII the group was a huge amalgam of divisions and public companies. During the war it made warplanes ships explosives and beer.

The zaibatsu were dissolved by US occupation forces and Mitsubishi was split into 139 entities. After the occupation the Japanese government encouraged many of the former business groups to reunite around the old zaibatsu banks. In 1954 Mitsubishi Trading became the leader of the Mitsubishi Group and established Mitsubishi International (US) which became a leading exporter of US goods.

The 1964 merger of three Mitsubishi companies created Mitsubishi Heavy Industries a top Japanese maker of ships aircraft plants and heavy machinery. Mitsubishi Kasei separated from Asahi Glass and Mitsubishi Rayon by a US fiat became Japan's #1 chemical concern. Mitsubishi Electric emerged as one of the country's leading electrical equipment and electronics manufacturers. In 1971 Chrysler invested in Mitsubishi Motors which began making cars for the US automaker. That year Mitsubishi Trading was renamed Mitsubishi Corporation.

Through the 1980s Japan seemed economically invincible. Then its "bubble economy" burst. The group fell behind in electronics and autos in the US consumer demand dried up at home and Mitsubishi Bank was left with a heavy burden of bad loans. Group members which traditionally provided materials supplies and sales outlets for each other began loosening old keiretsu ties during Japan's recession of the 1990s.

In 1993 Chrysler sold its stock in Mitsubishi Motors and two years later the companies severed production ties. This loss and declining demand in the US for Mitsubishi cars hurt auto sales.

Mitsubishi Bank merged with Bank of Tokyo in 1996 to form the biggest bank in the world The Bank of Tokyo-Mitsubishi (BTM). In 1997 several Mitsubishi companies admitted paying off a corporate racketeer setting off a wave of executive resignations.

By 1999 BTM had tumbled from the top spot and was unable to keep the money freely flowing to fellow Mitsubishi members.

Hit hard by the Asian economic crisis all the struggling Mitsubishi companies had to look outside of the keiretsu for help. In 1999 Mitsubishi Motors found a foreign partner Volvo for its truck making operations. Mitsubishi Oil merged with an outsider Nippon Oil to form Nippon Mitsubishi Oil (later renamed Nippon Oil). In 2000 DaimlerChrysler (now Chrysler and Daimler) acquired a controlling stake in Mitsubishi Motors for $2.1 billion.

Executives at Mitsubishi Motors were charged in 2001 after they allegedly kept the lid on thousands of reported defects in Mitsubishi cars instead of issuing recalls. Stung by this and the after-effects of scandals from the previous decade Mitsubishi unveiled a new corporate philosophy as part of a strategy to revive the group's reputation.

In 2003 Mitsubishi disbanded its information technology and electronics business unit. The unit's operations were divided between the new business and machinery groups. In 2004 the company formed an alliance with GE Yokogawa Medical Systems (GEYMS) to provide GEYMS with help in developing its presence in the Japanese diagnostic imaging market.

In 2004 the company formed a food distribution joint venture with five Japanese food wholesalers comprising national wholesaler Meidi-ya and four regional companies. The joint venture called Alliance Network became one of Japan's largest food wholesalers. Mitsubishi had a 51% stake in Alliance Network. Later in 2004 Mitsubishi acquired the food beverage additive and pharmaceutical active and excipient businesses of Ashland Distribution.

In 2006 Mitsubishi bolstered its automotive operations when it acquired shares in Isuzu from General Motors; Mitsubishi ended up with a 10% stake in Isuzu. Mitsubishi and Isuzu soon after formed a European joint venture to market light-duty trucks throughout the continent. Later that year Mitsubishi bought the Avon Automotive subsidiary of Avon Rubber in a deal worth $120 million.

The following year Mitsubishi bought majority control of Nosan Corporation a manufacturer of livestock feed. In late 2007 the company acquired the majority interest in Kentucky Fried Chicken Japan.

On the medical health care front Mitsubishi shifted the focus of certain of its subsidiaries to providing services to hospitals and nursing care facilities. It established the Trinity Healthcare Fund in 2007 to provide management support for the restructuring of hospitals and other medical institutions. Other Mitsubishi subsidiaries focused on medical services include ProCure which is a medical equipment wholesale distributor and Apprecia which provides hospital construction consulting services.

During 2007 the group began investing in energy-related assets as part of this strategy. It acquired nearly 40% of Encore Energy Pte. which in turn owns 51% of Medco Energy an Indonesian oil and gas concern. The deal was valued at about $350 million and gave Mitsubishi a 20% stake in Medco. Mitsubishi was already working with Medco on an Indonesian gas plant and the two companies plan to pursue further international energy partnerships.

In 2009 it entered the solar energy business buying 34% of a subsidiary of Spanish renewable energy firm Acciona SA

Mitsubishi in 2010 it merged subsidiaries Mitsubishi Corporation Unimetals and Mitsubishi Shoji Light Metal Sales Corporation. The resulting company was named Mitsubishi Corporation

Unimetals and remained a subsidiary of Mitsubishi. The merger was made to concentrate the company's management expertise in the non-ferrous metals industry.

EXECUTIVES

SEVP, Eiichi Tanabe
EVP; Group CEO Business Service Group, Toshimitsu Urabe
EVP; Regional CEO East Asia, Shunichi Matsui
President and CEO, Takehiko Kakiuchi
EVP; Group CEO Machinery Group, Kazushi Okawa
EVP Corporate Communications, Yasuhito Hirota
EVP; Group CEO Energy Business Group, Hajime Hirano
EVP; Group CEO Metals Group, Kanji Nishiura
EVP Regional Strategy, Kazuyuki Mori
EVP; Regional CEO North America, Hidemoto Mizuhara
EVP and CFO, Kazuyuki Masu
EVP; Group CEO Global Environmental and Infrastructure Business Group, Hiroshi Sakuma
EVP; Regional CEO Europe and Africa, Haruki Hayashi
EVP; Group CEO Chemicals Group, Takeshi Hagiwara
EVP; Group CEO Industrial Finance Logistics and Development Group, Shinya Yoshida
EVP; Group CEO Living Essentials Group, Yutaka Kyoya
SVP; Regional CEO Latin America and the Caribbean, Masaji Santo
SVP; Regional CEO Middle East and Central Asia, Katsuya Nakanishi
Chairman, Ken Kobayashi
Auditors: Deloitte Touche Tohmatsu LLC

LOCATIONS

HQ: Mitsubishi Corp
2-3-1 Marunouchi, Chiyoda-ku, Tokyo 100-8086
Phone: (81) 3 3210 2121
Web: www.mitsubishicorp.com

2016 Sales

	% of total
Japan	66
U.S.A	9
Other countries	25
Total	**100**

PRODUCTS/OPERATIONS

2016 Sales

	% of total
Living Essentials	37
Energy Business	20
Chemicals	19
Machinery	11
Metals	10
Industrial Finance Logistics & Development	2
Global Environmental & Infrastructure Business	1
Total	**100**

Selected Products and Services

Metals
  Bullion and metals futures
  Fabricated steel structures
  Metallurgical and thermal coal
  Nonferrous metal products
  Nonferrous metals
  Nuclear fuel and components
  Precious metals
  Raw materials for steel
  Semifinished products
  Steel materials
  Specialty steel
Living Essentials
  Apparel
  Canned foods
  Ceramic materials
  Cigarettes

Coffee beans coffee and beverages
Confections and snacks
Contract food services
Dairy foods and processed foods
Fabrics
Feedstuffs
Fresh and frozen foods
Grains and agricultural products
Marine products
Meat and livestock
Mineral water
Oils and fats
Photosensitized materials
Pulp paper and packaging materials
Soft drinks
Sweeteners
Textile raw materials
Textiles for industrial use
Tires
Wood wood products and construction materials
Machinery
　Automobiles
　Commercial aviation
　Defense systems and equipment
　Electronics products
　Industrial agricultural construction and other general
　machinery
　Plant and machinery for power generation electricity
　oil/gas/chemicals steel/cement and environmental
　protection
　Project development and construction
　Satellite communications
　Ships
　Space systems
　Transportation systems
Energy
　Carbon materials and products
　Crude oil
　LNG
　LPG
　Orimulsion
　Petroleum products
Industrial Finance Logistics and Development
　Commerce services
　Consumer services
　Financial services
　Logistics
Chemicals
　Fertilizers
　Fine and specialty chemicals
　Inorganic chemicals
　Petrochemicals
　Plastics

COMPETITORS

ITOCHU	Samsung Group
Marubeni	Sime Darby
Mitsui	Sumitomo

HISTORICAL FINANCIALS

Company Type: Public

Income Statement

FYE: March 31

	REVENUE ($ mil.)	NET INCOME ($ mil.)	NET PROFIT MARGIN	EMPLOYEES
03/16	61,672	(1,330)	—	82,203
03/15	63,923	3,338	5.2%	90,048
03/14	73,970	3,500	4.7%	86,190
03/13	63,435	3,826	6.0%	83,891
03/12	67,851	5,532	8.2%	82,792
Annual Growth	(2.4%)	—	—	(0.2%)

2016 Year-End Financials

Debt ratio: 0.3%
Return on equity: (-2.9%)
Cash ($ mil.): 13,366
Current ratio: 1.48
Long-term debt ($ mil.): 40,608
No. of shares (mil.): 1,584
Dividends
　Yield: 2.6%
　Payout: —
Market value ($ mil.): 53,878

	STOCK PRICE ($) FY Close	P/E High/Low	Earnings	PER SHARE ($) Dividends	Book Value
03/16	34.00	— —	(0.83)	0.89	25.81
03/15	40.45	0 0	2.05	1.42	28.65
03/14	37.12	0 0	2.12	1.19	29.78
03/13	37.53	0 0	2.32	1.24	26.97
03/12	46.76	0 0	3.36	1.74	25.99
Annual Growth	(7.7%)	— —	—	(15.3%)	(0.2%)

Mitsubishi Electric Corp.

Auditors: KPMG AZSA LLC

LOCATIONS

HQ: Mitsubishi Electric Corp.
2-7-3 Marunouchi, Chiyoda-ku, Tokyo 100-8310
Phone: (81) 3 3218 2272
Web: www.mitsubishielectric.co.jp

HISTORICAL FINANCIALS

Company Type: Public

Income Statement

FYE: March 31

	REVENUE ($ mil.)	NET INCOME ($ mil.)	NET PROFIT MARGIN	EMPLOYEES
03/16	39,131	2,034	5.2%	135,160
03/15	36,031	1,956	5.4%	129,249
03/14	39,279	1,486	3.8%	124,305
03/13	37,911	738	1.9%	120,958
03/12	44,367	1,366	3.1%	117,314
Annual Growth	(3.1%)	10.5%	—	3.6%

2016 Year-End Financials

Debt ratio: 0.0%
Return on equity: 12.3%
Cash ($ mil.): 5,112
Current ratio: 1.69
Long-term debt ($ mil.): 2,560
No. of shares (mil.): 2,143
Dividends
　Yield: 2.0%
　Payout: 50.1%
Market value ($ mil.): 44,876

	STOCK PRICE ($) FY Close	P/E High/Low	Earnings	PER SHARE ($) Dividends	Book Value
03/16	20.93	0 0	0.95	0.43	7.64
03/15	23.86	0 0	0.91	0.37	7.16
03/14	22.62	0 0	0.69	0.24	6.89
03/13	16.40	1 0	0.34	0.24	6.45
03/12	17.78	0 0	0.64	0.32	6.44
Annual Growth	4.2%	— —	10.5%	8.3%	4.4%

Mitsubishi Heavy Industries Ltd.

Japanese industrial behemoth Mitsubishi Heavy Industries (MHI) is heavy into machinery manufacturing for a myriad of markets. A member of the Mitsubishi keiretsu the group builds and supplies everything from nuclear power plants bridges and aircraft to engines ships and air conditioners to various industries and customers around the world. MHI operates through six business segments: Power Systems Machinery & Steel Structures Aerospace General Machinery & Special Vehicles Shipbuilding & Ocean Development and Others. The company's core market is Japan but it also does business in other parts of Asia North America Europe Central and South America Africa and the Middle East.

As the world continues to transition to a low-carbon society MHI is focused on four key areas for growth. It is trying to meet growing demand for gas turbines especially as industrialized nations work to replace aging facilities in line with tougher environmental regulations. To this end it is trying to commercialize its J-series gas turbines which offer the highest level of heat efficiency in the world. Second it reached an agreement with UK-based utility Scottish and Southern Energy to develop low-carbon energy. Third it took a capital stake in Italy's ATLA to strengthen its gas turbine service network in Europe. Overall service business sales are projected to account for 35% of sales by fiscal 2014. And fourth the company seeks to expand into fast-growing emerging markets such as India and China.

MHI is specifically pushing for greater localization in these emerging markets. Through two joint ventures with Mumbai-based Larsen & Toubro MHI completed two plants in India to manufacture supercritical-pressure boilers as well as steam turbines and generators in response to India's strong electricity demand. In 2010 it launched a Shanghai subsidiary to oversee its air conditioning and refrigeration business. The subsidiary will manufacture commercial air conditioners and truck refrigeration systems with the goal of doubling sales within the first two years.

In more developed countries like the US MHI is building gas and wind turbine assembly plants to expand its network of overseas production sites. In Japan the group's largest market by sales MHI continues to receive orders for gas turbine combined-cycle thermal power plants to replace aging facilities. In the wake of the catastrophic earthquake that struck eastern Japan in early 2011 the company's efforts are focused on trying to improve the safety of its pressurized water reactor plants and collaborating with Hitachi Ltd. to support recovery and stabilize operations at the Fukushima Daiichi Nuclear Power Plant.

In fiscal 2011 MHI's consolidated net sales remained around the same level as in 2010. Sales in 2010 fell nearly 13% from their record high in 2009 as a result of the global economic crisis. Net sales for 2011 rose in the Shipbuilding & Ocean Development segment on increased deliveries of new vessels and in General Machinery & Special Vehicles on increased orders for engines in China turbochargers in Europe and forklifts in Asia and the Middle East. The Others segment consisting of air conditioning and refrigeration systems also reported both in an increase in orders and higher sales of automotive thermal systems and residential and commercial air conditioners. However net sales decreased in the Power Systems Aerospace and Machinery & Steel Structures segments. Lackluster sales of wind turbines commercial aircraft and defense- and space-related products as well as customer postponement of steel and transportation projects contributed to the decrease in sales in these segments.

EXECUTIVES

President and CEO, Shunichi Miyanaga, age 68
EVP, Masahiko Arihara, age 64

SEVP and President and CEO Commercial Aviation and Transportation Systems, Yoichi Kujirai, age 65

EVP and President and CEO Integrated Defense & Space Systems, Hisakazu Mizutani, age 65

EVP and Senior General Manager Nuclear Energy Systems Division Energy & Environment, Ei Kadokami

SEVP and President and CEO Energy and Environment, Kenji Ando

EVP, Koji Hasegawa

EVP Human Resources Labor Relations and Global Personnel, Mutsuo Hiroe

EVP and General Counsel, Takashi Funato, age 64

EVP Chief Regional Officer Latin America and President of Mitsubishi Industrias Pesadas do Brazil Ltda., Yukio Kodama, age 62

EVP President and CEO Machinery Equipment and Infrastructure and Head of Marketing and Innovation Headquarters, Kazuaki Kimura

EVP CFO and Head of Business Strategy Office, Masanori Koguchi

EVP CTO Head of Technology and Innovation Headquarters and Head of Global Business Planning & Operations Headquarters, Michisuke Nayama

EVP Assistant to President and CEO Commercial Aviation and Transportation Systems and President. Mitsubishi Aircraft Corporation, Hiromichi Morimoto

EVP and President Mitsubishi Heavy Industries America Inc., Kiyoshi Okazoe

Chairman, Hideaki Omiya, age 70

Auditors: Ernst & Young ShinNihon LLC

LOCATIONS

HQ: Mitsubishi Heavy Industries Ltd.
2-16-5 Konan, Minato-ku, Tokyo 108-8215
Phone: (81) 3 6716 3111   **Fax:** (81) 3 6716 5800
Web: www.mhi.co.jp

2016 Sales

	% of total
Asia	
Japan	44
Other countries	18
North America	19
Europe	9
Africa	3
Middle East	3
Central and South America	3
Other regions	1
Total	**100**

PRODUCTS/OPERATIONS

2016 Sales

	% of total
Energy & environment	38
Machinery equipment and infrastructure	35
Commercial aviation & transportation systems	14
Integrated defense & space systems.	12
Others	1
Total	**100**

Selected Products

Aerospace
  Aeroengines
  Civil aircraft
  Defense aircraft
  Guided weapon systems
  Laser radar surveillance system
  Launch vehicles
  Rocket engines
  Space stations
General Machinery & Special Vehicles
  Agricultural machinery
  Construction machinery
  Forklift trucks
  Medium- and small-sized engines
  Tractors
  Turbochargers
Machinery & Steel Structures
  Air brakes
  Automated people movers
  Chemical plants
  CO2 recovery plants
  Crane and material handling systems
  Flue gas desulphurization plants
  Injection molding machines
  Monorails
  Production robots
  Rail transit systems
  Sludge treatment systems
  Testing equipment
Power Systems
  Boilers
  Desalination plants
  Fans and blowers
  Diesel engines
  Gas turbines
  Hydraulic equipment (actuators generators motors pumps and water pressure systems)
  Instrumentation and control systems
  Lithium-ion secondary batteries
  Solid oxide fuel cells
  Steam turbines
  Thin-film photovoltaic module
  Wind turbines
Shipbuilding & Ocean Development
  Cargo ships
  Floating facilities
  Marine engines
  Marine machinery
  Passenger ships
  Pure car carriers
  Special-purpose ships
  Tankers
Others
  Air conditioning and refrigeration systems
  Automotive thermal systems
  Centrifugal chillers
  Machine tools

COMPETITORS

ALSTOM
Aker Solutions
BWX Technologies
Baltija Shipbuilding
Bharat Heavy Electricals
Caterpillar
Chiyoda Corp.
DSME
Doosan Heavy Industries
GE
Hanjin Heavy Industries & Construction
Hitachi
Hyundai Heavy Industries
IHI Corp.
Kajima
Kawasaki Heavy Industries
Komatsu
Kubota
MAN
Marubeni
Mitsui Engineering & Shipbuilding
Nippon Sharyo
Nishimatsu Construction
Obayashi
Samsung Heavy Industries
Siemens AG
Sumitomo Heavy Industries
Suzlon Energy Limited
Taisei

HISTORICAL FINANCIALS

Company Type: Public

Income Statement

FYE: March 31

	REVENUE ($ mil.)	NET INCOME ($ mil.)	NET PROFIT MARGIN	EMPLOYEES
03/16	36,036	568	1.6%	100,784
03/15	33,273	920	2.8%	98,442
03/14	32,451	1,554	4.8%	80,583
03/13	29,948	1,034	3.5%	68,213
03/12	34,388	299	0.9%	68,887
Annual Growth	**1.2%**	**17.4%**	**—**	**10.0%**

2016 Year-End Financials

Debt ratio: 0.1%
Return on equity: 3.6%
Cash ($ mil.): 2,765
Current ratio: 1.36
Long-term debt ($ mil.): 5,630

No. of shares (mil.): —
Dividends
  Yield: —
  Payout: —
Market value ($ mil.): —

Mitsubishi Motors Corp. (Japan)

Mitsubishi Motors is a small fish in the big pond of global car manufacturing. The company sells about a million cars per year (far below rival Toyota) worldwide. The 20 models of cars trucks minivans and SUVs are made at its plants in Asia Europe and the US. Mitsubishi products include the Lancer Pajero Triton Mirage and Outlander vehicles. It also offers an electric minicar under its i-MiEV model. Mitsubishi Corporation and Mitsubishi Heavy Industries together own about a 30% stake in Mitsubishi Motors which traces its roots to Heavy Industries' 1917 "Mitsubishi Model A" project. About 80% of sales come from outside of Japan. In 2016 Nissan bought 34% of Mitsubishi Motors for $2.2 billion.

Geographic Reach

Mitsubishi's largest market is Europe representing 24% of net sales. Other major markets include Japan (20%) Asia (19%) North America (13%) Oceania (10%) and other countries (14%). The company operates through seven facilities in four countries; six car manufacturing facilities in four countries; 12 car manufacturing facilities of affiliated companies and business partners in 11 countries and regions; and eight engine transmission and parts manufacturing facilities in five countries.

Operations

Mitsubishi sees its future in electric vehicles which it has been developing since 1966. The company develops plug-in hybrids and other electric vehicles through its research and development facilities and through joint ventures with other auto makers. In 2014 it announced a partnership with Nissan and other car makers to develop and manufacture new electric minicars and promote a charging network.

Mitsubishi already has an electric minicar the i-MiEV on the market in Japan and Europe. (Minicars are a popular vehicle class in the Japanese and European markets and are gaining popularity in other parts of the world.) While it sells in Japan under its own brand the MiEV is sold in Europe through an agreement with French car maker Peugeot S.A. which buys and resells MiEV under a different brand.

Financial Performance

In 2015 Mitsubishi's net sales increased by 4% in 2015 compared to 2014. The growth was driven by increased sales from both its automobile and automobile financing businesses. Stronger North American sales were driven by brisk sales of the Outlander Sport and Mirage as an economic recovery within the US grew stronger.

Mitsubishi's net income also climbed 13% from 2014 to 2015 due to increased sales decreased advertising and promotion expenses an absence of a share issuance cost and gains on a revision of its retirement benefit plan.

Strategy

As it has in years past the company also continues to turn to emerging markets to increase its sales and boost profits. It has been targeting its products to customers in emerging markets like China Russia the Ukraine and other countries in Asia and Eastern Europe. Other sales-boosting initiatives featured a new plant being launched in the Philippines in January 2015. The new plant is continuing with the production of the Adventure and L300 models and produces up to 50000 units per year exceeding the production capacity at a previous plant.

The company was hit by a major scandal in 2016 after it was revealed that it had cheated on fuel economy tests for several years.

In 2014 Mitsubishi acquired Asian Transmission Corporation (ATC) from Mitsubishi Motors Philippines Corporation (MMPC) and Sojitz Corporation (Sojitz) A production base for components ATC supplies transmissions and engines for automobiles and the deal will reinforce Mitsubishi 's production base in the ASEAN countries where the automobile market is expected to experience sustainable growth.

Company Background

Mitsubishi Motors Corporation was created in 1970 when Mitsubishi Heavy Industries spun off its motor vehicle division. Mitsubishi Heavy Industries was created in 1934 by the merger of Mitsubishi Aircraft and Mitsubishi Shipbuilding (which had been making cars since 1917).

EXECUTIVES

EVP Development and Director, Mitsuhiko (Mike) Yamashita

Managing Director and Executive Corporate General Manager Overseas Operations Group Headquarters and Corporate General Manager ASEAN Office, Osamu Masuko

EVP Overseas Operations，Global After Sale and Director, Kozo Shiraji

COO, Trevor Mann

EVP Finance Controlling and Accounting CFO and Director, Koji Ikeya

SVP Head Officer of the Headquarters Production Group Headquarters and Director, Takeshi Ando

Auditors: Ernst & Young ShinNihon LLC

LOCATIONS

HQ: Mitsubishi Motors Corp. (Japan)
5-33-8 Shiba, Minato-ku, Tokyo 108-8410
Phone: (81) 3 3456 1111
Web: www.mitsubishi-motors.com

2015 Sales

	% of total
Europe	24
Japan	20
Asia	19
North America	13
Oceania	10
Other regions	14
Total	**100**

PRODUCTS/OPERATIONS

2015

	%
Automobiles	99
Financial services	1
Total	**100**

Selected Models

Challenger
Colt
Diamante
Eclipse
Eclipse Spyder
Endeavor
Galant
i MiEV
Lancer
Lancer Evolution
Mirage
Outlander
Raider

COMPETITORS

BMW	Kia Motors
Caterpillar	Land Rover
Daihatsu	Mazda
Deere	Nissan
FCA US	Peugeot
Fiat Chrysler	Renault
Ford Motor	Suzuki Motor
Fuji Heavy Industries	Toyota
General Motors	Volkswagen
Hino Motors	Volvo
Honda	smart GmbH
Isuzu	

HISTORICAL FINANCIALS

Company Type: Public

Income Statement

FYE: March 31

	REVENUE ($ mil.)	NET INCOME ($ mil.)	NET PROFIT MARGIN	EMPLOYEES
03/16	20,195	646	3.2%	34,070
03/15	18,175	984	5.4%	35,822
03/14	20,281	1,014	5.0%	30,280
03/13	19,290	403	2.1%	29,822
03/12	22,032	291	1.3%	30,777
Annual Growth	**(2.2%)**	**22.0%**	**—**	**2.6%**

2016 Year-End Financials

Debt ratio: 0.0%
Return on equity: 10.8%
Cash ($ mil.): 4,037
Current ratio: 1.43
Long-term debt ($ mil.): 4

No. of shares (mil.): 983
Dividends
  Yield: —
  Payout: —
Market value ($ mil.): 7,091

	STOCK PRICE ($) FY Close	P/E High/Low		PER SHARE ($) Earnings	Dividends	Book Value
03/16	7.21	0	0	0.66	0.00	6.08
03/15	9.03	0	0	1.00	0.00	5.58
03/14	10.41	—	—	1.01	0.00	5.42
03/13	1.09	—	—	0.39	0.00	6.14
03/12	1.15	—	—	0.03	0.00	0.58
Annual Growth	**58.2%**	—	—	**117.7%**	—	**79.6%**

Mitsubishi Shokuhin Co., Ltd.

Mitsubishi Shokuhin is a leading wholesale food distributor in Japan. It supplies retailers throughout the country with a wide assortment of products including processed foods seasonings and sauces chilled and frozen foods confectionery and canned goods. In addition the company distributes both alcoholic and non-alcoholic beverages. Trading company Mitsubishi Corporation owns just more than 50% of Mitsubishi Shokuhin. Formerly named Ryoshoku the company adopted the Mitsubishi Shokuhin moniker in 2011. It also began absorbing three of its food wholesaling operations —San-Esu Food Service Network and Meidi-ya. The integration is expected to be completed in 2012.

EXECUTIVES

President and CEO, Toru Moriyama
CFO, Daiichiro Suzuki
Division COO Information System Division, Michihiro Taniguchi
President and CEO Mitsubishi Shikoku, Yoichi Ichiura
Auditors: Deloitte Touche Tohmatsu LLC

LOCATIONS

HQ: Mitsubishi Shokuhin Co., Ltd.
6-1-1 Heiwajima, Ota-ku, Tokyo 143-6556
Phone: (81) 3 3767 5111
Web: www.mitsubishi-shokuhin.com

PRODUCTS/OPERATIONS

2016 sales

	% of total
Frozen and chilled foods business	39
Processed food business	32
Alcoholic beverages business	18
Confectioneries business	11
Total	**100**

COMPETITORS

ITOCHU	Kokubu
Kato Sangyo	

HISTORICAL FINANCIALS

Company Type: Public

Income Statement

FYE: March 31

	REVENUE ($ mil.)	NET INCOME ($ mil.)	NET PROFIT MARGIN	EMPLOYEES
03/16	21,221	111	0.5%	6,616
03/15	19,480	81	0.4%	7,022
03/14	23,137	93	0.4%	5,598
03/13	24,644	121	0.5%	5,757
03/12	26,233	149	0.6%	5,867
Annual Growth	**(5.2%)**	**(7.2%)**	**—**	**3.0%**

2016 Year-End Financials

Debt ratio: 0.0%
Return on equity: 8.7%
Cash ($ mil.): 2
Current ratio: 1.11
Long-term debt ($ mil.): —

No. of shares (mil.): 57
Dividends
  Yield: —
  Payout: —
Market value ($ mil.): —

Mitsubishi UFJ Financial Group Inc

Mitsubishi UFJ Financial Group (MUFG) is the largest banking group in Japan (ahead of Mizuho Financial and Sumitomo Mitsui Financial) and one of the largest in the world. The group provides retail banking corporate banking asset management securities brokerage leasing and trust services. Subsidiary The Bank of Tokyo-Mitsubishi UFJ (BTMU) boasts over 1100 branches across Japan and another 1150 across more than 40 countries. Mitsubishi UFJ Trust and Banking (MUTB) oversees some ¥30 trillion ($250 billion) in assets under management. Other holdings include investment bank Mitsubishi UFJ Securities California-based MUFG Union Bank and private bank Mitsubishi UFJ Morgan Stanley PB Securities (MUMSS).

OperationsMUFG operates an integrated business group system that concentrates on five main business areas: Retail Banking which includes its domestic retail banking trust banking and securities business; Corporate Banking which includes its domestic corporate-focused commercial banking investment banking trust banking and securities businesses; Trust Assets Business Group which covers asset management and administrative services for pension trusts and security trusts through MUTB and globally through BTMU; Global covers its overseas commercial investment retail and trust banking and securities; and Global Markets which provides asset and liability management and strategic investments of BTMU and MUTB and sales and trading of financial products for BTMU MUTB and MUSHD.

The firm's variety of service offerings give it a diversified revenue stream. About 40% of its total revenue comes from loan interest (including fees) while about 20% comes from interest income on investments trading account assets and deposits in other banks. Fees and Commissions income makes up 30% of total revenue while investment security gains and equity earnings (if applicable) make up the remainder.

MUFG is a member of the Mitsubishi group a melange of about 30 different companies —active in manufacturing transportation insurance and other industries —that shared common ownership before WWII but have been operated autonomously since. The group also includes credit card company Mitsubishi UFJ NICOS and Mitsubishi UFJ Lease & Finance.

Geographic Reach

The company operates in the US Japan and more than 40 countries in Europe Asia/Oceania. About 52% of its revenue came from Japan in fiscal 2015 (ended March 31) down from 70% in FY2014. Another 12% came from the US.

Sales and Marketing

MUFG mainly markets its products through sales agents.

Financial Performance

Note: Growth rates may differ after conversion to US dollars.

MUFG's revenues and profits have trended higher over the past few years thanks to a combination of growing loan and deposit business growing non-interest revenues from its investment businesses lower interest expenses in the low-interest environment a declining loan loss provisions as as its loan portfolio's credit quality has improved with higher property valuations in the strengthened economy.

The group's revenue rose more than double digits to nearly ¥5740 billion ($48 billion) fiscal 2015 (ended March 31) mostly thanks to net trading account profits of ¥1.15 billion (compared to net trading account losses of ¥34 billion in FY2014) which were buoyed by higher foreign bond valuations and lower interest rates in the US. MUFG's interest income and fee and commission revenue also grew in the high-single digits.

Higher revenue and declines in loan loss provisions helped MUFG's net income jump more than 50% to ¥1531 billion ($12.8 billion) in FY2015. The group's operating cash levels more than doubled to ¥2384 billion ($20 billion) thanks to higher cash earnings.

Strategy

With the stagnant Japanese economy MUFG has increasingly looked to emerging markets in Asia Latin America and Central and Eastern Europe for growth. In 2015 it continued its plans to expand its businesses in the fast-growing Southeast Asia region (including through select acquisitions of large banks like it did with its $5 billion-acquisition of Krungsri bank) and grow its consumer banking business in Asia targeting India Indonesia and the Philippines. Toward that end in 2015 MUFG showed interest in acquiring United Coconut Planters Bank from the Philippine government who wanted to sell its 74% stake in the bank for $350 million.

MUFG has also begun pivoting toward growing its asset management business in recent years. In 2015 it purchased an investment management unit from UBS Group AG Global Asset Management. In 2014 MUFG and MUTB and MUFJ Securities Holdings effectively created a new organization structure to strengthen the group's asset management business after merging Mitsubishi UFJ Asset Management (MUAM) with KOKUSAI Asset Management Co (KAM).

In the US subsidiary MUFG Union Bank has been expanding through the acquisition of other community banks. MUFG is also looking to strengthen its alliance with Morgan Stanley to grow its global investment banking operations.

Mergers and AcquisitionsIn mid-2015 as part of its asset management expansion strategy MUFG agreed to purchase UBS Group AG Global Asset Management's Alternative Fund Services unit which offers investment services for ¥30 billion ($250 million).

In December 2013 the company expanded its banking business further into Southeast Asia after subsidiary The Bank of Tokyo-Mitsubishi UFJ (BTMU) acquired a 72% stake in Thailand-based The Bank of Ayudhya Public Company (Krungsri) for ¥545.8 billion (around $5 billion) cash. Krungsri became a subsidiary of BTMU after the deal.

In November 2013 US subsidiary MUFG Union Bank acquired First Bank Association Bank Services a unit of first bank that offered a full suite of banking services to homeowners associations and community management companies which added $570 million in deposits as part of the deal.

In September 2013 bolstered its asset management lines after its subsidiary MUTB purchased Butterfield Fulcrum Group for ¥30.2 billion ($250 million) cash and changed its name to Mitsubishi UFJ Fund Services Holdings Limited.

Company Background

In 2010 MUFG became the first Japanese bank to acquire an interest in a Chinese asset manager when it bought out BNP Paribas Asset Management's 33% stake in a joint venture with Shenyin & Wanguo Securities. The following year it acquired some 15% of AMP Limited in Australia. The moves should allow it to expand its investment services to pension funds and other institutional investors as part of a plan to expand its trust operations.

MUFG was formed in the 2005 merger of Mitsubishi Tokyo Financial Group and UFJ Holdings.

HISTORY

Company BackgroundMitsubishi Bank emerged from the exchange office of the original Mitsubishi zaibatsu (industrial group) in 1885. It evolved into a full-service bank by 1895 and became independent in 1919 though its primary customers were Mitsubishi group companies. The bank survived WWII but a US fiat dismantled the zaibatsu after the war. Mitsubishi Bank reopened as Chiyoda Bank in 1948. After reopening offices in London and New York the bank readopted the Mitsubishi name.

In the 1950s Mitsubishi Bank became the lead lender for the reconstituted Mitsubishi group (keiretsu). In the 1960s it followed its Mitsubishi partners overseas helping finance Japan's growing international trade. In 1972 it acquired the Bank of California and began doing more business outside the group.

Japan's overinflated real estate market of the 1980s devastated many of the country's banks including Nippon Trust Bank of which Mitsubishi owned 5%. Japan's Ministry of Finance (MoF) urged Mitsubishi to bail Nippon out; as a reward for raising its stake in Nippon to 69% and assuming a mountain of unrecoverable loans the MoF allowed Mitsubishi to begin issuing debt before other Japanese banks. In 1995 Mitsubishi Bank and Bank of Tokyo agreed to merge.

Bank of Tokyo (BOT) was established in 1880 as the Yokohama Specie Bank; the Iwasaki family founders of the Mitsubishi group served on its board. With links to the Imperial family the bank was heavily influenced by government policy. With Japan isolated after the Sino-Japanese War its international operations suffered greatly even before WWII. Completely dismantled after WWII the bank was re-established in 1946 as the Bank of Tokyo a commercial city bank bereft of its foreign exchange business. During the 1950s the government restored it as a foreign exchange specialist but regulations limited its domestic business.

BOT evolved into an investment bank in the 1970s; its reputation as the leading foreign exchange bank brought in international clients and successful derivatives trading and overseas banking. By the time BOT and Mitsubishi Bank agreed to merge BOT had 363 foreign offices (only 37 in Japan) with more foreign than Japanese employees.

The two banks merged in 1996 to form The Bank of Tokyo-Mitsubishi (BTM); Mitsubishi was the surviving entity. Their California banks merged to create Union Bank of California (UnionBanCal). The next year BTM reorganized its operations but had problems assimilating its disparate corporate cultures.

In 1998 Japanese banking regulators doled out nearly $240 billion to the industry to prop up failing banks and to strengthen healthier ones. Also that year BTM was fined for bribing MoF officials with entertainment gifts and posted a huge loss after writing off $8.4 billion in bad debt. Losses continued in 1999 and the bank responded by reorganizing operationally cutting jobs and offices and selling stock in UnionBanCal.

In 2000 BTM announced plans to form a financial group with Mitsubishi Trust Bank and Nippon Trust Bank. The following year the three banks unified and formed Mitsubishi Tokyo Financial Group. Before rolling into Mitsubishi Trust Financial Group BTM paid back the money showered upon it by the Japanese government in 1998.

In 2004 MTFG introduced a new organizational structure that focused on its three core markets — retail corporate and trust asset businesses. The company planned to unify business within each division and to improve decision-making company-wide. The group also introduced a new executive officer system with the idea of separating company oversight and business execution. A mechanism for credit risk control was also added.

It was all to change in 2005 however. During this time Mitsubishi Tokyo Financial Group merged with UFJ Holdings emerging (at that time) as the world's largest bank by assets. As a result of the merger the group was renamed Mitsubishi UFJ Financial Group (MUFG).As with most of its peers MUFG was not immune to the global credit crisis that began in 2007. Its NICOS consumer lending subsidiary had a disappointing year due to the credit crunch. The unit sold its installment credit car loan and car leasing businesses to JACCS in 2008. In 2009 MUFG announced plans to close 50 branches and cut nearly 1000 jobs as a part of a long-term restructuring plan. In addition the bank shut down some 200 ATMs and relocated another 1000 employees.

In 2008 the group bought the rest of UnionBanCal and Mitsubishi UFJ NICOS it didn't already own and acquired a stake in bulge-bracket firm Morgan Stanley. MUFG also bought a 10% stake in UK-based Aberdeen Asset Management that year. (It later upped its interest to around 17%.)

EXECUTIVES

President and CEO Bank of Tokyo-Mitsubishi UFJ and Director, Takashi Oyamada, age 61
Senior Managing Executive Officer Group CSO and Group CHRO and Director, Tadashi Kuroda
President and Group CEO Mitsubishi UFJ Financial Group and Chairman Bank of Tokyo-Mitsubishi UFJ, Nobuyuki Hirano, age 65
Deputy Chairman President and CEO Mitsubishi UFJ Securities Holdings Company and President and CEO Mitsubishi UFJ Morgan Stanley Securities Company, Takashi Nagaoka
Managing Executive Officer Group Chief Risk Officer and Director, Masamichi (Mitch) Yasuda, age 55
Senior Managing Executive Officer Group CFO and Director, Muneaki Tokunari
Chairman Mitsubishi UFJ Trust and Banking Corporation and Director, Tatsuo Wakabayashi
Chief Executive and Managing Officer Europe Middle East and Africa (EMEA), Masahiro Kuwahara
Deputy Chairman, Mikio Ikegaya
Chairman, Kiyoshi Sono
Auditors: Deloitte Touche Tohmatsu LLC

LOCATIONS

HQ: Mitsubishi UFJ Financial Group Inc
7-1, Marunouchi 2-chome, Chiyoda-ku, Tokyo 100-8330
Phone: (81) 3 3240 8111   **Fax:** (81) 3 3240 7073
Web: www.mufg.jp

2014 Sales

	% of total
Asia/Oceania	
Japan	72
Other countries	13
US	5
Europe	3
Other regions	7
Total	**100**

PRODUCTS/OPERATIONS

2014 Sales

	% of total
Interest	
Loans including fees	38
Investment securities	8
Trading account assets	9
Other	2
Noninterest	
Fees & commissions	29
Investment securities gains	6
Other	8
Total	**100**

COMPETITORS

Aozora Bank	ORIX
BNP Paribas Bangkok	Resona
Citigroup	Shinsei Bank
HSBC	Sony
Japan Post	Sumitomo Mitsui
Mizuho Financial	Sumitomo Mitsui Trust
Mizuho Trust & Banking Ltd	Holdings

HISTORICAL FINANCIALS

Company Type: Public

Income Statement

FYE: March 31

	ASSETS ($ mil.)	NET INCOME ($ mil.)	INCOME AS % OF ASSETS	EMPLOYEES
03/16	2,605,329	7,144	0.3%	139,900
03/15	2,341,122	12,761	0.5%	137,200
03/14	2,457,493	9,837	0.4%	135,300
03/13	2,450,358	11,362	0.5%	112,100
03/12	2,623,454	5,074	0.2%	110,500
Annual Growth	**(0.2%)**	**8.9%**	**—**	**6.1%**

2016 Year-End Financials

Return on assets: 0.2%
Return on equity: 5.5%
Long-term debt ($ mil.): —
No. of shares (mil.): —
Sales ($ mil): 40,279
Dividends
Yield: 3.1%
Payout: 30.8%
Market value ($ mil.): —

	STOCK PRICE ($) FY Close	P/E High/Low		PER SHARE ($) Earnings	Dividends	Book Value
03/16	4.59	0	0	0.51	0.15	9.22
03/15	6.22	0	0	0.90	0.16	8.73
03/14	5.54	0	0	0.68	0.14	8.35
03/13	6.00	0	0	0.79	0.13	7.97
03/12	4.98	0	0	0.34	0.15	7.40
Annual Growth	**(2.0%)**	—	—	**10.6%**	**(0.1%)**	**5.7%**

Mitsui & Co., Ltd.

Auditors: Deloitte Touche Tohmatsu LLC

LOCATIONS

HQ: Mitsui & Co., Ltd.
1-3 Marunouchi 1-chome, Chiyoda-ku, Tokyo 100-8631
Phone: (81) 3 3285 1111   **Fax:** (81) 3 3285 9821
Web: www.mitsui.com

HISTORICAL FINANCIALS

Company Type: Public

Income Statement

FYE: March 31

	REVENUE ($ mil.)	NET INCOME ($ mil.)	NET PROFIT MARGIN	EMPLOYEES
03/16	42,384	(742)	—	54,395
03/15	45,048	2,554	5.7%	58,257
03/14	55,531	3,391	6.1%	60,660
03/13	52,200	3,272	6.3%	61,898
03/12	64,020	5,296	8.3%	64,218
Annual Growth	**(9.8%)**	**—**		**(4.1%)**

2016 Year-End Financials

Debt ratio: 0.3%
Return on equity: (-2.2%)
Cash ($ mil.): 13,275
Current ratio: 1.67
Long-term debt ($ mil.): 34,178
No. of shares (mil.): 1,792
Dividends
Yield: 4.5%
Payout: —
Market value ($ mil.): 412,227

	STOCK PRICE ($) FY Close	P/E High/Low		PER SHARE ($) Earnings	Dividends	Book Value
03/16	229.94	—	—	(0.41)	10.36	16.79
03/15	269.00	2	1	1.42	12.04	19.06
03/14	282.07	2	1	1.86	9.11	20.62
03/13	279.00	2	1	1.79	10.54	18.53
03/12	330.63	2	1	2.90	13.14	17.64
Annual Growth	**(8.7%)**			**—**	**(5.8%)**	**(1.2%)**

Mitsui Life Insurance Co., Ltd.

Auditors: Deloitte Touche Tohmatsu LLC

LOCATIONS

HQ: Mitsui Life Insurance Co., Ltd.
1-1-20 Aomi, Koto-ku, Tokyo 135-8222
Phone: (81) 3 6831 8000
Web: www.mitsui-seimei.co.jp

HISTORICAL FINANCIALS

Company Type: Public

Income Statement

FYE: March 31

	ASSETS ($ mil.)	NET INCOME ($ mil.)	INCOME AS % OF ASSETS	EMPLOYEES
03/15	61,967	84	0.1%	10,085
03/14	69,986	125	0.2%	10,259
03/13	76,823	81	0.1%	11,552
03/12	87,382	167	0.2%	12,118
03/11	87,242	171	0.2%	12,610
Annual Growth	**(8.2%)**	**(16.3%)**	**—**	**(5.4%)**

2015 Year-End Financials

Return on assets: 0.1%
Return on equity: 2.5%
Long-term debt ($ mil.): —
No. of shares (mil.): 278
Sales ($ mil): 6,640
Dividends
Yield: —
Payout: —
Market value ($ mil.): —

Mitsui OSK Lines Ltd

It's OK with Mitsui O.S.K. Lines if you send your freight over the ocean. Known as MOL the company is one of the world's largest marine transportation companies and operates a fleet of more than 930 vessels with an overall capacity of 66 million deadweight tons (DWT). The company's fleet includes containerships bulk cargo carriers car carriers oil tankers chemical products carriers and liquefied natural gas (LNG) carriers. MOL also operates cruise ships tugboats and domestic ferries and offers marine consulting services. In addition the company provides logistics services such as warehousing and freight forwarding operates marine terminals and holds stakes in finance and real estate businesses.

EXECUTIVES

Senior Managing Executive Officer, Takeshi Hashimoto
EVP, Kenichi Nagata
President, Junichiro Ikeda
Senior Managing Executive Officer, Masahiro Tanabe
Senior Managing Executive Officer, Shizuo Takahashi
Senior Managing Executive Officer, Masaaki Nemoto
President, Koichi Muto
Auditors: KPMG AZSA LLC

LOCATIONS

HQ: Mitsui OSK Lines Ltd
2-1-1 Toranomon, Minato-ku, Tokyo 105-8688
Phone: (81) 3 3587 7026
Web: www.mol.co.jp

PRODUCTS/OPERATIONS

2016 Sales

	% of total
Bulkships	49
Containerships	42
Associated busines	6
Ferry & Domestic transport	3
Others	-
Total	**100**

Selected Services

Associated Businesses
Car Carriers
Containerships
Cruise Ship
Dry Bulkers
Ferries and Coastal Liners
Logistics
Offshore Business
Tankers
Terminal

COMPETITORS

A.P. M₋ller - M|rsk
CMA CGM
China COSCO
Compa±a Sud
  Americana de Vapores
Dynagas LNG Partners
  LP
Evergreen Marine
Frontline
Hanjin Shipping
Hapag-Lloyd
Hyundai Merchant
  Marine
Kawasaki Kisen
MISC
Mediterranean Shipping
  Company
NORDEN
NYK Line
Neptune Orient
Orient Overseas
Sankyu
Stolt-Nielsen
Teekay

HISTORICAL FINANCIALS

Company Type: Public

Income Statement
FYE: March 31

	REVENUE ($ mil.)	NET INCOME ($ mil.)	NET PROFIT MARGIN	EMPLOYEES
03/16	15,247	(1,517)	—	12,681
03/15	15,144	353	2.3%	12,682
03/14	16,755	556	3.3%	10,289
03/13	16,039	(1,900)	—	9,465
03/12	17,496	(317)	—	9,431
Annual Growth	**(3.4%)**	**—**		**7.7%**

2016 Year-End Financials

Debt ratio: 0.4% No. of shares (mil.): 1,196
Return on equity: (-25.5%) Dividends
Cash ($ mil.): 1,302 Yield: 0.0%
Current ratio: 0.98 Payout: —
Long-term debt ($ mil.): 7,738 Market value ($ mil.): 7,679

	STOCK PRICE ($) FY Close	P/E High/Low		Earnings	PER SHARE ($) Dividends	Book Value
03/16	6.42	—	—	(1.27)	0.20	4.05
03/15	10.60	0	0	0.27	0.15	5.47
03/14	11.48	—	—	0.46	0.00	6.35
03/13	10.50	—	—	(1.59)	0.00	5.51
03/12	13.93	—	—	(0.27)	0.00	7.33
Annual Growth	**(17.6%) (13.8%)**	**—**	**—**	**—**	**—**	**—**

Mizrahi Tefahot Bank Ltd

Auditors: Brightman Almagor Zohar & Co.

LOCATIONS

HQ: Mizrahi Tefahot Bank Ltd
7 Jabotinsky Street, P.O. Box 3450, Ramat Gan 5252007
Phone: (972) 3 7559000   **Fax:** (972) 3 7559210
Web: www.mizrahi-tefahot.co.il

HISTORICAL FINANCIALS

Company Type: Public

Income Statement
FYE: December 31

	ASSETS ($ mil.)	NET INCOME ($ mil.)	INCOME AS % OF ASSETS	EMPLOYEES
12/15	53,474	289	0.5%	5,864
12/14	51,099	278	0.5%	5,864
12/13	51,761	310	0.6%	5,827
12/12	43,527	288	0.7%	5,670
12/11	39,300	273	0.7%	5,518
Annual Growth	**8.0%**	**1.5%**	**—**	**1.5%**

2015 Year-End Financials

Return on assets: 0.5% Dividends
Return on equity: 9.9% Yield: —
Long-term debt ($ mil.): — Payout: 7.2%
No. of shares (mil.): 234 Market value ($ mil.): —
Sales ($ mil): 1,729

Morrison (Wm.) Supermarkets Plc

Wm Morrison Supermarkets moved up the UK food chain with the acquisition of its larger rival Safeway plc. As the UK's fourth-largest grocery chain Morrison runs about 515 stores and nearly 155 convenience stores throughout England and Scotland. Morrison's supermarkets offer a variety of food and nonfood items most notably through its Market Street specialty departments. About 330 of the locations sell gas. Founded by its namesake in 1899 its purchase of the UK's Safeway chain transformed Wm Morrison into a national brand with about an 11% share of the UK grocery market.

OperationsThe chain is known as the master of small to medium-sized supermarkets as most of the company's stores fall into the 25000-to-40000 sq. ft. range. The shops are noted for their Market Street departments a collection of in-store specialty shops that ring the perimeter of the store. They include a bakery butcher shop and deli. Market Street departments also offer pizza pies and curry. Outlets also have in-store cafes. As the UK's second-largest fresh food manufacturer Morrison is vertically integrated including operating facilities for processing packing and distributing meat and produce. Its Farmers Boy unit supplies its stores with fresh food including pizzas cooked meats and other prepared foods. The company operates seven distribution centers and one national center that serviced its supermarkets and three convenience distribution centers.

The company generated more than 75% of its revenue from its online and in-store sales in fiscal 2015 (ended February 1) while another 21% of revenue came from fuel sales from its gas stations.

Geographic Reach

Morrison boasts more than 500 stores scattered across the UK in East England East Midlands Greater London North East North West Scotland South East South West Wales West Midlands Yorkshire and Gibraltar.

Sales and Marketing

The retailer spent £291 million ($438 million) on advertising and marketing in FY2015 (ended February 1) up from £280 million ($460 million) in FY2014.

Financial Performance

Note: Growth rates may differ after conversion to US dollars.

Wm Morrison's sales and profits have been in decline over the past few years due to declining same-store sales amidst intense competition in the grocers market and stagnating consumer finances with sluggish economic growth in the UK. The retailer's revenue fell by 5% to £16.8 billion ($25.3 million) in fiscal 2015 (ended February 1) mostly as comparable physical store sales declined by 6% (online sales grew by 0.6%) and new store sales fell by nearly 3%. Fuel sales also shrank by 10% as the retailer passed lower oil prices on to the customer.

Wm Morrison went even deeper into the red in FY2015 with a loss of £761 million ($1.14 billion) mostly due to a combination of lower revenue and £372 million ($560 million) in additional impairment and onerous lease provision costs during the year as its property and brand value deteriorated compared to its book asset values. The retailer's operating cash levels rose by 21% to £874 ($1.32 billion) as the company received £10 million ($15 million) in tax benefits compared to tax payments of £220 million ($331.2 million) in FY2014.

Strategy

Wm Morrison outlined its strategic objectives in 2015 which involved a £1 billion investment over three years through: permanently lowering prices to attract new customers; making fewer more selective promotions; boosting the value of its Morrison brand products and Market Street credentials; continually improve its product quality and range; improving its store layout to boost sales; and offering customer-loyalty-focused reward programs.

Toward its low-cost growth strategy the retailer continues to lower its prices to drive customers from competitors. During fiscal 2015 the retailer cut prices on 130 high-volume everyday product lines by an average of 22%. In 2014 it cut its prices by an average of 17% on some 1200 store products starting with Produce and Meat products through its "I'm Cheaper" campaign. It also launched its Match & More price-match and points card program to gain customer loyalty (with special incentives for its Morrison-brand products) and take customer market share from top competitors Aldi and Lidl. For FY2016 the company targeted another £800 million more in cost savings for customers.

Wm Morrison has also been making a number of moves to cut operational costs and boost profits with plans to unlock £1 billion worth of savings from 2014 through 2017. During FY2015 the retailer developed a sales-based ordering program with plans to roll it out to its Frozen food category and others to optimize its stocking inventories for significant cost savings. Also that year the company restructured its in-store teams to make lines of responsibility clearer and boost in-store efficiencies and focused on reducing its shrinkage waste and markdown costs.

It's also been expanding its store base particularly its convenience stores. During FY2015 the retailer opened 68 new stores of which 57 were convenience stores.

HISTORY

Company BackgroundA former grocer's apprentice William Morrison founded his company in Bradford UK in 1899 as a wholesale seller of eggs and butter. Named William Morrison (Provisions) the business eventually expanded into retail by opening grocery stalls and by the 1920s was operating counter service shops as well.

Self-service stores became popular in the UK during the late 1940s and 1950s and the company began opening self-service outlets during that time. William's son Ken (born when William was 57 years of age) joined the company in 1950 and became chairman in 1956. The chain opened its first supermarket in Bradford in 1962 by converting an abandoned cinema. Wm Morrison Supermarkets went public five years later.

In 1979 Wm Morrison moved into Lancashire by purchasing the 10-store grocery chain Whelans Discount founded by Dave Whelan an ex-football star who also founded JJB Sports. Two years later it bought the Mainstop chain. The company's sales grew by a factor of 10 during the 1980s and 1990; it added about 50 stores in the 1990s. In 1993 Wm Morrison began opening stores on Sundays and in 1997 it teamed up with Midland Bank to offer in-store banking.

The company had operated mostly in northeastern England but a new distribution center that opened in 1996 in Cheshire allowed it to handle more distribution duties and gave it the base to expand west. Wm Morrison also turned south opening superstores in three southern regions (Oxford Essex and Kent) in 1998. The retailer also acquired two stores from Food Giant and three superstores (one near London) from Co-operative Retail Services that year. Wm Morrison expanded its Farmers Boy food processing operations by opening a new 180000-sq.-ft. facility in 1999. It opened four new stores in 2000 and bought three others.

The company's highly regarded Managing Director John Dowd resigned in March 2002 because of ill health. Soon after Marie Melnyk and Robert Stott were promoted to the positions of joint managing director. Morrison added six stores in fiscal year 2003 (ended January 2003).

On January 9 2003 Morrison made an offer of 1.32 Morrison shares for each share of Safeway plc. In March the company's bid for its rival lapsed after the Office of Fair Trading referred the bid to the Competition Commission.

Following clearance from Britain's High Court the company's acquisition of Safeway closed on March 8 2004. (Morrison shareholders own 60% of the enlarged company with Safeway shareholders left with 40%.)

In June 2006 the company named Marc Bolland formerly COO of brewer Heineken as CEO succeeding Bob Stott who retired. Stott became CEO in 2005.

Sir Kenneth Morrison retired as chairman in March 2008 after 55 years with the company. Morrison who was named honorary president was succeeded by former deputy chairman Sir Ian Gibson. The grocery chain opened eight new supermarkets in fiscal 2008.

In 2009 Morrisons acquired about 40 Co-operative Group and former Somerfield stores for about £220 million (about $330 million). In November Bolland resigned to join Marks and Spencer. He was succeeded by Dalton Philips who joined the business in March 2010.

In 2011 Morrisons acquired about 18 Netto UK stores from ASDA. In June it bought Flower World an importer and wholesaler of flowers in the UK in a bid to improve the flower offering at its supermarkets.

EXECUTIVES

CEO, Dalton T. Philips, age 48
CFO, Trevor Strain
CIO, Daniel Beecham
Chairman, Andrew T. Higginson, age 58
Auditors: PricewaterhouseCoopers LLP

LOCATIONS

HQ: Morrison (Wm.) Supermarkets Plc
Hilmore House, Gain Lane, Bradford BD3 7DL
Phone: (44) 845 611 5000
Web: www.morrisons.co.uk

PRODUCTS/OPERATIONS

2012 Sales

	% of total
Food & general merchandise	76
Fuel	23
Total	**100**

COMPETITORS

ALDI	Lidl
ASDA	Marks & Spencer
BP	Musgrave Retail
Co-operative Group	Partners
Exxon Mobil	Royal Dutch Shell
J Sainsbury	SPAR (UK)
John Lewis	Tesco

HISTORICAL FINANCIALS

Company Type: Public

Income Statement

FYE: January 31

	REVENUE ($ mil.)	NET INCOME ($ mil.)	NET PROFIT MARGIN	EMPLOYEES
01/16*	23,072	317	1.4%	120,913
02/15	25,366	(1,147)	—	119,778
02/14	29,105	(391)	—	127,403
02/13	28,681	1,024	3.6%	128,705
01/12	27,743	1,083	3.9%	131,207
Annual Growth	**(4.5%)**	**(26.4%)**	**—**	**(2.0%)**

*Fiscal year change

2016 Year-End Financials

Debt ratio: 33.9%
Return on equity: 6.0%
Cash ($ mil.): 698
Current ratio: 0.48
Long-term debt ($ mil.): 2,866
No. of shares (mil.): —
Dividends
Yield: 0.0%
Payout: 551.1%
Market value ($ mil.): —

	STOCK PRICE ($) FY Close	P/E High/Low	PER SHARE ($) Earnings	Dividends	Book Value
01/16*	12.62	157 104	0.14	0.75	2.30
02/15	13.46	— —	(0.49)	0.91	2.32
02/14	19.81	— —	(0.17)	0.93	3.31
02/13	19.74	91 74	0.42	0.79	3.53
01/12	22.89	97 79	0.41	0.83	3.35
Annual Growth	**(13.8%)**	**— —**	**(24.1%)**	**(2.6%)**	**(8.9%)**

*Fiscal year change

MS&AD Insurance Group Holdings

MS&AD Insurance Group has insurance in Japan covered. MS&AD Insurance Group is the holding company for several large Japanese insurance companies including Mitsui Sumitomo Insurance (MSI) Aioi Nissay Dowa Insurance (ADI) Mitsui Direct General MSI Aioi Life and MSI Primary Life. Together the insurance companies offer property/casualty (e.g. auto personal fire marine) and life insurance as well as asset management (mutual funds financial consulting) and risk management services. MS&AD Insurance's 50 subsidiaries which serve individuals and businesses in Japan also offer products and services to customers in more than 40 countries in Europe Asia and the Americas.

Operations

The group has five primary operating divisions: domestic non-life (property/casualty) insurance domestic life insurance overseas business financial services and risk-related services. Each of its non-life firms underwrites policies in the fire and allied marine personal accident automobile and other arenas. The life insurers underwrite individual policies individual annuity insurance group insurance and other products.

Subsidiary MSI provides insurance and financial services around the world. In Japan it has a network of some 500 sales offices nearly 40000 agencies and about 230 service centers. MSI Primary Life is one of Japan's top individual annuity providers.

Sales and Marketing

MSI has 500 sales offices and more than 200 service centers in Japan. It also has about 900 locations in 40 countries around the globe. ADI has an almost identical range of domestic and international locations.

Mitsui Direct General sells automobile policies directly to individuals online and via telephone. MSI Aioi Life markets its products through financial institutions life insurance agencies and a direct sales force.

Financial Performance

Revenue increased 7% to ¥4689.6 billion in fiscal 2015 (ended March) primarily due to an increase in net premiums written and deposit premiums. Investment income also grew that year. With the increase in revenue net income rose 45% to ¥136 billion.

Cash flow from operations rose 28% to ¥628 billion in fiscal 2015.

Strategy

MS&AD is focused on expanding its domestic property/casualty operations its domestic life insurance business and its overseas operations. Its Next Challenge 2017 strategic plan was designed to promote the group's development.

Part of that plan included restructuring operations by function with MS&AD Holdings MSI ADI and MSI Aioi Life as its core businesses. Among the initiatives already completed was the 2014 establishment of ADI and MSI Aioi Life and the integration of certain business systems. Another key initiative is to promote enterprise risk management.

To expand abroad subsidiaries Mitsui Sumitomo Marine Management (U.S.A.) and Aioi Nissay Dowa Insurance Company of America opened new offices in the Dallas area during 2014. The group is also seeking acquisitions in Southeast Asia.

Mergers and Acquisitions

In 2014 subsidiary ADI and its European subsidiary acquired a 75% stake in UK-based telematics automobile insurer Box Innovation Group.

Company Background

Formed in 2008 as a holding company for the Mitsui Sumitomo operations MS&AD Insurance became the parent of a larger group of insurance companies through a three-way merger between Mitsui Sumitomo Aioi Insurance and Nissay Dowa General Insurance in 2010.

EXECUTIVES

Chairman MSI, Toshiaki Egashira, age 68
President CEO and Representative Director, Yasuyoshi Karasawa, age 66
Executive Officer Marketing and Sales, Masaaki Nishikata
Executive Officer Administration and Information Systems, Tetsuya Yoshikawa
Chairman, Hisahito Suzuki, age 66
Auditors: KPMG AZSA LLC

LOCATIONS

HQ: MS&AD Insurance Group Holdings
27-2, Shinkawa 2-chome, Chuo-ku, Tokyo 104-0033
Phone: (81) 3 5117 0270
Web: www.ms-ad-hd.com

PRODUCTS/OPERATIONS

2015 Sales

	% of total
Underwriting income	83
Investment income	17
Other ordinary income	.
Total	**100**

Selected Products

Compulsory Automobile Liability
Fire and Allied Insurance
Life
Marine

Personal Accident
Voluntary Automobile

COMPETITORS

Allianz	Prudential
Allstate	Prudential plc
Citigroup	Samsung Fire & Marine
Dai-ichi Life	Sompo Holdings
Fuji Fire and Marine	Sumitomo Life
Hyundai Marine & Fire	Tokio Marine
ING	Zurich Insurance Group

HISTORICAL FINANCIALS

Company Type: Public

Income Statement

FYE: March 31

	REVENUE ($ mil.)	NET INCOME ($ mil.)	NET PROFIT MARGIN	EMPLOYEES
03/16	42,764	1,616	3.8%	50,790
03/15	38,637	1,135	2.9%	47,354
03/14	42,171	905	2.1%	37,055
03/13	45,785	888	1.9%	36,643
03/12	45,775	(2,065)	—	36,929
Annual Growth	**(1.7%)**	**—**	**—**	**8.3%**

2016 Year-End Financials

Debt ratio: —   No. of shares (mil.): 603
Return on equity: 6.3%   Dividends
Cash ($ mil.): 17,025   Yield: 2.0%
Current ratio: —   Payout: —
Long-term debt ($ mil.): —   Market value ($ mil.): 8,373

	STOCK PRICE ($) FY Close	P/E High/Low		PER SHARE ($) Earnings	Dividends	Book Value
03/16	13.87	0	0	2.66	0.29	39.80
03/15	14.01	0	0	1.84	0.26	40.94
03/14	11.38	—	—	1.46	0.27	35.72
03/13	11.02	—	—	1.43	0.00	34.55
03/12	10.26	—	—	(3.32)	0.00	29.64
Annual Growth	**7.8%**	**—**	**—**	**—**	**—**	**7.6%**

Muenchener Hypothekenbank EG (Germany, Fed. Rep.)

EXECUTIVES

Vorstandsvorsitzender, Konrad Irtel
Auditors: DGRV - Deutscher Genossenschafts- und Raiffeisenverband e.V.

LOCATIONS

HQ: Muenchener Hypothekenbank EG (Germany, Fed. Rep.)
Karl-Scharnagl-Ring 10, Munich D-80539
Phone: (49) 89 5387 800   **Fax:** (49) 89 5387 900
Web: www.muenchenerhyp.de

HISTORICAL FINANCIALS

Company Type: Public

Income Statement

FYE: December 31

	ASSETS ($ mil.)	NET INCOME ($ mil.)	INCOME AS % OF ASSETS	EMPLOYEES
12/15	41,497	24	0.1%	493
12/14	44,171	19	0.0%	462
12/13	48,046	9	0.0%	351
12/12	48,297	7	0.0%	410
12/11	48,308	6	0.0%	375
Annual Growth	**(3.7%)**	**40.1%**	**—**	**7.1%**

2015 Year-End Financials

Return on assets: 0.0%   Dividends
Return on equity: 1.8%   Yield: —
Long-term debt ($ mil.): —   Payout: —
No. of shares (mil.): —   Market value ($ mil.): —
Sales ($ mil): 1,256

Muenchener Rueckversicherungs- Gesellschaft AG (Germany)

Some companies live with risk... Münchener Rückversicherungs-Gesellschaft (Munich Re) on the other hand thrives on risk. Reinsurance coverage (insurance for insurers) includes fire life motor and liability policies on both a facultative (individual risk) and treaty (categorized risk) basis. The company also provides direct insurance including life health and property coverage through Germany-based ERGO and other subsidiaries and it provides asset management services through MEAG MUNICH ERGO. Through Munich Re America Munich Re enjoys greater access to the US market. As one of the world's largest reinsurance and risk management firms the company operates in some 160 countries.

Operations

The company operates in six segments: life reinsurance property/casualty reinsurance ERGO life and health Germany ERGO property/casualty Germany ERGO international and Munich health (global health reinsurance and non-German health coverage). Reinsurance operations accounted for more than half of Munich Re's earnings in 2014 while ERGO accounted for 35%; Munich Health represented another 11%.

Munich Re's reinsurance and primary insurance segments respectively account for about 50% and 40% of annual premiums. After focused growth efforts in the primary insurance segment the ERGO division has grown to insure clients in 30 countries in Europe and Asia.

The company's health insurance operations are handled through the company's Deutsche Krankenversicherung unit (DKV a subsidiary of ERGO) in Germany and through the Munich Health division (which also holds Munich Re's health reinsurance operations) in international countries. The MEAG asset management unit holds some euro 200 billion ($260 billion) in investments.

Geographic Reach

North America is Munich Re's largest market accounting for about 45% of gross premiums written in 2014 (up from 25% in 2010 due to acquisitions and organic growth in the US). Europe is its second-biggest market (accounting for about 30% of premiums in 2014) and the company has expanded its European presence over the years through acquisitions and internal growth programs.

Financial Performance

Revenues declined 4% to euro 47.3 billion in 2014 primarily due to a decline in the reinsurance segments including both life and property/casualty reinsurance earnings. Canada life reinsurance sales went down primarily as the result of the restructuring of a large-volume treaty. Europe and Latin America property/casualty reinsurance also slowed down as did the special and financial risks division. Munich Health slipped 16% that year while primary insurance dropped mainly due to the sale of the Windsor Health Group.

Due to the revenue decline net income fell 5% to euro 3.1 billion in 2014. However cash flow from operations more than tripled to euro 7.5 billion due to a change in deposits retained and accounts receivable and payable.

Strategy

Though reinsurance is its largest operating segment the company hopes to continue the growth of its traditional insurance segment in the core German market and other European markets focusing on personal lines. As part of this strategy the company is widening the presence of the ERGO brand across its insurance operations in its European markets (especially in Germany).

Additionally Munich Re is working to extend the ERGO brand into new markets especially in emerging markets in Eastern Europe and parts of Asia.

In the North American market Munich Re is expanding in the specialty property/casualty and health insurance markets primarily through acquisitions. It is also working to expand its presence in the growing health care insurance arena in emerging markets like India.

Ownership

Billionaire investment mogul Warren Buffett who controls a number of insurance and reinsurance players through Berkshire Hathaway has taken notice of Munich Re. Buffett increased his stake in the company to 10% in 2010.

HISTORY

Company Background

Investors Carl Thieme and Theodor Cramer-Klett founded Munich Re in 1880. Within a month Munich Re opened offices in Hamburg Berlin Vienna and St. Petersburg establishing treaties with German and Danish insurers. In 1888 Munich Re went public; two years later it opened an office in London and helped finance the creation of Allianz which would soon come to dominate the German insurance industry. In 1892 the firm opened a branch in the US (it incurred severe losses from the 1906 San Francisco earthquake).

WWI interrupted Munich Re's UK and US operations. The company recovered after 1918 only to be hobbled again by the Great Depression. In 1933 Munich Re executive Kurt Schmitt became minister of economic affairs for the Nazis. Objecting to the evolving policies of National Socialism he left after a year returning to Munich Re where he became chief executive in 1938.

Hitler's ignition of WWII wasn't quite the boom Munich Re needed; its international business was again disrupted. After the war the Allies further limited overseas operations. Because of his involvement with the Nazi government Schmitt was replaced by Eberhard von Reininghaus in 1945. The

division of Germany further hampered the company's recovery.

Jump-started by the Marshall Plan in 1950 the West German Wirtschaftswunder (economic miracle) kicked into high gear as the devastated country rebuilt. Relaxation of occupation-era trading limits also helped as the company rebuilt its foreign business. By 1969 Munich Re's sales topped DM 2 billion. Amid the global oil crisis and a rash of terrorist acts in Germany the firm reported its first-ever reinsurance loss in 1977.

German reunification in 1990 provided new markets for Munich Re but advantages from new business in the East were wiped out by claims arising from that year's harsh winter.

In 1992 an investigation by the German Federal Cartel Office prompted a realignment in the insurance business —Allianz ceded its controlling interests in three life insurers (Hamburg-Mannheimer Versicherungs Karlsruher Lebensversicherung and Berlinische Lebensversicherung) to Munich Re bringing it into direct insurance. Munich Re took over Deutsche Krankenversicherung (DKV) in 1996. Also that year Munich Re acquired American Re.

During the 1990s reinsurance sales dwindled as competition increased forcing lower premiums and alternatives to insurance and reinsurance became more common. Munich Re looked to direct insurance particularly individual property/casualty and life insurance to compensate. In 1997 it merged Hamburg-Mannheimer and DKV with another insurer Victoria AG to form ERGO Versicherungsgruppe. Within a year ERGO's insurance income accounted for half of all revenues.

Munich Re and ERGO launched asset management firm MEAG Munich ERGO AssetManagement in 1999. That year Munich Re experienced its worst year ever after natural disasters hit its reinsurance business hard. To recoup its losses the next year the firm expanded both its reinsurance and primary insurance operations into key markets in Europe North and South America and Asia. Also in 2000 Munich Re bought CNA Financial's life reinsurance operations. Together with Swiss Re the company launched Inreon an online reinsurance exchange in 2001.

As one of the companies hit hardest financially by the World Trade Center tragedy Munich Re paid out some $2 billion in claims. In 2003 Allianz and Munich Re terminated their cooperation agreement as their shareholdings in each other fell to under 15%. (The two companies gradually sold off nearly all of their ownership interests in following years.)

In 2004 Munich Re entered its first Asian market by forming a joint venture in China.

EXECUTIVES

Management Board Member Reinsurance Corporate Underwriting and Information Technology, Torsten Jeworrek, age 56, $600,000 total compensation

Management Board Member Germany Asia Pacific and Africa Division, Ludger Arnoldussen, age 55, $400,000 total compensation

Management Board Member Special and Financial Risks Division, Thomas Blunck, age 51, $432,500 total compensation

Management Board Member Life Division, Joachim Oechslin, age 51

Management Board Member Europe and Latin America Division, Giuseppina Albo, age 54

Management Board Member Health Division, Doris H **Ŧ**oke, age 50

Senior Vice President Chief Financial Officer, Gary Gray

Chairman Management Board, jur. Nikolaus von Bomhard, age 60

Chairman Supervisory Board, Ing. Bernd Pischetsrieder

Deputy Chairman Supervisory Board, Marco N **Ŧ**enberg

Auditors: KPMG Bayerische Treuhandgesellschaft AG

LOCATIONS

HQ: Muenchener Rueckversicherungs-Gesellschaft AG (Germany)
Koeniginstrasse 107, Munich D-80802
Phone: (49) 89 38 91 0   **Fax:** (49) 89 39 90 56
Web: www.munichre.com

2014 Premiums

	% of total
Europe	30
North America	45
Asia & Australasia	17
Latin America	5
Africa Near & Middle East	3
Total	**100**

PRODUCTS/OPERATIONS

2014 Sales

	% of total
Reinsurance	
Property/casualty	34
Life	20
ERGO	
Life and health Germany	21
Property/casualty Germany	7
International	7
Munich Health	11
Total	**100**

Selected Brands

ERGO (primary insurance)
   Deutscher Automobil Schutz (D.A.S. auto insurance)
   Deutsche Krankenversicherung (DKV)
   ERV
ERGO Direkt (commercial customer consulting)
DKV (domestic health insurance)
Munich Health (international health insurance domestic and international health reinsurance)
Munich Re
Munich Re America
   American Modern Insurance (specialty property/casualty insurance life insurance reinsurance)
   Hartford Steam Boiler (HSB specialty property/casualty insurance and reinsurance)

COMPETITORS

AEGON	Manulife Financial
AIG	MetLife
AXA	Nippon Life Insurance
Allianz	OdysseyRe
Allstate	PartnerRe
Berkshire Hathaway	Prudential plc
Bloise-Holding	Reinsurance Group of
Chubb Limited	America
Everest Re	RenaissanceRe
General Re	Swiss Re
Hannover Re	Transatlantic Holdings
Helvetia Group	XL Group plc
ING	

HISTORICAL FINANCIALS

Company Type: Public

Income Statement

FYE: December 31

	ASSETS ($ mil.)	NET INCOME ($ mil.)	INCOME AS % OF ASSETS	EMPLOYEES
12/15	301,188	3,384	1.1%	43,554
12/14	331,807	3,832	1.2%	43,316
12/13	350,087	4,561	1.3%	44,665
12/11	340,531	4,211	1.2%	45,437
12/11	320,232	908	0.3%	47,206
Annual Growth	(1.5%)	38.9%	—	(2.0%)

2015 Year-End Financials

Return on assets: 1.1%
Return on equity: 10.2%
Long-term debt ($ mil.): —
No. of shares (mil.): 162
Sales ($ mil.): 68,236

Dividends
Yield: 2.8%
Payout: —
Market value ($ mil.): 3,253

	STOCK PRICE ($) FY Close	P/E High/Low		PER SHARE ($) Earnings	Dividends	Book Value
12/15	19.99	1	1	20.40	0.57	205.21
12/14	19.84	1	1	22.26	0.69	216.63
12/13	22.24	1	1	25.47	0.62	199.46
12/12	18.03	1	1	23.70	0.55	199.76
12/11	12.28	4	3	5.10	0.56	166.33
Annual Growth	12.9%	—	—	41.4%	0.3%	5.4%

Nanto Bank, Ltd.

The Nanto Bank primarily serves the Nara region of Japan. The bank operates from about 135 offices branches and other facilities located in the Hyogo Kyoto Mie Nara Osaka Tokyo and Wakayama areas of the country. Nanto Bank provides a selection of financial services including consumer banking credit card services securities leasing and lending. The bank traces its historical roots back to 1934. Major subsidiaries include Nanto Credit Guarantee Co. Nanto Lease co. Nanto Estate Co. Nanto Staff Service Co. and Nanto Investment Management Co.

Strategy

The Nanto Bank aims to increase its balance of loans deposits and assets by expanding its branch net work mainly through the establishment of new branches. In Osaka Prefecture identified as an important strategic area two new branches –the Eiwa branch and the Wakaeiwata branch –were built and opened in Higashiosaka City in September 2012. The company also opened in 2013 its Joto corporate business office and the Hokusetsu corporate business office with a plan to eventually developing these into branches.

EXECUTIVES

President, Takashi Hashimoto
Chairman, Ryuji Sakamoto
Auditors: KPMG AZSA LLC

LOCATIONS

HQ: Nanto Bank, Ltd.
16 Hashimoto-cho, Nara 630-8677
Phone: (81) 742 22 1131
Web: www.nantobank.co.jp

COMPETITORS

Aozora Bank
Kiyo Bank
Mitsubishi UFJ
Financial Group
Shizuoka Bank
Towa Bank

HISTORICAL FINANCIALS

Company Type: Public

Income Statement

FYE: March 31

	ASSETS ($ mil.)	NET INCOME ($ mil.)	INCOME AS % OF ASSETS	EMPLOYEES
03/16	49,027	108	0.2%	3,771
03/15	44,413	82	0.2%	3,791
03/14	50,254	87	0.2%	2,866
03/13	53,405	81	0.2%	2,889
03/12	58,631	42	0.1%	2,928
Annual Growth	(4.4%)	26.5%	—	6.5%

2016 Year-End Financials

Return on assets: 0.2%
Return on equity: 4.9%
Long-term debt ($ mil.): —
No. of shares (mil.): 268
Sales ($ mil): 680

Dividends
Yield: —
Payout: —
Market value ($ mil.): —

National Australia Bank Ltd.

National Australia Bank (NAB) is one of Australia's Big Four banks (along with ANZ Westpac and Commonwealth Bank of Australia). It provides banking wealth management and investment banking services in Australia as well as in New Zealand through its Bank of New Zealand (BNZ) subsidiary. NAB also offers debt risk management and investment products for institutional clients. The company and its subsidiaries have more than 1500 branches and service centers in the two regions. During 2015 the bank announced it would sell its Clydesdale Bank and Yorkshire Bank subsidiaries in the UK and its Great Western Bancorp subsidiary in the US to focus on its top markets in Australia and New Zealand.

OperationsNAB operates three business segments: Australian Banking which generated 69% of the company's operating income in fiscal 2015 (ended September 30 2015) and counts its business in Australia; NAB Wealth (10% of operating income) which counts NAB's insurance and investment solutions for retail corporate and institutional clients; and NZ Banking (10% of operating income) which counts NAB's business in New Zealand through BNZ. NAB's fourth segment UK Banking (10% of operating income) was discontinued in 2015 after it sold its Clydesdale Bank and Yorkshire Bank subsidiaries.

Broadly speaking NAB generated 70% of its total revenue from interest income (mostly on loans) during FY2015 while investment revenue made up another 12%. The rest came from premium and related revenue (4% of total revenue) fee income (1%) financial instrument gains (4%) and other operating income (9%).

Sales and Marketing

NAB served more than 12 million customers during FY2015. Its Australian Banking segment serves retail and business customers ranging from small and medium-sized enterprises to Australia's largest institutions. Its NAB segment serves retail corporate and institutional clients. BNZ serves retail business corporate agribusiness and insurance clients in New Zealand.

NAB spent A$248 million ($173 million) on advertising and marketing expenses in FY2015 compared to A$242 million ($211 million) in FY2014.

Financial PerformanceNote: Growth rates may differ after conversion to US dollars. This analysis uses financials from the company's annual report.

NAB's annual operating income (including net interest income) and profits have been trending higher since 2011 mostly thanks to 20% growth in loan assets over the period.

The bank's revenue dipped 3% to A$43.65 billion ($30.5 billion) in fiscal 2015 (ended September 30 2015) mostly due to a decrease in investment revenue during the year. Its net interest income however grew by 4% on higher housing and business lending volumes lower borrowing costs and favorable interest rate risk outcomes. The company's NAB Wealth segment grew the fastest (27% growth in cash earnings) thanks to strong insurance results and rising investment markets.

Despite revenue declines in FY2015 NAB's net income climbed 20% to A$6.34 billion ($4.4 billion) for the year mostly thanks to favorable foreign exchange rate movements and non-recurring items though low borrowing costs helped as well. The bank's operations used A$13 billion ($9.1 billion) for the year nearly twice as much cash as in FY2014 mostly because it used more cash to extend loans and advances to customers but also because of deposit repayments and various unfavorable working capital changes.

Strategy

Australia remains the core market for NAB making up nearly 70% of its total revenue in FY2015. As such the company continues to invest in building its business banking personal banking and wealth businesses; improving its loan asset quality; and drive mortgage and deposit growth at home.Abroad NAB has been exiting certain geographic markets and business lines in recent years. In October 2015 NAB reached a broad agreement to sell 80% of its life insurance business to Japan's Nippon Life for a little more than ¥2 billion. If the deal goes through the bank will retain 20% ownership of the business and will continue to market insurance products at its branches. Also in 2015 the bank sold its US-based subsidiary Great Western Bancorp in July and also announced it would exit the UK market by selling its Clydesdale Bank and Yorkshire Bank subsidiaries (slated for completion in February 2016).

HISTORY

Company BackgroundFormed in 1858 in Melbourne National Bank of Australasia (NBA) just missed the peak of the Victoria gold rush. The bank expanded across the territory and was one of the first to lend to farmers and ranchers using land deeds as security. In the late 1870s drought imperiled Victoria. Seeking greener pastures NBA entered New South Wales in 1885 then headed into Western Australia. Economic instability continued; in 1893 the bank experienced its first panic and was shuttered for eight weeks. NBA reopened only to close a quarter of its branches between 1893 and 1896.

During the Australian commonwealth's early years Western Australia was the bank's salvation as the economies in Victoria and South Australia stagnated. NBA helped fund Australia's WWI efforts through public loans. A postwar consolidation wave in banking swept up NBA which made acquisitions in 1918 and 1922.

Overdue farm and ranch loans weakened the bank during the Depression. As WWII raged the Commonwealth Bank (established in 1912) took greater control of Australia's banks. With competition among banks primarily limited to branch growth NBA acquired Queensland National Bank in 1948 and Ballarat Banking Co. in 1955. The bank diversified into consumer finance through acquisition. In the 1960s Australia experienced an economic boom as immigration and industrialization grew. The boom went bust in the 1970s as the world sunk into recession. Still under the Commonwealth Bank's tight control the banks watched business that had once been theirs lost to building societies merchant banks and credit unions.

The 1980s brought banking deregulation. To vie with foreign banks entering Australia NBA in 1981 merged with Commercial Banking Co. of Sydney and became the National Commercial Banking Corp. of Australia in 1982. (It took its present name in 1984.) Throughout the 1980s the bank diversified and moved into the US and Japan. It invested in property and made loans to foreign countries. All too quickly though property values sank and countries defaulted on loans.

To fight recession NAB looked abroad for opportunities. In 1987 it bought Clydesdale Bank Northern Bank and National Irish Bank from Midland Bank Group (now part of HSBC Holdings). Three years later NAB bought Yorkshire Bank then turned the four banks around by linking them and tightening loan operations. In 1992 it bought the troubled Bank of New Zealand again tightening loan operations. Three years later NAB claimed Michigan National in the US.

After the mid-1990s economic recovery NAB bought HomeSide to try to adapt the US mortgage firm's efficient operations for all its banks.

NAB in 2000 bought Lend Lease's MLC fund management group. It also announced plans to launch a separate stock for its European businesses fueling speculation it might be on the prowl to buy or merge with a large UK bank. The Australian Competition and Consumer Commission (ACCC) that year accused NAB of credit card transaction price-fixing; the bank faced a possible fine of nearly $6 million but the ACCC dropped litigation against the group the following year.

Also in 2001 NAB sold US-based Michigan National Bank to ABN AMRO and sold mortgage lender HomeSide International to Washington Mutual the following year. In fiscal year 2002 the bank cut some 2000 jobs mostly in back-office operations.

During fiscal year 2003 the company booked pre-tax losses of some $360 million due to unauthorized trading in the company's foreign currency options department. By the end of March 2004 chairman Charles Allen chief executive Frank Cicutto and the heads of global markets and foreign exchange had resigned. Three more executives and at least five traders were fired. The fallout continued the next year as the company struggled to regroup.

NAB sold its Irish banks —National Irish Bank and Northern Bank —to Danske Bank in 2005. It retained its UK banks Yorkshire Bank (England) and Clydesdale Bank (Scotland).

In 2006 NAB sold its Custom Fleet vehicle leasing division to GE Capital as well as its Asian life insurance and wealth management operations. The downsizing was part of the company's move to streamline operations.

To establish a foothold in the US NAB acquired Great Western Bancorporation for $A836 million (nearly US$800 million) in 2008.

Also that year NAB took a 20% stake in Chinese property trust Union Trust and Investment. The deal made NAB the first foreign bank to buy into a Chinese trust firm.

EXECUTIVES

Managing Director and Group CEO, Andrew Thorburn
Group Chief Risk Officer, David Gall
Acting Chief Customer Officer Corporate and Institutional Banking, Cathryn Carver

Managing Director and CEO Bank of New Zealand, Anthony J. Healy
Chief Customer Officer Consumer Banking and Wealth Management, Andrew Hagger
COO and Group Executive Customer Products and Services, Antony Cahill
Chief Customer Officer Business and Private Banking, Angela Mentis
CFO, Gary Lennon
Acting Chief Technology and Operations Officer, Bob Melrose
Chairman, Kenneth R. (Ken) Henry
Auditors: Ernst & Young

LOCATIONS

HQ: National Australia Bank Ltd.
Level 1, 800 Bourke Street, Docklands, Melbourne, Victoria 3008
Phone: (61) 3 8872 2461
Web: www.nabgroup.com

PRODUCTS/OPERATIONS

2015 Cash Earnings

	% of total
Australian banking	69
NZ banking	10
UK banking	10
NAB Wealth	8
Corporate function and others	3
Total	**100**

Selected Subsidiaries

Calibre Asset Management
Great Western Bancorporation
nabCapital (formerly Institutional Markets & Services)
National Australia Group Europe Limited
  Clydesdale Bank PLC
  Yorkshire Bank Home Loans Limited
  Yorkshire Bank Investments Limited
  National Australia Group Europe Services Limited
National Australia Group (NZ) Limited
  Bank of New Zealand
  BNZ International Funding Limited
National Australia Trustees Limited
National Wealth Management Holdings Limited
MLC Limited
  National Wealth Management International Holdings Limited

COMPETITORS

Australia and New Zealand Banking
Commonwealth Bank of Australia
Westpac Banking

HISTORICAL FINANCIALS

Company Type: Public

Income Statement

FYE: September 30

	ASSETS ($ mil.)	NET INCOME ($ mil.)	INCOME AS % OF ASSETS	EMPLOYEES
09/16	592,435	268	0.0%	34,567
09/15	671,228	4,454	0.7%	41,849
09/14	769,692	4,613	0.6%	42,602
09/13	753,097	5,078	0.7%	42,000
09/12	796,373	4,260	0.5%	0
Annual Growth	**(7.1%)**	**(49.9%)**	**—**	**—**

2016 Year-End Financials

Return on assets: 0.0%
Return on equity: 0.6%
Long-term debt ($ mil.): —
No. of shares (mil.): —
Sales ($ mil): 27,627

Dividends
  Yield: 9.5%
  Payout: 907.1%
Market value ($ mil.): —

STOCK PRICE ($)		P/E		PER SHARE ($)		
	FY Close	High/Low		Earnings	Dividends	Book Value
09/16	10.68	142	103	0.12	1.02	14.76
09/15	10.52	6	4	1.72	0.89	15.22
09/14	14.18	14	6	1.90	1.30	18.06
09/13	32.19	14	9	2.12	1.78	18.90
09/12	26.43	16	13	1.82	0.94	20.35
Annual Growth	**(20.3%)**	**—**	**—**	**(49.5%)**	**2.0%**	**(7.7%)**

National Bank of Abu Dhabi

Auditors: KPMG

LOCATIONS

HQ: National Bank of Abu Dhabi
  P.O. Box 4, Abu Dhabi
Phone:
Web: www.nbad.com

HISTORICAL FINANCIALS

Company Type: Public

Income Statement

FYE: December 31

	ASSETS ($ mil.)	NET INCOME ($ mil.)	INCOME AS % OF ASSETS	EMPLOYEES
12/15	110,691	1,424	1.3%	0
12/14	102,401	1,518	1.5%	0
12/13	88,500	1,288	1.5%	0
12/12	81,833	1,179	1.4%	0
12/11	69,606	1,009	1.5%	0
Annual Growth	**12.3%**	**9.0%**	**—**	**—**

2015 Year-End Financials

Return on assets: 1.3%
Return on equity: 12.8%
Long-term debt ($ mil.): —
No. of shares (mil.): —
Sales ($ mil): 3,672

Dividends
  Yield: —
  Payout: —
Market value ($ mil.): —

National Bank of Canada

What's the bank for the Quebecois? The National Bank of Canada says "C'est moi!" Also known as National Bank Financial Group the company offers personal and commercial banking services through about 450 branches in Canada primarily in Quebec. The bank's offerings include deposits mortgages loans and credit cards. Through subsidiaries it also provides insurance trust services wealth management online brokerage and private banking. The company with $185 billion in assets manages more than 50 proprietary mutual funds under the National Bank Omega and Altamira banners. Its Natbank unit has two branches in Florida for snowbirds.

Through some 85 locations the company's National Bank Financial subsidiary offers investments portfolio management and group insurance plans.

The unit manages more than $50 billion of client assets. It also performs investment banking and brokerage services such as mergers and acquisitions advice institutional trading securities clearing and corporate finance.

To boost its institutional services business National Bank of Canada agreed in late 2013 to acquire The Toronto-Dominion Bank's TD Waterhouse Institutional Services business for $250 million.

In 2012 National Bank of Canada sold its Natcan Investment Management arm to Fiera Sceptre (since renamed Fiera Capital) for more than $309 million. As part of the deal the bank received voting shares representing about 35% of Fiera. National Bank of Canada's strategy is to develop partnerships to grow in the wealth management business. In years prior the bank had been growing its wealth management segment hoping to capitalize on an aging Canadian populace investing toward retirement.

National Bank of Canada has benefited from a relatively strong Canadian economy and a rebound in employment in Quebec in particular. It reported more than $1 billion in net income in 2010 and enjoys one of the lowest loan loss ratios among financial institutions in the country. The company is focusing on referrals between its banking and financial markets segments to foment growth.

EXECUTIVES

President and CEO, Louis Vachon, age 54, $800,000 total compensation

EVP Human Resources and Corporate Affairs, Lynn Jeanniot

EVP Finance and Treasury and CFO, Ghislain Parent

EVP and Chief Transformation Officer, Ricardo Pascoe, $300,000 total compensation

EVP Risk Management, William Bonnell

EVP Operations, Brigitte Hebert

EVP Personal and Commercial Banking, Diane Giard

EVP Corporate Development and Chief Marketing Officer, Karen Leggett

EVP Information Technology, Dominique Fagnoule

Co-President and Co-CEO National Bank Financial; EVP Wealth Management, Martin Gagnon

EVP Financial Markets, Denis Girouard

Chairman, Jean Houde

Auditors: Deloitte LLP

LOCATIONS

HQ: National Bank of Canada
600 De La Gauchetiere Street West, 4th Floor, Montreal, Quebec H3B 4L2
Phone: 514 394-5000 **Fax:** 514 394-8434
Web: www.nbc.ca

PRODUCTS/OPERATIONS

2010 Sales

	% of total
Interest	
Loans	37
Securities & other	18
Noninterest	
Trust services & mutual funds	7
Securities brokerage commissions	6
Securitization revenue	5
Underwriting & advisory fees	5
Deposit & payment service charges	4
Lending fees	3
Other	15
Total	**100**

Selected Subsidiaries

Natbank (banking US)
NATCAN (75% portfolio management and investments)

National Bank Direct Brokerage (online brokerage)
National Bank Financial (investment banking)
National Bank General Insurance (home and auto coverage)
National Bank Insurance Firm (insurance brokerage)
National Bank Life Insurance Company
National Bank Securities (mutual funds)
National Bank Trust (trust services)

COMPETITORS

BMO Financial Group	Laurentian Bank
CIBC	RBC Financial Group
Caisses centrale	Scotiabank
Desjardins	TD Bank

HISTORICAL FINANCIALS

Company Type: Public

Income Statement

FYE: October 31

	ASSETS ($ mil.)	NET INCOME ($ mil.)	INCOME AS % OF ASSETS	EMPLOYEES
10/16	173,567	834	0.5%	21,770
10/15	164,216	1,142	0.7%	19,764
10/14	183,589	1,277	0.7%	19,955
10/13	179,938	1,375	0.8%	19,691
10/12	178,387	1,522	0.9%	19,920
Annual Growth	(0.7%)	(13.9%)	—	2.2%

2016 Year-End Financials

Return on assets: 0.5%
Return on equity: 10.2%
Long-term debt ($ mil.): —
No. of shares (mil.): 338
Sales ($ mil): 5,799

Dividends
  Yield: 4.5%
  Payout: 76.1%
Market value ($ mil.): 12,055

	STOCK PRICE ($) FY Close	P/E High/Low		PER SHARE ($) Earnings	Dividends	Book Value
10/16	35.66	11	8	2.46	1.65	24.97
10/15	33.01	9	7	3.43	1.55	23.78
10/14	46.87	19	9	3.86	1.73	26.34
10/13	86.95	19	16	4.21	3.35	23.88
10/12	77.36	17	14	4.67	3.06	22.44
Annual Growth	(17.6%)	—	—	(14.8%)	(14.3%)	2.7%

National Bank Of Greece S A

Like the ancient ruins that dominate the landscape of Greece National Bank of Greece (NBG) dominates the banking landscape of the Mediterranean. In addition to holding the top position at home NBG has taken a leading position in the Balkans by acquiring controlling stakes in banks throughout the region. The bank offers such services as commercial and consumer banking asset management investment banking brokerage services financing and insurance. It has more than 500 domestic branches and another 1200 in nearly a dozen outside countries. NBG once served as the Greek central bank but the government sold its stake in the company in 2004.

OperationsBroadly speaking NBG generates 75% of its revenue in the form of interest income (mostly from loans) while the remainder comes from a mix of insurance income deposit account charges and other fees and commissions credit card fees and gains available-for-sale securities.

NBG's Turkish Operations is the bank's largest segment generating more than 40% of the bank's total revenue. The unit offers a variety of commercial banking services through Finansbank and its subsidiaries in Turkey.

The Retail Banking division makes up another 20% of revenue and serves individual customers professionals small-medium and small sized companies (identified as businesses with revenues up to euro 2.5 million or roughly $2.8 million) in Greece. Corporate & Investment Banking (20% of revenue) lends to large and medium-sized companies and also offers shipping finance and investment banking services.

The bank's International business (roughly 10% of revenue) offers commercial banking services including commercial and retail credit trade financing foreign exchange and traditional deposit banking to countries outside of Greece and Turkey. In addition to Finansbank in Turkey NBG's seven other non-Greek subsidiaries include: United Bulgarian Bank (UBB) Vojvodjanska Banka Banca Romaneasca Stopanska Banka the National Bank of Greece (Cyprus) Ltd. (NBG Cyprus) Banka NBG (NBG Albania) South African Bank of Athens (SABA) and NBG Bank (Malta) Ltd. (NBG Malta).

NBG also has an Insurance business (5% of revenue) as well as a Global Markets & Asset Management business. Other services include proprietary real estate management and hotel and warehousing services which make up less than 5% of revenue.

Geographic Reach

In addition to Greece NBG operates banks in Albania Bulgaria Cyprus Egypt Romania Serbia and FYROM South Africa and Turkey. While most of the bank's revenue comes from its home country about 40% of revenue comes from its operations in Turkey while another roughly 10% comes from countries outside of Greece and Turkey.

Sales and Marketing

NBG markets its products and services through agents and independent insurance brokers. It spent euro 53 million ($64.4 million) on promotion and advertising in 2014 up from euro 68 million ($82.65 million) in 2013.

Financial Performance

Note: Growth rates may differ after conversion to US dollars.

The bank has come a long way from its low point in 2011 caused by heavy trading losses and political turmoil in its home country. Still after two years of growth revenue in 2014 plunged by 27% to euro 5.09 billion ($6.19 billion) mostly due to losses on its derivative investments but also because the bank collected less interest income from a rise in non-performing loans. NBG returned to the red in 2014 reporting a net loss of euro 2.5 billion ($3 billion) mostly due to a combination of lower revenue and higher loan loss provisions as the quality of its domestic loan portfolio worsened in the midst of intense political uncertainty and bad economic conditions in Greece. The bank's operations provided more cash in 2014 as most of its losses were related to non-cash loan loss provisions. StrategyGiven the poor economic climate in Greece and heated political battles ensuing related to the country's debt levels NBG has been operating in a challenging business climate. To turn around its struggling loan portfolio which has been suffering from domestic property devaluations in troubled Greece and resulting loan asset impairments the bank has been focusing on strengthening its capital position in raising cash from share offerings and selling off riskier loan assets in favor of safer ones. The bank has also been relying heavily on its Turkish Operations to generate loan business in Turkey where roughly 40% of its revenue came from in 2014. Mergers and AcquisitionsIn 2013 NGB made several acquisitions to expand its branch reach and loan business. In mid-2013 for example it purchased selected assets from the troubled banks Probank S.A. and First Business Bank S.A. (FBB) for a total of around euro 1 billion ($1.3 billion) adding 19 FBB branches and 112 Probank branches to the NBG branch network.

HISTORY

Company BackgroundThe National Bank of Greece (NBG) can trace its banking heritage back to Pasion a metic (non-Greek) former slave living in Athens in the fourth century BC. To help his former master rebuild after one of Greece's many wars he obtained a small private bank that had been formed a few decades earlier and became one of Athens' greatest bankers.

The bank as it exists today though was established in 1841 and for most of its existence served as Greece's central bank. It listed on the Athens Stock Exchange in 1880. NBG survived WWI and Germany's occupation of Greece during WWII. It weathered the civil war in the late 1940s the military coup that overthrew the constitutional monarchy in the 1960s and democratic reformation in the 1970s.

As the 1980s dawned and Andreas Papandreou's socialist government came to power in Greece the bank launched a joint venture in Paris with Credit Lyonnais and other investors. NBG caused plenty of problems for its privately owned competitors during the early part of the decade — as deposits declined profits shrank and labor costs rose the bank was able to undercut competitors thanks to its government backing.

A banking scandal involving NBG and Papandreou helped topple the socialist government in the late 1980s. The bank's US subsidiary Atlantic Bank of New York was one of two Greek banks charged with money laundering to the tune of $700 million. Rival political parties called for Papandreou already ailing to resign. (In 1992 the former leader was acquitted of corruption charges stemming from the scandal.)

Under the leadership of a different government in the early 1990s the bank looked to shake up its holdings to improve profits. It sold off a number of subsidiaries including a chain of luxury hotels an insurance unit and Traders Credit Bank a small commercial bank. These divestitures were just the beginning as the Greek government looked to privatize a number of its holdings. Turmoil in the Greek economy in the mid-1990s forced the bank to limit withdrawals hike interest rates and take other conservative measures as the government tried to prevent a devaluation of the native currency.

In the late 1990s Greece looked to join the Euro zone and its institutions began shaping up. Doing its part NBG took measures to clean up its balance sheet writing off a number of bad loans it had been pressured to make by the government. The bank focused on retail operations absorbed the National Mortgage Bank and transformed its ETEVA development banking subsidiary into a full-fledged investment bank. It began shoring up flagging overseas operations listed on the NYSE (1999) and looked to expand in the Balkans.

In 1997 the bank opened offices in Albania and three years later bought controlling interests in Macedonia's Skopanska Banka and United Bulgarian Bank. As the 20th century drew to a close NGB won more freedom from the Greek government when the finance ministry announced it would no longer appoint the bank's executive officers instead allowing NGB's board of directors and shareholders to make the decisions.

In 2000 the company launched subsidiary NBG Venture Capital which concentrates on Greece southeast Europe and the eastern Mediterranean.

The government sold 10% of its stake in the bank in 2003 as part of its privatization program. Although the move dropped its holdings to 30% the government retained management control. The state divested its interest in the company in 2004.

EXECUTIVES

General Manager Treasury Global Markets and Private Banking, Petros Christodoulou, age 56, $299,693 total compensation

General Manager Risk Management, Michael Oratis, age 59, $323,450 total compensation

General Manager of Strategy & International Activities Chief Economist of the Group, Paul Mylonas, age 58, $292,390 total compensation

General Manager of Corporate Banking Chairman of the Board of Directors at Ethniki Insurance Co, Dimitrios G. Dimopoulos, age 70, $213,254 total compensation

General Manager of Retail Banking, Nelly Tzakou-Lambropoulou, age 55, $205,284 total compensation

General Manager Real Estate, Aristotelis Karytinos, age 61, $344,833 total compensation

CEO, Leonidas Fragkiadakis, age 51, $241,674 total compensation

Chief Financial Officer, Paula N. Hadjisotiriou, age 59

General Manager Group Retail Collections, Marianna Politopoulou

Chief of Operations, Damianos Charalampidis

Chief Credit Officer, Dimitris Frangetis

Group CIO, Nikos Christodoulou

Chair, Louka T. Katseli

Auditors: Deloitte Hadjipavlou Sofianos & Cambanis S.A.

LOCATIONS

HQ: National Bank Of Greece S A
  86 Eolou St., Athens 10232
Phone: (30) 210 334 1000   **Fax:** (30) 210 334 2235
Web: www.nbg.gr

PRODUCTS/OPERATIONS

2014 Sales

	% of total
Turkish operation	41
Retail banking	19
International	12
Insurance	5
Corporate and investment banking	21
Others	2
Total	**100**

COMPETITORS

Alpha Bank	Emporiki Bank
Bank of Cyprus	HSBC
Citibank	Piraeus Bank S.A.
EFG Eurobank Ergasias	Royal Bank of Scotland

HISTORICAL FINANCIALS

Company Type: Public

Income Statement   FYE: December 31

	ASSETS ($ mil.)	NET INCOME ($ mil.)	INCOME AS % OF ASSETS	EMPLOYEES
12/13	147,091	50	0.0%	37,591
12/12	133,328	(3,344)	—	35,573
12/11	133,829	(18,806)	—	34,530
Annual Growth	4.8%	—	—	4.3%

2013 Year-End Financials

Return on assets: 0.0%	Dividends
Return on equity: ***.***.*%	Yield: —
Long-term debt ($ mil.): —	Payout: —
No. of shares (mil.): 159	Market value ($ mil.): 895
Sales ($ mil): 9,707	

Stock price table:

	STOCK PRICE ($) FY Close	P/E High/Low	PER SHARE ($) Earnings	Dividends	Book Value
12/13	5.60	17 1	0.62	0.00	20.05
12/12	1.79	— —	(523.92)	0.00	(1,262)
12/11	1.98	— —	(2,952.95)	0.00	(864)
Annual Growth	—	— —	—	—	—

National Grid plc

It's not gridlock but a lock on the Grid that is a good thing for National Grid. It is the sole owner and operator of the electricity transmission system in England and Wales. It transmits electricity through about 4500 miles of overhead and underground lines to distribution utilities serving more than 52 million people. National Grid also operates the UK natural gas transmission and distribution system (serving 10.9 million homes and businesses) through its National Grid Gas subsidiary. However it is the company's Northeastern US gas distribution and power generation transmission and distribution operations led by National Grid USA that bring in the bulk of the company's revenues.

Geographic Reach

In fiscal 2015 (March year end) the US accounted for 53% of revenues; the UK 47%.

Operations

In the US the company distributes power to about 3.5 million customers in Massachusetts New Hampshire New York and Rhode Island and natural gas to 3.6 million clients in those states. It also manages the electricity distribution network in Long Island.

National Grid owns the high-voltage electricity transmission network in England and Wales and operates the high pressure gas transmission system in Britain.

The electricity industry connects generation sources to homes and businesses through transmission and distribution networks. National Grid produces electricity from fossil fuel and nuclear power stations as well as renewable sources such as wind and solar. In the US National Grid owns and operates 50 fossil fuel-powered stations on Long Island and 4.6 MW of solar generation in Massachusetts.

It operates the transmission network in England and Wales and also operates Scottish networks. The company is working in a joint venture with Scottish Power Transmission to construct an interconnector to reinforce the transmission system between Scotland and England and Wales. In the US it jointly operates transmission facilities spanning upstate New York Massachusetts New Hampshire Rhode Island and Vermont.

The company's gas industry connects producers processors storage transmission and distribution network operators as well as suppliers to industrial commercial and domestic users. Gas used in the UK is mainly sourced from gas fields in the North and Irish seas piped from Europe and imported as LNG. Gas used in the US is produced mainly in North America. National Grid owns and operate Grain LNG an importation terminal and storage facility at the Isle of Grain in Kent.

Sales and Marketing

The company sells electricity under a long-term contract power supply agreement. It delivers gas to 10.9 million consumers in the UK and 3.6 million customers in the US. The customers buy gas in U.S. via independent providers.

Financial Performance

In fiscal 2015 National Grid's net revenues increased by 3% (in local currency) driven by higher revenues in the UK Electricity Transmission business reflecting increases in allowed Transmission Owner revenues and higher core allowances and pass-through costs in UK Gas Transmission.

Revenues in the UK Gas Distribution business were slightly lower as a result of changes in allowed revenues for replacement expenditure. US Regulated businesses revenues were also lower as a result of the end of the LIPA Management Services Agreement in the previous year partially offset by revenue increases from existing rate plans together with additional income from gas customer growth and the impact of the strengthening US dollar.

Net income decreased by 18% (in local currency) due to an increase in operating costs as the result of higher controllable costs (including the impact of inflation and additional costs to improve data quality and bring regulatory filings up to date); higher US bad debt costs following an exceptionally cold winter; and higher depreciation and amortization as a result of continued investment programs. These cost increases were partly offset by a reduction in spend on US financial systems implementation and stabilization upgrades.

National Grid's cash from operating activities increased by 25% (in local currency) due to changes in exceptional items re-measurements and stranded cost recoveries working capital (principally in the US due to the collection of high winter charges and other settlements including Superstorm Sandy reinsurance claims and LIPA receipts).

Strategy

The company's long-term strategy is to focus on large-scale power and gas systems in the UK and the US and to better integrate its various operations.

National Grid continues to work on developing additional interconnector projects (including opportunities for interconnection with Iceland Denmark and a further link with France). In the UK it is expanding gas system enhancement investment programs and developing electric grid modernization plans.

The company also continues investments in US programs investing in electricity and gas infrastructure to improve resilience and help reduce the impact of service interruptions. It is also investing in mobile technology.

HISTORY

Company Background

The National Grid Company was formed in 1990 as part of the privatization of the electricity industry in England and Wales. Until then the Central Electricity Generating Board (CEGB) a state monopoly responsible for power generation in England and Wales owned the national power grid (transmission system) and sold power to 12 area boards the regional authorities that distributed electricity to customers.

The Electricity Act of 1989 paved the way for competition; in 1990 the CEGB was split into The National Grid Company and three power-generating firms: National Power PowerGen and Nuclear Electric. The 12 area boards transferred their assets to 12 regional companies which jointly owned National Grid. The company keeping its monopoly status was charged to develop and operate an efficient coordinated and economical transmission system and to facilitate competition among power producers.

The company moved outside the UK when it invested in Citelec in 1993. An international consortium Citelec controlled Transener the surviving transmission system after Argentina privatized its electric utilities.

Also in 1993 National Grid set up Energis as a telecommunications firm to provide service to businesses. Piggybacking its fiber-optic lines on National Grid's transmission network Energis introduced national services in 1994 and by 1996 it had won several major customers including the BBC and Microsoft.

In 1995 National Grid went public as The National Grid Group. It also secured concessions to build transmission lines in Pakistan but in 1997 a new Pakistani government put the project on hold. That year it also upped its stake in Citelec from 15% to 41% which increased its control over the development of Argentina's transmission system. With partner CINergy Global it also acquired 80% of the Power Division of Zambia Consolidated Copper Mines in 1997 and it was chosen as a joint venture partner by India's Karnataka Electricity Board to build a transmission line in that state.

The company sold 26% of Energis in 1997; in 1998 it announced plans to sell the rest of Energis and launch a new company under the National Grid banner to set up telecom firms overseas. That year it laid plans to enter the US by agreeing to acquire New England Electric System (NEES). (The $3.2 billion purchase closed in 2000.)

In 1999 the company cut its stake in Energis to 46% and announced plans to shop for more US energy holdings. A deal was struck to purchase New York Utility Niagara Mohawk Holdings the following year. (The deal was completed in 2002.) Also in 2000 and 2001 the company continued to slim its stake in Energis (33%).

National Grid sold some noncore businesses in 2001 including UK metering company Datum Services and US energy marketer Allenergy and pulled out of the transmission project in India. It also agreed to manage the Alliance Regional Transmission Organization (RTO) in the US. In 2002 National Grid sold Niagara Mohawk's 50% interest in Canadian Niagara Power to Canadian utility Fortis.

The firm changed its name to National Grid Transco in 2002 upon completion of its acquisition of Lattice Group in a $21.5 billion deal.

In 2005 National Grid Transco sold four of its regional gas distribution networks; the North England network was acquired by a consortium that includes United Utilities and Cheung Kong Infrastructure; the South of England and Scotland networks were sold to Scottish and Southern Energy Borealis Infrastructure and Ontario Teachers' Pension Plan; and the Wales & West distribution network was purchased by a consortium managed by Macquarie Bank Limited. The company dropped Transco from its name in 2005.

National Grid dramatically boosted its North American assets in 2007 by acquiring gas distributor KeySpan for more than $7 billion. To comply with federal regulations connected to the KeySpan deal in 2008 National Grid sold its 2480-MW Ravenswood Generating Station in New York City to TransCanada for $2.9 billion.

In the second half of the decade to raise cash and narrow its operational focus the company jettisoned a number of noncore operations. National Grid sold its stakes in the alternative telecommunications network industry. The company also sold its telecom interests in Chile Argentina and Poland and wrote off its 33% stake in bankrupt UK telecommunications firm Energis which uses fiber-optic cable strung along National Grid's power lines. National Grid also sold former Lattice Group subsidiary 186k (fiber-optic networking) to Hutchison Whampoa and exited its telecom venture in

Brazil. It also sold its electricity interconnector linking Australia to the island state of Tasmania.

In 2010 a National Grid and TenneT joint venture began laying the first section of a high-voltage cable that will link the power grids in the UK and the Netherlands bolstering power supply in both countries. The project will help the companies meet environmental goals by facilitating power flows from low-carbon generation plants.

With an eye on meeting ambitious European Union goals for carbon emission reductions in 2009 National Grid released a report that by 2020 half of the UK's heating needs could be provided by biogas (converted from sewage and injected into the national gas distribution system) compensating for a decline in North Sea gas supply. In 2010 the company had one renewable gas plant under development in the US and two in the UK.

The company reported a major jump in revenues and income in 2010 primarily driven by a rebounding economy (prompting increased demand for power and gas) and by improved rates in the US market. Revenues grew by 40% in 2011 and net income by 30% thanks to strong demand and higher prices in the UK and increased rates in the US.

In 2011 National Grid announced plans to save $200 million in a restructuring of its US operations including cutting 1200 jobs. Late in 2011 the company sold the Seneca-Upshur Petroleum subsidiary for approximately $152 million. The deal is a further move to return to core business operations in gas and electricity distribution. That year it also agreed to sell its non-regulated metering business in the UK (Onstream) to Macquarie Bank for about $440 million.

EXECUTIVES

Finance Director, Andrew R. J. Bonfield, age 53, $712,000 total compensation
President US, Dean S. Seavers, age 56
CEO, John Pettigrew
CIO, Rich Adduci
Chairman, Peter Gershon, age 69
Auditors: PricewaterhouseCoopers LLP

LOCATIONS

HQ: National Grid plc
1-3 Strand, London WC2N 5EH
Phone: (44) 20 7004 3000   **Fax:** (44) 20 7004 3004
Web: www.nationalgrid.com

2014 Sales

	% of total
US	53
UK	47
Total	**100**

PRODUCTS/OPERATIONS

2014 Sales

	% of total
US Regulated	52
UK Electricity Transmission	25
UK Gas distribution	12
UK Gas Transmission	6
Other activities	5
Total	**100**

COMPETITORS

Con Edison	Northern Ireland
Enterprise Group	Electricity
Eversource Energy	Northern Powergrid
HomeServe	Scottish and Southern
IBERDROLA	Energy
Northern Electric	

HISTORICAL FINANCIALS

Company Type: Public

Income Statement

FYE: March 31

	REVENUE ($ mil.)	NET INCOME ($ mil.)	NET PROFIT MARGIN	EMPLOYEES
03/16	21,756	3,729	17.1%	25,068
03/15	22,466	2,983	13.3%	24,274
03/14	24,654	4,122	16.7%	23,909
03/13	21,820	3,487	16.0%	25,224
03/12	22,164	3,262	14.7%	25,645
Annual Growth	(0.5%)	3.4%	—	(0.6%)

2016 Year-End Financials

Debt ratio: 69.2%
Return on equity: 20.2%
Cash ($ mil.): 182
Current ratio: 0.82
Long-term debt ($ mil.): 35,601

No. of shares (mil.): —
Dividends
  Yield: 4.6%
  Payout: —
Market value ($ mil.): —

	STOCK PRICE ($) FY Close	P/E High/Low	PER SHARE ($) Earnings	Dividends	Book Value
03/16	71.42	105 85	0.99	3.29	5.21
03/15	64.61	132 112	0.79	3.45	4.73
03/14	68.74	106 90	1.10	3.15	5.14
03/13	58.01	93 77	0.95	0.00	4.24
03/12	50.48	93 79	0.91	0.00	4.15
Annual Growth	9.1%	— —	2.1%	—	5.8%

National Westminster Bank Plc

One of the retail banking arms of The Royal Bank of Scotland (RBS) National Westminster Bank (NatWest) provides banking and financial services to individual and small business clients in the UK. The bank offers deposits mortgages credit cards and personal loans through a network of 1500 bank branches. It also offers phone and Internet banking as well as a network of cash machines and mobile banking units. Subsidiary Ulster Bank has some 240 branches across the island of Ireland. Other offerings include life insurance pensions private banking services carbon offsets and other more prosaic business services as well as investment and retirement management.

NatWest was formed by the 1968 merger of National Provincial Bank (established in 1833) and Westminster Bank (1836). RBS acquired the company in 2000 in the UK's largest bank takeover to date.

The bank has struggled through the global financial crisis which deeply crippled parent RBS. RBS became 84% owned by the UK government after it received a series of bailouts in 2008 and 2009. NatWest reported a loss in 2010 as the result of lower gains on redemption of own debt higher costs and higher impairment losses.

As part of RBS' agreement with the European Commission the company is selling more than 300 of its branches and locations including seven NatWest branches in Scotland to Spanish bank Santander. The transaction (aimed at cutting costs) is expected to close in 2012.

EXECUTIVES

Chief Executive, Stephen A. M. Hester, age 51
Chairman, Philip Hampton, age 63
Auditors: Deloitte LLP

LOCATIONS

HQ: National Westminster Bank Plc
  135 Bishopsgate, London EC2M 3UR
Phone: (44) 131 626 4099   **Fax:** (44) 131 626 3081
Web: www.natwest.com

PRODUCTS/OPERATIONS

Services

Personal Banking
Credit card
Insurance
Loans
Mortgages
Saving Account
Private Banking
Credit Cards
Current Accounts
Insurance
Loans
Mortgages
Business Banking
International business
Startup business

COMPETITORS

AIB
Barclays
Clydesdale Bank
Grupo Santander

HSBC
Lloyds Banking Group
Yorkshire Bank

HISTORICAL FINANCIALS

Company Type: Public

Income Statement

FYE: December 31

	ASSETS ($ mil.)	NET INCOME ($ mil.)	INCOME AS % OF ASSETS	EMPLOYEES
12/15	448,184	(1,785)	—	29,200
12/14	482,268	2,705	0.6%	24,600
12/13	584,120	(9,854)	—	25,600
12/12	612,451	(5,280)	—	24,100
12/11	567,814	(5,950)	—	26,900
Annual Growth	(5.7%)	—	—	2.1%

2015 Year-End Financials

Return on assets: (-0.3%)
Return on equity: (-7.6%)
Long-term debt ($ mil.): —
No. of shares (mil.): 1,678
Sales ($ mil): 12,503

Dividends
  Yield: 7.4%
  Payout: —
Market value ($ mil.): 43,465

	STOCK PRICE ($) FY Close	P/E High/Low	PER SHARE ($) Earnings	Dividends	Book Value
12/15	25.90	— —	(0.00)	1.94	13.09
12/14	26.12	— —	(0.00)	1.94	15.68
12/13	25.18	— —	(0.00)	1.94	12.68
12/12	24.78	— —	(0.00)	1.94	19.88
12/11	16.78	— —	(0.00)	1.87	14.85
Annual Growth	11.5%	— —	—	1.0%	(3.1%)

NATIXIS SA

Auditors: Deloitte & Associés

LOCATIONS

HQ: NATIXIS SA
  30, avenue Pierre Mendes France, Paris 75013
Phone: (33) 1 58 32 30 00
Web: www.natixis.com

HISTORICAL FINANCIALS

Company Type: Public

Income Statement

FYE: December 31

	ASSETS ($ mil.)	NET INCOME ($ mil.)	INCOME AS % OF ASSETS	EMPLOYEES
12/15	544,885	1,463	0.3%	20,617
12/14	717,663	1,383	0.2%	20,287
12/13	702,315	1,217	0.2%	19,632
12/12	696,417	1,187	0.2%	20,198
12/11	656,701	2,020	0.3%	20,451
Annual Growth	(4.6%)	(7.7%)		0.2%

2015 Year-End Financials

Return on assets: 0.2%
Return on equity: 7.0%
Long-term debt ($ mil.): —
No. of shares (mil.): —
Sales ($ mil): 21,437

Dividends
  Yield: 6.5%
  Payout: 82.9%
Market value ($ mil.): —

NEC Corp

Radio and t.v. communications equipment
Auditors: KPMG AZSA LLC

LOCATIONS

HQ: NEC Corp
  5-7-1 SHiba, Minato-ku, Tokyo 108-8001
Phone: (81) 3 3454 1111
Web: www.nec.co.jp

HISTORICAL FINANCIALS

Company Type: Public

Income Statement

FYE: March 31

	REVENUE ($ mil.)	NET INCOME ($ mil.)	NET PROFIT MARGIN	EMPLOYEES
03/16	25,122	612	2.4%	98,726
03/15	24,466	477	2.0%	98,882
03/14	29,481	326	1.1%	100,914
03/13	32,644	323	1.0%	102,375
03/12	37,020	(1,344)	—	109,102
Annual Growth	(9.2%)	—	—	(2.5%)

2016 Year-End Financials

Debt ratio: 0.1%
Return on equity: 8.4%
Cash ($ mil.): 1,501
Current ratio: 1.51
Long-term debt ($ mil.): 2,848

No. of shares (mil.): —
Dividends
  Yield: —
  Payout: —
Market value ($ mil.): —

Nedbank Group Ltd

Nedbank Group provides commercial and personal financial services in South Africa and other parts of the continent. The company offers a range of wholesale and retail banking services through principal business clusters Nedbank Corporate Nedbank Retail Nedbank Wealth Nedbank Business Banking and Nedbank Capital (investment banking and capital markets). Other services include property finance private banking credit card processing insurance and foreign exchange and securities trading. UK-based insurer Old Mutual owns a controlling stake in Nedbank Group.

In addition to about 500 retail and commercial banking branches located primarily in South Africa's urban and suburban areas Nedbank Group has some 400 banking outlets inside Pick 'n Pay grocery stores and more than 40 other locations elsewhere in southern Africa. To grow its retail business Nedbank is looking to underserved markets such as youth senior citizens and small and medium-sized enterprises. It is also building its wealth management operations. As part of an effort to increase its motor vehicle and asset finance business the company in 2010 acquired the nearly 49% of Imperial Bank that it did not already own.

Nedbank strengthened its presence in Africa in 2008 when it announced a strategic alliance with Ecobank an institution that operates mainly in west and central Africa. The deal which gives clients access to both banking networks covering more than 30 countries is part of Nedbank's overall strategy to expand internationally and within Africa.

UK-based global banking firm HSBC was in exclusive talks to acquire a majority stake in Nedbank from Old Mutual. However negotiations broke down in 2010 and the deal fell through. Neither side gave a reason why the talks came to an end. Also that year Mike Brown was named CEO of Nedbank. He succeeded Tom Boardman who retired but remained on the company's board of directors.

EXECUTIVES

CEO, Michael W. T. (Mike) Brown, age 49
Managing Executive Nedbank Capital, Brian Kennedy, age 55
Group Risk Officer, Philip Wessels, age 57
Managing Executive Nedbank Corporate, Mfundo Nkuhlu, age 49
Managing Executive Business Banking, Sandile Shabalala, age 48
CIO, Fred Swanepoel, age 52
CFO, Raisibe K. Morathi, age 47
Chief Risk Officer, Trevor Adams
COO, Graham Wayne Dempster
Chairman, Vassi Naidoo
Auditors: Deloitte & Touche

LOCATIONS

HQ: Nedbank Group Ltd
Nedbank 135 Rivonia Campus, 135 Rivonia Road, Sandown, Sandton, Johannesburg 2196
Phone: (27) 11 294 4444   **Fax:** (27) 11 294 6540
Web: www.nedbankgroup.co.za

COMPETITORS

Absa	Investec
Citigroup	Standard Chartered
FirstRand	

HISTORICAL FINANCIALS

Company Type: Public

Income Statement

FYE: December 31

	ASSETS ($ mil.)	NET INCOME ($ mil.)	INCOME AS % OF ASSETS	EMPLOYEES
12/15	59,366	687	1.2%	31,312
12/14	70,057	847	1.2%	30,499
12/13	71,165	819	1.2%	29,513
12/12	80,221	878	1.1%	28,748
12/11	80,032	764	1.0%	28,494
Annual Growth	(7.2%)	(2.6%)	—	2.4%

2015 Year-End Financials

Return on assets: 1.2%	Dividends
Return on equity: 15.1%	Yield: 5.3%
Long-term debt ($ mil.): —	Payout: 37.8%
No. of shares (mil.): 476	Market value ($ mil.): 5,835
Sales ($ mil): 5,307	

	STOCK PRICE ($) FY Close	P/E High/Low		Earnings	PER SHARE ($) Dividends	Book Value
12/15	12.25	1	0	1.42	0.65	10.06
12/14	21.45	1	1	1.77	0.70	12.46
12/13	20.07	1	1	1.73	0.68	12.48
12/12	22.54	1	1	1.87	0.73	13.86
12/11	17.66	3	1	1.66	0.61	13.28
Annual Growth	(8.7%)	—	—	(3.7%)	1.8%	(6.7%)

Nestle SA

With instant coffee baby food and bottled water in the mix Nestle crunches more than just chocolate. The world's #1 food and drinks company in terms of sales Nestle is also the world leader in coffee (Nescafe). It also makes coffee for the home-brewing system Nespresso. Nestle is one of the world's top bottled water makers (Nestle Waters) one of the biggest frozen pizza makers (DiGiorno) and a big player in the pet food business (Friskies Purina). Its most well-known global food brands include Buitoni Dreyer's Maggi Milkmaid Carnation and Kit Kat. The company also owns Gerber Products. North America is Nestle's most important market.

HISTORY

Henri Nestle purchased a factory in Vevey Switzerland in 1843 that made products ranging from nut oils to rum. In 1867 he developed a powder made from cow's milk and wheat flour as a substitute for mother's milk. A year earlier Americans Charles and George Page had founded the Anglo-Swiss Condensed Milk Company in Cham Switzerland using Gail Borden's milk-canning technology. In 1875 Nestle sold his eponymous company then doing business in 16 countries. When Anglo-Swiss launched a milk-based infant food in 1878 Nestle's new owners responded by introducing a condensed-milk product. In 1905 a year after Nestle began selling chocolate the companies ended their rivalry by merging under the Nestle name. Hampered by limited milk supplies during WWI the company expanded into regions less affected by the war such as the US. In 1929 it acquired Cailler the first company to mass-produce chocolate bars and Swiss General inventor of milk chocolate. An investment in a Brazilian condensed-milk factory during the 1920s paid an unexpected dividend when Brazilian coffee growers suggested the company develop a water-soluble "coffee cube." Released in 1938 Nescafe instant coffee quickly became popular. Other new products included Nestle's Crunch bar (1938) Quik drink mix (1948) and Taster's Choice instant coffee (1966). Nestle expanded during the 1970s with acquisitions such as Beringer Brothers wines (sold in 1995) Stouffer's and Libby's. Moving beyond foods in 1974 Nestle acquired a 49% stake in Gesparal a holding company that controls the French cosmetics company L'Oreal. It acquired pharmaceutical firm Alcon Laboratories three years later. Helmut Maucher was named chairman and CEO in 1981. He began beefing up Nestle's global pres-

ence. Boycotters had long accused Nestle of harming children in developing countries through the unethical promotion of infant formula and Maucher acknowledged the ongoing boycott by meeting with the critics and setting up a commission to police adherence to World Health Organization guidelines. Nestle bought Carnation in 1985. Maucher doubled the company's chocolate business in 1988 with the purchase of UK chocolate maker Rowntree (Kit Kat). Also in the 1980s Nestle acquired Buitoni pastas. The company expanded in the 1990s with the purchases of Butterfinger and Baby Ruth candies Source Perrier water Alpo pet food and Ortega Mexican foods. Company veteran Peter Brabeck-Letmathe succeeded Maucher as CEO in 1997. He cleaned out Nestle's pantry by selling non-core businesses (Contadina tomato products Libby's canned meat products) but restocked with San Pellegrino (mineral water) and Dalgety's Spillers (pet food) in 1998. By 1999 the company started rolling out its Nestle Pure Life bottled water. It also sold its Findus brand (fish vegetables) and its non-instant US coffee brands. That year Nestle merged its US novelty ice-cream unit with operations of Pillsbury's Häagen-Dazs to form Ice Cream Partners USA. In 2000 Nestle purchased snack maker PowerBar. In 2001 it bought Ralston Purina for $10.3 billion making it the world's largest pet food maker. To win FTC approval the companies agreed to sell Meow Mix and Alley Cat dry cat food brands to Hartz Mountain. In a deal that gives Nestle a 99-year license to use the Häagen-Dazs brand in the US the company agreed to pay $641 million to General Mills (which has bought Pillsbury from Britain's Diageo) for the other half of Ice Cream Partners. In 2002 Nestle acquired German ice-cream maker Schoeller Holding Group as well as US food company Chef America maker of Hot Pockets and Lean Pockets. That same year Nestle also spun off eyecare subsidairy Alcon Laboratories but retained about 75% ownership of it. The company renamed its water unit from Perrier Vittel SA to Nestle Waters and bought Russian bottled water company Saint Springs. The company sold its savory flavor business Food Ingredients Specialties (FIS) to Swiss flavoring company Givaudan and its UK and Ireland ambient foods business to HM Capital Partners (then named Hicks Muse Tate & Furst). It also formed a joint venture with New Zealand dairy co-op Fonterra to produce and distribute dairy products in the Americas. Nestle and Cadbury Schweppes (now Cadbury) made a joint $10.5 billion bid for The Hershey Company in 2002 but Hershey called the sale off later that year. While Nestle already owned 30% of US ice cream powerhouse Dreyer's in 2002 it proposed a merger of its US ice cream businesses. After months of antitrust scrutiny the final deal gave Nestle 67% of Dreyer's. Seeking to further strengthen its position in the worldwide ice cream market Nestle acquired the ice cream and related products of Mövenpick a Swiss food company 2003. The acquisition brought Nestle licensing agreements with companies in Egypt Finland Germany Norway Sweden and Saudi Arabia. Other transactions in 2003 included the Nestle USA unit selling its Ortega brand Mexican food products to B&G Foods and the parent company selling Mont Blanc France's leading dessert brand to French investment firm Activa Capital. Also that year the company added to its bottled-water business by acquiring Hutchison Whampoa's Powwow which operates in Denmark France Germany Italy the Netherlands Portugal and the UK. In addition it acquired Clear Water a bottled-water home-and-office delivery company located in Russia. In line with its strategy to concentrate on value-added products in 2004 Nestle sold its cocoa-processing facilities in Germany and the UK to Cargill. Also in

2004 the company acquired Finnish dairy company Valid's Valiojäätelö ice cream business and increased its stake in Israeli bakery company Osem to 53%. In addition Nestle sold its German frozen food distributor Eastman that year and Nestle España bought Nestle Portugal for about $682 million. Nestle was ordered by the Brazilian government to sell its Chocolates Garoto in 2004 on the grounds that ownership of Garoto presented unfair market competition. Later that same year CEO Peter Brabeck-Letmathe announced he was considering reducing the number of outside directorships that he held because of increased demands as the leader of Nestle. At the time Brabeck-Letmathe sat on the boards of Alcon Credit Suisse Dreyer's Grand Ice Cream L'Oreal Roche Holding and "Winterthur" Swiss Insurance Company. (He has since left the "Winterthur" board.) And that year in a tangle with a French union over retirement benefits Nestle threatened to sell Perrier or produce its popular water from another source. However the company reached a settlement with the union and the production of Perrier continued. Long-time chairman Rainer Gut retired in 2005 and Brabeck-Letmathe replaced him. In 2005 it became a 90% owner of Dreyer's Grand Ice Cream. The next year Nestle became the owner of more than 90% of Dreyer's as the result of an exercise of a Put Right whereby Nestle was required to purchase certain shareholders' Class A Callable Puttable Common Stock (or Class A shares). As a result of this "short form merger" Dreyer's ceased trading on the Nasdaq stock exchange. In keeping with its strategy to concentrate on value-added products during 2006 Nestle sold its cocoa processing facilities in Germany and the UK to Cargill. Adding to its dominance in the European ice cream sector the company acquired Finnish dairy company Valid's Valiojäätelö's ice cream business and Greece's Delta Ice cream which has operations in Bulgaria Greece Macedonia Montenegro Romania and Serbia. Later that year Nestle bought the Australian breakfast cereal snack and soup operations of Uncle Tobys from Burns Philp for $670 million. The cereal portion was integrated into Cereal Partners Worldwide. In another streamlining move the company agreed to sell its canned liquid milk businesses in Southeast Asia to Singapore-based Fraser and Neave. Hedging its bets considering its food products (candy bars ice cream) are on the opposite end of the waistline wars Nestle acquired Jenny Craig for $600 million in 2006. In 2007 the company purchased the medical-nutrition business of Novartis for euro 1.88 billion ($2.5 billion). The business which has operations in 40 countries worldwide makes food for hospital patients. The purchase was seen as a move by Nestle to concentrate on higher-margin products. Brands in the acquisition included Boost and Resource nutritional supplements and Optifast dieting products. Nestle divested some operations in France and Spain in order to settle competitive concerns surrounding the deal voiced by the European Commission. On the food front Nestle subsidiary Dreyer's purchased the Eskimo Pie and Chipwich brands from Canadian ice cream maker CoolBrands in 2007 for almost $19 million. Nestle spooned out $5.5 billion in cash to purchase Gerber Products from Novartis in 2007. The deal made Nestle the world's largest baby food company.

Due to the increased workload as chairman Peter Brabeck-Letmathe stepped down as CEO in 2008; he remained in an active role as board chairman. Paul Bulcke former head of Zone Americas for Nestle replaced Brabeck-Letmathe as CEO.

The company it added to its "out of home food and beverage" operations (i.e. foodservice) in 2009 with the purchase of Tampa-based Vitality Food-

service. Vitality provides commercial and non-commercial beverage services worldwide.

In August 2010 Nestle acquired Liverpool-based Vitaflo a maker of clinical nutrition products for people with metabolic disorders. Also in August it completed the sale of Alcon to Novartis. The pharmaceutical maker acquired Nestle's stake in Alcon in two steps beginning with the sale of a 25% stake for $11 billion in July 2008. Novartis exercised its option to buy Nestle's remaining percentage of Alcon for $28 billion in 2010.

In November 2011 Nestle acquired the Oscar stocks and sauces business from Paulig Group building Nestle Professional's presence in the culinary flavors sector.

In July 2014 Nestle acquired L'Oreal's 50% stake in Galderma a joint venture formed by the two companies in 1981. Going forward Galderma will operate as the pharmaceutical arm of Nestle Skin Health S.A. established in June 2014 as a fully-owned Nestle subsidiary.

EXECUTIVES

Deputy EVP GLOBE Programme Information Systems Strategic Supply Chain eNestle and Group Information Security, Chris Johnson, age 55
CEO and Director, Ulf M. (Mark) Schneider, age 50
EVP and Head of Zone EMENA (Europe Middle East and North Africa), Luis Cantarell, age 64
Chairman Nestle Deutschland, Patrice Bula, age 61
EVP and Head Asia Oceania and Africa (AOA), Wan Ling Martello
EVP Head of Nestle Waters, Marco Settembri, age 58
EVP and Head of Zone Americas (United States of America Canada Latin America Caribbean), Laurent Freixe, age 54
Deputy EVP and CEO Nestle Professional, Martial C. Rolland
EVP and CFO, François-Xavier Roger
EVP CTO and Head of Innovation Technology Research & Development, Stefan Catsicas
Deputy EVP Head of Human Resources and Centre Administration, Peter R. Vogt
EVP and Head of Operations, Magdi Batato
Deputy EVP and Head of Nestle Nutrition, Heiko Schipper, age 47
CEO Tribe Mediterranean Foods, John McGuckin
Chairman, Peter Brabeck-Letmathe, age 72
Chairman elect, Paul Bulcke, age 62
Auditors: KPMG SA

LOCATIONS

HQ: Nestle SA
Avenue Nestle 55, Vevey, Vaud CH-1800
Phone: (41) 21 924 2111   **Fax:** (41) 21 924 4800
Web: www.nestle.com

2014 Factories

	No.
Americas	163
Asia Oceania & Africa	143
Europe	136
Total	**442**

2014 Sales

	% of total
Zone Americas	30
Zone Asia Oceania and Africa	20
Zone Europe	17
Nestlé Nutrition	10
Nestlé Waters	8
Other businesses	15
Total	**100**

PRODUCTS/OPERATIONS

2014 Product Sales

	% of total
Powdered & liquid beverages	22
Milk products & ice cream	18
Prepared dishes & cooking aids	15
Nutrition & health care	14
Pet care	12
Confectionery	11
Water	8
Total	**100**

Selected Products and Brands

Bouillons soups seasonings pasta and sauces
 Buitoni
 Maggi
 Thomy
 Winiary
Chilled Nestlé
 Chiquitin
 La Laitière
 La Lechera
 LC1
 Molico
 Ski
 Sveltesse
 Svelty
 Yoco
Chocolate confectionery and biscuits
 Aero
 Baci
 Butterfinger
 Cailler
 Crunch
 Galak/Milkybar
 Kit Kat
 Nestlé
 Polo
 Smarties
Coffee
 Bonka
 Loumidis
 Nescafé
 Nespresso
 Ricoré Ricoffy
 Taster's Choice
 Zoégas
Foodservice and professional products
 Chef
 Davigel
 Minor's
 Santa Rica
Frozen foods (prepared dishes pizzas)
 Buitoni
 California Pizza Kitchen (licensed)
 Delissio (Canada only)
 Hot Pockets
 Jack's Pizza
 Lean Cuisine
 Maggi
 Stouffer's
 Tombstone
Healthcare and nutrition
 Clinutren
 Modulen
 Nutren
 Peptamen
Ice cream
 Antica Gelateria del Corso
 Chipwich
 Dreyer's
 Drumstick/Extrême
 Edy's
 Eskimo Pie
 Häagen-Dazs
 Maxibon/Tandem
 Mega
 Mövenpick
 Parar
 Sin Parar/Sem
Infant food and nutrition
 Beba
 Cérélac
 Gerber
 Good Start
 Guigoz
 Lactogen
 Nan
 Neslac
 Nestlé
 Nestogen
 Nestum
Other beverages
 Carnation

Caro
Libby' s
Milo
Nescau
Nesquik
Nestea
Performance nutrition
PowerBar
Pria
Pet care
Alpo
Beneful
Cat Chow
Dog Chow
Fancy Feast
Felix
Gourmet
Pro Plan
Purina Friskies
Purina ONE
Tidy Cats
Refrigerated products (cold meat products dough pasta
pizzas sauces)
Buitoni
Herta
Nestlé
Toll House
Shelf-stable products
Bear Brand
Carnation
Coffee-Mate
Gloria
Klim
La Lechera
Milkmaid
Moça
Molico
Nestlé Omega
Nido
Ninho
Svelty
Water
Acqua Panna
Al Manhal
Arrowhead
Contrex
Deer Park
Hépar
Ice Mountain
Levissima
Nestlé Aquarel
Nestlé Pure Life
Nestlé Vera
Ozarka
Perrier
Poland Spring
Quézac
S.Pellegrino
San Bernardo
Vittel
Zephyrhills

Selected Subsidiaries Joint Ventures and Affiliates

Beverage Partners Worldwide (50% with The Coca-Cola
Company US)
Cereal Partners Worldwide (50% with General Mills US)
Galderma and Laboratoires innéov (29% with
L' Oreal cosmetic and nutritional supplement
products)
Gerber Products Company (infant nutrition US)
Jenny Craig Inc. (weight-loss centers and foods US)
Uncle Tobys (soups breakfast cereal snacks Australia)

COMPETITORS

Abbott Labs	Kerry Group
Associated British	Lindt & Sprngli
Foods	Mars Incorporated
Atkins Nutritionals	Medifast
Bally Total Fitness	Mondelez International
Barilla	Nutrisystem
Beech-Nut	PepsiCo
Campbell Soup	Procter & Gamble
Coca-Cola	Revlon
ConAgra	Russell Stover
Danone	Slim-Fast
Danone Water	Smucker
Dean Foods	Starbucks

Dreyer' s	Suntory Holdings
Fit America	Tata Global Beverages
GNC	United Biscuits
General Mills	Weight Watchers
Goya	International
HMG	Wimm-Bill-Dann
Heinz	World' s Finest
Hershey	Chocolate
Indofood	eDiets.com
Kellogg	maxingvest
Kent Gida	

HISTORICAL FINANCIALS

Company Type: Public

Income Statement

FYE: December 31

	REVENUE ($ mil.)	NET INCOME ($ mil.)	NET PROFIT MARGIN	EMPLOYEES
12/15	89,701	9,128	10.2%	335,000
12/14	92,869	14,614	15.7%	339,000
12/13	103,667	11,239	10.8%	333,000
12/12	100,713	11,575	11.5%	339,000
12/11	89,041	10,084	11.3%	328,000
Annual Growth	0.2%	(2.5%)	—	0.5%

2015 Year-End Financials

Debt ratio: 17.2%
Return on equity: 13.6%
Cash ($ mil.): 5,845
Current ratio: 0.88
Long-term debt ($ mil.): 11,681

No. of shares (mil.): —
Dividends
Yield: 3.0%
Payout: 74.9%
Market value ($ mil.): —

	STOCK PRICE ($) FY Close	P/E High/Low		PER SHARE ($) Earnings	Dividends	Book Value
12/15	74.42	27	23	2.91	2.28	20.35
12/14	72.95	16	14	4.57	2.42	22.38
12/13	73.59	25	21	3.51	2.16	22.02
12/12	65.17	20	17	3.62	2.11	20.85
12/11	57.71	20	16	3.15	1.99	19.03
Annual Growth	6.6%	—	—	(1.9%)	3.4%	1.7%

Nippon Express Co., Ltd.

One of Japan's largest transportation companies Nippon Express moves all sorts of freight. The company's largest business motor transportation operates under brands including Arrow. Besides general freight transportation Nippon Express offers moving services and transportation of items such as cash and construction equipment. Nippon Express also provides warehousing services and air ocean and rail freight forwarding. The company operates from facilities throughout Japan which accounts for the vast majority of its sales and in more than 40 other countries around the world. Founded in 1937 Nippon Express also sells petroleum products and leases containers.

Geographic Reach

The company operates in Japan the Americas and Europe and stretching into the rapidly developing markets of East Asia South Asia and Oceania. It maintains a global presence with about 515 locations in 240 cities spanning 41 countries.

Financial PerformanceNippon Express has experienced strong revenue growth during the last five years. Its revenue increased by 10% in 2015 (ended March) due to growth from its Distribution & Transportation segments primarily Combined

Business Heavy Haulage & Construction and Air Freight Forwarding.

Strategy

Already a market leader at home Nippon Express aims to grow by expanding its operations outside Japan. The company is opening facilities in Eastern Europe South America and other Asia/Pacific countries to take advantage of opportunities created by economic growth in those regions.

In 2015 the company established its own subsidiary in the Republic of Indonesia - PT NEX Logistics Indonesia. The new company offers warehouse distribution services as part of its third-party logistics (3PL) operations.

EXECUTIVES

President and CEO, Kenji Watanabe, age 66
EVP, Jiro Nakamura, age 67
EVP, Keiji Hagio, age 68
Chairman, Masanori Kawai, age 73
Auditors: Ernst & Young ShinNihon LLC

LOCATIONS

HQ: Nippon Express Co., Ltd.
1-9-3 Higashi-Shimbashi, Minato-ku, Tokyo 105-8322
Phone: (81) 3 6251 1111
Web: www.nittsu.co.jp

PRODUCTS/OPERATIONS

2015 Sales

	% of total
Combined business	39
Goods sales	22
Air freight forwarding	11
Marine & harbor transportation	6
Others	22
Total	**100**

Selected Services

Air Freight
Fine Arts Transport
Heavy Haulage
Logistics Design & IT
Marine Transport
Moving Service

COMPETITORS

DHL	Mitsui-Soko
FedEx	NYK Line
Hub Group	Schenker
Janel World Trade	Seino Transportation
Japan Post	Co
Kintetsu	UPS
Mitsui O.S.K. Lines	Yamato Holdings

HISTORICAL FINANCIALS

Company Type: Public

Income Statement

FYE: March 31

	REVENUE ($ mil.)	NET INCOME ($ mil.)	NET PROFIT MARGIN	EMPLOYEES
03/16	17,000	317	1.9%	86,011
03/15	16,043	219	1.4%	85,099
03/14	16,978	255	1.5%	65,162
03/13	17,146	253	1.5%	64,834
03/12	19,846	328	1.7%	65,759
Annual Growth	(3.8%)	(0.8%)	—	6.9%

2016 Year-End Financials

Debt ratio: 0.2%
Return on equity: 6.7%
Cash ($ mil.): 1,685
Current ratio: 1.55
Long-term debt ($ mil.): 2,724

No. of shares (mil.): 1,000
Dividends
Yield: 0.0%
Payout: —
Market value ($ mil.): 26,345

	STOCK PRICE ($)	P/E		PER SHARE ($)		
	FY Close	High/Low	Earnings	Dividends	Book Value
03/16	26.32	1 1	0.32	0.53	4.65
03/15	32.82	1 1	0.22	0.50	4.43
03/14	27.43	— —	0.25	0.00	4.82
03/13	24.82	— —	0.24	0.00	5.25
03/12	22.14	— —	0.32	0.00	5.78
Annual Growth	4.4%	— —	0.2%	—	(5.3%)

Nippon Life Insurance Co. (Japan)

Nippon Life Insurance also known as Nissay is a top life insurer in Japan. The company which has some 10 million policyholders uses a door-to-door sales corps and other representatives to peddle its traditional insurance products including individual and group life and annuity policies to Japanese consumers. In addition to its life insurance products the company administers pension plans and medical coverage plans and provides asset management services. Through its affiliates and subsidiaries the company also sells auto and other property/casualty insurance in Japan and it has some international life insurance operations as well as select real estate and financial service assets.

Operations

In addition to the core insurance operations other Nippon Life subsidiaries and affiliates are involved in real estate investment mortgage lending and investment advisory among other financial services activities. Its operating group includes subsidiaries NLI Insurance Tokyo Agency of Nippon NLI Properties Nissay Asset Management and Nissay Capital.

Geographic Reach

Nippon Life operates about 50 subsidiaries and affiliates and has some 120 branch locations and more than 1500 sales offices. It operates in China India Indonesia Japan Continental Europe Thailand the UK and the US.

Sales and Marketing

Nippon Life primarily sells policies through its dedicated field sales force as well as through retail store locations call centers and online. It also sells through select insurance brokerages and via partnerships with financial services firms including banks.

Financial Performance

After years of steady revenue increases Nippon Life has seen its earnings drop in the past couple of years. Revenues decreased by 7% to ¥6.8 trillion ($66 billion) in 2014 due to a decline in insurance and reinsurance premiums plus a lower reversal of allowance for doubtful accounts. Net income increased 35% to ¥284 billion though as a result of declines in provisions for policy reserves and investment expenses. Cash flow from operations decreased 31% to ¥1521 billion due to losses on derivatives and an increase in income taxes paid.

Strategy

Nippon Life along with its competitors in Japan is faced with several market challenges including a declining population (meaning a smaller customer pool) an aging population (meaning more payouts on claims) and an uneven economic recovery (which translates to cutbacks in personal expenditures).

To combat some of these problems Nippon Life has been broadening its sales channels to include an agency network and partnerships with financial services firms. (Deregulation has allowed sales of some insurance products at banks.) It also struck a deal with National Australia Bank in 2015 whereby it will acquire an 80% stake in the bank's life insurance business. Nippon Life will pay a little more than ¥200 billion for those operations gaining a stronghold in the growing Australian market.

Nippon Life has also been adding more medical coverage products to appeal to older consumers and is working to offer more comprehensive and flexible life insurance coverage options. In 2013 it added an educational endowment insurance plan to help customers prepare for educational expenses; it sold 100000 policies in its initial year. Nippon Life is also investing in information technology system improvements to enhance customer service and it is expanding its international operations particularly in China India Thailand and the US. In 2014 the company formed a business alliance with Indonesian life insurer Sequis Life (a subsidiary of conglomerate Gunung Sewu Kencana).

It is also expanding its asset management business to diversify earnings. In 2014 the company established a new credit investment division to combine its bond investment operations at home and abroad.

Mergers and Acquisitions

Nippon Life owns a 26% stake in Reliance Capital Asset Management which it invested in to increase its operations in India. It intends to bump that stake up to 49%.

In 2015 Nippon agreed to buy fellow domestic insurer Mitsui Life for ¥334.5 billion. That deal signals a determination to pursue growth in Japan despite the nation's slowing market.

HISTORY

Company Background

Nippon Life known as Nissay was a product of the modernization that began after US Commodore Matthew Perry opened Japan's ports to foreigners in 1854. Industry and trade were Japan's first focus but financial infrastructure soon followed. The country's first insurer (Meiji Mutual) opened in 1881. In 1889 Osaka banker Sukesaburo Hirose founded Nippon Life as a stock company. It grew and opened branches in Tokyo (1890) and Kyushu (1895).

In the 20th century the company developed a direct sales force and began lending directly to businesses. Lending remained the backbone of its asset strategy through most of the century. The insurance market in Japan grew quickly until the late 1920s but had already slowed by the eve of the Depression.

After WWII the company reorganized as a mutual and began mobilizing an army of women to build its sales of installment-premium basic life policies. In 1962 the company began automating its systems and established operations in the US (1972) and the UK (1981).

As interest rates rose in the wake of oil price hikes in the 1970s the company began offering term life and annuities and slowly moved to diversify its asset holdings from mostly government bonds (whose yields declined as rates rose) to stocks. This movement accelerated in the 1980s as the businesses that traditionally borrowed from Nippon Life turned directly to capital markets to raise money through debt issues. Seeking to replace its shrinking lending business the company began investing in US real estate and businesses whose values rose in the mid-1980s. The company reached its zenith in 1987; it owned about 3% of all the stocks on the Tokyo Exchange held more real estate than Mitsubishi's real estate units

and had bought 13% of US brokerage Shearson Lehman from American Express.

By the end of the year thanks to the US stock market crash the value of the Shearson investment had fallen 40%. But the company felt confident enough of its importance as the world's largest insurance company (by assets) to crow its intentions to strong-arm Japan's Ministry of Finance into letting it diversify into trust and securities operations.

Then its bubble burst. In 1989 real estate crashed and the stock market lost more than half its value. Japan's economy failed to improve and Nippon Life was left struggling with nonperforming loans and assets whose value had declined. The company suffered further from policy cancellations and from the Ministry of Finance's focus on buoying banks. In 1997 the ministry asked Nippon Life to convert its subordinated debt from Nippon Credit Bank (now Aozora Bank) to stock. That year Nippon Life formed an alliance with Marsh & McLennan's Putnam Investments subsidiary to help manage its assets; the relationship deepened in 1998 when they began developing investment trust products.

The next year Nippon Life faced a shareholder lawsuit over its involvement in the collapse of Nippon Credit Bank; the company claims the Ministry of Finance tricked it into bailing out the bank even though it was beyond rescue. In 2001 the company merged its Nissay General subsidiary with Dowa Fire & Marine creating nonlife insurer Nissay Dowa.

EXECUTIVES

Senior Managing Executive Officer, Kazuo Kobayashi
President, Yoshinobu Tsutsui
EVP, Takeshi Furuichi
EVP, Kenichi Kobayashi
Senior Managing Executive Officer, Koji Aiba
Senior Managing Executive Officer, Yasuomi Matsuyama
Senior Managing Executive Officer, Masami Kuroda
Chairman, Kunie Okamoto, age 72
Vice Chairman, Sadao Kato, age 68

LOCATIONS

HQ: Nippon Life Insurance Co. (Japan)
3-5-12 Imabashi, Chuo-ku, Osaka 541-8501
Phone: (81) 6 6209 4500   **Fax:** 212 906-1933
Web: www.nissay.co.jp

PRODUCTS/OPERATIONS

Selected Products and Services
Products for Individuals
  Annuities
  Asset management
  Cancer Medical Insurance
  Dread Disease Insurance
  Endowment Insurance
  General Medical Insurance
  Limited Injury Insurance
  Non-life Insurance Products
  Nursing Care Insurance
  Physical Disability Insurance
  Products for Children
  Single-payment Products
  Term Life Insurance
  Term Life Insurance with Survival Benefits
  Whole Life Insurance
Products for Businesses
  Disability coverage
  Home buying preparation
  Medical coverage
  Retirement coverage
  Survivor coverage
  Various life plans

HISTORICAL FINANCIALS

Company Type: Public

Income Statement

FYE: March 31

	ASSETS ($ mil.)	NET INCOME ($ mil.)	INCOME AS % OF ASSETS	EMPLOYEES
03/15	522,162	2,567	0.5%	70,783
03/14	553,095	2,394	0.4%	70,806
03/13	586,294	2,635	0.4%	70,004
03/12	623,756	2,741	0.4%	69,620
03/11	603,214	2,721	0.5%	70,002
Annual Growth	(3.5%)	(1.4%)	—	0.3%

2015 Year-End Financials

Return on assets: 0.5%
Return on equity: 5.0%
Long-term debt ($ mil.): —
No. of shares (mil.): —
Sales ($ mil.): 61,794

Dividends
  Yield: —
  Payout: —
  Market value ($ mil.): —

Nippon Steel & Sumikin Bussan Corp

Nippon Steel & Sumikin Bussan is the steel-trading operation of Nippon Steel & Sumitomo Metal Japan's largest steelmaker. The company trades a range of products including steel bars hot- and cold-rolled coils and wire products in China Southeast Asia and the US. Nippon Steel & Sumikin Bussan also imports steelmaking raw materials –iron ore from Australia and India and coal from Australia China New Zealand Russia Vietnam and the US. Other materials the company trades include heavy machinery fuels and non-ferrous metals. Steel products account for nearly 80% of company sales. Nippon Steel & Sumitomo Metal owns 32% of the company; Mitsui 20%.

Operations Nippon Steel & Sumikin Bussan operates in four segments: Steel (almost 80% of total revenue); Industrial Supply and Infrastructure; Textiles; and Foodstuffs. The Steel segment is engaged in a full range of steelmaking activities from buying raw materials to the delivery of steel products to customers. Foodstuffs offers imported meats including beef pork and chicken and manages restaurants. Centering on OEM production for apparel makers Textiles is engaged in everything from materials development to product planning production and distribution. Industrial Supply and Infrastructure invests in new businesses with growth potential such as industrial machinery infrastructure businesses and materials. Geographic Reach Nippon Steel & Sumikin Bussan operates in 20 countries in North and Central America Asia Europe and Oceania.

Japan accounts for about 75% of total revenue.

Financial Performance

Note: Growth rates may differ after conversion to US Dollars.

The company's net sales dropped from ¥2104 billion in fiscal 2015 (March year end) to ¥1931 in fiscal 2016 primarily due to a slump in steel sales. Steel revenue was down by 10% due to a decrease in demand in Japan China and Southeast Asia.

Net income declined from ¥18.5 billion to ¥18.4 billion due to higher selling general and administrative expenses.

Strategy

In 2017 Nippon Steel & Sumikin Bussan was looking to take advantage of the recovery in steel demand in Japan (driven by increased demand from the automotive and construction sectors) and higher steel prices despite the drag of continued excess steel capacity in China.

The company's major growth initiatives in 2017 included increasing its steel products' market share by expanding its global network of locations and strengthening its competitiveness in the Japanese steel market by cutting costs.

In the Industrial Supply & Infrastructure segment Nippon Steel & Sumikin Bussan planned to expand an industrial park in Thailand and develop an industrial park in Mexico.

In the Textiles area it planned to increase international sales and move from an OEM focus to a ODM (Original Design Manufacturing) focus.

In the Foodstuffs segment Nippon Steel & Sumikin Bussan was eyeing developing its restaurant chain business across Asia by expanding the number of its Tsubohachi restaurants.

Company BackgroundIn 2013 Nippon Steel Trading merged with Sumikin Bussan to form Nippon Steel & Sumikin Bussan Corporation.

EXECUTIVES

President and Director, Tetsuo Imakubo, age 70
Senior Managing Executive Officer and Director, Yukio Watanabe
Senior Managing Executive Officer and Director, Ikuo Ebihara
Senior Managing Executive Officer and Director, Kazuo Yamaguchi
Senior Managing Executive Officer and Director, Yuji Yokoyama
Auditors: Deloitte Touche Tohmats LLC

LOCATIONS

HQ: Nippon Steel & Sumikin Bussan Corp
  8-5-27 Akasaka, Minato-ku, Tokyo, smc 107-8527
Phone: (81) 3 5412 5098   **Fax:** (81) 3 5412 5101
Web: www.nssb.nssmc.com

HISTORICAL FINANCIALS

Company Type: Public

Income Statement

FYE: March 31

	REVENUE ($ mil.)	NET INCOME ($ mil.)	NET PROFIT MARGIN	EMPLOYEES
03/16	17,194	154	0.9%	8,179
03/15	17,541	145	0.8%	8,179
03/14	13,988	220	1.6%	7,778
03/13	10,907	65	0.6%	2,228
03/12	13,257	83	0.6%	2,231
Annual Growth	6.7%	16.5%	—	38.4%

2016 Year-End Financials

Debt ratio: 0.2%
Return on equity: 10.1%
Cash ($ mil.): 176
Current ratio: 1.36
Long-term debt ($ mil.): 637

No. of shares (mil.): 309
Dividends
  Yield: —
  Payout: —
  Market value ($ mil.): —

Nippon Steel & Sumitomo Metal Corp

When it comes to steel Nippon Steel & Sumitomo Metal rates as Japan's heavy lifter. The company the world's second-largest steelmaker after ArcelorMittal manufactures pig iron and ingots steel bars plates sheets pipes and tubes as well as specialty processed and fabricated steel products. Nippon Steel & Sumitomo Metal's annual crude steel output is more than 47.3 million tons. The company's operations include engineering construction chemicals nonferrous metals ceramics electricity supply information and communications and urban development (theme parks and condominiums). In 2012 Nippon Steel acquired fellow Japanese steel maker Sumitomo Metal Industries to form a global metals giant.

Operations

Nippon Steel & Sumitomo Metal operates in five segments: Steelmaking and Steel Fabrication (more than 85% of total revenue); Engineering and Construction; Chemicals; New Materials; and System Solutions. Steelmaking and Steel Fabrication makes and markets steel products including pig iron and ingots steel bars plates sheets pipes and tubes and specialty processed and fabricated steel items.

Engineering and Construction makes and markets industrial machinery and equipment and steel structures. It also offers construction work under contract waste processing and recycling services and supplies electricity gas and heat. Chemicals makes and sells coal-based chemical products petrochemicals and electronic materials. New Materials manufactures and markets materials for semiconductors and electronic parts carbon fiber and composite products and technology products for metal processing and joining. The System Solutions segment includes computer system engineering and consulting services. Geographic Reach Nippon Steel & Sumitomo Metal has operations in the Americas Europe and the Middle East and the Asia-Pacific region.

Its main operations are in Japan but it also has major subsidiaries in Australia Brazil China Indonesia Thailand and the US. The company has plants in more than 15 countries. In Japan its has 16 steelworks three major research centers and six laboratories. Sales and Marketing Nippon Steel & Sumitomo Metal's customers include Daikin Industries Fuji Xerox Panasonic Royal Dutch Shell and Yamaha Motor.

Financial Performance

Note: Growth rates may differ after conversion to US Dollars.

Nippon Steel & Sumitomo Metal reported a decrease in sales volume in fiscal 2016 (March year end) due to a delayed recovery in steeldemand in Japan (and a related inventory adjustment) and a global decline in steel product prices caused by lower raw material prices. As a result the company saw drop of ¥702.6 billion in net sales to ¥4907.4 billion.

The company's ordinary profit decreased by ¥250.8 billion in fiscal 2016 to ¥200.9 billion due to weak domestic steel demand lower export sales and depressed sales to the energy sector (the result of lower oil prices) all of which outpaced the company's cost improvement measures.

Nippon Steel & Sumitomo Metal's free cash flow declined by ¥126.6 billion in fiscal 2016 to ¥320.7 billion due to lower profit attributable to owners of the company's parent. Cash from operating activities and cash generated from asset compression resulted in a ¥270 billion reduction in interest-bearing debt.

Strategy

The company is looking to strengthen its Japan-based manufacturing plants by prioritizing investments in new technology and by sharing some of the best practices in Japan with overseas manufacturing bases. It plans to consolidate its upstream processes in Japan to increase its cost competitiveness.

Nippon Steel & Sumitomo Metal is looking to make Nisshin Steel (the fourth largest blast furnace steelmaker in Japan) a subsidiary in order to secure a constant supply of steel slabs to the company.

Outside of Japan its plans to increase steel production capacity to 19 million tons.

In 2015/16 the company deepened its strategic partnership with Vallourec S.A. (steel pipes and tubes for the energy and resources market) by increasing its equity investment in the French firm and expanding cooperation in R&D and customer service. It also provided more capital to Brazil-based affiliate Usinas Siderurgicas de Minas Gerais S.A. Mergers and Acquisitions Boosting its market position in 2016 the company agreed to boost its stake in Nisshin Steel from 8% to between 51% and 66%.

Company Background

The $24 billion acquisition of Sumitomo Metal Industries in 2012 mating Japan's #1 and #3 steelmakers boosted the expended company's market share against ArcelorMittal and other Asian rivals in an increasingly competitive marketplace. Similar consolidation has been happening in other countries —particularly China and Russia — aimed at elevating their steel industries to compete in the international market.

HISTORY

Company Background

As Japan prepared for war the government in 1934 merged Yawata Works its largest steel producer and other Japanese steelmakers into one giant company —Japan Iron & Steel. During postwar occupation Japan Iron & Steel was ordered to dissolve. Yawata Iron & Steel and Fuji Iron & Steel emerged from the dissolution and with Western assistance the Japanese steel industry recovered from the war years. In the late 1960s Fuji Steel bought Tokai Iron & Steel (1967) and Yawata Steel took over Yawata Steel Tube Company (1968).

Yawata and Fuji merged in 1970 and became Nippon Steel the world's largest steelmaker. In the 1970s the Japanese steel industry was criticized in the US; American competitors complained that Japan was "dumping" low-cost exports. Meanwhile Nippon Steel aggressively courted China.

The company diversified in the mid-1980s to wean itself from dependence on steel. It created a New Materials unit in 1984 retraining "redundant" steelworkers to make silicon wafers and forming an Electronics Division in 1986. Nippon Steel began joint ventures with IBM Japan (small computers and software) Hitachi (office workstations) and C. Itoh (information systems for small and midsized companies) in 1988 as increased steel de-

mand for construction and cars in Japan's "bubble economy" took the company to new heights.

In an atmosphere of economic optimism the company spent more than four times the expected expense to build an amusement park capable of competing with Tokyo Disneyland. The company plowed ahead spending some $230 million on the park. Space World amusement park opened on the island of Kyushu in 1990. The company's bubble burst that year. (The theme park declared bankruptcy in May 2005 and was sold to Kamori Kanko later that year.)

In response Nippon Steel cut costs and intensified its diversification efforts by targeting electronics information and telecommunications new materials and chemicals markets. Seeking to remake its steel operations the company began a drastic phased restructuring in 1993 that included a step most Japanese companies try to avoid —cutting personnel. A semiconductor division was organized that year as part of the company's diversification strategy.

Upgrading its steel operations Nippon Steel and partner Mitsubishi in 1996 introduced the world's first mass-production method for making hot-rolled steel sheet directly from smelted stainless steel. Profits were hurt that year by a loss-making project in the information and communications segment and by a steep decline in computer memory-chip prices.

The company began operation of a Chinese steelmaking joint venture Guangzhou Pacific Tinplate in 1997. The next year its Singapore-based joint venture with Hitachi Ltd. began mass-producing computer memory chips in hopes of stemming semiconductor losses. But falling prices convinced Nippon Steel to get out of the memory chip business and in 1999 it sold its semiconductor subsidiary to South Korea's United Microelectronics.

That year the US imposed antidumping duties on the company's steel products. The next year Nippon Steel agreed to form a strategic alliance with South Korea-based Pohang Iron and Steel (POSCO) at that time the world's #1 steel maker. The deal called for the exploration of joint ventures shared research and joint procurement as well as increased equity stakes in each other (at 2%-3%). Also in 2000 Nippon Steel agreed to provide Sumitomo Metal Industries and Nisshin Steel Co. with stainless steel products.

Early in 2001 Nippon Steel formed a cooperative alliance —focused on automotive sheet products —with French steel giant Usinor (now a part of ArcelorMittal). At the end of the year Nippon Steel decided to form an alliance with Kobe Steel to pare down costs and share in distribution and production facilities. In 2002 the company continued its series of comprehensive alliances by forming alliances with Japanese steelmaker Nippon Metal Industry to exchange its semi-finished stainless steel technologies and with POSCO to build environment-related businesses.

The company reported a loss of ¥51.69 billion ($430 million) for fiscal 2003 due to securities valuation losses and group restructuring charges. In 2004 Nippon Steel formed a joint venture with Baoshan Iron & Steel and Arcelor to manufacture high-grade automotive steel sheets.

Nippon Steel moved into the South American market in 2006 forming alliances with steelmaker Usiminas and iron miner CVRD. And the next year it created a JV with Baosteel and ArcelorMittal that produces automotive steel sheets.

The company joined up with Sumitomo Metal Industries in 2009 when the two companies agreed to form a joint venture that will combine their arc-welded stainless steel pipe and tube operations. Sumitomo will own 60% of the JV. The operations that make up the new company which will be called Sumikin & Nippon Steel Stainless Steel Pipe

Co. achieved sales of more than $250 million in 2008.

EXECUTIVES

President and COO, Hiroshi Tomono, age 71
Chairman and CEO, Shoji Muneoka, age 70
EVP, Syuichiro Kozuka, age 68
EVP, Masakazu Iwaki, age 67
EVP, Kosei Shindo
EVP, Shinya Higuchi
EVP, Katsuhiko Ota
EVP, Akihiro Miyasaka
Auditors: KPMG AZSA LLC

LOCATIONS

HQ: Nippon Steel & Sumitomo Metal Corp
2-6-1 Marunouchi, Chiyoda-ku, Tokyo 100-8071
Phone: (81) 3 6867 4111   **Fax:** (81) 3 6867 5607
Web: www.nssmc.com

2012 Sales

	% of total
Asia	
Japan	67
Other countries	24
Other regions	9
Total	**100**

PRODUCTS/OPERATIONS

2015 Sales

	% of total
Steelmaking & Steel Fabrication	86
Engineering	6
Chemicals	4
Systems Solutions	3
New Materials	1
Total	**100**

Selected Products and Services

Steelmaking and Steel Fabrication
  Fabricated and processed steels
  Pig iron and ingots
  Pipes and tubes
  Plates and sheets
  Sections
  Specialty sheets
Engineering and Construction
  Building construction
  Civil engineering
  Marine construction
  Plant and machinery
  Technical cooperation
Chemicals
  Aluminum products
  Ammonium sulfate
  Cement
  Ceramic products
  Coal tar
  Coke
  Ferrite
  Metallic foils
  Slag products
System Solutions
  Communications services
  Computers and equipment
  Data processing
  Systems development and integration
Urban Development
  Condominiums
  Theme parks
New Materials
  Semiconductor bonding wire
  Silicon wafers
  Titanium products
  Transformers
Other operations
  Services
  Energy services
  Financial services
  Insurance services
  Transportation
  Loading and unloading
  Marine and land transportation
  Warehousing

Selected Subsidiaries and Affiliates

Subsidiaries
Nippon Steel & Sumikin Coated Sheet Corporation
Nippon Steel & Sumikin Metal Products Co. Ltd.
Nippon Steel & Sumikin Stainless Steel Corporation
Nippon Steel & Sumikin Welding Co. Ltd.
Nippon Steel Australia Pty. Limited
Nippon Steel Blast Furnace Slag Cement Co. Ltd.
Nippon Steel Drum Co. Ltd. 1654
Nippon Steel Logistics Co. Ltd.
Nippon Steel Shipping Co. Ltd.
Nippon Steel Transportation Co. Ltd.
Nippon Steel U.S.A. Inc.
Nittetsu Cement Co. Ltd.
Nittetsu Elex Co. Ltd.
Nittetsu Finance Co. Ltd.
Nittetsu Steel Pipe Co. Ltd. 4832
Nittetsu Tokai Steel Wire Co. Ltd.
NS Preferred Capital Limited
Osaka Steel Co. Ltd.
Siam Nippon Steel Pipe Co. Ltd.
The Siam United Steel (1995) Co. Ltd.

Affiliates
Daiwa Can Company
Geostr Corporation
Godo Steel Ltd.
Japan Casting & Forging Corporation
Krosaki Harima Corporation
Mitsui Mining Co. Ltd.
Nichia Steel Works Ltd.
Nippon Steel Trading Co. Ltd.
Sanko Metal Industrial Co. Ltd.
Sanyo Special Steel Co. Ltd.
Sanyu Co. Ltd.
Suzuki Metal Industry Co. Ltd.
Taihei Kogyo Co. Ltd.
Topy Industries Ltd.

COMPETITORS

ArcelorMittal	POSCO
BlueScope Steel	Tata Europe
JFE Holdings	ThyssenKrupp Steel
Kobe Steel	United States Steel
Marubeni	Vale
Mitsubishi Corp.	Yamato Kogyo

HISTORICAL FINANCIALS
Company Type: Public

Income Statement
FYE: March 31

	REVENUE ($ mil.)	NET INCOME ($ mil.)	NET PROFIT MARGIN	EMPLOYEES
03/16	43,700	1,294	3.0%	100,170
03/15	46,758	1,786	3.8%	100,189
03/14	53,441	2,351	4.4%	84,361
03/13	46,655	(1,323)	—	83,187
03/12	49,871	712	1.4%	60,508
Annual Growth	(3.2%)	16.1%	—	13.4%

2016 Year-End Financials

Debt ratio: 0.2%
Return on equity: 5.0%
Cash ($ mil.): 760
Current ratio: 1.23
Long-term debt ($ mil.): 13,756
No. of shares (mil.): 902
Dividends
Yield: 15.7%
Payout: —
Market value ($ mil.): 17,150

	STOCK PRICE ($) FY Close	P/E High/Low		Earnings	PER SHARE ($) Dividends	Book Value
03/16	19.00	0	0	1.41	0.02	27.37
03/15	2.50	0	0	1.96	0.05	26.12
03/14	2.65	—	—	2.58	0.05	34.36
03/13	2.40	—	—	(1.72)	0.00	34.42
03/12	2.70	—	—	1.13	0.00	45.54
Annual Growth	62.9% (12.0%)	—	—	5.7%		

Nippon Telegraph & Telephone Corp (Japan)

Auditors: KPMG AZSA LLC

LOCATIONS

HQ: Nippon Telegraph & Telephone Corp (Japan)
Otemachi First Square, East Tower, 5-1 Otemachi, 1-
Chome, Chiyoda-Ku, Tokyo 100-8116
Phone: (81) 3 6838 5481   **Fax:** (81) 3 6838 5499
Web: www.ntt.co.jp

HISTORICAL FINANCIALS
Company Type: Public

Income Statement
FYE: March 31

	REVENUE ($ mil.)	NET INCOME ($ mil.)	NET PROFIT MARGIN	EMPLOYEES
03/16	102,772	6,569	6.4%	241,450
03/15	92,476	4,317	4.7%	241,600
03/14	105,844	5,672	5.4%	340,211
03/13	113,726	5,569	4.9%	324,713
03/12	128,091	5,701	4.5%	313,586
Annual Growth	(5.4%)	3.6%	—	(6.3%)

2016 Year-End Financials

Debt ratio: 0.1%
Return on equity: 8.3%
Cash ($ mil.): 9,691
Current ratio: 1.45
Long-term debt ($ mil.): 31,824
No. of shares (mil.): 2,096
Dividends
Yield: 1.7%
Payout: 60.2%
Market value ($ mil.): 90,637

	STOCK PRICE ($) FY Close	P/E High/Low		Earnings	PER SHARE ($) Dividends	Book Value
03/16	43.24	0	0	3.12	0.77	37.72
03/15	30.82	0	0	1.97	0.82	34.29
03/14	27.24	0	0	2.47	0.80	37.26
03/13	21.74	0	0	2.30	0.80	37.29
03/12	22.62	0	0	2.23	0.79	39.26
Annual Growth	17.6%	—	—	8.7%	(0.7%)	(1.0%)

Nippon Yusen Kabushiki Kaisha

Nippon Yusen Kabushiki Kaisha known as NYK Line is at home in ports around the globe. With a fleet of about 875 vessels the company is one of the world's largest marine transportation providers. The NYK Line fleet includes bulk carriers containerships tankers and a variety of specialized vessels including car carriers and liquefied natural gas (LNG) carriers; overall the fleet has a capacity of more than 50 million deadweight tons (DWT). In conjunction with its marine transportation business NYK Line offers such logistics services as customs clearance supply chain management and warehousing and operates more than 40 marine terminals.
Geographic Reach

NYK Line has some 450 logistics locations around the world. About 150 are located in South Asia and Oceania 88 in East Asia 76 in Europe 72 in Japan and 67 in the Americas.

Japan represented 75% of the company's total sales in 2015. Other markets include Asia (9%) North America (8%) Europe (7%).
Operations

NYK Line divides its operations into several segments. Global Logistics is its largest (and includes liner trade terminal and harbor transport air cargo and logistics) contributing 52% of the company's total sales in 2015. Bulk shipping generated 42% of the company's revenue. Its real estate operations accounted for the remainder of sales.
Financial Performance

NYK Line's revenues jumped 7% from 2014 to 2015 due to large gains from its Global Logistics segment particularly within North America Japan and Asia. Its net income also increased by 44% in 2015 compared to 2014. This was sparked by the increased revenue a gain on sales of shares of subsidiaries and affiliates and additional foreign exchange earnings.
Strategy

NYK Line is banking on increased demand for oil. About 80% of the company's new vessels are intended for use in the natural resources and energy transportation. Many of which are under long term contracts to customers in growing economies such as Brazil China and India.
Mergers and Acquisitions

The company often improves its geographical footprint through the use of acquisitions. In 2014 it purchased Tranco Terminal the largest car-terminal operating company in Kazakhstan. NYK Line projects that auto sales will rapidly increase in Kazakhstan. In addition the deal caters to the demand for transnational inland transport from the China and Russia areas bordering Kazakhstan and will provide a service to fulfill the various transport needs of its customers.

EXECUTIVES

Senior Managing Corporate Officer; Chief Executive Technical, Naoya Tazawa
EVP and CIO, Tadaaki Naito
Managing Corporate Officer; President and CEO Nippon Cargo Airlines, Fukashi Sakamoto
Senior Managing Corporate Officer and CFO, Kenji Mizushima
Senior Managing Corporate Officer; Chief Executive Energy Division, Hitoshi Nagasawa
Corporate Officer; President and CEO NYK Group Europe, Takuji Nakai
Managing Corporate Officer and CIO, Hidetoshi Maruyama
Senior Managing Corporate Officer; Chief Executive Automotive Transportation, Koichi Chikaraishi
Senior Managing Corporate Officer; Chief Executive Dry Bulk Division, Masahiro Samitsu
Managing Corporate Officer; Chief Executive General Affairs, Yoshiyuki Yoshida
Corporate Officer; Chairman and CEO NYK Ship Management, Tomoyuki Koyama
President, Yasumi Kudo
Auditors: Deloitte Touche Tohmatsu LLC

LOCATIONS

HQ: Nippon Yusen Kabushiki Kaisha
2-3-2 Marunouchi, Chiyoda-ku, Tokyo 100-0005
Phone: (81) 3 3284 6220
Web: www.nyk.com

2015 Sales

	% of total
Japan	75
Asia	9

North America 8
Europe 7
Other area 1
Total 100

PRODUCTS/OPERATIONS

2015 Sales

	% of total
Bulk shipping	42
Liner trade	28
Logistics	20
Air cargo transport	4
Cruise	2
Real estate	0
Other	4
Total	100

List of Items
Bulk Shipping Business
  Car Transport
  Dry Bulk Transport
  Offshore Business
  Tanker Transport (LNG Transport)
  Tanker Transport (Petroleum Chemical and LPG
  Transport)
Global Logistics
  Air Cargo Transportation Business
  Liner Trade Business
  Logistics Business
  Terminal and Harbor Transport Business
Real Estate Business
Others
  Worldwide Service Network

COMPETITORS

A.P. M∘ller - M∘rsk	Kawasaki Kisen
CMA CGM	Lufthansa Cargo
COSCO Group	Mediterranean Shipping
DHL	Company
DP World	Mitsui O.S.K. Lines
Dynagas LNG Partners	Mitsui-Soko
LP	Neptune Orient
Evergreen Marine	PSA International
Expeditors	Polar Air Cargo
Hanjin Shipping	
Hutchison Port	
Holdings	

HISTORICAL FINANCIALS

Company Type: Public

Income Statement

FYE: March 31

	REVENUE ($ mil.)	NET INCOME ($ mil.)	NET PROFIT MARGIN	EMPLOYEES
03/16	20,234	162	0.8%	40,059
03/15	20,018	396	2.0%	39,253
03/14	21,674	320	1.5%	32,342
03/13	20,162	200	1.0%	28,865
03/12	22,038	(887)	—	28,498
Annual Growth	(2.1%)	—	—	8.9%

2016 Year-End Financials

Debt ratio: 0.3%
Return on equity: 2.3%
Cash ($ mil.): 2,112
Current ratio: 1.55
Long-term debt ($ mil.): 7,439

No. of shares (mil.): 1,695
Dividends
  Yield: 3.8%
  Payout: 166.4%
Market value ($ mil.): 6,478

	STOCK PRICE ($) FY Close	P/E High/Low		PER SHARE ($) Earnings	Dividends	Book Value
03/16	3.82	1	0	0.10	0.15	4.06
03/15	5.75	0	0	0.23	0.09	3.98
03/14	5.84	—	—	0.19	0.08	4.42
03/13	5.07	—	—	0.12	0.00	4.38
03/12	6.26	—	—	(0.52)	0.00	4.47
Annual Growth	(11.6%)	—	—	—	—	(2.4%)

Nissan Motor Co., Ltd.

Nissan Motor one of Japan's leading automakers wants to get big by going small. Through its small-car initiative the company primarily produces low-cost and fuel-efficient small cars with standard comfort safety style and performance. Nissan's models include Maxima and Sentra cars and Altima and Infiniti upscale sedans as well as pickups SUVs and sports cars. It is also one of the world's largest manufacturers of forklifts. Renault holds a 43% stake in Nissan Motor and Nissan has a 15% stake in Renault constituting the Renault-Nissan Alliance. In 2016 the company agreed to buy 34% of Mitsubishi Motors for $2.2 billion.

Geographic Reach

Nissan manufactures in about 20 countries and sells and services products in more than 160 countries. The company operates 14 production facilities in Japan along with seven R&D facilities. Its facilities are also spread across North America (five production facilities); Europe (four); Asia (13); Oceania (one); Mexico Latin America and Caribbean (five); and the Middle East Gulf States and Africa (two).

Financial Performance

Nissan's net sales increased 20% in 2014 compared to 2013 and its net income spiked by 14%. In Japan total industry volumes rose by 9% to 5.7 million units as Nissan out-performed the market with unit sales up 11% to 719000 representing a market share of 12%. This improvement was driven by strong sales of its DAYZ series as well as strong demand for its first CMF model and the new X-Trail.

In China Nissan out-performed overall market growth. The total industry within China was up 14% to 20.75 million units while Nissan sales increased 17% to 1.27 million units. Its Qashqai and the all-new Sylphy along with new models from Venucia and Infiniti contributed to the improvement. In North America Nissan achieved significant sales growth. The total US industry was up 6% at 15.65 million units while Nissan sales volume increased by 13% to 1.29 million units amid strong demand for the new Rogue and the Altima.

Strategy

The Nissan Power 88 plan calls for attaining 8% global market share and an 8% operating profit margin by 2017. A major element of Power 88 is the development of about 90 new technologies including a next-generation XTRONIC continuously variable transmission technology. The plan additionally includes investing 70% of research and development expenses into green technology.

Nissan also has set a goal of increasing the percentage of fully built units that are locally made in the Americas to 85% by 2015. New plants in Brazil and Mexico are tasked with increasing production in the Americas from 1.2 million units a year in 2011 to 2 million units annually by 2014. The Great East Japan of Earthquake of 2011 and other contingencies also lead the company to create more efficient business continuity procedures for parts purchasing.

HISTORY

Company Background

In 1911 US-trained Masujiro Hashimoto established Tokyo-based Kwaishinsha Motor Car Works to repair import and manufacture cars. Kwaishinsha made its first car sporting its DAT ("fast rabbit" in Japanese) logo in 1913. Renamed DAT Motors in 1925 and suffering from a strong domestic preference for American cars the company consolidated with ailing Jitsuyo Motors in 1926. DAT in-

troduced the son of DAT in 1931 —the Datsun minicar ("son" means "damage or loss" in Japanese hence the spelling change).

Tobata Casting (cast iron and auto parts) bought Datsun's production facilities in 1933. Tobata's Yoshisuke Aikawa believed there was a niche for small cars and the car operations were spun off as Nissan Motors that year.

During WWII the Japanese government limited Nissan's production to trucks and airplane engines; Nissan survived postwar occupation in part due to business with the US Army. The company went public in 1951 and signed a licensing agreement the next year with Austin Motor (UK) which put it back in the car business. A 40% import tax allowed Nissan to compete in Japan even though it had higher costs than those of foreign carmakers.

Nissan entered the US market in 1958 with the model 211 using the Datsun name; it established Nissan Motor Corporation in Los Angeles in 1960. Exports rose as factory automation led to higher quality and lower costs. In the 1970s Nissan expanded exports of fuel-efficient cars such as the Datsun B210. The company became the leading US car importer in 1975.

The company's name change in the US from Datsun to Nissan during the 1980s confused customers and took six years to complete. In 1986 Nissan became the first major Japanese carmaker to build its products in Europe. It launched its high-end Infiniti line in the US in 1989.

EXECUTIVES

Chairman President and CEO, Carlos Ghosn, age 62
EVP and CFO, Joseph G. (Joe) Peter, age 53
Vice Chairman EVP and Chief Competitive Officer, Hiroto Saikawa, age 63
EVP Total Customer Satisfaction and Chairman Japan Asia and Oceania, Kimiyasu Nakamura
Corporate VP and CIO, Celso Guiotoko
VP Purchasing, Yasuhiro Yamauchi
EVP, Jose Munoz
SVP; President Dongfend Motor, Jun Seki
SVP; President Infiniti, Roland Kr ger
EVP Global Marketing and Sales EV and Battery, Daniele Schillaci
President Nissan Korea Co., Huh Sung-joong
CEO Infiniti Korea Co., Kang Seung-won
Vice Chairman, Toshiyuki Shiga
Auditors: Ernst & Young ShinNihon LLC

LOCATIONS

HQ: Nissan Motor Co., Ltd.
1-1-1 Takashima, Nishi-ku, Yokohama 220-8686
Phone: (81) 45 523 5523
Web: www.nissan-global.com

PRODUCTS/OPERATIONS

2014

	%
Automobile	94
Sales Financing	6
Total	100

Selected Products

Forklifts
  Engine-powerd forklifts
  Electric-powered forklifts
  Warehouse products
  Order pickers
  Pallet stackers
  Pallet transporters
  Reach trucks
Infiniti
  Infiniti G
  Infiniti G convertible
  Infiniti G coupe

Infiniti M
Infiniti EX
Infiniti FX
Infiniti JX
Infiniti QX
Nissan
  Altima
  Altima coupe
  Altima hybrid
  Armada
  Cube
  Frontier
  GT-R
  Maxima
  Murano
  Pathfinder
  Rogue
  Sentra
  Titan
  Versa
  Xterra
Nissan Marine outboard motors

COMPETITORS

BMW	Hyundai Motor
CLARK Material	Isuzu
Handling	Kia Motors
Crown Equipment	Mazda
Daihatsu	Mitsubishi Motors
Daimler	NACCO Industries
Deere	Peugeot
FCA US	Suzuki Motor
Fiat Chrysler	Tata Motors
Ford Motor	Toyota
Fuji Heavy Industries	Volkswagen
General Motors	Volvo
Honda	

HISTORICAL FINANCIALS
Company Type: Public

Income Statement
FYE: March 31

	REVENUE ($ mil.)	NET INCOME ($ mil.)	NET PROFIT MARGIN	EMPLOYEES
03/16	108,547	4,664	4.3%	174,043
03/15	94,809	3,813	4.0%	172,458
03/14	101,555	3,769	3.7%	147,939
03/13	102,342	3,639	3.6%	160,530
03/12	114,701	4,162	3.6%	157,365
Annual Growth	(1.4%)	2.9%	—	2.6%

2016 Year-End Financials

Debt ratio: 0.3%
Return on equity: 10.9%
Cash ($ mil.): 8,181
Current ratio: 1.59
Long-term debt ($ mil.): 33,307

No. of shares (mil.): —
Dividends
  Yield: 3.2%
  Payout: 59.6%
Market value ($ mil.): —

	STOCK PRICE ($) FY Close	P/E High/Low		PER SHARE ($) Earnings	Dividends	Book Value
03/16	18.51	0	0	1.11	0.61	9.42
03/15	20.33	0	0	0.91	0.57	(0.00)
03/14	17.87	—	—	0.90	0.84	10.08
03/13	19.20	—	—	0.87	0.00	9.64
03/12	21.47	—	—	1.00	0.00	9.37
Annual Growth	(3.6%)	—	—	2.8%	—	0.1%

NN Group NV (Netherlands)

Auditors: Ernst & Young Accountants LLP

LOCATIONS

HQ: NN Group NV (Netherlands)
  Schenkkade 65, Amsterdam 2595 AS
Phone: (31) 70 513 03 03
Web: www.nn-group.com

HISTORICAL FINANCIALS
Company Type: Public

Income Statement
FYE: December 31

	ASSETS ($ mil.)	NET INCOME ($ mil.)	INCOME AS % OF ASSETS	EMPLOYEES
12/15	176,617	1,704	1.0%	11,561
12/14	201,142	714	0.4%	12,486
12/13	200,670	13	0.0%	18,497
12/12	446,493	1,368	0.3%	25,693
Annual Growth	(26.6%)	7.6%	—	(23.4%)

2015 Year-End Financials

Return on assets: 0.9%
Return on equity: 7.3%
Long-term debt ($ mil.): —
No. of shares (mil.): 333
Sales ($ mil): 15,501

Dividends
  Yield: —
  Payout: —
Market value ($ mil.): 11,874

	STOCK PRICE ($) FY Close	P/E High/Low		PER SHARE ($) Earnings	Dividends	Book Value
12/15	35.60	8	6	4.89	0.00	70.06
12/14	30.65	18	16	2.03	0.00	74.11
12/13	0.00	—	—	(0.00)	0.00	
435,262.59						
Annual Growth	(94.6%)	—	—	—	—	—

Noble Group Ltd

Noble Group Limited obliges its customers by maintaining an unlimited appetite for raw materials. The investment holding company is principally engaged in the international supply of raw materials to customers in the agriculture energy metals minerals and ores and logistics markets. Noble Group conducts business through a network of more than 120 offices in almost 40 countries providing supply chain services for the sourcing marketing processing and transportation of industrial and agricultural products. The group is also involved in technical ship management services trade finance and coal mining. In 2016 it agreed to sell its North American energy business to Calpine for $1.05 billion.

The company relies on its diversified portfolio and integrated supply chains to offset downturns in particular sectors and create more operational efficiencies. Noble Group's "pipeline" supply chain strategy allows it to indentify and secure profits at every step of a product's journey from raw material to finished good (such as in the case of an agricultural product through seeking profits from fertilizer sales storage fees refining fees etc).

The company gets the bulk of its profit from agricultural and energy commodities and is investing heavily in both sectors and in 2009 and 2010 has invested in $214 million oil tank terminal in Netherlands warehouses and sugar refineries in Brazil and coal mining assets in Indonesia and Australia. Further diversifying its portfolio in 2010 the company acquired 51% of PT Henrison Inti Persada of Indonesia marking the company's first move into palm oil production. It also picked up the Sempra Energy Solutions unit of RBS Sempra Commodities' joint venture for $318 million.

In 2010 as part of its expansion in South America Noble Group acquired two mills from Brazilian ethanol producer Grupo Cerradinho for a $941 million.

With commodity prices rebounding from the 2009 global recession in 2010 the company reported a jump in revenues and net income led by the strong performance of its energy segment which doubled its revenues that year.

Korea Investment Corporation (KIC) acquired a 21% stake in Noble Group Limited in 2011. KIC and Noble established a co-operative business and strategic partnership to jointly invest in infrastructure assets and supply chain management activities. Investment firm China Investment Corp. is also a strategic partner in agricultural projects across Asia.

Also in 2011 to raise cash Noble Group sold its Donaldson Coal holdings to its 65%-owned Australian coal miner group Gloucester Coal in a transaction valued at $381 million. The deal bolsters Gloucester's production capacity and provides access to additional port capacity.

In 2012 Chinese-controlled coal miner Yancoal Australia (a subsidiary of Yanzhou Coal Mining Company) acquired Noble's Gloucester Coal in a cash-and-stock deal for about $637.4 million. As part of the deal Noble will ultimately get about 22% of the merged company.

EXECUTIVES

Vice Chairman and CFO, Stephen J. Marzo
Executive Director and President, William Randall
CEO and Executive Director, Yusuf A. Alireza
Chairman and Executive Director, Richard Samuel Elman
Auditors: Ernst & Young

LOCATIONS

HQ: Noble Group Ltd
  18th Floor, MassMutual Tower, 38 Gloucester Road,
Phone: (852) 2861 3511   **Fax:** (852) 2527 0282
Web: www.thisisnoble.com

2014 Sales

	% of total
North America	65
Asia-Pacific	17
Europe	9
South America	6
Africa	3
Total	100

PRODUCTS/OPERATIONS

2014 Sales

	% of total
Energy	85
Metals Minerals & Ores	15
Total	100

COMPETITORS

ADM	Marubeni
Cargill	Mitsui
Glencore	Sime Darby
ITOCHU	

HISTORICAL FINANCIALS
Company Type: Public

Income Statement
FYE: December 31

	REVENUE ($ mil.)	NET INCOME ($ mil.)	NET PROFIT MARGIN	EMPLOYEES
12/15	66,712	(1,672)	—	1,500
12/14	85,816	132	0.2%	1,900
12/13	97,878	243	0.2%	15,649
12/12	94,045	471	0.5%	15,000
12/11	80,732	431	0.5%	14,000
Annual Growth	(4.7%)	—	—	(42.8%)

2015 Year-End Financials

Debt ratio: 34.6%
Return on equity: (-39.9%)
Cash ($ mil.): 1,953
Current ratio: 1.42
Long-term debt ($ mil.): 3,433

No. of shares (mil.): —
Dividends
Yield: 0.0%
Payout: —
Market value ($ mil.): —

	STOCK PRICE ($)		P/E		PER SHARE ($)		
	FY Close		High/Low		Earnings	Dividends	Book Value
12/15	0.28		—	—	(0.26)	0.01	0.51
12/14	0.85		74	46	0.02	0.04	0.75
12/13	0.85		30	18	0.03	0.02	0.78
12/12	0.95		17	12	0.07	0.02	0.79
12/11	0.88		27	12	0.07	0.03	0.72
Annual Growth	(25.2%)		—	—	—	(27.7%)	(8.3%)

Nomura Holdings Inc

Nomura Holdings is the parent company of Nomura Securities Japan's leading investment bank and brokerage house. The company performs trading equity and bond underwriting research and mergers and acquisitions (M&A) advisory services. It also makes private equity and venture capital investments and oversees some ¥110 trillion in retail client assets. Subsidiary Nomura Asset Management is Japan's largest asset management firm in terms of assets under management in investment trusts which it offers to retail investors and through institutional funds. Nomura Holdings has operations in more than 30 countries; Nomura Securities International is the company's US trading and investment banking unit.

OperationsNomura operates through three business divisions. Wholesale which generated 50% of revenue in fiscal 2015 (ended March 31) includes the firm's global markets and investment banking operations and provides corporate and institutional products and services. Its Retail division (30% of revenue) provides investment products and offers investment consultation services to individuals and businesses from nearly 160 Nomura Securities locations across Japan. Its Asset Management division (6% of revenue) which operates through Nomura Asset Management develops and manages investment trusts and provides investment advisory services. Additional units include Nomura Trust & Banking big-ticket financing firm Nomura Babcock & Brown and the Nomura Institute of Capital Markets Research.

The firm's revenue streams are fairly diversified. About 23% of its total revenue came from commissions in FY2015 with another 5% coming from its investment banking fees. The firm's interest and dividend income and asset management/portfolio service fees made up 23% and 11% of total revenue respectively. The remainder of its revenue came from non-recurring sources such as net gains on trading (28% of revenue) and gains on equity investments (1%).

Geographic Reach

Nearly 70% of the firm's revenue came from Japan in fiscal 2015 (ended March) while business in the Americas and Europe each made up 13% of revenue. The remaining 5% of revenue came from the Asia and Oceania region. Its operations are mostly in Japan but subsidiaries are also in the US the UK Singapore and Hong Kong Special Administrative Region.

Sales and Marketing

The firm offers its variety of financial services to individuals corporations financial institutions governments and governmental agencies.

Financial Performance

Note: Growth rates may differ after conversion to US dollars.

Nomura Holdings has struggled to grow its revenues in recent years though its profits have been steadily climbing as its managed to cut non-interest expenses and pay lower income tax rates with more deductible expenses related to foreign subsidiaries.

The firm's revenue climbed 6% to ¥1.9 trillion in fiscal 2015 (ended March 31) mostly thanks to a double-digit jump in net gains on trading. The firm's Wholesale business drove most of the recurring revenue growth with its income rising by 3% on weaker Yen an increase in overseas equity revenue and higher overseas M&A and fundraising activity. Its Asset Management business grew by 15% as its assets under management grew with inflows from its investment trust and investment advisory businesses and from new revenue from its recently acquired subsidiary in Taiwan. Nomura's retail business shrank by 7% on decreasing commissions from the distribution of investment trusts and brokerage services.

Higher revenue during FY2015 drove Nomura's net income higher by 5% to ¥224.8 million for the year. The firm's cash levels fell sharply with operations using ¥77 million during the year mostly as it purchased more securities under agreements to resell. Strategy

Nomura is well-positioned to take advantage of expected growth in other Asian nations. The company expressed in 2015 that it expected Asia to account for half of global GDP by 2050 providing Nomura with Wholesale business opportunity as corporations continue to develop with higher demand for funding. It also expected that the region's growing middle class would increase demand for personal financial services over the next several decades creating another growth opportunity for its retail business.Additionally the firm's wide variety of financial services gives its tremendous cross-selling opportunities that integrate both its Retail and Wholesale operations.

HISTORY

Company BackgroundTokushichi Nomura started a currency exchange Nomura Shoten in Osaka in 1872 and began trading stock. His son Tokushichi II took over and in 1910 formed Nomura's first syndicate to underwrite part of a government bond issue. It established the Osaka Nomura Bank in 1918. The bond department became independent in 1925 and became Nomura Securities. The company opened a New York office in 1927 entering stock brokerage in 1938.

The firm rebuilt and expanded retail operations after WWII. It encouraged stock market investing by promoting "million ryo savings chests" —small boxes in which people saved cash (ryo was an old form of currency). When savings reached 5000 yen savers could buy into investment trusts. Nomura distributed more than a million chests in 10 years.

Nomura followed clients overseas in the 1960s helped underwrite a US issue of Sony stock and opened a London office. It became Japan's leading securities firm after a 1965 stock market crash decimated rival Yamaichi Securities. The firm grew rapidly in the 1970s ushering investment capital in and out of Japan and competing with banks by issuing corporate debt securities.

As the Japanese economy soared in the 1980s the company opened Nomura Bank International in London (1986) and bought 20% of US mergers and acquisitions advisor Wasserstein Perella (1988 sold 2001).

Then the Japanese economic bubble burst. Nomura's stock toppled 70% from its 1987 peak and underwriting plummeted. In 1991 and 1992 amid revelations that Nomura and other brokerages had reimbursed favored clients' trading losses the firm was accused of manipulating stock in companies owned by Japanese racketeers. Nomura's chairman and president —both named Tabuchi —resigned admitting no wrongdoing.

The firm trimmed staff and offices and focused on its most efficient operations. From 1993 to 2000 it seesawed from red to black and back again.

Junichi Ujiie became president after the payoff scandal; he restructured operations to prepare for Japan's financial deregulation. Nomura invested in pub chain Inntrepreneur and William Hill a UK betting chain. It also created an entertainment lending unit to lend against future royalties or syndication fees and spun off a minority stake in its high-risk US real estate business which ceased lending altogether the next year.

In 1998 Nomura was dealt a double blow when Asian economies collapsed and Russia defaulted on its debts. Incurring substantial losses the firm refocused on its domestic market and reduced overseas operations. That year it teamed with Industrial Bank of Japan for derivatives sales in the UK and pension plan consulting in Japan.

In 1999 Nomura bailed out ailing property subsidiary Nomura Finance which had been crippled by the sinking Japanese real estate market. It also invested heavily in UK real estate and bought 40% of the Czech beer market with South African Breweries.

The next year the firm agreed to buy the business services arm of Welsh utilities firm Hyder; it also bought 114000 flats in Germany with local government authorities its first European deal outside the UK. Also in 2000 Nomura sold its assets in pachinko parlors and "love" hotels Japanese cultural traditions with less-than-sparkling reputations. British authorities that year fined Nomura traders in relation to charges of trying to rig Australia's stock market in 1996.

The company converted to a holding company structure in 2001 and months later made its debut on the NYSE. It made two big deals in the UK that year buying hotel chain Le Meridien and becoming the nation's largest pub owner via the purchase of some 1000 locations from Bass. The company also bought a stake in Thomas Weisel Partners to increase its participation in M&A action between US and Japanese firms. In 2002 the company decided to sell the network of more than 4100 pubs to a consortium of private investors for some $3 billion.

In 2007 Nomura acquired global agency brokerage Instinet. The deal allowed the company to begin offering electronic trading services.

In 2008 Japanese regulators chose a consortium led by Nomura to take control of troubled Ashikaga Bank from the government; Nomura's private equity arm took a stake of about 45% in Ashikaga. The deal marked Nomura's first foray into retail banking.

The global financial crisis heavily impacted Nomura which reported steep declines in 2008 and 2009. The company lost some ¥208 billion ($2 billion) in 2009 alone on trading and equity investments. The US subprime mortgage bust further hurt the group which lost money on mortgage-backed securities.

In response Nomura cut operating costs and fine-tuned its offerings. The following year the company boosted its global investment banking capabilities by acquiring parts of the fallen bulge-bracket firm Lehman Brothers including operations in Asia Europe and the Middle East as well as the India-based back office operations. (In its post-acquisition transition the company laid off some 11% of its UK workforce or about 1000 employees in its London office.) In an effort to boost its domestic asset management business Nomura bought NikkoCiti Trust and Banking from Citigroup in 2009. The company also exited the US residential mortgage-backed securities business entirely.

The Lehman Brothers acquisition helped boost Nomura's profile in European equities and fixed-income trading. Adding on to that purchase Nomura bought London-based Tricorn Partners —a move that further complements its UK corporate finance advisory business.

Nomura Asset Management also bought a 35% stake in LIC Mutual Fund Asset Management Company of India. The deal gave Nomura a larger foothold in the Indian market and strengthened its credentials as an international asset manager.

EXECUTIVES

President and COO, Atsushi Yoshikawa, age 62
Senior Managing Director, Paul Spanswick
Executive Managing Director; CEO Wholesale, Tetsu Ozaki, age 59
Senior Managing Director; Regional Co-CEO Europe Middle East and Africa, Yasuo Kashiwagi
Senior Managing Director and Regional CEO Americas; Chairman and CEO Nomura Securities International, Shigesuke Kashiwagi, age 57
Senior Managing Director, Hiromasa Yamazaki
Senior Managing Director, Naoki Matsuba
Chairman and CEO China, Zhizhong Yang
Senior Managing Director and CIO, Masahide Nakamura
Executive Managing Director, Shoichi Nagamatsu, age 65
Senior Managing Director and Legal, Noriaki Nagai, age 59
Senior Managing Director, Yuji Nakata
Senior Managing Director, Noriaki Miyano
Senior Management Director, Toshihiro Iwasaki
CEO; President Nomura Securities, Koji Nagai
Senior Managing Director, Kenji Kimura
Senior Managing Director; Regional CEO Asia except Japan, Minoru Shinohara
Executive Managing Director; CEO Asset Management, Kunio Watanabe
Senior Managing Director, Kentaro Okuda
Senior Managing Director, Junko Nakagawa
Senior Managing Director; Regional CEO Americas, David Findlay
Senior Managing Director, Steven Ashley
Senior Managing Director; Regional Co-CEO Americas, Toshiya Hasegawa
Senior Managing Director, Eiji Miura
Senior Managing Director, Hisato Miyashita
Executive Managing Director; CEO Retail, Toshio Morita
Senior Managing Director, Lewis O'Donald
Senior Managing Director and Co-CIO, Naohiro Sako
Senior Managing Director; President and CEO Nomura Trust and Banking, Chie Shimpo
Senior Managing Director, Yo Akatsuka
Senior Managing Director, Juntaro Kimura
President and CEO India, Vikas Sharma
CEO Europe Middle East and Africa, Jonathan Lewis
Auditors: Ernst & Young ShinNihon LLC

LOCATIONS

HQ: Nomura Holdings Inc
9-1 Nihonbashi 1-chome, Chuo-Ku, Tokyo 103-8645
Phone: (81) 3 5255 1000
Web: www.nomuraholdings.com

2014 Sales

	% of total
Japan	69
Americas	13
Europe	13
Asia and Oceania	5
Total	**100**

PRODUCTS/OPERATIONS

2014 Sales

	% of total
Net gain on trading	28
Commissions	23
Interest and dividends	23
Asset management & portfolio service fees	11
Fees from investment banking	5
Gain on investments in equity securities	1
Other	9
Total	**100**

2014 Sales

	% of total
Wholesale	50
Retail	30
Asset Management	6
Others	14
Total	**100**

COMPETITORS

Bank of America	Goldman Sachs
Barclays	HSBC
Boom Securities	SMBC Nikko Securities
Daiwa Securities Group	UBS Investment Bank
Deutsche Bank	

HISTORICAL FINANCIALS

Company Type: Public

Income Statement
FYE: March 31

	ASSETS ($ mil.)	NET INCOME ($ mil.)	INCOME AS % OF ASSETS	EMPLOYEES
03/16	365,906	1,171	0.3%	28,865
03/15	348,253	1,873	0.5%	28,672
03/14	421,629	2,069	0.5%	27,670
03/13	403,248	1,139	0.3%	27,956
03/12	435,172	141	0.0%	34,395
Annual Growth	**(4.2%)**	**69.7%**	**—**	**(4.3%)**

2016 Year-End Financials

Return on assets: 0.3%	Dividends
Return on equity: 4.8%	Yield: 4.1%
Long-term debt ($ mil.): —	Payout: 63.9%
No. of shares (mil.): —	Market value ($ mil.): —
Sales ($ mil): 7,011	

	STOCK PRICE ($) FY Close	P/E High/Low		PER SHARE ($) Earnings	Dividends	Book Value
03/16	4.44	0	0	0.32	0.19	6.66
03/15	5.87	0	0	0.50	0.14	6.27
03/14	6.43	0	0	0.54	0.14	6.55
03/13	6.17	0	0	0.30	0.04	6.57
03/12	4.41	2	1	0.04	0.10	7.01
Annual Growth	**0.2%**			**69.5%**	**17.5%**	**(1.3%)**

Nordea Bank AB

Nordea Bank is one of the largest financial services groups in the Nordic and Baltic Sea regions. Sweden is its home but Nordea also has a major presence in Denmark Finland Norway and Russia.

The bank splits its operations into three main divisions: retail banking wholesale banking and wealth management. The bank also provides life and pension products. Originally founded in the 1820s Nordea Bank now boasts a network of about 700 branches and serves some 11 million customers including about 1 million corporate clients —a key customer segment for Nordea. About 55% of its lending activity is to corporations.

OperationsThe bank operates through three main segments. Retail Banking generates roughly 55% of the bank's overall income and offers a wide range of traditional deposit and loan products for both household customers and corporate clients mostly in the Nordic markets and the Baltic countries. Wholesale Banking brings in another 25% of total revenue and provides banking and other financial services to large Nordic and global corporate institutional and public companies. This division also serves financial sector clients with funds and equity products as well as consulting services within asset allocation and fund sales. Nordea Bank Russia offers a full range of bank services to corporate and private customers in Russia. Capital Markets unallocated includes the result in Capital Markets which is not allocated to the main business areas. Roughly 15% of revenue comes from the Wealth Management division which provides investment savings and risk management products. It also manages customers' assets and gives financial advice to affluent and high net worth individuals and institutional investors. Additionally Nordea offers financing and other services to clients in the Shipping Offshore & Oil Services industries. The bank also has a Life & Pensions business and an Asset Management division that is responsible for all actively-managed investment products.

Geographic Reach

Nordea Bank has an international network of branches subsidiaries and representative offices in almost 20 countries around the world with most of its operations in Denmark Finland Norway and Sweden. More than 30% of revenue comes from Denmark while Sweden generates another nearly 25%. Finland and Norway markets contribute more than 15% each. Other large markets include the Baltic countries and Russia.

Sales and Marketing

The bank serves private customers (from general retail to the highly-affluent) corporations financial institutions and other global institutional customers.

Nordea's mobile banking activity has been growing. In 2014 transaction volume from its mobile bank channels grew by 90% with the number of active mobile banking users growing by 1000 per day.

Financial Performance

Note: Growth rates may differ after conversion to US dollars.

Nordea's annual revenues have remained mostly stable for the past few years while profits have steadily been rising. Revenue in 2014 grew by 3% to euro 10.22 billion ($12.42 billion) mostly thanks to higher commission income from investment and lending services from the bank's growing Wealth Management and Retail Banking divisions.

Higher revenue in 2014 pushed profit higher for a third straight year with net income rising by 7% to euro 3.33 billion ($4.05 billion). Also helping the bank's bottom line net loan loss provisions declined by 26% as its loan portfolio gained credit strength.

Cash levels fell despite higher earnings in 2014 with operations using euro 10.82 billion ($13.15 billion) primarily as deposit funding from credit institutions and the broader public declined over the year.

Strategy

Nordea Bank has continued to focus more on its four key markets in the Nordic and Baltic regions (including Denmark Finland Norway and Sweden). In mid-2014 to better concentrate resources on these key markets Nordea exited its banking life and financing businesses in Poland through the sale of its Nordea Bank Polska S.A. to PKO Bank Polski SA for euro 694 million ($927 million). As the industry moves from brick-and-mortar branch banking to digital banking Nordea has also been expanding its electronic offerings via its mobile tablet Netbank and Facebook platforms. Indeed during 2014 the bank reported that the number of mobile transactions grew by 90% reflecting the change in consumer tastes in the banking industry. In late 2014 the company announced that it would increase its IT investments by 30-35% over the coming years building new core banking and payment platforms to keep up with the digital banking trend. Company Background

Sampo owns more than 20% of Nordea. The Swedish government held a nearly 20% stake in the bank but reduced that to 13% in 2011 as part of its plan to raise capital. It plans to sell more and possibly all of its Nordea stake over time.

Growth in European markets has been a focus for Nordea. In 2009 the company purchased a 75% stake in Russian bank JSB Orgresbank rebranding it as OJSC Nordea Bank. Nordea also bought the Polish life insurance operations of Finnish banking group Sampo doubling Nordea's customer base in Poland. However Nordea put the breaks on aggressive growth and completely halted branch expansion in Russia and the Baltic countries in light of the global financial crisis.

HISTORY

Company BackgroundNordea traces its roots to 1974 when two Swedish government-owned banks Postbanken and Sveriges Kreditbank merged to form the country's largest bank Post-och Kreditbanken (PKbanken) in order to compete with S-E-Banken and Svenska Handelsbanken.

PKbanken didn't hold on to the top spot long. By the early 1980s a recession and languid profits sank the company to third. However the firm did expand teaming with Norway's Christiana Bank og Kreditkasse to open joint offices in Hong Kong Houston London São Paolo and Singapore.

As regulatory restrictions in Sweden eased the government spun off 15% of its interest in the company on the Stockholm Stock Exchange in 1984.

PKbanken pulled out of its deal in London with Christiana Bank in 1986 but it bought a stake in London-based English Trust Group to expand its merchant banking services. In 1988 PKbanken acquired government-owned Carnegie Fondkommission Sweden's largest brokerage and in 1989 purchased the state-controlled Swedish Investment Bank a provider of funding to small and midsized businesses.

A year later PKbanken acquired regional Swedish bank Nordbanken and assumed the smaller firm's name. Soon after the government axed the combined firm's top officers and installed new management. The purging didn't help as another recession and a real estate market crash hammered the company's bottom line. In 1992 the Swedish government intervened again acquiring all of the outstanding shares of Nordbanken that it did not already own. The company rebounded quickly after selling bad loans to the state and cutting staff by a fifth.

In 1994 the Swedish government transferred its ownership of Gota Bank to Nordbanken. The company resumed trading on the Stockholm Stock Exchange the following year.

Across the border in Finland rivals Union Bank of Finland and Kansallis-Osake-Pankki merged in 1995 to create Merita Bank the country's largest.

In 1997 Nordbanken and Merita Bank combined to form MeritaNordbanken but their parents Nordbanken Holdings and Merita Ab remained separate. In 2000 the company bought Danish bank Unidanmark. MeritaNordbanken's holding companies united and assumed the name Nordic Baltic Holding. Later the company changed its name to Nordea an amalgamation of "Nordic" and "idea."

In 2001 Nordea bought Christiania Bank og Kreditkasse and later that year attached the Nordea Bank name to its banking subsidiaries in Denmark Finland Norway and Sweden.

By 2003 the company composed primarily of the four national banking groups —Nordea Bank Denmark Nordea Bank Finland Nordea Bank Norway and Nordea Bank Sweden —decided to change its complex legal structure and create one European company under the Nordea Bank banner.

Nordea acquired Denmark's Fionia Bank in 2009 including the bank's staff and its 29 branches but excluding some 2000 troubled corporate customers. The Denmark government had taken control of the failing bank earlier in the year.

EXECUTIVES

EVP Chief Risk Officer Head Group Risk Management Country Senior Executive Finland, Ari Kaperi, age 56
President and Group CEO, Casper von Koskull
EVP and Head of Retail Banking Country Senior Executive Sweden, Lennart Jacobsen, age 50
Deputy CEO and COO, Torsten Hagen J rgensen
Group CFO, Heikki Ilkka, age 46
EVP and Head of Wholesale Banking, Eric Ekman, age 47
EVP Deputy Head of Retail Banking and Country Senior Executive in Denmark, Mads G. Jakobsen, age 50
Chairman, Bj rn Wahlroos, age 64
Vice Chairman, Marie Ehrling, age 61
Auditors: Ohrlings PricewaterhouseCoopers AB

LOCATIONS

HQ: Nordea Bank AB
 Smalandsgatan 17, Stockholm SE-105 71
Phone: (46) 8 614 78 00   **Fax:** (46) 8 614 87 70
Web: www.nordea.com

2014 Sales

	% of total
Denmark	31
Sweden	24
Finland	18
Norway	17
New European markets	4
Other	6
Total	**100**

PRODUCTS/OPERATIONS

2014 Sales

	% of total
Banking products	61
Capital markets products	19
Savings products and asset management	10
Life and pensions	5
Other	5
Total	**100**

2014 Sales

	% of total
Retail Banking	56
Wholesale Banking	24
Wealth Management	16
Group Corporate Centre	4
Total	**100**

2014 Sales

	% of total
Net Interest income	54
Net Fee abd commission income	28
Net results on items at fair value	14
Other Operating income	4
Total	**100**

COMPETITORS

BNP Paribas	KBC
Citigroup	SEB AB
Danske Bank	Schroders
Deutsche Bank	Skandia
HSBC	Svenska Handelsbanken
JPMorgan Asset	
Management	

HISTORICAL FINANCIALS

Company Type: Public

Income Statement

FYE: December 31

	ASSETS ($ mil.)	NET INCOME ($ mil.)	INCOME AS % OF ASSETS	EMPLOYEES
12/15	704,575	3,988	0.6%	29,826
12/14	813,588	4,050	0.5%	29,397
12/13	867,940	4,289	0.5%	29,429
12/12	892,873	4,111	0.5%	31,466
12/11	926,375	3,397	0.4%	33,068
Annual Growth	(6.6%)	4.1%	—	(2.5%)

2015 Year-End Financials

Return on assets: 0.5%	Dividends
Return on equity: 12.0%	Yield: 6.0%
Long-term debt ($ mil.): —	Payout: 69.0%
No. of shares (mil.): —	Market value ($ mil.): —
Sales ($ mil): 15,890	

	STOCK PRICE ($) FY Close	P/E High/Low	PER SHARE ($) Earnings	Dividends	Book Value
12/15	11.13	15 11	0.99	0.67	8.37
12/14	11.55	16 13	1.01	0.59	8.99
12/13	13.51	18 13	1.06	0.44	9.97
12/12	9.61	13 10	1.03	0.35	9.23
12/11	7.82	18 10	0.84	0.38	8.32
Annual Growth	9.2%	— —	4.2%	15.6%	0.1%

North Pacific Bank Ltd

Sapporo Hokuyo Holdings supposes it has what customers need in the way of banking and financial services. The company was formed in 2001 to serve as the holding company for North Pacific Bank and The Sapporo Bank; together the regional banks have some 230 offices in Hokkaido as well as an office in Tokyo and two offices in China. North Pacific Bank which is the largest bank in Hokkaido accounts for most of the holding company's sales; the bank traces its roots to 1917. The company also has subsidiaries active in credit cards and leasing; bank subsidiaries engage in such activities as financing.

EXECUTIVES

President, Ryuzo Yokouchi
Auditors: KPMG AZSA LLC

LOCATIONS

HQ: North Pacific Bank Ltd
3-7 Odori Nishi, Chuo-ku, Sapporo, Hokkaido 060-8661
Phone: (81) 11 261 1311
Web: www.hokuyobank.co.jp

COMPETITORS

Hokkoku Bank	Mizuho Financial
Hokuhoku Financial	Resona
Group	Sumitomo Mitsui
Hyakujushi Bank	
Mitsubishi UFJ	
Financial Group	

HISTORICAL FINANCIALS

Company Type: Public

Income Statement

FYE: March 31

	ASSETS ($ mil.)	NET INCOME ($ mil.)	INCOME AS % OF ASSETS	EMPLOYEES
03/16	75,376	160	0.2%	5,412
03/15	68,031	131	0.2%	5,403
03/14	76,415	842	1.1%	3,744
03/13	83,029	206	0.2%	3,808
03/12	93,947	294	0.3%	3,730
Annual Growth	(5.4%)	(14.1%)	—	9.8%

2016 Year-End Financials

Return on assets: 0.2%	Dividends
Return on equity: 4.8%	Yield: —
Long-term debt ($ mil.): —	Payout: —
No. of shares (mil.): 398	Market value ($ mil.): —
Sales ($ mil): 1,323	

Novartis AG Basel

Auditors: PricewaterhouseCoopers AG

LOCATIONS

HQ: Novartis AG Basel
Lichtstrasse 35, Basel CH-4056
Phone: (41) 61 324 1111   **Fax:** (41) 61 324 7826
Web: www.novartis.com

HISTORICAL FINANCIALS

Company Type: Public

Income Statement

FYE: December 31

	REVENUE ($ mil.)	NET INCOME ($ mil.)	NET PROFIT MARGIN	EMPLOYEES
12/16	49,436	6,712	13.6%	118,393
12/15	50,387	17,783	35.3%	118,700
12/14	53,634	10,210	19.0%	133,413
12/13	58,831	9,175	15.6%	135,696
12/12	57,561	9,505	16.5%	127,724
Annual Growth	(3.7%)	(8.3%)	—	(1.9%)

2016 Year-End Financials

Debt ratio: 18.2%	No. of shares (mil.): —
Return on equity: 8.8%	Dividends
Cash ($ mil.): 7,007	Yield: 0.0%
Current ratio: 1.12	Payout: 97.0%
Long-term debt ($ mil.): 17,897	Market value ($ mil.): —

	STOCK PRICE ($) FY Close	P/E High/Low	PER SHARE ($) Earnings	Dividends	Book Value
12/16	72.84	31 24	2.80	2.72	31.52
12/15	86.04	14 11	7.29	2.67	32.46
12/14	92.66	23 19	4.13	2.76	29.50
12/13	80.38	21 17	3.70	2.43	30.64
12/12	63.30	16 13	3.89	2.48	28.54
Annual Growth	3.6%	— —	(7.9%)	2.3%	2.5%

Novo-Nordisk A/S

Until there is a cure for diabetes Novo Nordisk will stay busy and as long as diabetes is on the rise it will likely stay profitable. It is one of the world's leading producers of human insulin insulin analogues injection devices and education materials. It makes modern insulin analogues Levemir and NovoLog (which mimic natural insulin regulation more closely than human insulin) and Saxenda which treats obesity. The firm also has products in the areas of hemostasis management (blood clotting) human growth hormone and estrogen replacement therapy. The not-for-profit Novo Nordisk Foundation through its Novo A/S subsidiary controls the voting power in Novo Nordisk.

Operations

The company operates in two business segments: diabetes care (which covers insulins oral anti-diabetic drugs and obesity) and biopharmaceuticals (which covers hemophilia care growth hormone therapy and hormone replacement therapy). Novo Nordisk is the world's leader with 47% of the total insulin market in volume as well as 46% of the market for modern and new-generation insulins.

Drawing upon its familiarity in working with chronic disorders Novo Nordisk has built up a stable group of non-diabetic biopharmaceuticals. NovoSeven is used to treat hemophilia in patients who have developed inhibitors to other treatments and to treat patients who develop hemophilia later in life. Norditropin is the company's liquid human growth hormone which is given to children and adults with a growth hormone deficiency. It has extended the line of products to include easier-to-use injection devices. Its line of female hormone replacement therapies are used to reduce symptoms of menopause.

Geographic Reach

Novo Nordisk has production facilities around the globe but keeps the production of its active pharmaceutical ingredients close to home in Denmark. As with most biopharmaceutical enterprises Novo Nordisk engages in alliances with medical institutions and other drug companies to further its research and marketing activities.

Its primary markets are North America (about 50% of revenues) China Japan and major countries in Europe. The company's business in other markets including Algeria Argentina Australia Brazil India Russia and Turkey is also growing.

Financial Performance

The company has seen revenue growth over the past five years. In 2014 revenue grew 6% to DKK 88.8 billion as North America and China sales rose. Both the diabetes care and biopharmaceuticals segments have seen increased sales primarily driven by modern insulin and two products —Levemir and Victoza (which together account for more than three-fourths of the sales growth). In biopharmaceuticals a 6% increase in Norditropin sales

in North America as well as increased demand for the pre-filled FlexPro device helped boost revenues.

Net income rose 5% to DKK 26.4 billion in 2014 largely due to the increased revenue. Cash flow from operations grew 22% to DKK 31.7 billion as a result of the higher profits and a decline in income tax paid.

Strategy

Novo Nordisk has worked to keep its pipeline of products robust and productive. In 2014 it was granted marketing authorization for type 2 diabetes treatment Xultophy in Europe while in the US its Saxenda obesity treatment was given approval. The company launched recombinant factor VIII (NovoEight) in Japan and in some European nations for the treatment of hemophilia. Other launches that year include the NovoFine Plus 32G 4mm ultra-thin universal pen needle and its Ryzodeg insulin in Mexico.

Expanding its production capabilities the company opened a new modern insulin manufacturing facility in Russia in 2015. In 2014 it acquired a manufacturing facility in New Hampshire and began building new laboratories in its R&D campus in Måløv Denmark. Novo Nordisk has also broken ground on two new production facilities —one in Clayton North Carolina and another in Kalundborg Denmark —both of which should be operational by 2020.

After the anti-IL-20 treatment for rheumatoid arthritis failed to show effectiveness in phase 2 trials Novo Nordisk discontinued its inflammatory disorders operations. It didn't expect to make any product launches in that area before the late 2020s.

Mergers and Acquisitions

Further boosting its portfolio of diabetes and obesity intellectual property the company is acquiring two US biopharmaceutical research firms (Calibrium and MB2) for undisclosed amounts.

HISTORY

Company Background

Novo Nordisk was formed by the 1989 merger of Danish insulin producers Novo and Nordisk.

Soon after Canadian researchers first extracted insulin from the pancreases of cattle Danish researcher August Krogh (winner of the 1920 Nobel Prize in physiology) and physician Marie Krogh his wife teamed up with H. C. Hagedorn also a physician to found Nordisk Insulinlaboratorium. One of their lab workers was an inventor named Harald Pedersen and in 1923 Nordisk hired Pedersen's brother Thorvald to analyze chemicals. The relationship was unsuccessful however and the brothers left the company.

The Pedersens decided to produce insulin themselves and set up operations in their basement in 1924. Harald also designed a syringe that patients could use for their own insulin injections. Within a decade their firm Novo Terapeutisk Laboratorium was selling its product in 40 countries.

Meanwhile Nordisk introduced a slow-acting insulin in 1936. NPH insulin launched in the US in 1950 soon became the leading longer-acting insulin. Nordisk later became a major maker of human growth hormone.

During WWII Novo produced its first enzyme trypsin used to soften leather. It began producing penicillin in 1947 and during the 1950s developed Heparin a trypsin-based drug used to treat blood clots. The company unveiled more industrial enzymes in the 1960s.

In 1981 Novo began selling its insulin in the US through a joint venture with E. R. Squibb (now part of Bristol-Myers Squibb). The next year Novo was the first to produce human insulin (actually a modified form of pig insulin) and in 1983 Nordisk introduced the Nordisk Infuser a pump that constantly released small quantities of insulin. Two years later Novo debuted the NovoPen a refillable injector that looked like a fountain pen.

Novo was the world's #2 insulin maker (and the world's largest maker of industrial enzymes) when it merged with #3 Nordisk in 1989. By combining their research and market share they were better able to compete globally with then-#1 Eli Lilly. After the merger Novo Nordisk introduced the NovoLet the world's first prefilled disposable insulin syringe.

Novo Nordisk introduced drugs for depression (Seroxat 1992) epilepsy (Gabitril 1995) and hemophilia (NovoSeven 1995). The company entered a joint marketing alliance with Johnson & Johnson subsidiary LifeScan the world's #1 maker of blood glucose monitors in 1995. It also began working with Rhône-Poulenc Rorer on estrogen replacement therapies.

Eli Lilly raised a new challenge in 1996 with the FDA approval of Humalog (the US's first new insulin product in 14 years) which is absorbed faster giving users more flexibility in their injection schedule. (Novo Nordisk's own fast-acting insulin product NovoLog received FDA approval four years later.) A 1998 marketing pact with Schering-Plough signaled Novo Nordisk's desire to boost sales of its diabetes drugs in the US where Eli Lilly had historically dominated.

In 2000 Novo Nordisk split its health care and enzymes businesses; the split left Novo Nordisk with all the health care operations while a new company Novozymes was formed to carry out the enzyme business. It bought out the remaining shares in its Brazilian subsidiary Biobras in 2001. In 2002 the company spun off its US-based biotechnology firm ZymoGenetics. It retained a one-third of the company until selling its shares to Bristol-Myers Squibb in 2010.

EXECUTIVES

EVP and CFO, Jesper Brandgaard, age 53, $5,800,000 total compensation

EVP and Chief Science Officer, Mads Krogsgaard Thomsen, age 56, $5,800,000 total compensation

EVP and Chief of Staffs, Lars Fruergaard Jørgensen, age 50, $4,400,000 total compensation

EVP North America Operations, Jakob Riis, age 50, $4,400,000 total compensation

EVP International Operations, Maziar Mike Doustdar, age 46

EVP Product Supply, Henrik Wulff, age 46

Vice Chairman, Jeppe Christiansen

Chairman, Göran Ando

Auditors: PricewaterhouseCoopers Statsautoriseret Revisionsaktieselskab

LOCATIONS

HQ: Novo-Nordisk A/S
Novo Alle, Bagsvaerd DK-2880
Phone: (45) 4444 8888   **Fax:** (45) 4449 0555
Web: www.novonordisk.com

PRODUCTS/OPERATIONS

2014 Sales

	% of total
Diabetes care	
NovoRapid/Novolog	20
Levemir	16
Victoza	15
NovoMix/NovologMix	11
Human insulin	11
Protein-related products	3
Oral antidiabetic products	2
New-generation insulin	1
Biopharmaceuticals	
NovoSeven	10
Norditropin	7
Other products	4
Total	**100**

Selected Products

Diabetes products
  Human insulins
  Actrapid
  Insulatard
  Mixtard 30
  Glucagon-like Peptide-1
  Victoza
  Modern insulins
  Levemir
  NovoMix
  NovoRapid
  Oral antidiabetic agents
  NovoNorm
  PrandiMet
Biopharmaceuticals
  NovoSeven (recombinant hemophilia therapy)
  Norditropin (human growth hormone)
  Hormone replacement therapy
  Activelle
  Estrofem
  Novofem
  Vagifem

COMPETITORS

Animas	MannKind
Baxter International	Marina Biotech
Becton Dickinson	Medtronic
Biogen	Novartis
Eli Lilly	Pfizer
Genentech	Sanofi
GlaxoSmithKline	Wockhardt

HISTORICAL FINANCIALS

Company Type: Public

Income Statement

FYE: December 31

	REVENUE ($ mil.)	NET INCOME ($ mil.)	NET PROFIT MARGIN	EMPLOYEES
12/16	15,876	5,386	33.9%	41,971
12/15	15,752	5,088	32.3%	40,638
12/14	14,497	4,323	29.8%	40,957
12/13	15,424	4,647	30.1%	37,978
12/12	13,785	3,786	27.5%	34,286
Annual Growth	3.6%	9.2%	—	5.2%

2016 Year-End Financials

Debt ratio: 0.0%
Return on equity: 82.0%
Cash ($ mil.): 2,654
Current ratio: 1.26
Long-term debt ($ mil.): —

No. of shares (mil.): —
Dividends
  Yield: 0.0%
  Payout: 45.6%
Market value ($ mil.): —

	STOCK PRICE ($) FY Close	P/E High/Low		PER SHARE ($) Earnings	Dividends	Book Value
12/16	35.86	4	2	2.12	0.97	2.57
12/15	58.08	4	3	1.97	0.53	2.69
12/14	42.32	17	3	1.64	0.61	2.54
12/13	184.76	21	17	1.73	0.23	2.94
12/12	163.21	22	15	1.37	0.18	2.65
Annual Growth	(31.5%)			11.5%	51.7%	(0.8%)

NTT DoCoMo Inc

Mobile phone carrier NTT DoCoMo is one of the world's largest wireless network operators in terms of subscribers behind global leader Vodafone. NTT DoCoMo (which means "anywhere") boasts about 65 million subscribers to its FOMA-branded wireless voice network in Japan (giving it about half of market share) while about 49 million customers subscribe to its i-mode mobile Internet services.

The company also sells wireless telephone handsets under the DoCoMo brand and it provides emergency satellite services primarily for maritime use. NTT DoCoMo is the wireless spinoff of Japan's leading telecommunications carrier Nippon Telegraph and Telephone (NTT); NTT owns two-thirds of NTT DoCoMo.

The company saw sales slip in 2010 mainly due to the decline of its core voice segment. Meanwhile NTT DoCoMo improved its profits for the year due to decreased costs of equipment and reduced network costs. The company has said that it expects profits to increase in 2011 due to ongoing efforts to further bring down costs as well as initiatives to drive customer usage of data services by offering reduced pricing options and expanded mobile services such as original content delivery and wireless Internet tethering between wireless devices and portable computers.

DoCoMo means "anywhere" and NTT DoCoMo is everywhere in the Japanese market for mobile communication services. However faced with a mature market and stiff competition at home NTT DoCoMo has renewed its efforts to tap into growth markets abroad particularly in the Asia/Pacific region.

In 2011 the company agreed to a deal with JG Summit that gives it the option to buy additional shares in Philippine Long Distance Telephone (PLDT) for around $263 million. NTTDoCoMo already owns about 10% of PLDT.

Its largest purchase in this overseas push was the 2009 acquisition of about one-quarter of India-based Tata Teleservices for about $2.7 billion. The company hopes to tap into the burgeoning Indian market through this alliance with the telecommunications arm of the Tata Group. Also that year NTT DoCoMo bought a 35% stake in US multimedia software maker PacketVideo to bolster its internal efforts to develop applications for mobile video services. It acquired the rest of the company from parent NextWave Wireless for about $115 million in 2010.

NTT DoCoMo's efforts to garner higher subscription fees from its existing customer base in Japan and improve retention have included an increase in the variety of mobile services it offers the introduction of cell phones offering a broader set of features (email music playback and gaming) and ongoing investments in its network infrastructure to enable bandwidth-hungry streaming content such as video programming. The company is counting on increased data usage to fuel profits as sales of voice services decline.

HISTORY

Formed in 1952 by the Japanese Ministry of Communications to rebuild Japan's war-ravaged phone system Nippon Telegraph and Telephone (NTT) enjoyed a monopoly on phone services for more than four decades.

NTT first went into mobile communications with a maritime phone service in 1959 and in 1968 the company began offering paging services. Other telecommunications services followed: car phone service (1979) in-flight phone service (1986) and mobile phone service (1987).

In 1991 NTT established a subsidiary to adopt these wireless segments; it launched operations in 1992 as NTT Mobile Communications Network under the leadership of NTT executive Kouji Ohboshi. The firm quickly took on the DoCoMo nickname. The year closed with slightly more than a million analog mobile phone users in Japan —a market DoCoMo shared with upstart telecom companies DDI and IDO (later bought by DDI). Paging service was more popular and DoCoMo won more than 3 million customers.

DoCoMo in 1993 launched digital mobile phone service based on a scheme called PDC (personal digital cellular) —a system incompatible with the digital standards that would take root in Europe and the US. Liberalization of the cellular phone market in 1994 triggered unexpected growth: Customers who previously had to lease mobile phones from the network operators could now buy them at retail stores. Further competition emerged in 1995 with the launch of personal handyphone services or PHS (parent company NTT was among the companies providing PHS) but DoCoMo's subscriber count passed 3.5 million mobile phone users —about half the market.

DoCoMo's pager business peaked in 1996 before commencing a long-term decline; the mobile phone market where DoCoMo had more than 8 million subscribers overtook it. The company launched a satellite-based mobile phone system that year to serve customers beyond the range of cell sites reaching ships and mountainous regions.

Financial crises rocked the Pacific Rim in 1997 and Japan's Fair Trade Commission rocked NTT by ordering it to cut its 95% ownership of DoCoMo. Customers continued to flock to mobile phones despite economic turmoil and DoCoMo passed the 15-million-subscriber mark. In 1998 DoCoMo gave hope to Japan's low-flying market when it left the nest: Its mammoth IPO raised more than $18 billion.

Meanwhile DDI (now KDDI) had become the first Japanese carrier to launch a digital mobile phone network based on CDMA (code division multiple access) technology. Though DoCoMo still used PDC it redoubled its efforts to help develop and standardize a next-generation wideband version of CDMA.

In 1999 DoCoMo took over NTT's unprofitable PHS unit and rolled out a high-speed data service over the PHS network. That year it acquired a 19% stake in the telecom unit of Hong Kong's Hutchison Whampoa but failed expectations led the company to sell its stake in Hutchison 3G UK to Hutchison Whampoa in 2005 for euro 120 million.

In 2000 the company adopted NTT DoCoMo as its corporate name. To promote its new data services NTT DoCoMo launched a joint venture in Japan with Microsoft (Mobimagic). It took the i-mode service international in 2001 when the company teamed up with Telecom Italia Mobile to introduce the 3G service in Europe. The next year NTT DoCoMo became the largest shareholder in America Online Japan but it sold the more than 40% stake to America Online in 2003.

The company staked its claim in the US too by paying $9.8 billion for a 16% stake in AT&T Wireless in 2001. NTT DoCoMo sold its stake following the 2004 takeover of AT&T Wireless by rival Cingular Wireless (now AT&T Mobility) in a deal valued at $41 billion.

The company in 2002 took full ownership of its eight majority-owned regional operating subsidiaries and began consolidating operations. The company also has liquidated several other subsidiaries including an operating unit in Brazil and it has reorganized its European holdings under a single subsidiary DoCoMo Europe Ltd.

It also continued to advance digital wireless technologies through partnerships that include an alliance (formed in 2000) with Hutchison Whampoa and Dutch mobile phone company KPN Mobile to bid on European operating licenses. It also paid $4.5 billion for a 15% stake in KPN Mobile. (The stake was reduced to 2% then sold back to parent firm KPN. An i-mode affiliation continues however.)

After the number of paging service subscribers fell to less than 300000 from a high of 6.5 million (in 1996) NTT DoCoMo ended the service in early 2007. It additionally dissolved allucher a marketing and consulting services provider to mobile phone users and its animation-related Web portal management and marketing business known as Hive. NTT DoCoMo also discontinued its Personal Handyphone Service (PHS) and its CITYPHONE digital mobile service in 2008.

NTT DoCoMo in 2008 bought stakes in operators in Bangladesh (TM International 30%) and the Philippines (PLDT 20%). Additionally the company has i-mode network technology licensing agreements with about a dozen GSM network operators in Europe including Russia and Greece as well as in the Asia/Pacific region.

EXECUTIVES

EVP Managing Director Smart-life Business Division and Smart-life Solutions and Director, Toshiki Nakayama, age 59
President and CEO, Kazuhiro Yoshizawa, age 60
EVP Managing Director R&D Innovation Division CTO and Director, Seizo Onoe
EVP Managing Director Corporate Strategy and Planning and Director, Hiroyasu Asami
SEVP Managing Director Sales and Marketing Division and Director, Yoshikiyo Sakai
SEVP and Director, Akira Terasaki
EVP and CFO, Hirotaka Sato, age 58
EVP Managing Director Corporate Sales and Marketing Division and TOHOKU Reconstruction Support, Kazuhiro Takagi
EVP Network and Preparation for 2020 and Director, Kiyohiro Omatsuzawa
EVP Managing Director Hunam Resources Management and Director, Hajime Kii
Auditors: KPMG AZSA LLC

LOCATIONS

HQ: NTT DoCoMo Inc
Sanno Park Tower, 11-1, Nagata-cho 2-chome, Chiyoda-ku, Tokyo 100-6150
Phone: (81) 3 5156 1111   **Fax:** (81) 3 5156 0271
Web: www.nttdocomo.co.jp

PRODUCTS/OPERATIONS

2013 Sales

	% of total
Mobile communication services	71
Equipment sales	17
Other operating revenues	12
Total	**100**

Selected Services
Cellular
i-mode (wireless Internet access)
In-flight telephone
Mobile multimedia
Satellite mobile communications
Third-generation (3G) wireless (W-CDMA)
World Call (direct international calling)

Selected Regional Operating Subsidiaries
DOCOMO Business Net Inc.
DOCOMO Engineering Chugoku Inc.
DOCOMO Engineering Hokkaido Inc.
DOCOMO Engineering Hokuriku Inc.
DOCOMO Engineering Inc.
DOCOMO Engineering Kansai Inc.
DOCOMO Engineering Kyushu Inc.
DOCOMO Engineering Shikoku Inc.
DOCOMO Engineering Tohoku Inc.
DOCOMO Engineering Tokai Inc.
DOCOMO I Kyushu Inc.
DOCOMO Mobile Inc.
DOCOMO Mobile Tokai Inc.
DOCOMO Mobile Media Kansai Inc.
DOCOMO Service Chugoku Inc.
DOCOMO Service Hokkaido Inc.
DOCOMO Service Hokuriku Inc.
DOCOMO Service Inc.
DOCOMO Service Kansai Inc.
DOCOMO Service Kyushu Inc.
DOCOMO Service Shikoku Inc.
DOCOMO Service Tohoku Inc.
DOCOMO Service Tokai Inc.
DOCOMO Support Inc.
DOCOMO Systems Inc.
DOCOMO Technology Inc.

COMPETITORS

BT	Optus
China Mobile	SK Telecom
EMOBILE	SOFTBANK MOBILE
Hutchison Telecommunications	Telstra
	Vodafone
KDDI	

HISTORICAL FINANCIALS
Company Type: Public

Income Statement
FYE: March 31

	REVENUE ($ mil.)	NET INCOME ($ mil.)	NET PROFIT MARGIN	EMPLOYEES
03/16	40,313	4,883	12.1%	37,888
03/15	36,534	3,418	9.4%	37,412
03/14	43,220	4,502	10.4%	36,253
03/13	47,507	5,267	11.1%	35,426
03/12	51,688	5,655	10.9%	32,244
Annual Growth	**(6.0%)**	**(3.6%)**	**—**	**4.1%**

2016 Year-End Financials
Debt ratio: 0.0%
Return on equity: 10.2%
Cash ($ mil.): 3,156
Current ratio: 2.12
Long-term debt ($ mil.): 1,960
No. of shares (mil.): —
Dividends
Yield: 2.3%
Payout: 53.8%
Market value ($ mil.): —

	STOCK PRICE ($) FY Close	P/E High/Low		PER SHARE ($) Earnings	Dividends	Book Value
03/16	22.77	0	0	1.26	0.54	12.56
03/15	17.43	0	0	0.85	0.55	11.55
03/14	15.77	0	0	1.09	0.61	13.18
03/13	14.87	0	0	1.27	0.62	13.91
03/12	16.67	0	0	1.36	0.66	14.88
Annual Growth	**8.1%**	**—**	**—**	**(2.0%)**	**(4.8%)**	**(4.2%)**

Obayashi Corp. (Japan)

Obayashi's buildings shake rattle and roll —but they don't fall. A leading global contractor and one of Japan's top four general contractors the company is a pioneer in the development of earthquake-resistant building techniques. Obayashi serves as architect consultant engineer and systems designer for buildings and large-scale civil engineering projects worldwide. Some of its projects have included the Dubai Urban Rail Transit System; the bobsled and luge runs used in the 1998 Winter Games in Nagano; the Ted Williams tunnel in Boston; and restoration of port facilities in Kobe Japan damaged by a 1995 earthquake.

OperationsObayashi operates four core business segments. Its Domestic Building Construction business (which generated 54% of net sales in fiscal 2015 ended March) builds offices condos commercial facilities factories hospitals and schools and designs for customers concerned with environmental harm energy conservation seismic resistance and disaster readiness. Its Domestic Civil Engineering business (18% of net sales) builds various types of infrastructure as well as environmentally-friendly waste disposal facilities. The company's Overseas Construction business (22% of net sales) builds infrastructure such as roads bridges and schools. Its Real Estate business (4% of net sales) works on redevelopment projects across Japan as a project partner or specified agent and sells properties for lease in favorable locations (mainly urban areas). The company's Domestic Civil Engineering and Real Estate businesses boast the highest profit margins with each of these segments contributing 35% to Obayashi's overall operating income in FY2015 despite contributing a much smaller share of total revenue than the company's Domestic Building Construction Business. By comparison the Domestic Building Construction business and the Overseas Construction business contributed just 16% and 8% to overall operating income. Geographic ReachAbout 77% of Obayashi's net sales came from Japan in FY2015 while the rest came from North America (23% of sales) Asia (9%) and other regions (less than 1%). The Japan-based company's overseas offices are in London San Francisco Sydney Singapore Guam Taipei Hanoi Kuala Lampur Bangkok Yangon Dubai Auckland and Jakarta. Financial PerformanceNote: Growth rates may differ after conversion to US dollars. This analysis uses financials from the company's annual report.

Obayashi's net sales and profits have been rising over the past several years as its order volumes have increased with the strengthened economy in Japan and elsewhere and as its operation margins have remained stable.

The company's net sales rose 10% to a record ¥1773 billion ($14.8 billion) mostly thanks to firm orders from both public and private sectors in the domestic construction market. Obayashi's profit jumped 10% to a record ¥28.7 billion ($240 million) thanks to increases in gross profit on completed construction contracts and the company's Real Estate Development business. Its operating cash doubled to ¥74.6 billion ($575 million) for the year thanks to higher cash earnings mostly from its domestic construction business.

Strategy

As part of of the company's Medium-Term Business Plan in 2015 and as Japan's aging and shrinking demographics continue to threaten its core domestic construction business Obayashi would continue to diversify its revenue stream and selectively expand overseas. Indeed Obayashi's overseas building and civil construction businesses have been growing faster than its domestic businesses in recent years; its total overseas business accounted for 23% of its overall net sales in FY2015 up from 19% the year before. The company's overseas construction business is known for its work on national projects such as the Taiwan High Speed Rail and the Colorado River Bridge at the Hoover Dam which used "world-renowned technological capabilities like seismic resistance and shield tunneling."After countering the downturn in Japan's construction industry Obayashi began venturing into environmental services including hazardous and radioactive waste containment. It has also committed itself to green building practices.

HISTORY

Company BackgroundWith the first wave of Japanese modernization in 1892 Yoshigoro Ohbayashi opened a small construction operation in Osaka. He won the bid for construction of the Abe Paper Mill. In 1898 he joined with partner Kamezo Shirasugi to lay the foundations for the Obayashi Corporation.

Obayashi's first big contract came in 1901 for the construction of buildings for Osaka's Fifth National Industry Fair. During the Russo-Japanese War the young corporation built 100 barracks in three weeks a feat that helped it win a contract to build Tokyo Station (completed 1914). Obayashi executives were invited to the US by the Fluor Company in the early 1920s to study advanced construction techniques. After a 1923 earthquake and firestorm leveled much of Tokyo Obayashi applied the technology it learned from Fluor to build quake-resistant fireproof buildings.

Like many Japanese companies Obayashi is quiet about its history in the years leading up to WWII and the rebuilding that followed. However the Korean War increased demand for company projects such as the Tokyo Station annex the Japan Broadcasting Corporation building and the first of 50 major dam projects.

In the 1960s Obayashi became the first Japanese construction firm to build an internal R&D facility. Its Technical Research Institute developed the OWS-Soletanche Diaphragm Wall Construction Method which it used on the New Osaka building in 1961 and has adapted to many other buildings since. In 1965 the company began its first major civil engineering project overseas doing its part in a 32-year-long excavation in Singapore that reclaimed about 3% of that country's land mass from the sea. Also that year Obayashi completed the first high-rise in Japan Yokohama's 21-story Hotel Empire.

Expo '70 in Osaka showcased Obayashi's air-membrane dome and roof lift-up method. During the 1970s the company played key roles in Japan's massive highway-building projects. In 1979 it was the first Japanese construction company to be awarded a public works contract in the US.

Obayashi completed thousands of projects during the 1980s. It helped build the Tsukuba Expo '85 and restored the Katsura Rikyu Detached Palace a national treasure.

In 1994 two former Obayashi executives were found guilty of giving a 10 million yen (about $100000) bribe to the mayor of Sendai two years earlier. The company was one of several major construction companies involved in the scandal.

In the 1990s Obayashi "mole" machines chewed through the earth to create the Tokyo Bay Aqualine tunnel. In 1996 the company developed anti-earthquake construction methods for structures built on soft ground (almost a fifth of buildings in Tokyo).

Obayashi was hard hit in 1998 and 1999 as financial crises created turmoil in Japan's construction industry. The company responded by reducing its workforce by about 5% taking advantage of economies of scale in materials purchasing and working with subcontractors to cut costs. Beefing up its project orders is another key strategy. New projects secured by Obayashi in 2000 included the Taiwan North-South High Speed Rail Project and a new head office for Japanese advertising giant Dentsu.

In 2002 the group completed the NHK Osaka Broadcasting Station and the renovation of Kobe Wing Stadium a site for part of the 2002 World Cup soccer finals. Obayashi and Kobe Steel won the contract to operate the stadium for 15 years.

Obayashi was caught in a building scandal in its home country in 2005 when it came to light that an outside architect had falsified documents regarding earthquake resistance for one of its projects a hotel. Obayashi said that the falsifications were too skillfully done to catch at the construction stage.

EXECUTIVES

President, Toru Shiraishi, age 69
EVP, Tadahiko Noguchi, age 69
EVP, Makoto Kanai, age 68
Senior Managing Executive Officer, Makoto Kishida, age 65
EVP, Shozo Harada, age 67
Senior Managing Executive Officer, Akihisa Miwa, age 64
Senior Managing Executive Officer, Kenichi Shibata, age 67
Senior Managing Executive Officer, Nao Sugiyama, age 67
Chairman, Takeo Obayashi, age 62
Auditors: Ernst & Young ShinNihon LLC

LOCATIONS

HQ: Obayashi Corp. (Japan)
2-15-2 Konan, Minato-ku, Tokyo 108-8502
Phone: (81) 3 5769 1017
Web: www.obayashi.co.jp

2014 Sales

	% of total
Japan	81
Overseas	
North America	10
Asia	8
Others	1
Total	**100**

Obayashi has operations in Cambodia China Indonesia Japan Malaysia the Philippines Singapore Taiwan Thailand the UK the US and Vietnam.

PRODUCTS/OPERATIONS

2014 Sales

	% of total
Domestic Building Construction Business	56
Domestic Civil Engineering Business	20
Overseas Construction Business	18
Real Estate Business	3
Other Business	3
Total	**100**

Selected Subsidiaries and Affiliates

Atelier G&B Co. Ltd.
E.W. Howell Co. Inc. (US)
James E. Roberts-Obayashi Corporation (50% housing projects US)
Mutsuzawa Green Co. Ltd. (golf club and restaurant operations)
Naigai Technos Corporation
Obayashi Real Estate Corporation
Obayashi Road Corporation
OC Finance Corporation
OC Real Estate Management LLC (US)
SOMA Environment Service Corporation
Taiwan Obayashi Corporation
Thai Obayashi Corporation Limited (49%)

COMPETITORS

ABB	Kumagai Gumi
Bechtel	Parsons Corporation
CSCEC	Penta-Ocean
Fluor	Construction
Hazama	Shimizu
Hyundai Engineering	TOA
and Construction	Taisei
ITOCHU	Takenaka
Kajima	

HISTORICAL FINANCIALS

Company Type: Public

Income Statement

FYE: March 31

	REVENUE ($ mil.)	NET INCOME ($ mil.)	NET PROFIT MARGIN	EMPLOYEES
03/16	15,831	564	3.6%	17,754
03/15	14,785	239	1.6%	17,090
03/14	15,624	209	1.3%	12,856
03/13	15,392	140	0.9%	12,838
03/12	15,186	62	0.4%	12,870
Annual Growth	**1.0%**	**73.3%**	**—**	**8.4%**

2016 Year-End Financials

Debt ratio: 0.1%
Return on equity: 12.3%
Cash ($ mil.): 1,467
Current ratio: 1.05
Long-term debt ($ mil.): 1,594

No. of shares (mil.): 718
Dividends
Yield: —
Payout: —
Market value ($ mil.): 6,858

	STOCK PRICE ($) FY Close	P/E High/Low		PER SHARE ($) Earnings	PER SHARE ($) Dividends	PER SHARE ($) Book Value
03/16	9.55	0	0	0.79	0.00	6.40
03/15	6.32	0	0	0.33	0.00	5.89
03/14	5.77	—	—	0.29	0.00	6.04
03/13	4.71	—	—	0.20	0.00	6.14
03/12	4.45	—	—	0.09	0.00	6.20
Annual Growth	21.0%		—	— 73.3%		— 0.8%

Ogaki Kyoritsu Bank, Ltd.

The Ogaki Kyoritsu Bank provides banking and other financial services in the Gifu prefecture in central Japan. The bank serves consumers and businesses from more than 140 domestic branch locations and from 3 international offices in Hong Kong Shanghai and New York. Services include banking credit cards credit guaranty and leasing. Ogaki Kyoritsu Bank was established in 1896.

EXECUTIVES

President, TAKASHI TSUCHIYA
Managing Director, Takeo Ushijima
Auditors: KPMG AZSA LLC

LOCATIONS

HQ: Ogaki Kyoritsu Bank, Ltd.
3-98 Kuruwa-machi, Ogaki, Gifu 503-0887
Phone: (81) 584 74 2111
Web: www.okb.co.jp

COMPETITORS

Aozora Bank
Mitsubishi UFJ
Financial Group
Shizuoka Bank

HISTORICAL FINANCIALS
Company Type: Public

Income Statement
FYE: March 31

	ASSETS ($ mil.)	NET INCOME ($ mil.)	INCOME AS % OF ASSETS	EMPLOYEES
03/16	47,992	126	0.3%	4,451
03/15	42,988	94	0.2%	4,503
03/14	47,234	92	0.2%	3,417
03/13	48,836	106	0.2%	3,346
03/12	52,878	97	0.2%	3,285
Annual Growth	(2.4%)	6.6%	—	7.9%

2016 Year-End Financials

Return on assets: 0.2%
Return on equity: 5.3%
Long-term debt ($ mil.): —
No. of shares (mil.): 347
Sales ($ mil): 1,087

Dividends
Yield: —
Payout: —
Market value ($ mil.): —

Oil and Natural Gas Corp. Ltd.

The crown jewel of India's oil and gas assets state-owned Oil & Natural Gas Corporation (ONGC) is India's largest exploration and production company. It is also the country's largest multinational corporation. In a country reliant on imported fuels ONGC which has estimated proved and probable reserves of 6.4 billion metric tonnes of oil equivalent accounts for the 78% of India's oil and gas production. ONGC operates a more than 15000-km. pipeline network and owns nearly 72% of Mangalore Refinery & Petrochemicals Ltd. (MRPL). International exploration and production subsidiary ONGC Videsh has established exploration activities in 17 countries. India's government owns 74% of ONGC.

ONGC has been searching for ways to expand its stakes in oil patches around the world.

Through its ONGC Videsh subsidiary the company joined rival China National Petroleum Corporation (CNPC) to acquire a 38% stake in Syria's largest oil company from Petro-Canada. The Syrian company Al Furat Petroleum is 62%-owned by Royal Dutch Shell. ONGC had lost out to CNPC in an earlier bid in 2005 for PetroKazakhstan.

In 2006 ONGC acquired Exxon Mobil's 30% stake in a field in the Campos Basin of Brazil for $1.4 billion. Other partners in the field are the state-owned Petrobras and Royal Dutch Shell which each own 35%. ONGC had lost out to Chinese rivals in previous bids for assets in South America.

In 2008 ONCG Videsh announced plans to acquire Imperial Energy for $2.6 billion giving it a foothold in the Siberian oil market.

EXECUTIVES

Chairman and Managing Director, Dinesh K. Sarraf, age 59
Managing Director ONGC Videsh, Narendra K. Verma
Director Technology and Field Services, Shashi Shanker
Director Offshore, Tapas K. Sengupta
Director Onshore, Ved P. Mahawar
Director Exploration, Ajay K. Dwivedi
Director Finance, A. K. Srinivasan
Auditors: Khandelwal Jain and Co.

LOCATIONS

HQ: Oil and Natural Gas Corp. Ltd.
Tel Bhavan, Dehradun, Uttaranchal 248 003
Phone: (91) 135 275 9561   **Fax:** (91) 11 2331 6413
Web: www.ongcindia.com

COMPETITORS

BP
Cairn Energy
Exxon Mobil
Occidental Petroleum
Repsol Oil & Gas
Royal Dutch Shell
TOTAL

HISTORICAL FINANCIALS
Company Type: Public

Income Statement
FYE: March 31

	REVENUE ($ mil.)	NET INCOME ($ mil.)	NET PROFIT MARGIN	EMPLOYEES
03/15	266,779	29,313	11.0%	33,185
03/14	302,058	44,144	14.6%	33,988
03/13	309,278	44,615	14.4%	32,923
03/12	298,969	55,319	18.5%	32,909
03/11	277,788	50,366	18.1%	33,273
Annual Growth	(1.0%)	(12.7%)	—	(0.1%)

2015 Year-End Financials

Debt ratio: 0.2%
Return on equity: 10.4%
Cash ($ mil.): 25,736
Current ratio: 1.06
Long-term debt ($ mil.): 76,078

No. of shares (mil.): —
Dividends
Yield: —
Payout: —
Market value ($ mil.): —

Olam International Ltd.

Olam International is likely "the man behind the curtain" when it comes to many foods. A global leader in the supply-chain management of agricultural products and food ingredients its stable of products includes confectionary and beverage ingredients (cocoa and coffee) food staples and packaged foods (rice sugar coffee cocoa and other packaged foods) fiber and wood products (cotton and wood items) and edible nuts spices and beans. The Singaporean company which has operations in more than 65 countries sources raw materials from some 200000 suppliers and then processes distributes and markets about 20 agricultural products. Olam supplies its food products to more than 13800 customers globally.

Acquisitions and joint ventures in Africa have kept the company busy. During 2012 Olam purchased Zambia's largest coffee estate Northern Coffee Corp. (NCC) for about $6 million. NCC consists of five estates on 5866 hectares on land yielding about 4500 metric tons of Arabica coffee beans annually. Previously it bought Nigerian-based Kayass Enterprises for $66.5 million. Kayass' business includes manufacturing and selling branded dairy products and beverages under brands such as Blue Goat Nature's Fresh and Yo-Jus. In early 2012 Olam paid $167 million for Titanium Holdings which owns the OK banner considered Nigeria's second largest biscuits and sugar candy maker. The purchase is anticipated to boost Olam's Packaged Foods business by improving its already significant African capacity in raw material sourcing processing logistics warehousing and distribution.

Olam has also agreed to acquire a 75% stake in Macao Commodities Trading (MCT) a provider of food ingredients (including cocoa power cocoa beans dried fruits and dairy products) to Iberia and North Africa for about euro 15 million ($20 million). Under the terms of the deal Olam has an option to acquire the remaining shares by the end of 2016. The purchase will speed Olam's entry into Spain and the larger Iberian market.

On the wood products side of business Olam acquired Timber International for about $50 million in early 2011. The purchase added more than 1 million hectares of natural hardwood forest concessions in the Republic of Congo and the Republic of Gabon to Olam's holdings. Also in 2011 the company set up an 80/20 fertilizer processing joint venture with Gabon's government. The $1.3 billion project will produce 1.3 million tons of ammonia urea per year beginning in 2014.

Olam has also focused its attention on the US. In mid-2010 the company paid $250 million in cash for ConAgra's Gilroy Foods & Flavors vegetable operations which included dehydrated garlic onion and capsicum businesses as well as its Controlled Moisture GardenFrost Redi-Made and fresh vegetable operations and half a dozen manufacturing plants in California Nevada New Mexico and Oregon. The purchase furthered Olam's goal of increasing its US dehydrated vegetable business. In 2009 the company acquired the bankrupt California tomato processor SK Foods and its subsidiary RHM Industrial/Specialty Foods. The $39 million all-cash deal increased Olam's presence in the food-ingredient dehydrated food and spice sectors and introduced the company to the US tomato-processing business. SK had a 5% global market share in tomato processing; its customers included Campbell Soup Kraft Foods and General Mills.

After acquiring an initial 14% stake in Zealand Farming Systems Uruguay (NZFSU) in 2009 Olam has been incrementally increasing its share of the dairy farm with operations in New Zealand and Uruguay. However its attempt in 2011 to buy 100% of NZFSU failed and Olam's stake topped out at about 86%.

Moving over to the big island the 2009 acquisition of 8000 hectares (about 20000 acres) of Australian almond orchards from bankrupt Timber Corporation made Olam that country's largest almond grower as well as one of the top three worldwide. Olam paid A$128 million ($111 million) in cash for the land and associated permanent water rights. The purchase is also in line with Olam's strategy to increase its value-added products. In addition Australia's proximity to the export markets of China and India is a plus for Olam in its new nut-growing venture.

In India Olam acquired Hemarus Industries a sugar mill and power plant operator for about $74 million in 2011. The purchase garnered sugar milling assets in a large sugar producing country that provides a relative cost advantage. Previously Olam acquired Giridharilal Sugar and Allied Industries in 2008. India is the world's second-largest sugar producer and #1 sugar consumer.

Olam sealed a deal valued at $38 million in late 2011 to boost its hazelnut production in Turkey. The company acquired Progida Group which boasts a total capacity of 40000 metric tons of kernel per annum and two leased cracking units in a key hazelnut growing region in Turkey.

Citibank Nominees Singapore Kewalram Singapore and DBS Nominees each own about 20% of the company. DBSN Services and Temasek Holdings each own about 15%.

EXECUTIVES

Managing Director and Global Head Spices and Vegetable Ingredients and Country Head USA, Greg Estep

Group Managing Director and CEO, Sunny G. Verghese

Managing Director and Global Head Cotton Division, Ashok Hegde

SVP and Regional Head West Africa, Ranveer S. Chauhan

Senior Managing Director and regional Head Australia Asia and North South and Central America and Russia, Sridhar Krishnan

Managing Director Cocoa, Gerard A. (Gerry) Manley

Managing Director and Global Head Risk Market Compliance and Internal Audit, Jagdish Parihar

Managing Director and Global Head Coffee Dairy Products and CFS, Vivek Verma

Managing Director Cashew and Spices, Ashok Krishen

Managing Director Africa and Middle East, Venkataramani Srivathsan

Executive Director and Group COO, A. Shekar

Managing Director and Global Head Dairy and Sugar, Joe Kenny

Managing Director and Global Head Grains, K.C. Suresh

Group CFO, Neelamani (Muthu) Muthukumar

Deputy Chairman, Kwa Chong Seng, age 69

Auditors: Ernst & Young LLP

LOCATIONS

HQ: Olam International Ltd.
9 Temasek Boulevard, #11-02 Suntec Tower Two, 038989
Phone: (65) 6339 4100 **Fax:** (65) 6339 9755
Web: www.olamgroup.com

2013 Sales

	% of total
Asia & the Middle East	41
Africa	23
Europe	21
Americas	15
Total	**100**

PRODUCTS/OPERATIONS

2013 Sales

	% of total
Food staples & packaged foods	35
Edible nuts spices & beans	25
Confectionery & beverage ingredients	22
Industrial raw materials	18
Commodity financial services	-
Total	**100**

COMPETITORS

Adani Enterprises	ITOCHU
Amsterdam Commodities	Intraco
Barry Callebaut	Louis Dreyfus
Big Heart Pet Brands	Commodities
Cargill	MGP Ingredients
ConAgra	McCormick & Company
Corbion	Nestle
Danisco A/S	Plains Cotton
Dunavant Enterprises	Sensient
FFM	Sensient Dehydrated
Fonterra	Flavors
Food Corporation of India	Staplcotn
	Tate & Lyle
Heinz	Weil Brothers Cotton
ITC	Wonderful Company

HISTORICAL FINANCIALS

Company Type: Public

Income Statement

FYE: December 31

	REVENUE ($ mil.)	NET INCOME ($ mil.)	NET PROFIT MARGIN	EMPLOYEES
12/15*	20,073	69	0.3%	62,500
06/14	15,925	487	3.1%	23,000
06/13	16,527	286	1.7%	22,638
06/12	13,513	292	2.2%	18,000
06/11	12,962	349	2.7%	17,000
Annual Growth	**9.1%**	**(27.5%)**	**—**	**29.7%**

*Fiscal year change

2015 Year-End Financials

Debt ratio: 41.8%
Return on equity: 1.4%
Cash ($ mil.): 1,546
Current ratio: 1.61
Long-term debt ($ mil.): 4,797

No. of shares (mil.): —
Dividends
 Yield: 5.7%
 Payout: 1,544.3%
Market value ($ mil.): —

	STOCK PRICE ($) FY Close	P/E High/Low	PER SHARE ($) Earnings	Dividends	Book Value
12/15*	25.81	986808	0.02	1.47	1.31
06/14	40.55	158 92	0.19	1.23	1.38
06/13	25.60	230147	0.11	1.20	1.22
06/12	29.08	285163	0.12	0.71	1.12
06/11	44.00	271203	0.15	0.36	0.82
Annual Growth	**(12.5%)**	— —	**(33.3%)**	**32.3%**	**9.8%**

*Fiscal year change

Old Mutual Plc

The name belies its demutualized status: Financial services group Old Mutual provides banking insurance and asset management services in about 30 nations in southern Africa Europe Asia and the Americas. Founded in 1845 Old Mutual owns a majority stake of South Africa's Nedbank Group which provides commercial banking finance investment banking and other services. It also owns Old Mutual (US) Holdings also known as Old Mutual Asset Management (US) or OMAM (US). Skandia Insurance offers insurance products and mutual funds primarily in the UK and Sweden. Old Mutual has some £262 billion (some $357 billion) in funds under management.

Operations

Old Mutual operates through several business lines: long-term savings and investments US asset management banking and short-term insurance. Long-term savings and investments accounted for 70% of the company's fiscal 2012 revenue.

Old Mutual's Asset Management arm offers clients access to more than 115 investment strategies through its affiliated investment firms.

Geographic Reach

London-based Old Mutual generated more than 40% of its fiscal 2012 revenue from emerging markets. This includes business in Africa operations in Colombia and Mexico and joint ventures in India and China.

Sales and Marketing

The financial firm boasts more than 14 million customers worldwide. Clients buy products directly from Old Mutual or indirectly through an intermediary such as an independent financial advisor. Old Mutual reaches out to customers through a combined strategy of tied agents and independent financial advisors as well as via the Internet and call center functionality.

It sponsored the England rugby team's 2016 Autumn International series against Argentina Australia Fiji and South Africa.

Strategy

Old Mutual aims to expand in South Africa Africa and other selected emerging markets. It's also working to develop and grow its Old Mutual Wealth and US Asset Management businesses even including a partial IPO of its US Asset Management unit when economic conditions are favorable. For its Nedbank business Old Mutual is focused on boosting non-interest revenue growing the retail business via client-centered strategies and effective risk management and shifting the focus of its portfolio on profit-enhancing products and services.

In 2016 the company announced plans to split its four primary businesses —Old Mutual Emerging Markets Old Mutual Wealth Nedbank and OM Asset Management. The phased split a move to exit the holding company structure and allow each business freer access to the capital markets should be complete by the end of 2018.

The company fully exited continental Europe in early 2017 with the sale of Old Mutual Wealth Italy to Phlavia Investimenti which is owned by private investment firm Cinven. The disposal comes as part of Old Mutual's strategy of debt reduction and refocusing on core operations.

Mergers and Acquisitions

Old Mutual Wealth acquired Cheshire-based financial advice first JW Financial Planning in late 2016 adding over £100 million towards Old Mutual's goal of £1 billion in assets under advice.

HISTORY

Company Background

Old Mutual was founded in 1845 as the Mutual Life Assurance Society of the Cape of Good Hope to sell life insurance in the Cape Colony. When South Africa gained self-governance from the UK in 1910 Old Mutual chairman John Merriman became the colony's first premier. In 1927 the company made its first international expansion into Zimbabwe (then called Rhodesia).

Life insurance remained the firm's sole line of business until 1948 when it acquired a controlling stake in what would become Mutual & Federal a general insurer. To better administer its mutual fund and trust businesses the firm formed the South African Mutual Unit Trust Company in 1966.

Old Mutual diversified in 1986 buying a controlling stake in the Nedcor banking group. Also that year the firm made its first major acquisition outside Africa buying UK life insurer Providence Capitol. In 1995 the firm expanded into Hong Kong and the US where it opened Old Mutual Investment Advisers in Boston. Seeking a way into the UK financial services market the company acquired asset managers Capel-Cure Myers and Albert E Sharp in 1997 and 1998 respectively merging them into Capel-Cure Sharp.

The firm further globalized its asset management operations in 1999 establishing an alliance with Japanese insurer Sumitomo Life to cross-market trust and investment services. Also that year its Nedcor banking subsidiary launched a hostile takeover bid for Standard Bank Investment Corporation (of which Old Mutual already owned 20%); the merger would have created South Africa's largest bank but government regulators nixed the deal.

Old Mutual demutualized in 1999 listing on both the London and Johannesburg stock exchanges. In 2000 the company sold its UK insurance operations to XL Mid Ocean Reinsurance and Century Group then acquired UK brokerage Gerrard Group and started an infrastructure investment joint venture with Australia's Macquarie Bank. Old Mutual also bought US-based United Asset Management (selling its Murray Johnstone Holdings subsidiary to Aberdeen Asset Management). Meanwhile Nedcor (now Nedbank) bought 50.1% of Imperial Bank a South African bank with a large vehicle finance business.

While the firm's Old Mutual (US) operations proved successful other areas of growth were less salutary. Three years after forming Gerrard Limited in 2000 as part of a bid to boost the UK business the asset manager was sold to Barclays.

Old Mutual gained control of insurer and mutual fund manager Skandia Insurance in 2006 through a nearly £4 billion ($7 billion) hostile takeover bid. The acquisition brought more life insurance asset management and banking to Old Mutual and gave it deeper access into Asia Europe Latin America and the UK.Satisfied with the results of its asset management operations in the

US the company began expanding its asset management services in South Africa and the UK. In a shift from operating its businesses regionally the company took to grouping them by their primary operations.

EXECUTIVES

Group Finance Director, Ingrid Johnson, age 49
Group Chief Executive and Director, J. Bruce Hemphill, age 53
Group Strategy Director, Ian Gladman
Group Risk Officer, Sue Kean
CEO Africa, Jonas Mushosho
Chairman, Patrick H. O'Sullivan, age 67
Auditors: KPMG LLP

LOCATIONS

HQ: Old Mutual Plc
  5th Floor, Millennium Bridge House, 2 Lambeth Hill, London EC4V 4GG
Phone:
Web: www.oldmutual.com

Selected Subsidiaries
Old Mutual (South Africa) Ltd
Old Mutual Africa Holdings (Pty) Ltd
Old Mutual Life Assurance Company (South Africa) Ltd
Old Mutual Investment Group (South Africa) (Pty) Ltd
Nedbank Group Ltd
Nedbank Ltd
Mutual & Federal Insurance Company Ltd
Old Mutual Life Assurance Company (Namibia) Ltd
Old Mutual (US) Holdings Inc
Old Mutual (Bermuda) Ltd
Acadian Asset Management LLC
Barrow Hanley Mewhinney & Strauss LLC
Rogge Global Partners plc
OM Group (UK) Ltd
Old Mutual Wealth Management Limited

PRODUCTS/OPERATIONS

2012 Revenue

	% of total
Long-term savings	
Emerging markets	43
Old mutual wealth	27
NedBank	25
M&F	3
US Asset Management	2
Total	**100**

COMPETITORS

Absa	FirstRand
Alliance Trust	Investec
Allianz	PineBridge Investments
Aviva	Russell
Fidelity Worldwide	Sanlam
Investment	Standard Bank Group

HISTORICAL FINANCIALS
Company Type: Public

Income Statement
FYE: December 31

	ASSETS ($ mil.)	NET INCOME ($ mil.)	INCOME AS % OF ASSETS	EMPLOYEES
12/15	197,910	909	0.5%	64,043
12/14	222,470	908	0.4%	61,583
12/13	231,908	1,165	0.5%	56,812
12/12	231,298	1,890	0.8%	54,368
12/11	250,861	1,030	0.4%	57,430
Annual Growth	(5.8%)	(3.1%)	—	2.8%

2015 Year-End Financials

Return on assets: 0.4%
Return on equity: 8.7%
Long-term debt ($ mil.): —
No. of shares (mil.): —
Sales ($ mil): 20,078

Dividends
Yield: 0.0%
Payout: 539.3%
Market value ($ mil.): —

OMV AG (Austria)

Oil and chemicals group OMV is Austria's largest industrial company. A leading oil and gas company in Central and Eastern Europe it explores for natural gas and crude oil; refines crude oil; and imports transports and stores gas. In 2014 OMV reported proved reserves of 1.1 billion barrels of oil equivalent; it produced about 309000 barrels of oil equivalent per day and sold 13 billion cu. ft. of gas. The bulk of OMV's sales come from refining and marketing with the company operating three refineries and more than 4100 gas stations in 11 countries. OMV is focusing on growing its exploration and production assets.

Geographic Reach

OMV gets the bulk of its oil and gas from Austria and Romania but it also has assets in Africa Norway and the UK. The company operates refineries in Schwechat (Austria) Burghausen (Germany) and Petrobrazi (Romania).

Operations

The company operates in three major segments. OMV Exploration and Production's core countries in Romania and Austria OMV is focusing on reducing the natural decline and on enhancing the recovery rates from mature fields. It is looking to find new growth areas within the Caspian Middle East and Africa regions.

OMV Gas and Power ensures the supply of natural gas to its customers via a 2000 km gas pipeline in Austria. Its natural gas network serving about 90% of Austria's natural gas demand draws gas supplies from Russia Norway and Germany as well as from domestic reserves. Austria's gas market now dominated by OMV is slated for full competition and OMV is among state-controlled companies set for full privatization.

The company operates a gas pipeline network in Austria and owns gas storage facilities with a capacity of 2.7 bcm (30 TWh).

OMV Refining and Marketing serves about 1.5 million people a day through retail gas stations in 11 countries and is the market leader in Central and South Eastern Europe.

A fourth segment OMV Solutions is the integrated shared service center for all of the OMV Group companies. Its portfolio spans IT financial services and human resources administration.

Sales and Operations

The company sells its product through industrial customers local distribution companies and wholesalers which focus on multi-country customers.

Financial Performance

OMV's revenues decreased by 15% in 2014 primarily due to decrease in gas and power sales due to the impairments of the Brazi power plant in Romania and the goodwill related to the Petrol Ofisi acquisition.

The company's net income declined by 69% in 2014 due to lower revenues and changes in interest expenses.

	STOCK PRICE ($) FY Close	P/E High/Low	PER SHARE ($)		
			Earnings	Dividends	Book Value
12/15	21.84	223152	0.18	0.98	2.01
12/14	23.50	208169	0.18	0.97	2.36
12/13	25.40	199152	0.23	0.90	2.45
12/12	23.00	92 58	0.37	0.19	2.58
12/11	16.88	139 93	0.18	0.00	2.26
Annual Growth	6.7%	— —	0.0%	—	(2.9%)

OMV's cash inflow decreased by 11% that year primarily due to lower net income and changes in working capital as a result of changes in short-term provisions.

Strategy

To raise cash in 2016 OMV sold its 49% minority stake in Gas Connect Austria to Allianz and Snam for $627.26 million.

Reorganizing to be more operationally efficient in 2015 OMV integrated the Gas and Power and Refining and Marketing business segments. In 2014 the company sold its 45% stake in the German Bayernoil refinery network. The remaining OMV refineries are integrated into crude and/or petrochemicals with the associated competitive advantages in its core markets. Exploration and production is the growth driver of OMV. As part of OMV's strategy to build up a new exploration business in the region of Sub-Saharan Africa in 2014 the company signed an agreement with Tullow Oil an exploration-led company successful in finding and developing new resources in Africa. The first steps were taken with entries into offshore Madagascar Gabon and Namibia.

In 2013 the company announced plans to direct more than two-thirds of future investments towards exploration and production of oil and gas. It also plans to grow its integrated natural gas assets and restructure its downstream business by selling non-core refining and marketing assets.

Mergers and Acquisitions

As part of OMV's strategy of focusing on exploration and production in politically stable markets in 2013 the company acquired assets in Norway and the UK (West of Shetland area) from Statoil. It bought 19% in the producing Gullfaks field and 24% in the Gudrun field; both offshore oil and gas fields on the Norwegian Continental Shelf. In addition OMV took over 30% in Rosebank and 5.88% in Schiehallion both located west of the Shetland Islands and assets where OMV already holds a stake in.

Ownership

OMV's largest shareholders are Austrian state holding company ÖIAG (32%) and the International Petroleum Investment Company (IPIC) of Abu Dhabi (20%).

HISTORY

Company Background

Oil exploration began in Austria in the 1920s largely as joint ventures with foreign firms such as Shell and Socony-Vacuum. Full-scale production did not get underway until 1938 when the Anschluss (the absorption of Austria by Germany) paved the way for Germany to exploit Austria's natural resources to fuel its growing war machine. In the division of spoils following WWII Russia gained control of Austria's oil reserves.

The Russian-administered oil assets were transferred to the new Austrian government in 1955 which authorized the company Österreichische Mineralölverwaltung (ÖMG) in 1956 to control state oil assets. ÖMG state-controlled by the Austrian Mineral Oil Administration set about building a major refinery in 1960 and acquiring marketing companies Martha and ÖROP in 1965.

In 1968 ÖMG became the first Western company to sign a natural gas supply contract with Russia. In 1974 the company commissioned the Trans-Austria Gas Pipeline which enabled the supply of natural gas to Italy. That year ÖMG changed its name to ÖMV Aktiengesellschaft (ÖMV became OMV in 1995 for international markets).

During the 1970s OMV expanded its crude supply arrangements tapping supplies from Iran Iraq Libya and other Middle Eastern countries. It moved into oil and gas exploration in the mid-1980s forming OMV Libya (acquiring 25% of Occidental's Libyan production) and OMV UK.

With Austria moving toward increasing privatization in 1987 about 15% of OMV's shares were sold to the public. The government sold another 10% two years later. In 1989 OMV acquired PCD Polymere. With the aim of merging state-owned oil and chemical activities OMV acquired Chemie Linz in 1990. The company also opened its first OMV-branded service station that year. In 1994 OMV reorganized itself as an integrated oil and gas group based in Central Europe with international exploration and production activities and with other operations in the chemical and petrochemical sectors.

In 1995 OMV acquired TOTAL-AUSTRIA expanding its service stations by 59. The company introduced OMV lubricants to the Greek market in 1996. It also expanded its OMV service station network in Hungary to 66 stations after acquiring 31 Q8 (Kuwait) sites. In 1997 the Stroh Company's retail network in Austria was merged into OMV.

Expanding its retail network even farther OMV acquired BP's retail network in the Czech Republic Slovakia and Hungary in 1998. It also sold its stake in Chemie Linz and acquired a 25% stake in major European polyolefin producer Borealis which in turn acquired PCD Polymere. In 1999 the company pushed its retail network into Bulgaria and Romania. That year OMV also acquired Australian company Cultus Petroleum.

OMV and Shell agreed to develop North Sea fields together in 2000. That year OMV also formed a joint venture with Italy's Edison International to explore in Vietnam and acquired more than 9% of Hungarian rival MOL. It upped that stake to 10% in 2001.

In 2002 OMV opened its first gas station in Serbia and Montenegro. It also increased its German gas station count from 79 to 151 with the purchase of 32 units from Royal Dutch Shell and 40 stations from Martin GmbH & Co.

In 2003 the company acquired Preussag Energie's exploration and production assets for $320 million. That year the company moved into Bosnia-Herzegovina opening nine gas stations.

During 2004 the company bought up 51% of Romania's Petrom making it the top oil and gas producer in Central Europe. As part of the deal OMV chose to divest itself of its quarter-chunk of Rompetrol.

In 2006 Russian energy giant Gazprom signed long-term contracts for gas deliveries with OMV.

In a major consolidation move in 2006 OMV agreed to buy Austrian power firm Verbund for $17 billion but the move was rebuffed by government regulators. The next year the company announced plans to merge with Hungary's energy powerhouse MOL but those plans were called off as well due to European Commission regulatory concerns in 2008.

After plans to merge with Hungary's MOL went south OMV the next year sold its 21% stake in it to Russian oil company Surgutneftegas for euro 1.4 billion ($1.85 billion). Also in 2009 in keeping with its focus on retail markets in the Danube region southeastern Europe and the Black Sea region OMV sold subsidiary OMV Italia; San Marco Petroli acquired the network of about 100 gas stations in the northern Italian region of Triveneto.

OMV has been disposing of some of its heating oil operations. In 2008 it unloaded Bayern GmbH and it plans to sell its OMV Wärme Vertriebsgmbh by the end of 2010. At that point the sale of heating oil to private clients will be handled by partners but OMV will continue to service corporate customers.

Eyeing new areas of exploration that year OMV also acquired a 10% stake in Pearl Petroleum giving it access to gas-condensate fields in Iraq.

In 2010 the company boosted its share of Turkey-based oil products company Petrol Ofisi (renamed OMV Petrol Ofisi) from 42% to 96% by acquiring a 54% stake from Doğan Holding for about $1.4 billion. The deal gave OMV access to not only Turkey but the Caspian region and the Middle East.

The acquisition of full control (in 2010) of Petrol Ofisi Turkey's leading filling station and retail business with the only nationwide filling station network in the country (approximately 2300 stations) built a strategic bridge in the growth market of Turkey.

In a further push to grow in the Middle East in 2011 the company acquired two Tunisia-based exploration and production units from Pioneer Natural Resources for $866 million. It also boosted its footprint in Pakistan acquiring Petronas Carigali (Pakistan) Ltd. in 2011.

In 2012 the company sold its gas station subsidiary in Croatia. That year it boosted it E&P assets entering Abu Dhabi and acquiring natural gas assets in Norway.

EXECUTIVES

CEO, Rainer Seele, age 56
Executive Board Member Downstream (Refining Gas and Power and Marketing), Manfred Leitner
CFO, Reinhard Florey, age 52
Executive Board Member Upstream, Johann Pleininger, age 54
Deputy Chairman, Wolfgang C. Berndt, age 74
Chairman, Peter Oswald, age 54
Auditors: Ernst & Young Wirtschaftspruefungsgesellschaft m.b.H

LOCATIONS

HQ: OMV AG (Austria)
Trabrennstrasse 6-8, Vienna 1020
Phone: (43) 1 40440 0   **Fax:** (43) 1 40440 27900
Web: www.omv.com

COMPETITORS

BP	MOL
Eni	PKN ORLEN
Exxon Mobil	Royal Dutch Shell
Hellenic Petroleum	Unipetrol

HISTORICAL FINANCIALS
Company Type: Public

Income Statement
FYE: December 31

	REVENUE ($ mil.)	NET INCOME ($ mil.)	NET PROFIT MARGIN	EMPLOYEES
12/15	24,536	(1,198)	—	24,124
12/14	43,652	433	1.0%	25,505
12/13	58,393	1,600	2.7%	26,863
12/12	56,213	1,796	3.2%	28,658
12/11	44,046	1,375	3.1%	29,800
Annual Growth	(13.6%)	—	—	(5.1%)

2015 Year-End Financials

Debt ratio: 16.9%	No. of shares (mil.): 326
Return on equity: (-9.4%)	Dividends
Cash ($ mil.): 1,468	Yield: 3.5%
Current ratio: 1.06	Payout: —
Long-term debt ($ mil.): 5,001	Market value ($ mil.): 9,380

	STOCK PRICE ($) FY Close	P/E High/Low		PER SHARE ($) Earnings	Dividends	Book Value
12/15	28.74	—	—	(3.67)	1.02	38.95
12/14	26.55	39	22	1.32	1.28	43.47
12/13	47.79	15	11	4.89	1.16	49.01
12/12	36.70	9	7	5.50	1.05	48.09
12/11	30.38	13	8	4.36	0.96	43.52
Annual Growth	(1.4%)	—	—	—	1.5%	(2.7%)

ONEX Corp (Canada)

Investment firm Onex holds equity interests in over a dozen companies across several industries worldwide. It mainly invests in electronics manufacturing services and health care imaging companies but also in companies that deal in building products health and human services insurance and customer care services. While large-cap private equity is its biggest focus Onex also invests in debt and credit securities and real estate including real estate investment trusts commercial real estate loans and residential developments. Its ONCAP family of private equity funds invests in mid-cap firms. Altogether Onex has some $11.8 billion in third-party capital under management and about $22 billion in all.

Operations

The company's portfolio includes direct interests in electronics manufacturer Celestica and business process outsourcer Sitel in addition to minority stakes in more than a dozen companies including healthcare companies such as Res-Care Genesis Healthcare and Carestream Health. Onex also owns US insurance brokerage firm USI.

Geographic Reach

Onex is stationed in Ontario Canada and has other offices in London and New York. The US accounted for more than 50% of its revenue in 2014 while the rest came from Europe (21%) the Asia and Oceania region (17%) and Canada (5%).

Financial Performance

Onex's revenues have been rising in recent years with income-boosting company acquisitions. The firm has been struggling with years of losses however as its revenues have been eaten up by high cost of sales and operating expenses combined with amortization expenses on its assets. The firm's revenue fell by 29% to $19.8 billion in 2014 mostly due to income lost after it sold The Warranty Group Spirit AeroSystems and Skilled Healthcare Group during the year.

Revenue declines in 2014 caused Onex to suffer a net loss of $115 million though losses improved from $354 million in 2013 as the firm's operating costs declined. Onex's operating cash levels fell 38% to $989 million mostly due to unfavorable changes in working capital items and lower cash earnings.

Strategy

When considering acquisitions Onex seeks out growth investments restructurings and subsidiaries or divisions being sold by large corporations. It prefers to take a controlling position in its holdings which enables it to make strategic decisions though Onex does not usually get involved in the day-to-day activities of its companies.Some of Onex's recent company acquisitions and investments include: its $4.6 billion-purchase of Swiss packaging company SIG Combibloc in 2015; its 2015 $680 million-acquisition of UK-based mission-critical military equipment provider Survitec;

its late-2014 $1.33 billion-purchase of risk and claims management and managed care services provider York Risk Services; its $102 million investment in a 46% stake in Mavis Tire Supply LLC (Mavis Discount Tire) in late 2014; and its late-2014 $204-million investment for a 40% stake in Advanced Integration Technology which provides automation and tooling maintenance services and aircraft components to the aerospace industry. Regarding add-on acquisitions in 2014 Onex subsidiary USI agreed to acquire more than 40 insurance brokerage and consulting locations nationwide from financial services company Wells Fargo & Company; while subsidiary Schumacher Group acquired Hospital Physician Partners the fourth-largest provider of emergency and hospital medicine clinical staffing services.

Onex has historically been successful with its private equity exits as well. Since its founding in 1984 the company has made 480 acquisitions with a total value of $53 billion and has generated an average of 3 times its original investment representing a 28% gross compound IRR on realized substantially realized and publicly-traded investments. During 2014 the firm and its partners realized $6.1 billion in proceeds (a record year for realizations) after selling its remaining shares in: Allison Transmission Holdings for net proceeds of $770 million (from an original investment of $237 million); Spirit AeroSystems for net proceeds of $1 billion (original investment: $108 million); Gates Corporation for net proceeds of $727 million (original investment: $315 million); The Warranty Group for net proceeds of $509 million (original investment: $157 million); and Mister Car Wash for net proceeds of $168 million (original investment: $23 million).

EXECUTIVES

Senior Managing Director, Seth M. Mersky, age 56
Senior Managing Director, Anthony Munk, age 56
Managing Director and CFO, Ewout R. (Eve) Heersink, age 66
Senior Managing Director, Robert M. (Bobby) Le Blanc, age 49
VP Taxation, Christopher A. (Chris) Govan
Director Information Technology, Jason MacKenzie
President and CEO, Michael Dana
Auditors: PricewaterhouseCoopers LLP

LOCATIONS

HQ: ONEX Corp (Canada)
49th Floor, 161 Bay Street, P.O. Box 700, Toronto, Ontario M5J 2S1
Phone: 416 362-7711   Fax: 416 362-6803
Web: www.onex.com

2014 Sales

	% of total
United States	51
Europe	21
Asia & Oceania	17
Canada	5
Other	6
Total	100

PRODUCTS/OPERATIONS

2014 Sales

	% of total
Electronic manufacturing services	28
Building Products	18
Health care	12
Health and human services	9
Customer support services	7
Insurnace provider	6
Other	20
Total	100

Selected Holdings

Carestream Health
Celestica
Center for Diagnostic Imaging
Hawker Beechcraft
JELD-WEN
Res-Care
RSI Home Products
Sitel
Skilled Healthcare Group
Spirit AeroSystems
Sport Supply Group
Tomkins
The Warranty Group

COMPETITORS

Berkshire Hathaway	HM Capital Partners
Blackstone Group	Heico Companies
Brookfield Asset Management	Investor AB
	KKR
Caisse de dep°t et placement du Quebec	Power Financial
	Street Capital
Clayton Dubilier & Rice	TPG
	Thomas H. Lee Partners

HISTORICAL FINANCIALS

Company Type: Public

Income Statement

FYE: December 31

	REVENUE ($ mil.)	NET INCOME ($ mil.)	NET PROFIT MARGIN	EMPLOYEES
12/15	19,681	(573)	—	0
12/14	19,793	(115)	—	192,000
12/13	27,809	(354)	—	232,000
12/12	27,443	(121)	—	250,000
12/11	24,642	1,327	5.4%	246,000
Annual Growth	(5.5%)	—	—	—

2015 Year-End Financials

Debt ratio: 50.4%	No. of shares (mil.): 105
Return on equity: (-178.2%)	Dividends
Cash ($ mil.): 2,313	Yield: 0.0%
Current ratio: 1.44	Payout: —
Long-term debt ($ mil.): 17,643	Market value ($ mil.): 6,521

	STOCK PRICE ($) FY Close	P/E High/Low		PER SHARE ($) Earnings	Dividends	Book Value
12/15	61.52	—	—	(5.36)	0.18	(1.54)
12/14	58.36	—	—	(1.04)	0.16	7.40
12/13	53.95	—	—	(3.12)	0.13	10.35
12/12	42.27	—	—	(1.05)	0.11	14.18
12/11	33.11	3	3	11.31	0.11	15.80
Annual Growth	16.8%	—	—	—	12.8%	—

Orange

For many in Europe and elsewhere the telecom landscape has an Orange glow. Formerly France Telecom Orange provides fixed-line and mobile voice and data services to consumers and commercial clients around the world. The company serves some 250 million customers in about 30 countries. It is a leading European wireless operator and broadband service provider with more than 190 million mobile customers and some 16 million broadband subscribers. Orange's services for corporate clients are provided by its Orange Business Services unit which offers a wide range of managed business networking and data services. The company had been coalescing around its Orange brand since 2006 culminating in the mid-2013 name change.

Geographic Reach

Orange divides up its primary business –mobile and fixed-line telephony along with Internet access services –by region with France comprising nearly half of total operations. Spain and Portugal are its other two major regions with these services. The rest of the world makes up nearly a fifth of total revenues. The remaining business about 15% of sales is largely the company's enterprise services operations.

Sales and Marketing

Most of Orange's sales come through its own retail locations as well as other retail outlets In France the company operates nearly 550 stores.

Financial Performance

Orange reported its seventh straight year of declining revenue in 2014 with sales off 15% for the year. The company has been hit by pricing competition diminishing demand for legacy landline services and regulation of data transfer prices for customers traveling abroad. Net income drop 56% in 2014 on lower revenue and higher taxes. Cash flow from operations rose slightly for 2014 from 2013.

Strategy

In 2015 Orange unveiled Essentials 2020 a strategic plan to provide customers will a full spectrum of digital communications services. A top goal is to triple average data speeds on fixed and mobile networks in four years ending 2018. The company is investing in fiber networks in France Spain and Poland. In France for example the company intends to increase the number of homes it serves with high-speed service from 3.6 million in 2014 to 12 million in 2018 and to 20 million in 2022.

The company's near-term strategy includes looking beyond France for new business including doubling revenues in Africa and the Middle East by 2015 and expanding in Europe. That expansion will not only benefit Orange's core business but also its enterprise services success.

Mergers and Acquisitions

Orange acquired Jazztel in Spain making Orange the second biggest fixed-line broadband operator and a significant element Spain's mobile market.

HISTORY

Early History

Shortly before he abdicated King Louis Philippe laid the groundwork for France's state-owned telegraphic service. Established in 1851 the operation became part of the French Post Office in the 1870s about the time Alexander Graham Bell invented the telephone. The French government licensed three private companies to provide telegraph service and during the 1880s they merged into the Societe Generale de Telephones (SGT). In 1883 the country's first exchange was initiated in Rheims. Four years later an international circuit was installed connecting Paris and Brussels. The government nationalized SGT in 1889.

By the turn of the century France had more than 60000 phone lines and in 1924 a standardized telephone was introduced. Long-distance service improved with underground cabling and phone exchanges in Paris and other leading cities became automated during the 1930s.

WWII proved a major setback to the French government's telephone operations Direction Generale des Telecommunications (DGT) because a large part of its equipment was destroyed or damaged. For the next two decades France lagged behind other nations in telephony infrastructure development. An exception to this technological stagnation was Centre National d'Etudes des

Telecommunications (CNET) the research laboratory formed in 1944 that eventually became France Telecom's research arm.

In 1962 DGT was a key player in the first intercontinental television broadcast between the US and France via a Telstar satellite. The company began to catch up with its peers when it developed a digital phone system in the mid-1970s. In 1974 CNET was instrumental in the launch of France's first experimental communications satellite. In another technological advance DGT began replacing its paper directories with the innovative Minitel online terminals in 1980.

The French government created France Telecom in 1988. In 1993 France Telecom and Deutsche Telekom (DT) teamed up to form the Global One international telecommunications venture and Sprint joined the next year. Global One was formally launched in 1996. Also that year France Telecom began providing Internet access though Minitel still reigned as the country's top online service.

In 1997 the government sold about 20% of France Telecom to the public. With Europe's state telephone monopolies ending in 1998 France Telecom reorganized and brought prices in line with those of its competitors.

EXECUTIVES

Deputy CEO European Operations, Gervais Pellissier, age 57

EVP Group Human Resources, Bruno Mettling, age 58

Chairman and CEO, Stephane Richard, age 55

EVP Group General Secretary and France Carriers Division, Pierre Louette, age 54

Deputy CEO Customer Experience and Mobile Financial Services, Marc Rennard, age 59

SEVP Communication and Brand, Beatrice Mandine

Deputy CEO Chief Finance and Strategy Officer, Ramon Fernandez, age 49

SEVP Corporate Social Responsibility Diversity Partnerships and Philanthropy, Christine Albanel, age 61

Deputy CEO Orange Business Services (OBS), Thierry Bonhomme, age 60

CEO Orange Spain, Laurent Paillassot

SEVP Human Resources, Jer´me Barre

SEVP Orange France, Fabienne Dulac

CEO Orange Healthcare, Elie Lobel

CEO Orange Egypt, Jean Marc Harion

SEVP Innovation Marketing and Technologies, Mari-No ‹lle Jego-Laveissi ¨re, age 48

CEO Orange Belgium, Michael Trabbia

Auditors: KPMG SA

LOCATIONS

HQ: Orange
78 rue Olivier de Serres, Paris 75015
Phone: (33) 1 44 44 22 22
Web: www.orange.com

2014 Sales

	% of total
France	47
Enterprise	18
Spain	15
Poland	9
Rest of the world	7
International carriers & shared services	4
Total	**100**

PRODUCTS/OPERATIONS

Selected Operations

Audience and advertising (Internet advertising business)
Content (partnerships with content providers and development of related technology platforms)

Enterprise communication services (communication services to companies)
Health (services to the health care industry)
Home communication services (residential communication services especially fixed-line broadband)
Personal communication services (communication services for individuals using mobile devices)

COMPETITORS

AT&T	Sky plc
BT	TalkTalk
Bouygues	Tele2
COLT Group	Telecom Italia
Cable & Wireless	Telefnica
Deutsche Telekom	Telefnica Europe
Equinix Group	Tiscali
HP Enterprise Services	Unisys
IBM Global Services	Virgin Mobile
KPN	Vivendi
Maroc Telecom	Vodafone
Proximus	

HISTORICAL FINANCIALS

Company Type: Public

Income Statement

FYE: December 31

	REVENUE ($ mil.)	NET INCOME ($ mil.)	NET PROFIT MARGIN	EMPLOYEES
12/15	43,784	2,888	6.6%	0
12/14	47,684	1,124	2.4%	156,233
12/13	56,063	2,578	4.6%	165,488
12/12	57,009	1,080	1.9%	170,531
12/11	58,438	5,038	8.6%	171,949
Annual Growth	(7.0%)	(13.0%)	—	—

2015 Year-End Financials

Debt ratio: —
Return on equity: 8.7%
Cash ($ mil.): 4,867
Current ratio: 0.66
Long-term debt ($ mil.): —

No. of shares (mil.): —
Dividends
Yield: 4.0%
Payout: 66.6%
Market value ($ mil.): —

	STOCK PRICE ($) FY Close	P/E High/Low	PER SHARE ($) Earnings	Dividends	Book Value
12/15	16.63	20 15	1.00	0.67	12.71
12/14	16.92	57 34	0.38	0.92	13.56
12/13	12.35	21 14	0.98	0.68	12.77
12/12	11.05	52 34	0.41	1.84	12.19
12/11	15.66	15 10	1.89	1.72	13.54
Annual Growth (1.6%)	1.5%	—	— (14.7%)	(21.0%)	

Orix Corp. (Japan)

An international financing leviathan ORIX is one of Japan's largest public financial services firms. The company finances leases of everything from computers and measuring equipment to aircraft and ships; it rents out some 30000 different items and is adding more. ORIX also engages in consumer and corporate finance investment banking brokerage car rental and property development and management services in Japan and more than 35 other countries. Its retail offerings include banking life insurance credit cards and trust services. ORIX even has its own professional baseball team the Kobe-based ORIX Buffaloes.

OperationsORIX operates six main business segments: Corporate Financial Services which is the lending leasing and fee business; Maintenance

Leasing which provides automobile leasing and rentals car sharing and test and measurement instruments as well as IT-related equipment rentals and leasing; Real Estate which focuses on development rental and financing facility operation REIT asset management and real estate investment advisory services; Investment and Operation which invests in environment and energy-related business principal investment and loan servicing (asset recovery); Retail which offers life insurance banking and card loans; and Overseas Business which provides leasing lending investment in bonds investment banking asset management and ship- and aircraft-related financing.

Overall ORIX generated 35% of its total revenue from services income in fiscal 2015 (ended March 31) while sales of goods and real estate contributed another 20%. Life insurance premiums (and related investment income) and operating lease income each made up more than 15% of revenues. The remainder of revenues came from finance revenues (9%) and investment gains and dividends (3%).

ORIX USA acts as the holding company for the firm's operations in the US. Among its holdings are Los Angeles-based investment bank Houlihan Lokey which specializes in middle-market mergers and acquisitions. The firm also owns Japanese condominium builder DAIKYO.

Geographic Reach

The company operates nearly 1300 offices in Japan (where it earns more than 70% of its revenues) and 540 more overseas. The Americas is ORIX's second-largest market comprising another 10% of total revenues.

Sales and Marketing

ORIX has ramped up its advertising spend in recent years. It spent ¥20329 million ($215.7 million) on advertising in fiscal 2015 (ended March 31) compared to ¥15270 million ($162 million) and ¥11579 million ($122.9 million) in FY2014 and FY2013 respectively.

Financial Performance

Note: Growth rates may differ after conversion to US dollars.

ORIX's revenues and profits have been rising in recent years thanks to its growing life insurance real estate and services businesses coupled with declining interest expenses as its debt interest has been shrinking.

The firm's revenue jumped by 58% to ¥2174.3 billion ($21 billion) in fiscal 2015 (ended March 31) mostly thanks to exceptional growth across its Retail Investment and Operation and Overseas divisions. The firm's Investment and Operation division (its largest) revenues swelled by 181% thanks to continued growth in environment and energy business with government support newly acquired subsidiaries and the consolidation of its DAIKYO real estate builder subsidiary. Its Retail division (its 2nd largest) nearly doubled its revenues thanks to a gain on the sale of shares of Monex Group acquired revenue from its acquisition of Hartford Life Insurance KK an increase in finance revenue from the banking business and policy number growth in the life insurance business. Its Overseas Business revenues rose by 36% thanks to higher fee revenues from operations in the US and by the acquired asset management business of Robeco.

Higher revenue in FY2015 drove ORIX's net income higher by 25% to a record ¥234.95 billion (around $2 billion). The firm's operating cash fell by 46% to ¥257.6 billion (more than $2 billion) despite higher earnings mostly due to a net decrease in policy liabilities and policy account balances after its consolidation of Hartford Life Insurance KK.

Strategy

ORIX reiterated in 2015 that it plans to strengthen its non-finance business in the US expand its leasing business and make new investments in Asia build its quality asset base in the ship- and aircraft-related business and grow its asset management business through it recently acquired Robeco subsidiary. It also plans to continue expanding its already diverse array of offerings by moving into energy and environmental products. To this end in 2014 ORIX partnered with its asset manager subsidiary Robeco and the Asian Development Bank to launch a private equity fund to invest in environment and energy-related projects including low-carbon projects in Asia with plans to expand the business in the years ahead. Mergers and AcquisitionsIn July 2014 subsidiary ORIX Life Insurance Corporation bought Tokyo-based Hartford Life Insurance KK for ¥98355 million (roughly $970 million) with the goal of enhancing its capital strength and improving its management to accelerate its growth.

In July 2013 ORIX purchased a 90% equity stake in mid-size global asset manager Robeco Groep from Cooperative Centrale Raiffeisen-Boerenleenbank (Rabobank) for a total price of ¥255163 million (around $2.5 billion).

EXECUTIVES

President ORIX Baseball Club, Hiroaki Nishina, age 72
Deputy President and CIO, Tamio Umaki, age 68
Corporate EVP, Shintaro Agata, age 66
CEO ORIX USA, Brian F. Prince
Corporate EVP, Yuki Oshima, age 69
Deputy President and CFO, Haruyuki Urata, age 62
EVP; President ORIX Real Estate, Yoshiyuki Yamaya, age 60
SVP; President ORIX Auto, Katsunobu Kamei
EVP; President NS Lease, Katsutoshi Kadowaki
President and COO, Mikoto Inoue, age 64
Corporate EVP, Kazuo Kojima
SVP; President ORIX Credit, Masatoshi Kemmochi
Auditors: KPMG AZSA LLC

LOCATIONS

HQ: Orix Corp. (Japan)
World Trade Center Building, 2-4-1 Hamamatsu-cho, Minato-ku, Tokyo 105-6135
Phone: (81) 3 3435 1273   **Fax:** (81) 3 3435 1276
Web: www.orix.co.jp

2015 Sales

	% of total
Japan	73
Americas	10
Others	17
Total	**100**

PRODUCTS/OPERATIONS

2015 Sales

	% of total
Service income	35
Goods and real estate	20
Operating leases	17
Life insurance premiums and related investments income	16
Finance revenue	9
Gains on investment securities and dividends	3
Total	**100**

Selected Subsidiaries and Segments

ORIX Aircraft (aircraft leasing)
ORIX Asset Management & Loan Services Corporation (commercial mortgage servicing)
ORIX Auto (car rental and leasing)
ORIX Baseball Club (professional baseball team)
ORIX Life Insurance
ORIX Real Estate (real estate development and investment)
ORIX Real Estate Investment Advisors (asset management)

ORIX Rentec (rental operations)
ORIX Trust and Banking
ORIX USA
SUN Leasing Corporation (medical equipment leasing)

COMPETITORS

CIT Group	Mizuho Financial
GE Capital	Rentokil Initial
ILFC	Sumitomo
Mitsubishi UFJ Financial Group	

HISTORICAL FINANCIALS

Company Type: Public

Income Statement

FYE: March 31

	ASSETS ($ mil.)	NET INCOME ($ mil.)	INCOME AS % OF ASSETS	EMPLOYEES
03/16	97,927	2,316	2.4%	33,333
03/15	95,380	1,958	2.1%	31,035
03/14	87,865	1,809	2.1%	25,977
03/13	89,696	1,189	1.3%	19,043
03/12	101,851	1,050	1.0%	17,488
Annual Growth	**(1.0%)**	**21.9%**	**—**	**17.5%**

2016 Year-End Financials

Return on assets: 2.3%	Dividends
Return on equity: 11.6%	Yield: 3.2%
Long-term debt ($ mil.): —	Payout: 144.2%
No. of shares (mil.): 1,309	Market value ($ mil.): 93,486
Sales ($ mil): 21,130	

	STOCK PRICE ($) FY Close	P/E High/Low		Earnings	PER SHARE ($) Dividends	Book Value
03/16	71.39	0	0	1.77	2.33	15.71
03/15	70.34	0	0	1.49	1.12	13.71
03/14	70.47	1	0	1.38	0.65	14.20
03/13	63.58	1	0	0.93	0.48	14.30
03/12	48.25	1	0	0.82	0.48	15.83
Annual Growth	**10.3%**			**21.3%**	**48.5%**	**(0.2%)**

Oversea-Chinese Banking Corp. Ltd. (Singapore)

Singapore bank Oversea-Chinese Banking Corporation (OCBC Bank) operates more than 470 branches and offices in 15 countries including some 350 offices in Indonesia through its Bank OCBC NISP subsidiary. The company offers traditional banking services for individuals and businesses as well as financial services such as brokerage and asset management. Private banking for high-net-worth families is offered through the Bank of Singapore while Great Eastern Holdings which provides life and property/casualty insurance is the largest insurance company in Singapore and Malaysia. OCBC Bank was founded in 1912 to serve the Chinese business community of Singapore and other parts of Asia but now serves the general public.

Geographic Reach

The bank's main operations are in its home country of Singapore which accounts for 60% of business. Malaysia where it operates as OCBC Bank Malaysia and offers Islamic banking services through OCBC Al-Amin Bank accounts for about 20% of business. Indonesia and China each account for less than 10% of business.

In addition to its core markets OCBC also has a presence in Australia Brunei Dubai Hong Kong Japan The Philippines South Korea Taiwan Thailand the UK the US (in New York and Los Angeles) and Vietnam through branches and representative offices.

Strategy

With Singapore's population only 5 million people the bank has targeted China Indonesia and Malaysia as international growth markets. It plans to increase its Islamic banking and insurance operations in Malaysia home to almost 30 million people. In Indonesia (population 247 million) the bank consolidated its banking subsidiaries in order to grow the OCBC NISP brand there. And in China with 1.3 billion people the bank plans to cater to wealthy citizens by offering private banking services through the Bank of Singapore.

EXECUTIVES

SEVP Group Operations and Technology, Ching Wei Hong, age 56
Group CEO, Samuel N. (Sam) Tsien, age 61
SEVP and Head of Global Treasury and Investment Banking, Lam Kun Kin, age 53
Executive Vice President, Gilbert Kohnke, age 57
Head Group Operations and Technology, Lim Khiang Tong, age 56
CFO, Darren S. P. Tan, age 45
Head of Global Commercial Banking, Linus T. L. Goh, age 53
EVP and Head of Global Corporate Banking, George L. W. Lee
CEO Bank of Singapore, Renato de Guzman
CEO OCBC Bank China, Kng Hwee Tin
CEO OCBC Bank Malaysia, Ong Eng Bin
Chairman, Ooi Sang Kuang, age 68
Auditors: KPMG LLP

LOCATIONS

HQ: Oversea-Chinese Banking Corp. Ltd. (Singapore)
65 Chulia Street, #10-00 OCBC Centre East, 049513
Phone: (65) 6318 7222   **Fax:** (65) 6534 3986
Web: www.ocbc.com

2012 Sales

	% of total
Singapore	63
Malaysia	20
Indonesia	7
China	7
Rest of Asia	2
Rest of world	1
Total	**100**

PRODUCTS/OPERATIONS

2012 Sales

	% of total
Interest	59
Noninterest	
Fees & commissions	12
Life insurance	7
General insurance	1
Rental income	1
Dividends	1
Other	19
Total	**100**

Selected Subsidiaries

Banking
Bank of Singapore Limited
OCBC Al-Amin Bank Berhad
OCBC Bank (Malaysia) Berhad
Singapore Island Bank Limited
Insurance
Great Eastern Life Assurance (Malaysia) Berhad
Overseas Assurance Corporation (Malaysia) Berhad

The Great Eastern Life Assurance Company Limited
The Overseas Assurance Corporation
Asset management
Lion Global Investors Limited
Great Eastern Holdings Limited
Stockbroker
OCBC Securities Private Limited

COMPETITORS

ABN AMRO Group	Citigroup
AmBank Group	DBS Group Holdings
BNP Paribas	HSBC
Bank Central Asia	Hong Leong Finance
Bank Danamon Indonesia	Maybank
Bank Mandiri	Standard Chartered
Bank Rakyat	United Overseas Bank

HISTORICAL FINANCIALS

Company Type: Public

Income Statement

FYE: December 31

	ASSETS ($ mil.)	NET INCOME ($ mil.)	INCOME AS % OF ASSETS	EMPLOYEES
12/15	276,049	2,761	1.0%	29,847
12/14	303,690	2,908	1.0%	29,512
12/13	267,902	2,190	0.8%	25,350
12/12	241,962	3,264	1.3%	24,628
12/11	213,713	1,779	0.8%	22,892
Annual Growth	**6.6%**	**11.6%**	**—**	**6.9%**

2015 Year-End Financials

Return on assets: 0.9%
Return on equity: 11.8%
Long-term debt ($ mil.): —
No. of shares (mil.): —
Sales ($ mil): 15,523

Dividends
Yield: 6.4%
Payout: 65.3%
Market value ($ mil.): —

	STOCK PRICE ($) FY Close	P/E High/Low		PER SHARE ($) Earnings	Dividends	Book Value
12/15	12.54	15	13	0.67	0.81	5.94
12/14	15.33	16	14	0.78	0.81	5.91
12/13	15.71	23	21	0.60	0.48	5.79
12/12	15.93	14	11	0.92	0.45	6.15
12/11	11.90	23	18	0.50	0.41	5.05
Annual Growth	**1.3%**	**—**	**—**	**7.5%**	**18.9%**	**4.1%**

P.T. Bank Negara (Indonesia)

Auditors: Kantor Akuntan Publik Tanudiredja, Wibisana & Rekan

LOCATIONS

HQ: P.T. Bank Negara (Indonesia)
Gedung BNI, Jl. Jend. Sudirman Kav. 1, PO Box 1946, Jakarta 10220
Phone: (62) 21 251 1946   **Fax:** (62) 21 251 1214
Web: www.bni.co.id

HISTORICAL FINANCIALS

Company Type: Public

Income Statement

FYE: December 31

	ASSETS ($ mil.)	NET INCOME ($ mil.)	INCOME AS % OF ASSETS	EMPLOYEES
12/16	44,865	843	1.9%	28,390
12/15	36,837	656	1.8%	0
12/14	33,555	868	2.6%	26,536
12/13	31,779	744	2.3%	26,100
12/12	34,520	729	2.1%	24,861
Annual Growth	**6.8%**	**3.7%**	**—**	**3.4%**

2016 Year-End Financials

Return on assets: 2.0%
Return on equity: 14.2%
Long-term debt ($ mil.): —
No. of shares (mil.): —
Sales ($ mil): 4,102

Dividends
Yield: —
Payout: —
Market value ($ mil.): —

	STOCK PRICE ($) FY Close	P/E High/Low		PER SHARE ($) Earnings	Dividends	Book Value
12/16	0.00	0	0	0.05	0.00	0.42
12/15	7.93	0	0	0.04	0.00	0.36
Annual Growth	**—**	**—**	**—**	**6.5%**	**—**	**4.4%**

Panasonic Corp

Panasonic has been one of the world's most prolific electronics manufacturers since 1919. The company spans multiple fields: Its consumer business consists of AVC (audio video and communications) equipment along with hardware and software for linking it together and home appliances (washing machines vacuum cleaners personal grooming aids and commercial HVAC). In the field of devices Panasonic covers multimedia and eco-car equipment industrial electronic components and batteries. The company's solutions equipment targets environmentally conscience businesses manufacturers and health care firms.

Geographic Reach

The company sells its products and services in Asia Europe and North and South America. Japan accounts for just over 50% of net sales while other major markets include North and South America (16%) and Europe (10%).

Operations

Within the company's businesses are five segments: automotive and industrial systems (34% of net sales) appliances (23%) eco solutions (20%) AVC networks (14%) and other (9%).

Panasonic is financially diversified across its segments with the digital AVC networks segment consisting of imaging equipment AVC network equipment such as flat-panel TVs blu-ray disc recorders digital cameras notebook PCs projectors and in-flight entertainment systems. Its appliances segment manufactures products like air conditioners refrigerators washing machines and other home appliances.

Eco solutions supplies lighting fixtures electric lamps wiring devices solar photovoltaic systems interior furnishing materials water-related products ventilation and air-conditioning equipment and air purifiers among other products. The automotive and industrial segment maintains a broad spectrum of expertise across car-use-multimedia-related equipment automotive electronics electronics components automation controls electronic materials semiconductors batteries systems optical devices and manufacturing facility systems.

Sales and Marketing

Panasonic's consumer products are mainly sold to mass-merchandisers through sales subsidiaries. Housing products are sold through agencies and sales subsidiaries. AVC networks products are sold through retail distributors logistics service providers and public institutions. The company also markets its products through print ads and TV commercials.

Financial Performance

Panasonic's overall sales for fiscal 2015 (ends March 31) declined marginally by under 1% due to declines from its appliances and eco solutions segments. These segments were negatively affected by weakening demand after a consumption tax hike and a negative impact from sharp price declines of TVs in Japan.

Strategy

In Japan Panasonic is expanding into the housing improvement market where future growth is expected. In addition to renovating its showrooms in Japan to make them more compatible with the housing improvement market and targeting new customers the company is strengthening its direct marketing to clients through PanaHome Reform Corporation which was established in 2014.

Mergers and AcquisitionsThe company is using acquisitions as a means for growth within its satellite-based communications portfolio. In 2015 it acquired ITC Global a provider of satellite communication services for the energy mining and maritime markets. With regional headquarters in Houston; Sion Switzerland; and Perth Australia ITC Global serves customers at more than 1200 remote sites across 70 countries and all the world's oceans.

HISTORY

Company Background

Grade school dropout Konosuke Matsushita took $50 in 1918 and went into business making electric plugs (with his brother-in-law Toshio Iue founder of SANYO). His mission to help people by making high-quality low-priced conveniences while providing his employees with good working conditions earned him the sobriquet "god of business management." Matsushita Electric Industrial grew by developing inexpensive lamps batteries radios and motors in the 1920s and 1930s.

During WWII the Japanese government ordered the firm to build wood-laminate products for the military. Postwar occupation forces prevented Matsushita from working at his firm for four years. Thanks to unions' efforts he rejoined his namesake company shortly before it entered a joint venture with Dutch manufacturer Philips in 1952. The following year it moved into consumer goods making televisions refrigerators and washing machines and later expanding into high-performance audio products. Matsushita bought a majority stake in Victor Company of Japan (JVC originally established by RCA Victor) in 1954. Its 1959 New York subsidiary opening began Matsushita's drive overseas.

Sold under the National Panasonic and Technics names the firm's products were usually not cutting-edge but were attractively priced. Under Masaharu Matsushita the founder's son-in-law who became president in 1961 the company became Japan's largest home appliance maker introducing air conditioners microwave ovens stereo components and VCRs in the 1960s and 1970s. JVC developed the VHS format for VCRs which beat out Sony's Betamax format.

Matsushita built much of its sales growth on new industrial and commercial customers in the 1980s. The company expanded its semiconductor

office and factory automation auto electronics audio-visual housing and air-conditioning product offerings that decade. Konosuke died in 1989.

EXECUTIVES

Managing Director and Board Member; Director Tokyo Branch, Yasuo Katsura, age 69
Managing Director Industrial Sales and Board Member, Yoshihiko (Yoshi) Yamada, age 65
President, Kazuhiro Tsuga
Managing Executive Officer; President Panasonic Electronic Devices, Toshiaki Kobayashi
Executive Officer; Director Corporate Management Division Asia and Oceania and President Panasonic Asia Pacific, Ikuo Miyamoto
Managing Executive Officer and Head China and Northeast Asia, Hidetoshi Osawa
Executive Officer; Director Corporate Management Division for North America; Chairman and CEO North America, Joseph M. (Joe) Taylor
Managing Director; President AVC Networks Company, Yoshiyuki Miyabe
Managing Director and Board Member; President Home Appliances Company In Charge Of Lighting Company, Kazunori Takami, age 62
Managing Director Accounting and Finance, Hideaki Kawai
Regional Head for Europe & CIS Chairman & CEO Panasonic Europe Ltd. Managing Director Panasonic Marketing Europe GmbH, Laurent Abadie
EVP and President Eco Solutions Company, Shusaku Nagae
Managing Executive Officer and Head Asia the Middle East and Africa, Yorihisa Shiokawa
Managing Director Technology Intellectual Property and Information Systems, Mamoru Yoshida
President Panasonic Healthcare Co. Ltd., Kenji Yamane
President CEO*, Patrick D. O'Brien
Chairman, Kunio Nakamura, age 77
Vice Chairman, Masayuki Matsushita, age 71
Chairman, Fumio Ohtsubo, age 71
Auditors: KPMG AZSA LLC

LOCATIONS

HQ: Panasonic Corp
1006 Oaza Kadoma, Kadoma, Osaka 571-8501
Phone: (81) 6 6908 1121
Web: www.panasonic.co.jp

2015 Sales

	% of total
Japan	49
North & South America	16
Europe	9
Asia & others	26
Total	**100**

PRODUCTS/OPERATIONS

2015 Sales

	% of total
Automotive and industrial systems	34
Appliance	23
Eco Solutions	20
AVC network	14
Other	9
Total	**100**

Selected Segments and Products

AVC Networks
  Camcorders
  Computer drives (CD-ROM DVD-ROM/RAM)
  Computers (PCs)
  Digital cameras
  DVD players and recorders
  Fax machines

  Printers
  Telephones
  TVs (color LCD plasma display)
PEW and PanaHome
  Automation controls
  Beauty and personal care products
  Electronic and plastic materials
  Home security systems
  Interior furnishings
Home appliances
  Air conditioners and purifiers
  Dishwashers
  Dryers
  Fans
  Refrigerators
  Vacuum cleaners
  Water heaters
  Washing machines
Components and devices
  Batteries (dry rechargeable)
  Displays (CRTs LCDs PDPs)
  Electric motors
  General components (capacitors resistors printed circuit boards)
  Magnetic recording heads
  Semiconductors

Selected Brands

National
Panasonic
Quasar
Technics
Victor

COMPETITORS

A123 Systems	Konica Minolta
Apple Inc.	LG Electronics
BSH Bosch und Siemens	Motorola Solutions
Hausgeräte	NEC
BYD	Nokia
Canon	Olympus
Dell	Philips Electronics
Eastman Kodak	Procter & Gamble
Electrolux	Samsung Electronics
Fujitsu Technology	Sharp Corp.
Solutions	Sony
GE Appliances &	TE Connectivity
Lighting	Technicolor
HP	Toshiba
Haier Group	Truly International
IBM	Whirlpool
Intel	Yuasa Battery Thailand

HISTORICAL FINANCIALS

Company Type: Public

Income Statement

FYE: March 31

	REVENUE ($ mil.)	NET INCOME ($ mil.)	NET PROFIT MARGIN	EMPLOYEES
03/16	67,265	1,720	2.6%	49,520
03/15	64,303	1,495	2.3%	254,084
03/14	74,952	1,166	1.6%	271,789
03/13	77,615	(8,016)	—	293,742
03/12	95,650	(9,413)	—	330,767
Annual Growth	**(8.4%)**	**—**		**(37.8%)**

2016 Year-End Financials

Debt ratio: 0.1%	No. of shares (mil.): —
Return on equity: 10.9%	Dividends
Cash ($ mil.): 9,033	Yield: 1.8%
Current ratio: 1.28	Payout: 23.8%
Long-term debt ($ mil.): 6,270	Market value ($ mil.): —

	STOCK PRICE ($) FY Close	P/E High/Low	PER SHARE ($) Earnings	PER SHARE ($) Dividends	PER SHARE ($) Book Value
03/16	8.96	0 0	0.74	0.16	6.58
03/15	13.13	0 0	0.65	0.14	6.62
03/14	11.44	0 0	0.50	0.05	6.53
03/13	7.33	— —	(3.47)	0.05	5.85
03/12	9.25	— —	(4.07)	0.12	10.18
Annual Growth (10.3%)	(0.8%)	— —	—	7.5%	

Pegatron Corp

Pegatron might not be a sibling of the Transformer character Megatron but it is effective in transforming manufacturing contracts into money. The company is a contract manufacturer of components for computers communications devices and consumer electronics for a variety of companies that include Apple Corp. It make PCs notebooks smartphones game consoles and other devices. What's more Pegatron is moving into new markets such as automotive information and entertainment systems and manufacturing automation systems. Pegatron has emerged as an alternative to FoxConn and other contract manufacturers. The company formed in 2008 when computer maker ASUSTeK spun off its contract manufacturing business.

Operations

Pegatron divides its operation into Design Manufacturing and Service (DMS) and the Strategic Investment Group.

The DMS unit handles the design and manufacture of computer communication and consumer electronics' end products (3C Products as Pegatron calls them) and provides after-sales service. The Strategic Investment Group works on the upstream and downstream chains and includes strategic and other investments. As might be expected DMS is Pegatron's cash cow bringing in 92% of revenue with the rest coming from the investment arm.

Geographic Reach

A 61% surge of business in Europe made the region the biggest source of revenue for Pegatron in 2015 accounting for 42% of the total. Customers in the US and Taiwan where Pegatron is based accounted for 23% and 15% respectively.

The company's manufacturing sites and service and repair stations are in its key geographic markets Europe North America and Asia.

Sales and Marketing

Pegatron's major customers are well-known global brands in the computing communication and consumer electronics markets. Two customers contributed 70% of sales in 2015.

Financial Performance

Pegatron posted robust increases in revenue and profit in 2015. Revenue rose 19% as DMS sales jumped 21% while profit rose 53% on the higher revenue. Cash flow from operations slowed 80% in 2015 from 2014.

Strategy

Making components for companies like Apple has enabled Pegatron to reach new revenue highs each year. It views its efforts in computing consumer electronics and communications as solid foundation as it moves into other areas where it expects growth. Key areas for the future are the internet of things automation technology manufacturing efficiency and automotive infotainment systems.

EXECUTIVES

President, Tzu Hsien Tung
Auditors: KPMG

LOCATIONS

HQ: Pegatron Corp
5/F., No. 76, Ligong Street, Beitou District, Taipei 112
Phone: (886) 2 8143 9001   **Fax:** (886) 2 8143 7984
Web: www.pegatroncorp.com

2015 Sales

	% of total
Europe	42
USA	23
Taiwan	15
China	8
Japan	7
Others	5
Total	**100**

PRODUCTS/OPERATIONS

2015 Sales

	% of total
3C Products	92
Other	8
Total	**100**

2015 Sales

	% of total
DMS	92
Strategic Investment Group	8
Total	**100**

COMPETITORS

BenQ	Jabil
Compal Electronics	Lite-On Technology
Elitegroup Computer	MiTAC
Systems	Micro-Star
First International	International
Computer	Nam Tai
Flextronics	Quanta Computer
Foxconn International	TPV Technology
Foxconn Technology	TriGem
Giga-Byte Technology	Universal Scientific
Hedy Holding	Venture Corp.
Hon Hai	Wistron
Inventec	

HISTORICAL FINANCIALS

Company Type: Public

Income Statement
FYE: December 31

	REVENUE ($ mil.)	NET INCOME ($ mil.)	NET PROFIT MARGIN	EMPLOYEES
12/15	36,935	724	2.0%	7,376
12/14	32,204	462	1.4%	6,783
12/13	31,848	320	1.0%	0
12/12	30,363	219	0.7%	177,948
12/11	19,793	109	0.6%	112,318
Annual Growth	**16.9%**	**60.6%**	**—**	**(49.4%)**

2015 Year-End Financials

Debt ratio: 0.3%
Return on equity: 16.7%
Cash ($ mil.): 3,121
Current ratio: 1.46
Long-term debt ($ mil.): 374
No. of shares (mil.): —
Dividends
  Yield: —
  Payout: —
Market value ($ mil.): —

Peoples Insurance Company (Group) of China Ltd (The)

Auditors: Deloite Touche Tohmatsu Certified Public Accountants LLP

LOCATIONS

HQ: Peoples Insurance Company (Group) of China Ltd (The)
28 Qinghua West Road, Haidian District, Beijing 100084
Phone: (86) 10 6261 6611   **Fax:** (86) 10 6262 4880
Web: www.picc.com

HISTORICAL FINANCIALS

Company Type: Public

Income Statement
FYE: December 31

	ASSETS ($ mil.)	NET INCOME ($ mil.)	INCOME AS % OF ASSETS	EMPLOYEES
12/15	129,873	3,008	2.3%	193,687
12/14	126,035	2,112	1.7%	184,644
12/13	124,765	1,341	1.1%	0
Annual Growth	**2.0%**	**49.8%**	**—**	**—**

2015 Year-End Financials

Return on assets: 2.4%
Return on equity: 18.7%
Long-term debt ($ mil.): —
No. of shares (mil.): —
Sales ($ mil): 63,515
Dividends
  Yield: —
  Payout: —
Market value ($ mil.): —

	STOCK PRICE ($) FY Close	P/E High/Low	PER SHARE ($) Earnings	PER SHARE ($) Dividends	PER SHARE ($) Book Value
12/15	10.03	27 19	0.07	0.00	0.42
12/14	0.00	— —	0.05	0.00	0.35
12/13	0.00	— —	0.03	0.00	0.28
Annual Growth	**—**	**— —**	**50.2%**	**—**	**23.0%**

PetroChina Co Ltd

If you want petroleum in China or elsewhere then PetroChina is your company. A subsidiary of state-owned China National Petroleum Corporation (CNPC) PetroChina produces two-thirds of China's oil and gas. The company has proved reserves of 10.8 billion barrels of oil and 69.3 trillion cu. ft. of natural gas. In China it owns more than 53400 kilometers of natural gas and refined products pipeline and operates 29 refineries and 13 chemical plants. PetroChina was created in 2000 as a separate company to initially manage the domestic operations —and in recent years some key international assets —of CNPC.

Strategy

PetroChina is taking advantage of the growing consumption of natural gas in China by expanding its transmission infrastructure. It is also expanding its oil reserves and refining operations through the purchase of international oil fields and refineries including several assets from its parent.

In 2015 the company agreed to sell 50% of Central Asia Natural Gas Pipeline Co. to Mansong Holdings Ltd a subsidiary of China Reform Holdings Corp. Ltd. for 15 billion to 15.5 billion yuan.

EXECUTIVES

Vice Chairman and President, Wang Dongjin
VP and General Manager Exploration and Production, Zhao Zhengzhang, age 59
VP and General Manager PetroChina Natural Gas and Pipelines, Huang Weihe, age 58
Chief Engineer, Lin Aiguo, age 57
VP and General Manager PetroChina Refining and Chemical, Xu Fugui
VP and General Manager PetroChina International Company Limited (China National United Oil Corporation), Wang Lihua
VP and General Manager PetroChina International Exploration and Development and China National Exploration and Development, Lv Gongxun
VP and General Manager PetroChina Marketing Company, Tian Jinghui
CFO, Chai Shouping, age 55
Chairman, Wang Yilin, age 63
Vice Chairman, Zhang Jianhua, age 51
Auditors: KPMG Huazhen (Special General Partnership)

LOCATIONS

HQ: PetroChina Co Ltd
No. 9 Dongzhimen North Street, Dongcheng District, Beijing 100007
Phone: (86) 10 5998 6270   **Fax:** (86) 10 6209 9557
Web: www.petrochina.com.cn

2013 Sales

	% of total
Mainland China	67
Other countries	33
Total	**100**

PRODUCTS/OPERATIONS

2013 Sales

	% of total
Marketing	51
Refining & chemicals	23
Exploration & production	20
Natural gas & pipeline	6
Total	**100**

COMPETITORS

Bangchak Petroleum	Exxon Mobil
Public	Sinopec Shanghai
CNOOC	Petrochemical
Chevron	

HISTORICAL FINANCIALS

Company Type: Public

Income Statement

FYE: December 31

	REVENUE ($ mil.)	NET INCOME ($ mil.)	NET PROFIT MARGIN	EMPLOYEES
12/15	265,673	5,468	2.1%	521,566
12/14	367,841	17,268	4.7%	534,652
12/13	373,003	21,407	5.7%	544,083
12/12	352,134	18,498	5.3%	548,355
12/11	318,353	21,123	6.6%	552,810
Annual Growth	**(4.4%)**	**(28.7%)**	**—**	**(1.4%)**

2015 Year-End Financials

Debt ratio: 3.4%	No. of shares (mil.): —
Return on equity: 3.0%	Dividends
Cash ($ mil.): 11,205	Yield: 3.4%
Current ratio: 0.74	Payout: 7,431.4%
Long-term debt ($ mil.): 66,898	Market value ($ mil.): —

STOCK PRICE ($) FY Close	P/E High/Low	PER SHARE ($) Earnings	Dividends	Book Value
12/15	65.59	685334	0.03	2.25	0.99
12/14	110.96	251157	0.10	4.70	1.04
12/13	109.74	211145	0.12	4.21	1.02
12/12	143.78	246189	0.10	4.47	0.93
12/11	124.31	223156	0.12	4.90	0.87
Annual Growth	**(14.8%)**	**—**	**(29.1%)**	**(17.7%)**	**3.3%**

Petroleo Brasileiro S.A.

PETROLEO BRASILEIRO (PETROBRAS) isn't brash but it is Brazil's top company. The integrated energy company (controlled by the Brazilian government) explores for oil and gas and produces refines and transports oil and gas products. With extensive offshore assets in 2014 PETROBRAS reported proved reserves of 16.6 billion barrels of oil equivalent. In Brazil it also operates 15 refineries an extensive oil and gas pipeline network and more than 7710 gas stations. Petrobras Distribuidora is Brazil's #1 retailer of oil products and fuel alcohol. Petrobras Argentina is a top Argentine oil firm. Other units operate electricity (10 power plants) petrochemicals and natural gas assets.

Geographic Reach

Petrobras Internacional also known as Braspetro conducts exploration worldwide including in Angola Nigeria Tanzania Portugal the US and across Latin America. PETROBRAS has a presence in 17 countries.

Operations

The company operates through six business segments: Exploration and Production (crude oil NGL and natural gas exploration development and production in Brazil). In 2014 the company reported proved developed oil and gas reserves of 8.1 billion barrels of oil equivalent and proved undeveloped reserves of 4.6 billion barrels of oil equivalent in Brazil. The bulk of PETROBRAS' production comes from its operations in Brazilian waters; the company is recognized as a leader in offshore drilling technology and deepwater wells. Refining Transportation and Marketing (refining logistics transportation trading operations oil products and crude oil exports and imports and petrochemical investments in Brazil).

Distribution (oil products ethanol biodiesel and natural gas to wholesalers and through PETROBRAS' Petrobras Distribuidora S.A. retail network in Brazil).Gas and Power (transportation and trading of natural gas and LNG produced in or imported into Brazil as well as generation and trading of electric power and the fertilizer business.

Biofuel (production of biodiesel and its co-products and ethanol-related activities such as equity investments production and trading of ethanol sugar and the excess electricity generated from sugarcane bagasse). PETROBRAS is a major ethanol producer and plans (through Petrobras Transporte S.A. which oversees oil and derivatives ethanol biofuels and natural gas transportation and storage activities) to invest billions of dollars in biofuel development to ensure Brazil's fuel independence as its economy and population grows.

International (exploration and production of oil and gas refining transportation and marketing distribution and gas and power operations).

PETROBRAS main subsidiaries include Petrobras Distribuidora S.A. Petrobras Biocombustivel

Petrobras Transporte S.A. Petrobras Gas S.A. and Liquigas Distribuidora S.A.

Sales and Marketing The company serves industries such as Automotive Industrial Agriculture Rail Maritime and Aviation. It distributes its oil products through a company-owned retail network wholesale channels and by supplying other fuel wholesalers and retailers.

Financial Performance

PETROBRAS' net revenues increased by 2% in 2014 due to an increase in Gas & Power and Distribution sales.

The increase was primarily driven by higher oil product prices in the Brazil due to diesel and gasoline price increases applied in 2013 and 2014 and the impact of the appreciation of the US dollar against the real (9%) on the price of oil products adjusted to reflect international prices (such as jet fuel and naphtha) as well as higher electricity and natural gas prices.

Revenues were also affected by a 3% increase in the demand for oil products in Brazil mainly diesel (2%) gasoline (5%) and fuel oil (21%) and higher crude oil export volumes (12%) partially offset by a decrease in oil product export volumes (15%).

Foreign currency translation effects reduced the increase of sales revenues in US dollars. Excluding those effects sales revenues increased by 11% when expressed in reals.

PETROBRAS posted a net loss of 166% in 2014 primarily due to an increase in impairment of assets resulting from individualized impairment testing of a second refining unit of Refinaria Abreu e Limaand Complexo Petroquimico do Rio de Janeiro and lower international crude oil prices and lower valuataion of petrochemical assets.

In 2014 the company's cash inflow increased by 1% due to changes in working capital as a result of a decrease in inventories and increase in other liabilities.

Strategy

The company's 2014-2018 Business and Management Plan foresees investments in the order of $220.6 billion. Exploration & Production will get $153.9 billion mainly to develop the pre-salt and the post-salt production. Downstream will see investments of $38.7 billion to enhance refining capacity and achieve operational improvements.As per the 2030 Strategic Plan PETROBRAS is aiming to produce an average of 4 million barrels of oil equivalent per day between 2020 and 2030 and keep growing in biofuels ethanol and biodiesel to support the Brazilian diesel and gasoline markets.

To raise cash in 2015 PETROBRAS sold a 49% stake in its natural gas distribution subsidiary Gaspetro to Mitsui for $490.2 million.

HISTORY

Company Background
"O petroleo e nosso!"

"The oil is ours!" proclaimed the Brazilian nationalists' slogan in 1953 and President Getulio Vargas approved a bill creating a state-run monopoly on petroleum discovery development refining and transport. The same year that PETROLEO BRASILEIRO (PETROBRAS) was created a team led by American geologist Walter Link reported that the prospects of finding petroleum in Brazil were slim. The report outraged Brazilian nationalists who saw it as a ploy for foreign exploitation. PETROBRAS proved it could find oil but Brazil continued to import crude oil and petroleum products. By 1973 the company produced about 10% of the nation's needs.

When oil prices soared during the Arab embargo the government instead of encouraging exploration for domestic oil pushed PETROBRAS into a program to promote alcohol fuels. The company was forced to raise gasoline prices to make the more costly gasohol attractive to consumers. During the 1979 oil crunch the price of gasohol was fixed at 65% of gasoline. But during the oil glut of the mid-1980s PETROBRAS' cost of making gasohol was twice what it cost to buy gasoline —in other words PETROBRAS lost money.

PETROBRAS soon began overseas exploration. In 1980 it found an oil field in Iraq an important trading partner during the 1980s. The company also drilled in Angola and through a 1987 agreement with Texaco in the Gulf of Mexico.

In the mid-1980s PETROBRAS began production in the deepwater Campos basin off the coast of Rio de Janeiro state. Discoveries there in 1988 in the Marlim and Albacora fields more than tripled its oil reserves. It plunged deep into the thick Amazon jungle in 1986 to explore for oil and by 1990 Amazon wells were making a significant contribution to total production. That year to ease dependence on imports PETROBRAS launched a five-year $16.9 billion plan to boost crude oil production. It also began selling its mining and trading assets.

Before the invasion of Kuwait Brazil relied heavily on Iraq trading weapons for oil. After the invasion spawned increases in crude prices PETROBRAS raised pump prices but yielding to the government's anti-inflation program still did not raise them enough to cover costs. It lost $13 million a day.

The company sold 26% of Petrobras Distribuidora to the public in 1993 and privatized several of its petrochemical and fertilizer subsidiaries. A 1994 presidential order bent on stabilizing Brazil's 40%-per-month inflation cut the prices of oil products. In 1995 the government loosened its grip on the oil and gas industry and allowed foreign companies to enter the Brazilian market. In the wake of this reform PETROBRAS teamed up with a Japanese consortium to build Brazil's largest oil refinery.

In 1997 PETROBRAS appealed a $4 billion judgment from a 1992 shareholder lawsuit; the suit alleged PETROBRAS had undervalued shares during the privatization of the loss-making Petroquisa affiliate. (The appeal was granted in 1999.)

As part of an effort to boost oil production PETROBRAS also began to raise money abroad in 1999. The next year PETROBRAS and Spanish oil giant Repsol YPF agreed to swap oil and gas assets in Argentina and Brazil in a deal worth more than $1 billion.

In 2000 the company announced plans to change its corporate name to PETROBRAX but fierce political and popular reaction forced the company to abort this plan in 2001. In an even greater public relations disaster that year one of PETROBRAS' giant rigs sank off of Brazil and 10 workers were killed. In 2001 PETROBRAS announced that it was going to spend as much as $3 billion to buy an oil company in order to increase its production in the Gulf of Mexico.

In 2002 the company expressed an interest in buying Argentina's major oil company (YPF) from Spanish/Argentine energy giant Repsol YPF. That year PETROBRAS bought control (59%) of Argentine energy company Perez Companc in a deal valued at $1 billion. PETROBRAS also reported its first oil find in Argentina in 2002.

In 2006 the company acquired a 50% stake in a deepwater block in Equatorial Guinea from a private group of companies for an undisclosed sum.

The company also restructured the Brazilian petrochemical industry to make it more efficient. Its actions included the purchase of the petrochemical assets of the Ipiranga Group in 2007 and

Suzano Petroquimica a leader in Latin American polypropylene resin production in 2008.

In 2007 PETROBRAS announced a major offshore oil discovery in the Tupi. In 2008 it reported it had discovered a major natural gas field near the Tupi find.

In 2011 it was operating more than 130 production platforms. PETROBRAS has made a number of major offshore oil discoveries in offshore Brazil since 2000 including the Tupi field (found in 2007) and which has the potential to boost Brazil's oil reserves by 40%. In 2010 PETROBRAS announced another major discovery a 3.7 to 15 billion-barrels-of-oil-reserves find (offshore of Rio de Janeiro) that could double Brazil's known reserves.

Streamlining its Petrobras Argentina operations in 2011 the company acquired that unit's Brazilian petrochemicals business (Innova SA) for $332 million.

In 2012 it teamed up with GE Oil & Gas in a $1.1 billion deal through which the GE unit will supply 380 subsea wellhead systems to a number of PETROBRAS' oil and gas fields in offshore Brazil.

Brazil's government owns more than 55% of PETROBRAS.

EXECUTIVES

Chairman, Pedro Pullen Parente, age 63
CFO and Investor Relations Director, Ivan de Souza Monteiro, age 56
Exploration and Production Officer; Member of the Executive Board, Guilherme Estrella
CEO Transpetro, Ant´nio Rubens Silva Silvino
President, Ivan de S˜ Pereira
Chairman, Luiz Nelson Guedes de Carvalho
Auditors: PricewaterhouseCoopers Auditores Independentes–PwC

LOCATIONS

HQ: Petroleo Brasileiro S.A.
Avenida Republica do Chile, 65, Rio de Janeiro 20031-912
Phone: (55) 21 3224 4477
Web: www.petrobras.com.br

2010 Sales

	% of total
Brazil	74
Other countries	28
Total	**100**

PRODUCTS/OPERATIONS

2010 Sales

	% of total
Refining transportation & marketing	46
Exploration & production	26
Distribution	18
International	6
Gas & power	4
Total	**100**

Selected Subsidiaries

Downstream Participações S.A. (asset exchanges between Petrobras and Repsol-YPF)
Petrobras Argentina (59%; oil and gas Argentina)
Petrobras Comercializadora de Energia Ltda
Petrobras Distribuidora SA (BR; distribution and marketing of petroleum products fuel alcohol and natural gas)
Petrobras Gás SA (Gaspetro management of the Brazil-Bolivia pipeline and other natural gas assets)
Petrobras Internacional SA (Braspetro; overseas exploration and production marketing and services)
Petrobras International Finance Company - PIFCO (oil imports)
Petrobras Negócios Eletrônicos S.A.
Petrobras Química SA (Petroquisa petrochemicals)

Petrobras Transporte SA (Transpetro oil and gas transportation and storage)

COMPETITORS

Ashland Inc.	Marathon Oil
BHP Billiton	Norsk Hydro ASA
BP	Occidental Petroleum
Chevron	PEMEX
Devon Energy	Petr\leos de
Eni	Venezuela
Exxon Mobil	Royal Dutch Shell
Imperial Oil	Sunoco
Koch Industries Inc.	TOTAL

HISTORICAL FINANCIALS

Company Type: Public

Income Statement

FYE: December 31

	REVENUE ($ mil.)	NET INCOME ($ mil.)	NET PROFIT MARGIN	EMPLOYEES
12/15	97,314	(8,450)	—	78,470
12/14	143,657	(7,367)	—	80,908
12/13	141,462	11,094	7.8%	86,111
12/12	144,103	11,034	7.7%	85,065
12/11	145,915	20,121	13.8%	81,918
Annual Growth	**(9.6%)**	**—**		**(1.1%)**

2015 Year-End Financials

Debt ratio: 54.7%
Return on equity: (-9.3%)
Cash ($ mil.): 25,058
Current ratio: 1.52
Long-term debt ($ mil.): 111,521
No. of shares (mil.): —
Dividends
  Yield: —
  Payout: —
Market value ($ mil.): —

	STOCK PRICE ($) FY Close	P/E High/Low		PER SHARE ($) Earnings	Dividends	Book Value
12/15	4.30	—	—	(0.65)	0.00	5.00
12/14	7.30	—	—	(0.56)	0.61	8.91
12/13	13.78	24	14	0.85	0.21	11.39
12/12	19.47	37	21	0.85	0.86	12.87
12/11	24.85	27	14	1.54	0.93	13.48
Annual Growth	**(35.5%)**			**(22.0%)**		

Peugeot SA

Peugeot S.A is the top carmaker in France. The company makes cars and light commercial vehicles under the Peugeot and Citroën brands. Peugeot is among the top manufacturers in European passenger car and commercial vehicle sales. Also part of Peugeot's automotive operations are Faurecia (auto parts) GEFCO (transportation and logistics) and Banque PSA Finance (financial services for dealers and customers). Other group products include motorcycles and scooters. Peugeot makes most of its sales in Europe. The Peugeot family controls about 38% of the voting stock. PSA plans to acquire General Motor's German Opel business which may see Opel remain an independent firm.

HISTORY

In 1810 brothers Frederic and Jean-Pierre Peugeot made a foundry out of the family textile mill in the Alsace region of France and invented the cold-roll process for producing spring steel. Bicycle production began in 1885 at the behest of avid cyclist Armand Peugeot Jean-Pierre's grandson.

Armand turned to automobiles and built Peugeot's first car a steam-powered three-wheeler in 1889. A gas-fueled Peugeot tied for first place in the 1894 Paris-Rouen Trials the earliest auto race on record. That year the budding carmaker built the first station wagon followed in 1905 by the first compact the 600-pound "Le Bebe."

Peugeot built factories in France including one in Sochaux (1912) that remains the company's main plant. It made the first diesel passenger car in 1922. The 1929 introduction of the reliable 201 model was followed by innovations such as synchromesh gears in 1936. The company suffered heavy damage in WWII but quickly bounced back and began expanding overseas after the war.

In 1954 CEO Roland Peugeot rebuffed a board proposal calling for global expansion that would place the company in competition with US automakers. By 1976 the French government persuaded Peugeot to merge with Citroën.

Andre Citroën founded his company in 1915 and in 1919 it became the first in Europe to mass-produce cars. Citroën hit the skids during the Depression and in 1934 handed Michelin a large block of stock in lieu of payment for tires. Citroën never fully recovered though by 1976 the company's line ranged from the 2CV minicar (discontinued in 1990) to limousines.

In 1978 Peugeot bought Chrysler's aging European plants and withering nameplates including Simca (France) and Rootes (UK). Peugeot changed the nameplates to Talbot but sales continued to slide. It lost nearly $1.2 billion from 1980 to 1984.

Jacques Calvet took over as CEO in 1984. He cut 30000 jobs and spent heavily on modernization. Aided by the strong launch of the 205 superminicar Peugeot returned to profitability in 1985 and by 1989 had halved its production break-even point. In the 1980s Peugeot inked production deals with Renault (industrial vehicles motors gearboxes) and Fiat (light trucks) and introduced a reasonably priced electric van in 1990.

Peugeot withdrew from the US in 1991 after five years of declining sales. A year later Renault and Peugeot developed electric cars and set up servicing centers throughout France. Citing an economic slump in 1993 Peugeot suffered its first loss ($239 million) since 1985. A French government incentive to replace cars more than 10 years old boosted 1994 sales.

Peugeot and rival Renault together introduced a V6 engine in 1996. Jean Martin Folz replaced Calvet as managing board chairman in 1997; Folz headed up Peugeot for 10 years and was replaced by Christian Streiff in 2007. In 1998 the company began building Peugeots and Citroëns in the same plants and created its Faurecia unit when its ECIA subsidiary merged with car parts maker Bertrand Faure. In an effort to capitalize on the growing South American car market the company purchased more than 80% of Argentina's Sevel and built a plant in Brazil. In 1999 the company sold its flight systems supplier SAMM to TRW's Lucas Aerospace unit.

With demand for its cars falling steeply in South America due to the region's continuing economic crisis Peugeot restructured its Brazil operations in 2000 and formed a new subsidiary Citroën do Brasil.

In 2001 Peugeot announced that it was building an engine plant in Brazil and agreed to produce a subcompact car for the European market with Toyota. The following year Peugeot formed an alliance with BMW to develop and build a line of small diesel engines for use in vehicles made by both companies.

In 2005 Peugeot achieved a major milestone when for the first time it sold more than 1 million units outside its traditional market of Western Europe or 30% of total sales. Large gains were made in South America and even more so in China. In 2006 the company repeated the feat. With Western Europe a mature market Peugeot was looking to three key emerging markets to drive future growth: China the Mercosur region (Argentina Brazil Paraguay and Uruguay) and Central and Eastern Europe.

EXECUTIVES

EVP Mobility Services, Gregoire Olivier
EVP Director Supply Chain and Manufacturing, Yann Vincent, age 59
Chairman Managing Board, Carlos Tavares, age 57
EVP Operational Director India-Pacific, Emmanuel Delay
VP Purchasing, Jean-Christophe Quemard
Director General Citro «n Italia, Jean Philippe Imparato
EVP China and ASEAN, Denis Martin
Director French Sales Peugeot, Christophe Bergerand, age 52
EVP Finance, Jean-Baptiste de Chatillon
CEO DS Brand, Yves Bonnefont
EVP Operational Director Europe, Maxime Picat
CEO Citro «n Brand, Linda Jackson
EVP Research and Development, Gilles Le Borgne
EVP Purchasing, Yannick Bezard
EVP Operational Director Latin America, Carlos Gomes
EVP Programs and Strategy, Patrice Lucas
EVP Human Resources, Xavier Chereau
Chairman Supervisory Board, Louis Gallois, age 68
Vice Chairman Supervisory Board, Zhu Yanfeng, age 55
Vice Chairman Supervisory Board, Marie-Hel ¨ne Peugeot-Roncoroni
Vice Chairman Supervisory Board, Jack Azoulay
Auditors: ERNST & YOUNG et Autres

LOCATIONS

HQ: Peugeot SA
75, avenue de la Grande-Armee, Paris 75116
Phone: (33) 1 40 66 55 11   **Fax:** (33) 1 40 66 54 14
Web: www.psa-peugeot-citroen.com

2011 Sales

	% of total
Europe	73
Latin America	9
Asia	5
Russia	3
Rest of the world	10
Total	**100**

PRODUCTS/OPERATIONS

2011 Sales

% of sales		
Automotive division	66	
Faurecia	25	
Gefco	6	
Banque PSA Finance	3	
Total	**0**	**100**

2011 Sales

% of total		Units
Peugeot brand		60
Citroën brand		40
Total		**100**

Selected Subsidiaries

Citroën
Peugeot
Banque PSA Finance
Faurecia (57% automotive components)
GEFCO (transportation and logistics services)

COMPETITORS

BMW	Kia Motors

CRCAM IDF CCI	Mazda
Daimler	Nissan
FCA US	Piaggio & Co.
Fiat Chrysler	Renault
Ford Motor	Suzuki Motor
General Motors	Toyota
Honda	Volkswagen
Isuzu	Yamaha Motor

HISTORICAL FINANCIALS

Company Type: Public

Income Statement

FYE: December 31

	REVENUE ($ mil.)	NET INCOME ($ mil.)	NET PROFIT MARGIN	EMPLOYEES
12/15	59,553	979	1.6%	0
12/14	65,159	(858)	—	189,786
12/13	74,467	(3,189)	—	196,885
12/12	73,080	(6,603)	—	204,287
12/11	77,493	760	1.0%	0
Annual Growth	**(6.4%)**	**6.5%**	**—**	**—**

2015 Year-End Financials

Debt ratio: 17.3%	No. of shares (mil.): 799
Return on equity: 9.0%	Dividends
Cash ($ mil.): 11,868	Yield: —
Current ratio: 0.85	Payout: —
Long-term debt ($ mil.): 4,647	Market value ($ mil.): 13,911

	STOCK PRICE ($) FY Close	P/E High/Low		PER SHARE ($) Earnings	Dividends	Book Value
12/15	17.40	19	9	1.13	0.00	14.38
12/14	12.18	—	—	(1.40)	3.67	14.63
Annual Growth	**42.9%**	**—**	**—**	**—**	**—**	**(0.4%)**

Phoenix Group Holdings

Apparently a Phoenix Group can hatch out of the right kind of Pearl. Formerly known as Pearl Group Phoenix Group operates through two primary companies: IGNIS Asset Management and Phoenix Life. Phoenix Life is made up of a handful of life insurance companies including Phoenix Life Ltd. London Life and NPI Ltd. However its companies don't sell new policies but instead maintain blocks of life insurance policies and pension products bought from other insurers (called closed life funds). It has more than 6 million such policies in force. Ignis Asset Management manages £67 billion of assets for customers within and outside of Phoenix Group.

Operations

Phoenix's operations include subsidiaries Phoenix Life Scottish Provident Scottish Mutual and Resolution Asset Management.

Mergers and Acquisitions

In 2016 Phoenix Group bought AXA's UK pension operations AXA Wealth and SunLife. In a similar move it then agreed to buy the UK insurer Abbey Life from beleaguered German giant Deutsche Bank for £935 million. That purchase will add some £10 billion in assets under management.

Company Background

In 2009 the company was acquired by Virgin Islands-based investment firm Liberty Acquisition Holdings. Following the acquisition —which valued Pearl Group at about £1.6 billion ($2.6 billion) –Liberty Acquisition a special purpose acquisition vehicle (or "blank check" company) changed its name to Pearl Group and began to inject up to £600 million ($987 million) into the new company with a focus on investing in additional financial service entities.

The company streamlined a bit in 2009 by merging its two asset management businesses Axial Investment management and Ignis into one company: Ignis Asset Management. It then began rebranding some products under the Phoenix Life name which paved the way for renaming the company Phoenix Group Holdings in 2010.

Internal mergers continued in 2011 when the company consolidated some of its life insurance businesses into Phoenix Life Ltd. Ultimately the company intends to have two primary life insurance companies under the Phoenix Life banner.

EXECUTIVES

Group Chief Executive, Clive C R Bannister, age 57
Group Finance Director, Jim McConville
Group Chief Risk Officer, Wayne Snow
Group Chief Actuary, Simon True
Chairman, Henry E. Staunton, age 67
Auditors: Ernst & Young LLP

LOCATIONS

HQ: Phoenix Group Holdings
1st Floor, 32 Commercial Street, St. Helier, Jersey JE2 3RU
Phone:
Web: www.thephoenixgroup.com

PRODUCTS/OPERATIONS

2015 Sales

	% of total
Net investment income	91
Fees	8
Other	1
Total	**100**

COMPETITORS

AXA UK	Prudential plc
Aviva	Royal London Mutual
Legal & General Group	Standard Life
Liverpool Victoria	

HISTORICAL FINANCIALS

Company Type: Public

Income Statement

FYE: December 31

	ASSETS ($ mil.)	NET INCOME ($ mil.)	INCOME AS % OF ASSETS	EMPLOYEES
12/15	95,606	297	0.3%	741
12/14	107,403	483	0.5%	748
12/13	122,411	239	0.2%	1,200
12/12	138,772	631	0.5%	1,265
12/11	138,265	(202)	—	1,355
Annual Growth	**(8.8%)**	**—**		**(14.0%)**

2015 Year-End Financials

Return on assets: 0.3%
Return on equity: 8.3%
Long-term debt ($ mil.): —
No. of shares (mil.): 225
Sales ($ mil): 1,025
Dividends
  Yield: —
  Payout: —
Market value ($ mil.): 2,960

	STOCK PRICE ($) FY Close	P/E High/Low		PER SHARE ($) Earnings	Dividends	Book Value
12/15	13.13	15	13	1.33	0.00	16.00
12/14	12.52	9	7	2.15	0.00	16.40
12/13	12.03	18	15	1.13	0.00	14.03
12/12	8.13	4	3	3.65	0.00	15.31
12/11	7.75	—	—	(1.18)	0.32	14.63
Annual Growth	**14.1%**	—	—	—	—	**2.3%**

PICC Property and Casualty Co Ltd

PICC Property and Casualty (PICC P&C) is the leading property/casualty (P&C) insurer in bustling China. Founded in 1949 as the state-owned People's Insurance Company of China (now known as PICC Group) PICC P&C was spun off in 2003. It operates throughout most of China with more than 10000 branch offices providing primarily auto insurance (more than 70% of sales). Additional types of coverage include commercial property liability accident and homeowners insurance. PICC Group holds 70% of the company while US firm AIG holds 10% of its shares.

Founded just 20 days after ceremonies marking the founding of China PICC P&C survived a 20-year suspension of insurance activities within China. It eventually came to control 70% of the P&C market in spite of increasing competition both from China-based insurers and from foreign companies entering the burgeoning marketplace.

The company has sisters: PICC Life Insurance Company and PICC Health Insurance Company which offer complementary coverage.

EXECUTIVES

Chairman, Wu Yan
EVP, Wang He
Vice Chairman and President, Lin Zhiyong
Auditors: Deloitte Touche Tohmatsu Certified Public Accountants LLP

LOCATIONS

HQ: PICC Property and Casualty Co Ltd
Tower 2, No. 2 Jianguomenwai Avenue, Chaoyang District, Beijing 100022
Phone: (86) 10 85176084   **Fax:** (86) 10 85176084
Web: www.epicc.com.cn

COMPETITORS

Allianz Guangzhou	China Pacific Property
CNinsure	Insurance
China Life Insurance	Ping An Insurance

HISTORICAL FINANCIALS

Company Type: Public

Income Statement

FYE: December 31

	ASSETS ($ mil.)	NET INCOME ($ mil.)	INCOME AS % OF ASSETS	EMPLOYEES
12/15	64,734	3,363	5.2%	167,709
12/14	58,992	2,435	4.1%	161,310
12/13	52,763	1,744	3.3%	160,190
12/12	46,585	1,669	3.6%	156,364
12/11	42,203	1,275	3.0%	140,942
Annual Growth	**11.3%**	**27.4%**	**—**	**4.4%**

2015 Year-End Financials

Return on assets: 5.5%
Return on equity: 22.4%
Long-term debt ($ mil.): —
No. of shares (mil.): —
Sales ($ mil): 40,838
Dividends
  Yield: —
  Payout: —
Market value ($ mil.): —

Ping An Bank Co Ltd

Auditors: Ernst & Young Hua Ming

LOCATIONS

HQ: Ping An Bank Co Ltd
Shenzhen Devolopment Bank Building, No. 5047, Shennan East Road, Shenzhen, Guangdong Province 518001
Phone: (86) 755 82080387   **Fax:** (86) 755 82080386
Web: www.bank.pingan.com

HISTORICAL FINANCIALS

Company Type: Public

Income Statement

FYE: December 31

	ASSETS ($ mil.)	NET INCOME ($ mil.)	INCOME AS % OF ASSETS	EMPLOYEES
12/15	386,039	3,366	0.9%	0
12/14	352,292	3,190	0.9%	0
12/13	312,483	2,515	0.8%	0
12/12	257,695	2,149	0.8%	0
12/11	199,888	1,632	0.8%	0
Annual Growth	**17.9%**	**19.8%**	**—**	**—**

2015 Year-End Financials

Return on assets: 0.9%
Return on equity: 14.9%
Long-term debt ($ mil.): —
No. of shares (mil.): —
Sales ($ mil): 14,812
Dividends
  Yield: —
  Payout: —
Market value ($ mil.): —

Ping An Insurance (Group) Co of China Ltd.

Ping An Insurance is China's second-largest life insurance company (after China Life Insurance Company) and offers a variety of products including fire marine cargo and accident insurance as well as a home protection plan. The company also provides stock trading equity investment funds and bonds property leasing and asset management services through Ping An Trust; and its Shenzhen Ping An Bank subsidiary offers retail banking and other consumer services such as credit card and mortgage lending. In addition Ping An Insurance founded in 1988 has launched Ping An Health Insurance Company of China.

Strategy

While insurance is still the company's main staple it is hoping to secure a prime spot in China's developing asset management industry.

In other diversification efforts Ping An Insurance has been moving to invest in a variety of commercial entities. In 2016 it bought UK-based Mayborn Group which makes baby items including the Tommee Tippee line of baby bottles.

EXECUTIVES

Chairman and CEO, Ma Mingzhe
EVP, Sun A
Chief Investment Officer, Chen Dexian
Chief Actuary, Yao Bo
Auditors: PricewaterhouseCoopers Zhong Tian LLP

LOCATIONS

HQ: Ping An Insurance (Group) Co of China Ltd.
Offices at 15, 16, 17, 18 Floors, Galaxy Development Center, Fu Hua No. 3 Road, Futian District, Shenzhen, Guangdong Province 518048
Phone: (86) 400 8866 338   **Fax:** (86) 755 8243 1029
Web: www.pingan.com

PRODUCTS/OPERATIONS

Selected Subsidiaries and Affiliates
China Ping An Insurance Overseas (Holdings) Limited
  China Ping An Insurance (Hong Kong) Company Limited (75%)
  Ping An of China Asset Management (Hong Kong) Company Limited
China Ping An Trust & Investment Co. Ltd.
  Ping An Securities Co. Ltd.
Ping An Annuity Insurance Company of China Ltd.
Ping An Health Insurance Company of China Ltd.
Ping An Life Insurance Company of China Ltd.
Ping An Property & Casualty Insurance Company of China Ltd.
Shenzhen Ping An Bank Co. Ltd.

COMPETITORS

CNinsure	China Pacific Property
China Insurance	Insurance
China Life Insurance	PICC Property
China Pacific	
Insurance	

HISTORICAL FINANCIALS

Company Type: Public

Income Statement
FYE: December 31

	ASSETS ($ mil.)	NET INCOME ($ mil.)	INCOME AS % OF ASSETS	EMPLOYEES
12/15	733,717	8,345	1.1%	275,011
12/14	645,451	6,328	1.0%	235,999
12/13	555,066	4,650	0.8%	203,366
12/12	456,232	3,216	0.7%	190,284
12/11	363,088	3,094	0.9%	175,136
Annual Growth	19.2%	28.2%	—	11.9%

2015 Year-End Financials

Return on assets: 1.2%
Return on equity: 17.3%
Long-term debt ($ mil.): —
No. of shares (mil.): —
Sales ($ mil): 100,503

Dividends
  Yield: 1.5%
  Payout: 36.4%
  Market value ($ mil.): —

STOCK PRICE ($) FY Close	P/E High/Low		Earnings	PER SHARE ($) Dividends	Book Value
12/15	11.04	10	3	0.46	0.17	2.82
12/14	20.39	8	6	0.38	0.09	2.62
12/13	18.03	11	7	0.29	0.06	1.91
12/12	17.19	14	10	0.20	0.05	1.62
12/11	13.11	19	8	0.20	0.07	1.31
Annual Growth	(4.2%)	—	—	23.3%	25.9%	21.0%

Piraeus Bank SA

Greece is the word and Piraeus has most certainly heard. Piraeus Bank provides retail banking investment banking leasing and insurance services in the Mediterranean and in Central and Eastern Europe. Its network of branches across Greece numbers more than 1000 plus it has about 400 more in Albania (Tirana Bank) Romania Bulgaria Serbia the Ukraine and the US (New York's Marathon Bank). Piraeus Bank also provides its services through its electronic Winbank business which includes about 1900 ATMs Internet and phone banking. The company maintains a diverse loan portfolio with energy and transportation loans making up 30% of its portfolio. Piraeus Bank was founded in 1916 and under state control until 1991.Since Piraeus Bank was privatized it has grown rapidly through acquisitions of other banks in Greece. The company also has expanded internationally into Central and Eastern Europe and elsewhere in the Mediterranean. It acquired Bulgarian Eurobank (now Piraeus Bank Bulgaria) Atlas Bank (renamed Piraeus Bank Beograd) Egyptian Commercia Bank (Piraeus Bank Egypt) Share Capital of International Commerce Bank in the Ukraine and the Cyprus branch network of Arab Bank (Piraeus Bank Cyprus).

In 2009 Piraeus Bank teamed with BNP Wealth Management to begin offering wealth management services. In another partnership that year the company signed an agreement with Victoria General Insurance Group in order to offer insurance. Piraeus Bank continues to seek investments for further growth.

EXECUTIVES

General Manager Corporate and Investment Banking, Ilias D. Milis
General Manager Restructuring Portfolio, Spyros A. Papaspyrou, age 56
Acting CEO, Georgios Poulopoulos
General Manager Group Finance, Konstantinos Paschalis
General Manager Group Operations, I. Sgourovasilakis
General Manager Group Administration Support, K. Georgiou
General Manager Group Technology, I. Delis
Vice Chairman, Stavros M. Lekkakos, age 64
Vice Chairman, Apostolos S. Tamvakakis, age 59
Chairman, George Handjinicolaou
Auditors: PricewaterhouseCoopers S.A.

LOCATIONS

HQ: Piraeus Bank SA
4 Amerikis str., Athens 105 64
Phone: (30) 210 333 5000   **Fax:** (30) 210 333 5080
Web: www.piraeusbankgroup.com

Branch Locations

	No.
Greece	1,037
Romanis	140
Bulgaria	83
Albania	53
Serbia	42
Egypt	41
Ukraine	37
Cyprus	14
London	1
Frankfurt	1
Total	**1,449**

PRODUCTS/OPERATIONS

Selected Subsidiaries
ATEbank
ETBA Industrial Areas S.A.
Marathon Bank of New York (USA)
OJSC Piraeus Bank ICB (Ukraine)
Picar S.A.
Piraeus Asset Management Mutual Funds S.A.
Piraeus Bank AD Beograd (Serbia)
Piraeus Bank Bulgaria AD
Piraeus Bank (Cyprus) Ltd
Piraeus Bank Egypt SAE
Piraeus Capital Management
Piraeus Card Services
Piraeus Direct Services S.A.
Piraeus Insurance and Reinsurance Brokerage S.A.
Piraeus Insurance Agency S.A.
Piraeus Factoring S.A.
Piraeus Leaases SA
Piraeus Leasing Bulgaria
Piraeus Bank Romania S.A.
Piraeus Leasing Romania
Piraeus Private Equity
Piraeus Real Estate S.A.
Piraeus Securities S.A.
Piraeus Wealth Management
Tirana Bank S.A. (Albania)
Tirana Leasing (Albania)

COMPETITORS

Alpha Bank	Emporiki Bank
Bank of Cyprus	National Bank of
EFG Eurobank Ergasias	Greece

HISTORICAL FINANCIALS

Company Type: Public

Income Statement
FYE: December 31

	ASSETS ($ mil.)	NET INCOME ($ mil.)	INCOME AS % OF ASSETS	EMPLOYEES
12/15	95,336	(2,061)	—	20,719
12/14	108,532	(2,396)	—	22,372
12/13	126,672	3,505	2.8%	22,718
12/12	92,798	(671)	—	18,872
12/11	63,834	(8,554)	—	12,806
Annual Growth	10.5%	—	—	12.8%

2015 Year-End Financials

Return on assets: (-2.1%)
Return on equity: (-22.1%)
Long-term debt ($ mil.): —
No. of shares (mil.): —
Sales ($ mil): 3,823

Dividends
  Yield: —
  Payout: —
  Market value ($ mil.): —

STOCK PRICE ($) FY Close	P/E High/Low		Earnings	PER SHARE ($) Dividends	Book Value
12/15	0.61	—	—	(0.93)	0.00	1.24
12/14	2.18	—	—	(0.41)	0.00	1.44
12/13	4.11	5	1	1.28	0.00	1.81
12/12	6.45	—	—	(0.58)	0.00	(1.30)
12/11	6.45	—	—	(7.91)	0.00	(1.08)
Annual Growth	(44.6%)	—	—	—	—	—

PJSC Gazprom

With prominent gas assets Gazprom Russia's largest company has proved and probable oil and gas reserves of 29.2 billion tons of coal equivalent and produces about 513 billion cu. meters of natural gas a year. With 18% of the world's gas reserves it is also the world's #1 gas producer. Majority-owned by the Russiangovernment Gazprom is engaged in oil and gas exploration processing transport and marketing. It operates Russia's domestic gas pipeline network and delivers gas across Central Asia and Europe. It also holds stakes in Russian financial institutions a polypropylene plant and a telecom network and produces 17% of Russia's electricity. Gazprom accounts for about 25% of Russia's tax revenues.

Geographic Reach

Gazprom exports gas to more than 30 countries within and beyond the borders of the former Soviet Union. The company has offices in Algiers Astana Ashkhabad Bishkek Dokha Ekaterinburg Kiev Kishinev Krasnodar Minsk Moscow Novy Urengoy Peking Riga Rio de Janeiro Samara St. Petersburg Tehran Tomsk Khabarovsk and Yuzhno-Sakhalinsk.

Operations

Gazprom operates one of the largest gas pipeline systems in the world and is responsible for the major part of gas production and high pressure gas transportation in the Russian Federation and is a major supplier of gas to European countries. It is engaged in oil production refining activities electric and heat energy generation. Its reportable segments are: Production of gas; Transport; Distribution; Gas storage; Production of crude oil and gas condensate; Refining; and Electric and heat energy generation and sales.

The company owns the world's largest gas transmission network - the Unified Gas Supply System of Russia with the total length of over 168 thousand kilometers.

In addition to natural gas Gazprom holds a 5% global share of the production of liquefied natural gas (LNG). It also holds 79% of oil producer Gazprom Neft. It also holds stakes in Russian financial institutions a polypropylene plant and its own telecom network and produces 17% of Russia's electric power.

Financial Performance

In 2014 Gazprom's net sales increased by 6% (in local currency) due to higher sales from production of gas segment refining and gas storage.

Its net income dropped by 1 trillion rubles (87%) compared to 2013. In fiscal 2014 net cash provided by the operating activities increased by 12% (in local currency) primarily due to a change in other current assets settlements on tax payable and accounts payable and accrued charges excluding interest dividends and capital construction.

Strategy

Gazprom's strategic goal is to establish itself as a leader among global energy companies by diversifying sales markets ensuring reliable supplies increasing operating efficiency and exploring its scientific and technical potential.

To grow its gas and condensate transmission in Western Siberia the company is expanding and retrofitting the Urengoy Condensate Treatment Plant in order to increase its annual throughput to 12 million tons of de-ethanized condensate; completing treatment and transmission facilities for oil and Achimov condensate; building sections of the Urengoy Surgut condensate pipeline; as well as expanding and retrofitting its Surgut Condensate Stabilization Plant.Gazprom's export strategy is based on the long-term contract system under the take-or-pay principle with the contractual gas price pegged to the petroleum product price as the industry benchmark.

Gas exports to Europe are critical to Gazprom which is burdened by debt because of the insolvency of Russian consumers and hordes of non-paying customers. Gazprom holds strategic partnerships with Western energy companies including Germany's E.ON Ruhrgas. Other partners include Royal Dutch Shell Eni of Italy and Finland's Fortum. In addition Gazprom has a deal with German chemical conglomerate BASF that grants BASF minority shares in both the proposed North Europe Gas Pipeline and the West Siberia field that will feed it. The company is also working on the South Stream Pipeline a massive project aimed at linking Russia's southern gas fields to Western markets via Bulgaria.

Establishing a major new market (China) in 2014 the company tied up a 30-year $400 billion-plus gas supply deal with China National Petroleum.

While natural gas is its core asset the company is also ramping up its other segments as part of a diversification drive to broaden its revenue base and enhance its profile as an integrated energy producer

In the power industry the company is engaged in the diversification of tariff regulation risks optimization of the fuel balance and achieving synergies by combining natural gas and electric power businesses. The major focus is to be placed on construction of cutting-edge combined cycle power plants which will use of natural gas. By 2020 the aggregate capacity of Gazprom's generating facilities will reach 44.8 GW.

Mergers and Acquisitions

In 2014 Gazprom acquired 100% of the South Stream Transport B.V. (the company responsible for the offshore part of the South Stream project) by acquiring EDF International S.A.S. Wintershall Holding GmbH and ENI International B.V. shares in the project for Euro 883 million.

In 2013 it bought a 89.98% interest in OAO Moscow Integrated Power Company (OAO MIPC) and heat assets from the Moscow Government. The primary business activity of OAO MIPC is the-generation purchase and supply heating and hot water to commercial and residential customers in the City of Moscow.

HISTORY

Company Background

Following the breakup of the Soviet Union in the early 1990s one of the first priorities of the Russian government was to move some state monopolies toward a free-market economic system. A presidential decree in 1992 moved the company toward privatization by calling for the formation of a Russian joint-stock company to explore for and produce gas gas condensates and oil; provide for gas processing; operate gas wells; and build gas pipelines and storage facilities.

By 1993 the government had converted its natural gas monopoly Gazprom into a joint-stock company; the company had dated back to the 1940s and the USSR Ministry of the Gas Industry had kept all of its assets when it became a corporation in 1989.

The new Gazprom was 15%-owned by Gazprom workers and 28% by people living in Russia's gas-producing regions. The state retained about a 40% share (boosted to 51% in 2003). The company inherited all of the former Soviet republics' export contracts to Western and Central Europe.

Thanks to the power of Viktor Chernomyrdin (Gazprom's former Soviet boss and gas industry minister who became Russia's prime minister in 1992) the company was able to enjoy large tax breaks and maintain its role as a monopoly –even as other industries were being more deeply privatized. However the privatization of Gazprom was later attacked as being manipulated to profit the company's top management including Chernomyrdin. Top managers were rumored to have each received 1%-5% of shares –holdings potentially worth $1.2 billion-$10 billion each.

Needing to raise cash in 1996 Gazprom offered 1% of its stock to foreigners the first sale of stock to foreign investors. In 1997 Gazprom and Royal Dutch/Shell formally became partners. That year Gazprom began building its Blue Stream pipeline across the Black Sea to Turkey. Italian group Eni helped back the project and became a partner by 1999.

In 1998 Gazprom acquired a stake in Promstroibank Russia's fourth-largest financial institution. German energy powerhouse Ruhrgas acquired a 3% stake in Gazprom in 1998 which it increased to nearly 4% the next year. Also in 1999 Gazprom started building its Yamal-Europe pipeline which was to stretch to Germany for exports to Europe.

The next year an attempt by Gazprom to muscle into Hungary's chemicals sector by offering cheaper raw materials was blocked by Hungary's TVK and Borsodchem and their allies. Also in 2000 Gazprom became embroiled in a politically controversial issue when it called for the country's leading private media holding group Media-MOST to sell shares to the gas giant in order to settle millions of dollars of debt. Because Media-MOST held NTV television a major critic of Russian President Vladimir Putin the deal was alleged to have been directed by the Kremlin. A government probe into the deal was later ordered. (By 2002 Gazprom owned a significant stake in NTV which it sold that year so it could focus on its core energy businesses.)

The alignment of Gazprom's board changed in 2000 after the annual shareholder's meeting. For the first time in Gazprom's history company managers did not have a majority of seats. A new chairman Dmitri Medvedev second in command to Putin was elected to replace Chernomyrdin. In 2001 the board fired CEO Rem Vyakhirev and replaced him with Deputy Energy Minister Alexei Miller a Putin ally.

Gazprom had announced plans in 2004 to acquire Rosneft (effectively giving the Russian government control of Gazprom) though the deal was complicated by Rosneft's acquisition of the Yugansk assets acquired from YUKOS. In 2005 Gazprom abandoned plans to merge with Rosneft and acquired Sibneft in an effort to add significant oil operations to its business. Millhouse Capital a holding company controlled by Russian oligarch Roman Abramovich sold its majority stake in what was then a major exploration and production company called Sibneft (now Gazprom Neft) to Gazprom for a reported $13 billion. At the time Sibneft was Russia's fifth-largest oil company.

In 2006 Gazprom signed long-term contracts for gas deliveries with Austrian energy giant OMV. That year Royal Dutch/Shell agreed to give control of the $22 billion Sakhalin-2 project (run by Sakhalin Energy Investment) in Russia's Far East to Gazprom.

Former Gazprom chairman Dmitri Medvedev was elected president of Russia in 2008.

The company became embroiled in a pricing dispute with neighbor Ukraine in 2009 resulting in the disruption of gas supplies to Ukraine and because of its transnational pipelines to dozens of other countries in Europe.

Wanting to expand its Russian and international assets and diversify its profile in 2009 Gazprom acquired Italian energy titan ENI's 20% share in oil producer Gazprom Neft raising the Russian giant's direct ownership to 79%. ENI had acquired its stake in 2007 following the bankruptcy of YUKOS. Gazprom had the option to buy ENI's stake within two years and exercised that right in 2009 paying just more than $4 billion to ENI. Gazprom directly owns or indirectly controls through subsidiaries about 95% of Gazprom Neft.

In 2010 the company made its first entry into the US gas market when it began trading and marketing natural gas though Gazprom Marketing & Trading USA. It also signed a strategic partnership with Royal Dutch Shell to develop oil and gas assets in Russian Siberia and the Far East and process and market products in Russia and Europe.

To raise cash to pay down debt in 2010 the company sold its controlling stake in SeverEnergia (a natural gas project partly owned by ENI) to a joint venture owned by Gazprom Neft and OAO Novatek for $1.5 billion. To raise cash it sold 9% of its 19% stake in Novatek to Gazprombank for $2.8 billion.

In 2011 it installed 1.9 GW of combined heat and power generation units and deployed an offshore production platform at the Prirazlomnoye oil field in the Pechora Sea in the Arctic.

Expanding its energy footprint in 2011 Gazprom agreed to acquire power generation KES Holding (which owns four power companies) to create Russia's largest power company. KES Holding will hold 25% of the new joint venture.

To expand its gas supply in 2012 the company announced that it planned to spend 43 billion rubles (US $1.4 billion) that year to develop gas infrastructure projects (gas fields and pipelines) in the Sakhalin region of Eastern Russia. In 2011 Gazprom acquired TNK-BP's east Siberian Kovykta gas field for about $770 million. The purchase opens up the possibility of a major supply agreement with China.

EXECUTIVES

Deputy Chairman and CEO, Alexei B. Miller, age 55
Deputy Chairman Management Committee; Director General OOO Gazprom export, Alexander I. Medvedev, age 61
Member Management Committee; Head Marketing and Processing of Gas and Liquid Hydrocarbons Department; Director General OOO Mezhregiongaz, Kirill Gennadievich Seleznev, age 42
Member Management Committee; Head Legal Department, Nikolay N. Dubik, age 45
Member Management Committee; Director General OOO Gazprom komplektatsiya, Igor Y. Fyodorov, age 51
Head Information Policy Department, Alexander D. Bespalov, age 66
Member Management Committee and Head Department Gas Transportation Underground Storage and Utilization Department, Oleg E. Aksyutin
Member Management Committee; Head Gas Gas Condensate and Oil Production, Vsevolod Cherepanov, age 50
CFO, Alexander Ivannikov
Member of the Management Committee Department Head Gazprom, Sergey Prozorov, age 58
Head of Department 840, Natalia Borisenko, age 39
Chairman, Victor A. Zubkov, age 75
Auditors: ZAO PricewaterhouseCoopers Audit

LOCATIONS

HQ: PJSC Gazprom
Nametkina St., 16, V-420, GSP-7, Moscow 117997
Phone: (7) 495 719 3001   **Fax:** (7) 495 719 8333
Web: www.gazprom.com

PRODUCTS/OPERATIONS

2014 Sales

	% of total
Distribution	53
Refining	29
Electric and heat energy generation and sales	7
Production of crude oil and gas condensate	4
Transport	3
Gas storage	0
Production of gas	0
All other segments	4
Total	**100**

COMPETITORS

BP	Rosneft
Centrica	Sakhalin Energy
Gasunie	Surgutneftegas
LUKOIL	Tatneft
Qatar Petroleum	

HISTORICAL FINANCIALS

Company Type: Public

Income Statement

FYE: December 31

	REVENUE ($ mil.)	NET INCOME ($ mil.)	NET PROFIT MARGIN	EMPLOYEES
12/15	82,293	10,658	13.0%	462,400
12/14	94,585	2,701	2.9%	459,600
12/13	159,918	34,664	21.7%	459,500
12/12	156,607	38,850	24.8%	417,000
12/11	143,741	40,490	28.2%	401,000
Annual Growth	(13.0%)	(28.4%)	—	3.6%

2015 Year-End Financials

Debt ratio: 0.2%	No. of shares (mil.): —
Return on equity: 7.7%	Dividends
Cash ($ mil.): 18,404	Yield: 6.1%
Current ratio: 1.88	Payout: 186.3%
Long-term debt ($ mil.): 37,860	Market value ($ mil.): —

	STOCK PRICE ($) FY Close	P/E High/Low		PER SHARE ($) Earnings	Dividends	Book Value
12/15	3.67	0	0	0.46	0.23	6.24
12/14	4.53	1	1	0.12	0.68	7.26
12/13	8.65	0	0	1.51	0.29	12.34
12/12	9.73	0	0	1.69	0.46	12.00
12/11	10.68	1	0	1.76	1.02	10.06
Annual Growth	(23.4%) (11.3%)	—	—	(28.4%)	(31.4%)	

PJSC Lukoil

Russians look to LUKOIL for their energy needs. Russia's #1 integrated oil company produces refines and sells oil and oil products; it accounts for 16% of Russia's crude oil production. In 2012 LUKOIL reported proved reserves of 17.3 billion barrels of oil equivalent the majority of which is located in Russia. The company explores for oil and gas in Russia and in about a dozen other countries in Eastern Europe the Middle East Asia and South America. It owns refineries in five countries and marketing and distribution assets in nearly 30 including about 6000 gas stations. In addition LUKOIL has power generation assets in Russia Bulgaria Romania and Ukraine.

Operations

It operates five refineries in Russia one each in Ukraine Bulgaria Romania the Netherlands and

Italy; LUKOIL's gas stations are located in Russia the Baltic states Central and Eastern Europe and the US.

LUKOIL Russia's second-largest company behind natural gas monopoly Gazprom is steadily transforming itself from a top-heavy bureaucratic enterprise into a decentralized entrepreneurial company competing in free markets through joint ventures and strategic relationships.

Financial Performance

The company has seen a few years of robust growth in revenues and net income due in part to the expansion of its activities (including increased hydrocarbon production and the growth of its gas station network) but largely because of the recovering global economy's effect on increasing demand and lifting commodity prices.

Ownership

LUKOIL president Vagit Alekperov controls about 20% of the company. ING Bank Eurasia holds about 70% of LUKOIL's shares on behalf of other investors.

HISTORY

LUKOIL was formed from the combination of three major state-owned oil and gas exploration companies —Langepasneftegaz Uraineftegaz and Kogalymneftegaz —that traced their origins to the discovery of oil in western Siberia in 1964. More than 25 years later after the Soviet Union broke up the oil and gas sector was one of the first industries marked for privatization.

In 1992 the government called for Langepasneftegaz Uraineftegaz and Kogalymneftegaz to merge and LUKOIL was created the next year. (The LUK of LUKOIL comes from the initials of the three companies.) Russian president Boris Yeltsin appointed Siberian oil veteran Vagit Alekperov as the company's first president. The Russian government also formed several other large integrated oil companies including Yukos Surgutneftegaz Sidanco and Sibneft.

LUKOIL went public on the fledgling Russian Trading System in 1994. The next year the company absorbed nine other enterprises including oil exploration companies Astrakhanneft Kaliningradmorneftegaz and Permneft. That year LUKOIL became the first Russian oil company to set up an exploration and production trading arm. In 1996 LUKOIL acquired a 41% stake in Izvestia Russia's major independent newspaper.

Chevron and LUKOIL with seven other oil and gas companies and three governments agreed in 1996 to build a 1500-kilometer pipeline to link the Kazakhstan oil fields to world markets.

In 1997 LUKOIL became the first Russian corporation to sell bonds to international investors and the government sold 15% of its stake in the company. That year LUKOIL's 50%-owned Nexus Fuels unit opened its first gas stations located in the parking lots of US grocery stores (the partnership dissolved and Nexus went bankrupt in 2000).

LUKOIL began a partnership with Conoco (later ConocoPhillips) in 1998 to develop oil and natural gas reserves in Russia's northern territories. LUKOIL also acquired 51% of Romania's Petrorel refinery. In 1999 it acquired control of refineries in Bulgaria and Ukraine and in a petrochemical firm in Saratov. It also acquired oil company KomiTEK in one of Russia's largest mergers.

The government sold a 9% stake in LUKOIL to a Cyprus-based unit Reforma Investments held in part by LUKOIL's "boss of bosses" Vagit Alekperov (gained at the bargain price of $200 million). Critics cited the sale as Yeltsin's bid to gain Alekperov's political support.

The company announced the first major oil find in the Russian part of the Caspian Sea in 2000 and formed a joint venture (Caspian Oil Company) with fellow Russian energy giants Gazprom and Yukos to exploit resources in the Caspian. The next year LUKOIL acquired more than 1300 gas stations on the East Coast of the US when it bought Getty Petroleum Marketing.

That year LUKOIL also acquired Bitech a Canadian oil exploration and production firm with operations in the Republic of Komi in the Russian Federation. In 2002 the company sold its oil service business a move that cut its overall workforce by some 20000 and resulted in savings of $500 million annually.

With an appetite for expansion the company upped its production with refinery acquisitions and invested heavily in new oil patches such as the Caspian Sea. In 2005 LUKOIL acquired Finland-based Oy Teboil AB and Suomen Petrooli Oy affiliated refined oil products companies for an undisclosed amount. LUKOIL also acquired Nelson Resources which had oil and gas interests in Western Kazakhstan for about $2 billion.

The next year the company acquired Marathon Oil's assets in Khanty-Mansiysk Autonomous Region —Yugra of Western Siberia —for $787 million. LUKOIL also acquired 376 European gas stations from ConocoPhillips in 2006.

In 2007 LUKOIL signed a strategic exploration and production agreement with Qatar Petroleum.

In 2008 the company diversified its operations further creating a power generation segment which encompasses its own generators at well sites and a number of generating units in Bulgaria Romania and Ukraine.

In 2008 it began to re-engage in Iraq where it had held oil concessions prior to the US-led invasion in 2003. It also acquired a retail network in Turkey in 2008 for $500 million.

EXECUTIVES

First VP Economics and Finance, Sergei P. Kukura, age 63

Deputy Chairman and First EVP Exploration and Production, Ravil U. Maganov, age 62

President and Director, Vagit Y. Alekperov, age 66

SVP Finance, Alexander K. Matytsyn, age 55

VP; CEO of LUKOIL-West Siberia, Vladimir I. Nekrasov, age 59

SVP Oil and Gas Production, Azat Shamsuarov, age 53

VP Oil Sales and Supplies, Vadim Vorobyev

VP and General Counsel, Ivan Maslyaev, age 58

Chairman, Valery I. Grayfer, age 87

Auditors: ZAO KPMG

LOCATIONS

HQ: PJSC Lukoil
11 Sretensky Boulevard, Moscow 101000
Phone: (7) 495 627 4444   **Fax:** (7) 495 625 7016
Web: www.lukoil.com

2015 Sales

	% of total
Russia	30
Other countries	70
Total	**100**

PRODUCTS/OPERATIONS

2015 Sales

	% of total
Refining marketing and distribution	95
Exploration and production	4
Corporate and other	1
Total	**100**

2015 Sales

	% of total
Refined products	67
Crude oil	27

Gas & gas products	2
Petrochemicals	1
Sales of energy & related services	1
Other	2
Total	**100**

COMPETITORS

Ashland Inc.	PETROBRAS
BP	Petrleos de
Exxon Mobil	Venezuela
Gazprom Neft	Rosneft
Imperial Oil	Royal Dutch Shell
Norsk Hydro ASA	Surgutneftegas
Occidental Petroleum	TOTAL
PEMEX	Tatneft

HISTORICAL FINANCIALS

Company Type: Public

Income Statement

FYE: December 31

	REVENUE ($ mil.)	NET INCOME ($ mil.)	NET PROFIT MARGIN	EMPLOYEES
12/15	77,852	3,942	5.1%	106,200
12/14	144,167	4,746	3.3%	0
12/13	141,452	7,832	5.5%	0
12/12	139,171	11,004	7.9%	0
12/11	133,650	10,357	7.7%	0
Annual Growth	**(12.6%)**	**(21.5%)**	**—**	**—**

2015 Year-End Financials

Debt ratio: 0.2%
Return on equity: 17.6%
Cash ($ mil.): 3,483
Current ratio: 1.75
Long-term debt ($ mil.): 10,822

No. of shares (mil.): 712
Dividends
  Yield: 7.9%
  Payout: 35.8%
Market value ($ mil.): 23,160

	STOCK PRICE ($) FY Close	P/E High/Low		PER SHARE ($) Earnings	Dividends	Book Value
12/15	32.49	0	0	5.49	2.57	61.21
12/14	38.35	10	5	6.20	2.62	107.48
12/13	63.12	7	5	10.18	3.66	104.10
12/12	67.50	5	4	14.17	3.05	96.98
12/11	53.20	6	4	13.04	1.71	87.34
Annual Growth	**(11.6%)**	**—**	**—**	**(19.5%)**	**10.6%**	**(8.5%)**

Polski Koncern Naftowy Orlen S.A.

Crudely moving into the private market PKN ORLEN is the largest refiner and distributor of oil in Poland. The company owns a total of seven refineries (including three in the Czech Republic and one in Lithuania) and has some 2700 retail sites in the Czech Republic Germany Lithuania and Poland. PKN ORLEN owns chemical maker Anwil has holdings in several other Polish companies and controls Czech refiner and retailer UNIPETROL. Two former state monopolies Petrochemia Plock (Poland's largest refinery) and Centrala Produktow Naftowych (Poland's #1 petroleum distributor) merged in 1999 to create PKN ORLEN. The Polish government still owns 27% of the company.

The company also manufactures liquefied propane-butane gas (LPG) for use at industrial plants and for heating public buildings. Other PKN ORLEN products include polyvinyl chloride plastics used in foils containers bottles cable insulation

and auto parts; nitric fertilizers; asphalts for construction of roads airports and sports facilities; and basic industrial and engine oils.

Its Eko subsidiary burns hazardous waste while its ORLEN Transport division handles the distribution of fuel to its gas stations. Its Solino holdings (70%) produce salt and brine and use salt caverns for underground storage of petroleum and fuels.

HISTORY

The merger between Petrochemia Plock Poland's largest refiner and petrochemicals maker and CPN (Centrala Produktow Naftowych) the nation's largest motor fuel distributor created Polski Koncern Naftowy (PKN) in 1999.

Poland's oil industry stretches back to the late 1800s when five refineries were built in the nation's southern region. The Polish Oil Monopoly was formed in 1944 to oversee the country's oil distribution operations; it assumed the CPN name a year later.

While the rest of the world increasingly turned to oil as an energy source after WWII Poland continued to rely on coal and its oil industry grew slowly. CPN was split into 17 regional branches in 1955. The branches controlled local operations and the head office in Warsaw handled pricing and purchasing.

In the late 1950s the Soviet Union began building the Friendship pipeline to deliver crude oil to East Germany and Poland. The Polish government responded by forming Petrochemia to develop a refinery next to the pipeline in the city of Plock.

The Petrochemia refinery began producing refined products in 1964; four years later it started processing crude oil to make fuels lubricants and bitumen. The refinery also began making products such as detergents and plastics from processed refinery gases and other hydrocarbons. It added petrochemicals in 1970.

Because of the oil industry's slow growth in Poland the country managed to avoid some of the impact of the 1970s energy crisis. (Even as late as 1995 oil accounted for only 17% of Poland's energy consumption.) But it was forced to pay higher prices for Russian crude. In 1975 the government decided to expand its refining operations and created a second major refiner Rafineria Gdanska to focus on motor oils.

Locked behind the Iron Curtain Poland was not able to build its oil operations until the early 1990s. In 1992 Petrochemia began expanding its refinery facilities to reach a production capacity of 820000 barrels per day within 10 years.

After Communism's demise the Polish government started planning the privatization of its oil operations. After several plans were adopted and discarded in the early 1990s the government finally decided in 1996 to split CPN up among the nation's refineries. Holding company Nafta Polska was formed that year to own 75% stakes in Poland's refineries and in CPN and carry out the privatization process.

In 1997 CPN was stripped of its fuel depots and rail transport operations which were placed under the Nafta Polska umbrella. Displeased with the plan to carve up CPN the distributor's management rallied against the government's plan. The Polish government gave in and went back to the drawing board.

A successful plan was formed in 1998 namely to merge Petrochemia and CPN. The companies were combined in 1999 and 30% of the new PKN was floated on the Warsaw and London stock exchanges. The next year the government spun off an additional 42% stake and the company added ORLEN to its name (combining the Polish words for eagle and energy). Also in 2000 the government began preparing to float Refineria Gdanska. PKN hoped to get a piece of its regional rival but the state left PKN out of the bidding to encourage competition.

PKN acquired some 494 gas stations in Germany from BP who sold them to meet German antitrust regulations for its merger with Veba Oel in late 2002.

In 2004 PKN purchased 63% of UNIPETROL; the European Commission's Competition Directorate granted approval of the purchase in mid-2005.

EXECUTIVES

VP and CFO, Slawomir R. Jedrzejczyk, age 48
Member Management Board Refinery Operations,
  Krystian Pater, age 53
President and CEO, Dariusz J. Krawiec
Member of Management Board Petrochemical
  Operations, Piotr Chelminski
Auditors: KPMG Audyt Sp. z o.o.

LOCATIONS

HQ: Polski Koncern Naftowy Orlen S.A.
  Chemikow 7, Plock 09-411
Phone: (48) 24 256 81 80   **Fax:** (48) 24 367 77 11
Web: www.orlen.pl

2015 Sales

	% of total
Poland	41
Germany	19
Czech Republic	12
Lithuania Latvia Estonia	8
Other countries	20
Total	**100**

PRODUCTS/OPERATIONS

2015 Sales

	% of total
Downstream	65
Retail	35
Upstream	-
Total	**100**

COMPETITORS

BP	OMV
Exxon Mobil	Royal Dutch Shell
LUKOIL	Statoil
MOL	TOTAL

HISTORICAL FINANCIALS

Company Type: Public

Income Statement

FYE: December 31

	REVENUE ($ mil.)	NET INCOME ($ mil.)	NET PROFIT MARGIN	EMPLOYEES
12/15	22,568	724	3.2%	0
12/14	30,339	(1,650)	—	20,305
12/13	37,762	58	0.2%	21,565
12/12	38,822	758	2.0%	21,954
12/11	31,044	685	2.2%	22,380
Annual Growth	**(7.7%)**	**1.4%**	**—**	**—**

2015 Year-End Financials

Debt ratio: 4.8%
Return on equity: 13.8%
Cash ($ mil.): 599
Current ratio: 1.52
Long-term debt ($ mil.): 2,077

No. of shares (mil.): 427
Dividends
  Yield: —
  Payout: —
Market value ($ mil.): —

Poly Real Estate Group Co., Ltd.

EXECUTIVES

Chairman, Guangju Song
Auditors: Daxin Certified Public Accountants

LOCATIONS

HQ: Poly Real Estate Group Co., Ltd.
  29th - 33th Floor, South Tower, Poly International
  Building, No. 688, Yuejiang Zhonglu, Haizhu Distrct,
  Guangzhou, Guangdong Province 510308
Phone: (86) 20 89898833   **Fax:** (86) 20 89898666
Web: www.gzpoly.com

HISTORICAL FINANCIALS

Company Type: Public

Income Statement

FYE: December 31

	REVENUE ($ mil.)	NET INCOME ($ mil.)	NET PROFIT MARGIN	EMPLOYEES
12/15	19,005	1,901	10.0%	0
12/14	17,571	1,965	11.2%	0
12/13	15,255	1,775	11.6%	0
12/12	11,052	1,353	12.2%	0
12/11	7,472	1,037	13.9%	0
Annual Growth	**26.3%**	**16.3%**	**—**	**—**

2015 Year-End Financials

Debt ratio: 4.5%
Return on equity: 18.5%
Cash ($ mil.): 5,771
Current ratio: 1.73
Long-term debt ($ mil.): 13,057

No. of shares (mil.): —
Dividends
  Yield: —
  Payout: —
Market value ($ mil.): —

POSCO (South Korea)

POSCO has steeled itself for any set of business conditions. The company makes hot- and cold-rolled steel products (plate steel stainless steel electrical steel and wire rods) which it sells to the auto shipbuilding home appliance engineering and machinery industries. It produces more than 39 million tons of steel a year making it the world's #3 steelmaker behind ArcelorMittal and Nippon Steel. Majority-owned POSCO Engineering & Construction builds industrial facilities such as steel plants and energy plants. POSCO Energy is Korea's largest private power generator and subsidiary Daewoo International is a global steel and raw materials trading company. Most of POSCO's sales are to Korean markets.

POSCO's hot- and cold-rolled products segments account for about two-thirds of sales. Hot-rolled products are used in the construction of automobile chassis buildings and bridges industrial pipes and tanks and railway rolling stocks. The company's cold-rolled products such as cold-rolled coils and galvanized cold-rolled products are used in the automotive industry to manufacture car body panels and for other uses like household goods electrical appliances and engineering and metal parts. It produces most of its steel at its integrated steel facilities Pohang Works and Gwangyang Works. POSCO also engages in steel and raw materials trading and invests in energy

and mineral development projects around the world though its Daewoo International unit.

South Korea has little native iron ore and POSCO has had to look elsewhere for its raw materials. It purchases iron ore or coal from Australia Brazil Canada South Africa and the US from companies such as Vale Rio Tinto and BHP Billiton. To expand its production operations POSCO has developed joint ventures with companies in China Southeast Asia and Latin America.

In 2011 the company reported an 11% rise in revenues (a more than 40% increase in local revenues) thanks in part to higher selling prices for its steel and wire rod products but primarily because of a 200%-plus growth in trading revenues as the result of the Daewoo acquisition in 2010. However POSCO reported a drop of 13% in net income for the year as major cost increases related to the Daewoo purchase outpaced revenue growth.

To geographically expand its operations POSCO has an alliance with long-time rival Nippon Steel whereby each has taken a small stake in the other; it has also formed a joint venture with Steel Authority of India and plans to establish agreements with other steelmakers in China and Europe.

POSCO is looking to expand into the energy industry market for steel plate (used in the construction oil platforms). In 2012 it secured a steel supply contract from rig maker Samkang M&T for North Sea rigs and has set its sights on getting a 10% global share of the oil and gas industry's steel plate market by 2020.

In 2011 POSCO entered a $6 billion joint venture with Vale's Mozambique operations to mine coal in the southern part of that country. The mine expected to produce 11 million tons of metallurgical coal a year will help POSCO maintain a steady supply of raw materials for its steel mills. At the same time POSCO agreed to set up a similar joint mining venture in neighboring Zimbabwe with Anchor Holdings to develop chrome coal iron ore and other minerals.

That same year POSCO acquired a 20% stake in US-based graphene company XG Sciences in a move to diversify its business. Graphene is a raw material used to manufacture high-tension nanocarbon. POSCO also moved to acquire all of Thailand-based stainless steel producer Thainox Stainless pcl in 2011. POSCCO already owned a 16% stake but had waited for political stability to return to Thailand before acquiring the balance.

HISTORY

After the Korean War South Korea the US and its allies wanted to rebuild South Korea's infrastructure as quickly as possible. Steel was given a high priority and before long about 15 companies were making various steel products. Quality was a problem though as the companies used dated production processes.

With the backing of South Korean president Chung Hee Park momentum for a large steel plant grew in the late 1960s. In 1967 the South Korean government and Korean International Steel Associates (KISA) —a consortium of seven Western steelmakers - signed an agreement that called for the completion of an integrated mill by 1972. Pohang Iron & Steel Co. (POSCO) the operating company was incorporated in 1968. Efforts to raise the necessary capital failed however and KISA was dissolved in 1969.

Undaunted the South Koreans turned to the Japanese who arranged loans covering most of the mill's costs and the early phases of planning and construction. The Japanese also transferred the technology needed to run such a plant. Slow and deliberate planning resulted in a plant far away from Seoul (part of a plan to locate industries throughout the country) and a design that lent itself to future expansion. The first stage including a blast furnace and two steel converters was completed in 1973. By the time the fourth stage of construction began in 1979 the Koreans had gained enough confidence to take over many of the tasks. When the last stage was completed in 1981 the plant had an annual capacity of 8.5 million tons.

To ensure steel of acceptable quality POSCO focused first on plain high-carbon steel for general construction rather than on specialized (and difficult to produce) varieties. The company gradually broadened its specialized offerings.

In 1985 POSCO began construction on a second integrated steel plant located in Kwangyang. That plant was also built in four stages; its annual production capacity when it was completed in 1992 was 11.4 million tons. By 1987 POSCO was exporting almost 3 million tons of steel a year and using its knowledge to assist in plant construction projects in other countries.

By the mid-1990s POSCO was exporting 6 million tons of steel annually. The South Korean government sold a 5% stake in POSCO to the public in 1998 and vowed to open up the primary steel-making industry to competition. However facing a severe downturn in steel demand that year because of sluggishness in Asian and domestic markets the company canceled two projects in China and suspended two in Indonesia. In 1999 POSCO merged its two subsidiaries Pohang Coated Steel and Pohang Steel Industries to create Pohang Steel Co. That same year POSCO Machinery & Engineering POSEC-HAWAII and P.T. Posnesia Stainless Steel Industry were joined to form POSCO Machinery Co. The South Korean government continued selling off its 13% stake in 1999.

In 2000 POSCO sold its 51% stake in telecommunications company Shinsegi Telecom to SK Telecom in exchange for cash and a 6.5% stake in SK Telecom. It also formed a strategic alliance –exploration of joint ventures shared research and joint procurement –with Nippon Steel the world's #1 steelmaker. The deal also calls for each to take increased equity stakes (2% or 3%) in the other. After about 30 years of government control the South Korean government sold its remaining shares of POSCO in 2001.

In June 2002 Chairman Yoo was indicted for influencing POSCO subsidiaries and contractors to buy inflated shares of Tiger Pools International (South Korea's sole sports lottery business) for Kim Hong-Gul the third son of South Korean President Kim Dae-Jung. That same year Pohang Iron & Steel Co. officially changed its company name to POSCO to try and strengthen brand recognition.

In 2003 Yoo resigned ahead of the company's shareholder meeting amid his possible involvement in illegal stock transactions.

The company invested in its Mexican operations in 2006 announcing a joint venture coil processing facility with Daewoo International to serve local carmakers. In 2010 POSCO acquired a majority stake in Daewoo International. Daewoo shareholders voted to put the company's depressed shares up for sale after the South Korean government gave its approval for the deal early in 2010.

EXECUTIVES

President, Hwang Eun-Yeon, age 58
CEO, Oh-Joon Kwon, age 65
President and Head Steel Production Division, Jin-Il Kim, age 63
SEVP and Head Corporate Infrastructure Division, Dong-Jun Yoon, age 57
SEVP and Head Finance and Investment Division, Young-Hoon Lee, age 56
SEVP and Head Steel Business Division, In-Hwan Oh, age 57

SEVP and Department Manager Legal Affairs, Se-Bin Song, age 53
SEVP and Head Technical Research Laboratories, Sung-Ho Park, age 59
SEVP and General Superintendent Gwangyang Works, Tong-Il An, age 56
SEVP and General Superintendent Pohang Works, Hag-Dong Kim, age 56
SEVP and Department Manager Value Management, Chung-Myong Cho, age 55
EVP and Department Manager Corporate Audit, Woo-Kyu Lee, age 58
EVP and General Manager Europe, Chang-Hee Yim
EVP and Department Manager Labor and Outside Services, Suk-Bum Ko, age 58
EVP and Project Manager Regional Head Office Establishment Team Indonesia, Jhi-Yong Kim, age 54
EVP and Department Manager New Business Development Department, Seong Yu, age 59
EVP and Department Manager Steel Solution Marketing, In-Hwa Chang, age 60
EVP and Department Manager External Relation, Dong-chang Jung, age 57
EVP and Project Manager Regional Head Office Establishment Team Vietnam, Sik Nam, age 59
EVP and President PT Krakatau POSCO Co. Ltd., Kyung-Zoon Min, age 57
EVP and Department Manager Energy and Shipbuilding Materials Marketing, Tak Jeong, age 56
EVP and Department Manager safety and Production Strategy, Tae-Ju Lee, age 57
EVP and Department Manager Steel Planning, Hong-Soo Kim, age 58
EVP and Department Manager Steel Business Strategy, Chang Hwan Son, age 55
Auditors: Samjong Accounting Corporation (A Member Firm of KPMG)

LOCATIONS

HQ: POSCO (South Korea)
  6261 Donghaean-ro Nam-gu, Pohang-si,
  Gyeongsangbuk-do 790-300
Phone: (82) 54 220 0114   **Fax:** (82) 54 220 6000
Web: www.posco.co.kr

COMPETITORS

ArcelorMittal
Baosteel
Bechtel
Fluor
Hitachi
Hyundai Steel
JFE Holdings
Kobe Steel
Mitsubishi Steel Mfg.
Nippon Steel & Sumitomo Metal Corporation
Samsung Group
Severstal
Tata Steel
ThyssenKrupp Steel
United States Steel

HISTORICAL FINANCIALS

Company Type: Public

Income Statement

FYE: December 31

	REVENUE ($ mil.)	NET INCOME ($ mil.)	NET PROFIT MARGIN	EMPLOYEES
12/15	49,460	153	0.3%	17,045
12/14	59,499	572	1.0%	17,877
12/13	58,826	1,308	2.2%	17,832
12/12	59,571	2,305	3.9%	17,623
12/11	59,496	3,148	5.3%	17,553
Annual Growth	(4.5%)	(53.0%)	—	(0.7%)

2015 Year-End Financials

Debt ratio: 0.0%	No. of shares (mil.): 80
Return on equity: 0.4%	Dividends
Cash ($ mil.): 4,139	Yield: 5.0%
Current ratio: 1.45	Payout: 107.5%
Long-term debt ($ mil.): 10,921	Market value ($ mil.): 2,829

	STOCK PRICE ($) FY Close	P/E High/Low		PER SHARE ($) Earnings	Dividends	Book Value
12/15	35.36	0	0	1.57	1.78	438.12
12/14	63.81	0	0	6.79	1.91	475.17
12/13	78.00	0	0	16.55	1.77	501.12
12/12	82.15	0	0	29.85	2.09	478.38
12/11	82.10	0	0	40.76	2.16	428.55
Annual Growth	(19.0%)	—	—	(55.7%)	(4.7%)	0.6%

Power Corp. of Canada

Founded in the 1920s to develop hydroelectric power Power Corporation of Canada now generates cash not electricity. Through its majority stake in Power Financial the company controls one of Canada's leading mutual fund firms (IGM Financial) one of its largest life insurers (Great-West Lifeco) and other insurance firms. It also owns Gesca which publishes Montreal's La Presse and six other daily newspapers in Quebec and Ontario and a majority of Pargesa Group which has stakes in large companies involved in energy (TOTAL) utilities (GDF SUEZ) construction (Lafarge) wines and spirits (Pernod Ricard) and other sectors in Europe through a controlling stake in Groupe Bruxelles Lambert.

In addition Power Corporation has investments in hedge funds private equity fund managers in France and the US and companies involved in biotechnology clean tech digital media and television production. Through Great-West Lifeco the company owns US-based mutual fund manager Putnam which it acquired from insurance brokerage Marsh & McLennan in 2007. The nearly $4 billion deal gave Power Corporation a significant presence in the US.

The company proved to be rather resilient during the economic downturn as its portfolio companies for the most part performed relatively well. Earnings were up in 2010 as IGM Financial and Great-West Lifeco reported higher sales. Power Corporation continues to focus on its core asset management and retirement planning operations and build the online presence of its media holdings. In 2011 the company made a move to enter China's fast-growing fund management sector by arranging to buy a 10% state in China Asset Management.

Former chairman Paul Desmarais (whose sons Paul and Andre are co-CEOs) owns more than 60% of Power Corporation of Canada.

EXECUTIVES

SVP Power Corporation and Power Financial, Arnaud Vial, age 64, $475,000 total compensation
EVP, John A. Rae, $497,000 total compensation
Deputy Chairman President and Co-CEO, Andre R. Desmarais, age 60, $1,000,000 total compensation
Chairman and Co-CEO, Paul Desmarais, age 62, $1,000,000 total compensation
EVP and CFO, Gregory D. Tretiak
Vice Chairman Power Corporation and Power Financial, Henri-Paul Rousseau, age 67
Vice Chairman Power Corporation and of Power Financial, Michel Plessis-Belair
Auditors: Deloitte LLP

LOCATIONS

HQ: Power Corp. of Canada
751 Victoria Square, Montreal, Quebec H2Y 2J3
Phone: 514 286-7400   **Fax:** 514 286-7484
Web: www.powercorporation.com

2015 Sales

	% of total
Canada	48
Europe	31
US	21
Total	**100**

PRODUCTS/OPERATIONS

2015 Sales

	% of total
Premium income	64
Net investment income	13
Fees income	20
Other	3
Total	**100**

2015 Sales by Segment

	% of total
Great-West Lifeco	88
IGM Financial	8
Other	4
Total	**100**

Selected Investments

Communications
Gesca Ltée (newspaper publisher)
Square Victoria Communications Group Inc.
Square Victoria Digital Properties Inc.
Financial Services
Great-West Lifeco Inc. (68%)
The Canada Life Assurance Company
Great-West Life & Annuity Insurance Company
The Great-West Life Assurance Company
London Life Insurance Company
Putnam Investments LLC
IGM Financial Inc. (57%)
Investment Planning Counsel (91%)
Investors Group
Mackenzie Financial Corporation
Power Financial Corporation (66%)
Victoria Square Ventures Inc.
Other
Pergesa Holding S.A. (Switzerland)

COMPETITORS

AGF Management	Dundee Corp.
Berkshire Hathaway	Loews
Brookfield Asset	Manulife Financial
Management	Onex
CI Financial	Ontario Teachers'
CPP Investment Board	Pension Plan
Caisse de dep²t et	Street Capital
placement du Quebec	

HISTORICAL FINANCIALS

Company Type: Public

Income Statement

	ASSETS ($ mil.)	NET INCOME ($ mil.)	INCOME AS % OF ASSETS	EMPLOYEES
12/15	304,453	37	0.0%	26,500
12/14	326,232	44	0.0%	0
12/13	324,456	48	0.0%	0
12/12	273,127	50	0.0%	30,900
12/11	250,461	40	0.0%	30,700
Annual Growth	5.0%	(1.8%)	—	(3.6%)

2015 Year-End Financials

Return on assets: 0.0%
Return on equity: 0.4%
Long-term debt ($ mil.): —
No. of shares (mil.): 414
Sales ($ mil): 27,703
Dividends
Yield: 0.0%
Payout: 31.8%
Market value ($ mil.): 8,648

	STOCK PRICE ($) FY Close	P/E High/Low		PER SHARE ($) Earnings	Dividends	Book Value
12/15	20.87	6	5	2.76	0.88	24.37
12/14	27.32	10	9	2.37	1.00	25.07
12/13	30.09	15	11	1.96	1.09	25.27
12/12	25.58	15	12	1.80	1.17	24.70
12/11	23.33	12	9	2.27	1.14	23.43
Annual Growth	(2.7%)	—	—	5.0%	(6.2%)	1.0%

Power Financial Corp

Power Financial gets a charge out of insurance and investments. The holding company seeks controlling stakes in financial services companies in the US the UK and Canada. Core investments include 68%-owned Great-West Lifeco (subsidiaries include Great-West Life Assurance Canada Life and London Life Insurance leading providers of insurance in Canada). Lifeco's US subsidiary Great-West Life & Annuity Insurance provides employee benefits and retirement plans. Boston-based fund manager Putnam Investments is also part of the family. Power Financial owns about half of IGM Financial which owns Investors Group and Mackenzie Financial distributors of mutual funds and other investment products and services.

Power Financial also is a 50% partner in Dutch holding company Parjointco with the Frère-Bourgeois and CNP groups the joint venture that owns a 54% stake in Pargesa which invests in building materials utilities minerals and energy companies (with Groupe Bruxelles Lambert it owns stakes in Imerys and TOTAL).

In 2007 Power Financial surprised many when it purchased the once-venerable but recently disgraced Putnam Investments. Speculation turned to I-told-you-so the following year when Putnam like most money managers was slammed by the subprime mortgage and credit market collapse. In mid-2008 Power Financial brought in long-time Fidelity Investments COO Robert Reynolds as president and CEO of Putnam. The new leader trimmed staff tied pay to performance and started two new funds to attract fresh money.

Power Corporation of Canada the country's fifth largest firm by revenue owns two-thirds of Power Financial. Canada's well-known billionaire Desmarais family controls Power Corporation.

EXECUTIVES

President and CEO, R. Jeffrey Orr, $3,358,665 total compensation
EVP and CFO, Gregory D. Tretiak
Managing Director Power Financial Europe, Jocelyn Lefebvre
EVP, Claude Genereux
Co-Chairman, Andre R. Desmarais, age 60
Co-Chairman, Paul Desmarais, age 62
Vice Chairman, Henri-Paul Rousseau, age 67
Vice Chairman, Amaury de Seze
Vice Chairman, Michel Plessis-Belair
Auditors: Deloitte LLP

LOCATIONS

HQ: Power Financial Corp
751 Victoria Square, Montreal, Quebec H2Y 2J3
Phone: 514 286-7400   **Fax:** 514 286-7484
Web: www.powerfinancial.com

2015 Revenues

	% of total
Canada	48
Europe	32
US	20
Total	**100**

PRODUCTS/OPERATIONS

2015 Revenues

	% of total
Great-West Lifeco	92
IGM	8
Total	**100**

2015 Revenues

	% of total
Premium Income	67
Investment Income	12
Fee Income	21
Total	**100**

Selected Subsidiaries & Affiliates

Great-West Lifeco Inc. (68%)
Great-West Life & Annuity Insurance Company (US)
Great-West Life Assurance Company
Canada Life Financial Corporation
London Insurance Group Inc.
Putnam LLC
IGM Financial Inc. (57%)
Investment Planning Counsel (94%)
Investors Group Inc.
Mackenzie Financial Corporation

COMPETITORS

AXA Financial
Allstate
CIGNA
Industrial Alliance Insurance and Financial Servic
Manulife Financial
Prudential
RBC Financial Group
State Farm
Sun Life

HISTORICAL FINANCIALS

Company Type: Public

Income Statement

FYE: December 31

	ASSETS ($ mil.)	NET INCOME ($ mil.)	INCOME AS % OF ASSETS	EMPLOYEES
12/15	300,689	1,669	0.6%	25,720
12/14	322,832	1,844	0.6%	0
12/13	321,358	1,783	0.6%	0
12/12	270,058	1,634	0.6%	17,870
12/11	247,698	1,688	0.7%	29,100
Annual Growth	5.0%	(0.3%)	—	(3.0%)

2015 Year-End Financials

Return on assets: 0.5%
Return on equity: 12.6%
Long-term debt ($ mil.): —
No. of shares (mil.): 713
Sales ($ mil): 26,449
Dividends
Yield: 0.0%
Payout: 45.9%
Market value ($ mil.): 16,492

	STOCK PRICE ($) FY Close	P/E High/Low		PER SHARE ($) Earnings	Dividends	Book Value
12/15	23.12	9	7	2.33	1.07	19.74
12/14	31.27	10	9	2.59	1.21	20.65
12/13	34.02	13	10	2.47	1.32	21.31
12/12	27.29	13	11	2.31	1.41	19.89
12/11	25.07	13	10	2.36	1.37	18.72
Annual Growth	(2.0%)	—	—	(0.3%)	(6.0%)	1.3%

Prudential Plc

When it comes to life insurance a little prudence goes a long way. Working through its subsidiaries Prudential is the UK's largest life insurer and the largest European insurer operating in Asia. In addition to insurance Prudential UK's products include pensions annuities investment bonds and fund management. Its businesses include Prudential Corporation Asia; Jackson National Life Insurance Prudential's US subsidiary better known as Jackson; Prudential UK & Europe and its UK-focused asset management business M&G. Prudential plc was formed in 1848 to offer life insurance and loans to the middle class and is not affiliated with US insurance giant Prudential Financial.

Operations

Prudential serves more than 24 million policyholders through its global insurance divisions and it has a total of some £509 billion in assets under management. About 14 million of Prudential's customers are in Asia. Prudential's US operations conducted though subsidiary Jackson National Life is primarily focused on meeting the needs of the retiring and wealthy Baby Boomer generation; the US is Prudential's largest territory by revenue. Prudential's operation in the UK its original market offers long-term accumulation and retirement products.

Geographic Reach

Through its UK-based businesses Prudential has about 50 branch locations in the UK other European countries and India. Jackson National distributes products in all 50 US states from about 20 regional offices. In Asia Prudential has about 30 businesses that are spread over 14 markets and has strong market positions in China India Vietnam Hong Kong Philippines Indonesia Singapore Malaysia and Cambodia.

Sales and Marketing

Prudential conducts sales through independent brokers and agents institutional product distributors regional brokers captive agents banks investment advisors and via direct marketing means like telephone mail and the internet.

In addition to joint ventures with banks in China (with CITIC Group) and India (with ICICI Bank) Prudential has bank distribution agreements in other Asian markets. Its life accident and health insurance policies are sold in Singapore Indonesia and Thailand through the more than 500 branches of United Overseas Bank.

Financial Performance

Note: Growth rates may differ after conversion to US Dollars.

A trend of volatile revenue since the 2007 financial crisis (a result of a reliance on investment returns for more than 40% of Prudential's insurance income) continued in 2015 with revenue falling 31% on 2014 to £41.7 billion for the year. This sharp fall was due almost entirely to a £22 billion fall in investment return and spread between the three territories of Asia the US and the UK. Despite a fall in revenue profit for the year climbed 16% to £2.6 billion due to higher profits based on longer-term investment returns.

Cash flow from operating activities rose by £700 million to £2.5 billion tracking the rise in profits. Prudential has seen steadily climbing net income over the past five years as revenues outweigh expenses.

Strategy

A key part of Prudential's growth strategy and differentiation from its competitors is its presence in Asia particularly in markets including Southeast Asia Singapore and Hong Kong. It is working to increase sales of savings and insurance products to the emerging and increasingly self-reliant middle class in Asian markets. One manifestation of this is in heathcare insurance. 42% of heathcare spend in Asia is out-of-pocket (compared to 9% in the UK) and together with an increase in cancer survival rates (and a subsequent increase in recurrences) has driven a desire to reduce the financial anxiety - via insurance - that a second or third cancer brings.

Another strategic area of focus is retirement savings products (such as variable annuities) in the US. Its Jackson National Life Insurance targets the aging Baby Boomer demographic in the US the wealthiest in the world. Prudential views Baby Boomers as under-saved especially in the context of advancing life-expectancy and looks to provide products to grow assets and provide guaranteed lifetime income. In the UK the company is maximizing its asset management operations and focusing on core insurance markets.

HISTORY

Actually prudence almost killed Prudential before it ever got started. Founded in 1848 as Prudential Mutual Assurance Investment and Loan Association the firm initially insured middle-class customers. The Dickensian conditions of the working poor made them too risky for insurers. Unfortunately the company found few takers of the right sort and by 1852 Prudential was in peril.

Two events saved Prudential: The House of Commons pressed for insurance coverage for all classes and Prudential's own agents pushed for change. The company expanded into industrial insurance a modest coverage for the working poor. In 1864 to quell criticism of the insurance industry Prudential brought in independent auditors to confirm its soundness. This soon became a marketing tool and business took off. The Pru as it came to be known became the leading industrial insurer by the 1880s. It covered half the country's population by 1905. The firm's salesmen were known for making personal visits to customers (the "Man from the Pru" became a ubiquitous icon in the 1940s and was revived in 1997).

During the two world wars Prudential boosted its reputation by honoring the policies of war victims when it could have legally denied them. Between wars the company added fire and accident insurance in Europe.

The 1980s were volatile for insurance companies especially in the wake of Britain's financial deregulation in 1986. Therefore in 1982 under the direction of CEO Brian Corby the Pru reorganized product lines and in 1985 entered the real estate business. In 1986 it entered the US market by buying US-based Jackson National Life Insurance.

Prudential which had considered selling Mercantile and General Reinsurance in the early 1990s (purchased in 1969) sold the reinsurer back to Swiss Re in 1996. It also formed Prudential Bank and created an Asian emerging-market investment fund that year.

Insurance regulators reprimanded the company for mis-selling financial products in 1997. In 1998 Jackson National bought a California savings and loan enabling it to sell investment products in the US. Also that year the Pru sold its Australian and New Zealand businesses and Prudential Bank launched its pioneering Internet bank Egg Banking.

In 1999 Prudential bought investment manager M&G Group. The company then changed its name to Prudential plc and began talks with the Prudential Insurance Company of America to resolve confusion of their similar names as they expanded into new markets. Also in 1999 the Pru joined forces with the Bank of China to offer pension and asset management in Hong Kong.

The company announced plans in 2000 to sell a chunk of its institutional fund management business as well as its traditional balanced pension business to Deutsche Bank. That year the company spun off 20% of Egg (it sold the rest in 2007).

Entering the Japanese life insurance market Prudential bought Orico Life in 2001. Prudential's hopes of capturing the lucrative annuities market by acquiring American General were dashed that year as American General instead embraced American International Group leaving the Pru with a $600 million break-up fee. To consolidate operations the firm sold its general insurance business in 2001 to Swiss insurer Winterthur (a subsidiary of Credit Suisse).

In early 2006 Prudential rejected a takeover offer from larger rival Aviva valued at nearly $30 billion.

After helping oversee the shift in focus that brought the company growth in Asia and stability during the 2008 economic downturn CEO Mark Tucker stepped down at the end of September 2009. The company chose CFO Tidjane Thiam to replace him. Thiam a native of Ivory Coast became the first black CEO of a FTSE 100 company.

In early 2010 the company expanded its operations in Singapore by acquiring United Overseas Bank's life insurance unit for S$428 million ($307 million). Along with becoming owner of UOB Life Assurance Ltd. Prudential entered into an agreement through which UOB sells Prudential's life accident and health insurance policies for 12 years at the bank's more than 400 branches in Singapore Indonesia and Thailand giving Prudential a greater presence in those markets. In 2011 Prudential targeted the business of Singapore's class of "rising rich" individuals as an important area for growth.

Prudential made a splashy bid on AIG's Hong Kong-based American International Assurance (AIA) business in 2010. The $35.5 billion deal ($25 billion in cash $8.5 billion in securities and $2 billion in stock) would have made Prudential the largest life insurer in Hong Kong and allowed AIG to pay off a chunk of its debt to the US government. However Prudential's shareholders were not impressed and raised a ruckus over the deal. To appease them Prudential attempted to reduce its offer to $30 billion —which AIG coolly refused —and then simply withdrew its entire offer.

EXECUTIVES

Executive Director; Chief Executive The M&G Group, Michael G.A. McLintock, age 55, $320,000 total compensation
Group CEO, Mike Wells
Chairman and CEO Prudential North America, Barry L. Stowe, age 59, $646,000 total compensation
Chief Executive Prudential UK & Europe, Jackie Hunt, age 48
CFO, Nic Nicandrou
CEO Prudential Asia, Tony Wilkey
Group Investment Director and Interim Chief Risk Officer, John Foley
Chairman, Paul Manduca, age 64
Auditors: KPMG LLP

LOCATIONS

HQ: Prudential Plc
12 Arthur Street, London EC4R 9AQ
Phone: (44) 20 7220 7588
Web: www.prudential.co.uk

2015 Sales

	% of total
US	38
UK	32
Asia	24
Asset Management	6
Total	100

PRODUCTS/OPERATIONS

2015 Sales

	% of total
Insurance	94
Asset management	6
Total	**100**

COMPETITORS

AEGON	Lincoln Financial
AIA Group	Group
AIG	Lloyds Banking Group
AXA	Manulife Financial
Allianz	MetLife
Aviva	Mitsui Sumitomo
BlackRock	Insurance
Canada Life	Nationwide Financial
Cathay Life Insurance	New York Life
China Life Insurance	Nippon Life Insurance
China Pacific	Ping An Insurance
Insurance	Prudential
Citigroup	RSA Insurance
FMR	Samsung Life Insurance
Great Eastern Holdings	Schroders
HSBC	Standard Life
ING	State Farm
Invesco Perpetual	TIAA
Jupiter Fund	The Hartford
Management	Tokio Marine
Legal & General Group	Zurich Insurance Group

HISTORICAL FINANCIALS

Company Type: Public

Income Statement

FYE: December 31

	ASSETS ($ mil.)	NET INCOME ($ mil.)	INCOME AS % OF ASSETS	EMPLOYEES
12/15	573,490	3,821	0.7%	21,820
12/14	576,335	3,459	0.6%	20,544
12/13	538,628	2,224	0.4%	20,052
12/12	500,086	3,541	0.7%	27,619
12/11	422,641	2,301	0.5%	25,414
Annual Growth	7.9%	13.5%	—	(3.7%)

2015 Year-End Financials

Return on assets: 0.6%	Dividends
Return on equity: 20.8%	Yield: 2.6%
Long-term debt ($ mil.): —	Payout: 77.2%
No. of shares (mil.): —	Market value ($ mil.): —
Sales ($ mil): 61,564	

	STOCK PRICE ($) FY Close	P/E High/Low		PER SHARE ($) Earnings	Dividends	Book Value
12/15	45.08	52	39	1.50	1.18	7.46
12/14	46.17	56	43	1.35	1.17	7.18
12/13	45.00	85	55	0.87	0.94	6.23
12/12	28.55	34	24	1.39	0.81	6.53
12/11	19.74	41	28	0.91	0.76	5.53
Annual Growth	22.9%	—	—	13.3%	11.5%	7.8%

PTT Public Co Ltd.

Thailand fills its tanks thanks to integrated oil company PTT the nation's largest company. Its PTT Oil transportation and marketing unit operates more than 1200 gas stations. PTT Gas procures processes transports and distributes natural gas. PTT owns 49% of the nation's largest refiner Thai Oil. Other PTT units engage in oil and gas exploration and production (in Thailand and elsewhere) produce petrochemicals and mine coal. It is also has major oil and gas trading operations.

The company is majority-owned by the Government of Thailand.

Operations

PTT's core businesses are Exploration & Production and Gas and Oil.

PTT Exploration and Production Public Company Limited (PTTEP). PTT has also invested in natural gas-related corporations both in Thailand and abroad.

The Gas Business Group engages in natural gas supply procurement pipeline transmission separation and distribution.

The Oil Business Group engages in distribution of refined fuel and lubricating products covering retail marketing run through PTT service stations wholesale marketing and commercial marketing for government agencies industry sector airlines and oil vessels.

The International Trading Business Group covers procurement and import-export trading of crude oil condensate petroleum and petrochemical products .

On the investment side PTT invests in a wide range of its related businesses with an emphasis on petrochemical and oil refining businesses.

Financial Performance

The company's revenues increased by 28% in 2011 with a jump in profits of 25% reflected the success in natural gas procurement to meet growing demand efficiency improvement of gas separation plants (GSPs) and the commercial operation of GSP unit 6 (Rayong) which boosted production capacity.

Other factors include PTTEP's production increase (especially from the oil sands KKD project in Canada); production capacity expansion in the petrochemical group; improved returns from portfolio risk management investment and development programs; and pricing risk management for PTT and PTT group.

Strategy

The company sees its role as being the lead player in Thailand's oil and gas development and revenue production. PTT is relying on the synergy between various downstream businesses to add business value and reduce operating costs.

Ownership

The Government of Thailand owns 51% of PTT.

Company Background

Thailand which created PTT to secure energy supplies during the oil crunch of the late 1970s sold a third of the company in a 2001 IPO.

In 2008 as part of PTT's energy diversification drive the company opened the world's largest NGV (natural gas vehicle) gas station in Thailand to respond to the growing number of NGV vehicles in the country.

EXECUTIVES

CFO, Wirat Uanarumit
President and CEO, Tevin Vongvanich, age 58
COO Infrastructure, Surong Bulakul, age 61
COO Upstream Petroleum and Gas, Nuttachat Charuchinda
COO Downstream Petroleum, Sarun Rungkasiri
SEVP Petrochemicals and Refining, Sarakorn Kulatham
SEVP Human Resources and Organization Excellence, Pitipan Tepartimargorn
SEVP Corporate Strategy, Chansin Treenuchagron
SEVP Gas, Charcrie Buranakanonda
SEVP Oil, Chavalit Punthong
SEVP International Trading, Boobpha Amornkiatkajorn
SEVP Sustainability Management and Project Engineering, Auttapol Rerkpibook
Chairman, Piyasvasti Amranand
Auditors: The Office of the Auditor General of Thailand

LOCATIONS

HQ: PTT Public Co Ltd.
555 Vibhavadi-Rangsit Road, Chatuchak, Bangkok 10900
Phone: (66) 2 537 2000   **Fax:** (66) 2 537 3498 9
Web: www.pttplc.com

PRODUCTS/OPERATIONS

2011 Sales

	% of total
International trading	53
Oil	21
Natural gas	16
Exploration & production	6
Petrochemical	3
Coal	1
Other	-
Total	**100**

Selected Subsidiaries and Affiliates:

PetroAsia (Huizhou) Co. Ltd. (25%)
PTT Exploration and Production Public Co. Ltd. (66%)
PTT Mart Co. Ltd. (49%)
PTT Natural Gas Distribution Co. Ltd. (58%)
Star Petroleum Refining Co. Ltd. (36%)
Thai Lube Blending Co. Ltd. (49%)
Thai Oil Plc. (50%)

COMPETITORS

BP	Chevron

HISTORICAL FINANCIALS

Company Type: Public

Income Statement

FYE: December 31

	REVENUE ($ mil.)	NET INCOME ($ mil.)	NET PROFIT MARGIN	EMPLOYEES
12/15	56,256	553	1.0%	0
12/14	86,213	1,696	2.0%	25,986
12/13	86,831	2,891	3.3%	25,251
12/12	91,301	3,420	3.7%	20,816
12/11	77,158	3,345	4.3%	18,240
Annual Growth	(7.6%)	(36.2%)	—	—

2015 Year-End Financials

Debt ratio: 0.8%	No. of shares (mil.): —
Return on equity: 2.8%	Dividends
Cash ($ mil.): 6,660	Yield: —
Current ratio: 2.16	Payout: —
Long-term debt ($ mil.): 16,048	Market value ($ mil.): —

	STOCK PRICE ($) FY Close	P/E High/Low		PER SHARE ($) Earnings	Dividends	Book Value
12/15	6.30	1	1	0.19	0.00	6.77
12/14	10.00	1	0	0.59	0.00	7.43
12/13	8.96	0	0	1.01	0.00	7.30
12/12	10.79	0	0	1.20	0.00	6.93
12/11	9.50	0	0	1.17	0.00	6.18
Annual Growth	(9.8%)	—	—	(36.8%)	—	2.3%

Public Bank Berhad (Malaysia)

Public Bank stakes its success on providing banking services to the public. The company has about 250 branches throughout Malaysia where it is one of the top lenders and fund operators. Offerings include deposit accounts credit cards home loans and insurance plans. In addition to retail and commercial services it provides corporate banking brokerage investment banking wealth management and Islamic banking. Public Bank has more than 100 overseas branches in countries including Cambodia China Hong Kong Laos Sri Lanka and Vietnam. The company was founded in 1966 by chairman Tan Sri Dato' Sri Dr. Teh Hong Piow.

Auditors: Ernst & Young

LOCATIONS

HQ: Public Bank Berhad (Malaysia)
Menara Public Bank, 146 Jalan Ampang, Kuala Lumpur 50450
Phone: (60) 3 2176 6000   **Fax:** (60) 3 2163 9917
Web: www.publicbankgroup.com

PRODUCTS/OPERATIONS

652014325

COMPETITORS

AmBank Group	Hong Leong Bank
Bank Muamalat	Lloyds Banking Group
Bank Pembangunan	Maybank
CIMB Group	RHB Capital
HSBC	

HISTORICAL FINANCIALS

Company Type: Public

Income Statement

FYE: December 31

	ASSETS ($ mil.)	NET INCOME ($ mil.)	INCOME AS % OF ASSETS	EMPLOYEES
12/15	84,496	1,175	1.4%	18,373
12/14	98,869	1,292	1.3%	18,198
12/13	93,326	1,240	1.3%	17,924
12/12	89,694	1,263	1.4%	17,625
12/11	78,703	1,099	1.4%	17,511
Annual Growth	1.8%	1.7%	—	1.2%

2015 Year-End Financials

Return on assets: 1.4%
Return on equity: 17.0%
Long-term debt ($ mil.): —
No. of shares (mil.): —
Sales ($ mil): 4,205

Dividends
Yield: —
Payout: —
Market value ($ mil.): —

	STOCK PRICE ($) FY Close	P/E High/Low		PER SHARE ($) Earnings	Dividends	Book Value
12/15	4.20	3	3	0.30	0.00	1.88
12/14	5.55	5	4	0.35	0.00	2.08
12/13	4.00	—	—	0.35	0.00	1.78
12/12	4.00	—	—	0.36	0.00	1.67
12/11	4.00	4	4	0.31	0.00	1.34
Annual Growth	1.2%	—	—	(0.8%)	—	8.8%

Qatar National Bank

Auditors: Firas Qoussous (a member of Ernst & Young)

LOCATIONS

HQ: Qatar National Bank
P.O. Box 1000, Doha
Phone: (974) 44425 444   **Fax:** (974) 4441 3753
Web: www.qnb.com.qa

HISTORICAL FINANCIALS

Company Type: Public

Income Statement

FYE: December 31

	ASSETS ($ mil.)	NET INCOME ($ mil.)	INCOME AS % OF ASSETS	EMPLOYEES
12/16	197,642	3,395	1.7%	0
12/15	147,918	3,093	2.1%	0
12/14	133,632	2,872	2.1%	0
12/13	121,790	2,603	2.1%	0
12/12	100,734	2,289	2.3%	0
Annual Growth	18.4%	10.4%	—	—

2016 Year-End Financials

Return on assets: 1.9%
Return on equity: 18.8%
Long-term debt ($ mil.): —
No. of shares (mil.): 839
Sales ($ mil): 11,736

Dividends
Yield: —
Payout: —
Market value ($ mil.): —

QBE Insurance Group Ltd.

QBE Insurance Group may be one of Australia's leading insurers but it also has a hefty global reach. The company offers a variety of insurance and reinsurance through offices in about 50 countries. QBE provides general property/casualty policies as well as liability auto marine aviation energy accident workers' compensation and professional indemnity coverage. The company writes both individual and commercial insurance policies and also administers reinsurance coverage. It sells its products through direct and independent representative agencies.

Geographic Reach

QBE Insurance Group earns about three-fourths of its revenue outside of Australia.

Financial Performance

The company's revenue decreased in fiscal 2013 compared to the previous fiscal year. It reported about $16 billion in revenue for fiscal 2013 down from $17 billion in fiscal 2012. The decreased revenue caused the company to suffer a net loss of $251 million in fiscal 2013 after claiming a net income of $760 million in fiscal 2012.

QBE Insurance Group's cash flow also decreased significantly in fiscal 2013 compared to fiscal 2012 levels.

Strategy

After an extremely acquisitive period the company has been working to catch up to itself. Restructuring efforts have been made to cut costs; for example the company established a global processing center in the Philippines in 2013. In late 2014 QBE Insurance Group agreed to sell its operations in the Czech Republic Hungary and Slovakia to Fairfax Financial Holdings.

EXECUTIVES

CEO European Operations, Richard Pryce
CEO, John Neal, age 52
CEO Australian & New Zealand Operations, Patrick C. (Pat) Regan
CEO North America, Russell (Russ) Johnston
Group COO, Colin Fagen
CEO Emerging Markets Division, David Fried
Chief Risk Officer, Jason Brown
CEO Australian and New Zealand, Tim Plant
Chairman, Marty Becker
Auditors: PricewaterhouseCoopers

LOCATIONS

HQ: QBE Insurance Group Ltd.
Level 27, 8 Chifley Square, Sydney, New South Wales 2000
Phone: (61) 2 9375 4444   **Fax:** (61) 2 9231 6104
Web: www.qbe.com

COMPETITORS

AEGON	ING
AIG	Insurance Australia
AMP Limited	Loews
AXA	Munich Re Group
AXIS Capital Holdings	National Australia
Allianz	Bank
Allianz France	Nationwide
Allstate	RSA Insurance
Australia and New	Samsung Fire & Marine
Zealand Banking	Standard Chartered
Aviva	State Farm
Commonwealth Bank of	Suncorp-Metway
Australia	Swiss Re
GEICO	Travelers Companies
Generali	Westpac Banking

HISTORICAL FINANCIALS

Company Type: Public

Income Statement

FYE: December 31

	ASSETS ($ mil.)	NET INCOME ($ mil.)	INCOME AS % OF ASSETS	EMPLOYEES
12/15	42,176	687	1.6%	0
12/14	45,000	742	1.6%	19,442
12/13	47,271	(254)	—	17,000
12/12	50,762	761	1.5%	0
12/11	46,737	704	1.5%	0
Annual Growth	(2.5%)	(0.6%)	—	—

2015 Year-End Financials

Return on assets: 1.5%
Return on equity: 6.3%
Long-term debt ($ mil.): —
No. of shares (mil.): 1,370
Sales ($ mil): 12,587

Dividends
Yield: 3.2%
Payout: 58.5%
Market value ($ mil.): 12,460

	STOCK PRICE ($) FY Close	P/E High/Low		PER SHARE ($) Earnings	Dividends	Book Value
12/15	9.10	23	16	0.50	0.29	7.67
12/14	9.06	21	15	0.56	0.22	8.09
12/13	10.27	—	—	(0.23)	0.26	8.30
12/12	11.43	23	16	0.62	0.64	9.51
12/11	13.25	32	18	0.61	0.58	9.34
Annual Growth	(9.0%)	—	—	(4.8%)	(5.1%)	(15.8%)

Quanta Computer Inc

Quanta Computer is an original design manufacturer (ODM) serving some of the leading names in computer hardware including Dell Apple and HP. It is one of the world's largest manufacturers of notebook computers and also produces network servers television set-top boxes monitors LCD TVs and smartphones. Quanta Computer's other business units include Quanta Storage (data storage products) and RoyalTek Company (personal navigation devices and other GPS products). While well known for its notebooks and their smaller computer cousins the netbooks Quanta Computer is diversifying into other consumer electronics and IT products.

Geographic Reach The company is based in Taiwan with additional facilities in Asia Europe and North and South America.

Financial Performance Quanta Computer's 2011 revenue fell just over 1% to NT$1.1 trillion (around $37 billion). Its net income however rose by 22% for the same period to NT$23 billion (about $780 million) as a result of strict cost controls it put in place. The company is focused on inventory reductions and yield rate improvements among other measures.

Strategy The company is focusing its R&D efforts on cloud computing connectivity and client devices. All three areas are part of a broader cloud computing initiative that involves the design and manufacture of data storage products and servers (for providing cloud-computing services) next-generation data networking products (for enabling uninterrupted cloud-computing connections and service coverage) and client devices (for accessing cloud networks). Outside of notebooks other areas of focus include mobile devices automotive electronics high-definition video conferencing and satellite technology.

EXECUTIVES

CFO, Elton Yang
Vice Chairman and President, C.C. Leung
Chairman, Barry Lam
Auditors: KPMG

LOCATIONS

HQ: Quanta Computer Inc
No. 188, Wen Hwa 2nd Road, Guishan District, Taoyuan 33377
Phone: (886) 3 327 2345   **Fax:** (886) 3 327 1511
Web: www.quantatw.com

PRODUCTS/OPERATIONS

Products
QCI
Notebook
Server
OLPC
Camera
Industrial computer

COMPETITORS

ASUSTeK	Hon Hai
BenQ	Inventec
Celestica	MiTAC
China Techfaith	Pegatron
Compal Electronics	Super Micro Computer
First International Computer	Tatung
	TriGem
Flextronics	Wistron
Foxconn International	

HISTORICAL FINANCIALS

Company Type: Public

Income Statement

FYE: December 31

	REVENUE ($ mil.)	NET INCOME ($ mil.)	NET PROFIT MARGIN	EMPLOYEES
12/15	30,652	542	1.8%	90,167
12/14	29,254	596	2.0%	120,370
12/13	29,522	624	2.1%	76,349
12/12	35,317	794	2.2%	88,315
12/11	36,612	775	2.1%	108,872
Annual Growth	(4.3%)	(8.5%)	—	(4.6%)

2015 Year-End Financials

Debt ratio: 1.0%
Return on equity: 13.4%
Cash ($ mil.): 4,039
Current ratio: 1.28
Long-term debt ($ mil.): 636

No. of shares (mil.): —
Dividends
  Yield: —
  Payout: 325.9%
Market value ($ mil.): —

	STOCK PRICE ($) FY Close	P/E High/Low		PER SHARE ($) Earnings	Dividends	Book Value
12/15	0.00	—	—	0.14	0.45	1.05
12/14	11.75	2	2	0.15	0.46	1.08
12/13	8.87	—	—	0.16	0.52	1.07
12/12	8.87	—	—	0.20	0.53	1.08
Annual Growth	—	—	—	(9.2%)	(4.0%)	(0.7%)

Rallye S.A. Neuilly-Sur-Seine

Retail giant Rallye musters its businesses around not just the French flag but around flags worldwide. Rallye's Casino Guichard-Perrachon subsidiary operates over 15000 hypermarkets supermarkets and convenience stores in Europe (mostly France) Asia/Pacific and South America (including Brazil). It also has a foothold in the sporting goods and athletic shoe department with Courir and Groupe Go Sport which runs about 500 shops mostly in France. In addition to retailing the company is active in real estate development banking and a variety of investment vehicles. Foncière Euris controls about 55% of Rallye and nearly 75% of the voting rights.

Operations
Rallye's Casino subsidiary is a leading supermarket chain in France and has operation in a further 10 countries worldwide. Store banners include Casino Monoprix Franprix-Leader Price and Vindemia. In Latin America food sales are made through mainly the ?xito Disco Devoto and Libertad banners and GPA stores and electronics through Casas Bahia and Ponto Frio. In Asia business is conducted through Big C Thailand and Big C Vietnam. The Cnova e-commerce division operates Cdiscount and Cnova Brazil.

Geographic Reach
The Paris-based company operates in France Latin America and Asia.

Financial Performance
Note: Growth rates may differ after conversion to US Dollars.
In 2015 revenue fell 5% on prior year to euro 46.8 billion as a downturn in Brazil's equipment goods sector impacted Latam Electronics revenue. The company recorded a net loss again in 2015 and the scale of the loss increased from euro 33.0 million in 2014 to euro 166.0 million in 2015 as a result of lower net sales and an increase in operating expenses. Rallye subsidiary Casino sold its Thailand-listed Big C Thailand subsidiary for euro 3.1 billion to help pay down around half of Casino's net debt.

Cash from operating activities decreased by 2% on prior year to euro 2.8 billion.

Strategy
Rallye is furthering its position in expected high-growth countries in Latin America and the Asia-Pacific region.

Subsidiary Casino sold its Thailand unit Big C Thailand for euro 3.1 billion to TCC owned by

Thailand's richest man. The disposal will help Casino pay down around half of its net debt.

Casino Franprix Geant Leader Price and Monoprix. Casino is the #1 convenience store operator in France with stores under the Petit Casino Spar and Vival names. Casino has grown by purchasing stakes in supermarket hypermarket and convenience store companies with international locations. It plans to continue expanding globally focusing on South America and the Asia-Pacific region.

While Rallye exited the footwear retail business in the US with its sale of The Athlete's Foot the company plans to continue to expand Groupe Go Sport in Europe. The retailer was formed when Rallye merged two subsidiaries: Go Sport (France's #2 sporting goods retailer) with about 150 stores and Courir (France's #1 sports and leisure footwear retailer) with more than 200.

Rallye has increased its e-commerce activities through its majority stake of Cdiscount.com a French online retailer of CDs videos and more. Cdiscount belongs to the non-food group which also includes Mercialys (retail real estate development) Casino Cafeteria (corporate cafeterias) and Banque Casino (consumer lending).

HISTORY

Rallye has its roots in Casino Guichard-Perrachon which was formed after Geoffroy Guichard took over his father-in-law's general store in 1892.

In the early 1920s the company which would later become a Rallye holding opened factories to produce items that included food and soap. In 1924 Rallye was formed as a food retailer. Also that year a food distribution group that would become an important acquisition for Rallye in the 1990s Genty was founded (renamed Genty Cathiard in 1959).

By WWII Casino had 215 branches. During the war Casino's troubles included 70 stores leveled and 450 damaged in bomb attacks.

The firm launched its first supermarket (Grenoble) in 1960 and its first cafeteria in 1967. It expanded to Geant hypermarkets (Marseille) in 1970 and formed Casino USA in 1976.

Rallye entered sporting goods in 1981 through the purchase of France's 11-unit Athletic Attic chain and the acquisition of a minority stake of US sports footwear and apparel retailer The Athlete's Foot Group. Rallye then acquired majority control of Athlete's Foot in 1984.

Rallye's sales reached $4.4 billion in 1989. The next year it acquired the food distribution group Genty Cathiard which included retail units Go Sport (sporting goods) and Courir (sports footwear). The acquisition moved Rallye from #8 to #5 in French supermarket groups.

By 1991 Rallye operated 51 hypermarkets and 227 supermarkets. That year Euris headed by Jean-Charles Naouri bought a stake in Rallye which had heavy debt after borrowing funds to acquire Genty Cathiard. Rallye traded its food retail operations (close to 300 hypermarkets and supermarkets) with food giant Casino in exchange for a 30% stake in Casino in 1992.

Rallye merged with subsidiary Genty Cathiard in 1993 when the company went public. Also in 1993 Rallye began a major restructuring for Go Sport that lasted until 1996.

French supermarket chain Promodès made a hostile takeover attempt on Casino and Rallye in 1997 which would have made Promodès France's largest retailer. Rallye (which still had 30% of Casino and about 40% of voting rights) made a friendly counter bid; Promodès backed out and Rallye took control of Casino. By 1998 The Athlete's Foot Group had grown to more than 260 US outlets (company-owned) and more than 400 franchises (about 180 in the US).

Franchises were also located in 38 countries including Australia Canada France and Hong Kong. Go Sport operated 80 outlets in France and six in Belgium and there were more than 100 Courir stores (France) by the beginning of 1998. Rallye spun off nearly 20% of Courir in 1999.

Casino expanded its international markets in 1999 by acquiring stakes in food retailing companies in countries that included Brazil Colombia Thailand and Venezuela. Go Sport grew in 1999 by launching new stores in France Belgium and Poland –a new market.

In 2000 Casino bought a 51% stake in French online CD retailer Cdiscount.com. Although Rallye as a whole nearly doubled its net profit in 2000 Athlete's Foot suffered a loss of almost $29 million that year and began a three-year restructuring plan that included the closure of 84 unprofitable stores. Conversely 100 new Athlete's Foot franchises opened in 2001 including the first stores in Mexico and Hungary.

In June 2002 Casino acquired a nearly 40% stake in Laurus a leading retailer in the Netherlands.

In December 2003 Rallye sold its interest in The Athlete's Foot (TAF) to the chain's managers in a management-led buyout for an undisclosed sum. Accounting for less than 1% of Rallye's sales TAF had closed nearly 100 branches since 2001 but was still unprofitable.

François de Montaudouin resigned as managing director of Rallye in January 2004 and was succeeded by Chairman Jean-Charles Naouri.

In 2005 the company held an initial public offering for its shopping center real estate development company Mercialys.

EXECUTIVES

CEO, Didier Carlier, age 65
Deputy CEO, Franck Hattab
Chairman, Jean-Charles Naouri, age 67

LOCATIONS

HQ: Rallye S.A. Neuilly-Sur-Seine
83, rue du Faubourg Saint-Honore, Paris 75008
Phone: (33) 1 44 71 13 73   **Fax:** (33) 1 44 71 13 70
Web: www.rallye.fr

2015 Sales

	% of total
South America	46
France	44
Asia	9
Other regions	1
Total	**100**

2015 Sales

	% of total
France Retail	40
Latam Retail	32
Latam Electronics	11
Asia	9
E-commerce	7
Other activities	1
Total	**100**

PRODUCTS/OPERATIONS

2015 Sales

	% of total
Food & general	99
Sporting goods	1
Total	**100**

COMPETITORS

ALDI	Guyenne et Gascogne
Ahold Delhaize	ITM Entreprises
Auchan	Kering
Carrefour	METRO AG
E.Leclerc	Tesco
Galeries Lafayette	Wal-Mart

HISTORICAL FINANCIALS

Company Type: Public

Income Statement

FYE: December 31

	REVENUE ($ mil.)	NET INCOME ($ mil.)	NET PROFIT MARGIN	EMPLOYEES
12/15	51,009	(180)	—	330,433
12/14	59,748	(40)	—	340,060
12/13	67,881	238	0.4%	333,722
12/12	56,231	322	0.6%	321,385
12/11	45,344	19	0.0%	227,995
Annual Growth	**3.0%**	**—**	**—**	**9.7%**

2015 Year-End Financials

Debt ratio: 39.8%	No. of shares (mil.): 47
Return on equity: (-18.8%)	Dividends
Cash ($ mil.): 5,083	Yield: —
Current ratio: 0.84	Payout: —
Long-term debt ($ mil.): 12,822	Market value ($ mil.): —

Randstad Holding N.V.

Randstad Holding has the supply to meet nearly any demand. The company is one of the largest temporary staffing and employment services agencies in the world (behind Adecco). It operates primarily in Europe but also in Asia and North America under the Randstad brand and several others including Sapphire Technologies (IT staffing) Yacht (industrial staffing) and Tempo-Team (general staffing). Through almost 4200 locations in more than 40 countries Randstad supplies temporary workers for small assignments as well as large-scale deployments. It also offers permanent placement and HR project management and consultancy services. Randstad Holding was established in 1960.

Operations
Randstad's operations are divided across four business segments: staffing professionals HR solutions (payroll services HR consulting and vendor management services) and in-house services (works onsite with clients primarily residing in the manufacturing and logistics sectors).

Financial Performance
The company's total annual revenue increased from $22.5 billion in fiscal 2012 up to $22.8 billion in fiscal 2013. Randstad's net income increased from $48.5 million in fiscal 2012 to $317.5 million in fiscal 2013 on the strength of the gross annual revenue.

Strategy
Believing that the Japanese market is one of the largest staffing markets in the world Randstad is looking to the country as an important location for achieving growth.

Mergers and Acquisitions
In a highly acquisitive period in mid-2016 Randstad made five acquisitions - two technology related and three recruitment related. It acquired Obiettivo Lavoro an Italian recruitment firm for around $103 million; twago a leading European freelance marketplace; and online recruitment firm Monster for around $430 million. The acquisition of Monster one of the largest online jobsites is a significant step into online recruitment for Randstad.

The technology acquisitions are Japanese IT and engineering firm Careo Group and French company Ausy a consulting and engineering firm that will help Randstad broaden its technology and engineering capabilities.

HISTORY

Frits Goldschmeding founded Randstad Holding as Uitzendbureau Amstelveen near Amsterdam in 1960.

Originally part of a student project the company turned a small profit its first year and was renamed Randstad Uitzendbureau in 1964. ("The Randstad" is the densely populated area including Amsterdam Rotterdam and the Hague.)

It launched its first operation outside the Netherlands the next year establishing Interlabor Interim in Belgium. By 1970 Randstad had 32 branches in four countries including Germany and the UK.

Continuing its expansion across Europe (it entered France in 1973) the company was recast as Randstad Holding in 1978. The next year it opened its 100th branch and launched its Randon security business in the Netherlands in 1980. In 1985 Randstad celebrated its silver anniversary with 250 branches.

The company went public in 1990 listing its shares on the Amsterdam Stock Exchange. That year it moved its headquarters to the Amsterdam suburb of Diemen.

In 1993 Randstad entered the US market when it bought Atlanta-based Temp Force and later acquired Nashville-based Jane Jones Enterprises. It also expanded its staffing business into Spain that year. Randstad's US business later scored a coup when it became a sponsor of the 1996 Olympic Games in Atlanta. The company placed more than 16000 temporary employees to help out during the games. By 1997 the company had more than 1000 branches in Europe and North America.

Founder and CEO Goldschmeding resigned his post in 1998 and was replaced by Hans Zwarts. That year Randstad bought Strategix Solutions the commercial staffing unit of US-based AccuStaff (later MPS Group) for $850 million. The next year the company bought Germany's Time Power Personal-Dienstleistungen and Spain's Tempo Grup. Randstad and Dutch publisher VNU announced plans to create an online employment site covering Europe in 2000 (the site was closed in 2001).

The following year Randstad bought Spanish staffing firm Umano giving the company 150 additional locations throughout Spain. It also sold its security and cleaning businesses in 2001. Zwarts retired in 2002 and was replaced by 30-year company veteran Cleem Farla. In 2003 Ben Noteboom took over as CEO. In 2004 Randstad opened an office in Poland and bought staffing firm Take Air.

In 2007 Randstad almost doubled Randstad Switzerland's revenue through the acquisition of Job One. The Swiss staffing firm operated about two dozen branches and focuses on the technology health care and construction industries. In the biggest acquisition in its company's history Randstad acquired rival staffing agency Vedior in mid-2008. The deal catapulted Randstad ahead of other staffing rivals making it one of the largest in the world.

Striving to improve its position in Canada and the US Randstad purchased rival SFN Group for about $770 million in 2011.

EXECUTIVES

CFO and Vice Chairman Executive Board, Robert-Jan van de Kraats, age 56, $565,000 total compensation

CEO and Chairman of the Executive Board, Jacques van den Broek, age 56, $497,000 total compensation
President Randstad North America, Linda Galipeau, age 53
Managing Director Randstad Netherlands, Chris Heutink, age 54
Group President Randstad US, Traci L. Fiatte
President and CEO Randstad Group France, Fran $is Beharel, age 46
CEO Randstad Canada, Marc- tienne Julien
Chairman, Wout Dekker, age 60
Vice Chairman, Jaap Winter
Auditors: PricewaterhouseCoopers Accountants N.V.

LOCATIONS

HQ: Randstad Holding N.V.
  Diemermere 25, Diemen 1112 TC
Phone: (31) 20 569 59 11   **Fax:** (31) 20 569 55 20
Web: www.randstad.com

COMPETITORS

Adecco
Allegis Group
CDI
Kelly Services
ManpowerGroup

Robert Half
Technical Aid
Corporation
Volt Information

HISTORICAL FINANCIALS
Company Type: Public

Income Statement
FYE: December 31

	REVENUE ($ mil.)	NET INCOME ($ mil.)	NET PROFIT MARGIN	EMPLOYEES
12/15	20,933	551	2.6%	627,150
12/14	20,967	398	1.9%	609,020
12/13	22,810	300	1.3%	595,730
12/12	22,521	39	0.2%	611,020
12/11	20,986	231	1.1%	605,500
Annual Growth	(0.1%)	24.3%	—	0.9%

2015 Year-End Financials

Debt ratio: 4.5%
Return on equity: 14.1%
Cash ($ mil.): 145
Current ratio: 1.17
Long-term debt ($ mil.): 135

No. of shares (mil.): 182
Dividends
  Yield: 1.8%
  Payout: 18.0%
Market value ($ mil.): 5,662

	STOCK PRICE ($) FY Close	P/E High/Low		PER SHARE ($) Earnings	Dividends	Book Value
12/15	31.09	13	7	3.01	0.57	23.10
12/14	23.85	16	11	2.20	0.51	22.39
12/13	32.43	26	15	1.69	0.69	22.60
12/12	18.60	116	84	0.22	0.65	20.87
12/11	14.80	28	13	1.29	0.64	21.93
Annual Growth	20.4%	—	—	23.5%	(3.1%)	1.3%

Reliance Industries Ltd

Auditors: Deloitte Haskins & Sells LLP

LOCATIONS

HQ: Reliance Industries Ltd
  3rd Floor, Maker Chambers IV, 222, Nariman Point, Mumbai 400 021
Phone: (91) 22 2278 5000   **Fax:** (91) 22 2278 5111
Web: www.ril.com

HISTORICAL FINANCIALS
Company Type: Public

Income Statement
FYE: March 31

	REVENUE ($ mil.)	NET INCOME ($ mil.)	NET PROFIT MARGIN	EMPLOYEES
03/15	61,404	3,767	6.1%	24,930
03/14	73,854	3,746	5.1%	23,853
03/13	74,592	3,846	5.2%	23,519
03/12	71,684	3,876	5.4%	23,166
03/11	60,189	4,327	7.2%	22,661
Annual Growth	0.5%	(3.4%)	—	2.4%

2015 Year-End Financials

Debt ratio: 0.4%
Return on equity: 11.3%
Cash ($ mil.): 2,005
Current ratio: 0.99
Long-term debt ($ mil.): 19,310

No. of shares (mil.): —
Dividends
  Yield: —
  Payout: 22.7%
Market value ($ mil.): —

Renault S.A. (France)

Auditors: KPMG Audit

LOCATIONS

HQ: Renault S.A. (France)
  13-15, quai Le Gallo, Boulogne-Billancourt, Cedex 92513
Phone: (33) 1 76 84 04 04
Web: www.groupe.renault.com

HISTORICAL FINANCIALS
Company Type: Public

Income Statement
FYE: December 31

	REVENUE ($ mil.)	NET INCOME ($ mil.)	NET PROFIT MARGIN	EMPLOYEES
12/15	49,370	3,074	6.2%	120,136
12/14	49,902	2,297	4.6%	117,395
12/13	56,352	806	1.4%	121,807
12/12	54,395	2,335	4.3%	127,086
12/11	55,137	2,705	4.9%	128,322
Annual Growth	(2.7%)	3.2%	—	(1.6%)

2015 Year-End Financials

Debt ratio: 48.8%
Return on equity: 10.7%
Cash ($ mil.): 15,393
Current ratio: 1.01
Long-term debt ($ mil.): 6,216

No. of shares (mil.): 292
Dividends
  Yield: 2.1%
  Payout: 3.7%
Market value ($ mil.): 5,888

	STOCK PRICE ($) FY Close	P/E High/Low		PER SHARE ($) Earnings	Dividends	Book Value
12/15	20.16	2	1	11.21	0.43	104.36
12/14	14.12	2	2	8.37	0.00	101.48
Annual Growth	42.7%	—	—	7.6%	—	0.7%

Repsol S.A.

The sun shines on Repsol (formerly Repsol YPF) Spain's largest oil company. A fully integrated oil and gas company it operates in Latin America the Middle East and North Africa. Repsol operates five refineries in Spain and one in Peru and produces chemicals plastics and polymers. It sells gas under the brands Campsa Petronor and Repsol at 4500 service stations in Europe and Latin America. It is one of Spain's largest sellers of liquefied petroleum gas and liquefied natural gas. Repsol has proved reserves of 2.2 billion barrels of oil equivalent. Affiliate YPF conducts exploration production refining logistics marketing and chemicals in Argentina. Repsol also owns 30% of Gas Natural Fenosa.

Change in Company Type

In 2012 the Argentine government shocked the company when it seized control of subsidiary YPF as part of a nationalization drive.

Repsol had owned YPF Argentina's #1 oil company since 1999. However the Fernandez government took back a 51% stake in YPF. The bid reflects a growing trend towards nationalization of key industries (airlines private pension funds) that have drawn warnings from Argentina's trading partners.

Geographic ReachRepsol operates globally and has major assets primarily in Spain and Argentina. In 2011 Europe accounted for 63% of company's revenues.

Operations

Repsol upstream's division is engaged in oil and natural gas exploration and production activities based on key traditional regions located in Latin America (mainly Trinidad and Tobago Peru Venezuela Bolivia Colombia and Ecuador) and in North Africa (Algeria and Libya). Strategic areas for short and medium-term growth include the US Gulf of Mexico and offshore fields in Brazil.

The company's LNG activities include the liquefaction transportation marketing and regasification of liquefied natural gas in addition to electricity generation activities in Spain at the Bahia de Bizkaia Electricidad plan and natural gas marketing in North America.

Repsol's downstream business includes the supply and trading of crude and other products oil refining marketing of oil products and LPG and the production and marketing of chemicals.

Financial Performance

Higher oil prices and increased demand lifted Repsol's revenues by 6% in 2011. Net income decreased by 53% in 2011 due to the impact on revenues of the depreciation of the dollar against the euro and increase in personnel expense.

Strategy

Repsol plans to invest more than euro 21 billion (more than $26 billion) over the next few years in its operations particularly in exploration and production including its Spanish refineries which will receive an investment of about euro 4 billion (more than $4 billion).

To raise cash and to rebalance its global portfolio in 2011 Repsol sold about 4% of its stake in YPF to Lazard Asset Management for $639 million.

Repsol created the New Energies Business Unit in 2010 assigned to the Downstream Division to promote and new cleaner energy initiatives to reduce carbon dioxide emissions.

Mergers and Acquisitions

Growing its operations in 2015 Repsol acquired Canada-based Talisman Energy for $8.3 billion plus debt.

HISTORY

Repsol officially created in 1987 is actually the result of efforts that began as early as the 1920s to organize Spain's fragmented energy industry.

Following an era of dependency on foreign investment prior to and during Francisco Franco's dictatorship (1939-75) Spain began reorganizing its energy industry. In 1979 it set up the Instituto

Nacional de Hidrocarburos which in 1981 incorporated all public-sector firms involved in gas and oil under one government agency.

Repsol was formed six years later to provide central management to a Spanish oil company that could compete in the unified European market. The government chose the name Repsol after a well-known brand of Spanish lubricant products. The firm was charged with pursuing a global strategy to bring together all levels of the industry.

In 1989 Repsol offered 26% of the firm on the Madrid and New York stock exchanges raising more than $1 billion. That year Repsol increased its marine fleet with the purchase of the Naviera Vizcaina shipping company and bought Carless Refining & Marketing a UK business with a chain of 500 service stations operating mainly under the Anglo brand. Although Spain was opening its doors to foreign investment the Spanish government maintained control over the country's energy industry including a tightly guarded distribution network under state-controlled Campsa. Campsa oversaw a marketing/logistics system of pipelines storage terminals and sales outlets.

The European Community demanded that Spain open its markets to other EC members forcing Campsa in 1991 to divide its 3800 gasoline stations among its four major shareholders: Cepsa (Spain's largest private refiner) Petromed Ertoil and Repsol. Repsol gained 66% of the logistical network and use of the Campsa brand name.

Repsol and Spanish bank La Caixa merged their interests in natural gas in 1992 to create Gas Natural a new gas distributor. That year the Spanish government began reducing its majority holding and by 1996 its stake had dwindled to 10%. (It sold its remaining stock in 1997.)

Expanding its South American operations Repsol acquired control of Argentinian oil company Astra CAPSA and a Peruvian oil refinery in 1996. That year Repsol purchased a 30% stake in the Tin Fouye Tabankort field in Algeria.

In 1999 Repsol paid $2 billion for a 15% stake in giant oil company YPF which was auctioned off by Argentina's government. After acquiring another 83% of YPF for $13.2 billion Repsol changed its name to Repsol YPF. To help pay down debt incurred in the acquisition Repsol YPF sold its UK North Sea oil and gas operations to US independent Kerr-McGee for $555 million in 2000. That year the company (as part of its commitment to Argentina's government after acquiring YPF) agreed to swap some of its Argentine refining and marketing assets for Brazilian oil and gas operations owned by Petrobras.

In 2002 Repsol YPF sold oil and gas assets in Indonesia to CNOOC for about $585 million. Former chairman of Spain's top gas supplier Gas Natural S.A. Antonio Brufau replaced Alfonso Cortina de Alcocer in 2004 as chairman of Repsol.

In 2006 the company acquired BP's 28% stake in the Shenzi field in the Gulf of Mexico. The next year Repsol YPF began selling minority stakes in YPF to generate cash to support the Argentine company's growth.

EXECUTIVES

Executive Director of Management and Development Control, Miguel Mart nez San Mart n
Executive Managing Director Exploration and Production, Luis Cabra Due±as, age 59
CEO; Executive Director; Member Executive Committee, Josu Jon Imaz San Miguel, age 52
Executive Managing Director Downstream, Maria Victoria Zingoni
Chairman, Antonio Brufau Niubo
First Vice Chairman, Gonzalo Gort¯zar Rotaeche
Second Vice Chairman, Manuel Manrique Cecilia
Auditors: DELOITTE, S.L.

LOCATIONS

HQ: Repsol S.A.
Mendez Alvaro, 44, Madrid 28045
Phone: (34) 91 75 38 100   **Fax:** (34) 902 303 145
Web: www.repsol.com

PRODUCTS/OPERATIONS

2011 Sales

	% of total
Downstream	63
YPF	17
Gas Natural Fenosa	10
Upstream	6
LNG	4
Corporate	-
Total	**100**

COMPETITORS

Anadarko Petroleum	Norsk Hydro ASA
BHP Billiton	Occidental Petroleum
BP	PEMEX
Devon Energy	PETROBRAS
Endesa S.A.	Petrobras Argentina
Eni	Petr±eos de
Exxon Mobil	Venezuela
IBERDROLA	Pioneer Natural
Imperial Oil	Resources
Koch Industries Inc.	RasGas
Marathon Oil	Royal Dutch Shell
Murphy Oil	TOTAL
Noble Energy	

HISTORICAL FINANCIALS

Company Type: Public

Income Statement

FYE: December 31

	REVENUE ($ mil.)	NET INCOME ($ mil.)	NET PROFIT MARGIN	EMPLOYEES
12/15	42,711	(1,336)	—	27,111
12/14	55,448	1,959	3.5%	24,289
12/13	76,433	268	0.4%	30,296
12/12	77,152	2,715	3.5%	29,985
12/11	80,848	2,836	3.5%	46,575
Annual Growth	(14.7%)			(12.7%)

2015 Year-End Financials

Debt ratio: 30.4%	No. of shares (mil.): 1,400
Return on equity: (-4.3%)	Dividends
Cash ($ mil.): 2,666	Yield: 8.2%
Current ratio: 0.88	Payout: 87.5%
Long-term debt ($ mil.): 11,524	Market value ($ mil.): 15,586

	STOCK PRICE ($) FY Close	P/E High/Low		PER SHARE ($) Earnings	Dividends	Book Value
12/15	11.13	—	—	(0.95)	0.92	22.14
12/14	18.58	22	16	1.42	2.07	25.15
12/13	25.29	182	138	0.21	1.01	28.79
12/12	20.90	19	9	2.24	1.29	29.51
12/11	30.51	18	13	2.33	1.11	27.71
Annual Growth	(22.3%)	—	—	—	(4.6%)	(5.5%)

Resona Holdings Inc Osaka

Resona Holdings resonate in Japan's retail banking market. It's the holding company of Resona Bank and smaller regional banks Kinki Osaka Bank and Saitama Resona Bank which operate nearly 1450 branches across Japan mainly in the greater Tokyo area and the Kansai region. While it focuses on consumer and small business banking services Resona Bank also provides corporate pension management and real estate services corporate and personal trust services personal loans asset management and estate planning services. Altogether Resona Holdings boasts over ¥45 trillion ($375 billion) in total assets and ¥24 trillion ($20 billion) in trust assets.

OperationsResona Holdings operates three core business segments: Consumer Banking which provides consumer loans asset management and asset succession services; Corporate Banking which provides corporate loans trust asset management real estate services corporate pension management and asset succession services; and Market Trading which provides short-term lending borrowing bond purchase and sale and derivatives trading in financial markets.About 54% of its total revenue came from interest income in fiscal 2015 (ended March 31) while 23% came from non-trust fees and commissions and 3% came from trust fees. About 85% of its total loans and bills discounted were loans to small and medium-sized enterprises (SMEs). More than 60% of its deposits were from individuals.

Geographic Reach

Tokyo-based Resona Holdings has more than 1440 branches across Japan including more than 820 in the Kanto region and 579 in the Kansai region. Its Kinki Osaka Bank subsidiary has 128 manned branches mainly in the Kinki region. About 40% of its branches are manned while the majority are unmanned.

Financial Performance

Note: Growth rates may differ after conversion to US dollars.

Resona Holdings' revenues and profits have trended lower over the past several years mostly due to shrinking interest margins on loans amidst the low-interest environment.

The company had a breakout year in fiscal 2015 (ended March 31) however as its revenue rose by 4% to ¥861.4 billion ($7.2 billion) on higher fee and commission income from sales of its investment trust and insurance products. Its interest income continued to slide downward due to low interest margins.

Despite generating higher revenue in FY2015 the group's net income fell by 4% to ¥211.4 billion ($1.77 billion) mostly due to higher income taxes and a ¥23 billion charge related to the reversal of deferred tax assets in line with the reduction of the effective corporate tax rate. Resona's operating cash levels fell in half to ¥1103 billion ($9 billion) for the year mostly as it extended more of its cash toward loans and bills discounted.

Strategy

Resona Holdings in early 2015 launched its "New Mid-term Management Plan" for the next decade which set its sights on becoming the "No. 1 Retail Bank" through more proactive measures toward continued growth. Continuing to focus on its retail banking business and lending to SMEs the bank planned to "maximize customer value by maintaining its fundamental stance that 'Customers' joy and happiness are Resona's.' The company also in 2015 outlined its three "ACL" initiatives which included: "All Resona" which aimed to offer collaboration of companies and services to provide SME customers with management consulting and other services as they grew; "Cross-selling promotion" which aimed to cross sell life insurance to the group's mortgage customers which numbered 560000 borrowers and grew by 40000 new borrowers annually; and "Low-cost operations" which rely on productivity-boosting initiatives such as installed communication terminals that allow tellers to serve customers more securely and efficiently.

Resona Holdings has significant market strength in its key markets in the greater Tokyo metro area and the Kansai region (the most populated and economically active parts of Japan). During 2015 it held 40% of the deposit market in the Saitama and Osaka Prefectures and nearly 20% of the loan market in the region as well.

EXECUTIVES

President and Representative Executive Officer, Kazuhiro Higashi, age 59
President Saitama Resona Bank, Masahito Kamijo
Representative Executive Officer, Toshiki Hara
Representative Executive Officer, Tetsuya Kan
President The Kinki Osaka Bank, Koji Nakamae
Auditors: Deloitte Touche Tohmatsu LLC

LOCATIONS

HQ: Resona Holdings Inc Osaka
  1-5-65 Kiba, Koto-ku, Tokyo 135-0042
Phone: (81) 3 6704 3111
Web: www.resona-gr.co.jp

PRODUCTS/OPERATIONS

2014 Sales

	% of total
Interest income	57
Fees and commissions	23
Other operating income	4
Trust fees	3
Other	13
Total	**100**

Selected Subsidiaries

Daiwa Guarantee Co. Ltd. (credit guarantee)
Resona Bank Ltd. (bank)
Resona Guarantee Co. Ltd. (credit guarantee)
Saitama Resona Bank Ltd. (bank)
Kinki Osaka Shinyo Hosho Co. Ltd. (credit guarantee)
The Kinki Osaka Bank Ltd. (bank)
P.T. Bank Resona Perdania (bank)
Resona Kessai Service Co. Ltd. (collections agency)
Resona Card Co. Ltd. (credit cards)
Resona Capital Co. Ltd. (private equity)
Resona Research Institute Co. Ltd. (consulting)
Resona Business Service Co. Ltd. (staffing)

COMPETITORS

Aozora Bank	Mitsubishi UFJ
Bank of Yokohama	Financial Group
Chiba Bank	Mizuho Financial
Chugoku Bank	Nishi-Nippon
Fukuoka Financial	Shinsei Bank
Group	Shizuoka Bank
Gunma Bank	Sumitomo Mitsui
Hachijuni Bank	Sumitomo Mitsui Trust
Hokuhoku Financial	Holdings
Group	Yamaguchi Financial
Iyo Bank	Group
Juroku Bank	

HISTORICAL FINANCIALS

Company Type: Public

Income Statement

FYE: March 31

	ASSETS ($ mil.)	NET INCOME ($ mil.)	INCOME AS % OF ASSETS	EMPLOYEES
03/16	437,469	1,637	0.4%	28,096
03/15	388,288	1,762	0.5%	28,353
03/14	433,246	2,137	0.5%	16,536
03/13	458,175	2,924	0.6%	16,826
03/12	526,633	3,092	0.6%	16,881
Annual Growth	**(4.5%)**	**(14.7%)**	**—**	**13.6%**

2016 Year-End Financials

Return on assets: 0.3%		Dividends	
Return on equity: 9.6%		Yield: —	
Long-term debt ($ mil.): —		Payout: —	
No. of shares (mil.): —		Market value ($ mil.): —	
Sales ($ mil): 7,291			

	STOCK PRICE ($) FY Close	P/E High/Low		PER SHARE ($) Earnings	Dividends	Book Value
03/16	3.60	0	0	0.67	0.00	6.96
03/15	5.15	0	0	0.70	0.00	7.10
03/14	4.81	—	—	0.63	0.00	8.64
03/13	5.47	—	—	0.77	0.00	9.49
03/12	4.42	—	—	0.83	0.00	9.17
Annual Growth	**(5.0%)**	**—**	**—**	**(5.2%)**	**—**	**(6.7%)**

RHB Bank Berhad

RHB Capital is the holding company for RHB Banking Group which offers retail small business and commercial banking services (through RHB Bank) and insurance securities asset management unit trusts derivatives corporate finance and underwriting (through RHB Investment Bank and RHB Insurance). The group's RHB Islamic Bank unit offers retail and commercial banking services that are sensitive to Islamic and regional laws. RHB Capital operates through more than 200 locations mainly in Malaysia but also Brunei Cambodia Hong Kong Indonesia Singapore Thailand and Vietnam. In 2013 RHB Investment Bank bought OSK Investment Bank. RHB Capital acquired and merged Kwong Yik Bank with DCB Bank in 1997.
Auditors: PricewaterhouseCoopers

LOCATIONS

HQ: RHB Bank Berhad
  Level 9, Tower One, RHB Centre, Jalan Tun Razak,
  Kuala Lumpur 50400
Phone: (60) 3 9285 2233   **Fax:** (60) 3 9281 9314
Web: www.rhbgroup.com

COMPETITORS

AmBank Group	Hang Seng Bank
Bank of China	Malaysian Industrial
Bank of East Asia	Development Finance
CIMB Group	Maybank

HISTORICAL FINANCIALS

Company Type: Public

Income Statement

FYE: December 31

	ASSETS ($ mil.)	NET INCOME ($ mil.)	INCOME AS % OF ASSETS	EMPLOYEES
12/15	53,593	351	0.7%	16,117
12/14	62,730	582	0.9%	16,089
12/13	58,332	558	1.0%	16,692
12/12	61,754	582	0.9%	12,154
12/11	48,088	473	1.0%	11,299
Annual Growth	**2.7%**	**(7.2%)**	**—**	**9.3%**

2015 Year-End Financials

Return on assets: 0.6%	Dividends
Return on equity: 7.2%	Yield: —
Long-term debt ($ mil.): —	Payout: —
No. of shares (mil.): —	Market value ($ mil.): —
Sales ($ mil): 2,514	

RHB Bank Berhad (Malaysia)

RHB Bank Berhad lends a helping hand for Malaysians' financial future. The bank a subsidiary of RHB Capital Berhad offers a wide range of financial services such as personal and corporate loans savings accounts and credit cards. RHB Bank Berhad also provides a variety of Islamic products and online banking. The company operates a network of some 200 offices across Malaysia as well as branches throughout Singapore Bangkok and Brunei. It is purchasing an 80% stake in Indonesian financial institution Bank Mestika. RHB Bank Berhad was established through the merging of DCG Bank Berhad and Kwong Yik Berhad in 1997.

LOCATIONS

HQ: RHB Bank Berhad (Malaysia)
  Towers Two & Three, RHB Centre, Jalan Tun Razak,
  Kuala Lumpur 50400
Phone: (6) 3 9287 8888   **Fax:** (6) 3 9287 9000
Web: www.rhbgroup.com

COMPETITORS

AmBank Group	Maybank
CIMB Group	

HISTORICAL FINANCIALS

Company Type: Public

Income Statement

FYE: December 31

	ASSETS ($ mil.)	NET INCOME ($ mil.)	INCOME AS % OF ASSETS	EMPLOYEES
12/15	50,852	357	0.7%	0
12/14	58,522	533	0.9%	0
12/13	53,163	538	1.0%	0
12/12	55,410	589	1.1%	0
12/11	45,119	491	1.1%	0
Annual Growth	**3.0%**	**(7.7%)**	**—**	**—**

2015 Year-End Financials

Return on assets: 0.7%	Dividends
Return on equity: 9.4%	Yield: —
Long-term debt ($ mil.): —	Payout: —
No. of shares (mil.): —	Market value ($ mil.): —
Sales ($ mil): 2,202	

Ricoh Co., Ltd.

Ricoh may be best known for its imaging equipment but the company is more than just another copycat. One of the world's leading manufacturers of copiers and supplies Ricoh also makes fax machines scanners and printers. Other products from the company which operates about 230 subsidiaries and affiliates in more than 180 countries include digital cameras servers software for its products semiconductors printed circuit boards thermal paper labels and optical equipment. Ricoh is represented in the US and across the Americas by its Ricoh Americas subsidiary.
Geographic Reach

Sales in Japan account for about 42% of the company's revenues. Sales in the Americas and Europe were around the 25% mark for each.

Financial Performance

Ricoh's revenue increased 2% in 2015 (ended March) due to increase in Imaging & Solutions (1.6% higher) and Industrial Products (8% higher). New models of color multi-function printers sold well in Japan and overseas boosting Imaging & Solutions while the thermal business heated up sales for Industrial Products. Profits dropped 6% however on higher expenses in 2015.

Strategy

Although printers and office equipment are Ricoh's biggest moneymakers the company has moved beyond its core products into related services including managed document services document outsourcing services logistics financing leasing and IT service. The company is investing $300 million in its managed document services infrastructure through 2014. Ricoh leases its equipment through a separate publicly traded company in Japan named Ricoh Leasing.

Mergers and Acquisitions

In 2015 Ricoh expanded its activities in Malaysia with the acquisition of NASSION Systems a provider of information and telecommunications services in the country. In a 2014 acquisition Ricoh added PTIMarketing Technologies a software-as-a-service marketing asset management and marketing firm to its fold. Ricoh bolstered it IT services portfolio through the 2014 acquisition of mindSHIFT Technologies Inc. a managed IT cloud data center and professional services company that serves small and mid-sized organizations.

HISTORY

Early History

Ricoh began in 1936 as the Riken Kankoshi Company making photographic paper. With founder Kiyoshi Ichimura at the helm the company soon became the leader in Japan's sensitized paper market. It changed its name to Riken Optical Company in 1938 and started making cameras. Two years later it produced its first camera under the Ricoh brand.

By 1954 Ricoh cameras were Japan's #1 seller and also popular abroad. The next year it entered the office machine market with its compact mimeograph machine. Ricoh followed that in 1960 with an offset duplicator.

Ricoh built its business in the 1960s with a range of office machines including reproduction and data processing equipment and retrieval systems. The company began establishing operations overseas including US subsidiary Ricoh Industries U.S.A. in 1962. The US unit started marketing cameras but found greener pastures in the copier industry where Ricoh's products were sold under the Pitney Bowes and Savin brand names. It changed its name to Ricoh Company in 1963. Two years later Ricoh entered the emerging field of office computers and introduced an electrostatic copier. In 1968 Ichimura died and Mikio Tatebayashi took over as president for the next eight years.

EXECUTIVES

President and CEO, Zenji Miura, age 67
Group Executive Officer, Shiro Sasaki, age 67
Corporate EVP, Yohzoh Matsuura, age 60
Corporate EVP, Yoshinori Yamashita, age 59
Corporate EVP, Nobuo Inaba
Corporate EVP, Kunihiko Satoh
Chairman and CEO Ricoh Germany, Niculae Cantuniar
Chairman, Shiro Kondo
Auditors: KPMG AZSA LLC

LOCATIONS

HQ: Ricoh Co., Ltd.
Ricoh Bldg., 8-13-1 Ginza, Chuo-ku, Tokyo 104-8222
Phone: (81) 3 6278 2111
Web: www.ricoh.co.jp

2015 Sales

	% of total
Japan	42
The Americas	27
Europe Middle East Africa	23
Other	8
Total	**100**

PRODUCTS/OPERATIONS

2015 Sales

	% of total
Imaging & solutions	89
Industrial products	6
Other	5
Total	**100**

Selected Products

Imaging and Solutions
  Imaging Solutions
  Diazo copiers
  Digital duplicators
  Digital monochrome and color copiers
  Fax machines
  Imaging supplies and consumables
  Wide-format copiers
  Printing systems (laser multifunction)
  Scanners
  Network System Solutions
  Document management software
  Networking and applications software
  Network systems
  Personal computers
  Servers
  Services and support
Industrial
  Electronic components
  Measuring equipment
  Optical equipment
  Semiconductor devices
  Thermal media
Other
  Digital cameras and other photographic equipment
  Financing and logistics services
  Optical disks

COMPETITORS

3M	Lexmark
Brother Industries	NEC
CASIO COMPUTER	Nikon
Canon	Oce
Dell	Oki Electric
Eastman Kodak	Olympus
Epson	Panasonic Corp
FUJIFILM	SANYO
Fuji Xerox	Sharp Corp.
HP	Toshiba
Hitachi	Xerox
Konica Minolta	
Kyocera Document Solutions	

HISTORICAL FINANCIALS

Company Type: Public

Income Statement

FYE: March 31

	REVENUE ($ mil.)	NET INCOME ($ mil.)	NET PROFIT MARGIN	EMPLOYEES
03/16	19,671	560	2.9%	109,361
03/15	18,602	571	3.1%	109,951
03/14	21,272	705	3.3%	108,195
03/13	20,453	345	1.7%	107,431
03/12	23,204	(543)	—	109,241
Annual Growth	**(4.0%)**	—	—	**0.0%**

2016 Year-End Financials

Debt ratio: 0.2%	No. of shares (mil.): 724
Return on equity: 5.8%	Dividends
Cash ($ mil.): 1,492	Yield: 0.0%
Current ratio: 1.58	Payout: —
Long-term debt ($ mil.): 5,272	Market value ($ mil.): 7,611

	STOCK PRICE ($) FY Close	P/E High/Low		Earnings	PER SHARE ($) Dividends	Book Value
03/16	10.50	0	0	0.77	0.31	13.24
03/15	10.95	1	0	0.79	0.30	12.47
03/14	58.00	1	0	0.97	1.64	13.76
03/13	54.35	1	1	0.48	0.22	13.16
03/12	49.38	—	—	(0.75)	0.40	13.83
Annual Growth	**(32.1%)**	—	—	—	**(6.7%)**	**(1.1%)**

Rio Tinto Ltd

Rio Tinto is on the lookout for pay dirt. Rio Tinto Limited one of the world's largest mining operations (along with BHP Billiton and Vale) is the Australian half of dual-listed sister companies with Rio Tinto plc taking up residence in London. Although each company trades separately the two Rio Tintos operate as one business. Rio Tinto explores for a variety of commodities: bauxite coal copper diamonds gold iron ore minerals (borates and titanium dioxide) nickel and potash. Iron ore makes up about 44% of the group's sales. It also produces aluminum through its Rio Tinto Alcan unit. Most of its businesses are in Australia and North America but it is expanding its operations in China and Mongolia.

By focusing on a strategy of developing large-scale long-term mining operations and businesses Rio Tinto has tried to weather commodity prices that have dipped and risen over several years. The mining industry is affected by both oversupply and rising costs in raw materials. Like its rivals the company continues to seek acquisitions that will grow shareholder value as it cuts costs and improves productivity.

Despite a year of challenges including six fatalities at its mining sites and flooding that disrupted production in Australia Rio Tinto recorded revenues of $60.5 billion in 2011. Net income however fell about 59% —from $15.3 billion in 2010 to $6.8 billion in 2011. The company attributes an $8.9 billion impairment charge related to its aluminum assets as the cause of its precipitous fall in net earnings that year.

The company's iron ore business also contributed 78% of the group's net income in 2011. Rio Tinto is the world's second-largest supplier of iron ore which is used in steelmaking operations. Its key iron ore operations are in the Pilbara region of Western Australia and in Quebec in Canada.

In 2011 the company started trimming its aluminum operations. It placed 13 assets on the chopping block allowing Rio Tinto Alcan to focus on its high-quality tier one assets (mostly in Canada) and improve performance. The company also planned to transfer its stakes in six Australian and New Zealand operations to a new business unit Pacific Aluminium that would be managed and reported separately from Rio Tinto Alcan.

In 2011 to raise cash the company sold its talc business to Imerys for $340 million. That year Rio Tinto also increased its stake to 49% in Canada-based Ivanhoe Mines which manages the Oyu Tolgoi mine in Mongolia one of the world's largest undeveloped copper-gold projects. In 2012 it upped its holding in Ivanhoe Mines to 51% to become the majority owner. Commercial production at the mine may be delayed however because an agreement to supply electricity has not yet been reached between China and Mongolia.

In another strategic move in 2011 Rio Tinto made an all-cash offer for Canada-based uranium producer Hathor Exploration valued at $578 million after rival Cameco Corp. made a takeover bid for the company. In 2012 Rio Tinto was successful in acquiring Hathor which supplies about a fifth of the world's uranium.

In the first half of 2011 the company completed the acquisition of the Riversdale coal mine which has now been renamed Rio Tinto Coal Mozambique.

In 2012 the company began an overview of operations and announced that it may sell its diamond business. The company operates diamond mines in Canada Zimbabwe and Australia. At its Argyle mine in Australia the company unearthed a rare pink diamond in the rough in 2012. The Argyle mine is undergoing a $2.1 billion expansion and is the world's largest producer of pink diamonds. However in 2011 diamond operations made up only 2% of the company's total earnings before interest tax depreciation and amortization. Argyle's lower production also helped lead to an 86% drop in overall earnings for its diamonds unit that year.

Slimming down further in 2012 the company agreed to sell one of its noncore US operations Atlanta-based wire and cable business Alcan Cable to Kentucky-based General Cable for $185 million. General Cable makes and distributes copper aluminum and fiber-optic wire and cable products. Alcan Cable serves the energy and construction markets.

HISTORY

Rio Tinto Limited began life as the Zinc Corporation in 1905 to recover zinc from the tailings of the silver and lead mines around Australia's mineral-rich Broken Hill area. The company expanded steadily extending its operations into a wide range of mining and metallurgical activities primarily in Australia. By 1914 it had changed its name to Consolidated Zinc Corporation. The company discovered the world's largest deposit of bauxite (1955) and formed Hamersley Holdings with Kaiser Steel (1962) to mine iron ore.

Rio Tinto plc (UK) began with mining operations in Spain in 1873. It sold most of its Spanish holdings in 1954 and branched out to Australia Africa and Canada. In 1962 Rio Tinto and Australia's Consolidated Zinc merged to form RTZ. The companies merged their Australian interests as a partially owned subsidiary CRA (from Conzinc Riotinto of Australia).

In 1968 RTZ bought U.S. Borax which was built on one of the earth's few massive boron deposits. (The use of boron in cleansers was widespread in the late 19th century.) A 1927 discovery in the Mojave Desert led to development of a large boron mine. Until its Turkish mine was nationalized RTZ controlled the world's boron supply. It sold U.S. Borax's consumer products operations in 1988.

RTZ opened a large copper mine at Bougainville in Papua New Guinea in 1969. Subsidiary CRA discovered diamonds in Western Australia's Argyle region three years later. CRA then opened Australia's largest thermal-coal development at Blair Athol in 1984.

RTZ bought Kennecott Corporation in 1989 and expanded its copper operations. Kennecott had been formed by Stephen Birch and named for Robert Kennicott (a typo altered the spelling of the company's name); it had begun mining at Bing-

ham Canyon Utah in 1904. Kennicott had died in Alaska while trying to establish an intercontinental telegraph line. Backed by J.P. Morgan and the Guggenheims Birch also built a railroad to haul the ore. Kennecott merged its railroad and mine operations in 1915. Kennecott consolidated its hold on Chile's Braden copper mine (1925) and on the Utah Copper Company (1936) and other US mines. When copper prices slumped British Petroleum's Standard Oil of Ohio subsidiary bought Kennecott (1981). In 1989 RTZ purchased British Petroleum's US mineral operations including Kennecott.

By the 1990s RTZ and CRA (by then 49%-owned by RTZ) were increasingly competing for mining rights to recently opened areas of Asia and Latin America. RTZ sold the last of its nonmining holdings (building products group) in 1993. In 1995 RTZ brought CRA into its operations. Through Kennecott RTZ purchased US coal mine operators Nerco Cordero Mining Company and Colowyo Coal Company. Also in 1995 the company acquired 13% of Freeport-McMoRan Copper & Gold (sold in 2004).

The RTZ and CRA company names were changed to Rio Tinto plc and Rio Tinto Limited respectively in 1997. Rio Tinto bought a Wyoming coal mine from Kerr-McGee for about $400 million in 1998. The next year Rio Tinto bought 80% of Kestrel (coal Australia) increased its ownership of Blair Athol from 57% to 71% and increased its stake in Comalco (aluminum) to 72%.

In 2000 CEO Leon Davis retired; his position passed to energy group executive Leigh Clifford. In a move that sparked an outcry from union officials Davis accepted a position as non-executive deputy chairman (he retired from the board in 2005). Later that year Rio Tinto acquired both North Limited and Ashton Mining. The company also bought Comalco's outstanding shares and the Peabody Group's Australian subsidiaries.

Rio Tinto sold its Norzink Zink Smelter to Outokumpu in 2001. It also increased its holdings in Queensland Alumina Coal & Allied Industries and Palabora Mining and it began developing the Hail Creek Coal Project in Australia which is based on one of the largest coking coal deposits in the world. In 2003 Rio Tinto sold its 25% stake in Minera Alumbrera (Argentina) and Peak Gold Mine (Australia) to Wheaton River Minerals for around $210 million.

Rio Tinto had owned 14% of Lihir Gold but divested its stake in the company. Prior to that decision the company had controlled Lihir and its management. In late 2005 though Rio Tinto reliquished its management rights and decided to sell its entire stake in Lihir.

Tom Albanese succeeded Clifford in 2007.

In 2007 Rio Tinto swooped in and made a successful $38 billion offer to buy Alcan then the world's #3 aluminum producer. That came not long after Alcoa #2 in the world had offered $33 billion. The deal combined Rio Tinto's own aluminum operations with Alcan's to form the new world leader Rio Tinto Alcan based in Canada. Rio Tinto's operations were located in Australia New Zealand and Africa as well as in Italy and the UK. Alcan's geographic strengths were in North America throughout Europe and in the Asia/Pacific region.

After that acquisition Rio Tinto announced a major divestment program saying it wanted to sell off $15 billion worth of assets. In early 2008 it began that program selling stakes in two North American properties to Hecla Mining and Barrick Gold. The properties had been a part of Kennecott Minerals and netted Rio Tinto about $2.5 billion. Later that year the company spun off most of its North American coal operations into a company called Cloud Peak Energy which it spun off

through a public offering in 2009 using the almost $750 million it received to help recoup expenses from the purchase of Alcan. A major step in the divestment plan was taken in early 2009 when the company sold its undeveloped potash assets and a Brazilian iron ore mine to Vale for about $1.5 billion.

The company's most significant deals though have been the ones that didn't happen. In 2008 BHP Billiton approached Rio Tinto with an offer to buy its Anglo-Australian rival at a price that valued the company at nearly $150 billion. Rio Tinto's Board rejected the notion but BHP Billiton kept up its pursuit. The combination would have created the world's largest minerals company and one of the largest companies of any sort in terms of market cap. Months later though at the end of a year mired by the global economic meltdown BHP Billiton announced that the deal no longer provided value to its shareholders and called it off.

In an effort to obstruct BHP Billiton's takeover bid for Rio Tinto in 2008 Alcoa and Aluminum Corporation of China (Chinalco) had acquired 14% of Rio Tinto for $14 billion. Early the next year Chinalco stepped in with an offer to assist Rio Tinto out of a portion of its debt which was considerable. The complicated arrangement would have given Rio Tinto $19.5 billion through investments in aluminum copper and iron ore joint ventures as well as through convertible bonds. Chinalco's stake in Rio Tinto would have been raised to 19% and the Chinese company would have had the right to name two members to Rio Tinto's Board.

However the transaction —never popular with domestic investors —fell through by mid-2009. Rio Tinto instead went with a rights issue hoping to raise $15 billion and an agreed-upon joint venture with BHP Billiton that would have combined the two companies' iron ore projects in Western Australia. However that deal fell through also after German authorities ruled in 2010 that it was anticompetitive.

In late 2010 Rio Tinto made a $3.5 billion tender offer for Australian coal producer Riversdale Mining Ltd. but ran into problems convincing two large institutional shareholders to sell their stakes. Rio Tinto upped the offer to about $4 billion in early 2011 but India's Tata Steel and Brazil's CSN —which together held about 47% of Riversdale — were still not willing to part with their shares. A couple of deadline extensions and price bumps later Rio Tinto acquired both the CSN and Tata stakes to control close to 100% of Riversdale's shares.

EXECUTIVES

Chairman, Jan P. du Plessis, age 61

Group executive Organisational Resources, Hugo Bague

Chief executive Rio Tinto Alcan, Alfredo (Alf) Barrios

CEO, Jean-Sebastien Jacques

CFO, Christopher Lynch

CEO Energy and Minerals, Bold Baatar

Group Executive Health Safety and Environment; Managing Director Australia, Joanne Farrell

Group Executive Growth and Innovation, Stephen McIntosh

Chief Executive Iron Ore, Chris Salisbury

Chief Executive Copper and Diamonds, Arnaud Soirat

Auditors: PricewaterhouseCoopers

LOCATIONS

HQ: Rio Tinto Ltd
Level 33, 120 Collins Street, Melbourne, Victoria 3000
Phone: (61) 3 9283 3333   **Fax:** (61) 3 9283 3707
Web: www.riotinto.com

2015 Sales

	% of total
China	42
US	15
Other Asia	14
Japan	11
Europe (Excluding UK)	8
Canada	4
Australia	3
UK	1
Other	2
Total	**100**

PRODUCTS/OPERATIONS

2015 Sales

	% of total
Iron Ore	41
Aluminum	27
Copper	9
Coal	8
Industrial Minerals	6
Gold	3
Diamonds	2
Other	4
Total	**100**

Selected Holdings

Aluminum
Bell Bay
Boyne Island (59% smelting)
Queensland Alumina Ltd. (80%)
Tiwai Point (79% New Zealand)
Weipa (Australia)
Iron Ore
Hamersley Iron Pty. Ltd.
Channar (60%)
Marandoo mine (Pilbara Australia)
Nammuldi
Iron Ore Co. of Canada (59%)
Robe River Iron Associates (53%)
Energy & Minerals
Coal
Bengalla (30% Australia)
Blair Athol Coal (71%)
Hail Creek Coal (82%)
Hunter Valley Operations (76%)
Kestrel (80%)
Mt Thorley (61%)
Warkworth (42%)
Rio Tinto Diamonds & Minerals
Rio Tinto Diamond (diamonds Australia Canada Zimbabwe)
Rio Tinto Minerals (borates titanium dioxide Argentina/Australia/US)
Copper Products
Escondida (30% Chile)
Grasberg (40% Indonesia)
Kennecott Utah Copper (US)
Northparkes (80%)
Palabora (58% South Africa)
Gold
Barneys Canyon (US)
Bingham Canyon (US)
Escondida (30% Chile)
Rawhide (51% US)

COMPETITORS

ALROSA	Glencore
ASARCO	Goldcorp
Anglo American	Grupo Mexico
AngloGold Ashanti	ITOCHU
Arconic	Kaiser Aluminum
BHP Billiton	Marubeni
Barrick Gold	Newmont Mining
CONSOL Energy	Norsk Hydro ASA
Cliffs Natural Resources	RUSAL
	Recylex
Codelco	Southern Copper
Fortescue Metals	Teck
Freeport-McMoRan	Vale

HISTORICAL FINANCIALS

Company Type: Public

Income Statement

FYE: December 31

	REVENUE ($ mil.)	NET INCOME ($ mil.)	NET PROFIT MARGIN	EMPLOYEES
12/15	34,829	(866)	—	54,938
12/14	47,664	6,527	13.7%	59,775
12/13	51,171	3,665	7.2%	66,331
12/12	50,967	(2,990)	—	61,305
12/11	60,537	5,826	9.6%	56,965
Annual Growth	**(12.9%)**	**—**	**—**	**(0.9%)**

2015 Year-End Financials

Debt ratio: 25.8%
Return on equity: (-2.0%)
Cash ($ mil.): 9,366
Current ratio: 1.52
Long-term debt ($ mil.): 21,140

No. of shares (mil.): 1,798
Dividends
  Yield: —
  Payout: —
Market value ($ mil.): 59,090

	STOCK PRICE ($) FY Close	P/E High/Low		PER SHARE ($) Earnings	Dividends	Book Value
12/15	32.86	—	—	(0.48)	0.00	20.77
12/14	46.70	18	12	3.51	0.00	25.02
12/13	61.06	37	24	1.97	0.00	24.82
12/12	68.06	—	—	(1.62)	0.00	25.18
12/11	61.46	30	18	3.01	0.00	27.81
Annual Growth	**(14.5%)**	**—**	**—**	**—**		**(7.0%)**

Rio Tinto Plc

No you are not seeing double. Rio Tinto plc one of the world's largest mining operations (along with BHP Billiton and Vale) is the British half of a tandem of dual-listed companies. Rio Tinto plc's Australian counterpart is Rio Tinto Limited which has its headquarters in Melbourne. Rio Tinto explores for a variety of commodities: bauxite coal copper diamonds gold iron ore minerals (borates and titanium dioxide) nickel and potash. Iron ore makes up about 46% of the group's sales. The company also produces aluminum through its Rio Tinto Alcan unit.

Geographic Reach

The company operates in Australia and North America with significant businesses in Asia Europe Africa and South America. China is Rio Tinto's largest geographic segment accounting for 38% of 2014 revenues.

Operations

Rio Tinto engages in the exploration and mining and processing of metals and other mineral resources. Its products include aluminum copper diamonds thermal and metallurgical coal uranium gold industrial minerals (borax titanium dioxide and salt) and iron ore.

Financial Performance

In 2014 the company's net revenue decreased by 7% due to lower iron ore and energy sales as a result of lower prices. That year Rio Tinto improved its net loss to $28 million (compared to a net loss of $2.8 billion in 2013) primarily due to lower operating expenses and impairment charges and a decrease in losses on external debt.

In 2014 the company's cash flow decreased by 5% due to lower taxes and lower net interest paid.

Strategy

By focusing on a strategy of developing large-scale long-life mining operations Rio Tinto has tried to weather commodity prices that have dipped and risen over several years. Rio Tinto's tight-fisted operating style while providing exceptional margins for its industry has drawn the ire of unions which have been critical of the company's employment and environmental records.

To raise cash in 2017 Rio Tinto agreed to sell most of its underperforming Australian coal assets to China-backed Yanzhou Coal in a deal worth up to $2.45 billion.

In 2014 it sold Rio Tinto Coal Mozambique to International Coal Ventures Private Limited and 50.1% of its Clermont Joint Venture to GS Coal Pty Ltd a company jointly owned by Glencore and Sumitomo.

That year the company signed an option agreement with LNG Canada (a joint venture owned by Shell Canada Energy Phoenix Energy Holdings Limited Kogas Canada LNG Ltd and Diamond LNG Canada Ltd) to buy or lease a wharf and associated land at its port facility at Kitimat British Columbia.

HISTORY

Company Background

Following a tough 2009 in which the global recession depressed commodity prices Rio Tinto rebounded strongly in 2010 posting a 35% increase in overall revenues due primarily to increased sales volumes and prices generated by the beginnings of an economic recovery. Leading the pack for Rio Tinto was its Iron Ore segment which saw an increase of 91% over the previous year followed by the Copper segment with a hike of 24% and the Energy unit with 15%. Profitability soared in 2010 as net income jumped more than 184% due to lower operating costs and significant reductions in debt.

Despite its failed effort the previous year to hike its 9% stake in Rio Tinto to 19% Aluminum Corporation of China (Chinalco) formed a joint venture with Rio Tinto in 2010 to operate an iron ore project in Guinea West Africa. A Chinalco subsidiary will hold 47% of Rio Tinto's Simandou project which is expected to begin producing up to 70 million tons of ore per year by 2015.

In 2011 Rio Tinto and Chinalco teamed up again on a new joint venture that will focus on mineral exploration in China. Chinalco is seeking to find and develop domestic sources of copper coal and potash to offset the cost of importing those raw materials. Chinalco will hold a 51% interest in the joint venture Chinalco Rio Tinto Exploration with Rio Tinto holding the remaining 49%.

One of the world's largest producers of copper Rio Tinto operates the Oyu Tolgoi project in Mongolia along with Canada's Ivanhoe Mines and the Mongolian government. Vancouver-based Ivanhoe controlled one of the world's largest untapped copper and gold deposits in Mongolia and Rio Tinto expects the mine to be one of the world's top 10 copper producers as well as one of the top gold producers by 2018. In 2012 Rio Tinto upped its holding in Ivanhoe from 49% to 51% to become the majority owner.

Also in early 2012 Rio Tinto completed its offer for Canada-based uranium producer Hathor Exploration valued at $578 million after rival Cameco Corp. made a takeover bid for the company in 2011. Hathor supplies about a fifth of the world's uranium.

In 2011 the company also started slimming its aluminum operations. It placed 13 assets on the chopping block allowing Rio Tinto Alcan to focus on its high-quality tier one assets (mostly in Canada) and improve performance. The company also planned to transfer its stakes in six Australian and New Zealand operations to a new business unit Pacific Aluminium.

The new unit managed and reported separately from Rio Tinto Alcan would include the company's Gove bauxite mine and alumina refinery Boyne Smelters and Gladstone Power Station Tomago smelter and Bell Bay smelter in Australia. In New Zealand it would include the New Zealand Aluminium Smelters.

For at least a while longer the company is holding on to seven noncore assets managed by Rio Tinto Alcan including operations in France Germany the UK and the US. The company is in no hurry to sell and may wait until the economy improves before divesting certain operations. Rio Tinto has tried a similar divestment strategy before. It embarked on a divestment plan in the mid-2000s with the long-term goal of turning out $15 billion from its divestments. By 2010 the company had gained more than $10 billion from the divestment program.

Rio Tinto was formed in 1972.

EXECUTIVES

CFO, Christopher J. (Chris) Lynch, age 62
Group Executive Organisational Resources, Hugo Bague, age 55
Chief Executive Energy and Minerals, Alan Davies
Chief Executive Copper and Diamonds, Arnaud Soirat
Chief Executive Aluminium, Alfredo Barrios, age 50
Chief Executive, Jean-Sebastien Jacques, age 44
Chief Executive Iron Ore, Chris Salisbury
Chief Executive Growth and Innovation, Stephen McIntosh
Global Head of Health Safety Environment and Communities, Joanne Farrell
Chairman, Jan P. du Plessis, age 61
Auditors: PricewaterhouseCoopers LLP

LOCATIONS

HQ: Rio Tinto Plc
6 St. James' s Square, London SW1Y 4AD
Phone: (44) 20 7781 2000   **Fax:** (44) 20 7781 1800
Web: www.riotinto.com

2014 Sales by Destination

	% of total
Asia	
China	38
Japan	15
Other countries	16
North America	
US	13
Canada	3
Europe	
UK	1
Other countries	9
Australia	2
Other Countries	3
Total	**100**

PRODUCTS/OPERATIONS

2014 Sales

	% of total
Iron ore	46
Aluminum	24
Copper	12
Energy	9
Diamonds & minerals	8
Other	1
Total	**100**

COMPETITORS

ALROSA	Glencore
ASARCO	Goldcorp
Anglo American	Grupo Mexico
AngloGold Ashanti	ITOCHU
Arconic	Kaiser Aluminum
BHP Billiton	Marubeni
Barrick Gold	Newmont Mining

CONSOL Energy	Norsk Hydro ASA
Cliffs Natural	Phelps Dodge
Resources	Placer Dome
Codelco	RUSAL
DeBeers	Southern Copper
Falconbridge	Teck
Fortescue Metals	Vale
Freeport-McMoRan	WMC Resources

HISTORICAL FINANCIALS

Company Type: Public

Income Statement

FYE: December 31

	REVENUE ($ mil.)	NET INCOME ($ mil.)	NET PROFIT MARGIN	EMPLOYEES
12/15	34,829	(853)	—	54,938
12/14	47,664	(28)	—	59,775
12/13	51,171	(2,586)	—	66,331
12/12	50,967	(14)	—	71,219
12/11	60,537	939	1.6%	67,930
Annual Growth	(12.9%)	—	—	(5.2%)

2015 Year-End Financials

Debt ratio: —	No. of shares (mil.): 1,374
Return on equity: (-2.0%)	Dividends
Cash ($ mil.): 9,366	Yield: 7.5%
Current ratio: 1.52	Payout: —
Long-term debt ($ mil.): —	Market value ($ mil.): 40,012

	STOCK PRICE ($) FY Close	P/E High/Low		PER SHARE ($) Earnings	Dividends	Book Value
12/15	29.12	— —		(0.48)	2.21	27.18
12/14	46.06	17 12		3.51	2.02	32.73
12/13	56.43	30 20		1.97	1.76	32.48
12/12	58.09	— —		(1.62)	1.66	33.21
12/11	48.92	25 14		3.01	1.17	36.57
Annual Growth	(12.2%)	— —		—	17.2%	(7.2%)

Roche Holding Ltd

Roche operates two segments —pharmaceuticals and diagnostics —and sells its products in some 190 countries. Roche's prescription drugs include cancer therapies MabThera/Rituxan and Avastin Perjeta and Kadcyla for HER2-positive breast cancer hepatitis drug Pegasys idiopathic pulmonary fibrosis drug Esbriet macular degeneration therapy Lucentis and Tamiflu which is used to prevent and treat influenza (including pandemic strains). The company markets many of its bestsellers through subsidiary Genentech and affiliate Chugai Pharmaceutical. Roche's diagnostics arm offers clinical lab supplies genetic tests diabetes monitoring supplies and point-of-care diagnostics for health care providers.

Operations

Roche's pharmaceuticals division accounts for more than three-fourths of annual revenues with oncology drugs making the largest sales contribution (77% of revenues in 2014). The smaller yet faster-growing diagnostics segment is a leading maker of in vitro clinical diagnostic tests through its professional diagnostics segment; it is also an established provider of diabetes tests and glucose monitors.

Some of Roche's pipeline products include Anti-PDL1 immunotherapy medicine for bladder cancer Lampalizumab for geographic atrophy of the eye Cobimetinib and Zelboraf for advanced melanoma and ACE910 bispecific antibody for hemophilia A.

The company treated more than 19 million patients in 2014.

Geographic Reach

The largest geographic markets for the pharma segment are the US and Western Europe. Product marketing efforts in the US are conducted through Roche's main US subsidiary Genentech which is one of the world's largest biotech companies. The company also has a solid stance in the Japanese drug market through its 61.5% stake in Chugai Pharmaceutical and it is experiencing growth in Latin America and Asia.

In the Asia/Pacific region Roche's SPHERE (Scientific Partnership for HER2Testing Excellence) program helps to improve awareness and tests and treats breast and gastric cancers. It operates in a dozen markets: Bangladesh China Hong Kong India Indonesia Korea Malaysia Myanmar the Philippines Taiwan Thailand and Vietnam.

North American operations accounted for 40% of Roche's revenues in 2014 followed by Europe (31%) and other regions.

Financial Performance

As one of the top 10 global pharmaceutical companies Roche has steadily grown its revenues and profits over the last decade. Revenue increased by just under 2% in 2014 to CHF 47.5 billion thanks to growth in both the pharmaceutical and diagnostics segments. The pharmaceutical arm grew 4% that year due to growth in its oncology and immunology portfolios particularly increased sales of its Acemtra treatment for rheumatoid arthritis and its Xolair treatment for chronic hives and asthma. The rising sales of Perjeta and Kadcyla helped offset any declines of Xeloda. The diagnostics arm grew 6% driven by growth in the professional diagnostics and molecular diagnostics operations.

Net income fell 16% to CHF 9.5 billion that year though as expenses related to R&D marketing and distribution rose. Cash flow from operations grew a modest 1% to CHF 15.8 billion due to several factors (including an increase in working capital and a decline in cash used in income tax paid).

Strategy

In order to expand its pharmaceutical product offerings and stave off revenue losses from patent expirations and other competitive pressures Roche invests heavily in internal research and development programs to expand its pipeline of small-molecule and biotechnology drug candidates. The company has about 100 drugs in clinical development stages the bulk of which aim to treat oncology cardiovascular metabolic viral inflammatory autoimmune and central nervous system disorders. In 2014 the company invested CHF 9 billion in core R&D (representing 19% of sales).

Roche also pursues acquisitions and site expansions.

The firm has also widened its R&D programs by forming partnerships with other drugmakers such as Biogen Idec and Pharmasset as well as through acquisitions. In addition to new drug formulas Roche conducts R&D programs on existing drugs to gain regulatory approval for new indications which typically helps to extend a drug's patent protection and increase sales volumes. In 2014 the company signed 55 new agreements including three acquisitions four product transactions 37 research and technology collaborations and 11 product out-licensing agreements.

In 2015 the US FDA provided 510(k) clearance for the cobas MRSA/SA test for the early detection of methicillin-resistant Staphylococcus aureus (MRSA) and methicillin-resistant Staphylococcus aureus (SA) from nasal specimens; it also approved the cobas TaqScreen MPX test v2.0 for the detection of HIV HCV and HBV in blood and plasma donations. The prior year Roche received Breakthrough Therapy designation for three medicines (anti-PDL1 Lucentis and Esbriet). Also in

2014 the company launched a new test to determine fertility levels as well as a test to predict the likelihood of preeclampsia in pregnancy.

Not one to neglect its smaller division Roche has been aggressively adding to its diagnostic testing stable through R&D partnership and acquisition efforts. In addition to clinical and diabetes tests focus areas for the diagnostics division include tissue-based cancer diagnostics (through its Ventana Medical Systems subsidiary) life science (gene sequencing) technologies and molecular diagnostics which include personalized (or companion) tests that are used to determine the best treatment regimen for a specific patient.

In 2014 Roche signed a distribution agreement with Sigma-Aldrich for its biochemical reagents portfolio which includes cellular analysis kits.

Mergers and Acquisitions

Acquisitions are also key elements in Roche's R&D growth strategy and have expanded its pharmaceutical segment in focused therapeutic areas. For example in 2014 it acquired Seragon Pharmaceuticals out of California for $988 million; it gained rights to Seragon's portfolio of selective estrogen receptor degraders to potentially treat hormone receptor-positive cancers. It also bought Santaris Pharma out of Denmark Austria's Dutalys and California's InterMune (for $8.8 billion) adding Esbriet to its portfolio. The following year it purchased Ariosa Diagnostics a molecular diagnostics company.

In 2013 it enhanced its diagnostics business and strengthened its hematology offerings with the $220 million purchase (plus contingent payments) of Constitution Medical Investors which makes tests for blood diseases. Two years later it bought a controlling stake in Foundation Medicine which makes the FoundationOne cancer test for just over $1 billion. It also acquired Genia Technologies (California) which is developing a single-molecule semiconductor-based DNA sequencing platform; IQuum (Massachusetts) developer of the Laboratory-in-a-tube or Liat system; and Bina Technologies (California) which provides Roche with a big data platform for centralized management and processing of next-generation sequencing data.

The company also announced plans to buy private French company Trophos which makes olesoxime (an experimental treatment for spinal muscular atrophy a debilitating genetic neuromuscular disease) for an upfront payment of euro 120 million ($140 million) plus further payments up to euro 350 million.

Ownership

Descendants of the founding Hoffmann and Oeri families own about half of Roche. In addition fellow Swiss drugmaker Novartis owns 33% of the company.

HISTORY

Company Background

Fritz Hoffmann-La Roche backed by family wealth began making pharmaceuticals in a lab in Basel Switzerland in 1894. At the time drug compounds were mixed at pharmacies and lacked uniformity. Hoffmann was not a chemist but saw the potential for mass-produced standardized branded drugs.

By WWI Hoffman had become successful selling Thiocal (cough medicine) Digalen (digitalis extract) and other products on four continents. During the war the Bolsheviks seized the firm's St. Petersburg Russia facility and its Warsaw plant was almost destroyed. Devastated Hoffmann sold company shares outside the family in 1919 and died in 1920.

As WWII loomed Roche divided its holdings between F. Hoffman-La Roche and Sapac which held many of Roche's foreign operations. US opera-

tions became more important during the war. Roche synthesized vitamins C A and E (eventually becoming the world's top vitamin maker) and built plants and research centers worldwide.

Roche continued to develop such successful products as tranquilizers Librium (1960) and Valium (1963) —the world's best-selling prescription drug prior to anti-ulcer successors Tagamet (SmithKline Beecham now part of GlaxoSmithKline) and Prilosec (AstraZeneca). Roche made its first fragrance and flavor buy Givaudan in 1963.

In the 1970s after several governments accused it of price-gouging on Librium and Valium Roche agreed to price restraints. The company was fined for vitamin price-fixing in 1976. It was also rapped that year for its slow response to an Italian factory dioxin leak that killed thousands of animals and forced hundreds of families to evacuate.

Roche became one of the first drugmakers to sell another's products when it agreed to sell Glaxo's Zantac ulcer treatment in the US in 1982. The move let Roche maintain its large US sales force at the time when Valium went off patent decimating the company's drug sales.

Roche acquired a product pipeline when it bought a majority stake in genetic engineering firm Genentech in 1990. In 1994 it bought the struggling Syntex solidifying its position in North America. The company gained Aleve and other products in 1996 when it bought out its joint venture with Procter & Gamble and also acquired Cincinnati-based flavors and fragrances firm Tastemaker.

In its biggest acquisition ever Roche bought Corange in 1998 for $10.2 billion; its subsidiary Boehringer Mannheim was renamed Roche Molecular Biochemicals. In 1999 Roche announced it had located the gene that causes osteoarthritis. The company began to market anti-obesity pharmaceutical Xenical in the US that year despite reports of some unpleasant side effects.

EXECUTIVES

Head of Genentech Research and Early Development (gRED), Michael D. Varney
Chairman and CEO Chugai, Osamu Nagayama, age 69
Chief Financial and IT Officer, Alan Hippe, age 49
CEO, Severin Schwan, age 49
Head Roche Molecular Diagnostics, Daniel O'Day, age 52
COO Diagnostics, Roland Diggelmann, age 49
Head of Roche Partnering, Sophie Kornowski-Bonnet, age 53
Head of Pharma Research and Early Development, John C. Reed, age 58
Chairman, Christoph Franz, age 56
Vice Chairman, Andre Hoffman, age 58
Auditors: KPMG AG

LOCATIONS

HQ: Roche Holding Ltd
Grenzacherstrasse 124, Basel CH-4070
Phone: (41) 61 688 22 72   **Fax:** (41) 61 688 13 96
Web: www.roche.com

2014 Sales

	% of total
North America	40
Europe	31
Asia	19
Latin America	7
Africa Australia & Oceania	3
Total	**100**

PRODUCTS/OPERATIONS

2014 Sales

	% of total
Pharmaceuticals	
Oncology	48
Immunology	11
Infectious disease	7
Ophthalmology	3
Neuroscience	1
Other	7
Diagnostics	23
Total	**100**

Selected Products

Top 20 Products (listed alphabetically)
Actemra/RoActemra (rheumatoid arthritis)
Activase/TNKase (cardiovascular)
Avastin (colorectal cancer non-small cell lung cancer breast cancer kidney cancer)
Bonviva/Boniva (osteoporosis)
CellCept (transplantation)
Herceptin (HER2-positive breast cancer)
Lucentis (wet age-related macular degeneration diabetic macular edema)
MabThera/Rituxan (non-Hodgkin's lymphoma rheumatoid arthritis chronic lymphocytic leukemia)
Madopar (Parkinson's disease restless leg syndrome)
Mircera (predialysis)
NeoRecormon/Epogen (anemia oncology)
Neutrogin/Neupogen (neutropenia associated with chemotherapy)
Nutropin (growth hormone deficiency)
Pegasys (hepatitis B and C)
Pulmozyme (cystic fibrosis)
Tamiflu (treatment and prevention of influenza)
Tarceva (advanced non-small cell lung cancer advanced pancreatic cancer)
Valcyte/Cymevene (cytomegalovirus infection)
Xeloda (colorectal cancer breast cancer colon cancer)
Xolair (asthma)
Other Products
Anaprox (pain fever and inflammation)
Bactrim (anti-infective)
Bondronat (bone disease in breast cancer patients)
Dilatrend (hypertension)
Dormicum (sedation)
Erivedge (basal cell carcinoma)
Fuzeon (HIV)
Invirase (HIV)
Kytril (nausea and vomiting induced by chemotherapy or radiation therapy)
Lariam (malaria)
Perjeta (breast cancer)
Roaccutane/Accutane (acne)
Rocaltrol/Calcitriol (osteoporosis)
Rocephin (bacterial infections)
Roferon-A (hepatitis C hairy cell leukemia AIDS-related Kaposi's sarcoma)
Toradol (acute pain)
Valium (anxiety disorders)
Vesanoid (leukemia)
Viracept (HIV)
Xenical (weight loss weight control)
Zelboraf (metastatic melanoma)
Zenapax (transplant rejection)

Selected Acquisitions

COMPETITORS

Abbott Labs	Gilead Sciences
Allergan plc	GlaxoSmithKline
Amgen	Johnson & Johnson
Astellas	Merck
AstraZeneca	Merck KGaA
Bayer AG	Novartis
Becton Dickinson	Pfizer
Biogen	Sanofi
Bristol-Myers Squibb	Takeda Pharmaceutical
Eisai	Teva
Eli Lilly	

Income Statement
FYE: December 31

	REVENUE ($ mil.)	NET INCOME ($ mil.)	NET PROFIT MARGIN	EMPLOYEES
12/15	50,753	8,924	17.6%	91,747
12/14	50,411	9,434	18.7%	88,509
12/13	54,555	12,528	23.0%	85,080
12/12	51,755	10,405	20.1%	82,089
12/11	46,889	9,930	21.2%	80,129
Annual Growth	2.0%	(2.6%)	—	3.4%

2015 Year-End Financials

Debt ratio: 30.9%	No. of shares (mil.): 160
Return on equity: 43.7%	Dividends
Cash ($ mil.): 3,756	Yield: 2.9%
Current ratio: 1.19	Payout: 9.4%
Long-term debt ($ mil.): 17,218	Market value ($ mil.): 5,515

	STOCK PRICE ($) FY Close	P/E High	P/E Low	PER SHARE ($) Earnings	PER SHARE ($) Dividends	PER SHARE ($) Book Value
12/15	34.47	3	3	10.35	1.00	132.03
12/14	33.99	6	3	10.93	1.11	123.75
12/13	70.20	5	4	14.51	0.97	135.33
12/12	50.50	5	4	12.17	0.92	98.82
12/11	42.55	4	3	11.67	0.87	80.49
Annual Growth	(5.1%)	—	—	(3.0%)	3.6%	13.2%

Rolls Royce Holdings Plc

Rolls-Royce Holdings doesn't make cars so luxurious you'll cry (see Motor Cars) but it sure can make an aircraft engine whine. One of the world's largest aircraft engine makers Rolls-Royce through its Civil and Defense Aerospace businesses makes commercial and military engines for a broad customer base including airlines corporate and utility aircraft and helicopter operators and armed forces around the world. Beyond aviation its Energy unit supplies gas turbine power generation to the oil and gas industry while its Marine segment makes propulsion systems that power 70 navies worldwide. Rolls-Royce has operations in North America Europe and Asia with an emerging presence in the Middle East.

Operations

The company operates two divisions: Aerospace and Land & Sea.

The Aerospace division covers both civil and military aviation for which it develops manufactures markets and sells engines and power systems. The division's engines are found in the aircraft such as the Airbus A380 and on the defense side of things Rolls-Royce commands approximately one-quarter of the world's military engine manufacturing market share. Its portfolio covers all major sectors —combat helicopters unmanned and tactical aircraft training and transport. The Land & Sea division has three interests of power systems marine propulsion and nuclear power generation and propulsion. Its PWR2 nuclear propulsion system is found in the Royal Navy's Trident submarine fleet.

Geographic Reach

Headquartered in London Rolls-Royce has operations in over 50 countries and customers in over 150 worldwide. Europe is the company's biggest market at around 35% of sales followed by North America at 30% and Asia at 20%.

Financial Performance

Note: Growth rates may differ after conversion to US Dollars.

After a few years of growth from 2011 sales have flattened coming in at £13.7 billion in 2014 and 2015. Sales in Land & Sea were marginally lower than prior year due to weakness in Marine sales. Net income nudged up £14 million in 2015 to £83 million due to a decrease in taxation and commercial and administrative costs. Cash flow from operations fell 16% to £1.1 billion due to changes in provisions.

Strategy

The company undertook a restructuring initiative in 2014 and 2015 to enhance operational efficiency which included the axing of 600 management jobs since mid-2015 and the consolidation of its Civil Aerospace repair and overhaul activities allowing for the closure of sites in Brazil and the UK. It sold its Michell Bearings business in November 2015 for £12.6 million.

Rolls-Royce expects to see an uptick in its overseas business following the sharp fall in value of the Pound Sterling subsequent to the EU referendum in mid-2016.

Rolls-Royce is possibly weighing up an escalation of its nuclear activities after the UK government announced a £250 million competition to encourage development of small modular reactor (SMR) technologies which have potential uses as part of a 7 gigawatt network of SMRs.

Mergers and Acquisitions

In mid-2016 Rolls-Royce announced the purchase of the remaining 53% of shares in Industria de Turbo Propulsores (ITP) for euro 720 million in order to strengthen its large engine growth program. ITP brings with it long-term aftermarket revenue including the high volume Trent 1000 and Trent XWB engines. The acquisition is expected to complete in 2017.

In 2015 the company acquired R.O.V Technologies which makes products that allow for the remote inspection and cleaning of boiling/pressurized water reactors complementing Rolls-Royce's existing nuclear activities.

HISTORY

In 1906 automobile and aviation enthusiast Charles Rolls and engineer Henry Royce unveiled the Silver Ghost an automobile that earned Rolls-Royce a reputation as maker of the best car in the world.

A year after Rolls' 1910 death in a biplane crash Royce suffered a breakdown. From his home Royce continued to design Rolls-Royce engines such as the Eagle its first aircraft engine in 1914 and other engines used to power airplanes during WWI —but management of the company fell to Claude Johnson who remained chief executive until 1926.

Although the company returned primarily to making cars after WWI its engines were used in several history-making flights and in 1931 set world speed records for land sea and air. Rolls-Royce bought the Bentley Motor Company that year. In 1933 it introduced the Merlin engine which powered the Spitfire Hurricane and Mustang fighters of WWII. Rolls-Royce began designing a jet engine in 1938 and over the years it pioneered the turboprop engine turbofan and vertical takeoff engine.

Realizing that it had to break into the lucrative US airliner market to stay alive Rolls-Royce bought its main British competitor Bristol-Siddley Engines in 1966. With Bristol-Siddley came its contract to build the engine for the Anglo-French Concorde in 1976 and a US presence.

Lockheed ordered the company's RB211 engine for its TriStar in 1968 but Rolls-Royce underestimated the project's technical and financial challenges and entered bankruptcy in 1971. The British government stepped in and nationalized the aerospace division and sold the auto group. The RB211 entered service on the TriStar in 1972 and on the Boeing 747 in 1977.

Rolls-Royce was reprivatized in 1987. In a diversification effort two years later the company bought mining marine and power plant specialist Northern Engineering Industries. In the early 1990s the aerospace market was hurt by military spending cutbacks and a recession; the company cut more than 18000 jobs.

A joint venture with BMW launched the BR710 engine for Gulfstream and Canadair's long-range business jets in 1990. The company bought Allison Engine in 1995.

Rolls-Royce sold Parsons Power Generation Systems to Siemens in 1997. Also that year it won a contract to supply Trent 892 engines for Boeing 777 jets being built for American Airlines (a subsidiary of AMR Corporation) in a deal worth $1 billion.

In 1998 the British government approved a repayable investment of about $335 million in the company to develop a new model of Trent aircraft engines. Narrowing its focus the company sold its power transmission and distribution business to Austria-based VA Technologie.

Rolls-Royce pumped up its gas and oil equipment business in 1999 by buying the rotating compression equipment unit of Cooper Cameron (now Cameron International); it became one of the world leaders in marine propulsion by acquiring Vickers. The company then bought the aero and industrial engine repair service of First Aviation Services and took full control of its aircraft-engine joint venture with BMW; in return BMW received a 10% stake in Rolls.

In 2000 subsidiary Rolls-Royce Energy Systems India Private was awarded its first order: producing a Bergen gas engine for Garden Silk Mills for powering a textile plant in India. That year Rolls-Royce won a contract to supply engines for Israel's El Al airline's Boeing 777s. Late in 2000 it was reported that the company would cut about 5000 jobs over three years.

Early in 2001 Rolls-Royce sold most of its Vickers Turbine Components business. In October the company cut about 11% of its workforce in response to the worldwide crisis in the commercial jet business.

In 2002 the company announced that it had inked a 10-year $2 billion deal to supply engines to Gulfstream Aerospace. That year Rolls-Royce sold its Vickers Defence Systems unit which made tanks and armored vehicles to Alvis Plc. In 2003 Sir Ralph Robins who had been executive chairman for more than a decade retired from his post.

Early in 2004 Rolls-Royce and GE Aircraft Engines were picked to supply engines for Boeing's upcoming 787 Dreamliner. Rolls-Royce was also selected to supply engines for Airbus' upcoming behemoth A380.

In late 2007 it scored one of its largest contracts a $42 million project to provide steering gear and deck machinery for Chinese shipbuilder Sinopacific.

In 2008 it entered into a joint venture with Goodrich Corporation called Aero Engine Controls to produce engine controls for Rolls-Royce aircraft. It also partnered with France's AREVA to construct the first new nuclear reactors built in the UK in more than 20 years.

In 2009 the company focused on developing four advanced manufacturing research centers in the US the UK and Singapore. Rolls-Royce invested £300 million (more than $450 million) in its UK factories as part of its almost £2 billion (over $3 billion) capital replacement plan to be carried out over a period of 10 years. That year Rolls-Royce engines allowed the BAE Systems' Mantis UAV and AgustaWestland's Lynx Wildcat helicopter to take flight.

Rolls-Royce's nuclear market was strengthened in 2009 by its agreement with electric service provider EDF Energy (formerly known as London Electricity Group) to enter into a joint venture with EDF Energy giving support to the UK facility. The following year the company introduced its STOVL (short take-off and vertical landing) Rolls-Royce LiftSystem.

The bell of financial crisis knelled in 2008 causing the company to implement cost-cutting measures which included headcount reductions of almost 10%. The company in partnership with GE Aviation continued development of the F136 engine for the F-35 Joint Strike Fighter and its Trent 1000 engine took its first flight in the Boeing 787 Dreamliner. Also in 2008 Rolls-Royce established its civil nuclear business to tap a growing global market.

Auditors: KPMG LLP

LOCATIONS

HQ: Rolls Royce Holdings Plc
  62 Buckingham Gate, London SW1E 6AT
Phone: (44) 20 7222 9020   **Fax:** (44) 20 7227 9170
Web: www.rolls-royce.com

2015 Sales

	% of total
Europe	36
North America	30
Asia	21
Middle East	6
South America	3
Australasia	2
Africa	1
Other	1
Total	**100**

PRODUCTS/OPERATIONS

2015 Sales (by market)

	% of total
Civil Aerospace	52
Power Systems	18
Defence Aerospace	15
Marine	10
Nuclear	5
Total	**100**

Selected Products and Services

Aircraft engines
Automation and control equipment
Bearings and seals
Diesel and gas turbine engines
Electric propulsion systems
Engine support services
Helicopter engines
Fuel cells
Generators
Offshore drilling equipment
Overhaul and repair services
Ship designs
Technical publications
Training

Selected Subsidiaries

Civil aerospace
  Optimized Systems and Solutions Limited (OSyS)
  (advanced controls and predictive data management)
  Rolls-Royce Leasing Limited (engine leasing)
  Rolls-Royce Total Care Services Limited (aftermarket
  support services)
Corporate
  Rolls-Royce International Limited (international
  support and commercial information services)

Rolls-Royce Power Engineering plc (power generation and marine systems)
Energy
  Rolls-Royce Fuel Cell Systems Limited (fuel cell system development)
  Rolls-Royce Power Development Limited (project development)
  Tidal Generation Limited (development of tidal generation systems)
Marine
  ODIM ASA (offshore drilling naval and power generation equipment)
  Rolls-Royce Marine Electrical Systems Limited (marine electrical systems)
  Rolls-Royce Power Development Limited (generation of electricity from independent power projects)
  Rolls-Royce Marine Power Operations Limited (nuclear submarine propulsion systems)
  Rolls-Royce Power Engineering plc (energy and marine systems)
p>#

COMPETITORS

Emerson Electric	McDermott
GE Aviation	Pratt & Whitney
GE Honda Aero Engines	SAFRAN
HEICO	Siemens AG
Honeywell Aerospace	Volvo
IHI Corp.	
Kawasaki Heavy	
Industries	

HISTORICAL FINANCIALS

Company Type: Public

Income Statement

FYE: December 31

	REVENUE ($ mil.)	NET INCOME ($ mil.)	NET PROFIT MARGIN	EMPLOYEES
12/15	20,339	123	0.6%	50,500
12/14	21,442	107	0.5%	54,100
12/13	25,636	2,259	8.8%	55,200
12/12	19,601	3,676	18.8%	42,800
12/11	17,184	1,313	7.6%	40,400
Annual Growth	**4.3%**	**(44.7%)**	**—**	**5.7%**

2015 Year-End Financials

Debt ratio: 21.9%
Return on equity: 1.4%
Cash ($ mil.): 4,706
Current ratio: 1.48
Long-term debt ($ mil.): 4,272

No. of shares (mil.): 1,838
Dividends
  Yield: 4.0%
  Payout: 521.6%
Market value ($ mil.): 15,666

	STOCK PRICE ($) FY Close	P/E High/Low	PER SHARE ($) Earnings	Dividends	Book Value
12/15	8.52	1741168	0.07	0.35	4.04
12/14	67.19	27431662	0.06	0.36	5.29
12/13	106.03	143100	1.20	0.31	4.93
12/12	71.79	59 48	1.96	0.28	5.24
12/11	57.73	126 93	0.70	0.25	3.73
Annual Growth	**(38.0%)**	**— —**	**(44.5%)**	**8.9%**	**2.0%**

Rosneft Oil Co OJSC (Moscow)

Integrated oil giant Rosneft conducts oil and gas exploration and production activities in Siberia the North Caucasus the Black Caspian and Azov Seas and in other regions. It also has exploration projects in Algeria Kazakhstan and Turkmenistan. It has proved reserves of 33 billion barrels of oil

equivalent and seven refineries (4.9 million barrels of oil equivalent a day). Rosneft operates shipping and pipeline companies and a national network of 2630 gasoline stations. In 2016 Rosneft bought the Russian government's 50.1% stake in refiner Bashneft for $5.2 billion. That year Russia agreed to sell 19.5% of Rosneft to Glencore and Qatar's sovereign wealth fund for $11 billion.

Geographic ReachRosneft is widely engaged in exploration and production across all of Russia's major hydrocarbon regions: Western Siberia Southern and Central Russia Timan-Pechora Eastern Siberia and the Far East. In addition the company participates in several exploration projects in Kazakhstan and Algeria. Rosneft's seven major refineries have convenient locations throughout the country from the Black Sea coast to Asia and its retail network covers 41 regions of the Russian Federation. Rosneft also owns 50% of Ruhr Oel which holds stakes in four refineries in Germany.
  Operations
Rosneft ranks among the world's top publicly traded oil and gas companies. It is primarily engaged in exploration and production of hydrocarbons production of petroleum products and petrochemicals and marketing of refined products. The company's major exploration projects are located in Russia's most promising oil & gas regions such as Eastern Siberia the shelf of Russia's Black Caspian and Azov seas and the Russian Far East. It has a network of gas stations in 44 regions of Russia.
  Financial Performance
Increased industrial demand and higher oil prices helped to lift the company's revenues by 53% in 2013. It also saw its net income increase by 51% that year.
  Strategy
Rosneft's development strategy includes both increasing shareholder value and attaining the highest corporate governance standards especially in terms of transparency and responsible business management.

It also seeks to grow through acquisitions of other oil companies and by partnerships as a way to gain hydrocarbon assets and industry expertise.

In 2014 Rosneft and SANORS Holding Limited (Novokuibyshevsk Petrochemical Company) signed a deal to build anew world-class petrochemical complex in the Samara region of Russia.
  Mergers and Acquisitions
In 2014 Rosneft agreed to buy 49% of Petrocas Energy International Limited creating the joint venture for its activities in the South Caucasus region. Through the JV (Petrocas owns and operates high-quality storage assets in one of the main oil and oil products logistics hub in the region) Rosneft will expand its presence in the area and further diversify its supply routes options. In 2014 Rosneft and Lukoil signed deal regarding Rosneft's acquisition of 20% of National Oil Consortium LLC (NOC) boosting it holdings in NOC to 80%. The remaining 20% is owned by Gazprom Neft.

Other 2014 purchases included the Bishkek Oil Company Group a leader in the oil products market in Bishkek eight companies (part of the Weatherford group) involved in drilling operations in Russia and Venezuela and Orenburg Drilling Company (a key to the re-equipment of Rosneft's fleet of drilling units).

In a major expansion in 2013 Rosneft bought BP's 50% stake in TNK-BP (it already held 50%) in a $55 billion deal. Rosneft paid BP $17.1 billion in cash plus shares.

HISTORY

Company Background
Rosneft was formed in 1993.

In 2004 Rosneft acquired YUKOS' main oil unit –Yugansk –in a controversial $9.4 billion deal. The acquisition of Yugansk (also known as Yuganskneftegaz) has been more complicated than Rosneft may have wished as questions were raised about how the deal was handled and how the transaction was funded. In 2004 the company agreed to merge with Russian energy giant Gazprom. The Yugansk acquisition threw the merger with Gazprom into disarray with Rosneft claiming that terms of the deal should be renegotiated to account for the change in value of Rosneft's assets. In addition Group Menatep (majority owner of YUKOS) called for Rosneft to repay a loan estimated at about $900 million that is secured by Yugansk assets. In response Rosneft filed an $11 billion suit against YUKOS for unpaid taxes related to Yugansk.

In 2005 Rosneft approved the deal with Gazprom though the acquisition would exclude the Yugansk assets acquired from YUKOS. After months of conflicting reports state-controlled Gazprom abandoned the deal.

In 2006 Rosneft and BP teamed up to develop energy projects in Russia's Arctic. Rosneft raised $10.4 billion in a 2006 IPO (during which BP acquired a $1 billion stake).

In a move toward becoming a global oil company in 2011 Rosneft formed a strategic alliance with BP (involving a stock swap of 5% of BP's shares for 9.5% of Rosneft's) to help fund the exploration of three blocks on the Russian Arctic continental shelf. The blocks have a production capacity on a par with the UK North Sea. However rival Russian partners at TNK-BP (BP's established Russian joint venture) objected to the proposed deal saying that have the legal right to have first choice on BP expansion activities in Russia. An arbitration tribunal in the UK supported their position. BP subsequently agreed to pursue the Rosneft deal through TNK BP. This move was unsuccessful and in May 2011 the BP/Rosneft deal fell through.

It followed this by forming a joint venture with Exxon Mobil to explore oil and gas fields in the Arctic. (This plan was stymied by US sanctions imposed in 2014).

Growing its European refinery footprint in 2011 it also acquired a 50% stake in German refinery Ruhr Oel from PDVSA for about $1.6 billion. BP owns the other 50%.

Beefing up its Russian assets in 2012 also bought 51% of NGK ITERA LLC one of the largest independent producers and traders of natural gas in Russia for RUB 7 billion (US $227 million).

EXECUTIVES

President and Director, Eduard Khudainatov, age 56
VP Finance and Economics, Pavel Fyodorov
Auditors: Ernst & Young LLC

LOCATIONS

HQ: Rosneft Oil Co OJSC (Moscow)
26/1, Sofiyskaya Embankment, Moscow 115035
Phone: (7) 499 517 88 99   **Fax:** (7) 499 517 72 35
Web: www.rosneft.com

PRODUCTS/OPERATIONS

2013 Sales

	% of total
Oil & gas	52
Petroleum products & petrochemicals	47
Support services & other revenues	1
Equity share in profits of associates & joint ventures	-
Total	**100**

COMPETITORS

Exillon Energy	LUKOIL
Gazprom	Tatneft

HISTORICAL FINANCIALS

Company Type: Public

Income Statement

FYE: December 31

	REVENUE ($ mil.)	NET INCOME ($ mil.)	NET PROFIT MARGIN	EMPLOYEES
12/15	69,740	4,807	6.9%	261,500
12/14	93,493	5,912	6.3%	248,900
12/13	142,824	16,582	11.6%	228,000
12/12	101,114	11,202	11.1%	166,110
12/11	84,202	9,789	11.6%	160,837
Annual Growth	(4.6%)	(16.3%)	—	12.9%

2015 Year-End Financials

Debt ratio: 0.4%
Return on equity: 12.3%
Cash ($ mil.): 7,569
Current ratio: 1.32
Long-term debt ($ mil.): 30,915

No. of shares (mil.): —
Dividends
  Yield: 0.0%
  Payout: 23.5%
Market value ($ mil.): —

	STOCK PRICE ($) FY Close	P/E High/Low		PER SHARE ($) Earnings	Dividends	Book Value
12/15	3.41	0	0	0.45	0.11	3.69
12/14	3.60	0	0	0.56	0.21	4.60
12/13	7.85	0	0	1.61	0.31	8.97
12/12	8.85	0	0	1.19	0.10	7.93
Annual Growth	(27.2%) (17.4%)	—	—	(21.4%)	2.4%	

Royal Bank of Canada (Montreal, Quebec)

Royal Bank of Canada is Canada's #1 bank by assets and market capitalization and is a leading North American financial services company. Royal Bank of Canada and its subsidiaries operate under the brand name RBC providing a diversified set of personal and commercial banking wealth management insurance investor and wholesale banking services globally. RBC serves large and small personal business public sector and institutional clients through offices in Canada the US and about 49 other countries including the UK and other select parts of Europe and Asia/Pacific. Its 2015 acquisition of City National Corp added 75 branches to its network in the US.

Operations
The company has realigned its business segments into five units. It eliminated its International Banking segment and created a new Investor & Treasury Services segment which offers advisory custodial and financing services to safeguard assets and manage risk to institutional investors. That segment includes RBC Investor Services the largest custodian in Canada and formerly a joint venture called RBC Dexia. The company also operates a Personal & Commercial Banking segment which includes personal and business banking operations and certain investment businesses in Canada the US and the Caribbean.

Wholesale banking business Capital Markets continues to provide a full suite of products and services –including corporate and investment banking equity and debt origination and structur-

ing and trading –to public and private companies institutional investors governments and central banks. Rounding out RBC's business segments are Wealth Management and Insurance.

Geographic Reach
Canada is RBC's largest market accounting for more than two-thirds of total revenue. The remainder of revenue is balanced between the US and other international markets (which include Europe and Asia).

Financial Performance
The company has seen stable growth in its revenues over the past few years. RNC's revenues increased by 9% in 2013 due to higher interest and non interest income. Net interest income rose due to solid volume growth of 5% across most of its businesses in the Canadian Banking segment and higher trading-related net interest income (and higher lending activity) in Capital Markets. RBC's net income increased by 8% in 2013 due to a decline in the provision for loan losses.

Strategy
With Canada generating more than two-thirds of RBC's revenue it's no surprise that the company's primary strategy in that market is to remain the undisputed leader in financial services. Other initiatives the company is undertaking to achieve its growth strategy are tightly managing costs deepening client relationships increasing price competitiveness and investing in technology.

Outside of Canada in an effort to be a leading provider of capital markets and wealth management services the company is focusing on high-net-worth corporate and institutional clients in the US the UK and key emerging markets like Hong Kong and Singapore. RBC is the sixth-largest global wealth manager by assets under management. Streamlining its operations in 2014 RBC sold RBC Royal Bank (Jamaica) Limited and RBTT Securities Jamaica Limited to Sagicor Group Jamaica Limited.

Mergers and AcquisitionsIn November 2015 RBC purchased City National Corporation along with some 75 City National Bank branches in the US (mostly in California) for a total consideration valued around $5 billion. The acquisition added $33.5 billion in assets and expanded RBC's reach into the US. Planning to make City National Corporation its American retail banking franchise RBC intended to keep the City National name on the acquired branches and promote product and service cross-selling between City National and RBC.

In 2013 growing its specialty financing business RBC acquired the Canadian auto finance and deposit business of Ally Financial in a deal valued at $1.4 billion. The deal positions RBC as a leader in the Canadian auto finance business.

Diversifying its portfolio that year the bank acquired the Athena Energy Group a market leading natural gas supplier in Quebec.

Company Background
In 2012 RBC acquired the Latin American Caribbean and African private banking business of Coutts the wealth management division of Royal Bank of Scotland to increase market share with high-net-worth clients.

RBC in 2012 also shed its money-losing US retail bank operations RBC Bank (USA) and a US credit card business selling them to PNC Financial for $3.6 billion. RBC said those operations lacked the scale to accomplish what the company wanted to do in the US. RBC had also been struggling with credit losses in the US following the economic downturn.

RBC was created as Merchants Bank in 1864 and was incorporated in 1869. It changed its name to The Royal Bank of Canada in 1901 and to Royal Bank of Canada in 1990.

HISTORY

Royal Bank of Canada (RBC) has looked south of the border ever since its 1864 creation as Merchants Bank in Halifax Nova Scotia a port city bustling with trade spawned by the US Civil War. After incorporating in 1869 as Merchants Bank of Halifax the bank added branches in eastern Canada. Merchants opened a branch in Bermuda in 1882. Gold strikes in Canada and Alaska in the late 1890s pushed it into western Canada.

Merchants opened offices in New York and Cuba in 1899 and changed its name to Royal Bank of Canada in 1901. RBC moved into new Montreal headquarters in 1907 and grew by purchasing such banks as Union Bank of Canada (1925). In 1928 it moved into the 42-story Royal Bank Building then the tallest in the British Empire.

The bank faltered during the Depression but recovered during WWII. After the war RBC financed the expanding minerals and oil and gas industries. When Castro took power in Cuba RBC tried to operate its branches under communist rule but sold out to Banco Nacional de Cuba in 1960.

RBC opened offices in the UK in 1979 and in West Germany Puerto Rico and the Bahamas in 1980. As Canada's banking rules relaxed RBC bought Dominion Securities in 1987. The US Federal Reserve approved RBC's brokerage arm for participation in stock underwriting in 1991.

The bank faced a $650 million loss in 1992 after backing the Reichmann family's Olympia & York property development company which failed under the weight of its UK projects. The next year an ever-diversifying RBC bought Royal Trustco Canada's #2 trust company and Voyageur Travel Insurance its largest retail travel insurer. A management shakeup in late 1994 ended with bank president John Cleghorn taking control of the company.

In 1995 RBC listed on the New York Stock Exchange and the next year joined with Heller Financial (an affiliate of Japan's Fuji Bank) to finance trade between Canada and Mexico. It began offering PC home banking in 1996 and Internet banking in 1997. That year RBC became one of the world's largest securities-custody service providers with its acquisition of The Bank of Nova Scotia's institutional and pension custody operations.

The company and Bank of Montreal agreed to merge in 1998 but Canadian regulators fearing the concentration of banking power seen in the US rejected the merger. In response the bank trimmed its workforce and orchestrated a sale-leaseback of its property portfolio (1999).

In the late 1990s RBC grew its online presence by purchasing the Internet banking operations of Security First Network Bank (now Security First Technologies 1998) the online trading division of Bull & Bear Group (1999) and 20% of AOL Canada (1999). It also bought several trust and fiduciary services businesses from Ernst & Young.

It acquired US mortgage bank Prism Financial and the Canadian retail credit card business of BANK ONE in 2000. RBC also sold its commercial credit portfolio to U.S. Bancorp. The company agreed to pay a substantial fine after institutional asset management subsidiary RT Capital Management came under scrutiny from the Ontario Securities Commission for alleged involvement in illegal pension-fund stock manipulation. RBC ended up selling RT Capital to UBS AG the following year.

Also in 2001 RBC made another US purchase: North Carolina's Centura Banks (now RBC Centura Banks). It sold Houston-based home lender RBC Mortgage to New Century Financial in 2005. Also that year it acquired private bank Abacus Financial which adding locations in the UK and Amsterdam.

RBC spent the decade prior to the global recession building up its US operations. The company moved into the US trust business in 2006 when it purchased American Guaranty & Trust a unit of National Life Insurance Company. In 2007 it bought the electronic brokerage business of New York boutique Carlin Financial Group. Other acquisitions made during that period include debt securities investor Access Capital Strategies energy advisory firm Richardson Barr and DC-area investment bank Ferris Baker Watts.

In 2008 RBC acquired community banks in Alabama Georgia and Florida including Alabama National BanCorporation. That same year RBC agreed to buy back some $850 million in auction-rate securities and pay the New York State attorney general's office a nearly $10 million fine. Auction-rate securities were sold to investors as a low-risk investment but as the economy worsened in 2007 and 2008 banks canceled the regular auctions rendering the securities worthless. Customers and regulators claimed that banks continued to sell them the securities even though they knew the investments had become very high risk.

Also in 2008 RBC Bank expanded its finance operations when it bought the Canadian commercial leasing business of ABN AMRO. It renamed the unit RBC Equipment Finance Group.

To cement its place among the world's 10 largest wealth managers RBC bought UK-based fixed income specialist BlueBay Asset Management for some $1.5 billion in 2010. Also that year it bought BNP Paribas Fortis' Hong Kong wealth management business.

In 2010 it also sold Liberty Life its US life insurance subsidiary that had posted losses for two years to Apollo affiliate Athene Holding. To boost brand recognition of another US unit the company changed the name of Voyageur Asset Management to RBC Global Asset Management (US).

EXECUTIVES

President and CEO, David I. (Dave) McKay, age 53, $500,000 total compensation

Chair and CEO RBC Capital Markets; Group Head Capital Markets and Investor and Treasury Services, A. Douglas McGregor

Group Head Personal and Commercial Banking, Jennifer Tory

Group Head Technology and Operations, Bruce Ross

CFO, Rod Bolger

Group Head RBC Wealth Management and RBC Insurance, Douglas A. Guzman

Chairman, Kathleen P. Taylor

Auditors: PricewaterhouseCoopers LLP

LOCATIONS

HQ: Royal Bank of Canada (Montreal, Quebec)
Royal Bank of Canada, 200 Bay Street, Toronto, Ontario M5J 2J5
Phone: 416 974-8393   **Fax:** 416 974-3535
Web: www.rbc.com

2015 Sales

	% of total
Canada	63
US	19
Other international	18
Total	**100**

PRODUCTS/OPERATIONS

2015 Sales

	% of total
Personal & commercial banking	40
Capital markets	22
Wealth management	19
Insurance	13
Investor & treasury services	6
Total	**100**

COMPETITORS

AGF Management	Dundee Corp.
BMO Financial Group	Goldman Sachs
Bank of America	Great-West Lifeco
Barclays	Guardian Capital Group
CI Financial	HSBC Bank Canada
CIBC	JPMorgan Chase
Caisse de dep⁻ t et	Laurentian Bank
placement du Quebec	National Bank of
Caisses centrale	Canada
Desjardins	Nomura Securities
Canadian Western Bank	Power Financial
Central 1 Credit Union	Scotiabank
Citigroup	TD Bank
Deutsche Bank	UBS

HISTORICAL FINANCIALS

Company Type: Public

Income Statement

FYE: October 31

	ASSETS ($ mil.)	NET INCOME ($ mil.)	INCOME AS % OF ASSETS	EMPLOYEES
10/16	882,207	7,777	0.9%	80,000
10/15	816,337	7,542	0.9%	0
10/14	840,559	7,962	0.9%	0
10/13	823,013	7,965	1.0%	0
10/12	827,347	7,462	0.9%	80,000
Annual Growth	**1.6%**	**1.0%**	**—**	**0.0%**

2016 Year-End Financials

Return on assets: 0.9%
Return on equity: 15.5%
Long-term debt ($ mil.): —
No. of shares (mil.): 1,484
Sales ($ mil): 34,627

Dividends
Yield: 5.1%
Payout: 67.6%
Market value ($ mil.): 92,735

	STOCK PRICE ($) FY Close	P/E High/Low		PER SHARE ($) Earnings	Dividends	Book Value
10/16	62.48	9	7	5.07	2.42	35.76
10/15	56.83	9	8	5.11	2.34	32.73
10/14	71.17	12	10	5.36	2.57	32.67
10/13	67.18	12	9	5.30	2.48	32.22
10/12	57.03	12	9	4.94	2.27	30.72
Annual Growth	**2.3%**	**—**	**—**	**0.6%**	**1.6%**	**3.9%**

Royal Bank of Scotland Group Plc

If you have overdraft protection for your checking account you can thank The Royal Bank of Scotland (RBS) which introduced the service in 1728. Today RBS is one of Europe's largest banking groups. Through subsidiaries Royal Bank of Scotland and National Westminster Bank it has the UK's largest bank network of more than 2000 branches. RBS offers private banking and insurance products through Coutts Group and Adam & Company. Other divisions include Ulster Bank which operates in Ireland and Northern Ireland; and US transaction processor RBS Lynk. After a series of bailouts in 2008 and 2009 the UK government owns 73% of RBS. RBS sold its remaining stake in US-based Citizens Financial Group in late 2015.

OperationsRBS operates three franchises and seven operating segments. Personal & Business Banking (PBB) which made up 33% of RBS' revenue in 2014 comprises the UK Personal & Business Banking segment including Williams & Glyn and Ulster Bank. It serves retail mass-affluent and small business customers (with up to £2 million in annual revenues).

Commercial & Private Banking (CPB) comprises the Commercial Banking (18% of 2014 revenues) and Private Banking (6% of 2014 revenues) segments and serves commercial and mid-corporate customers and high-net worth individuals with trade and foreign exchange services as well as private banking services to business owners and entrepreneurs.

Corporate & Institutional Banking (CIB) which made up 22% of 2014 revenues provides debt financing risk management and trade services for corporate and international clients mostly in the UK and Western Europe or multinational clients in the US and Asia with substantial trade and investment links in the region. The group's US-based Citizens Financial Group (CFG) which it sold in late 2015 generated 16% of its revenue in 2014 and provided retail and corporate banking services through the Citizens and Charter One brands through branches in 11 US states and offices in other states. RBS Capital Resolution (RCR) which became operational in January 2014 manages a £29 billion pool of high credit risk and troubled asset types.

Geographic Reach

UK-based RBS operates in Europe Asia the Middle East and North America. About 80% of its revenue came from the UK in 2014 while its business in Europe and the US contributed 9% and 7% respectively.

Financial Performance

Note: Growth rates may differ after conversion to US dollars.

RBS' annual losses have been deepening over the past several years as low interest margins have been hurting the bank's top line and bad loan debt has led to elevated (and profit-eating) loan impairment provisions. Further the bank has been forced to sell off riskier loan assets to improve its loan portfolio situation which has led to shrinking loan business over the years.

The group's revenue fell by 14% to £19.8 million ($30.8 million) in 2014 mostly as the bank continued to de-risk its loan portfolio and trading assets which led to a double-digit decline in interest income and a 50% dive in income from trading activities respectively. Despite lower revenue in 2014 RBS did manage to significantly cut its losses to less than £3 billion ($4.8 billion) compared to £8.5 billion ($14 billion) in 2013 as its impairment provisions on bad loan debt improved considerably thanks to its continued de-risking measures. Its cash levels also improved with operations using £20.4 billion ($31.7 billion) for the year thanks mostly to reduced losses and a smaller decrease in bank and customer deposit cash.

Strategy

RBS has structured its business "around the needs of its customers" in recent years repositioning itself in 2014 into three franchises and seven operating segments to offer a wide variety of services available for cross-sell to its customer base of two million in Scotland. The reorganized bank would "be a UK-focused retail and corporate bank with an international footprint to drive its corporate business."

Keeping its business more focused on core banking operations RBS has exited several business lines and geographic regions over the past several years. In late 2015 for example RBS sold its remaining stake in US-based Citizens Financial Group to exit its retail banking business in the US. That year it also agreed to sell its internationally-managed Private Banking and Wealth Management business to Union Bancaire Privee (UBP) in-

cluding its client relationships outside the British Isles. The bank would continue serving its UK Private Banking and Wealth Management clients as well as international clients with strong ties to the UK.

RBS has also worked to strengthen its balance sheet in recent years selling off riskier loan assets and freeing up resources for surer loan deals. In 2015 it sold a portfolio of US and Canadian loan commitments and certain associated derivatives as well as coverage banking debt capital markets syndicate and associated capabilities related to the loan commitments. Company BackgroundThe group was crippled by both the global financial crisis and its ambitious international expansion primarily its disastrous 2007 investment in Dutch bank ABN AMRO. In late 2008 the UK took a 60% stake in RBS but the bank still ended up reporting an annual loss of some £28 billion ($41 billion) —the largest loss in British corporate history. The government stepped in at least twice more to help RBS manage its debt and interest payments intervening with the contingency that RBS make significant efforts to get back on solid ground.

HISTORY

Company BackgroundRoyal Bank of Scotland was founded in 1727 but its roots go back to the Darien Company a merchant expedition that was established to set up a Scottish trading colony in Panama. The Darien expedition ended disastrously in 1699. In 1707 England voted to compensate Scottish creditors for the colony's failure (in part because England had promised support then reneged contributing to the collapse) and a small industry sprang up around paying creditors and loaning them money. In 1727 the Equivalent Company the combined entity of these organizations was granted a banking charter and became Royal Bank of Scotland.

In 1826 the Parliament voted to take away Scottish banks' right to issue banknotes for less than five pounds which would have required banks to use gold or silver. Few banks had such reserves and the move sparked an outcry. Novelist Sir Walter Scott's The Letters of Malachi Malagrowther which defended the Scottish one-pound note helped shoot down the proposal.

RBS expanded throughout Scotland over the next 50 years. It opened a London branch in 1874; it didn't establish a branch outside London until it bought Williams Deacon's Bank which had a branch network in North England. RBS continued to use the Williams Deacon's name as it did with Glyn Mills & Co. which it purchased in 1939.

In 1968 RBS took on its modern persona as a public company when it merged with National Commercial Bank. The company moved overseas during the 1970s establishing offices in Hong Kong and major US cities.

RBS spent the next 20 years trying to achieve another merger of the same scale as National Commercial. In 1981 the bank was wooed by Standard Chartered Bank and Hongkong and Shanghai Bank (now part of HSBC Holdings) but British regulators denied both suitors.

The bank moved into telephone operations in 1985 when it set up Direct Line for selling car insurance. In 1988 RBS bought New England bank Citizens Financial (but it plans to divest that business). In 1989 the company entered into an alliance with Banco Santander (now Santander Central Hispano) Spain's largest banking group. The alliance created a cross-pollination of ideas and strategies that boosted both banks' operations. The first fruit of the alliance came in 1991 with the launch of Interbank On-line Systems (IBOS) which

connected several European banks and allowed for instantaneous money transfers.

In the 1990s RBS was linked with a variety of partners. It even made a bid for the much larger bank Barclays in a move regarded as cheeky but was rebuffed. In 1997 it announced a joint venture with Richard Branson's Virgin Group called Virgin Direct to offer personal banking. The company also bought Angel Trains Contract a rolling stock leasing company and established a transatlantic banking transfer system (similar to IBOS) with US bank CoreStates (now owned by First Union).

In 2000 RBS acquired NatWest after a prolonged takeover battle with rival Bank of Scotland (now part of HBOS plc). The bank sold Gartmore Investment Management its fund management unit to Nationwide Mutual Insurance Company. Royal Bank also sold the assets of NatWest's Equity Partners unit and launched NatWest Private Banking to target wealthy investors.

In 2004 RBS made several acquisitions to boost its US presence: It paid about $360 million for the credit card business of Connecticut-based People's Bank and bought payments processor Lynk Systems (now RBS Lynk) while Citizens Financial bought Cleveland-based bank Charter One Financial. Also that year Ulster Bank bought Ireland-based retail financial services provider First Active.

In 2007 RBS led the consortium that acquired the Dutch bank for euro 71 billion in a deal that was called the largest ever in the banking industry. The buyers carved ABN AMRO into pieces; RBS took the global wholesale and international retail operations in Asia Eastern Europe and the Middle East. The ambitious takeover preceded the global economic crisis though and RBS was among the hardest hit financial groups.

The troubled company made several moves to try and raise capital. Early in 2008 the company announced a £12 billion rights issue. RBS also tried but failed to find a buyer for its insurance arm. However other assets were divested that year. The company sold rolling stock leasing firm Angel Trains to Babcock & Brown and others and it sold its joint venture Tesco Personal Finance back to supermarket giant Tesco. The efforts proved inadequate though. The government took a controlling stake in the group in 2008 the same year that RBS reported the largest corporate loss in British history.

Also as part of the government rescue RBS went through a management shakeup. Fred Goodwin the architect of the bank's international expansion was removed as CEO. He was replaced by Stephen Hester formerly the CEO of British Land Company. Johnny Cameron chairman of the group's global banking and markets segment (which lost the group's most money in 2008) was also ousted and chairman Tom McKillop retired early.

RBS also shuffled its corporate structure in 2009. It split its UK retail and commercial banking division into three segments (retail commercial and wealth) and made Ulster Bank its own segment. The group folded its operations support division into other arms and established a segment to manage the selling and runoff of noncore operations. RBS retained the Global Banking & Markets Global Transaction Services US Retail & Commercial and RBS Insurance (including Churchill Insurance) segments although several of their components were transferred to the noncore segment.

RBS has scaled back on the international growth that weakened the group during the economic fallout with the ultimate goal of reducing non-UK operations to less than a quarter of its assets. In 2009 the group sold its 4% stake in Bank of China for some £1.6 billion ($2.4 billion); it also sold most of its operations in Southeast Asia to Australia and New Zealand Banking Group for about $550 million. RBS divested units in Argentina

Colombia Chile the United Arab Emirates Kazakhstan and Pakistan —all assets gained as part of its ABN AMRO transaction.

With the government having to step in at least twice to bail out the bank by 2011 RBC was forced to cut costs and sell non-core operations to refocus on its core banking business. In 2010 it sold more than 300 branches and offices to Banco Santander for some £1.65 billion ($2.6 billion). RBS sold its factoring and invoice financing unit to GE Capital and its payment services unit Global Merchant Services to Advent International and Bain Capital. It also sold its interest in RBS Sempra Commodities. In 2012 the company sold the international private banking business of Coutts to Royal Bank of Canada. Other divisions have been simply wound down and closed. RBS was ordered by the Federal Reserve in 2011 to improve its US operations or risk losing permission to do business in America. In October 2012 RBS sold a 30% stake in Direct Line Group part of its insurance group in an IPO valued at £2.6 billion ($4.2 billion).

EXECUTIVES

Chief Executive RBS Citizens Financial Group, Bruce W. Van Saun, age 58, $333,000 total compensation

Global Head Global Restructuring Group, Derek S. Sach, age 61

Chief Executive Personal and Business Banking, Les Matheson

Finance Director, Nathan Bostock, age 55

Chief Executive Retail Direct, Chris Sullivan, age 58

Executive Chairman Corporate and Institutional Banking, Donald Workman

CEO Markets, Peter Nielsen

CEO RBS Insurance, Paul Geddes, age 46

Chief Executive, Ross McEwan

CEO UK Corporate and Institutional Banking, Mark Catton

Chief Executive Commercial and Private Banking, Alison Rose

Managing Director GTS Cash, Stuart Lawson

President Dmitry Medvedev, Igor Yurgens

Co-CEO CIB, Chris Marks

Co-CEO CIB, Mark Bailie

Chief Executive Williams & Glyn, Jim Brown

Chairman RBS Scotland, Malcolm Buchanan

Chairman, Howard J. Davies, age 66

Auditors: Deloitte LLP

LOCATIONS

HQ: Royal Bank of Scotland Group Plc
P.O. Box 1000, Gogarburn, Edinburgh EH12 1HQ
Phone: (44) 131 626 0000   **Fax:** (44) 131 626 3081
Web: www.rbs.com

2014 Sales

	% of total
UK	80
Rest of Europe	9
US	7
Other countries	4
Total	**100**

PRODUCTS/OPERATIONS

2014 Sales by Segment

	% of total
Personal & Business Banking	
UK Personal & Business Banking	33
Ulster Bank	5
Commercial and Private Banking	
Commercial Banking	18
Private Banking	6
Corporate and Institutional Banking	22
Citizen financial group	16
RBS Capital Resolution	·
Total	**100**

Selected Subsidiaries

Citizens Financial Group Inc. (banking US)
Coutts & Co (private banking)
Direct Line Insurance Group plc
National Westminster Bank Plc
The Royal Bank of Scotland plc
Ulster Bank Limited (Northern Ireland)

COMPETITORS

AIB	JPMorgan Chase
Bank of America	Lloyds Banking Group
Bank of Ireland	PNC Financial
Barclays	Santander UK
Citigroup	Standard Chartered
HSBC	Standard Life
ING Direct UK	permanent tsb

HISTORICAL FINANCIALS
Company Type: Public

Income Statement
FYE: December 31

	ASSETS ($ mil.)	NET INCOME ($ mil.)	INCOME AS % OF ASSETS	EMPLOYEES
12/15	1,208,390	(2,802)	—	90,158
12/14	1,640,265	(4,840)	—	108,700
12/13	1,698,649	(14,783)	—	114,900
12/12	2,115,244	(9,600)	—	137,200
12/11	2,327,889	(3,085)	—	142,600
Annual Growth	**(15.1%)**	**—**		**(10.8%)**

2015 Year-End Financials

Return on assets: (-0.2%)
Return on equity: (-3.4%)
Long-term debt ($ mil.): —
No. of shares (mil.): —
Sales ($ mil): 25,030

Dividends
Yield: —
Payout: —
Market value ($ mil.): —

	STOCK PRICE ($) FY Close	P/E High/Low	Earnings	Dividends	Book Value
12/15	8.87	— —	(0.25)	0.00	6.81
12/14	12.11	— —	(0.47)	0.00	1.56
12/13	11.33	— —	(1.33)	0.00	1.70
12/12	10.79	— —	(0.88)	0.00	1.92
12/11	6.37	— —	(0.28)	0.00	10.49
Annual Growth	**8.6%**				
(10.2%)					

Royal Bank of Scotland plc

Auditors: Deloitte LLP

LOCATIONS

HQ: Royal Bank of Scotland plc
36 St Andrew Square, Edinburgh EH2 2YB
Phone: (44) 131 556 8555
Web: www.rbs.com

HISTORICAL FINANCIALS
Company Type: Public

Income Statement
FYE: December 31

	REVENUE ($ mil.)	NET INCOME ($ mil.)	NET PROFIT MARGIN	EMPLOYEES
12/15	24,398	(2,932)	—	90,158
12/14	28,599	(5,048)	—	84,200
12/13	41,180	(12,078)	—	106,100
12/12	40,424	(6,210)	—	111,000
12/11	42,138	(2,541)	—	113,700
Annual Growth	**(12.8%)**	**—**		**(5.6%)**

2015 Year-End Financials

Debt ratio: —
Return on equity: (-3.9%)
Cash ($ mil.): 117,672
Current ratio: —
Long-term debt ($ mil.) —

No. of shares (mil.): —
Dividends
Yield: —
Payout: —
Market value ($ mil.): —

	STOCK PRICE ($) FY Close	P/E High/Low	Earnings	Dividends	Book Value
12/15	0.00	— —	(0.25)	0.00	6.81
12/14	39.71	— —	(0.00)	0.00	11.05
12/13	36.24	— —	(0.00)	0.00	12.20
12/12	27.70	— —	(0.00)	0.00	14.46
Annual Growth	**—**	**— —**	**—**	**—**	**—**
(17.2%)					

Royal Dutch Shell Plc

Royal Dutch Shell which sits on an oil and gas throne higher than that of #2 oil company Exxon Mobil has worldwide proved reserves of 13.9 billion barrels of oil equivalent. Most of the oil giant's crude is produced in Nigeria Oman the UK and the US. It is also investing in the Athabasca Oil Sands Project which converts Alberta oil sands to synthetic oil. The company operates 44000 gas stations (the world's largest retail fuel network). Royal Dutch Shell also produces refined products and chemicals at more than 30 refineries transports natural gas trades gas and electricity and develops renewable energy. In a major move in 2016 the company bought BG Group for $53 billion.

Geographic Reach

The company operates around the world in more than 70 countries including in Australia Brazil Brunei Canada China Denmark Germany Malaysia the Netherlands Nigeria Norway Oman Qatar Russia the UK and the US.

Operations

Royal Dutch Shell operates in three segments: Upstream Downstream and the Corporate segment.

Through Upstream International and Upstream Americas the company explores for and produces crude oil natural gas and natural gas liquids; transports oil and gas; and operates the upstream and midstream infrastructure required to deliver oil and gas to market. Upstream International also manages liquefied natural gas (LNG) and gas-to-liquids (GTL) businesses. Upstream Americas also extracts bitumen from oil sands in Canada which is converted into synthetic crude oil.

In 2013 Royal Dutch Shell added 1.6 billion barrels of oil equivalent of gross proved reserves.

The Downstream segment is engaged in the manufacturing supply distribution and marketing of oil products and chemicals; alternative energy (excluding wind); and CO2 management.

Downstream accounted for about 88% and Upstream accounted for 10% of Royal Dutch Shell's total revenues in 2013.

In 2013 the company produced 3.2 million barrels of oil equivalent a day and sold about 19.6 million tons of LNG.

The segment's Supply and Distribution infrastructure has more than 1500 storage tanks and 150 distribution facilities in 25 countries. It supplies more than 100 grades of lubricants and 20 different types of fuel serving more than 15000 vessels worldwide.

Royal Dutch Shell's Corporate segment manages the company's non-operating activities including Shell's holdings and treasury organization its headquarters and central functions as well as its self-insurance activities.

Financial Performance

The company's revenues declined by 5% in fiscal 2013 primarily due to lower Downstream segment sales decreased interest and lower other income received; partially offset by higher Upstream revenues.

Upstream revenues rose thanks to an 1.4% increase in global oil demand driven by emerging economies. Synthetic crude oil prices posted a 7% increase while gas prices were 6% higher than in 2012. These gains were partially offset by lower liquids prices.

In the Downstream segment oil products sales volumes dipped by 1% in 2012 reflecting lower marketing and trading volumes partly offset by the increased Refinery intake volumes. The drop was also caused by field declines and the impact of the challenging operating environment in Nigeria.

Royal Dutch Shell's net income decreased by 38% in 2013 due to lower revenues and high depreciation charges as a result of impairments and a change in financial reporting requirements.

Strategy

The company's key strengths include the development and application of technology the financial and project-management skills to deliver large field development projects and the management of integrated value chains.

In 2016 the company bought BG Group for $53 billion bolstering the company's position in liquefied natural gas Brazilian oil business and deep water assets.

Following the acquisition to free up cash and pay down debts Royal Dutch Shell has embarked on a $30 billion divestment program slated to completion by 2018. So far the company has in 2017 agreed to sell $3.8 billion in North Sea assets to Chrysaor an exploration firm. It is also to sell its stake in a Thai gas field for $900 million.

In 2016 Shell agreed to sell a 31% stake in Showa Shell Sekiyu to Japan-based refiner Idemitsu Kosan for $1.35 billion. It planned to retain a 2% stake in Showa Shell.

The same year it also agreed to sell 206000 net acres of non-core oil and gas properties in Western Canada to Tourmaline Oil for more than a $1 billion. In 2015 the company sold its Norwegian retail assets. In France it sold its Butagaz LPG business to DCC Energy for EUR464 million.

In 2014 Royal Dutch Shell also agreed to sell its Australian downstream businesses to Vitol for A$2.9 billion (US$2.6 billion).

Royal Dutch Shell committed about 85% of its capital investment in 2014 to Upstream activities. It's long term strategy includes developing shale oil and gas plays and future opportunities such as heavy oil plays and new fields in the Arctic Iraq Kazakhstan and Nigeria. However plummeting oil prices led the company to exit the Arctic in 2015.

Looking to focus its onshore US drilling program on a few of the more prolific formations in an effort to boost profitability in 2014 Royal Dutch Shell agreed to sell drilling rights in shale formations in Louisiana and Wyoming for $2.1 billion in two transactions. In one of the deals the company will also receive drilling rights to land in Ohio and Pennsylvania.

While committed to developing clean energy as a way to reduce carbon emissions Royal Dutch Shell is focusing on clean oil production technology (such as carbon sequestration) and biofuels which are more in line with its core oil and gas competencies rather than on wind power and solar energy.

Boosting its research and development capability in 2013 the company relaunched its Shell Technology Center Houston as the global base for a number of specific technology focus areas across the upstream and downstream segment. Royal Dutch Shell spends more than a billion dollars a year on research and development activities.

Expanding its Canadian oil and gas production activities in 2012 Royal Dutch Shell announced plans to ramp up production at its Athabasca Oil Sands project in Alberta and to develop shale gas and an LNG export terminal in British Columbia.

Mergers and Acquisitions

In 2014 the company acquired Repsol's LNG portfolio outside of North America including supply positions in Peru and Trinidad and Tobago for about $4 billion.

Growing its North America shale portfolio in 2012 Royal Dutch Shell acquired 618000 net acres in the Permian Basin in West Texas (with production of 26000 barrels of oil equivalent per day) from Chesapeake Energy for $2 billion.

It also agreed to buy Hess' stake in the North Sea Beryl area fields and the Scottish Area Gas Evacuation System for $525 million.

In a move to expand its position as a provider of shallow water drilling services in Asia Africa and the Middle East in 2012 it formed Shell Drilling Holdings which bought 37 jackup drilling rigs one swamp barge and associated operations from Transocean for $1.05 billion.

HISTORY

Company Background

In 1870 Marcus Samuel inherited an interest in his father's London trading company which imported seashells from the Far East. He expanded the business and after securing a contract for Russian oil began selling kerosene in the Far East.

Standard Oil underpriced competitors to defend its Asian markets. Samuel secretly prepared his response and in 1892 unveiled the first of a fleet of tankers. Rejecting Standard's acquisition overtures Samuel created "Shell" Transport and Trading in 1897.

Meanwhile a Dutchman Aeilko Zijlker struck oil in Sumatra and formed Royal Dutch Petroleum in 1890 to exploit the oil field. Young Henri Deterding joined the firm in 1896 and established a sales force in the Far East.

Deterding became Royal Dutch's head in 1900 amid the battle for the Asian market. In 1903 Deterding Samuel and the Rothschilds (a French banking family) created Asiatic Petroleum a marketing alliance. With Shell's non-Asian business eroding Deterding engineered a merger between Royal Dutch and Shell in 1907. Royal Dutch shareholders got 60% control; "Shell" Transport and Trading 40%.

After the 1911 Standard Oil breakup Deterding entered the US building refineries and buying producers. Shell products were available in every state by 1929. Royal Dutch/Shell joined the 1928 "As Is" cartel that fixed prices for most of two decades.

The post-WWII Royal Dutch/Shell profited from worldwide growth in oil consumption. It acquired 100% of Shell Oil its US arm in 1985 but shareholders sued maintaining Shell Oil's assets had been undervalued in the deal. They were awarded $110 million in 1990.

Management's slow response to two 1995 controversies —environmentalists' outrage over the planned sinking of an oil platform and human rights activists' criticism of Royal Dutch/Shell's role in Nigeria —spurred a major shakeup. It began moving away from its decentralized structure and adopted a new policy of corporate openness.

In 1996 Royal Dutch/Shell and Exxon (now Exxon Mobil) formed a worldwide petroleum additives venture. Shell Oil joined Texaco (now part of Chevron) in 1998 to form Equilon Enterprises combining US refining and marketing operations in the West and Midwest. Similarly Shell Oil Texaco and Saudi Arabia's Aramco combined downstream operations on the US's East and Gulf coasts as Motiva Enterprises.

In 1999 Royal Dutch/Shell and the UK's BG plc acquired a controlling stake in Comgas a unit of Companhia Energetica de São Paulo and the largest natural gas distributor in Brazil for about $1 billion.

In 2000 the company sold its coal business to UK-based mining giant Anglo American for more than $850 million. To gain a foothold in the US power marketing scene Royal Dutch/Shell formed a joint venture with construction giant Bechtel (called InterGen). The next year the company agreed to combine its German refining and marketing operations with those of RWE-DEA. Royal Dutch/Shell tried to expand its US natural gas reserves in 2001 by making a $2 billion hostile bid for Barrett Resources but the effort was withdrawn after Barrett agreed to be acquired by Williams for $2.5 billion.

In 2002 in connection with Chevron's acquisition of Texaco Royal Dutch/Shell acquired ChevronTexaco's (now Chevron) stakes in the underperforming US marketing joint ventures Equilon and Motiva. That year the company through its US Shell Oil unit acquired Pennzoil-Quaker State for $1.8 billion. Also that year Royal Dutch/Shell acquired Enterprise Oil for $5 billion plus debt. In addition it purchased RWE's 50% stake in German refining and marketing joint venture Shell & DEA Oil (for $1.35 billion).

In 2004 the group signed a $200 million exploration deal with Libya signaling its return to that country after a more than decade-long absence. Also that year the company reported that it had overestimated its reserves by 24%. The bad news resulted in the ouster of the chairman and CFO.

The Anglo-Dutch entity restructured to stay competitive. Revelations of overestimated oil reserves in 2004 prompted a push for greater transparency in the company's organizational structure. This led to the 2005 merger of former publicly traded owners Royal Dutch Petroleum and The "Shell" Transport and Trading Company into Royal Dutch Shell.

Searching for new oil assets in 2006 the company acquired a large swath of oil sands acreage in Alberta Canada. Further boosting its oil sands business in 2007 the company acquired the 22% of Shell Canada that it did not already own. The company also began investing some $12 billion (in addition to the $2.6 billion already spent) in offshore projects near Dubai. In 2008 Royal Dutch Shell expanded its exploration assets in Alaska by acquiring 275 lease blocks in the Chukchi Sea for $2.1 billion.

In 2009 the company made significant oil discoveries in the deepwater eastern Gulf of Mexico at West Boreas Vito and the Cardamom Deep and in 2010 at the Appomattox prospect in the Mississippi Canyon block. The finds expanded Shell Oil's long-term development plans in the area.

Further expanding its unconventional natural gas resources in 2010 the company spent $4.7 billion to acquire East Resources which holds 1 million acres of Marcellus Shale one of the fastest-growing shale plays in the US.

On the conventional side of the oil business the Gulf of Mexico produces 370000 barrels of oil per day or about 15% of Royal Dutch Shell's worldwide production. In 2010 the company claimed an industry record starting production at the deepest floating drilling and production platform in the world. The Perdido Development operates in 8000 ft. of water in the Gulf of Mexico. In response to the BP oil rig disaster in the Gulf of Mexico the company joined forces with Exxon Mobil Chevron and ConocoPhillips to form a $1 billion rapid-response joint venture that will be able to better manage and contain future deepwater spills.

With an eye toward raising cash and focusing on its majority holdings and joint ventures rather than on minority held businesses in 2010 Royal Dutch Shell sold 10% of its 34% in Australian oil and gas enterprise Woodside Petroleum for $3.3 billion. Royal Dutch Shell also announced that it would seek to sell the rest of its stake in Woodside Petroleum over time. (Earlier in the year the company formed a $3.5 billion joint venture with PetroChina which acquired Arrow Energy a company with major natural gas assets in Northern Australia).

As part of its strategy of selling noncore downstream assets to raise cash in 2010 Royal Dutch Shell sold its Finnish and Swedish operations (including a refinery in Gothenburg and 565 gas stations) to Finland-based St1 for $640 million. In 2011 it sold its UK-based Stanlow refinery to India's Essar Group for $350 million.

In 2010 the company formed a $12 billion joint venture with Brazil's Cosan to ramp up ethanol production.

EXECUTIVES

CFO, Simon Henry, age 55, $449,000 total compensation
CEO and Director, Ben van Beurden, age 58
Director Downstream, John Abbott
Director Projects and Technology, Harry Brekelmans
Director Upstream, Andrew Brown
CFO, Jessica Uhl
Integrated Gas and New Energies Director, Maarten Wetselaar
Chairman, Charles O. (Chad) Holliday, age 68
Deputy Chairman, Hans Wijers, age 66
Auditors: PricewaterhouseCoopers LLP

LOCATIONS

HQ: Royal Dutch Shell Plc
Carel van Bylandtlaan 30, The Hague 2596 HR
Phone: (31) 70 377 9111   **Fax:** (44) 20 7934 5153
Web: www.shell.com

2015 Sales

	$ mil.	% of total
Europe	95,223	35
Africa Asia Oceania	95,892	35
US	50,666	19
Other Americas	23,179	9
Share of joint ventures & other income	7,196	2
Total	**272,156**	**100**

PRODUCTS/OPERATIONS

2015 Sales

	$ mil.	% of total
Downstream	236,384	88
Upstream	28,480	10
Share from joint ventures & other income	7,196	2
Corporate & other	96	-
Total	**272,156**	**100**

COMPETITORS

7-Eleven	Koch Industries Inc.
Ashland Inc.	Marathon Oil
BHP Billiton	Norsk Hydro ASA
BP	Occidental Petroleum
Chevron	PEMEX
ConocoPhillips	PETROBRAS
Dow Chemical	PetroKazakhstan
DuPont	Petróleos de
Eastman Chemical	Venezuela
Eni	Repsol
Exxon Mobil	Sinopec Shanghai
FEC Resources	Petrochemical
Hess Corporation	Sunoco
Huntsman International	TOTAL
Imperial Oil	

HISTORICAL FINANCIALS

Company Type: Public

Income Statement

FYE: December 31

	REVENUE ($ mil.)	NET INCOME ($ mil.)	NET PROFIT MARGIN	EMPLOYEES
12/15	272,156	1,939	0.7%	93,000
12/14	431,344	14,874	3.4%	94,000
12/13	459,599	16,371	3.6%	92,000
12/12	481,700	26,592	5.5%	87,000
12/11	484,489	30,918	6.4%	90,000
Annual Growth	(13.4%)	(50.0%)	—	0.8%

2015 Year-End Financials

Debt ratio: 17.1%
Return on equity: 1.1%
Cash ($ mil.): 31,752
Current ratio: 1.32
Long-term debt ($ mil.): 52,849
No. of shares (mil.): —
Dividends
  Yield: 8.1%
  Payout: 1,253.3%
Market value ($ mil.): —

	STOCK PRICE ($) FY Close	P/E High/Low	PER SHARE ($) Earnings	Dividends	Book Value
12/15	45.79	216 140	0.30	3.76	25.46
12/14	66.95	35 26	2.36	3.72	27.25
12/13	71.27	28 24	2.60	3.56	28.50
12/12	68.95	17 14	4.24	3.42	29.77
12/11	73.09	16 12	4.98	3.36	27.10
Annual Growth	(11.0%)	— —	(50.5%)	2.9%	(1.6%)

Royal London Mutual Insurance Society Ltd (United Kingdom)

The Royal London Mutual Insurance Society wants to give its customers the royal treatment. The company and its subsidiaries collectively known as the Royal London Group offer products and services including life insurance pensions savings products investment products property/casualty insurance credit insurance and investment management under such brands as Royal London Asset Management Scottish Life and Bright Grey among others. The company is one of the UK's largest mutual life and pensions insurers with about 4 million customers and more than £46 billion (almost $75 billion) under management. The Royal London Group sells both directly and through financial advisors in the UK and the Isle of Man. Although the economic environment in the UK and the world is uncertain and likely to remain so for some time the group remains calm and carries on. Its capital strength and stability in fact continue to improve. In 2011 Royal London Group had record life and pension new business levels. Increased capital reflected this along with positive investment returns added to its assets.

During 2011 the group acquired Royal Liver Assurance and successfully integrated the business; its Royal London Asset Management (RLAM) business carries out its asset management. Royal London Group is looking to add new business in 2012 as well by acquiring The Co-op-erative Banking Group's life pensions and asset management businesses representing some 2 million policyholders and £20 billion (more than $32 billion) funds under management.

The acquisitive moves are part of the company's strategy to grow its business provide security for its policyholders and members and allow for the delivery of good financial returns.

Royal London combined its Scottish Life International Insurance and Scottish Provident International Life Assurance into Royal London 360° in 2008. The new entity emerged as an investment savings and tax planning company with $3 billion under management. The moves were part of other plans and consolidations. The company also bought Scottish Provident offering individual life insurance and Phoenix Life Assurance now Royal London Retail from Pearl Group in 2008.

LOCATIONS

HQ: Royal London Mutual Insurance Society Ltd (United Kingdom)
55 Gracechurch Street, London EC3V 0RL
Phone: (44) 845 050 2020
Web: www.royallondongroup.co.uk

PRODUCTS/OPERATIONS

Selected Brands

Ascentric/IFDL (wrap platform investment administration and consolidation services)
Bright Grey (protection insurance)
Caledonian Life (return on investment protection products brokered in Ireland)
MoneyVista (online financial planning for consumers)
Royal London 360° (international division; offshore investment)
Royal London Asset Management (fund management; fixed income cash property and equity asset management)
Royal London Plus (life and pensions administration)
Scottish Life (pensions specialist)
Scottish Provident (personal mortgage and business protection)

COMPETITORS

AXA UK	Lloyds Banking Group
Aviva	Prudential plc
Clerical Medical	Standard Life
Legal & General Group	

HISTORICAL FINANCIALS

Company Type: Public

Income Statement

FYE: December 31

	ASSETS ($ mil.)	NET INCOME ($ mil.)	INCOME AS % OF ASSETS	EMPLOYEES
12/15	111,006	185	0.2%	3,130
12/14	115,412	232	0.2%	2,801
12/13	105,970	614	0.6%	3,050
12/12	64,070	419	0.7%	2,787
12/11	59,875	135	0.2%	2,692
Annual Growth	16.7%	8.0%	—	3.8%

2015 Year-End Financials

Return on assets: 0.1%
Return on equity: —
Long-term debt ($ mil.): —
No. of shares (mil.): —
Sales ($ mil): 4,764
Dividends
  Yield: —
  Payout: —
Market value ($ mil.): —

RWE AG

RWE doesn't stand for Runs With Electricity but it could. RWE is one of Germany's top two electricity suppliers (along with E.ON). Through its subsidiaries the energy conglomerate provides electricity and gas to residential and business customers primarily in Central and Western Europe. It also owns major UK-based utilities and German-based electricity and gas supplier RWE npower. RWE owns oil and gas exploration and production unit RWE-DEA; other businesses include companies engaged in gas transportation and storage power generation energy trading information technology and coal mining. In 2017 RWE spun off its renewable network and retail energy operations into a separate entity innogy.

Geographic ReachRWE operates in Germany the Netherlands/Belgium the UK and in Central Eastern and South Eastern Europe. Germany accounted for more than 50% of the company's revenues in 2011.

Operations

In addition to generating power and distributing electricity and gas in its core geographic markets the company also develops renewable power through RWE Innogy; explores for and produces oil and gas through RWE-DEA; and engages in energy trading and gas midstream activities through RWE Supply & Trading.

Financial Performance

The company's revenues decreased by 3% in 2011 due to a drop in revenues from the Germany power generation Netherlands/Belgium and Trading/Gas Midstream segments. Power generation revenues declined due to the German government's shift in energy policy (exiting nuclear power) following the reactor disaster at Fukushima. Netherlands/Belgium revenues declined due to a drop in Essent's gas midstream business caused by a drop in electricity generation margins. Trading/Gas Midstream revenues declined due to a drop in the realization of successful forward transactions and in some of its gas purchase contracts.

The company's net income decreased by 45% in 2011 due to a decrease in revenues and operating income caused by an increase in the costs of material depreciation amortization and impairment losses and other operating expenses.

Strategy

RWE plans its investments in power stations networks and raw material production facilities in terms of decades not in terms of years. It is looking to compete more effectively in the deregulated German power and gas markets order by restructuring its regional energy businesses. The company's former German utility unit RWE Energie lost its regional monopoly status because of deregulation and RWE has responded by splitting its domestic power generation distribution and supply operations into new units. RWE has also responded by acquiring utilities and energy services companies in the Czech Republic Hungary Poland and Slovakia and by targeting expansion in Europe.

RWE is also focusing on the expansion of renewable energy in Germany the UK the Netherlands Poland Spain and Italy.

In 2011 the company acquired Energy Resources Holding B.V. which has owns 30 % of EPZ a Dutch electricity generator.

To meet antitrust requirements in 2011 RWE sold its 75% stake in the German natural gas transmission grid business (Thyssengas) to Macquarie Group. To pay down debt in 2011 it also sold its German long-distance power grid to a consortium of five pension funds of German and Swiss insurers for $1.4 billion. RWE retained operational control of the grid.

A possible merger between RWE and Spanish power giant IBERDROLA fell through in 2011 due to market and political concerns.

HISTORY

Founded at the end of the 19th century RWE mirrored the industrialization of Germany in its growth. It was formed as Rheinisch-Westfalisches Elektrizitatswerk in 1898 by Erich Zweigert the mayor of Essen and Hugo Stinnes an industrialist from Mulheim to provide electricity to Essen and surrounding areas. The company began supplying power in 1900.

Stinnes persuaded other cities —Gelsenkirchen and Mulheim —to buy shares in RWE in 1905. In 1908 RWE and rival Vereinigte Elektrizitatswerk Westfalen (VEW) agreed to divide up the territories that each would supply.

Germany's coal shortages caused by WWI prompted RWE to expand its coal operations and it bought Rheinische Aktiengesellschaft für Braunkohlenbergbau a coal producer in 1932. RWE also built a power line network completed in 1930 to connect populous northern Germany with the south. By 1939 as WWII began the company had plants throughout most of western Germany. However the war destroyed much of its infrastructure and RWE had to rebuild.

The company continued to rely on coal for most of its fuel needs in the 1950s but in 1961 RWE and Bayern Atomkraft sponsored the construction of a demonstration nuclear reactor the first of several such projects at Gundremmingen. The Gundremmingen plant was shut down in 1977 and to replace it RWE built two 1300-MW reactors that began operation in 1984.

RWE began to diversify and in 1988 it acquired Texaco's German petroleum and petrochemical unit which became RWE-DEA. By 1990 RWE's operations also included waste management and construction. RWE reorganized creating RWE Aktiengesellschaft as a holding company for group operations.

RWE-DEA acquired the US's Vista Chemical in 1991 and RWE's Rheinbraun mining unit bought a 50% stake in Consolidation Coal from DuPont. (The mining venture went public in 1999 as CONSOL Energy.) RWE led a consortium that acquired major stakes in three Hungarian power companies in 1995.

Hoping to play a role in Germany's telecommunications market RWE teamed with VEBA in 1997 to form the o.tel.o joint venture and RWE and VEBA gained control of large German mobile phone operator E-Plus. The nation's telecom market was deregulated in 1998 but Mannesmann and former monopoly Deutsche Telekom proved to be formidable competitors. In 1999 RWE and VEBA sold o.tel.o's fixed-line business (along with the o.tel.o brand name) and cable-TV unit Tele Columbus. The next year the companies sold their joint stake in E-Plus.

Faced with deregulating German electricity markets RWE Energie had begun restructuring as soon as the market opened up in 1998. It agreed to buy fellow German power company VEW in a $20 billion deal that closed in 2000. RWE also joined with insurance giant Allianz and France's Vivendi in a successful bid for a 49.9% stake in state-owned water distributor Berliner Wasserbetriebe (Vivendi later spurned an RWE offer to buy its energy businesses).

After taking advantage of deregulating markets in Germany RWE moved to pick up other European utilities: It acquired UK-based Thames Water (later renamed RWE Thames Water) in 2000 and bought a majority stake in Dutch gas supplier Intergas the next year. In 2002 the company issued an exchange offer to acquire UK electricity supplier Innogy (later renamed RWE npower) for a total of about $4.4 billion in cash and $3 billion in assumed debt. It also completed a $3.7 billion purchase of Czech Republic gas supplier Transgas.

In a move to further streamline operations RWE sold its 50% stake in refinery and service station subsidiary Shell & DEA Oil to Deutsche Shell and Shell Petroleum. To do battle in an increasingly competitive utility industry RWE is acquiring stakes in other European utilities. In 2003 RWE also acquired North American utility American Water Works which was combined with the US operations of RWE Thames Water for $4.6 billion in cash and $4 billion in assumed debt.

Recognizing that its international acquisitions of water utilities in the early 2000s had left it overextended RWE has been to selling its water assets in order to save cash and streamline its operations around its core power businesses. Overextended in 2006 the company sold its Thames Water unit to Kemble Water Limited a consortium led by Macquarie Bank's European Infrastructure Funds. It spun off its American Water unit in 2008.

The company saw its revenues drop in 2009 as the global recession hammered gas prices. However the same lower gas prices helped RWE to save costs enabling it to post an improved net income that year.

After being outmaneuvered by EDF in its plan to grow its Pan-European power footprint by acquiring British Energy RWE in 2009 acquired top Dutch power utility Essent for $10.7 billion. The deal boost its position as one of the top electricity and gas utilities in Europe.

Growing its energy sources in 2009 it also formed a joint venture with E.ON to develop 6000 MW of nuclear power capacity in the UK. In a move to reduce its dependency on the wholesale gas markets in 2009 RWE acquired 70% of the Breagh North Sea gas field for about $350 million.

The company announced CEO Jürgen Großmann who fought Germany's decision to phase out nuclear power stepped down in July 2012. Großmann was replaced by Peter Terium the CEO of Essent. COO Rolf Martin Schmitz was named Deputy CEO.

EXECUTIVES

Chairman and CEO, Rolf Martin Schmitz, age 59
CFO and CEO RWE Supply and Trading, Markus Krebber
Deputy Chairman, Frank Bsirske
Auditors: PricewaterhouseCoopers Aktiengesellschaft Wirtschaftsprüfungsgesellschaft

LOCATIONS

HQ: RWE AG
Opernplatz 1, Essen 45128
Phone: (49) 201 12 00   **Fax:** (49) 201 12 15199
Web: www.rwe.com

2014 Sales

	% of total
Germany	57
UK	21
Other EU	22
Rest of Europe	0
Other countries	1
Total	**100**

PRODUCTS/OPERATIONS

2014 Sales

	% of total
Supply/ Distribution Networks Germany	52
Supply United Kingdom	19

Supply Netherlands/ Belgium	9
Central Eastern and South Eastern Europe	8
Trading/ Gas Mid-Stream	7
Conventional Power Generation	4
Renewables	1
Other Consolidation	0
Total	**100**

Selected Divisions and Subsidiaries

RWE Energy (German and continental European downstream energy operations)
RWE npower (affiliated with RWE Innogy electricity and gas supply UK)
RWE Supply & Trading (power gas coal and oil trading)
RWE-DEA AG (oil and gas exploration production and storage)
RWE Power (upstream energy operations)

COMPETITORS

BP	Enel
Centrica	Exxon Mobil
E.ON	Royal Dutch Shell
Electricite de France	Vattenfall
Endesa S.A.	

HISTORICAL FINANCIALS
Company Type: Public

Income Statement
FYE: December 31

	REVENUE ($ mil.)	NET INCOME ($ mil.)	NET PROFIT MARGIN	EMPLOYEES
12/15	50,492	(185)	—	59,350
12/14	56,094	2,071	3.7%	61,715
12/13	70,754	(3,795)	—	66,341
12/12	66,918	1,721	2.6%	70,208
12/11	63,577	2,335	3.7%	72,068
Annual Growth	(5.6%)	—	—	(4.7%)

2015 Year-End Financials

Debt ratio: 26.2%
Return on equity: (-2.0%)
Cash ($ mil.): 2,746
Current ratio: 1.11
Long-term debt ($ mil.): 18,209
No. of shares (mil.): 575
Dividends
Yield: 6.2%
Payout: —
Market value ($ mil.): 7,272

	STOCK PRICE ($) FY Close	P/E High/Low		Earnings	PER SHARE ($) Dividends	Book Value
12/15	12.63	—	—	(0.30)	0.79	12.86
12/14	30.95	14	11	3.37	1.01	21.31
12/13	36.80	—	—	(6.18)	1.90	24.96
12/12	41.64	23	16	2.81	1.93	33.94
12/11	34.93	22	8	4.33	3.38	35.37
Annual Growth	(22.5%)	—	—	—	(30.6%)	
	(22.4%)					

S-Oil Corp

S-Oil aims to become the most S-uccessful refiner in South Korea and beyond. The company is one of its country's leading refiners and a major provider of lubricants and gasoline. S-Oil is capable of producing 669000 barrels per day at its Onsan refinery and its product menu includes gasoline kerosene diesel lube base oil automotive and industrial oils and petrochemical products such as benzene and toluene. S-Oil operates a naphtha reforming plant with a daily capacity of 45000 barrels and a BTX production plant with an annual capacity of 900000 tons. Its joint venture with Saudi Arabia's Aramco –signed in 1991 –ensures a steady supply of crude oil.

OperationsThe company operates the Onsan Refinery and other facilities at that location that can produce petrochemicals and lube base oil. S-Oil produces and supplies high quality oil products based on the world-class Bunker-C Cracking Center and the xylene Center a paraxylene plant with the world's highest production capacity for a single facility.

Geographic Reach

S-Oil exports more than 60% of its annual production to about 30 countries around the world.

Financial Performance

Thanks to high oil prices and the expansion of its refining capacity S-Oil's 2011 revenues increased by 56% and its net income by 69%.

Business Strategy

The company's long-term strategy includes further investment in the refining business integration with the petrochemical business and growing its renewable energy business.

Buoyed by increasing demand for petroleum products from China and other Asian countries in 2011 S-Oil completed its Onsan refinery expansion project. The expansion doubles the plant's production of paraxylene and benzene to 2.4 million tons a year. It also increased its refining capacity from 580000 barrels per day to 669000 barrels per day.

Company Background

S-Oil began commercial operations in 1980. The company broke off from SsangYong Group in 1999 and changed its name to S-Oil a year later.

EXECUTIVES

CEO, Othman Al-Ghamdi
Auditors: Samil Accounting Corporation (A Member Firm of PircewaterhouseCoopers)

LOCATIONS

HQ: S-Oil Corp
192 Baekbeom-ro Mapo-gu, Seoul 121-805
Phone: (82) 2 3772 5151   **Fax:** (82) 2 782 4879
Web: www.s-oil.com

COMPETITORS

GS Caltex	SK Group
LG International	

HISTORICAL FINANCIALS
Company Type: Public

Income Statement
FYE: December 31

	REVENUE ($ mil.)	NET INCOME ($ mil.)	NET PROFIT MARGIN	EMPLOYEES
12/15	15,205	536	3.5%	2,865
12/14	26,101	(263)	—	2,796
12/13	29,628	275	0.9%	2,749
12/12	32,521	548	1.7%	2,671
12/11	27,542	1,027	3.7%	2,622
Annual Growth	(13.8%)	(15.0%)	—	2.2%

2015 Year-End Financials

Debt ratio: 0.0%
Return on equity: 12.2%
Cash ($ mil.): 171
Current ratio: 1.77
Long-term debt ($ mil.): 1,706
No. of shares (mil.): 112
Dividends
Yield: 1.3%
Payout: 10.2%
Market value ($ mil.): 3,940

	STOCK PRICE ($) FY Close	P/E High/Low		Earnings	PER SHARE ($) Dividends	Book Value
12/15	35.00	0	0	4.61	0.47	40.69
12/14	22.30	0	0	(2.26)	0.50	39.85
12/13	37.20	0	0	2.36	1.24	45.22
12/12	51.00	0	0	4.73	1.70	44.72
12/11	40.75	0	0	8.85	1.63	40.06
Annual Growth	(3.7%)	—	—	(15.1%)	(26.7%)	0.4%

Safran S.A.

Auditors: ERNST & YOUNG et Autres

LOCATIONS

HQ: Safran S.A.
2, boulevard du General Martial-Valin, Paris, Cedex 15 75724
Phone: (33) 1 40 60 80 80   **Fax:** (33) 1 40 60 81 02
Web: www.safran-group.com

HISTORICAL FINANCIALS
Company Type: Public

Income Statement
FYE: December 31

	REVENUE ($ mil.)	NET INCOME ($ mil.)	NET PROFIT MARGIN	EMPLOYEES
12/15	21,429	(461)	—	0
12/14	20,217	(153)	—	68,945
12/13	21,522	1,908	8.9%	66,289
12/12	19,515	1,716	8.8%	62,558
12/11	16,000	618	3.9%	59,805
Annual Growth	7.6%	—	—	—

2015 Year-End Financials

Debt ratio: 10.0%
Return on equity: (-7.1%)
Cash ($ mil.): 2,009
Current ratio: 0.80
Long-term debt ($ mil.): 1,908
No. of shares (mil.): 416
Dividends
Yield: 1.9%
Payout: —
Market value ($ mil.): 7,179

	STOCK PRICE ($) FY Close	P/E High/Low		Earnings	PER SHARE ($) Dividends	Book Value
12/15	17.24	—	—	(1.11)	0.34	14.72
12/14	15.26	—	—	(0.36)	0.55	18.25
12/13	17.24	20	5	4.58	0.32	21.94
12/12	43.25	14	10	4.13	0.87	19.21
12/11	30.20	33	23	1.53	0.25	15.70
Annual Growth	(13.1%)	—	—	—	8.4%	(1.6%)

SAIC Motor Corp Ltd

SAIC Motor Corporation is the largest automotive manufacturer listed on the A-Shares market in China. The Shanghai Automotive Industry Corporation subsidiary makes automobiles (including passenger and commercial vehicles) and spare parts (including engines transmissions powertrain chassis interior and exterior trim electronic appliances). It is also engaged in auto financing logistics vehicle information second-hand cars and other car service and trading businesses. Its operations include Shanghai Volkswagen Shanghai GM SAIC-GM-Wuling Nanjing Iveco SAIC-Iveco-Hongyan and Shanghai Sunwin.

Financial Performance

In 2012 SAIC Motors sold 4.5 million cars with a year-on-year growth of 12% maintaining its edge as market leader edge in the Chinese domestic automotive market.

The company's revenues increased by 19% in 2011 while its net profit increased by 23%. The increase in net profit was due to the increase in total revenues (due to a strong increase in the sales of cars) partially offset by a 4% increase SG&A mainly due to the increase of sales-related expenses including transportation and logistics expenses and advertising expenses and a 25% increase in administrative expenses mainly due to the increase in research and development expenditure royalty expenses employee salaries and welfare costs.

Strategy

To help address China's smog issues by increasing the adoption of electric vehicles in 2012 SAIC Motors and Shanghai International Automotive City (Group) Co. (SIAC) signed a memorandum of understanding to develop a new energy vehicle demonstration project at Shanghai Automotive Museum with an eye toward wider implementation of the vehicle. In addition SAIC Motor SIAC and Shanghai Gaozhan New Energy Vehicle Sales and Service Co. Ltd. reached an agreement to develop the Roewe E50 pure electric vehicle under which 200 units of Roewe E50 pure electric vehicle will be produced on a test basis.

Company Background

SAIC Motor Corporation was established in 1984 as Shanghai Volkswagen Automotive a 50-50 joint venture with Volkswagen.

EXECUTIVES

President, Chen Zhixin, age 57
VP; General Manager Passenger Vehicle Co.; Head Technology Center, Wang Xiaoqiu, age 52
VP; General Manager Shanghai General Motors Wuling, Shen Yang, age 55
VP; General Manager Commercial Vehicle and Shanghai Commercial Vehicle Co., Lan Qingsong, age 52
Acting CFO, Wei Yong, age 44
Chief Engineer, Cheng Jinglei, age 49
Chairman, Chen Hong, age 55
Auditors: Deloitte Touche Tohmatsu

LOCATIONS

HQ: SAIC Motor Corp Ltd
No. 489, Weihai Road, Jingan District, Shanghai 200041
Phone: (86) 21 22011138 **Fax:** (86) 21 22011199
Web: www.saicmotor.com

2015 Sales

	% of total
China	98
Others	2
Total	**100**

PRODUCTS/OPERATIONS

2015 Revenue by products

	% of total
Vehicles	75
Parts	19
Trading	1
Finance	1
Service and others	3
Total	**100**

2015 Revenue by Segment

	% of total
Vehicles and parts	99
Finance	1
Total	**100**

COMPETITORS

BMW	Honda
BYD	Hyundai Motor
Daimler	Kia Motors
Dongfeng Peugeot	Mazda
FCA US	Nissan
Fiat Chrysler	Peugeot
Ford Motor	Suzuki Motor
General Motors	Toyota

HISTORICAL FINANCIALS
Company Type: Public

Income Statement
FYE: December 31

	REVENUE ($ mil.)	NET INCOME ($ mil.)	NET PROFIT MARGIN	EMPLOYEES
12/15	103,232	4,587	4.4%	0
12/14	101,508	4,507	4.4%	0
12/13	93,461	4,097	4.4%	0
12/12	77,151	3,328	4.3%	0
12/11	69,077	3,212	4.7%	5,379
Annual Growth	**10.6%**	**9.3%**	**—**	**—**

2015 Year-End Financials

Debt ratio: 0.4%
Return on equity: 17.9%
Cash ($ mil.): 11,189
Current ratio: 1.05
Long-term debt ($ mil.): 1,479
No. of shares (mil.): —
Dividends
  Yield: —
  Payout: —
Market value ($ mil.): —

Samba Financial Group

The sound of money is music to Samba Financial Group's ears. The bank offers retail banking corporate banking investment banking asset management credit cards loans and related services through about 70 branches (25 are ladies only) and some 500 ATMs across Saudi Arabia and branches in London Dubai and Qatar. In Pakistan Samba Financial is the majority owner of Samba Bank Limited with about 30 branches. Its financial products are also Shariah-compliant. In 2014 the company launched a new SambaMobile app for smart phones and tablets. Samba Financial was set up in 1980 when it took over the two Saudi branches owned by Citibank; Citibank sold the last of its stake in the company in 2004.

EXECUTIVES

CEO, Rania Mahmoud Nashar
Auditors: PricewaterhouseCoopers

LOCATIONS

HQ: Samba Financial Group
King Abdul Aziz Road, P.O.Box. 833, Riyadh 11421
Phone: (966) 1 477 4770 **Fax:** (966) 1 477 4770
Web: www.samba.com.sa

COMPETITORS

Al Rajhi Banking	Dallah Albaraka Group
Arab Banking Corp.	Qatar National Bank
Arab National Bank	Riyad Bank
Banque Saudi Fransi	Saudi British Bank

HISTORICAL FINANCIALS
Company Type: Public

Income Statement
FYE: December 31

	ASSETS ($ mil.)	NET INCOME ($ mil.)	INCOME AS % OF ASSETS	EMPLOYEES
12/15	62,659	0	0.0%	3,723
12/14	57,935	1,333	2.3%	3,404
12/13	54,667	1,202	2.2%	3,306
12/12	53,119	1,154	2.2%	3,329
12/11	51,406	1,147	2.2%	3,057
Annual Growth	**5.1%**	**(85.5%)**	**—**	**5.1%**

2015 Year-End Financials

Return on assets: 0.0%
Return on equity: 0.0%
Long-term debt ($ mil.): —
No. of shares (mil.): 2,000
Sales ($ mil): 2,198
Dividends
  Yield: —
  Payout: —
Market value ($ mil.): —

Samsung Electronics Co Ltd

Auditors: Samil Accounting Corporation (A Member Firm of PircewaterhouseCoopers)

LOCATIONS

HQ: Samsung Electronics Co Ltd
129, Samseong-ro, Yeongtong-gu, Suwon-si, Gyeonggi-do 443-742
Phone: (82) 31 200 1114 **Fax:** (82) 31 200 7538
Web: www.samsung.com

HISTORICAL FINANCIALS
Company Type: Public

Income Statement
FYE: December 31

	REVENUE ($ mil.)	NET INCOME ($ mil.)	NET PROFIT MARGIN	EMPLOYEES
12/15	170,545	15,889	9.3%	96,898
12/14	188,470	21,097	11.2%	99,382
12/13	217,461	28,356	13.0%	95,794
12/12	188,351	21,715	11.5%	90,700
12/11	142,403	11,529	8.1%	101,970
Annual Growth	**4.6%**	**8.3%**	**—**	**(1.3%)**

2015 Year-End Financials

Debt ratio: 0.0%
Return on equity: 11.1%
Cash ($ mil.): 19,240
Current ratio: 2.47
Long-term debt ($ mil.): 1,272
No. of shares (mil.): 127
Dividends
  Yield: 0.0%
  Payout: 16.2%
Market value ($ mil.): 130,582

	STOCK PRICE ($) FY Close	P/E High/Low	Earnings	PER SHARE ($) Dividends	Book Value
12/15	1,025.00 1,153.38	0 0	107.35	17.47	
12/14	1,100.00 1,138.46	0 0	139.93	13.07	
12/13	1,375.00 1,049.15	0 0	188.09	7.65	
12/12	1,350.00	0 0	144.19	5.15	838.14
12/11	835.00	0 0	76.80	4.75	646.02
Annual Growth	**5.3%**	**—**	**8.7%**	**38.5%**	**15.6%**

Samsung Fire & Marine Insurance (South Korea)

Chances are that when you think of Samsung you think TVs DVDs and mobile phones. But in South Korea Samsung also means insurance. Samsung Fire & Marine is the largest casualty insurance company in the region offering auto fire marine aviation pension and long-term health coverage. The company has streamlined operations to compete in an increasingly deregulated market — one that allows foreign competition. The firm has entered foreign markets such as China Europe Indonesia Japan and Vietnam forming business alliances with People's Insurance Company of China and Tokio Marine.

Geographic Reach

Based in South Korea Samsung Fire & Marine has an overseas presence in Indonesia China Vietnam Singapore England and the US. It has representative offices in Europe Asia North America South America the United Arab Emirates and Russia.

Sales and Marketing

Samsung Fire & Marine sells its products through company agents general agents banks and via telemarketing.

Financial Performance

Revenue rose 33% to 18.8 trillion Won in fiscal 2014 due to an increase in premium income as sales of general automotive and long-term insurance and reinsurance rose. Net income rose 63% to 838 billion Won that year as a result of higher interest earnings dividend income and gains on foreign exchange transactions.

However cash flow from operations fell 6% to 3.4 trillion Won in 2014 as more cash was used in deposits loans and payment of retirement benefits.

Strategy

The company's primary strategies for growth include expanding abroad and developing new health care insurance products. It is focused on increasing its agent capacity as well as expansion in China of its online automobile coverage operations.

EXECUTIVES

President, Min Soo An
Auditors: Samjong Accounting Corporation (A Member Firm of KPMG)

LOCATIONS

HQ: Samsung Fire & Marine Insurance (South Korea)
87 Samsung Insurance Building, Euljiro 1-ga, Choong-gu, Seoul 100-191
Phone: (82) 2 1588 5114　　**Fax:** (82) 505 161 1614
Web: www.samsungfire.com

PRODUCTS/OPERATIONS

2014 Sales

	% of total
Premium income	95
Reinsurance income	3
Other	2
Total	**100**

2014 Premium Income

	% of total
Long-Term insurance	55
Automobile insurance	21
General insurance	12
Pension insurance	12
Total	**100**

Selected Affiliates

Cheil Communication Inc.
Cheil Industries Inc.
S1 Corporation
Samsung Card Co. Ltd.
Samsung Corporation
Samsung Economic Research Institute
Samsung Electro-Mechanics Co. Ltd.
Samsung Electronics Co. Ltd.
Samsung Engineering Co. Ltd.
Samsung Fine Chemicals Ltd.
Samsung Foundation of Culture
Samsung Investment Trust Management Co. Ltd.
Samsung Life Insurance Co. Ltd.
Samsung Securities Co. Ltd.
Samsung Welfare Foundation
Samsung-BP Chemicals Co. Ltd.
The Shilla Hotels and Resorts Co. Ltd.

COMPETITORS

Allianz	MS&AD Holdings
Dongbu	Sompo Holdings
Hyundai Marine & Fire	Tokio Marine
Kyobo Life Insurance	

HISTORICAL FINANCIALS

Company Type: Public

Income Statement

FYE: December 31

	REVENUE ($ mil.)	NET INCOME ($ mil.)	NET PROFIT MARGIN	EMPLOYEES
12/15	18,155	689	3.8%	5,692
12/14	18,990	763	4.0%	5,498
12/13*	14,697	486	3.3%	5,782
03/13	17,523	694	4.0%	5,808
03/12	15,343	701	4.6%	5,510
Annual Growth	**4.3%**	**(0.4%)**	**—**	**0.8%**

*Fiscal year change

2015 Year-End Financials

Debt ratio: —	No. of shares (mil.): 40
Return on equity: 8.2%	Dividends
Cash ($ mil.): 1,465	Yield: —
Current ratio: —	Payout: —
Long-term debt ($ mil.): —	Market value ($ mil.): —

San-In Godo Bank, Ltd. (The) (Japan)

The San-in Godo Bank provides banking services in the Tottori and Shimane prefectures in western Japan. The bank also serves the adjacent Sanyo and Hyogo regions. It does business from more than 100 branches and 13 subsidiary companies. San-in Godo Bank operates overseas from offices in Dalian and Shanghai China and New York City. The bank was established in 1941.

EXECUTIVES

President, FUMIO ISHIMARU
Auditors: Ernst & Young ShinNihon LLC

LOCATIONS

HQ: San-In Godo Bank, Ltd. (The) (Japan)
10 Uomachi, Matsue, Shimane 690-0062
Phone: (81) 852 55 1000　　**Fax:** (81) 852 27 3398
Web: www.gogin.co.jp

COMPETITORS

Aozora Bank	Shizuoka Bank
Mitsubishi UFJ Financial Group	

HISTORICAL FINANCIALS

Company Type: Public

Income Statement

FYE: March 31

	ASSETS ($ mil.)	NET INCOME ($ mil.)	INCOME AS % OF ASSETS	EMPLOYEES
03/16	45,954	114	0.3%	3,185
03/15	39,857	101	0.3%	3,144
03/14	43,390	108	0.2%	2,146
03/13	45,082	104	0.2%	2,167
03/12	50,314	125	0.3%	2,184
Annual Growth	**(2.2%)**	**(2.3%)**	**—**	**9.9%**

2016 Year-End Financials

Return on assets: 0.2%	Dividends
Return on equity: 3.7%	Yield: —
Long-term debt ($ mil.): —	Payout: —
No. of shares (mil.): 158	Market value ($ mil.): —
Sales ($ mil): 814	

Sanofi

Auditors: ERNST & YOUNG et Autres

LOCATIONS

HQ: Sanofi
54, Rue La Boetie, Paris 75008
Phone: (33) 1 53 77 40 00　　**Fax:** (33) 1 53 77 43 03
Web: www.sanofi.com

HISTORICAL FINANCIALS

Company Type: Public

Income Statement

FYE: December 31

	REVENUE ($ mil.)	NET INCOME ($ mil.)	NET PROFIT MARGIN	EMPLOYEES
12/15	37,970	4,669	12.3%	115,631
12/14	41,459	5,336	12.9%	113,496
12/13	45,853	5,117	11.2%	112,128
12/12	47,393	6,546	13.8%	111,974
12/11	45,345	7,363	16.2%	113,719
Annual Growth	**(4.3%)**	**(10.8%)**	**—**	**0.4%**

2015 Year-End Financials

Debt ratio: 17.6%	No. of shares (mil.): 1,301
Return on equity: 7.5%	Dividends
Cash ($ mil.): 9,964	Yield: 3.7%
Current ratio: 1.48	Payout: 45.4%
Long-term debt ($ mil.): 14,288	Market value ($ mil.): 55,519

	STOCK PRICE ($) FY Close	P/E High/Low		PER SHARE ($) Earnings	Dividends	Book Value
12/15	42.65	17	12	3.54	1.61	48.57
12/14	45.61	16	13	4.01	1.91	52.08
12/13	53.63	21	16	3.83	1.79	59.14
12/12	47.38	13	9	4.93	1.69	57.12
12/11	36.54	9	7	5.55	3.23	54.93
Annual Growth (3.0%)	3.9%	—	—	(10.6%)	(16.0%)	

SAP SE

SAP's software forms a company's nerve centre. Its enterprise resource planning software integrates back-office functions such as analytics accounting distribution and human resources and comes in on-premises and cloud-linked forms. While the sale and servicing of its legacy on-premises offering brings in the majority of the company's revenue SAP is going all-in on cloud computing and the digitalization of business with the release of S/4HANA in 2015 as an alternative to its existing SAP Business Suite. The company serves over 300000 customers in 25 different industries across 190 countries.

Operations

SAP sells its software and services in two segments. Software and software-related services account for 71% of revenue. The segment includes SAP's on-premise software and its cloud-based software products. The biggest chunk of revenue - 49% - comes from payment for support of the company's software.SAP's Cloud services and support accounts for 11% of revenue but is growing rapidly and doubled in size in 2015 on the back of the success of its SAP S/4HANA platform. The product launched in early 2015 and had picked up 2700 customers by the end of the year.

Professional services offered by SAP generate the other 18% of revenue.SAP products cover functionality such as analytics enterprise management supply chain management financial management and customer relationship management among others. The products are scaled and tailored to fit companies of varying size and in a diversity of industries.

Companies working in the consumer and energy and natural resources industries are SAP's biggest market segments accounting for around 23% of revenue each. Discrete manufacturing brings in 18% services 16% public services 10% and financial services 9%. Geographic ReachHeadquartered in Walldorf Germany SAP has facilities in more than 130 countries. In 2015 the US was SAP's biggest single market accounting for 33% of the company's revenue. Germany was the next biggest market with 13%. Including Germany the EMEA region contributed 44% of revenue. About 15% of revenue came from the Asia-Pacific region and Japan. Sales and MarketingMost of SAP's sales are generated by the direct sales staffs within the organization although it also sells through partners. Financial PerformanceNote: Growth rates may differ after conversion to US Dollars.SAP spent much of 2015 on cloud nine after its new SAP S/4HANA system an update of its initial cloud offering proved fantastically successful. Revenue in SAP's Cloud segment more than doubled to euro 2.3 billion accounting for over a third of the 18% top-line revenue growth for a company record of euro 20.8 billion. The software licenses and support segment

which still accounts for some 72% of revenue grew at a slower but still impressive 14% to euro 14.9 billion.

Net income in 2015 was up 15% to euro 2.7 billion mostly in line with the increase in revenue. Cash flow from operating activities climbed 40% to euro 1.8 billion for the same reason.

Strategy

SAP is going big in cloud. The company takes the view that connectivity is still in its relative infancy and has vast potential for growth. Its proprietary HANA platform released in 2010 marked a step away from the three pillars of master data transactional data and aggregations of transactional data and allows for business processes and analytics to run on the same platform.

In the past five years revenue from cloud subscriptions and support has risen explosively from euro 18 million in 2011 to euro 2.3 billion in 2015 and the company hopes the release of its latest S/4HANA platform will usher in a new era of enterprise resource planning. Uptake of the new software surpassed SAP's expectations in its first year of release with customers numbering 2700. Furthermore as more companies with the new software report performance improvements SAP can expect to see an increase in enthusiasm among its customer base of large and conservative companies.

The ‘Internet of Things' (IoT) - the interconnectivity of small machines and devices via the internet - is an area of digitalization that is expected to grow rapidly over the coming years. SAP has worked to ready itself for the coming wave by baking IoT capability into S/4HANA.

Mergers and Acquisitions

SAP entered into a flurry of acquisition activity in 2012-14 as its bought its way into the cloud computing space. In the period it acquired Ariba a provider of a cloud-based B2B marketplace ($4.3 billion); travel and expenses firm Concur ($8.3 billion); and contract workforce management software company Fieldglass (+$1 billion). The combined network of the three companies is worth some $600 billion. Additionally in a ‘fill-in' acquisition in 2015 SAP bought French cloud-computing firm Multiposting (80 employees) a provider of software that allows for the automatic posting of jobs and internships on the internet.

HISTORY

Early History

Former IBM software engineers Hasso Plattner Hans-Werner Hector Dietmar Hopp Claus Wellenreuther and Klaus Tschira started SAP in 1972 when the project they were working on for IBM was moved to another unit.

While rival software firms made many products to automate the various parts of a company's operations these engineers decided to make a single system that would tie a corporation together. In 1973 they launched an instantaneous accounting transaction-processing program called R/1. By 1979 they had adapted the program to create R/2 mainframe software that linked external databases and communication systems.

The company went public in 1988. That year Plattner began a project to create software for the computer network market. In 1992 as sales of its R/2 mainframe software lagged SAP introduced its R/3 software which would later become its flagship SAP ERP.

EXECUTIVES

CEO, William R. (Bill) McDermott, age 54, $1,279,900 total compensation
President SAP Business One SAP Anywhere and SAP Business ByDesign, Barry Padgett

President Global Customer Operations, Robert (Rob) Enslin
COO, Christian Klein, age 35
CIO, Thomas Saueressig, age 31
CFO, Luka Mucic
Chairman, Hasso Plattner, age 72
Deputy Chairperson, Margret Klein-Magar
Auditors: KPMG AG Wirtschaftsprufungsgesellschaft

LOCATIONS

HQ: SAP SE
  Dietmar-Hopp-Allee 16, Walldorf D-69190
Phone: (49) 0 6227 7 47474   **Fax:** (49) 0 6227 7 57575
Web: www.sap.com

2015 Sales

	% of total
Europe Middle East & Africa	
Germany	13
Other countries	31
Americas	
US	33
Other countries	8
Asia/Pacific	15
Total	**100**

PRODUCTS/OPERATIONS

2015 Sales by Type

	% of total
Software & Support	
Support	48
Licenses	23
Cloud Subscription & Support	11
Services	18
Total	**100**

2015 Sales by Market

	% of total
Consumer	24
Energy	23
Discrete Manufacturing	18
Services	16
Public Services	10
Financial Services	9
Total	**100**

Selected Customers

Aigo
City of Cape Town South Africa
Danone
Beaumont Health System
McLaren Group

Selected Software

SAP Business All-in-One
SAP Business ByDesign
SAP Business One
SAP Business Suite
SAP ERP
SAP HANA
SAP NetWeaver

Selected Services

Application hosting
Business consulting
Custom development
Financing
Implementation
Maintenance
Training

Selected Acquisitions

Concur (2014) Travel and expense management software for companies
Hybris (2014) Real-time customer engagement and commerce platformSeeWhy (2014) Cloud-based behavioral target marketing softwareTicket-Web (2013) Ticketing software and customer relationship management (CRM) software for sports and entertainment.KMS Softw
Right Hemisphere (2012; enterprise visualization)
TechniData (2010; environmental health and safety)
Sybase (2010 business intelligence and database management)
Clear Standards (2009 environmental)

Highdeal (2009 billing)
Visiprise (2008 manufacturing process management)
Business Objects (2008 business intelligence)
OutlookSoft (2007 business performance management)
Pilot Software (2007 business performance management)

COMPETITORS

BMC Software	IBM
CA Inc.	MicroStrategy
CDC Software	Microsoft
Electronic Data	Oracle
Processing	Software AG
Epicor Software	Workday Inc.
HP	salesforce.com

HISTORICAL FINANCIALS

Company Type: Public

Income Statement

FYE: December 31

	REVENUE ($ mil.)	NET INCOME ($ mil.)	NET PROFIT MARGIN	EMPLOYEES
12/15	22,647	3,328	14.7%	76,986
12/14	21,344	3,986	18.7%	74,406
12/13	23,149	4,579	19.8%	66,572
12/12	21,382	3,720	17.4%	64,422
12/11	18,409	4,446	24.2%	55,765
Annual Growth	5.3%	(7.0%)	—	8.4%

2015 Year-End Financials

Debt ratio: 25.0%	No. of shares (mil.): 1,197
Return on equity: 14.2%	Dividends
Cash ($ mil.): 3,715	Yield: 1.1%
Current ratio: 1.24	Payout: —
Long-term debt ($ mil.): 9,455	Market value ($ mil.): 94,758

	STOCK PRICE ($) FY Close	P/E High/Low	PER SHARE ($) Earnings	Dividends	Book Value
12/15	79.10	32 23	2.79	0.88	21.15
12/14	69.65	28 22	3.33	0.99	19.83
12/13	87.14	32 26	3.83	0.80	18.50
12/12	80.38	34 23	3.12	1.02	15.66
12/11	52.95	21 15	3.74	0.00	13.80
Annual Growth	10.6%	— —	(7.1%)	—	11.3%

Saudi Basic Industries Corp - SABIC (Saudi Arabia)

SABIC stands for Saudi Basic Industries Corporation but it could also stand for "seriously a big industrial company." Saudi Arabia's largest non-oil company SABIC operates through six units: chemicals performance chemicals polymers (polyolefins PVC and polyester) plastics (including SABIC Innovative Plastics) fertilizers and metals (steel and aluminum). SABIC is one of the world's top makers of polyethylene and polypropylene. The company which introduces some 150 new products per year operates 60 manufacturing and compounding plants in more than 40 countries as well as numerous distribution centers offices and storage facilities. SABIC is majority owned (70%) by the Saudi government.

Geographic Reach

The company's corporate offices and headquarters are in Riyadh Saudi Arabia while its major industrial operations are in Al-Jubail on the Arabian

Gulf as well as in Yanbu on the Red Sea. SABIC operates across more than 40 countries in the Middle East Asia Europe and the Americas.

Operations

A leading industrial player in Saudi Arabia the company primary leverages by-products of oil production to create value-added export commodities (chemicals polymers and fertilizers) and provides the commodity and financial basis for industrial diversification (such as steel production) within and outside of the Kingdom.

The company's European subsidiary produces more than 2 million metric tons of polymers and more than 5 million metric tons of basic chemicals.

The chemicals segment (87% of SABIC's revenues in 2014) includes chemicals polymers performance chemicals and innovative plastic products; metals (5%) offers steel products; fertilizers (3%) ; and the corporate segment (5%) include corporate operations technology and innovation centers investment activities and SABIC Industrial Investments Company.

Sales and Marketing

SABIC serves markets such as transportation agrinutrients construction medical devices packaging clean energy and electrical and electronics.

Financial Performance

In 2014 SABIC's net revenues decreased by 0.5% due to a sales decline in the Chemicals and Metals Segments. The company's net income dropped by 8% that year due to a decrease in net revenues and higher selling general and administrative expenses.

In 2014 SABIC's cash flow decreased by 10% as the result of lower net income and changes in working capital due to changes in accounts payable and changes in accruals and other current liabilities.

Strategy

The company's strategy focuses on improving existing assets creating profitable growth globally developing new platforms and continuously developing its capabilities. To meet the growing trend for medical device manufacturers shift from metal or other fiber-filled materials to plastic in their applications in 2014 SABIC introduced two new grades of high-modulus carbon fiber reinforced thermoplastics. The company signed an agreement with HTE- the high throughput experimentation company to establish a satellite laboratory for high throughput experimentation to increase its R&D efficiency. This will include advanced testing equipment which will be hosted exclusively at HTE's newly constructed laboratory building in Heidelberg Germany.

In 2014 SABIC and the Korea-based SK Global Chemical signed a 50-50 joint venture agreement in Seoul South Korea for a total investment of $595 million to manufacture a range of high-performance polyethylene products using SK's cutting edge Nexlene technology. The joint venture located in Singapore is expected to operate a series of manufacturing plants the first of which was recently completed by SK Global Chemical at its complex in Ulsan South Korea with an expected annual capacity of 230000 tons. The plants will produce metallocene linear low density polyethylene polyolefin plastomers and polyolefin elastomers that will meet the growing needs of diverse industries such as advanced packaging automotive healthcare footwear and electrical and lighting.

Company Background

SABIC was founded in 1976.

EXECUTIVES

Vice Chairman and CEO, Mohamed H. Al-Mady
EVP Corporate Strategy and Planning, Yousef Al-Zamel
EVP Fertilizers, Khaled Al-Mana
EVP Corporate Human Resources, Fahad Al-Sheaibi
EVP Polymers, Mosaed Al-Ohali
EVP Innovative Plastics, Keith J. Smith
EVP Chemicals, Yousef A. Al-Benyan
EVP Metals, Abdulaziz S. Al-Humaid
EVP Performance Chemicals, Abdullah S. Al-Rabeeah
EVP Technology and Innovation, Ernesto Occhiello
EVP Shared Services, Omar A. Al-Amoudi
EVP Manufacturing, Awadh Al-Maker
Chairman, Saud bin Abdullah bin Thenayan Al-Saud

LOCATIONS

HQ: Saudi Basic Industries Corp - SABIC (Saudi Arabia)
P.O. Box 5101, Riyadh 11422
Phone: (966) 1 225 8000   **Fax:** (966) 1 225 9000
Web: www.sabic.com

PRODUCTS/OPERATIONS

2014 Sales

	% of total
Chemicals	87
Metals	5
Corporate	5
Fertilizers	3
Total	**100**

Selected Subsidiaries & Affiliates

Al-Jubail Petrochemical Co
Aluminum Bahrain
Arabian Industrial Fibers Co
Arabian Petrochemical Co
Eastern Petrochemical Co
Gulf Aluminum Rolling Mill Co
Gulf Petrochemical Industries Co
Jubail Fertilizer
Jubail United Petrochemical Co
Mááden Phosphate Co.
National Chemical Carrier Company
National Chemical Fertilizer Co
National Industrial Gases Co
National Methanol Co
SABIC Innovative Plastics
Saudi Arabian Fertilizer Co
Saudi Iron & Steel Co
Saudi Kayan Petrochemical Co
Saudi Methanol Co
Saudi Organometallic Chemicals Co
Saudi Petrochemical Co
Saudi Specialty Chemicals Co
Saudi-Yanbu Petrochemical Co
Saudi-European Petrochemical Co
Sinopec SABIC Tianjin Petrochemical Co
Yanbu National Petrochemical

COMPETITORS

A. Schulman
ArcelorMittal
BASF SE
Covestro
Dow Chemical
DuPont
ExxonMobil Chemical
INEOS AG
Lucite
LyondellBasell
Nippon Steel & Sumitomo Metal Corporation
POSCO
Shell Chemicals
Sumitomo Chemical

HISTORICAL FINANCIALS

Company Type: Public

Income Statement

FYE: December 31

	REVENUE ($ mil.)	NET INCOME ($ mil.)	NET PROFIT MARGIN	EMPLOYEES
12/15	39,444	4,999	12.7%	40,000
12/14	50,364	6,221	12.4%	40,000
12/13	50,400	6,739	13.4%	40,000
12/12	50,400	6,607	13.1%	40,000
12/11	50,639	7,797	15.4%	33,000
Annual Growth	(6.1%)	(10.5%)	—	4.9%

2015 Year-End Financials

Debt ratio: 5.8%
Return on equity: 11.6%
Cash ($ mil.): 10,294
Current ratio: 2.75
Long-term debt ($ mil.): 15,789

No. of shares (mil.): —
Dividends
Yield: —
Payout: —
Market value ($ mil.): —

Sberbank Russia

Whether you do your saving in Siberia or your asset management in Moscow the Savings Bank of the Russian Federation or Sberbank has a branch for you. With a history going back some 170 years Sberbank is one of the largest banking institutions in Russia serving about 70% of nation's population. It has some 17000 branches throughout the country (crossing 11 time zones) offering banking services ranging from savings to private and investment banking and a complete range of lending and credit services to more than 1 million corporate and 135 million retail customers. The Central Bank of the Russian Federation also known as The Bank of Russia controls Sberbank with a 50% ownership stake.

OperationsIn addition to its main retail banking services Sberbank also boasts a trade finance and an investment banking business. It also provides health life third-party liability and other insurance products for both retail and corporate clients. Its insurance business serves more than 8.5 million individuals and 192000 corporate clients. Sberbank makes about three-fourths of its revenues from loan interest. The company generated 46% of its total revenue from interest on loans to corporate customers in 2014 while another 28% of revenue came from interest on loans to individuals. About 16% of its total revenue came from fee and commission income.

Geographic Reach

While 80% of its assets are in Russia Sberbank also has foreign subsidiary banks in 22 countries including the UK Central and Eastern Europe Turkey and others. Its DenizBank AS subsidiary has branches in Austria Russia Northern Cyprus-Germany and Bahrain. Sberbank Europe AG Austria (SBE) and its subsidiary banks serve the Czech Republic Slovakia Hungary Croatia Slovenia Bosnia Herzegovina and Ukraine.

Sales and Marketing

Sberbank serves individuals institutions and medium to large-sized businesses and corporations.

Financial Performance

Note: Growth rates may differ after conversion to US dollars.Sberbank's revenues and profits have been on the uptrend in recent years thanks to continued growth in its corporate and retail loan businesses. The bank's revenue jumped by 26% to R$2.25 trillion ($39.6 billion) in 2014 mostly as its

corporate loan and retail loan businesses grew by 40% and nearly 30% respectively. The group's net fee and commission income also rose by nearly 28% as the bank received more income from cash and settlement transactions with individuals and legal entities and as its investment banking and financial market businesses grew slightly during the year. (Note: In terms of US$ revenue fell sharply due to the decline in the Ruble.) Despite revenue growth in 2014 Sberbank's net income dropped 20% to R$290.3 billion ($5.1 billion) as the cost of funding rose sharply in December (interest expenses increased by 33% for the year) and as loan provision charges particularly with foreign exchange loans grew with the reduced valued of the Ruble and the overall quality deterioration of the bank's loan portfolio amidst political tensions in the Ukraine and Russia. Sberbank's operating cash nearly doubled to R$830 billion ($14.6 billion) despite lower earnings in 2014 mostly as the bank borrowed more cash from other banks.

Strategy

Sberbank continued to dominate the Russian deposit and loan market in 2015. Beyond reporting that a whopping 70% of the population of Russia used its services during the year the bank boasted a 53% market share of the mortgage loan market and kept its firm grip on more than half of the country's deposits. As part of its "Strategy 2018" goal to diversify and expand its revenue streams the bank plans to grow in the insurance and pension markets in future years. To this end in 2014 Sberbank launched its Sberbank Insurance and Sberbank Insurance Broker subsidiaries to start getting a foothold in the insurance business.

To grow its existing business with customers Sberbank regularly releases new banking products many of which are tied to government programs as part of a "one-stop-shop" for government and banking services. During 2014 it launched a slew of new products including: government subsidy programs like consumer loans for military personnel and government-supported education loans; its PRO100 bankcards for personal or payroll card use in the Russian Payment system; and a popular Cash Management service (which grew its user base by 60% during the year) that allowed customers to receive cash flow data between their accounts at different commercial banks.Sberbank has also been moving toward digital banking channels that are quickly taking the industry by storm allowing the bank to slow expensive branch-expansion plans and cut operating costs significantly while giving customers faster access to banking services. As of 2015 Sberbank had 90000 self-service machines as well as 72.2 million subscribers to its Mobile Banking SMS-services with more than 20 million active users.

Mergers and Acquisitions

In early 2012 to build its investment banking practice the company bought Moscow-based Troika Dialog from Standard Bank and Troika's management for some $1.25 billion.

Ownership

The Central Bank of the Russian Federation (The Bank of Russia) is the founder and principal shareholder of Sberbank commanding a 50% stake plus one voting share of the Russian bank.

EXECUTIVES

Deputy Chairman, Sergey Gorkov
Deputy Chairman, Stanislav K. Kuznetsov
Deputy Chairman, Alexander Torbakhov, age 44
Deputy Chairman, Bella Zlatkis
Deputy Chairman, Alexander Morozov
First Deputy Chairman, Lev Khasis, age 50

Chairman of the Board and Chief Executive Officer of Sberbank of Russia, Herman Gref, age 52
First Deputy Chairman, Maxim Poletaev
Deputy Chairman, Andrey Donskih
Deputy Chairman, Vadim Kulik
Vice President Director of the Financial Department, Nikolay Tsekhomskiy
Auditors: CJSC Ernst & Young Vneshaudit

LOCATIONS

HQ: Sberbank Russia
19 Vavilova St., Moscow 117997
Phone: (7) 495 500 55 50   **Fax:** (7) 495 957 5731
Web: www.sberbank.ru

PRODUCTS/OPERATIONS

2014 Sales

	% of total
Interest	
Loans	74
Securities	7
Due from other banks	1
Noninterest	
Fee and commission income	16
Net gain on trading in forieng currency	1
Other	1
Total	**100**

Selected Subsidiary

DenizBank A.S.
Sberbank Europe AG
Sberbank Kazakhstan
BPS-Sberbank (Belarus)
Sberbank Ukraine

Selected Group companies

Auction House of the Russian Federation OJSC
Auction LLC
Sberbank Asset Management CJSC
Sberbank Ast CJSC
Sberbank Capital LLC
Sberbank CIB
Sberbank Insurance Company LLC
Sberbank Leasing CJSC
Sberbank Private Pension Fund
Status Registrar Society CJSC
Strategy Partners Group CJSC
United Credit Bureau CJSC

COMPETITORS

Alfa Group
Deutsche Bank (Moscow)
MDM Bank
Sistema
VTB

HISTORICAL FINANCIALS

Company Type: Public

Income Statement

FYE: December 31

	REVENUE ($ mil.)	NET INCOME ($ mil.)	NET PROFIT MARGIN	EMPLOYEES
12/15	37,608	3,023	8.0%	330,700
12/14	36,928	4,964	13.4%	0
12/13	53,177	11,069	20.8%	0
12/12	45,370	11,458	25.3%	286,019
12/11	31,876	9,795	30.7%	266,187
Annual Growth	4.2%	(25.5%)	—	5.6%

2015 Year-End Financials

Debt ratio: —
Return on equity: 10.1%
Cash ($ mil.): 31,601
Current ratio: —
Long-term debt ($ mil.): —

No. of shares (mil.): —
Dividends
Yield: 0.5%
Payout: 17.2%
Market value ($ mil.): —

	STOCK PRICE ($) FY Close	P/E High/Low		Earnings	PER SHARE ($) Dividends	Book Value
12/15	5.79	1	0	0.14	0.03	1.49
12/14	3.87	1	0	0.23	0.61	1.59
12/13	12.57	1	1	0.51	0.24	2.64
12/12	12.56	1	1	0.53	0.19	2.35
12/11	9.94	1	1	0.45	0.00	1.82
Annual Growth	(12.6%)	—	—	(25.4%)	—	(4.9%)

Schlumberger Ltd.

Measuring and controlling devices nec n

EXECUTIVES

President Directeur General, Pascal PANETTA
Auditors: PricewaterhouseCoopers LLP

LOCATIONS

HQ: Schlumberger Ltd.
42 Rue Saint-Dominique, Paris 75007
Phone: 713 513-2000
Web: www.slb.com

HISTORICAL FINANCIALS

Company Type: Public

Income Statement

FYE: December 31

	REVENUE ($ mil.)	NET INCOME ($ mil.)	NET PROFIT MARGIN	EMPLOYEES
12/16	28,010	(1,687)	—	100,000
12/15	35,711	2,072	5.8%	95,000
12/14	48,871	5,438	11.1%	120,000
12/13	46,459	6,732	14.5%	123,000
12/12	42,321	5,490	13.0%	118,000
Annual Growth	(9.8%)	—		(4.1%)

2016 Year-End Financials

Debt ratio: 25.1%
Return on equity: (-4.3%)
Cash ($ mil.): 9,257
Current ratio: 1.59
Long-term debt ($ mil.): 16,463
No. of shares (mil.): 1,391
Dividends
Yield: 0.0%
Payout: —
Market value ($ mil.): 116,814

	STOCK PRICE ($) FY Close	P/E High/Low		Earnings	PER SHARE ($) Dividends	Book Value
12/16	83.95	—	—	(1.24)	2.00	29.52
12/15	69.75	58	41	1.63	2.00	28.36
12/14	85.41	28	19	4.16	1.60	29.68
12/13	90.11	19	14	5.05	1.25	30.19
12/12	69.30	19	14	4.10	1.10	26.16
Annual Growth	4.9%	—	—	—	16.1%	3.1%

Schneider Electric SE

If you're hungry for power this company can help. Schneider Electric is a leading global manufacturer of equipment for electrical power distribution and for industrial control and automation. The company helps power generators distribute electricity; designs automation systems for the automo-bile and water treatment industries; builds electric networks and utility management systems for energy water treatment oil and gas and marine applications; and manages electric power in residential industrial and commercial buildings. It sells its products to the construction electric power industrial and infrastructure markets.

Geographic ReachSchneider has operations in over 100 countries. The Asia Pacific contributes about 28% of net sales. Other major markets include Western Europe (27%) and North America (25%). The remaining stems from the rest of the world.

Operations

Schneider operates through four operating segments: Buildings and Partner (43% of net sales) Industry (22%) Infrastructure (21%) and Information Technology (IT; 14%).

Sales and Marketing

Distributors account for approximately 42% of its total revenues through an extensive network in 190 countries all over the world. Schneider Electric serves 113 global customers including Apple BHP Billiton EDF ExxonMobil Nestle and Veolia Environment.

Financial Performance

Schneider's revenues jumped 7% and its profits increased 45% from 2013 to 2014 due to increased sales from its Buildings and Partner and Industry segments. These segments experienced solid OEM demand growth from all regions especially Western Europe. (Note: the company's 2013 annual statement was restated due to discontinued operations.)

Mergers and Acquisitions

Schneider has been enhancing its product portfolio through the use of acquisitions. In mid-2015 the company announced it was combining its software operations with British engineering IT firm Aveva in a reverse takeover. The deal will see Aveva acquire Schneider's software division on a debt-free cash-free basis and Schneider will then pay Aveva £550m for new Aveva shares which will result in it owning 54% of the enlarged company. Aveva provides design software for the industrial plant power and shipping industries.

HISTORY

Company Background

Schneider Electric's predecessor was founded in 1782 to make industrial equipment. After the upheavals of the French Revolution and the Napoleonic Wars the company came under the control of brothers Adolphe and Eugene Schneider in 1836. Within two years they had built the first French locomotive (the country's first rail line opened in 1832).

Schneider became one of France's most important heavy industry companies branching into a variety of machinery and steel operations. However the country's industrial development continued to trail that of Britain and Germany due to recurrent political strife including the revolution of 1848 and the Franco-Prussian War. France also possessed fewer coal and iron deposits.

During WWI Schneider was a key part of France's war effort. It entered the electrical contracting business in 1929 and fought off nationalization attempts in the mid-1930s. The blitzkrieg of 1939 brought much of France under Nazi occupation and the Schneider factories that were not destroyed were commandeered by the Germans.

The company rebuilt after the war aided by the French government. It was restructured as a holding company and its operating units were split into three subsidiaries: civil and electrical engineering industrial manufacturing and construction. Charles Schneider the last family member to lead the company died in 1950.

In 1963 Schneider concluded an alliance with the Empain Group of Belgium and by 1969 three years after Schneider went public the two companies merged to become Empain-Schneider. It was a period when the company made numerous noncore acquisitions entering such fields as ski equipment fashion publishing and travel.

Schneider began reorganizing in 1980. The effort entered its final phase in 1993 with a major recapitalization that saw the merger of its former parent company Societe Parisienne d'Entreprises et de Participations with Schneider SA and the issue of new stock to existing stockholders.

EXECUTIVES

President and CEO North America Operations and Group Supply Chain Officer, Annette K. Clayton, age 53
Chairman and CEO, Jean-Pascal Tricoire, age 53
EVP Global Marketing and Chief Marketing Officer, Chris Leong
EVP Technology and CTO, Prith Banerjee, age 55
EVP Buildings and Partner, Philippe Delorme, age 45
EVP Europe Operations, Leonid Mukhamedov
EVP Information Systems and CIO, Herve Coureil, age 46
EVP China Operations, Zhu Hai
EVP France Operations and President Schneider Electric France, Luc Remont
EVP Infrastructure, Frederic Abbal
EVP Global Human Resources, Olivier Blum
EVP Industry, Peter Herweck
President Middle East and Africa, Caspar Herzberg
EVP Strategy, Emmanuel Lagarrigue
EVP Global Solutions, Daniel Do mo
Auditors: ERNST & YOUNG et Autres

LOCATIONS

HQ: Schneider Electric SE
35, rue Joseph Monier, CS 30323, Rueil-Malmaison, Cedex 92506
Phone: (33) 1 41 29 70 00   **Fax:** (33) 1 41 29 71 00
Web: www.schneider-electric.com

2014 Sales

	% of total
Asia/Pacific	28
Western Europe	27
North America	25
Rest of the world	20
Total	**100**

PRODUCTS/OPERATIONS

2014 Sales

	% of total
Buildings & Partner	43
Industry	22
Infrastructure	21
IT	14
Total	**100**

Selected Products

Advanced human-machine interface terminals
Camera sensors
Centralized building management systems
Circuit breakers
Customized sensors
Disconnectors
Electric vehicle charging infrastructure
Electrical panels
Indicator lights
InRow Cooling Systems
Installation & control systems
Medium voltage cells
Network power control
Optimum temperature control
Power supply
Programmable regulators
Renewable energies integration

Security monitoring equipment
Server cabinets
Software for the integrated management of mission critical infrastructure
Supervision Control & Data Acquisition (SCADA) management systems
Transformers
Uninterruptable power supply
  Monophase
  Three-phase

COMPETITORS

ABB	Legrand
ALSTOM	Leonardo
Alcatel-Lucent	Measurement
Bechtel	Specialties
Beghelli	Mitsubishi Electric
Bharat Heavy	Nissin Electric
Electricals	Rockwell Automation
Checkpoint Systems	Roper Technologies
Danaher	Sentry Technology
EMCOR	Siemens AG
Electricite de France	Technology Research
Emerson Electric	Corp.
Endress + Hauser	Transtector
Fluor	Vicon Industries
GE	Woodhead Industries
Itron	Yokogawa Electric
Johnson Controls	

HISTORICAL FINANCIALS

Company Type: Public

Income Statement

FYE: December 31

	REVENUE ($ mil.)	NET INCOME ($ mil.)	NET PROFIT MARGIN	EMPLOYEES
12/15	29,016	1,532	5.3%	181,362
12/14	30,313	2,359	7.8%	185,965
12/13	32,423	2,599	8.0%	152,784
12/12	31,562	2,425	7.7%	152,384
12/11	28,956	2,354	8.1%	140,491
Annual Growth	0.1%	(10.2%)	—	6.6%

2015 Year-End Financials

Debt ratio: 19.5%
Return on equity: 6.9%
Cash ($ mil.): 3,266
Current ratio: 1.36
Long-term debt ($ mil.): 6,682

No. of shares (mil.): 565
Dividends
  Yield: 3.7%
  Payout: —
Market value ($ mil.): 6,415

	STOCK PRICE ($) FY Close	P/E High/Low		PER SHARE ($) Earnings	Dividends	Book Value
12/15	11.35	7	4	2.68	0.43	40.16
12/14	14.41	5	4	4.10	0.50	41.98
12/13	17.55	5	4	4.68	0.49	42.77
12/12	14.79	4	3	4.43	0.43	40.11
12/11	10.51	5	3	4.33	0.00	38.10
Annual Growth	1.9%	—	—	(11.3%)	—	1.3%

Schweizer Verband der Raiffeisenbanken (Switzerland)

EXECUTIVES

President, Johannes R egg

LOCATIONS

HQ: Schweizer Verband der Raiffeisenbanken (Switzerland)
Raiffeisenplatz, St. Gallen CH-9001
Phone: (41) 71 225 88 88   **Fax:** (41) 71 225 88 87
Web: www.raiffeisen.ch

HISTORICAL FINANCIALS

Company Type: Public

Income Statement

FYE: December 31

	ASSETS ($ mil.)	NET INCOME ($ mil.)	INCOME AS % OF ASSETS	EMPLOYEES
12/15	47,115	0	—	1,900
12/14	38,048	0	—	1,892
12/13	36,754	0	—	1,846
12/12	35,217	0	—	1,810
12/11	165,698	0	—	9,770
Annual Growth	(27.0%)	—	—	(33.6%)

SCOR S.E. (France)

This company knows the score in the global reinsurance market. SCOR provides treaty (groups of risks) and facultative (individual risks) reinsurance covering the risks of insurance underwriters around the globe. The company reinsures property/casualty life accident and health insurance lines. Most of SCOR's business comes from Europe and North America and is divided into two distinct business segments: Global Life (including long-term care and disability products) and Global P&C (including treaty corporate and specialty property/casualty lines). It serves customers in some 170 countries through offices that specialize in the needs of a specific industry or market.

Operations

The company's life insurance unit SCOR Global Life accounts for about 53% of revenue while SCOR Global P&C (property and casualty) brings in about 47%. Outside of its reinsurance operations the company has a third smaller business named SCOR Global Investments which provides asset and investment management services to the other operating SCOR facilities.

Geographic Reach

SCOR has about 40 offices in nearly 25 cities throughout in the Americas Europe and Asia. Europe contributed about 42% of revenue with France Germany Spain and Italy leading the charge. North America brings in about 40% and the rest comes from Asia and other countries (Australia and South Africa mainly).

Sales and Marketing

Reinsurance is written either through brokers or directly. SCOR employs both methods but breaks it down differently depending on the operating unit. Global Life is 90% direct and 10% broker while Global P&C is 63% broker and 37% direct.

Financial Performance

In 2013 the company reported a 7% increase in revenue as its Life unit performed well on the strength of an earlier acquisition of life insurance provider Generali US. Net income shot up 31% based on improved revenue gains made on the Generali purchase and increased investment returns. Cash flow however dropped due to cash used for acquisitions and investments.

Strategy

SCOR is focused on growing organically through new products and new markets and growing through acquisitions. It followed a large 2011 purchase with the acquisition of Generali US a life insurance provider. The company has also realigned its business portfolio to prioritize North America Asia and the rest of the world.

Mergers and Acquisitions

In 2013 SCOR purchased Italian insurer Assicurazioni Generali's US unit Generali US to boost its life insurance business. The $750 million price tag included Generali US' Kansas City office and staff; it created the country's largest life reinsurance company.

In 2011 the company acquired Transamerica Reinsurance from Dutch insurance giant AEGON for $912.5 million. The purchase included all of Transamerica Re's mortality risk reinsurance (pure life reinsurance) operations while AEGON retained the annuity guarantee business. The purchase made SCOR a top player in the US life reinsurance market and was folded in with the SCOR Global Life team.

HISTORY

SCOR was founded in 1970 by the French government to compete against reinsurers like Munich Re and Swiss Reinsurance; the government eventually ceded control to a group of French insurers including AXA UAP Re and Groupe des Assurances Nationales. By 1972 SCOR was expanding internationally.

Growth continued throughout the 1970s and '80s. In 1989 the firm acquired Deutsche Continental Rückversicherungs in Germany. A year later the firm listed on the Paris stock exchange.

In the early 1990s SCOR's owners began setting up their own reinsurance operations and selling off their holdings in the company. In 1995 AXA and Assurances Generales de France were the last to sell their stakes. Also that year SCOR consolidated ownership in its subsidiaries and streamlined its Asian operations.

The year 1996 was a big one in the US for SCOR. It acquired the reinsurance business of Allstate and also listed on the New York Stock Exchange. As worldwide property/casualty markets took a downturn in 1996 and 1997 SCOR began expanding its life accident and health reinsurance.

Numerous natural disasters in 1998 and 1999 hobbled SCOR's already slumping property/casualty unit; losses were offset by increased business in other lines. SCOR acquired full control of its Commercial Risk Partners subsidiary in 1999 bolstering its specialty reinsurance business. In 2000 SCOR reorganized its industrial risk business to further offset recent losses. That year the company bought Partner Re's US subsidiary PartnerRe Life and Switzerland-based Veritas property/casualty reinsurance portfolio.

In 2001 SCOR joined Inreon an online reinsurance exchange set up by industry bigwigs Swiss Re and Munich Re. In 2002 it liquidated and sold off subsidiary Commercial Risk Partners to reduce costs. Expanding internationally the company opened offices in Korea and India in 2004 and 2005.

In 2007 SCOR acquired Swiss reinsurer Converium Holding beginning with a buy-up of about a third of the company's shares. The purchase agreement went through several drafts (one resulting in a lawsuit alleging that SCOR had deliberately undervalued Converium) but was eventually accepted by both boards of directors. The acquisition added customers in Austria Germany Switzerland and the UK and boosted SCOR into a spot among the top five global life reinsurers.

Also in 2007 SCOR transformed itself into a Societas Europaea a legal structure that allows it more financial freedom in its European operations. In addition the company voluntarily delisted from the New York Stock Exchange.

EXECUTIVES

Deputy CEO Global P&C SE; CEOSCOR Switzerland, Benjamin Gentsch, age 56
Chairman and CEO, Denis Kessler, age 64, $500,000 total compensation
CEO SCOR Global P&C SE, Victor Peignet, age 59, $203,000 total compensation
CEO SCOR Global Life SE, Paolo De Martin, age 46
CEO SCOR Global Investments SE, Fran $is De Varenne, age 50
CIO, Marc Philippe, age 48
CFO, Mark Kociancic, age 45
Chief Risk Officer, Frieder Kn pling, age 46
Deputy CEO SCOR Global Life SE, Simon Pearson, age 50
Managing Director and CFO Americas Hub, Paul Christoff, age 45
Managing Director Asia-Pacific Hub, Eric Pooi, age 48
Auditors: Mazars

LOCATIONS

HQ: SCOR S.E. (France)
5 avenue Kleber, Paris 75016
Phone: (33) 1 58 44 70 00   **Fax:** (33) 1 58 44 85 00
Web: www.scor.com

2013 Gross Written Premiums

	% of total
Europe	42
Americas	39
Asia-Pacific & other regions	19
Total	**100**

PRODUCTS/OPERATIONS

2013 Premiums

	% of total
Global P&C	53
Global Life	47
Total	**100**

COMPETITORS

AXIS Capital Holdings	Reinsurance Group of
Endurance Specialty	America
Everest Re	RenaissanceRe
General Re	Scottish Re Group
Hannover Re	Swiss Re
Munich Re America	Transatlantic Holdings
Munich Re Group	XL Group plc
PartnerRe	

HISTORICAL FINANCIALS

Company Type: Public

Income Statement
FYE: December 31

	ASSETS ($ mil.)	NET INCOME ($ mil.)	INCOME AS % OF ASSETS	EMPLOYEES
12/15	45,316	699	1.5%	2,706
12/14	45,175	622	1.4%	2,555
12/13	47,030	755	1.6%	2,450
12/12	42,955	550	1.3%	2,284
12/11	40,509	426	1.1%	2,184
Annual Growth	**2.8%**	**13.1%**	**—**	**5.5%**

2015 Year-End Financials

Return on assets: 1.6%	Dividends
Return on equity: 10.6%	Yield: 4.1%
Long-term debt ($ mil.): —	Payout: 4.1%
No. of shares (mil.): 185	Market value ($ mil.): 706
Sales ($ mil): 15,229	

	STOCK PRICE ($) FY Close	P/E High/Low		Earnings	PER SHARE ($) Dividends	Book Value
12/15	3.80	1	1	3.68	0.16	37.07
12/14	2.98	1	1	3.31	0.18	37.19
12/13	3.62	1	1	4.01	0.16	36.68
12/12	2.76	2	1	2.95	0.14	34.51
12/11	2.23	2	1	2.29	0.14	30.82
Annual Growth	**14.2%**	**—**	**—**	**12.6%**	**2.4%**	**4.7%**

Sekisui House, Ltd. (Japan)

Sekisui House could have written the book on Zen and the art of house building. One of Japan's leading homebuilders Sekisui House designs prefabricates and builds steel wooden and concrete houses and condominiums. It has built 2.2 billion homes. It is also involved in selling land detached houses and condominiums. Its real estate operations include leasing and managing houses lowrise apartments and commercial and retail buildings. Other operations include contract remodeling and landscaping. The company is also focusing on green building and sustainability in its new line of homes and adds such features as fuel cells to its houses. Sekisui Chemical owns 10% of the company which dates back to 1929.

EXECUTIVES

President CEO and Director, Isami Wada
EVP and CFO, Shiro Inagaki
Executive Officer, Toshinori Abe
EVP and Director, Tetsuo Iku
Auditors: Ernst & Young ShinNihon LLC

LOCATIONS

HQ: Sekisui House, Ltd. (Japan)
1-1-88 Oyodonaka, Kita-ku, Osaka 531-0076
Phone: (81) 6 6440 3111   **Fax:** (81) 6 6440 3369
Web: www.sekisuihouse.co.jp

PRODUCTS/OPERATIONS

Selected Subsidiaries and Affiliates
Sekisui House Umeda Operation Co. Ltd.
Sekiwa Real Estate Chubu Ltd.
Sekiwa Real Estate Chugoku Ltd.

Sekiwa Real Estate Kansai Ltd.
Sekiwa Real Estate Kyushu Ltd.
Sekiwa Real Estate Sapporo Ltd.
Sekiwa Real Estate Tohoku Ltd.
SGM Operation Co. Ltd

COMPETITORS

Daikyo	Shimizu
Daiwa House Industry	Sumitomo Forestry
Minaean	Sumitomo Realty
Mitsubishi Estate	Taisei
Mitsui Fudosan	

HISTORICAL FINANCIALS

Company Type: Public

Income Statement
FYE: January 31

	REVENUE ($ mil.)	NET INCOME ($ mil.)	NET PROFIT MARGIN	EMPLOYEES
01/16	15,371	697	4.5%	23,089
01/15	16,245	766	4.7%	22,913
01/14	17,657	780	4.4%	22,379
01/13	17,723	510	2.9%	21,476
01/12	20,036	379	1.9%	21,275
Annual Growth	**(6.4%)**	**16.4%**	**—**	**2.1%**

2016 Year-End Financials

Debt ratio: 0.1%	No. of shares (mil.): 700
Return on equity: 7.9%	Dividends
Cash ($ mil.): 1,614	Yield: —
Current ratio: 1.72	Payout: —
Long-term debt ($ mil.): 974	Market value ($ mil.): 11,021

	STOCK PRICE ($) FY Close	P/E High/Low		Earnings	PER SHARE ($) Dividends	Book Value
01/16	15.73	—	—	0.99	0.00	12.61
01/15	12.85	—	—	1.06	0.00	13.11
01/14	13.80	—	—	1.08	0.36	13.45
01/13	10.92	—	—	0.71	0.28	13.32
01/12	9.40	—	—	0.54	0.23	14.63
Annual Growth	**13.7%**	**—**	**—**	**16.4%**	**—**	**(3.7%)**

Seven & i Holdings Co. Ltd.

Japan's biggest retail conglomerate Seven & i Holdings caters to six of the so-called seven deadly sins (saving wrath for its competition). The "seven" of the company's title reflects the seven areas of business that it is involved with: convenience stores general merchandise and department stores restaurants supermarkets banks and IT services. The "holding" part of the firm's name consists of its subsidiaries: Seven-Eleven Japan (parent of 7-Eleven in the US) Ito-Yokado Sogo & Seibu Co. Seven & i Food Systems Seven Bank and York-Benimaru. Created in 2005 after stock-transfer agreements absorbing its subsidiaries into the company took effect Seven & i operates some 41900 stores worldwide.

After two years of decline the holding company's fiscal 2011 (ends February) total sales inched up a bit while net income more than doubled vs. the previous year. Seven & i's convenience stores posted a sales gain while sales at its superstores and department stores were flat. Already the world's #1 convenience store operator Seven & i's worldwide network of c-stores topped 40000 in fiscal 2011. (Convenience stores account for about 40% of the group's total worldwide sales.) By March 2014 the company is planning to open a record 1500 c-stores (for a net gain of more than 900) as it works to cater to "housewives and the elderly."

While Seven & i rings up more than two-thirds of its total sales at home the holding company oversees about 100 operating companies in 15 other countries in Asia North America and Europe. With the Japanese economy in a prolonged slump and reeling from the effects of the massive earthquake in March 2011 it's looking beyond its borders for growth opportunities. China is an important emerging market for Seven & i Holdings: It currently operates more than 4800 stores and restaurants in Taiwan and supermarkets stores and restaurants in Beijing Chengdu and Shanghai. Indeed in early 2009 Seven & i Food Systems formed a joint venture company with a large Chinese corporation to establish the family restaurant chain "AllDay's" there.

Seeking to further expand its retail empire the company and Ain Pharmaciez formed Seven Health Care which plans to open drugstores inside superstores and shopping malls operated by Seven & i Holdings and to develop generic drugs. Seven Health Care is jointly owned by Seven & i Holdings (10%) and its subsidiaries Ito-Yokado (50%) and Seven-Eleven Japan (10%) as well as Ain Pharmaciez (30%). More recently the company also boosted its entertainment holdings by doubling its stake in Tower Records Japan in 2011 to about 45%. The move made Seven & i the largest shareholder in the music retail chain (ahead of NTT DoCoMo with 42%).

While the global appetite for convenience store fare is growing the hunger for department store merchandise is not. As the Japanese department store industry struggles with weak personal consumption the company rearranged its department store holdings when it merged holding company Millennium Retailing with Sogo and Seibu department stores to form Sogo & Seibu Co. in August 2009. The merger was effected to capitalize on the well-known Sogo and Seibu names reduce costs and to foster collaboration with Seven & i.

The "i" of Seven & i Holdings stands for "innovation" as well as for the similar-sounding Japanese word for "love."

EXECUTIVES

President, Ryuichi Isaka
Chairman Seven Bank, Takashi Anzai
President and COO York-Benimaru, Zenko Ohtaka
Managing Executive Officer and Chief Administrative Officer, Katsuhiro Goto
President and COO Ito-Yokado, Atsushi Kamei
Executive Officer and CFO, Kunio Takahashi
President Sogo & Seibu, Ryu Matsumoto
President Seven & i Food Systems, Tsuneo Okubo
Auditors: KPMG AZSA LLC

LOCATIONS

HQ: Seven & i Holdings Co. Ltd.
8-8 Niban-cho, Chiyoda-ku, Tokyo 102-8452
Phone: (81) 3 6238 3000
Web: www.7andi.com

2016 Sales

	% of total
Japan	67
North America	31
Other regions	2
Total	**100**

PRODUCTS/OPERATIONS

2016 Sales

	% of total
Convenience stores	44
Superstores	34
Department stores	14
Financial services	3
Mail order services	3
Food services	1
Others	1
Total	**100**

Selected Subsidiaries

Convenience stores
  7-Eleven Inc.
  Seven-Eleven (Beijing) Co. (65%)
  Seven-Eleven China Co.
  Seven-Eleven (Hawaii) Inc.
  Seven-Eleven Japan Co.
Superstores
  Chengdu Ito-Yokado (74%)
  Hua Tang Yokado (76%)
  Ito-Yokado
  York Mart
  York-Benimaru
Department stores
  Gottsuo Bin Co.
  The Loft Co. (71%)
  Shell Garden Co.
  Sogo & Seibu Co.
Financial services
  K.K. York Insurance
  Seven & i Financial Center
  Seven Bank (49%)
  Seven Card Service (96%)
Food services
  Seven & i Food Systems
  Seven & i Restaurant (Beijing) Co. (75%)

COMPETITORS

A.S. Watson	Isetan Mitsukoshi
AEON	J. Front
Asahi Kasei	Kirin Holdings Company
Carrefour	Kokubu
Couche-Tard	LAWSON
Daiei	McDonald's
Dairy Farm International	Nisshin Seifun Group
	Seiyu
FamilyMart UNY	Takashimaya
Fast Retailing	Yamazaki Baking

HISTORICAL FINANCIALS
Company Type: Public

Income Statement
FYE: February 29

	REVENUE ($ mil.)	NET INCOME ($ mil.)	NET PROFIT MARGIN	EMPLOYEES
02/16	53,519	1,424	2.7%	145,460
02/15	50,610	1,449	2.9%	148,307
02/14	55,282	1,724	3.1%	55,364
02/13	54,169	1,498	2.8%	55,011
02/12	59,516	1,614	2.7%	51,888
Annual Growth	**(2.6%)**	**(3.1%)**	**—**	**29.4%**

2016 Year-End Financials

Debt ratio: 0.1%
Return on equity: 6.8%
Cash ($ mil.): 9,737
Current ratio: 1.20
Long-term debt ($ mil.): 6,735
No. of shares (mil.): 884
Dividends
  Yield: 1.5%
  Payout: 20.6%
Market value ($ mil.): 17,630

	STOCK PRICE ($) FY Close	P/E High/Low		PER SHARE ($) Earnings	Dividends	Book Value
02/16	19.94	0	0	1.61	0.30	23.78
02/15	19.03	0	0	1.64	0.30	21.82
02/14	74.77	—	—	1.95	1.31	24.68
02/13	58.40	—	—	1.69	1.59	24.50
02/12	55.21	—	—	1.83	1.47	26.19
Annual Growth	**(22.5%)**	**—**	**—**	**(3.1%)**	**(32.5%)**	**(2.4%)**

Shanghai Construction Group Co., Ltd.

Auditors: PricewaterhouseCoopers Zhong Tian CPAs Limited Company

LOCATIONS

HQ: Shanghai Construction Group Co., Ltd.
No. 666, Dongdaming Road, Shanghai 200080
Phone: (86) 21 35100838   **Fax:** (86) 21 55886222
Web: www.shconstruction.cn

HISTORICAL FINANCIALS
Company Type: Public

Income Statement
FYE: December 31

	REVENUE ($ mil.)	NET INCOME ($ mil.)	NET PROFIT MARGIN	EMPLOYEES
12/15	19,313	288	1.5%	0
12/14	18,313	285	1.6%	0
12/13	16,854	267	1.6%	0
12/12	14,942	256	1.7%	0
12/11	13,163	215	1.6%	24,324
Annual Growth	**10.1%**	**7.5%**	**—**	**—**

2015 Year-End Financials

Debt ratio: 2.9%
Return on equity: 9.3%
Cash ($ mil.): 5,977
Current ratio: 1.14
Long-term debt ($ mil.): 2,868
No. of shares (mil.): —
Dividends
  Yield: —
  Payout: —
Market value ($ mil.): —

Shanghai Jinfeng Investment Co Ltd

Auditors: Ernst & Young Hua Ming Certified Public Accountants

LOCATIONS

HQ: Shanghai Jinfeng Investment Co Ltd
29th Floor, Tianan Center, No. 338, Nanjing West Road, Shanghai 200003
Phone: (86) 21 63592020   **Fax:** (86) 21 63586115
Web: www.ehousee.com

HISTORICAL FINANCIALS
Company Type: Public

Income Statement
FYE: December 31

	REVENUE ($ mil.)	NET INCOME ($ mil.)	NET PROFIT MARGIN	EMPLOYEES
12/15	31,955	1,060	3.3%	0
12/14	17	(58)	—	0
12/13	147	11	7.8%	0
12/12	70	16	23.8%	0
12/11	145	32	22.0%	0
Annual Growth	**284.7%**	**139.6%**	**—**	**—**

2015 Year-End Financials

Debt ratio: 6.1%
Return on equity: 25.0%
Cash ($ mil.): 6,745
Current ratio: 1.54
Long-term debt ($ mil.): 26,774

No. of shares (mil.): —
Dividends
  Yield: —
  Payout: —
Market value ($ mil.): —

Shanghai Pharmaceuticals Holding Co Ltd

Auditors: PricewaterhouseCoopers Zhong Tian LLP

LOCATIONS

HQ: Shanghai Pharmaceuticals Holding Co Ltd
Shanghai Pharmaceutical Building, No. 200, Taicang Road, Shanghai 200020
Phone: (86) 21 63730908   **Fax:** (86) 21 63289333
Web: www.sphchina.com

HISTORICAL FINANCIALS

Company Type: Public

Income Statement

FYE: December 31

	REVENUE ($ mil.)	NET INCOME ($ mil.)	NET PROFIT MARGIN	EMPLOYEES
12/15	16,246	442	2.7%	41,173
12/14	14,887	417	2.8%	39,891
12/13	12,921	370	2.9%	39,646
12/12	10,920	329	3.0%	38,355
12/11	8,722	324	3.7%	37,249
Annual Growth	**16.8%**	**8.1%**	**—**	**2.5%**

2015 Year-End Financials

Debt ratio: 2.1%
Return on equity: 9.9%
Cash ($ mil.): 1,853
Current ratio: 1.41
Long-term debt ($ mil.): 14

No. of shares (mil.): —
Dividends
  Yield: —
  Payout: 27.5%
Market value ($ mil.): —

Sharp Corp (Japan)

Best known for its consumer electronics Sharp is a well-known maker of electronic components and computer hardware and peripherals. The company's flagship products are LCDs which are used in everything from airplane cockpits to PCs to pinball machines. The company also produces flash memory laser diodes and optical sensors. Sharp also makes printers and cell phones; consumer audio and video products such as Blu-ray disc players and LCD TVs; and a variety of appliances such as air purifiers and steam ovens. The 100-year-old company is also one of the world's largest manufacturers of photovoltaic solar cells.

Geographic Reach

Sharp gets more than half of sales from customers located outside of Japan. The company has established regional headquarters in the Americas China and in Europe as it looks to expand internationally.

Financial Performance

Sharp's financial performance dulled in 2015 (ended March) with revenues falling 18% resulting in a net loss for the year. The loss was the third on the past four years. The company reported lower sales in its major product categories including TVs mobile phones and air conditioners. Sales in the company's business solutions segment rose about 7% based on sales of multi-purpose printers overseas. Cash flow from operations also fell in 2015.

Strategy

In mid-2015 Sharp sold its TV business in the US and other markets in the Americas to the Hisense Group based in China. The sale which includes a manufacturing plant in Mexico was for $27 million. The deal is one of several steps Sharp has taken to restructure and refocus its business as it has lost ground to rivals. Sharp has taken outside investment in the past year and is seeking more. The company is cutting about 10% of its work force —about 5000 jobs.

Sharp has taken steps to expand its business in the Asia-Pacific Region. It opened a manufacturing plant in Indonesia and expanded and bolstered sales networks in Myanmar and Sri Lanka. The company also is seeking to expand in emerging markets in the Middle East and Africa.

The company is looking to new technology to revive its display sales. It has developed a manufacturing process that enables it to make displays of various shapes —not just rectangles.

HISTORY

Early History

Tokuji Hayakawa got started in manufacturing in 1912 when he established Hayakawa Electric Industry to make a type of belt buckle he had designed. Three years later he invented the first mechanical pencil named the Ever-Sharp which was a commercial success. After an earthquake leveled much of Tokyo in 1923 including Hayakawa's business he moved to Osaka and sold the rights to his pencil to finance a new factory. He introduced Japan's first crystal radio sets in 1925 and four years later debuted a vacuum tube radio.

Following WWII Hayakawa Electric developed an experimental TV which it began mass-producing in 1953. The company was ready with color TVs when Japan initiated color broadcasts in 1960. Hayakawa Electric grew tremendously during the 1960s introducing microwave ovens (1962) solar cells (1963) the first electronic all-transistor-diode calculator (1964) and the first gallium arsenide LED (1969). The firm opened a US office in 1962.

In 1970 the company began to make its own semiconductor devices and changed its name to Sharp Corporation a nod to the name of its first product. It began mass production of LCDs in 1973. Sharp later introduced the first electronic calculator with an LCD (1973) solar-powered calculators (1976) and a credit card-sized calculator (1979).

EXECUTIVES

Senior Executive Managing Officer and President of Consumer Electronics Company, Yoshisuke Hasegawa, age 61
EVP and Head of Accounting and Finance Group, Katsuaki Nomura
Executive Managing Officer and President of Display Device Company, Taimi Oketani
EVP Consumer Electronics Company Head of Global Sale and Marketing and Chairman Sharp Electronics (Malaysia) Sdn. Bhd., Akira Atarashi
Executive Managing Officer and President of Business Solutions Company and Chairman Sharp Business Solutions Corporation, Kazushi Mukai
Chairman and President Sharp Electronics Corporation, Toshiyuki Osawa
President, Tai Jeng-wu
Executive Managing Officer and President of Electronic Components and Devices Company, Kazuhiro Moritani
CEO Greater China Business Chairman and President Sharp (China) Investment Co.Ltd. and Chairman Sharp Electronics Sales (China) Co.Ltd., Akihiko Imaya
President Energy Solutions Company, Hiroshi Sasaoka
Chairman, Shigeaki Mizushima, age 61
Auditors: KPMG AZSA LLC

LOCATIONS

HQ: Sharp Corp (Japan)
22-22 Nagaike-cho, Abeno-ku, Osaka 545-8522
Phone: (81) 6 6621 1221
Web: www.sharp.co.jp

PRODUCTS/OPERATIONS

2015 Sales

	% of total
Products business	54
Device business	46
Total	**100**

Selected Products

Consumer/information products
  Audiovisual and communication equipment
  Audio amplifiers
  Blu-ray disc players
  Digital cameras
  High-definition televisions
  Liquid crystal display DVD televisions
  Liquid crystal display televisions
  Liquid crystal display video projectors
  Mobile phones
  Video cameras
  Information equipment
  Calculators
  Digital copiers
  Fax machines
  Mobile business tools
  Personal computers
  Printers
  Home appliances
  Air cleaning systems
  Superheated steam ovens
Electronic components
  Flash memory
  Integrated circuits
  Laser diodes and other optoelectronic devices
  Radio-frequency components
  Satellite broadcasting components
  Solar cells and other photovoltaic devices

COMPETITORS

AU Optronics	NEC
Broadcom	Oki Electric
CASIO COMPUTER	Panasonic Corp
Canon	Philips Electronics
Electrolux	Pioneer Corporation
Epson	Ricoh Company
Ericsson	SANYO
First Solar	Samsung Electronics
Fujitsu	SolarWorld
HP	Sony
Hanwha Q Cells	SunPower
Hisense	Suntech Power
Hitachi	TCL
IBM	TPV Technology
Konica Minolta	Tatung
Kyocera	Toshiba
LG Electronics	Xerox
Lexmark	Yingli
Mitsubishi Electric	

HISTORICAL FINANCIALS
Company Type: Public

Income Statement
FYE: March 31

	REVENUE ($ mil.)	NET INCOME ($ mil.)	NET PROFIT MARGIN	EMPLOYEES
03/16	21,920	(2,279)	—	43,511
03/15	23,222	(1,853)	—	49,096
03/14	28,358	111	0.4%	50,253
03/13	26,342	(5,795)	—	50,647
03/12	29,938	(4,584)	—	56,756
Annual Growth	(7.5%)	—	—	(6.4%)

2016 Year-End Financials
Debt ratio: 0.4%
Return on equity: ***.***.*%
Cash ($ mil.): 2,452
Current ratio: 0.70
Long-term debt ($ mil.): 714

No. of shares (mil.): 1,690
Dividends
  Yield: —
  Payout: —
Market value ($ mil.): 1,944

	STOCK PRICE ($) FY Close	P/E High/Low	Earnings	Dividends	Book Value
03/16	1.15	— —	(1.38)	0.00	(0.23)
03/15	1.92	— —	(1.10)	0.00	0.15
03/14	3.01	— —	0.08	0.00	1.19
03/13	2.78	— —	(5.21)	0.00	1.23
03/12	7.38	— —	(4.17)	0.00	7.15
Annual Growth	(37.2%)	—	—	—	—

Shiga Bank, Ltd.

Shiga Bank established in 1933 has grown to become the largest bank in the Shiga prefecture. The bank and its 14 subsidiaries provide customers with typical banking products and services credit card leasing and venture capital financing services and accepts negotiable certificates of deposits and installment-deposits fixed-term savings products. Shiga Bank's primary customers are individuals and small and medium-sized businesses. The bank which operates nearly 140 offices and branches in Japan Hong Kong and Thailand (as well as 10 agents) is banking on the region's expanding economy to improve local economies in the Kyoto and Shiga prefectures. Shiga Bank if controlled by Japan Trustee Service Bank.

EXECUTIVES
President, SHOJIRO TAKAHASHI
Chairman, Yutaka Hirono
Auditors: Deloitte Touche Tohmatsu LLC

LOCATIONS
HQ: Shiga Bank, Ltd.
  1-38 Hamamachi, Otsu, Shiga 520-8686
Phone: (81) 77 524 2141
Web: www.shigagin.com

COMPETITORS
Nanto Bank
Oita Bank
Toho Bank

HISTORICAL FINANCIALS
Company Type: Public

Income Statement
FYE: March 31

	ASSETS ($ mil.)	NET INCOME ($ mil.)	INCOME AS % OF ASSETS	EMPLOYEES
03/16	44,751	138	0.3%	3,715
03/15	41,648	113	0.3%	3,714
03/14	46,284	106	0.2%	2,508
03/13	49,547	58	0.1%	2,530
03/12	55,141	100	0.2%	2,602
Annual Growth	(5.1%)	8.3%	—	9.3%

2016 Year-End Financials
Return on assets: 0.3%
Return on equity: 4.5%
Long-term debt ($ mil.): —
No. of shares (mil.): 260
Sales ($ mil): 854

Dividends
  Yield: —
  Payout: —
Market value ($ mil.): —

Shin Kong Financial Holding Co., Ltd.

Commercial banking securities dealing asset management and insurance all find a home beneath Shin Kong's umbrella. Also known as SKFH the holding company offers an array of banking and financial services through subsidiaries Shin Kong Life Insurance (SKL) Shin Kong Investment Trust (SKIT) Taiwan Shin Kong Insurance Brokers (SKIB) and Taiwan Shin Kong Commercial Bank (SKB). The company has expanded its product offerings and market presence with a focus on mainland China for growth opportunities. SKFH was established in 2002.

EXECUTIVES
Chief Information Officer; Group Head - Technology and Operations, Jan Verplancke
Chief Executive - Consumer Banking; Group Executive Director, Steve Bertamini
Chairman of the Board, John Peace
Auditors: Deloitte & Touche

LOCATIONS
HQ: Shin Kong Financial Holding Co., Ltd.
  Level 38, No. 66, Section 1, Chung-Hsiao West Road, Taipei 100
Phone: (886) 2 23895858
Web: www.skfh.com.tw

PRODUCTS/OPERATIONS

2014 Sales

	% of total
Interest income	31
Other income	69
Total	**100**

COMPETITORS
Cathay Financial Holding
Chinatrust Financial
First Financial Holding
Fubon Financial
Hua Nan Financial
SinoPac Holdings
Taiwan Business Bank

HISTORICAL FINANCIALS
Company Type: Public

Income Statement
FYE: December 31

	ASSETS ($ mil.)	NET INCOME ($ mil.)	INCOME AS % OF ASSETS	EMPLOYEES
12/15	90,172	175	0.2%	16,433
12/14	88,358	217	0.2%	20,820
12/13	85,014	334	0.4%	20,279
12/12	79,583	338	0.4%	20,677
12/11	70,479	181	0.3%	20,653
Annual Growth	6.4%	(0.7%)	—	(5.6%)

2015 Year-End Financials
Return on assets: 0.2%
Return on equity: 5.2%
Long-term debt ($ mil.): —
No. of shares (mil.): —
Sales ($ mil): 7,117

Dividends
  Yield: —
  Payout: —
Market value ($ mil.): —

Shin Kong Life Insurance Co Ltd

LOCATIONS
HQ: Shin Kong Life Insurance Co Ltd
  Shin Kong Life Tower, 66, Chung-Hsiao W. Rd. Sec. 1, Taipei 100
Phone: (886) 2 2389 5858   **Fax:** (886) 2 2375 8688
Web: www.skl.com.tw

HISTORICAL FINANCIALS
Company Type: Public

Income Statement
FYE: December 31

	ASSETS ($ mil.)	NET INCOME ($ mil.)	INCOME AS % OF ASSETS	EMPLOYEES
12/15	64,317	4	0.0%	12,483
12/14	62,276	53	0.1%	13,542
12/13	60,515	218	0.4%	13,214
12/12	56,748	190	0.3%	13,737
12/11	51,225	81	0.2%	14,797
Annual Growth	5.9%	(52.6%)	—	(4.2%)

2015 Year-End Financials
Return on assets: 0.0%
Return on equity: 0.2%
Long-term debt ($ mil.): —
No. of shares (mil.): —
Sales ($ mil): 9,030

Dividends
  Yield: —
  Payout: —
Market value ($ mil.): —

Shinhan Financial Group Co. Ltd.

Shinhan Financial Group one of South Korea's largest financial companies in terms of assets provides retail and corporate banking credit cards insurance asset management securities brokerage and credit reporting services to almost 30 million customers. Its primary subsidiary is Shinhan Bank which has one of the largest branch networks in the country with more than 900 locations. It also owns a stake in the 40-branch Jeju Bank. Shinhan Financial Group has international operations in about a half-dozen other countries including Shinhan Bank America in New York. Other units include Shinhan Investment Corp. (about 100 offices) and Shinhan Life Insurance (about 200 offices).

OperationsShinhan Financial which operates mainly through Shinhan Bank centers its business around three core segments: Retail Banking which provides traditional banking products and services to retail and affluent individuals and non-profit organizations; Corporate and Investment Banking services which makes loans to corporations and small to medium-sized businesses; International Banking which counts the business of Shinhan's overseas branch operations and other international businesses along with securities trading and administrative operations. Through its more than 30 direct and indirect subsidiaries the bank also provides insurance brokerage and asset management services as well as credit card products and services. Shinhan Financial generated roughly 75% its 2014 operating income from interest income one-third of which came from its retail loan business one-fifth coming from its credit card business and just over one-tenth coming from its corporate loan business. The majority of the remaining 25% of total revenue came from fee and commission income mostly from its retail banking and credit card businesses.

Geographic Reach

Shinhan Financial generated 96% of its operating income from South Korea in 2014. It had three-fourths of its 1250 locations in Korea with more than one-third of the its offices in the Seoul metropolitan market alone and about 20% of offices in the Kyunggi province. The rest of the Korean branches in the cities of Incheon Busan Kwangju Taegu Ulsan and Taejon. Shinhan Bank's international branches are in some 16 countries including Cambodia Canada China Germany Hong Kong India Japan Kazakhstan Myanmar Poland Singapore the UK the US and Vietnam. It has representative offices in Mexico and Uzbekistan.

Sales and Marketing

The company serves retail and affluent individuals small and mid-sized businesses non-profit organizations (such as hospitals airports and schools) and corporations. Its Shinhan Card business primarily sells through the banking and credit card branch network sales agents and business partnerships and affiliations with vendors.Altogether the firm spent Wan$229.64 billion ($208.9 million) on advertising in 2014 up from W$211.3 billion ($192.2 million) and W$188.36 billion ($171.4 million) in 2013 and 2012 respectively.

Financial Performance

Note: Growth rates may differ after conversion to US dollars.Shinhan Financial's revenues and profits have been trending lower in recent years due to shrinking interest margins on loans amidst the low-interest environment.

The firm's revenue dipped by 2% to W$16135 billion ($15.43 billion) in 2014 mostly as its interest income on loans dipped by 4% due to a continued decline in interest margins on both its retail loans and corporate loans. Shinhan's net fees and commission income however grew by 6% as its credit card fee income increased with higher consumer credit balances.

Despite lower revenues in 2014 Shinhan's net income jumped by 10% to W$2.08 billion ($1.89 million) mostly thanks to significant unrealized fair value gains of the firm's available-for-sale financial assets. The firm's cash levels fell sharply despite higher earnings during the year with operations using W$2.08 billion ($1.89 million) after adjust-

ing Shinhan's earnings for non-cash interest expenses net insurance loss and net trading loss items.

StrategyShinhan Financial Group reiterated in 2015 that its long-term strategy (which it's followed since 2001) included: balanced growth among its banking and non-banking businesses; expansion of its service offerings to grow revenues and differentiate the bank from competitors; and strengthening of its management systems and core expertise in effort to become the market leader in Korea and a world-class financial holding company. To that end in 2015 the company planned to introduce more differentiated financial services; and continue its international expansion efforts by localizing its product offerings and operations and bolstering its local marketing expertise and distribution channels. Shinhan Financial is also moving toward digital banking channels that are quickly taking the industry by storm allowing the bank to slow the growth of its costly branch network and cut operating costs significantly. Indeed more than 8.6 million Shinhan customers –about one-third of its customer base —were enrolled in the firm's smart phone banking service in 2014; nearly double the size of its "Smart" customer base in 2012. Additionally about 59% of all Shinhan bank transactions were done over the bank's internet or mobile banking services while just 5% of transactions were at physical branch locations.

Mergers and Acquisitions

In June 2015 Shinhan Bank purchased a 75% stake in Centratama Nasional Bank along with its $81 million in assets and 41 offices in Indonesia. Similarly in April 2015 Shinhan obtained regulatory approval to acquired a 40% equity interest in Jakarta-based Bank Metro Express a small bank in Indonesia and expected to close the transaction in late 2015. The bank planned to merge the two Indonesian banks in 2016 to strengthen its operations in the Southeast Asia region.

EXECUTIVES

Chairman and CEO, Han Dong Woo, age 68
Chairman and CEO, Cho Yong-Byoung, age 59
Deputy President and Chief Strategic Officer, Kim Hyung-jin, age 57
Deputy President and CFO, Yim Bo-hyuk
EVP, Lee Chang-goo, age 56
EVP Corporate and Investment Banking Business, Woo Young-woong, age 57
Auditors: Samjong Accounting Corporation (A Member Firm of KPMG)

LOCATIONS

HQ: Shinhan Financial Group Co. Ltd.
20 Sejong-daero 9-gil Jung-gu, Seoul 100-724
Phone: (82) 2 6360 3071   **Fax:** (82) 2 6263 3098
Web: www.shinhangroup.com

PRODUCTS/OPERATIONS

2014 Sales

	% of total
Interest income	
Loans	57
Available for sale financia assets	3
Held to maturity financial assets	5
Trading assets	3
Cash and due from banks	1
Other interest income	2
Non Interest income	
Fee and commission income	21
Dividend income	1
Net trading income	2
Net gain on sale of available for sale financial assets	1
Net foreign currency transaction gain	4
Total	**100**

2014 Sales

	% of total
Banking	67
Credit card	25
Securities	4
Life insurance	4
Other	—
Total	**100**

Selected Subsidiaries

Jeju Bank (68.9%)
SHC Management
Shinhan AITAS (99.8%)
Shinhan Bank
Shinhan BNP Paribas Asset Management (65%)
Shinhan Capital
Shinhan Card
Shinhan Credit Information
Shinhan Data System
Shinhan Investment Corp.
Shinhan Life Insurance
Shinhan Private Equity Investment Management
Shinhan Savings Bank

COMPETITORS

Busan Bank	KB Financial Group
Daegu Bank	Korea Exchange Bank
Hana Bank	Samsung Life Insurance
Industrial Bank of Korea	Woori

HISTORICAL FINANCIALS

Company Type: Public

Income Statement

FYE: December 31

	ASSETS ($ mil.)	NET INCOME ($ mil.)	INCOME AS % OF ASSETS	EMPLOYEES
12/15	314,940	2,011	0.6%	147
12/14	308,948	1,902	0.6%	155
12/13	296,009	1,809	0.6%	148
12/12	281,771	2,175	0.8%	155
12/11	248,656	2,675	1.1%	158
Annual Growth	**6.1%**	**(6.9%)**	**—**	**(1.8%)**

2015 Year-End Financials

Return on assets: 0.6%
Return on equity: 7.8%
Long-term debt ($ mil.): —
No. of shares (mil.): 474
Sales ($ mil): 13,340
Dividends
Yield: 2.5%
Payout: 19.5%
Market value ($ mil.): 15,928

	STOCK PRICE ($) FY Close	P/E High/Low		PER SHARE ($) Earnings	Dividends	Book Value
12/15	33.59	0	0	4.07	0.87	55.28
12/14	40.39	0	0	3.83	0.63	56.25
12/13	45.70	0	0	3.63	0.62	55.23
12/12	36.64	0	0	4.39	0.66	51.97
12/11	68.21	0	0	5.03	0.65	44.40
Annual Growth	**(16.2%)**	**—**	**—**	**(5.2%)**	**7.5%**	**5.6%**

Shinsei Bank Ltd. (Japan)

Shinsei Bank provides retail and corporate banking and several other financial services from 35 branches throughout Japan. Shinsei used to focus on financing Japan's large industrial firms but has been cultivating its retail and small business banking operations. It offers retail banking services such as deposits mortgages and investments as well as higher-margin services such as wealth management market services and institutional asset management bond sales and underwriting trust services and specialty financing in the public and real estate sectors. Founded as the Long-Term Credit Bank of Japan in 1952 the company was reborn as Shinsei (Japanese for "new birth") Bank in 2000.

OperationsShinsei Bank group operates three main business segments. The Individual Group segment (which generated 58% of Shinsei Bank's total revenue and 22% of its profit in fiscal 2015 ended March 31) provides retail banking personal loans credit cards mutual funds insurance housing loans and overseas remittance services. The Institutional Group (which contributed 32% to revenue and 65% to profit) provides public sector finance real estate finance specialty finance health care finance private equity and credit trading (through Shinsei PI Group) leasing and property management services (through Showa Leasing Co) and trust services (through Shinsei Trust). The Global Markets Group (7% of revenue 8% of profit) provides market wealth management and asset management services through subsidiaries such as Shinsei Investment Management and Shinsei Securities. Broadly about 53% of the bank's revenue came from interest income (mostly from loans) in FY2015 while 16% came from fee and commission income. Around 4% of its revenue came from net trading income while the remaining 23% of its revenue came from (non-recurring) net gains on sales of certain non-trading assets.

While Shinsei Bank lends to a variety of different industries across Japan about 27% of its entire loan portfolio's value was tied to loans to customers in the finance and insurance and real estate industries. About 7% of its portfolio went to customers in the services industries while another 15% was lent to customers in the manufacturing electric power/gas/heat/water and transportation/postal service industries. Geographic ReachShinsei Bank had 35 branch outlets across Japan in fiscal 2015 (ended March 31) with about one-third of them around Tokyo nine in the Kinki region seven in the Konto region (excluding Tokyo) and one each in the Chugoku Tohoku Tokai Shikoku Kyushi Hokkaido and Hokuriku/Koshinetsu regions of Japan. The bank also had over 43960 ATM locations in Japan with nearly 40% of them located in the Kanto/Tokyo region and another 15% in the Kinki region. Additionally it had ATMs in all the other regions where there were branches along with 434 ATM locations in Okinawa.

Financial Performance

Note: Growth rates may differ after conversion to US dollars. This analysis uses financials from the company's annual report. In domestic currency terms Shinsei Bank's annual revenues and profits have been trending higher since fiscal 2013 (ended March 31 2013) thanks to loan business growth and non-interest growth from fees and commissions and sales of investment products. The bank's total revenue (defined by the company as the total of net interest income and non-interest income) grew to ¥235.3 billion in FY2015 thanks to a combination of: higher net interest income as the bank decreased its funding costs and collected higher dividend income from securities investments in the Institutional Group; and non-interest income growth thanks to an improvement in market-related transaction revenues including ALM operations (the company's corporate internal trading division) as well as a rise in revenue from the installment sales finance business of the consumer finance business. Higher revenue and a decline in loan loss provisions in FY2015 boosted Shinsei Bank's net income up 64% to ¥67.8 billion

($567 million) for the year. The bank's operating cash levels declined sharply despite higher earnings with operations using ¥509 billion or $4.25 billion (operations provided ¥524 billion in FY2014) as the bank's deposit levels fell and as its loan balances grew. Company BackgroundDuring the late 2000s Shinsei had been battered by its exposure to toxic assets including loans to failed Lehman Brothers and structured asset-backed securities. It had also taken a hit in the domestic real estate market in which the company had been a significant lender. Record losses reported for 2008 sparked rumors that Shinsei would merge with Aozora Bank another struggling midsized bank that was nationalized in 2001. The two banks reached a merger agreement in 2009 but called those plans off due to strategic differences.

HISTORY

Company BackgroundThe Japanese government nationalized Shinsei Bank's debt-ridden Long-Term Credit Bank in 1998. It sold the bank to an international group led by US-based Ripplewood Holdings in 2000 making it one of the few major Japanese banks to come under foreign control. Ripplewood spun off the bank in 2004 placing it on the Tokyo Stock Exchange.

In 2007 Shinsei acquired a minority stake in global advisory firm Duff & Phelps. In 2008 it acquired GE's consumer finance business in Japan consisting of credit card personal lending and mortgage operations. In 2010 Shinsei Bank sold Shinsei Asset Management its Mumbai-based asset management operation to Daiwa Bank. The company would use the proceeds to pay down its debt.

EXECUTIVES

President and CEO, Shigeki Toma, age 68
Senior Managing Executive Officer, Hitomi Sato, age 68
Senior Managing Executive Officer and Group CIO, Michiyuki Okano, age 56
Senior Managing Executive Officer, Sanjeev Gupta, age 56
Deputy President, Yukio Nakamura, age 62
Senior Managing Executive Officer and CFO, Shigeru Tsukamoto, age 66
Managing Executive Officer, Norio Funayama, age 59
Managing Executive Officer, Toru Myochin, age 51
Managing Executive Officer, Yoshiaki Kozano, age 54
Managing Executive Officer, Hironobu Satou, age 56
Managing Executive Officer, Shinichirou Seto, age 55
Managing Executive Officer, Masashi Yamashita, age 58
Auditors: Deloitte Touche Tohmatsu LLC

LOCATIONS

HQ: Shinsei Bank Ltd. (Japan)
2-4-3 Nihonbashi-Muromachi, Chuo-ku, Tokyo 103-8303
Phone: (81) 3 6880 7000
Web: www.shinseibank.com

PRODUCTS/OPERATIONS

2014 Sales

	% of total
Net interest income	54
Noninterest income	
Net fee and commission	12
Net trading income	7
Others	27
Total	**100**

COMPETITORS

Aozora Bank
Bank of Yokohama
Mitsubishi UFJ
 Financial Group
Mizuho Financial
Mizuho Trust & Banking
 Ltd
Resona
Sumitomo Mitsui
Sumitomo Mitsui Trust
 Holdings

HISTORICAL FINANCIALS

Company Type: Public

Income Statement

FYE: March 31

	ASSETS ($ mil.)	NET INCOME ($ mil.)	INCOME AS % OF ASSETS	EMPLOYEES
03/16	79,510	542	0.7%	6,668
03/15	74,094	565	0.8%	6,687
03/14	90,303	400	0.4%	5,064
03/13	95,962	542	0.6%	4,863
03/12	104,957	78	0.1%	4,830
Annual Growth	**(6.7%)**	**62.2%**		**8.4%**

2016 Year-End Financials

Return on assets: 0.6%	Dividends
Return on equity: 8.0%	Yield: 0.6%
Long-term debt ($ mil.): —	Payout: 8.7%
No. of shares (mil.): —	Market value ($ mil.): —
Sales ($ mil): 3,361	

	STOCK PRICE ($) FY Close	P/E High/Low		PER SHARE ($) Earnings	Dividends	Book Value
03/16	2.69	0	0	0.20	0.02	2.62
03/15	4.06	0	0	0.21	0.02	2.30
03/14	3.91	—	—	0.15	0.02	2.64
03/13	4.57	—	—	0.20	0.00	2.74
03/12	2.58	—	—	0.03	0.00	2.88
Annual Growth	**1.0%**	—	—	**62.3%**	—	**(2.3%)**

Shizuoka Bank, Ltd. (Japan)

Auditors: Deloitte Touche Tohmatsu LLC

LOCATIONS

HQ: Shizuoka Bank, Ltd. (Japan)
1-10 Gofuku-cho, Aoi-ku, Shizuoka 420-8761
Phone: (81) 54 261 3131
Web: www.shizuokabank.co.jp

HISTORICAL FINANCIALS

Company Type: Public

Income Statement

FYE: March 31

	ASSETS ($ mil.)	NET INCOME ($ mil.)	INCOME AS % OF ASSETS	EMPLOYEES
03/16	98,998	426	0.4%	6,622
03/15	93,627	416	0.4%	6,734
03/14	103,642	452	0.4%	4,246
03/13	109,624	605	0.6%	4,269
03/12	118,194	453	0.4%	4,257
Annual Growth	**(4.3%)**	**(1.5%)**	—	**11.7%**

2016 Year-End Financials

Return on assets: 0.4%
Return on equity: 5.1%
Long-term debt ($ mil.): —
No. of shares (mil.): 613
Sales ($ mil): 1,992

Dividends
  Yield: —
  Payout: 243.2%
  Market value ($ mil.): 69,512

	STOCK PRICE ($) FY Close	P/E High/Low		PER SHARE ($) Earnings	Dividends	Book Value
03/16	113.25	—	—	0.65	1.59	13.37
03/15	113.25	—	—	0.63	1.34	12.51
03/14	113.25	—	—	0.68	0.00	12.59
03/13	94.51	—	—	0.93	0.00	13.29
03/12	105.92	—	—	0.69	0.00	13.96
Annual Growth	1.7%	—	—	(1.2%)	—	(1.1%)

Showa Shell Sekiyu K.K.

Show and tell? When is comes to oil and petroleum products Showa Shell Sekiyu has plenty to show and talk about. Showa Shell 33%-owned by Royal Dutch Shell and 15% by Saudi Aramco is one of Japan's leading oil refiners. The company imports refines and distributes petroleum products. The firm's three local refining affiliates Showa Yokkaichi Toa Oil and Seibu Oil have a collective refining capacity of 395000 barrels a day. Showa Shell markets its products through 3800 gas stations; it also has solar power electricity city gas (liquefied petroleum gas) and property businesses. In 2016 Royal Dutch Shell agreed to sell all but 2% of its stake in Showa Shell to Japan-based refiner Idemitsu Kosan.

OperationsThe company operates the Yokkaichi Refinery of Showa Yokkaichi Sekiyu Co. Ltd. (210000 barrels per day) the Keihin Refinery of Toa Oil Co. Ltd. (65000 barrels per day) and the Yamaguchi Refinery of Seibu Oil Co. Ltd. (120000 barrels per day). These refineries produce fuel oils such as gasoline; diesel oil; kerosene; basic materials for petrochemical products such as mixed xylene benzene and propylene; lubricants; asphalt; and other products.

Showa Shell markets its products through 3800 gas stations;

The company has developed the technology for manufacturing next-generation CIS thin-film solar panels.

It also operates Ohgishima Power which has two natural gas-fired power plants as a joint venture with Tokyo Gas. Electricity produced at the plants is sold primarily to customers in or near Tokyo.

Sales and Marketing

Showa Shell sells petroleum products in Japan primarily through its gas station network. Products sold include gasolines kerosene and a range of automotive lubricants. The company also directly sells fuel oil gas oil naphtha lubricants bitumen and LP gas to construction firms electric power and gas utilities fishing fleets manufacturers and shipping companies. Showa Shell's international sales include aviation fuel to airlines and marine bunker fuels and lubricants to shipping firms.

Financial Performance

Showa Shell's revenues increased by 18% in 2011 due to a 17% hike in prices on petroleum products which rose in tandem with higher crude oil prices pushing up sales for the oil business. The increase in crude oil prices also had a positive effect on inventory valuation. In addition the sales volume increased for kerosene and other middle

distillates; and 128% increase in Energy Solution Businesses due to the greater scale of sales in the solar business stemming from the start of operations at the third Miyazaki Plant.

Net income increased by 45% in 2011 thanks to higher prices on petroleum products and higher net sales. It also benefited from increased demand for heating fuels due to particularly cold weather at the beginning of the year as well as a recovery in petroleum product margins.

Strategy

In addition to growing its core refining and petroleum products businesses the company is expanding its solar energy assets. In 2011 it launched the Kunitomi Plant its Solar Frontier unit's third Miyazaki plant and one of the largest solar plants in the world.

Company Background

The company was founded in 1985 through a merger between Japan's Showa Oil and Royal Dutch Shell's Shell Sekiyu.

EXECUTIVES

Corporate Executive Officer, Hiroshi Watanabe
VP, Tomonori Okada
CEO, Tsuyoshi Kameoka
Corporate Executive Officer, Yuri Inoue
Corporate Executive Officer, Katsuaki Shindome
COO Energy Solutions Business, Misao Hamamoto
COO Oil Business, Masayuki Kobayashi
Corporate Executive Officer, Kenichi Morishita
Corporate Executive Officer, Makoto Abe
Auditors: PricewaterhouseCoopers Aarata

LOCATIONS

HQ: Showa Shell Sekiyu K.K.
  2-3-2 Daiba, Minato-ku, Tokyo 135-8074
Phone: (81) 3 5531 5594   **Fax:** (81) 3 5531 5598
Web: www.showa-shell.co.jp

PRODUCTS/OPERATIONS

2015 sales

	% of total
Oil business	93
Energy solution business	6
Others	1
Total	**100**

COMPETITORS

Cosmo Oil	JX Nippon Mining & Metals
Exxon Mobil	
Idemitsu Kosan	JX Nippon Oil & Energy
JX Holdings	SK Innovation

HISTORICAL FINANCIALS

Company Type: Public

Income Statement

FYE: December 31

	REVENUE ($ mil.)	NET INCOME ($ mil.)	NET PROFIT MARGIN	EMPLOYEES
12/15	18,089	(228)	—	4,765
12/14	25,127	(81)	—	6,039
12/13	28,139	574	2.0%	5,829
12/12	30,526	11	0.0%	5,848
12/11	35,812	298	0.8%	5,947
Annual Growth	(15.7%)	—		(5.4%)

2015 Year-End Financials

Debt ratio: 0.1%
Return on equity: (-11.1%)
Cash ($ mil.): 137
Current ratio: 0.94
Long-term debt ($ mil.): 857

No. of shares (mil.): 376
Dividends
  Yield: —
  Payout: —
Market value ($ mil.): 3,023

	STOCK PRICE ($) FY Close	P/E High/Low		PER SHARE ($) Earnings	Dividends	Book Value
12/15	8.03	—	—	(0.61)	0.00	5.37
12/14	10.12	—	—	(0.22)	0.00	6.60
12/13	10.40	—	—	1.53	0.00	8.23
12/12	5.75	—	—	0.03	0.00	8.44
12/11	10.75	—	—	0.79	0.00	9.58
Annual Growth	(7.0%)	—	—	(13.5%)	—	—

Siam Commercial Bank Public Co Ltd (The)

One of Thailand's largest commercial banks by total assets deposits and loans The Siam Commercial Bank (SCB) hails from royal beginnings. It is the country's oldest bank established by King Rama V in 1906 in response to the proliferation of foreign financial institutions in Thailand. It offers a variety of financial services such as corporate and personal lending retail and wholesale banking credit cards life insurance foreign currency trading and investment banking among others. SCB operates through a network of about 1200 branches and 9140 ATMs; it is expanding regionally. In 2014 SCB had Baht 2553 billion in total assets Baht 1781 billion in deposits and Baht 1733 billion in loans.

EXECUTIVES

CFO, Kittiya Todhanakasem, age 58
SEVP; Head Special Business, Sarunthorn Chutima
President and CEO, Arthid Nanthawithaya
SEVP and Chief Legal and Control Officer, Wallaya Kaewrungruang
SEVP and Chief Risk Officer, Anucha Laokwansatit
SEVP and Chief Strategic Officer, Jens Lottner
CTO, Colin R. Dinn
Chairman, Anand Panyarachun
Auditors: KPMG Phoomchai Audit Ltd.

LOCATIONS

HQ: Siam Commercial Bank Public Co Ltd (The)
  9 Ratchadapisek Road,, Jatujak, Bangkok 10900
Phone: (66) 2 544 1000   **Fax:** (66) 2 937 7721
Web: www.scb.co.th

PRODUCTS/OPERATIONS

2013 Sales

	% of total
Interest income	56
Net earned insurance premiums	23
Fees & service income	14
Net trading income	4
Dividend income	2
Net gain on investments	1
Total	**100**

Selected Group Companies

SCB Asset Management
SCB Life Assurance
SCB Securities
The Siam Commercial Bank

COMPETITORS

Bangkok Bank	TMB Bank
Bank of Ayudhya	Thanachart Capital
KASIKORNBANK	

Company Type: Public

Income Statement
FYE: December 31

	ASSETS ($ mil.)	NET INCOME ($ mil.)	INCOME AS % OF ASSETS	EMPLOYEES
12/15	76,999	1,309	1.7%	0
12/14	82,107	1,622	2.0%	0
12/13	77,408	1,534	2.0%	0
12/12	74,179	1,314	1.8%	20,994
12/11	59,670	1,152	1.9%	19,566
Annual Growth	6.6%	3.2%	—	—

2015 Year-End Financials

Return on assets: 1.7%	Dividends
Return on equity: 15.9%	Yield: 4.4%
Long-term debt ($ mil.): —	Payout: —
No. of shares (mil.): —	Market value ($ mil.): —
Sales ($ mil): 6,308	

	STOCK PRICE ($) FY Close	P/E High/Low		PER SHARE ($) Earnings	Dividends	Book Value
12/15	12.95	1	1	0.39	0.57	2.51
12/14	21.41	1	1	0.48	0.51	2.56
12/13	17.16	2	1	0.45	0.54	2.22
12/12	23.65	2	2	0.39	0.11	2.10
Annual Growth	(18.2%)	—	—	(0.1%)	52.5%	4.7%

Siemens AG (Germany)

For Siemens one of the largest electronics and industrial engineering companies in the galaxy everything comes down to seven segments: Power and Gas; Wind Power and Renewables; Energy Management; Building Technologies; Mobility; Digital Factory; and Process Industries and Drives. Siemens makes everything from automation equipment and building technologies for manufacturers and construction companies to diagnostic and imaging systems for hospitals and clinics. Other products include power generation and distribution equipment for the oil and gas and renewable energy sectors. Siemens Energy Siemens Healthcare Siemens Industry and Siemens Infrastructure & Cities are a few of its primary segments.

Geographic Reach

All in all the company operates through more than 290 major production and manufacturing plants in 200 countries worldwide. The EMEA region accounted for 54% of its net sales in 2014. Other major markets include the Americas (26%) and Asia and Australia (20%).

Operations

Siemens in late 2014 restructured its operations from four segments to seven: Power and Gas (PG); Wind Power and Renewables (WP); Energy Management (EM); Building Technologies (BT); Mobility (MO); Digital Factory (DF); and Process Industries and Drives (PD).

PG offers products for generating electricity from fossil and renewable fuels and for transporting oil and natural gas and WP offers products and services for on- and offshore wind power. EM is a supplier of products systems equipment and services for transmission and distribution of electrical energy while BT manufactures and supplies energy-efficient buildings and infrastructure systems. MO is a provider of passenger and freight transportation systems and services; DF offers automation technology industrial switchgear industry software and services primarily to the manufacturing industry; and PD offers process products systems and services to industry sectors.

In addition to its main segments Siemens operates a financial services division that offers corporate financing fund management insurance and risk management services. It also makes hardware and software for the communications industry through its enterprise communications business.

While its operations are diverse Siemens' long-term strategy focuses on developing and producing products that are attuned to global trends. Addressing climate environmental and energy concerns the company makes wind turbines for the renewable energy industry and energy-efficient building technologies for the construction industry. Siemens' products are also used to build transit systems water and wastewater facilities and other systems that in effect facilitate population growth in mature and emerging urban markets.

Financial Performance

After experiencing two straight years of revenue growth Siemens saw its revenue dip 11% from $103 billion in 2013 to $91 billion in 2014. Profits jumped 17% from nearly $5.8 billion in 2013 to $6.8 billion in 2014 driven by a decrease in expenses. (Note the company's 2013 annual revenue was restated due to discontinued operations.)

Siemens' declines for 2014 primarily reflected weaker orders in power generation and fewer orders from power transmission products. Its former health care segment experienced declines due to reduced orders in Asia Australia and the Americas in addition to a decline in the company's diagnostics business.

Strategy

Siemens' focus on urbanization in emerging markets has been growing particularly more intense in recent years especially in China India and Russia where economies and urban populations have been exploding. The company has been bolstering its presence in these markets by entering into joint ventures and partnerships with native companies. The company also has a growing presence in emerging markets in South America through subsidiaries in Brazil Argentina Chile and other countries.

Siemens has been selling various operations in an effort to weather the turbulence in the global economy and refocus its operations on its core business segments. In 2015 it sold its hospital information system business to Cerner for $1.3 billion. The business was focused on administrative hospital IT and electronic patient records not the lab and medical equipment-based IT software that is more aligned with Siemens' business. The divestiture included 6000 employees in the US Europe (particularly Germany) and Asia.

To bolster its railroad operations Siemens in 2013 bought Invensys Rail the rail signaling business of British engineering firm Invensys. Shelling out $2.8 billion for the purchase Siemens enhanced its market share in the rail automation sector and merged Invensys Rail with its Siemens Infrastructure & Cities segment.

Mergers and Acquisitions

In 2016 Siemens agreed to acquire Mentor Graphics for $4.5 billion. The move fills out a part of Siemens strategy for building out its software capabilities. With Mentor Graphics Siemens can handled a wide range of work for electronics products.

HISTORY

Company Background

In 1847 electrical engineer Werner von Siemens and craftsman Johann Halske formed Siemens & Halske. The firm's first major project linked Berlin and Frankfurt with the first long-distance telegraph system in Europe (1848). In 1870 it completed a 6600-mile telegraph line from London to Calcutta India and in 1874 it made the first transatlantic cable linking Ireland to the US.

The company's history of firsts includes Europe's first electric power transmission system (1876) the world's first electrified railway (1879) and one of the first elevators (1880). In 1896 it patented the world's first X-ray tube and completed the first European subway in Budapest Hungary.

By the next century it had formed light-bulb cartel OSRAM with German rivals AEG and Auer (1919) and created a venture with Furukawa Electric called Fuji Electric (1923). It developed radios and traffic lights in the 1920s and began producing electron microscopes in 1939.

Siemens & Halske played a critical role in Germany's war effort in WWII and suffered heavy losses. During the 1950s it recovered by developing data processing equipment silicates for semiconductors and the first implantable pacemaker. It moved into the nuclear industry in 1959 when its first reactor went into service at Munich-Garching. In 1966 the company reincorporated as Siemens AG.

EXECUTIVES

President and CEO, Joe Kaeser, age 59, $780,000 total compensation
CEO Financial Services, Roland W. Chalons-Browne, age 60
CEO Mobility, Jochen Eickholt, age 53
CTO Labor Director and Member of the Managing Board, Siegfried Russwurm, age 53, $780,000 total compensation
Member of the Managing Board and CEO Infrastructure and Cities Sector, Roland Busch, age 52
CFO and Member of the Managing Board, Ralf P. Thomas, age 55
CEO Energy Management, Ralf Christian
Head Healthcare, Michael Sen, age 48
CEO Building Technologies Division, Matthias Rebellius
EVP CTO and Member Managing Board Siemens AG, Klaus Helmrich, age 58
CEO Industry Automation Division, Anton S. Huber
CEO Siemens Corporation USA; CEO Power and Gas Division the Wind Power and Renewables Division the Power Generation Services Division the Region North America and the Region South America, Lisa Davis, age 53
CEO Power and Gas Division, Willi Meixner, age 51
CEO Process Industries and Drives Division, Jurgen Brandes, age 55
CEO Energy Management Division, Jan Mrosik
CEO Wind Power and Renewables, Markus Tacke
CEO Healthcare, Bernd Montag
CEO Power Generation Services, Tim O. Holt, age 46
CEO Siemens Qatar, Adrian Wood, age 50
CEO Siemens Kuwait, Herbert Klausner, age 52
CEO Siemens Middle East and UAE, Dietmar Siersdorfer
Head Asia Australia Business and Energy Management Division, Cedrik Neike, age 43
Second Deputy Chairman, Werner Wenning, age 70
Chairman, Gerhard Cromme, age 74
First Deputy Chairwoman, Birgit Steinborn, age 56
Auditors: Ernst & Young GmbH

LOCATIONS

HQ: Siemens AG (Germany)
Wittelsbacherplatz 2, Munich D-80333
Phone: (49) 89 636 33443   **Fax:** (49) 89 636 30085
Web: www.siemens.com

2014 Sales

	% of total
Europe CIS Africa Middle East	
Germany	15
Other countries	39
Americas	
US	18
Other countries	8
Asia Australia	
China	9
Other countries	11
Total	**100**

PRODUCTS/OPERATIONS

2014 Sales

	% of total
Energy	34
Infrastructure & Cities	26
Industry	23
Health care	17
Total	**100**

Selected Operations

Industry
  Building technology (heating and ventilation security fire safety systems)
  Industry automation (manufacturing and process automation)
  Industry solutions (systems integration for industrial plants)
  Mobility (transportation systems)
  Motion control (converters drives motors numerical control systems)
  OSRAM (light-emitting diodes light bulbs)
Energy
  Fossil power generation (gas and steam turbines and generators power plants)
  Oil and gas (extraction conversion and transportation systems)
  Power distribution (powergrid automation switch gear components)
  Power transmission (high-voltage equipment)
  Renewable energy (wind energy)
  Service rotating equipment (power plant services and operation)
Health care
  Diagnostics (immune diagnostics molecular analysis)
  Imaging and IT (imaging systems and networking)
  Workflow and solutions (health care systems and services)
Other
  BSH Bosch und Siemens Hausgeräte (equity investment)
  ELIN GmbH & Co. (equity investment)
  Enterprise Network Holdings (equity investment)
  Financial services (cross-sector)
Krauss-Maffei Wegmann GmbH & Co. (equity investment)
Siemens Corp. (US)
Siemens Energy (Germany and US)
Siemens Enterprise Communications GmbH (Germany)
Siemens Financial Services GmbH (Germany)
Siemens Healthcare (Germany and US)
Siemens Holdings plc (UK)
Siemens Industry Automation (US; subsidiary of Siemens Industry)
Siemens Industry Inc. (US)
Siemens Industry Inc. (US)
Siemens Ltda. (Brazil)
Siemens Osakeyhtiö Group (Finland)
Siemens Product Lifecycle Management Software Inc. (US; subsidiary of Siemens Industry)
Siemens Water Technologies Corp.(US; subsidiary of Siemens Industry)

COMPETITORS

ABB	Honeywell
ALSTOM	International
AREVA	Huawei Technologies
Abbott Labs	Johnson Controls
Alcatel-Lucent	MAN
Avaya	McKesson
Beckman Coulter	Mitsubishi Electric
Bharat Heavy	Mitsubishi Heavy
Electricals	Industries

Bombardier	Nichia
Capgemini	Nortel Networks
Cerner	OSRAM Licht
Computer Sciences	Philips Electronics
Corp.	Philips Healthcare
Danfoss Turbocor	Roche Diagnostics
Danieli	Rockwell Automation
Dassault	Schneider Electric
Dresser-Rand	Senvion
Emerson Electric	Sonova
FANUC	Toshiba
GE	United Technologies
GN ReSound	Varian Medical Systems
Gamesa	Veolia Environnement
Hitachi	Vestas Wind Systems
Hologic	

HISTORICAL FINANCIALS

Company Type: Public

Income Statement

FYE: September 30

	REVENUE ($ mil.)	NET INCOME ($ mil.)	NET PROFIT MARGIN	EMPLOYEES
09/16	88,907	6,083	6.8%	351,000
09/15	84,799	8,164	9.6%	348,000
09/14	90,537	6,763	7.5%	343,000
09/13	102,419	5,782	5.6%	366,400
09/12	101,236	5,764	5.7%	370,000
Annual Growth	(3.2%)	1.4%	—	(1.3%)

2016 Year-End Financials

Debt ratio: 27.5%	No. of shares (mil.): 808
Return on equity: 15.8%	Dividends
Cash ($ mil.): 11,837	Yield: 2.3%
Current ratio: 1.29	Payout: 38.9%
Long-term debt ($ mil.): 27,641	Market value ($ mil.): 94,827

	STOCK PRICE ($) FY Close	P/E High/Low		PER SHARE ($) Earnings	Dividends	Book Value
09/16	117.32	18	13	7.42	2.81	47.25
09/15	89.30	14	10	9.80	2.76	47.80
09/14	119.07	20	17	7.94	6.02	46.65
09/13	120.51	24	20	6.79	5.95	45.01
09/12	100.15	20	16	6.52	2.85	46.41
Annual Growth	4.0%	—	—	3.3%	(0.4%)	0.5%

SinoPac Financial Holdings Co Ltd

SinoPac is packing away financial services in Asia and on the US west coast. The holding company owns Bank SinoPac which has about 130 branches in Taiwan. Bank SinoPac was created in 2006 after the merger of a bank by that name and International Bank of Taipei or IBT. In the US SinoPac Bancorp owns (but is selling) Far East National Bank which serves California's Asian-American community through about 10 branches. Other holdings include SinoPac Securities which offers brokerage services corporate financing and underwriting. The company's SinoPac Credit Cards unit has issued more than 1.7 million cards. SinoPac Holdings' subsidiaries also have operations in China Hong Kong Macao the UK and Vietnam.

In addition to banking brokerage and credit card issuing SinoPac Holdings' subsidiaries are involved in insurance asset management factoring venture capital call centers and more.

EXECUTIVES

President, Shou Chuan Ho
Auditors: Deloitte & Touche

LOCATIONS

HQ: SinoPac Financial Holdings Co Ltd
3&6-13/F., No. 306, Section 2, Bade Road, Taipei 104
Phone: (886) 2 8161 8888   **Fax:** (886) 2 8161 8485
Web: www.sinopac.com

COMPETITORS

Bank of East Asia	HSBC
Cathay Financial	Hotung Investment
Holding	Holdings
Chang Hwa Bank	Hua Nan Financial
Chinatrust Financial	Mega Financial
E.Sun	Shin Kong
East West Bancorp	Taishin
First Financial	Taiwan Business Bank
Holding	Taiwan Cooperative
Fubon Financial	Bank

HISTORICAL FINANCIALS

Company Type: Public

Income Statement

FYE: December 31

	ASSETS ($ mil.)	NET INCOME ($ mil.)	INCOME AS % OF ASSETS	EMPLOYEES
12/15	48,314	330	0.7%	8,549
12/14	48,941	410	0.8%	8,783
12/13	49,158	361	0.7%	8,781
12/12	46,760	328	0.7%	8,294
12/11	42,888	101	0.2%	8,095
Annual Growth	3.0%	34.4%	—	1.4%

2015 Year-End Financials

Return on assets: 0.6%	Dividends
Return on equity: 8.4%	Yield: —
Long-term debt ($ mil.): —	Payout: —
No. of shares (mil.): —	Market value ($ mil.): —
Sales ($ mil): 1,379	

Sinopharm Group Co., Ltd.

EXECUTIVES

Chairman, Yulin Wei
Auditors: PricewaterhouseCoopers

LOCATIONS

HQ: Sinopharm Group Co., Ltd.
  Sinopharm Plaza, No. 1001 Zhongshan West Road, Changning District, Shanghai 200051
Phone: (86) 21 2305 2666
Web: www.sinopharmgroup.com.cn

HISTORICAL FINANCIALS

Company Type: Public

Income Statement

FYE: December 31

	REVENUE ($ mil.)	NET INCOME ($ mil.)	NET PROFIT MARGIN	EMPLOYEES
12/15	34,963	579	1.7%	54,735
12/14	32,246	463	1.4%	50,099
12/13	27,563	371	1.3%	45,415
12/12	21,780	316	1.5%	40,737
12/11	16,240	247	1.5%	35,394
Annual Growth	21.1%	23.6%	—	11.5%

SK C&C Co Ltd

EXECUTIVES

President, Jeong Ho Park

LOCATIONS

HQ: SK C&C Co Ltd
9 Seongnam-daero 343beon-gil Bundang-gu,
Seongnam, Gyeonggi-do 463-847
Phone: (82) 2 6400 0114   **Fax:** (82) 2 6400 0277
Web: www.skcc.co.kr

HISTORICAL FINANCIALS

Company Type: Public

Income Statement

	REVENUE ($ mil.)	NET INCOME ($ mil.)	NET PROFIT MARGIN	EMPLOYEES
12/15	33,632	4,543	13.5%	4,120
12/14	2,217	116	5.2%	4,063
12/13	2,188	179	8.2%	4,344
12/12	2,099	333	15.9%	4,013
12/11	1,468	378	25.8%	3,819
Annual Growth	**118.8%**	**86.2%**	—	**1.9%**

2015 Year-End Financials

Debt ratio: 0.0%   No. of shares (mil.): 55
Return on equity: 70.5%   Dividends
Cash ($ mil.): 5,945   Yield: —
Current ratio: 1.15   Payout: —
Long-term debt ($ mil.): 19,970   Market value ($ mil.): —

SK Hynix Inc

SK Hynix (formerly Hynix Semiconductor) may not live in the past but its business is based on memory- computing memory that is. SK Hynix makes DRAM and NAND flash memories for computers mobile phones and televisions as well as the growing number of devices such as smartphones and tablet PCs innovated by the IT industry. The company is battling to retain its spot among the world's top makers of DRAM chips; it trails Samsung Electronics and jockeys for market share with Elpida Memory and Micron Technology. SK Hynix operates three factories in South Korea and some 30 sales offices in more than 15 countries. South Korean telecommunications giant SK Telecom owns about 20% of the company.

HISTORY

Chung Ju-Yung went into business after WWII repairing trucks for the US armed forces in Korea. In 1947 Chung started Hyundai Engineering and Construction the first Korean contractor to win overseas construction projects. Chung's shrewd business gambles helped Hyundai become a major international player in construction.

In 1983 Hyundai Group took another gamble — for a company with no electronics manufacturing experience –and founded Hyundai Electronics Industries (HEI) to make semiconductors and microcomputer components. Chung's son Chung Mong-Hun (who also had no high-tech experience) became HEI's chairman.

To overcome its lack of technical expertise HEI manufactured chips and electronics for other companies. HEI continued to expand in the early 1990s even as Chung Mong-Hun was charged (and eventually jailed) by the South Korean government for tax evasion and diverting money to his father's opposition political party the Unification National Party.

In 1999 HEI acquired LG Semicon the semiconductor unit of LG Group; the combined operations enabled the company to battle Samsung Electronics (and later Micron Technology) atop the market for DRAM chips. At the same time though the acquisition brought with it LG Semicon's unwieldy debts.

Bowing to government pressure to replace family-run conglomerates with more efficient and transparent management systems Chung Mong-Hun resigned as chairman in 2000. Park Chong-Sup previously chairman of subsidiary Hyundai Electronics America was appointed chairman and CEO. Later that year the company spun off its automotive electronics division (Hyundai Autonet) and its monitors unit (Hyundai ImageQuest) and announced plans to cut its ties with Hyundai Group and become an independent company. (The company completed its disaffiliation from Hyundai Group in 2001 when it and other former members of the group dissolved their cross-ownership ties.)

Chung Ju-Yung died in 2001. Soon afterward HEI changed its name to Hynix Semiconductor. Also that year as it faced massive maturing debts the company announced plans to lay off 30% of its workforce and began to sell off assets.

In the course of 2001 Hynix spun off its satellite service business (Space Broadband Corporation) its customer service operations (Hyundai Digitech Service) its telecom handset unit (Hyundai CuriTel later sold to a consortium of Korean companies for about $125 million) its DSL Internet service unit (Hyundai Networks) and its main LCD business (Hyundai Display Technology).

Hynix seemed to have found its long-term salvation in 2002 when it struck a provisional agreement to sell its memory operations to US-based rival Micron. The complex deal called for Micron to pay about $3.4 billion for all of Hynix's memory operations and a small stake in its other lines. Although the agreement was reached by Hynix's executives and approved by its leading creditors the company's board of directors nixed the deal a week after it was announced. Most of that board of directors was replaced in mid-2002 after Hynix's creditors effectively took control of the company by exercising debt-for-equity swap rights. CEO Park Chong-sup stepped down; COO Park Sang-ho (no relation) succeeded him. A few months later director Woo Eui-je was appointed co-CEO (he subsequently became chairman as well).

Hynix stayed afloat through 2001 and 2002 thanks to multibillion-dollar bailout efforts led by the Seoul Guarantee Insurance Company Korea Exchange Bank Woori Bank (formerly Hanvit Bank and now part of Woori Financial Group) and other creditors. Many of these financiers –widely seen as the bulwark that kept Hynix from financial collapse –were partially controlled by South Korea's government. These connections led Micron and Infineon among others to claim that the bailout packages amounted to trade protectionism. Both the European Commission and the US Department of Commerce slapped stiff duties on Hynix DRAMs produced outside the US.

Late in 2002 Hynix sold its flat-panel LCD business (called Hydis) to China-based electronics maker BOE Technology Group for about $380 million. (Hynix's own creditors lent BOE half of the purchase price.) The BOE deal came about a year after Hynix announced a deal to sell most of Hydis to a Taiwanese consortium; that deal which valued Hydis at more than $800 million fell through a few months after it was announced.

Park Sang-ho resigned as president and co-CEO in 2003.

After on-again off-again talks that went on for a year Citigroup and Francisco Partners led an $830 million buyout of Hynix's non-memory chip operations in 2004. (Hynix creditors agreed to lend Citigroup $325 million to help finance the purchase.) Citigroup formed a company MagnaChip Semiconductor to receive the non-memory unit making chips used in flat-panel displays and digital still cameras.

In 2005 the World Trade Organization rejected US and EU claims that Hynix was illegally subsidized by the Korean government.

In 2005 Hynix found a buyer for its 47% stake in ImageQuest an exporter of LCDs and color display tubes. An investor consortium agreed to take over the stake for $35 million. The company also disposed of its 12% stake in Hyundai Autonet a South Korean car audio equipment manufacturer for $76.6 million.

In yet another move to reduce the company's debt its creditors agreed to a debt-discounting program that combined with proceeds from the sale to Citigroup reduced Hynix's debt by nearly $1 billion. Some 137 creditors additionally decided to sell a total 23.7% stake by the end of 2005.

In 2005 Hynix Semi pleaded guilty to fixing prices for memory chips from 1999 to 2002 and paid a fine of $185 million to the US Department of Justice which had brought a criminal complaint against Hynix and other large competitors in the memory chip market. The next year four executives of Hynix pleaded guilty to criminal charges stemming from the Justice Department's inquiry; they received jail sentences ranging from five to eight months apiece. Also in 2005 Hynix secured a contract to supply flash memory chips to Apple Computer (now Apple) through 2010.

A US District Court jury in 2006 found that Hynix had infringed on 10 patents held by Rambus and ordered the Korean company to pay nearly $307 million in damages to Rambus. The judge in the case however lowered the award to almost $134 million which Rambus accepted. Rambus also accused Hynix of anti-competitive business practices in a separate lawsuit in the US. Also in 2006 Hynix agreed to settle a class-action lawsuit regarding the price-fixing scandal; among the settlement terms was a payment of $73 million to the plaintiffs.

Creditor banks reduced their ownership in Hynix through the sale of 43 million shares to domestic and overseas investors in 2006. The number of creditors was reduced as well to nine from 46. The $1.5 billion share sale dropped the total equity ownership of Korea Exchange Bank and other Hynix creditors to around 37% from just over half of the company's equity.

Woo Eui-je resigned as chairman and CEO in 2007 after a year which saw Hynix post a sizable profit for 2006 and finish strongly to claim second place in the global DRAM market widely trailing DRAM leader Samsung Electronics but comfortably ahead of competitors Qimonda Micron Technology and Elpida Memory.

That same year Hynix signed patent cross-licensing agreements on memory device technology with both SanDisk and Toshiba. The company also established a 50/50 joint venture with SanDisk to manufacture memory components and to develop consumer products based on flash memory devices.

Also in 2007 Hynix broke ground on an advanced wafer fabrication plant (or fab) in Cheongju South Korea. The facility dubbed M11 cost more than $4 billion to build and equip. The company used the fab Hynix's third 300mm wafer fab to make high-density NAND flash memories on 300mm (12-inch) wafers.

In 2008 Hynix agreed to work together with Taiwan's ProMOS Technologies. The company licenses its 50nm DRAM stack process to ProMOS and the Taiwanese company makes DRAMs for Hynix on a contract basis. Hynix acquired an equity stake of 8% in ProMOS as part of the pact.

Also in 2008 the company ceased DRAM production at its Hynix Semiconductor Manufacturing America wafer fabrication facility in Eugene Oregon –its only plant in the US. Hynix made the move because of continuing oversupply and precipitously declining prices in the global DRAM market. The company is looking at utilization of its 200mm wafer fabrication facilities since they are less efficient than its 300mm wafer fabs. The Eugene plant is a 200mm fab. Hynix will decide later on what to do with the facility; under market conditions it may not be economical to change the fab to 300mm wafer fabrication or to utilize the facility for producing devices other than DRAMs such as photovoltaic solar cells.

Hynix closed 200mm DRAM fabs in Cheongju and Icheon South Korea and in Wuxi China in addition to the Oregon fab. Only one 200mm fab in Cheongju was remaining by the end of 2008 and it is focusing on specialty devices eschewing volume production of DRAMs or other commodity parts.

In 2008 the company sold part of its stake in the Chinese fab to Numonyx for $100 million. Hynix reduced its ownership in the plant from about 83% to around 72%.

Late in the year under pressure from plummeting chip demand and prices the company announced restructuring efforts that included dropping executive pay by up to 30% cutting its executive ranks by 30% and offering employees with more than 10 years on the job an early retirement package. The moves were expected to cut labor costs by 15% at a time when Hynix was asking its bank and shareholders for financial help.

Hynix started losing money in the last quarter of 2007 and was in the red throughout 2008. In 2009 the company completed two rights offerings with its creditors to raise cash and to ease its debt load. Korea Exchange Bank and other creditors agreed to convert $309 million in trade financing into longer-term debt and to extend about $148 million in new loans to the chip maker which also plans to sell new shares worth around $520 million.

Also in 2009 Hynix agreed to settle a long-running patent infringement case with Rambus by taking out a license for certain memory parts and paying royalties on sales of the devices. The Korean chip maker also committed to paying $397 million in damages to Rambus.

In 2010 Kim Jong Kap resigned as CEO and was succeeded by SVP Kwon Oh Chul who was selected by Hynix's creditors to run the company. Also in 2010 Hynix reached a settlement with the European Commission on a longstanding complaint regarding price fixing on memory chips from 1998 to 2002. The commission collected a total of about $408 million from memory chip suppliers in the case; Hynix's penalty was $63 million for colluding with other memory makers helping hike the prices consumers paid for PCs and other products.

Later that year Hynix acquired the minority stake in China-based Hynix-Numonyx Semiconductor Ltd. owned by Numonyx (acquired by Micron Technology in 2010). Hynix paid about $423 million for the 19% stake owned by its partner in the joint venture. The move came as competition between and Hynix and Micron heated up.

After spinning off its non-memory semiconductor business as MagnaChip Semiconductor Hynix is returning to chip markets other than DRAMs and flash memories. MagnaChip originally filed for an IPO in the US in 2007; it withdrew the registration statement in 2009 citing unfavorable market conditions for IPOs. MagnaChip filed another registration statement with the SEC in 2010.

EXECUTIVES

President CEO and Director, Oh Chul Kwon
EVP CTO and Director, Sung Wook Park
CFO and Director, Min Chul Kim
Auditors: Samjong Accounting Corporation (A Member Firm of KPMG)

LOCATIONS

HQ: SK Hynix Inc
2091, Gyeongchung-daero Bubal-eup, Icheon, Gyeonggi-do 467-734
Phone: (82) 31 630 4114   **Fax:** (82) 31 630 4103
Web: www.hynix.com

PRODUCTS/OPERATIONS

Selected Products
DRAM
DDR2 SDRAM
DDR3 SDRAM
DDR4 SDRAM
GDDR5 SDRAM
HBM
LPDDR3
LPDDR4
Module
NAND
eMMC
Multichip Package
Raw NAND
UFS
SSD
Client SSD
CMOS Image Sensor
Enterprise SSD
SSD Consumer Site

COMPETITORS

ACL Semiconductors
Cypress Semiconductor
Elpida Memory
IBM Microelectronics
Integrated Silicon
  Solution
Kingston Technology
Macronix International
Micron Technology
Mitsubishi Electric
Mosel Vitelic
Nanya
Netlist
Oki Semiconductor
OmniVision
  Technologies

Powerchip
Rambus
SMART Modular
  Technologies
Samsung Electronics
SanDisk
Sharp Electronics
Silicon Storage
TSMC
Tessera
Toshiba Semiconductor
  & Storage Products
UMC
Winbond Electronics

HISTORICAL FINANCIALS
Company Type: Public

Income Statement
FYE: December 31

	REVENUE ($ mil.)	NET INCOME ($ mil.)	NET PROFIT MARGIN	EMPLOYEES
12/15	15,977	3,673	23.0%	22,139
12/14	15,652	3,834	24.5%	21,551
12/13	13,469	2,731	20.3%	20,756
12/12	9,517	(148)	—	20,560
12/11	8,972	(48)	—	19,601
Annual Growth	15.5%	—	—	3.1%

2015 Year-End Financials

Debt ratio: 0.0%
Return on equity: 21.9%
Cash ($ mil.): 999
Current ratio: 2.02
Long-term debt ($ mil.): 2,384

No. of shares (mil.): 706
Dividends
  Yield: —
  Payout: 5.0%
Market value ($ mil.): —

SK Innovation Co Ltd

SK Innovation (formerly known as SK Energy) is the energy lubricants and chemicals affiliate of South Korea's SK Group. Korea's largest oil refiner SK Innovation controls about 34% of Korea's fuel retailing market. The firm holds stakes in 30 oil exploration and production projects in 16 countries and has proved reserves of more than 500 million barrels of oil equivalent. It imports liquid petroleum gas (LPG) and claims a 44% share of the Korean LPG market. SK Innovation supplies natural gas to Seoul and other cities in Korea. The company also makes lubricants low-pollutant gasoline petrochemicals and batteries for electric vehicles.

In 2011 in order to be a more flexible organization in dealing with a rapidly changing marketplace SK Innovation spun off its refining unit as SK Energy its chemical operations as SK Global Chemicals and its lubricant oil business as SK Lubricants. All the units are wholly-owned subsidiaries. A part of the innovative push the company's new corporate name claims the company is looking to expand in the field of alternative energy including pursuing new battery and carbon capture technologies.

SK Innovation is focusing on strengthening its overseas oil exploration and production operations. It has formed strategic alliances with other global oil concerns such as Nippon Oil and PERTAMINA to in order to expand activities in China Vietnam and Indonesia.

In 2010 it formed a joint venture with KBR to market and license SK Innovation's petrochemical and related process technologies. That same year it agreed to sell its Brazilian oil interests to Denmark's Mærsk Oil for $2.4 billion. SK Innovation plans to use the proceeds either to invest in developing oil and gas fields or to buy other international oil companies. That year the company signed a contract to operate and maintain Vietnam's first petrochemical plant.

On the innovative technology side of the ledger in 2010 Korea launched its first electric car a vehicle powered by an SK Innovation lithium-ion battery.

In 2008 the company merged with subsidiary SK Incheon Oil a major Korean refiner allowing the company to further its plans to be a major oil and fuels exporter to the growing China market.

President, Chul Khil Jeong
Auditors: Anjin & Co. (A Member Firm of Deloitte Touche Tohmatsu)

LOCATIONS
HQ: SK Innovation Co Ltd
26, Jong-ro Jongno-gu, Seoul 110-110
Phone: (82) 2 2121 5114   **Fax:** (82) 2 2121 2118
Web: www.skenergy.com

COMPETITORS
BHP Billiton	Idemitsu Kosan
Exxon Mobil	JX Nippon Oil & Energy
GS Caltex	POSCO Daewoo
Hyundai Corporation	Royal Dutch Shell

HISTORICAL FINANCIALS
Company Type: Public

Income Statement   FYE: December 31

	REVENUE ($ mil.)	NET INCOME ($ mil.)	NET PROFIT MARGIN	EMPLOYEES
12/15	41,100	692	1.7%	1,419
12/14	60,200	(538)	—	1,878
12/13	63,395	694	1.1%	1,892
12/12	68,680	1,110	1.6%	1,881
12/11	59,007	2,734	4.6%	1,642
Annual Growth	(8.6%)	(29.1%)	—	(3.6%)

2015 Year-End Financials
Debt ratio: 0.0%	No. of shares (mil.): 91
Return on equity: 5.2%	Dividends
Cash ($ mil.): 2,566	Yield: —
Current ratio: 1.71	Payout: —
Long-term debt ($ mil.): 5,210	Market value ($ mil.): —

SK Networks Co Ltd

Auditors: Hanyoung Accounting Corporation (A Member Firm of Ernst & Young International)

LOCATIONS
HQ: SK Networks Co Ltd
90 Namdaemun-ro, Jung-gu, Seoul 440-816
Phone: (82) 2 2221 2114   **Fax:** (82) 2 2221 0097
Web: www.sknetworks.co.kr

HISTORICAL FINANCIALS
Company Type: Public

Income Statement   FYE: December 31

	REVENUE ($ mil.)	NET INCOME ($ mil.)	NET PROFIT MARGIN	EMPLOYEES
12/15	17,301	62	0.4%	3,174
12/14	20,480	29	0.1%	3,301
12/13	24,699	(540)	—	3,661
12/12	26,164	45	0.2%	3,912
12/11	23,764	125	0.5%	4,085
Annual Growth	(7.6%)	(16.1%)	—	(6.1%)

2015 Year-End Financials
Debt ratio: 0.0%	No. of shares (mil.): 248
Return on equity: 2.9%	Dividends
Cash ($ mil.): 959	Yield: —
Current ratio: 0.92	Payout: —
Long-term debt ($ mil.): 1,065	Market value ($ mil.): —

Skandinaviska Enskilda Banken

Snow banks are a common winter sight in Sweden; SEB banks are easy to spot year-round. Skandinaviska Enskilda Banken (SEB) provides merchant banking retail banking wealth management and life insurance in some 20 nations mostly in Northern Europe. Its merchant banking division provides lending debt capital markets trading finance and custody services to corporate clients and financial institutions. Its retail division provides business services including loans and card services. SEB Wealth Management offers asset management and private banking services to institutional and wealthy clients. Founded in 1856 the bank boasts nearly SK$3 trillion (around $350 billion) in assets.

OperationsThe bank operates five main business segments: Merchant Banking which generated 38% of total revenue in 2014; Retail Banking (27% of revenue); Wealth Management (10% of revenue) which boasts around SK$1.8 billion ($208 million) in assets under management; Life (10% of revenue) which provides life insurance products; and Baltic (8% of revenue) which counts the bank's operations in the Baltic region.

More broadly SEB generated 48% of its total revenue from interest income in 2014 while 22% came from fee and commission income and 8% came from life insurance premium income. The remainder of the bank's revenue came from gains on the bank's investment securities.

Geographic Reach
SEB generated 60% of its operating income in Sweden in 2014. Its other top markets are in the Nordic countries of Denmark Finland Germany and Norway as well as in Baltic countries such as Estonia Latvia and Lithuania. Sales and MarketingRetail Banking served 1.7 million private customers and 200000 small and medium-sized businesses in 2014. Its Wealth Management division serves institutions life insurance companies and private individuals. SEB's corporate customers come from a broad range of industries and sectors including manufacturing and service companies as well as investment and property companies.

Financial Performance
Note: Growth rates may differ after conversion to US dollars.SEB's revenues and profits have been rising over the past several years mostly thanks to higher net interest income from its growing loan business and cheap borrowing rates as well as increasing fee and commission income from its growing corporate financing business. (Note: In terms of US Dollars the bank's revenue has struggled to grow due to unfavorable foreign exchange rates.)The bank's revenue jumped by 15% to SK$98 billion ($12.4 billion) in 2014 thanks to a combination of higher fee and commission income from higher volumes of Merchant Banking transactions (such as mergers and acquisitions initial public offerings and new issues) and gains on the bank's investment securities and assets and liabilities held for trading. The bank's insurance business also grew thanks to higher fund values and higher premium volumes. Higher revenue and strong staff cost controls in 2014 also pushed the bank's net income up by 30% to SK$19 billion ($2.46 billion). SEB's cash levels declined sharply with operations using SK$148 billion ($19 billion) during the year mostly due to a decrease in borrowing from credit institutions and a decline in short-term security issue funding compared to the prior year.

Strategy
SEB in 2015 continued to focus on growing its Merchant Banking and Retail divisions. Thanks to its heavy promotional investments in 2014 the bank landed 60 new large corporate and institutional customers 12700 new small and mid-sized enterprise (SME) customers and 27000 private customers.

In addition to growing on its own SEB also looks to acquire financial firms that complement its offerings and expand its geographic reach. In 2014 SEB acquisitions boosted its card business in two of its top Noridic markets: Finland and Norway. With events in Russia and Ukraine causing political turmoil financial capitalization has also been an important priority for the bank. Fortunately for SEB the European Central Bank's 2014 stress test confirmed the bank's capital strength and asset quality passed muster. Mergers and AcquisitionsIn 2014 SEB bolstered its card businesses in Finland and Norway after acquiring Nets' Business Eurocard operations and DNB's corporate card portfolio respectively.

HISTORY
Company BackgroundSkandinaviska Enskilda Banken (SEB) was incorporated in 1972 as a result of the merger between Stockholm's Enskilda Bank (founded in 1856 by the Wallenberg family) and Skandinaviska Banken (founded in 1864 and a pioneer in commercial lending in Scandinavia). By 1974 SEB had begun expanding its operations forming an investment management subsidiary. It then became one of the first Swedish banks to go international when it took a stake in the German Deutsch-Skandinavische Bank in 1976. By the end of the 1970s SEB had reached halfway around the world establishing a subsidiary in Singapore to handle Southeast Asian operations.

By the early 1980s SEB was leading the nation in industrial as well as private accounts largely due to deregulation and the introduction of new financial instruments including Swedish treasury bills a commercial paper market and market-rate state bonds. The bank continued to expand opening branches in the Cayman Islands Hamburg London and New York; it also began cross-border banking in Scandinavia through a regional alliance with Bergen Bank of Norway Privatbanken of Denmark and Union Bank of Finland.

In another step toward deregulation the Swedish government lifted the ban on foreign banking in 1985. Within a year a dozen international banks had established themselves in Sweden but SEB continued to expand; its investment banking subsidiary Enskilda Securities opened branches in Hong Kong London New York Paris and Singapore in the latter half of the 1980s.

In 1990 the bank acquired an option to buy about a third of Skandia Sweden's largest private insurance company. But facing strong resistance from Skandia's management SEB accepted defeat and sold most of its option to two Scandinavian insurance companies. Winds of change blew through Sweden in the early 1990s as the country suffered a severe economic recession. Deregulation in the mid-1980s followed by excessive lending to the property market led to inflated real estate prices and then a collapse of the market. Banks investing in property experienced huge losses; many banks (including SEB) had to turn to the government for help to strengthen their capital bases. The mid-1990s saw the bank still trying to recover selling several of its subsidiaries including a vehicle finance unit to GE Capital.

1997 saw SEB acquire Trygg-Hansa (now SEB Trygg Liv) one of Sweden's major insurers. The bank remained acquisitive in 1998 expanding aggressively into the Baltic by buying major stakes in banks in Estonia (Eesti Ühlspank) Latvia (Latvija Unibanken) and Lithuania (Vilniaus Bankas).

In 1999 the bank further emphasized its Internet business making it a separate unit. Also that year SEB sold Trygg-Hansa's non-life business to Denmark's Codan Insurance in exchange for Codan's banking subsidiary and other assets. In 2000 the bank acquired Germany's almost 200-branch BfG Bank from Credit Lyonnais; it then used BfG to create a cross-selling and Internet alliance with German insurer Gerling. Also in 2000 SEB upped its stake in Eesti Ühispank Vilniaus Bankas and Latvijas Unibanka.

The following year SEB announced plans to acquire fellow Swedish bank FöreningsSparbanken to create SEB SwedBank. EU regulators investigated the proposal and demanded significant concession. As a result the two banks dropped plans for the merger later in 2001.

SEB continued to boost its offerings and services —largely through acquisitions —during the early years of the 21st century. Purchases included Europay in Norway (2002) Danish life insurer Codan Pension (2004) Ukraine's Bank Agio (2005) and Russia's PetroEnergoBank (2006). In 2007 it acquired nearly all of Factorial Bank adding 65 branches in Eastern Ukraine. The following year it bought London-based hedge fund Key Asset Management.

EXECUTIVES

EVP and CFO, Jan Erik Back, age 55
EVP and Head Merchant Banking and Corporate and Institutions, Annika Falkengren, age 54
Deputy President and CEO, Magnus Carlsson, age 60
Country Manager SEB Germany, Fredrik Boheman, age 60
EVP and Head of Retail Banking, Mats Torstendahl, age 55
Country Manager SEB Denmark, Peter H .ltermand, age 53
Head of Baltic Division, David Teare, age 53
Country Manager SEB Norway, William Paus, age 49
Country Manager and President SEB Latvia, Ieva Tetere
Country Manager and President SEB Estonia, Allan Parik
Chief Risk Officer, Johan Andersson, age 59
Co-Head Merchant Banking Division, Joachim Alpen, age 49
Head of Life Division, Peter Dahlgren, age 44
Head of Wealth Management, Christoffer Malmer, age 41
Co-Head of Merchant Banking Division, Johan Torgeby, age 42
Country Manager SEB Finland, Marcus Nysten, age 56
Deputy Chairman, Urban Jansson, age 71
Vice Chairman, Jesper Ovesen, age 59
Chairman, Marcus Wallenberg, age 60
Auditors: PricewaterhouseCoopers AB

LOCATIONS

HQ: Skandinaviska Enskilda Banken
Kungstradgardsgatan 8, Stockholm SE-106 40
Phone: (46) 771 62 10 00
Web: www.sebgroup.com

2014 Operating Income

	% of total
Scandinavia	
Sweden	60
Norway	8
Denmark	7
Finland	4
Baltics	
Lithuania	3

Estonia	3
Latvia	2
Germany	7
Other	6
Total	**100**

PRODUCTS/OPERATIONS

2014 Sales by Segment

	% of total
Merchant Banking	38
Retail Banking	27
Life	10
Wealth Management	10
Baltic	8
Other	7
Total	**100**

COMPETITORS

Citigroup Global Markets	Morgan Stanley
	Nordea Bank
Danske Bank	Skandia
Deutsche Bank	Storebrand ASA
DnB NOR	Svenska Handelsbanken
Goldman Sachs	Swedbank AB
KBC	UBS Investment Bank

HISTORICAL FINANCIALS
Company Type: Public

Income Statement
FYE: December 31

	ASSETS ($ mil.)	NET INCOME ($ mil.)	INCOME AS % OF ASSETS	EMPLOYEES
12/15	296,065	1,966	0.7%	16,599
12/14	341,678	2,486	0.7%	16,742
12/13	387,577	2,303	0.6%	17,096
12/12	376,613	1,785	0.5%	18,168
12/11	342,561	1,610	0.5%	18,912
Annual Growth	(3.6%)	5.1%	—	(3.2%)

2015 Year-End Financials

Return on assets: 0.6%
Return on equity: 11.9%
Long-term debt ($ mil.): —
No. of shares (mil.): —
Sales ($ mill): 9,043
Dividends
Yield: —
Payout: 63.0%
Market value ($ mil.): —

Skanska AB

Auditors: KPMG AB

LOCATIONS

HQ: Skanska AB
Warfvinges vag 25, Stockholm SE-112 74
Phone: (46) 10 448 00 00   **Fax:** (46) 8 755 12 56
Web: www.skanska.com

HISTORICAL FINANCIALS
Company Type: Public

Income Statement
FYE: December 31

	REVENUE ($ mil.)	NET INCOME ($ mil.)	NET PROFIT MARGIN	EMPLOYEES
12/15	18,154	566	3.1%	48,470
12/14	18,540	497	2.7%	57,866
12/13	21,289	587	2.8%	57,105
12/12	19,855	437	2.2%	56,618
12/11	17,215	1,100	6.4%	52,557
Annual Growth	1.3%	(15.3%)	—	(2.0%)

2015 Year-End Financials

Debt ratio: —
Return on equity: 21.0%
Cash ($ mil.): 1,404
Current ratio: 1.24
Long-term debt ($ mil.): —
No. of shares (mil.): 411
Dividends
Yield: 0.0%
Payout: 58.7%
Market value ($ mil.): 7,855

	STOCK PRICE ($) FY Close	P/E High/Low		PER SHARE ($) Earnings	Dividends	Book Value
12/15	19.11	2	2	1.37	0.80	6.95
12/14	22.09	2	2	1.20	0.81	6.69
12/13	20.52	2	2	1.42	0.97	8.03
Annual Growth	(3.5%)	—	—	(1.0%)	(4.7%)	(3.6%)

Sky Plc

Auditors: Deloitte LLP

LOCATIONS

HQ: Sky Plc
Grant Way, Isleworth, Middlesex TW7 5QD
Phone: (44) 333 100 0333   **Fax:** (44) 333 100 0444
Web: www.sky.com/corporate

HISTORICAL FINANCIALS
Company Type: Public

Income Statement
FYE: June 30

	REVENUE ($ mil.)	NET INCOME ($ mil.)	NET PROFIT MARGIN	EMPLOYEES
06/16	16,062	894	5.6%	30,714
06/15	15,685	3,072	19.6%	27,060
06/14	13,006	1,474	11.3%	20,841
06/13	11,027	1,492	13.5%	19,413
06/12	10,595	1,413	13.3%	17,937
Annual Growth	11.0%	(10.8%)	—	14.4%

2016 Year-End Financials

Debt ratio: 68.8%
Return on equity: 20.0%
Cash ($ mil.): 2,868
Current ratio: 1.09
Long-term debt ($ mil.): 11,949
No. of shares (mil.): 1,719
Dividends
Yield: 4.3%
Payout: 341.1%
Market value ($ mil.): 78,748

	STOCK PRICE ($) FY Close	P/E High/Low		PER SHARE ($) Earnings	Dividends	Book Value
06/16	45.81	158	111	0.52	1.97	2.69
06/15	65.50	60	46	1.80	1.98	2.89
06/14	62.70	118	97	0.94	2.05	1.17
06/13	48.39	90	68	0.91	1.65	0.97
06/12	43.92	102	73	0.82	1.48	0.88
Annual Growth	1.1%	—	—	(10.8%)	7.4%	32.3%

Societe Generale

Auditors: ERNST & YOUNG et Autres

LOCATIONS

HQ: Societe Generale
29, Bd Haussman, Paris 75009
Phone: (33) 1 42 14 20 00
Web: www.societegenerale.com

HISTORICAL FINANCIALS
Company Type: Public

Income Statement
FYE: December 31

	ASSETS ($ mil.)	NET INCOME ($ mil.)	INCOME AS % OF ASSETS	EMPLOYEES
12/15	1,453,433	4,357	0.3%	145,703
12/14	1,590,086	3,272	0.2%	148,322
12/13	1,700,629	2,994	0.2%	148,324
12/12	1,648,479	1,020	0.1%	154,009
12/11	1,528,048	3,084	0.2%	159,616
Annual Growth	(1.2%)	9.0%	—	(2.3%)

2015 Year-End Financials

Return on assets: 0.3%
Return on equity: 7.0%
Long-term debt ($ mil.): —
No. of shares (mil.): 796
Sales ($ mil): 106,253

Dividends
Yield: 2.8%
Payout: 5.2%
Market value ($ mil.): 7,346

	STOCK PRICE ($) FY Close	P/E High/Low		PER SHARE ($) Earnings	Dividends	Book Value
12/15	9.22	2	2	4.89	0.26	80.71
12/14	8.32	4	3	3.54	0.27	85.40
12/13	11.65	5	3	3.30	0.12	90.47
12/12	7.82	12	6	0.84	0.00	87.07
12/11	4.36	4	1	4.11	0.46	81.50
Annual Growth	20.6%	—	—	4.4%	(13.4%)	(0.2%)

Societe Nationale des Chemins de Fer Francais (SNCF) (France)

Auditors: PricewaterhouseCoopers Audit

LOCATIONS

HQ: Societe Nationale des Chemins de Fer Francais (SNCF) (France)
1-7 place aux Etoiles, La Plaine ST Denis, Cedex 93212
Phone: (33) 1 42 85 63 13   **Fax:** (33) 1 42 85 63 16
Web: www.sncf.com

HISTORICAL FINANCIALS
Company Type: Public

Income Statement
FYE: December 31

	REVENUE ($ mil.)	NET INCOME ($ mil.)	NET PROFIT MARGIN	EMPLOYEES
12/15	31,909	(2,372)	—	196,152
12/14	33,114	735	2.2%	245,763
12/13	44,374	(247)	—	244,570
12/12	44,576	504	1.1%	249,343
12/11	42,224	161	0.4%	245,090
Annual Growth	(6.8%)	—	—	(5.4%)

2015 Year-End Financials

Debt ratio: 54.9%
Return on equity: (-39.3%)
Cash ($ mil.): 4,382
Current ratio: 0.84
Long-term debt ($ mil.): 16,503

No. of shares (mil.): —
Dividends
Yield: —
Payout: —
Market value ($ mil.): —

Sodexo

This company has a lot of mouths to feed. Formerly Sodexho Alliance Sodexo is the world's #2 contract foodservice provider (after Compass Group) with operations in about 80 countries. Its subsidiaries offer corporate foodservice and hospitality services vending services and foodservices for educational institutions and other public-sector clients. Other operations include event concessions health care foodservices and such outsourced on-site service solutions as cleaning groundskeeping and laundry. Its US-based subsidiary Sodexo Inc. is one of the largest contract foodservice providers in North America. The company has some 33900 service sites worldwide.

In addition to its core foodservice and facilities management services Sodexo is a leading provider of voucher cards in Europe and Latin America used to buy groceries clothing and other basic necessities. The company operates voucher systems for both employers that use the cards as a form of employee benefits as well as for government welfare programs. Vouchers include restaurant gift and childcare passes. (Sodexo refers to its voucher operations as motivation solutions.)

Sodexo's business strategy includes the following: to become a world leader in on-site service solutions and motivation solutions and to maintain its leadership in the foodservice sector. It sets forth these basic goals in order to meet challenges such as the recent and on-going worldwide economic turndown and the aging of the population (particularly in North America). It also faces diminishing sources of and rising costs of its raw materials (ex: energy and food). And finally as the world population continues to grow and at the same time societies' wealth grows Sodexo must to deal with quality-of-life issues with regard to the goods and services it provides.

Working to fulfill these strategies the company won the contract for organizing the 2010 Winter Olympics in Vancouver. During 2009 it increased its contract obligations with France's Ministry of Justice to deliver service solutions to 27 additional prisons. It also won the Microsoft Europe contract and renewed its contract with Procter & Gamble for which Sodexo provides a wide range of services at 38 sites in 13 European countries. It also signed a 30-year contract to design construct and manage a military training center for The Defense Training Review in the UK. (Sodexo hopes to realize euro 30 billion in revenue over the life of the contract.) In addition Sodexo made acquisitions in high-growth markets in 2009 including Zehnacker in Germany RKHS in India and Comfort Keepers in the US. Following that trend into 2011 the company acquired the Brazilian based Puras do Brazil for approximately euro 525 million mid year.

During 2008 it signed contracts to provide services to GlaxoSmithKline in Canada and Societe Generale in France. The company has also been making targeted acquisitions to expand both its services and geographical reach. It purchased a 90% stake in Zehnacker Group a facilities management services provider in Germany for more than euro 170 million ($234 million) in 2008. That same year it acquired Score Groupe in France.

The company changed its name in 2008 to Sodexo dropping both the word "Alliance" and the "h" as part of a global rebranding effort. The name change was intended to raise the company's profile and recognition by focusing on the singular name (that it also hopes is easier to spell and pronounce without the extra letter).

Chairman Pierre Bellon and his family own about 38% of the company.

HISTORY

The Bellon family had been luxury ship hospitality specialists since the turn of the century 60 years before Pierre Bellon founded Sodexho in 1966. By 1971 Bellon had his first contract outside France to provide foodservice to a Brussels hospital. Sodexho continued to expand its services into the late 1970s entering remote site management in Africa and the Middle East in 1975 and starting its service vouchers segment in Belgium and Germany in 1978.

Sodexho jumped the pond in 1980 expanding its businesses into North and South America. The company went public on the Paris Bourse exchange in 1983. Two years later it bought Seiler a Boston vending machine company-turned-restaurateur. Sodexho then bought San Francisco's Food Dimensions in 1987. After beefing up its American operations with four other US acquisitions the company merged Food Dimensions and Seiler in 1989. Sodexho's US river cruise company Spirit Cruises —an echo of the Bellon family's original calling —was also included in the merger. The merged US companies were renamed Sodexho USA in 1993.

The 1990s proved an era of growth and acquisitions for Sodexho. The company expanded into Japan Africa Russia and five Eastern European countries in 1993. The company acquired a 20% stake in Corrections Corporation of America the following year and virtually doubled its size with the acquisition of the UK's Gardner Merchant in 1995. The largest catering company in that region Gardner Merchant had holdings that spanned Australia Asia northern Europe the UK and the US — generally markets where Sodexho did not have a strong presence. That year the company also acquired Partena a Swedish security and care company from Volvo's Fortos.

Gardner Merchant's US business was officially merged with Sodexho USA in 1996 to make it the #4 foodservice company in the US. Also that year Sodexho acquired Brazilian service voucher company Cardapio. After a year of legal wrangling Sodexho also lost a fight for control of Accor's Eurest France to rival caterer Compass Group and sold off its minority interest. The next year Sodexho acquired 49% of Universal Ogden Services renamed Universal Services an American remote site manager. To signify its efforts to maintain the individuality of the companies it acquires Sodexho changed its name to Sodexho Alliance in 1997.

Marriott International merged its foodservice branch with Sodexho's North American foodservice operations in 1998. With a 48% stake Sodexho Alliance became the largest shareholder; former Marriott International stockholders took the rest with the Marriott family controlling 9%. Before the merger Sodexho USA was less than one-fourth the size of Marriott International's foodservice division. Sodexho acquired GR Servicios Hoteleros in 1999 thereby becoming the largest caterer in Spain. The following year it agreed to merge its remote site management operations with Universal Services and rename it Universal Sodexho (later Sodexo Remote Sites).

In 2001 its initial $900 million bid to buy the 52% of Sodexho Marriott Services it didn't already own was rebuffed by its subsidiary's shareholders. Sodexho Alliance made a better offer (about $1.1 billion) and finally reached an agreement to purchase the rest of Sodexho Marriott Services. The deal was completed later that year and Sodexho Marriott Services changed its name to Sodexho Inc. Also that year the company agreed to pay some $470 million for French rival Sogeres and US-based food management firm Wood Dining.

In 2002 the company announced it had detected accounting and management errors in its UK operations causing the value of its stock to fall by nearly one-third. In addition the company replaced its UK management team because of poor performance there.

Admitting no wrongdoing Sodexho settled an $80 million race-bias lawsuit just before it was to go to trial in 2005. The suit brought by the African-American employees of its American subsidiary Sodexho Inc. charged that African-Americans were routinely passed over for promotions and were segregated within the company. In addition to paying the monetary award Sodexho agreed to increase company diversity through promotion incentives monitoring and training.

In 2005 Bellon 75 stepped down as company CEO but remained chairman. He was replaced by Sodexho veteran Michel Landel. The company changed its name to Sodexo in 2008 a rebranding effort that eliminated both the word "Alliance" and the "h" from its name.

EXECUTIVES

CEO, Michel Landel, age 65, $843,447 total compensation
CEO Corporate Services Worldwide, Sylvia Metayer
CEO Energy and Resources Worldwide, Nicholas Japy, age 60
CEO Universities Worldwide, Patrick E. (Pat) Connolly
Group Chief Strategy Organization Research and Development and Innovation Officer, Damien Verdier, age 59
EVP and VP Group Executive Committee; CEO Europe On-Site Services, Pierre Henry, age 65
Region Chair North America and CEO Schools Worldwide, Lorna C. Donatone
CEO Benefits and Rewards Services Worldwide, Denis Machuel
CEO Service Operations Worldwide, Satya-Christophe Menard
CEO Government and Agencies and CEO Sports and Leisure Worldwide, Debbie White
CEO Engineering and Construction, Laurent Auzanneau
Group Chief Brand and Communication Officer, Ana Busto
Group CFO, Marc Rolland
Vice Chairman, Sophie Bellon
Auditors: PricewaterhouseCoopers Audit

LOCATIONS

HQ: Sodexo
255, quai de la Bataille de Stalingrad, Issy-les-Moulineaux, Cedex 9 92866
Phone: (33) 1 30 85 75 00
Web: www.sodexo.com

2016 Sales

	% of total
United States	41
France	13
United Kingdom	10
Other	36
Total	**100**

PRODUCTS/OPERATIONS

2016 Sales

	% of total
On-site Services	
Food services	67
Facilities management	29
Benefits and Rewards	4
Total	**100**

Selected Services

Benefits and Rewards Services
Employee Benefits

Expense Management
Incentive & Recognition Programs
On-site Services
Personal and Home Services

COMPETITORS

ARAMARK	Elior
Accor	Healthcare Services
Autogrill	ISS A/S
Berendsen	SSP
Cintas	SSP America
Compass Group	UniFirst
Delaware North	

HISTORICAL FINANCIALS

Company Type: Public

Income Statement

FYE: August 31

	REVENUE ($ mil.)	NET INCOME ($ mil.)	NET PROFIT MARGIN	EMPLOYEES
08/16	22,542	709	3.1%	425,594
08/15	22,211	784	3.5%	422,844
08/14	23,768	646	2.7%	419,317
08/13	24,357	581	2.4%	427,921
08/12	22,959	660	2.9%	421,391
Annual Growth	**(0.5%)**	**1.8%**	**—**	**0.2%**

2016 Year-End Financials

Debt ratio: 20.3%
Return on equity: 17.2%
Cash ($ mil.): 1,531
Current ratio: 0.96
Long-term debt ($ mil.): 2,800
No. of shares (mil.): 150
Dividends
  Yield: 2.1%
  Payout: —
Market value ($ mil.): 3,489

	STOCK PRICE ($) FY Close	P/E High/Low		PER SHARE ($) Earnings	Dividends	Book Value
08/16	23.16	6	4	4.62	0.49	27.11
08/15	17.59	23	4	5.09	0.41	27.31
08/14	97.97	33	27	4.21	0.00	27.71
08/13	88.10	34	26	3.81	0.00	25.81
08/12	78.85	23	18	4.34	0.38	25.36
Annual Growth	**(26.4%)**	**—**	**—**	**1.6%**	**6.6%**	**1.7%**

SoftBank Group Corp

Auditors: Deloitte Touche Tohmatsu LLC

LOCATIONS

HQ: SoftBank Group Corp
1-9-1 Higashi-Shinbashi, Minato-ku, Tokyo 105-7303
Phone: (81) 3 6889 2290
Web: www.softbank.jp

HISTORICAL FINANCIALS

Company Type: Public

Income Statement

FYE: March 31

	REVENUE ($ mil.)	NET INCOME ($ mil.)	NET PROFIT MARGIN	EMPLOYEES
03/16	81,512	4,222	5.2%	74,888
03/15	72,264	5,570	7.7%	72,978
03/14	64,587	5,105	7.9%	77,966
03/13	34,036	3,958	11.6%	32,862
03/12	39,039	3,824	9.8%	22,710
Annual Growth	**20.2%**	**2.5%**	**—**	**34.8%**

2016 Year-End Financials

Debt ratio: 0.5%
Return on equity: 17.3%
Cash ($ mil.): 22,882
Current ratio: 1.07
Long-term debt ($ mil.): 82,600
No. of shares (mil.): 1,146
Dividends
  Yield: 0.6%
  Payout: —
Market value ($ mil.): 27,417

	STOCK PRICE ($) FY Close	P/E High/Low		PER SHARE ($) Earnings	Dividends	Book Value
03/16	23.91	0	0	3.46	0.16	20.29
03/15	29.08	0	0	4.66	0.18	19.95
03/14	37.91	0	0	4.27	0.20	15.94
03/13	22.80	0	0	3.49	0.00	14.39
03/12	14.87	—	—	3.40	0.00	15.93
Annual Growth	**12.6%**	**—**	**—**	**0.4%**	**—**	**6.2%**

Sompo Holdings Inc

Sompo Holdings (formerly SompoJapan Nipponkoa Holdings) was created to hold two insurance companies: Sompo Japan and Nipponkoa Insurance. While already strong players in Japan's property/casualty (called non-life in Japan) and life insurance markets when merger mania hit the industry they didn't want to be left out and formed the joint holding company in 2010. The two companies merged into one entity Sompo Japan Nipponkoa Insurance in 2014. The holding company's businesses include domestic property/casualty and life insurance as well as overseas insurance asset and risk management services pension plans and some supplemental health insurance products.

Geographic Reach

Sompo Holdings has operations in some 230 cities in 32 countries in Africa the Americas Asia Europe the Middle East and Oceania. It earns the majority of its revenues in the Japanese market.

Sales and Marketing

Sompo Holdings markets its products through insurance agencies while Sonpo 24 and Saison Automobile and Fire sells directly to customers. Sompo Japan Nipponkoa Himawari Life markets through property/casualty insurance agencies promoting life insurance to property/casualty policyholders.

Financial Performance

The company's revenue increased 6% to ¥3 trillion in 2014 on an increase in net premiums written and life insurance premiums written. Investment income also rose that year. Predecessors Sompo Japan and Nipponkoa saw continued growth in net premiums written primarily due to the effect of rate revisions in automobile coverage. In South America the acquiring of additional shares of Brazil's Maritima Seguros boosted earnings.

Net income dropped 1% to ¥43.6 billion due to an increase in net commissions and brokerage fees and provisions for reserve for outstanding losses and claims and provisions for underwriting reserves incurred.

Sompo Holdings reported a cash inflow of ¥123 billion (versus a cash outflow in 2013) due to gains on investments and changes in reserves for outstanding losses and claims.

Strategy

Why merge in the first place? The company cites pressures on its industry from several sources including the country's declining birthrate its rapidly aging population and the effects of climate change. While those are real challenges to the industry the Sompo/Nipponkoa merger also took place at the same time as several other large mergers among Japanese insurance companies. When the dust settles there will be fewer but larger companies elbowing each other to claim market share.

To expand its reinsurance operations the company has established outposts in Hong Kong Kuala Lumpur and London. It opened a representative office in Johannesburg in 2014. And it acquired UK-based Canopius Group a specialty player that primarily works through insurance exhange Lloyds.

Also in 2014 Sompo Japan Nipponkoa became the first Japanese property/casualty insurer to receive approval to sell compulsory automobile accident coverage in China.

The company is entering new market sectors that complement its insurance operations. In 2015 it struck up a partnership with nursing care company MessageCo to provide nursing care services. It also acquired a majority stake in Japanese home remodeler FRESHHOUSE to build on its fire insurance sales.

Mergers and Acquisitions

Since the initial merger Sompo Holdings has been working to expand its operations outside the saturated Japanese market. To enter the overseas specialty market the company in 2014 purchased Canopius Group one of the top 10 insurers in the Lloyds insurance market. Further in 2016 the company agreed to acquire casualty insurer Endurance Specialty Holdings for $6.3 billion opening it up to the US market and becoming the latest Japanese insurer to make moves across the Pacific.

EXECUTIVES

President and Executive Officer (Group CEO) and Representative Director, Kengo Sakurada
Deputy President and Senior Managing Executive Officer (Group CIO) and Director, Keiji Nishizawa
Deputy President Senior Managing Executive Officer and Director, Shinji Tsuji
Managing Executive Officer and General Manager The Americas Regional Headquarters, Masato Fujikura
Executive Officer General Manager Global Business Planning Department and General Manager China & East Asia Regional Headquarters, Junichi Tanaka
Executive Officer and General Manager South Asia and Pacific Regional Headquarters, Nobuhiro Kojima
Executive Officer and General Manager Europe Regional Headquarters, Takashi Yoshino
Chairman, Masaya Futamiya
Auditors: Ernst & Young ShinNihon LLC

LOCATIONS

HQ: Sompo Holdings Inc
1-26-1 Nishi-Shinjuku, Shinjuku-ku, Tokyo 160-8338
Phone: (81) 3 3349 3000
Web: www.sompo-hd.com

COMPETITORS

Fuji Fire and Marine	Samsung Fire & Marine
MS&AD Holdings	Tokio Marine
Nippon Life Insurance	

HISTORICAL FINANCIALS

Company Type: Public

Income Statement

FYE: March 31

	REVENUE ($ mil.)	NET INCOME ($ mil.)	NET PROFIT MARGIN	EMPLOYEES
03/16	28,745	1,421	4.9%	80,668
03/15	27,213	452	1.7%	70,731
03/14	29,001	427	1.5%	35,904
03/13	30,071	463	1.5%	35,481
03/12	33,881	(1,124)	—	35,542
Annual Growth	(4.0%)	—	—	22.7%

2016 Year-End Financials

Debt ratio: —
Return on equity: 9.1%
Cash ($ mil.): 5,924
Current ratio: —
Long-term debt ($ mil.): —
No. of shares (mil.): 404
Dividends
Yield: —
Payout: —
Market value ($ mil.): 11,337

	STOCK PRICE ($) FY Close	P/E High	P/E Low	Earnings	PER SHARE ($) Dividends	PER SHARE ($) Book Value
03/16	28.05	0	0	3.51	0.00	36.23
03/15	30.95	0	0	1.11	0.00	37.24
03/14	24.90	—	—	1.03	0.00	32.75
03/13	21.95	—	—	1.11	0.00	32.89
03/12	22.66	—	—	(2.71)	0.00	29.40
Annual Growth	5.5%			—	—	5.4%

Sony Corp

Sony is synonymous with consumer electronics. It's especially big in TVs and game consoles like the new PlayStation4. Officially named Sony Kabushiki Kaisha the company designs makes and sells a host of electronic equipment instruments and devices for consumer professional and industrial markets. Professional products include semiconductors and components. A top global media conglomerate Sony boasts additional assets in the areas of music (Sony Music Entertainment) film (Sony Pictures Entertainment and Sony Digital Production) smartphones (Sony Mobile) DVDs (Sony Pictures Home Entertainment) and TV (Sony Pictures Television). Sony also has several financial services businesses and an advertising agency in Japan.

Geographic Reach

Sony's primary manufacturing facilities are located in Asia including Japan where it is headquartered. Japan is also its single largest market by sales (32% in fiscal 2012 ends March). The US China and Europe are also key markets.

Operations

Sony realigned its reportable segments in 2012 as part of a reorganization. The operations of the former Consumer Professional & Devices (CPD) and Networked Products & Services (NPS) segments are now part of the Consumer Products & Services (CPS) –the company's largest segment by sales –and Professional Device & Solutions (PDS) segments. CPS includes LCD televisions Blu Ray disc and DVD players digital and video cameras PCs and gaming consoles. Certain PlayStation products are marketed and distributed by Sony Computer Entertainment LLC and Sony Computer Entertainment Europe Ltd. PDS the company's second largest segment includes broadcast and other B2B products as well as semiconductors and components.

A smaller business segment Sony Ericsson was renamed Sony Mobile Communications in 2012. As a result of a reorganization that Sony is undertaking plans to even further realign its business segments are under way.

Sales and Marketing

Sony's products are marketed worldwide by sales subsidiaries and unaffiliated distributors as well as direct online sales.

Financial Performance

Sony's fiscal 2012 (ends March) sales fell 9% vs. the prior year while net income continued its steep decline. Indeed the company marked its fourth consecutive year of unprofitability in 2012 as its losses widened.

Sony's consumer products and services segment CPS remains the company's bread and butter accounting for 45% is its fiscal 2012 sales. But competition is fierce in this industry with Apple paving the way in music players with the iPod and Microsoft (Xbox 360) and Nintendo (Wii) jockeying for dominance in game console sales globally.

The rising Yen decreasing demand for its products pricing pressures and the lingering global economic crisis has sidelined Sony in recent years. After logging a record profit in 2007 the company has seen its business stall as consumers tightened their belts.

Strategy

The most pressing part of Sony's current strategy is turning around its electronics businesses. With a new management team established in April 2012 the company moves forward with a plan to strengthen certain core areas: digital imaging game and mobile. Sony is trying to develop new products expand its hardware and software offerings and integrate the operations of its smartphone business (operated by Sony Mobile) with its tablet and PC businesses. Another aspect of this strategy is to turn around its TV business to improve profitability there; TVs generate a large chunk of sales within the CPS segment.

The company may have a hit on its hands with the new PlayStation4 (PS4) which went on sale in North America in November 2013. Indeed Sony sold more than 1 million PS4s in the first 24 hours of sales. The new games console is the centerpiece of the new management team's turnaround strategy for Sony's consumer electronics and film businesses.

Sony also has been consolidating manufacturing facilities selling off businesses and facilities and reducing headcounts. Divestments include its TV production assets and personal computer division. It's closing 20 retail stores in the US and cutting 1000 jobs as part of a much larger reorganization.

In a very competitive electronics environment Sony is simultaneously trying to innovate and launch products in new markets such as it is doing with medical peripherals like printers monitors cameras and recorders. The company is drawing on its audio and visual expertise to build a 4K technology product lineup. 4K is said to deliver more than four times the resolution of full HD.

On the music side Sony's wholly owned subsidiary Sony Corporation of America (SCA) in 2012 led a group of investors in a high-profile high-dollar deal. Alongside the Estate of Michael Jackson David Geffen and Blackstone Group SCA acquired EMI Music Publishing for $2.2 billion from Citigroup. The company's Sony/ATV Music Publishing which owns more than 750000 copyrights now oversees EMI Music Publishing and its 1.3 million copyrights on behalf of the investor group. (Sony/ATV Music Publishing is co-owned by subsidiaries of SCA and trusts formed by the Estate of Michael Jackson.)

HISTORY

Akio Morita Masaru Ibuka and Tamon Maeda (Ibuka's father-in-law) started Tokyo Telecommunications Engineering in 1946 with funding from Morita's father's sake business. The company produced the first Japanese tape recorder in 1950. Three years later Morita paid Western Electric (US) $25000 for transistor technology licenses which sparked a consumer electronics revolution in Japan. His firm launched one of the first transistor radios in 1955 followed by the first Sony-trademarked product a pocket-sized radio in 1957. The next year the company changed its name to Sony (from "sonus" Latin for "sound" and "sonny" meaning "little man"). It beat the competition to newly emerging markets for transistor TVs (1959) and solid-state videotape recorders (1961).

Sony launched the first home video recorder (1964) and the first solid-state condenser microphone (1965). Its 1968 introduction of the Trinitron color TV tube began another decade of explosive growth. Sony bet wrong on its Betamax VCR (1976) which lost to rival Matsushita's (now Panasonic Corp.) VHS as the industry standard. However 1979 brought another success the Walkman personal stereo.

Pressured by adverse currency rates and competition worldwide Sony used its technology to diversify beyond consumer electronics and began to move production to other countries. In the 1980s it introduced Japan's first 32-bit workstation and became a major producer of computer chips and floppy disk drives. The purchases of CBS Records in 1988 ($2 billion) and Columbia Pictures in 1989 (a $4.9 billion deal which included TriStar Pictures) made Sony a major force in the rapidly growing entertainment industry.

The firm manufactured Apple's PowerBook but its portable CD player Data Discman was successful only in Japan (1991). In the early 1990s Sony joined Nintendo to create a new kind of game console combining Sony's CD-ROM drive with the graphic capabilities of a workstation. Although Nintendo pulled out in 1992 Sony released PlayStation in Japan (1994) and in the US (1995) to great success. Two years later in a joint venture with Intel it developed a line of PC desktop systems.

Rather than support an industry-wide standard in 1997 Sony teamed up with Philips Electronics to make another recording media called Super Audio CD which could replace videotapes and CDs. (Sony and Philips created the CD and continue to receive royalties from it.)

In 1998 Sony shipped its first digital high-definition TV to the US folded TriStar into Columbia Pictures merged its Loews Theatres unit with Cineplex Odeon and launched its Wega flat-screen TV.

Philips Sun Microsystems and Sony formed a joint venture in early 1999 to develop networked entertainment products. Also in 1999 Nobuyuki Idei became CEO and the company introduced a Walkman with the capability to download music from the Internet.

In 2000 Sony formed PlayStation.com Japan to sell game consoles and software online; it also introduced its 128-bit PlayStation 2 which plays DVD movies and connects to the Internet. The company later restructured placing all of its US entertainment holdings under a newly-formed umbrella company called Sony Broadband Entertainment.

In early 2001 Sony started an online bank with Japan's Sakura Bank and JP Morgan Chase. Struggling to coordinate its content units (music movies games etc.) with its manufacturing operations (TVs VCRs radios etc.) Sony announced yet another corporate restructuring plan; that move placed all electronics units under one upper-management group.

Adverse market conditions in 2001 aggravated by the September 11 attacks led Sony Pictures Entertainment to consolidate its two domestic television operations folding Columbia TriStar Network Television into Columbia TriStar Domestic Television (CTDT).

In February 2002 an investment group led by Onex Corporation acquired its Loews Theatres unit (which filed for bankruptcy in February 2001). In the course of the fiscal year ending March 2002 Sony laid off about 13700 employees primarily in its electronics and music businesses.

In an attempt to capitalize on the strength of its own brand Sony Pictures Entertainment renamed its Columbia TriStar Domestic Television (CTDT) and Columbia TriStar International Television (CTIT) divisions in September 2002 designating them as Sony Pictures Television (SPT) and Sony Pictures Television International (SPTI) respectively. In October 2002 Sony transformed its Aiwa unit into a wholly-owned subsidiary and absorbed the struggling firm in December 2002.

In 2003 Sony adopted a US-style corporate governance model (made possible by a revision in Japan's Commercial Code) and acquired CIS Corp. a Japanese information system consulting firm. In an effort to cut costs through manufacturing consolidation Sony closed its audio equipment plant in Indonesia that year.

Sony unveiled the Vaio Pocket in 2004 a portable music player designed to compete with Apple's iPod; Vaio Pocket debuted in the US later that year. Sony also introduced a similar product Network Walkman —its first Walkman with a hard drive —in 2004. In October 2004 the company launched a music download system in Japan dubbed MusicDrop. The system utilizes Microsoft's Windows Media Player.

To manage its financial units (Sony Life Insurance Company Sony Assurance and Sony Bank) it created Sony Financial Holdings in 2004. The company announced in 2005 that Idei would be succeeded by foreigner Howard Stringer who had been in charge of Sony's entertainment unit. In 2005 Sony sold its minority stake in music club Columbia House to BMG Direct a subsidiary of Germany's Bertelsmann. In December 2005 the company spun off Sony Communication Network the subsidiary that operates So-Net Internet service (which has nearly 3 million subscribers) through an IPO.

In June 2006 Sony created a holding company for its Japanese-based retail operations (Sony Plaza Sony Family Club B&C Laboratories CP Cosmetics Maxim's de Paris and Lifeneo) and sold 51% of the holding company to investment firm Nikko Principal Investments Japan.

In late 2008 Sony bought out NEC's 45% stake in joint venture Sony Optiarc.

The company in 2010 sold the measuring equipment business of Sony Manufacturing Systems to Mori Seiki a Japan-based precision tool maker in a deal valued at about ¥6 billion (nearly $70 million). It also sold off its 90% stake in Sony Baja California its main TV factory in North America located in Tijuana Mexico to Taiwanese company Hon Hai Precision Industry. It generated $217 million for its share in HBO Latin America which it sold to Time Warner.

In February 2012 Sony acquired Telefonaktiebolaget LM Ericsson's 50% stake in Sony Ericsson Mobile Communications AB marking the completion of the previously announced transaction. As a result Sony Ericsson became a wholly-owned subsidiary of Sony and was renamed "Sony Mobile Communications."

EXECUTIVES

President and CEO; Chairman Sony Corporation of America, Kazuo (Kaz) Hirai, age 56
Executive Deputy President Device Solutions Business and RDS Platform and President Device Solutions Business Group, Tomoyuki Suzuki
EVP Imaging Products and Solutions Business President Professional Solutions Group and Digital Imaging Business Group, Shigeki Ishizuka
SVP and President Home Entertainment and Sound Business Group, Masashi Imamura
EVP Legal Compliance Corporate Communications CSR and External Relations, Shiro Kambe
EVP and CFO, Kenichiro Yoshida
Auditors: PricewaterhouseCoopers Aarata

LOCATIONS

HQ: Sony Corp
7-1, KONAN 1-CHOME, MINATO-KU, Tokyo 108-0075
Phone: (81) 3 6748 2111   **Fax:** (81) 3 6748 2244
Web: www.sony.co.jp

2016 Sales

	% of total
Japan	29
Europe	23
US	21
Asia/Pacific (except Japan and China)	12
China	7
Other	8
Total	**100**

PRODUCTS/OPERATIONS

2016 Sales

	% of total
Game & Network services	18
Home entertainment & sound	14
Mobile communications	13
Financial services	13
Devices	11
Pictures	11
Imaging products & solutions	9
Music	7
Other	4
Total	**100**

Selected Products

Consumer Products & Services (CPS)
   Digital imaging
   Game hardware and software
   Home audio and video
   Personal and mobile products
   Televisions
Professional Device & Solutions (PDS)
   Broadcast and professional-use products
   Semiconductors
   Components

COMPETITORS

Apple Inc.	Motorola Solutions
Bertelsmann	Nintendo
Dell	Nokia
Disney	Panasonic Corp
Eastman Kodak	Philips Electronics
Fujitsu	Pioneer Corporation
HP	SANYO
IBM	Samsung Group
Intel	Sharp Corp.
Kyocera	Technicolor
LG Electronics	Universal Studios
Microsoft	

HISTORICAL FINANCIALS
Company Type: Public

Income Statement
FYE: March 31

	REVENUE ($ mil.)	NET INCOME ($ mil.)	NET PROFIT MARGIN	EMPLOYEES
03/16	72,181	1,316	1.8%	125,300
03/15	68,477	(1,050)	—	131,700
03/14	75,250	(1,243)	—	140,900
03/13	72,278	457	0.6%	146,300
03/12	79,156	(5,566)	—	162,700
Annual Growth	(2.3%)	—	—	(6.3%)

2016 Year-End Financials

Debt ratio: 0.0%	No. of shares (mil.): 1,261
Return on equity: 6.1%	Dividends
Cash ($ mil.): 8,759	Yield: 0.3%
Current ratio: 0.87	Payout: 8.5%
Long-term debt ($ mil.): 4,956	Market value ($ mil.): 32,444

	STOCK PRICE ($) FY Close	P/E High/Low		PER SHARE ($) Earnings	Dividends	Book Value
03/16	25.72	0	0	1.05	0.08	17.39
03/15	26.78	—	—	(0.94)	0.24	16.52
03/14	19.12	—	—	(1.21)	0.25	20.96
03/13	17.40	0	0	0.43	0.27	23.11
03/12	20.77	—	—	(5.55)	0.30	24.65
Annual Growth	5.5%	—	—	—	(28.2%)	(8.3%)

South African Reserve Bank

Auditors: SizweNtsalubaGobodo Inc.

LOCATIONS

HQ: South African Reserve Bank
370 Helen Joseph Street, Pretoria 0002
Phone: (27) 12 313 3911

HISTORICAL FINANCIALS
Company Type: Public

Income Statement
FYE: March 31

	ASSETS ($ mil.)	NET INCOME ($ mil.)	INCOME AS % OF ASSETS	EMPLOYEES
03/16	55,884	99	0.2%	2,233
03/15	54,842	46	0.1%	2,239
03/14	56,611	(132)	—	2,218
03/13	55,567	(152)	—	2,186
03/12	57,003	(77)	—	2,218
Annual Growth	(0.5%)	—	—	0.2%

2016 Year-End Financials

Return on assets: 0.2%	Dividends
Return on equity: 19.8%	Yield: —
Long-term debt ($ mil.): —	Payout: —
No. of shares (mil.): 2	Market value ($ mil.): —
Sales ($ mil): 912	

SSE PLC

Auditors: KPMG LLP

LOCATIONS

HQ: SSE PLC
Inveralmond House, 200 Dunkeld Road, Perth PH1 3AQ
Phone: (44) 17 38456000 **Fax:** (44) 17 38457005
Web: www.sse.com

HISTORICAL FINANCIALS
Company Type: Public

Income Statement
FYE: March 31

	REVENUE ($ mil.)	NET INCOME ($ mil.)	NET PROFIT MARGIN	EMPLOYEES
03/16	41,428	663	1.6%	21,118
03/15	46,783	802	1.7%	19,965
03/14	50,918	537	1.1%	19,894
03/13	43,012	647	1.5%	19,795
03/12	50,835	316	0.6%	19,489
Annual Growth	(5.0%)	20.3%		2.0%

2016 Year-End Financials

Debt ratio: 46.5%	No. of shares (mil.): 1,007
Return on equity: 8.1%	Dividends
Cash ($ mil.): 518	Yield: 6.0%
Current ratio: 0.82	Payout: 187.9%
Long-term debt ($ mil.): 8,989	Market value ($ mil.): 21,784

	STOCK PRICE ($) FY Close	P/E High/Low		PER SHARE ($) Earnings	Dividends	Book Value
03/16	21.62	53	42	0.66	1.32	7.42
03/15	22.24	45	39	0.82	1.35	9.05
03/14	24.71	84	64	0.55	1.34	8.74
03/13	22.71	51	44	0.68	1.22	8.74
03/12	21.51	110	90	0.34	1.15	7.78
Annual Growth	0.1%	—	—	18.3%	3.6%	(1.2%)

Standard Bank Group Ltd

Standard Bank Group sets the standard for sub-Saharan banking. Standard Bank South Africa's largest bank offers a variety of retail and commercial banking corporate and investment banking investment management and life insurance services through about 700 locations in its home country. The group also includes 500-plus additional branches more than 15 other African nations where it operates as Stanbic Bank. Beyond Africa the bank has offices in Asia Europe and the Americas including many emerging markets. It serves individuals and business and corporate customers. Standard Bank holds a controlling stake in South African insurance firm Liberty Holdings.

Geographic Reach

Contributing almost 85% of Standard Bank Group's revenue South Africa is its largest market by far. SBG also operates in 17 other African nations (from Angola to Zambia) as well as the UK and the US. Emerging markets include Argentina Brazil China Turkey and Russia.

Operations

In addition to personal commercial and corporate banking services SBG's insurance arm 53%-owned Liberty offers life insurance and investment and wealth management services to individuals and corporations in select African markets.

Financial Performance

Standard Bank Group struggled during the prolonged global recession. Low interest rates weak demand for credit and other financial factors impacted the company's revenues in 2009 and 2010. In 2011 the bank's revenue was essentially flat (up less than 1%) vs. the prior year while net income rose 23% over the same period. The modest uptick in revenue was credited to increase in banking activities partially offset by decreasing revenues at Liberty.

The personal and business banking division (up 8% in 2011 vs. 2010) outperformed the bank's other units. Revenue in South Africa the bank's largest market declined 1% while revenue from the rest of Africa was up 15% year over year. Revenue from outside of Africa fell 6%.

Strategy

Standard Bank Group is one of four full-service South African banks and claims to be the largest by assets and earnings. SBG aspires to be Africa's leading corporate and investment bank with a deep specialization in natural resources. To that end the bank is strengthening its focus on its core market and is looking to expand in Nigeria and Namibia. The company intends to grow its commercial banking operations there by building new branches. It opened more than 70 branches in Nigeria in 2010 alone.

Despite its Afro-centric focus SBG is also active in emerging markets worldwide including Russia. Indeed Standard Bank acquired about a third of Russian investment bank Troika Dialog in 2009. The partnership helped the group establish a presence in Russia where there is an opportunity to create a substantial domestic and cross-border franchise. However in early 2012 the company sold its stake in Troika Dialog to Russia's Sberbank for $372 million plus additional funds if Troika performs well. Standard Bank hopes to utilize its relationship with Troika to establish partnerships with Sberbank in the future. Other key emerging markets for the bank are Argentina Brazil and Turkey.

EXECUTIVES

Joint Group CEO, Simpiwe (Sim) Tshabalala, age 48
CEO CIB SBG and SBSA, David (Dave) Munro, age 45
Joint Group CEO, Ben Kruger, age 56
Group Financial Director and Director Standard Bank Group (SBG) and Standard Bank South Africa (SBSA) and Chairman Standard Bank London Holdings Limited and Standard Advisory London Limited, Simon Ridley, age 59
CEO PBB Group, Peter Schlebusch, age 49
CEO Offshore Group, Will Thorp
Chief Executive Standard Bank Wealth, Margaret Nienaber
Chairman, Thulani Gcabashe, age 58
Auditors: KPMG Inc.

LOCATIONS

HQ: Standard Bank Group Ltd
9th Floor, Standard Bank Centre, 5 Simmonds Street, Johannesburg 2001
Phone: (27) 11 636 9111 **Fax:** (27) 11 636 4207
Web: www.standardbank.com

2011 Total Income

	% of total
South Africa	84
Rest of Africa	10
Outside of Africa	5
Central and other	1
Total	**100**

Selected Markets

Africa
  Angola
  Botswana
  DRC
  Ghana
  Kenya
  Lesotho
  Malawi
  Mauritius
  Mozambique
  Namibia
  Nigeria
  South Africa
  Swaziland
  Tanzania
  Uganda
  Zambia
Americas
  Argentina
  Brazil
  US
Europe/Asia Pacific
  China
  Hong Kong
  Isle of Man
  Japan
  Jersey
  Russia
  Singapore
  Taiwan
  Turkey
  United Arab Emirates
  United Kingdom

PRODUCTS/OPERATIONS

2011 Revenue

	% of total
Liberty	45
Personal & business banking	34
Corporate & investment banking	21
Central & other	-
Total	**100**

COMPETITORS

Absa	Old Mutual
Citigroup	Sanlam
Commerzbank	Scotiabank
FirstRand	Standard Chartered
Nedcor	

HISTORICAL FINANCIALS

Company Type: Public

Income Statement

FYE: December 31

	ASSETS ($ mil.)	NET INCOME ($ mil.)	INCOME AS % OF ASSETS	EMPLOYEES
12/15	126,935	1,523	1.2%	54,361
12/14	164,717	1,549	0.9%	49,259
12/13	160,533	1,571	1.0%	48,808
12/12	181,381	1,937	1.1%	49,017
12/11	184,338	1,675	0.9%	52,127
Annual Growth	(8.9%)	(2.4%)	—	1.1%

2015 Year-End Financials

Return on assets: 1.2%
Return on equity: 15.8%
Long-term debt ($ mil.): —
No. of shares (mil.): 1,618
Sales ($ mil): 13,586

Dividends
Yield: 5.2%
Payout: 32.8%
Market value ($ mil.): 11,732

	STOCK PRICE ($) FY Close	P/E High/Low		PER SHARE ($) Earnings	Dividends	Book Value
12/15	7.25	1	0	0.95	0.38	6.20
12/14	12.33	1	1	0.96	0.40	7.62
12/13	12.48	1	1	0.96	0.38	7.89
12/12	14.23	1	1	1.21	0.00	8.47
Annual Growth (20.1%)		—	—	(5.9%)	—	(7.5%)

Standard Chartered Plc

While the British Empire isn't as global as it used to be that hasn't stopped Standard Chartered. The UK-based banking group known as Stanchart primarily operates in its target markets of Asia the Middle East and Africa which offer some of the world's fastest-growing economies. It also operates in Europe and the Americas. In all Stanchart has more than 1700 offices in more than 70 countries. The company operates four business segments revolved around retail banking (deposit accounts loans cards and investment products) and corporate and institutional banking (capital markets cash management international trade custody and clearing services). Stanchart traces its roots back more than 150 years.

OperationsBecause the bank's strategy is centered around client relationships it organizes its business around four client segment groups and five product groups. The bank made 26% of its operating income from its retail banking business in 2014 while transaction banking and financial market products and services each generated around 20%. The remainder of operating income comes from Corporate finance (14%) financial markets (19%) and private banking services (9%). Sorted by client Stanchart generates more than 55% of its operating income from corporate & institutional clients more than 30% from retail clients more than 5% from commercial clients (mid-sized companies) and the remainder from private banking clients (affluent individuals). Geographic Reach

The UK-based bank does business in more than 70 markets mostly in Asia Africa and the Middle East but also in Europe and the Americas. Standard generates about 30% of its operating income from China (its largest market) 20% from the ASEAN region and roughly 10% from each of the Africa South Asia North East Asia and MENAP (Middle East North Africa Afghanistan and Pakistan) regions. About 7% comes from Europe and 5% comes from the Americas.

Sales and Marketing

The Corporate & Institutional business serves financial institutions and global and local corporate clients; while the Retail group serves individuals and small businesses. Private Banking clients include high net worth individuals and Commercial Clients include mid-sized companies. The bank serves clients from a variety of sectors: including energy manufacturing commercial real estate consumer durables and construction.Looking to reinforce its commitment to making a positive impact in the communities where it operates Stanchart in 2012 rolled out an international advertising campaign that spanned multiple media such as TV print outdoor and digital.

Financial Performance

Stanchart's revenue in 2014 fell by 4% to $24.8 billion mostly driven by a $329 million decline in income from the Commercial Clients segment as its Private Equity business' investments underperformed compared to the prior year its renminbi (RMB) products received less demand in Financial Markets and because the division made a number of exits from under-performing business lines.

The bank's net income also dove by 36% to $2.7 billion over the period mostly from lower revenue but also because of impairment losses on loans and advances and other credit risk provisions as the credit-worthiness of its loan portfolio worsened. Cash from operations spiked by 458% to $52.8 billion primarily as the bank used less cash toward loans and advances to customers and banks and less cash toward buying other operating assets such as derivative financial instruments.

Strategy

Stanchart has been pursuing a new strategy in its consumer banking business shifting to a customer-focused business model and standardizing its processes in early 2014. It has leveraged its 2008 acquisition of American Express's international banking business to not only boost its private banking operations but strengthen its presence in key markets in Asia Africa and the Middle East. Stanchart has also aggressively added more branches and ATMs to its retail network and invested in making improvements to its online and mobile capabilities.Stanchart has also exited several markets that didn't align with its new strategy and broader portfolio to focus more on its target markets in Asia Africa and the Middle East. In late 2014 for example after witnessing disappointing results from the unit Stanchart sold its Hong Kong-based consumer finance business Prime-Credit to an investment consortium worth more than $600 million. Also in 2014 it exited its Consumer Finance businesses in Hong Kong China and Korea; its Retail Clients businesses in Germany and Lebanon; and its third-party sourcing channel for Retail Clients.

In addition the bank has been investing heavily in cost-saving measures across all segments while also making improvements to its online and mobile banking platforms. In mid-2015 to strengthen its balance sheet and free up resources Standard announced that it would slash its operating costs by $1.8 billion by 2018. In late 2014 it announced that it would invest more than $400 million toward productivity improvements in 2015 across Retail Clients Corporate & Institutional Clients and products and support functions. In the Retail Clients market for example the company will concentrate more on key cities as well as its digital and affluent segments (i.e. Priority and Business Clients). As part of this plan the company in 2015 closed its under-performing institutional cash equities equity research and equity capital markets activities; a move that was expected to deliver $100 million in cost savings by 2016 and outpace restructuring costs.

Mergers and AcquisitionsHelping to position Stanchart as a top South African custodian the company in 2013 acquired the South African custody and trustee business of Absa Bank which had developed a profitable custody model across more than 20 sub-Saharan African countries.

Company Background

Asia Africa and the Middle East have been among Stanchart's targeted areas for growth. It owns First Africa Group which provides mergers and acquisitions advisory services to companies wanting to invest in Africa. Stanchart bought Barclays Bank's custody business in 2010 adding operations in eight African nations. In late 2011 the company bought the performing segment of Barclays' credit card business in India at a discount. In 2012 to expand its wholesale banking business in Turkey Stanchart purchased Credit Agricole Yatirim Bankasi Turk A.S. (CAYBT) a fully-owned subsidiary of Credit Agricole Corporate and Investment Bank.

HISTORY

Company BackgroundStandard Chartered began in 1853 as the Chartered Bank of India Australia and China to finance trade between the UK and its Asian colonies. It began establishing offices in 1858. Over the next 40 years The Chartered Bank expanded throughout Asia. In the 20th century the bank opened branches in Germany and the US. In 1957 Chartered entered the Middle East by acquiring Eastern Bank. In 1969 it agreed to merge with Standard Bank.

In 1862 schoolmaster John Paterson established the Standard Bank of British South Africa Ltd. to fund trade with mining businesses. Within two years the bank had 15 branches. Like Chartered Standard had moved into Germany and the US by 1905 and operated in central and southern Africa by 1912.

In 1962 the bank was renamed The Standard Bank Ltd. Three years later it expanded into Gambia Ghana Nigeria and Sierra Leone but the end of colonialism meant instability; business was threatened and ruling parties often nationalized Standard's banks. In 1969 the bank agreed to merge with Chartered Bank.

Asian and Middle Eastern business flourished in the early 1970s while South African branches struggled under growing international pressure on the country's apartheid regime. In response the company diversified into metals trading and consumer finance. It also expanded in the US market with the purchase of Union Bancorp of California.

Standard Chartered failed in a 1981 attempt to gain entry to the UK market through purchasing Royal Bank of Scotland. Four years later that bank went public.

In 1986 Lloyds Bank tried to take over Standard Chartered but investors Robert Holmes a Court Yue-Kong Pao and Khoo Teck Puat acquired enough of the company to block the play. Meanwhile overseas financial deregulation brought more competition and Hong Kong Singapore and Malaysia sank into recession.

Hit by trade sanctions against South Africa the bank in 1987 sold its operations there. As the world tumbled deeper into recession Standard Chartered's loan losses climbed. But the bank began to recover the next year as it trimmed its US bank holdings.

Scandal hit the bank in the 1990s. In 1992 Standard Chartered paid $515 million in restitution after a broker in its Mumbai India office embezzled some $1.2 billion from Indian banks. In 1994 executives with Mocatta were convicted of bribery and the Hong Kong government banned Standard Chartered Securities (sold in 1996) from underwriting stock offerings for nine months after it falsified six IPOs.

In 1997 Standard Chartered refocused on retail banking with its 1998 purchase of what is now Banco Standard Chartered in Latin America and its bank/insurance tie-ups with CGU (now CGNU) and Prudential plc. The promotion of Rana Talwar to CEO brought a strategic focus on emerging markets from which other banks were withdrawing.

Standard Chartered in 1999 bought Thailand's Nakornthon Bank and the non-Swiss trade financing operations of UBS AG and expanded into China through a pact with the Bank of China. In 2000 the company bought Australia and New Zealand Banking Group's Grindlays operations in South Asia and the Middle East. The following year Stanchart began cutting 20% of its workforce. It also folded Grindlay's operations into its own while retaining the brand's name.

In 2004 Stanchart bought the majority of Australia and New Zealand Banking Group's project finance business which is headquartered in London. The business which cost Stanchart about $1.5 billion operates in four regions: the UK the US the Middle East and South Asia (especially India).

In 2005 the bank acquired Korea First Bank (now SC First Bank); the deal was the biggest foreign investment ever for South Korea's financial sector. The following year Stanchart paid about $1.2 billion for Taiwan's Hsinchu Bank making it the first foreign bank owner in that country. Also in 2006 the bank acquired 20% of China Bohai Bank.

In 2008 the UK government responded to the global financial crisis by investing £50 billion ($87.9 billion) in the nation's top banks including Stanchart. It agreed to guarantee another £250 billion ($438 billion) in bonds and provide additional liquidity of at least £200 billion ($350 billion) to the banks. The bailout plan was initiated to provide capital directly to the banks in order to revitalize lending activities.Also in 2008 the company made some acquisitions for further international expansion. It bought Asia Trust and Investment Corporation which added some 10 branches in the lucrative Taipei market. Stanchart also bought some of the Brazil operations of Lehman Brothers after that company filed for bankruptcy protection.

EXECUTIVES

Group CEO, William T. (Bill) Winters, age 55
Chief Executive India Operations, Zarin Daruwala
Regional CEO ASEAN and South Asia, Ajay Kanwal
Regional CEO India and South Asia, Sunil Kaushal
CEO Corporate and Institutional Banking, Simon Cooper
Group CIO, Michael Gorriz, age 56
Group Finance Director, Andy Halford
CEO Iraq, Andreas Meletiou
CEO Singapore, Judy Hsu
Director Compliance People and Communications and Regional CEO Europe and Americas, Tracy Clarke
CEO Retail Banking, Karen Fawcett
Group COO, Doris Honold
Regional CEO Greater China and North Asia, Benjamin P. C. (Ben) Hung
Group Chief Risk Officer, Mark Smith
Chairman, Jose Vi ±als
Auditors: KPMG Audit Plc

LOCATIONS

HQ: Standard Chartered Plc
32nd Floor, 4-4A Des Voeux Road, Central,
Phone: (44) 20 7885 8888
Web: www.sc.com

2014 Sales

	% of total
China	30
ASEAN	20
South Asia	10
MENAP	10
Africa	10
North East Asia	8
Europe	7
Americas	5
Total	**100**

PRODUCTS/OPERATIONS

2014 Sales

	% of total
Interest	69
Noninterest	
Fees & commissions	18
Net trading income	8
Other	5
Total	**100**

COMPETITORS

Bank of America	Hang Seng Bank
Bank of China	Lloyds Banking Group
Bank of East Asia	Maybank
Barclays	OCBC Bank
Citigroup	Royal Bank of Scotland
DBS Group Holdings	Standard Bank Group
Deutsche Bank	State Bank of India
Grupo Santander	United Overseas Bank
HSBC	Woori

HISTORICAL FINANCIALS

Company Type: Public

Income Statement

FYE: December 31

	ASSETS ($ mil.)	NET INCOME ($ mil.)	INCOME AS % OF ASSETS	EMPLOYEES
12/15	640,483	(2,194)	—	84,076
12/14	725,914	2,613	0.4%	90,940
12/13	674,380	4,090	0.6%	86,640
12/12	636,518	4,887	0.8%	89,058
12/11	599,070	4,849	0.8%	86,865
Annual Growth	**1.7%**			**(0.8%)**

2015 Year-End Financials

Return on assets: (-0.3%)
Return on equity: (-4.6%)
Long-term debt ($ mil.): —
No. of shares (mil.): —
Sales ($ mil): 21,168

Dividends
Yield: —
Payout: —
Market value ($ mil.): —

Standard Life Assurance Co. (United Kingdom)

EXECUTIVES

Director, Paul Matthews
Auditors: PricewaterhouseCoopers LLP

LOCATIONS

HQ: Standard Life Assurance Co. (United Kingdom)
Standard Life House, 30 Lothian Road, Edinburgh EH1 2DH
Phone: (44) 131 225 2552
Web: www.standardlife.com

HISTORICAL FINANCIALS

Company Type: Public

Income Statement

FYE: December 31

	ASSETS ($ mil.)	NET INCOME ($ mil.)	INCOME AS % OF ASSETS	EMPLOYEES
12/15	261,892	2,108	0.8%	6,431
12/14	317,822	785	0.2%	8,335
12/13	305,074	770	0.3%	8,224
12/12	280,627	1,125	0.4%	8,459
12/11	247,366	460	0.2%	8,789
Annual Growth	**1.4%**	**46.3%**	—	**(7.5%)**

2015 Year-End Financials

Return on assets: 0.7%
Return on equity: 32.8%
Long-term debt ($ mil.): —
No. of shares (mil.): 1,969
Sales ($ mil): 13,241

Dividends
Yield: —
Payout: —
Market value ($ mil.): —

State Bank of India

LOCATIONS

HQ: State Bank of India
  Central Office, Madam Cama Road, Nariman Point,
  Mumbai 400 021
Phone: (91) 22 2283 0535   **Fax:** (91) 22 2285 5348
Web: www.sbi.co.in

HISTORICAL FINANCIALS

Company Type: Public

Income Statement

FYE: March 31

	ASSETS ($ mil.)	NET INCOME ($ mil.)	INCOME AS % OF ASSETS	EMPLOYEES
03/15	417,125	2,717	0.7%	213,238
03/14	388,840	2,360	0.6%	222,033
03/13	380,690	3,300	0.9%	228,296
03/12	345,870	3,015	0.9%	215,481
03/11	76,389	570	0.7%	222,933
Annual Growth	52.9%	47.7%	—	(1.1%)

2015 Year-End Financials

Return on assets: 0.6%
Return on equity: 11.0%
Long-term debt ($ mil.): —
No. of shares (mil.): —
Sales ($ mil): 41,137

Dividends
  Yield: —
  Payout: —
Market value ($ mil.): —

	STOCK PRICE ($) FY Close	P/E High/Low	Earnings	PER SHARE ($) Dividends	Book Value
03/15	41.71	— —	0.36	0.00	1.50
03/14	55.36	— —	0.34	0.00	1.92
03/13	86.80	— —	0.49	0.00	1.57
03/12	94.32	— —	0.47	0.00	1.05
03/11	123.30	— —	0.54	0.00	1.06
Annual Growth	(23.7%)	— —	(9.5%)	—	9.1%

Statoil ASA

Crude petroleum and natural gas nsk

EXECUTIVES

Chairman Of The Board, Lars Johannes Nordli
Auditors: KPMG AS

LOCATIONS

HQ: Statoil ASA
  Forusbeen 50, Stavanger N-4035
Phone: (47) 51 99 00 00   **Fax:** (47) 51 99 00 50
Web: www.statoil.com

HISTORICAL FINANCIALS

Company Type: Public

Income Statement

FYE: December 31

	REVENUE ($ mil.)	NET INCOME ($ mil.)	NET PROFIT MARGIN	EMPLOYEES
12/15	54,781	(4,254)	—	21,581
12/14	83,920	2,951	3.5%	22,516
12/13	104,898	6,566	6.3%	23,413
12/12	129,328	12,317	9.5%	23,028
12/11	111,467	13,103	11.8%	31,715
Annual Growth	(16.3%)	—	—	(9.2%)

2015 Year-End Financials

Debt ratio: 3.3%
Return on equity: (-10.2%)
Cash ($ mil.): 8,623
Current ratio: 1.83
Long-term debt ($ mil.): 29,955

No. of shares (mil.): —
Dividends
  Yield: 6.0%
  Payout: —
Market value ($ mil.): —

	STOCK PRICE ($) FY Close	P/E High/Low	Earnings	PER SHARE ($) Dividends	Book Value
12/15	13.96	— —	(1.34)	0.85	12.67
12/14	17.61	4 2	0.93	1.72	16.15
12/13	24.13	2 2	2.06	1.15	18.40
12/12	25.04	1 1	3.86	1.07	17.95
12/11	25.61	1 1	4.11	1.05	14.58
Annual Growth	(14.1%)	— —	—	(5.3%)	(3.5%)

Ste Cooperative de Consommation Coop-Geneva

LOCATIONS

HQ: Ste Cooperative de Consommation Coop-Geneva
  Thiersteinerallee 12, Basel CH-4002
Phone: (41) 61 336 66 66   **Fax:** (41) 61 336 60 40
Web: www.coop.ch

HISTORICAL FINANCIALS

Company Type: Public

Income Statement

FYE: December 31

	REVENUE ($ mil.)	NET INCOME ($ mil.)	NET PROFIT MARGIN	EMPLOYEES
12/15	26,074	418	1.6%	79,953
12/14	27,459	475	1.7%	77,087
12/13	30,264	518	1.7%	74,955
12/12	29,160	493	1.7%	75,309
12/11	28,316	459	1.6%	75,296
Annual Growth	(2.0%)	(2.3%)	—	1.5%

2015 Year-End Financials

Debt ratio: —
Return on equity: 5.3%
Cash ($ mil.): 1,087
Current ratio: 1.22
Long-term debt ($ mil.): —

No. of shares (mil.): —
Dividends
  Yield: —
  Payout: —
Market value ($ mil.): —

Storebrand ASA

EXECUTIVES

Chairman Of The Board, Odd Arild Grefstad
Auditors: Deloitte AS

LOCATIONS

HQ: Storebrand ASA
  Professor Kohts vei 9, Lysaker NO-1327
Phone: (47) 22 31 50 50   **Fax:** (47) 22 48 98 90
Web: www.storebrand.no

HISTORICAL FINANCIALS

Company Type: Public

Income Statement

FYE: December 31

	ASSETS ($ mil.)	NET INCOME ($ mil.)	INCOME AS % OF ASSETS	EMPLOYEES
12/15	59,153	133	0.2%	2,298
12/14	66,344	278	0.4%	2,232
12/13	74,120	324	0.4%	2,138
12/12	75,119	179	0.2%	2,250
12/11	66,767	112	0.2%	2,221
Annual Growth	(3.0%)	4.5%	—	0.9%

2015 Year-End Financials

Return on assets: 0.2%
Return on equity: 4.6%
Long-term debt ($ mil.): —
No. of shares (mil.): 447
Sales ($ mil): 4,655

Dividends
  Yield: —
  Payout: —
Market value ($ mil.): —

	STOCK PRICE ($) FY Close	P/E High/Low	Earnings	PER SHARE ($) Dividends	Book Value
12/15	0.00	3 3	0.30	0.00	6.70
12/14	10.49	2 2	0.62	0.00	7.34
12/13	11.75	3 2	0.73	0.00	8.25
12/12	9.50	5 3	0.40	0.00	7.88
Annual Growth	—	— —	(7.2%)	—	(4.0%)

SUEZ SA

SUEZ Environnement conducts a variety of activities including the treatment production and distribution of drinking water; the collection recovery and treatment of wastewater; and the collection and processing of nonhazardous and hazardous waste recycling of waste and street cleaning. Supplying some 92 million people with drinking water the firm manages about 1200 drinking water production plants and 150000 kms (95000 miles) of sewage lines. It operates through subsidiaries such as Ondeo (drinking water and sanitation services) Degremont (water treatment services) and SITA (waste management services).

In 2010 SUEZ Environment acquired a 75% stake in Aguas de Barcelona a Spanish company dedicated to services distribution or treatment of water primarily in Europe but also in Asia North America and South America. The deal allows SUEZ Environment to add a "second pillar" to its European water business. It also owns 33% of Aguas de Valencia and looking to up its stake in the coastal Spanish water provider.

SUEZ Environnement was formed in 2002 by the regrouping of SITA (one of Europe's largest waste management companies) with French conglomerate SUEZ's Ondeo Degremont water unit. Other operations include FAIRTEC (waste service engineering) Ondeo Industrial Solutions (technical support and consulting for water operations) and Safege (consulting engineering for water operations).

EXECUTIVES

EVP Innovation and Business Performance, Thierry M. Mallet, age 56
SEVP Waste Activity Europe, Christophe Cros, age 57
EVP Human Resources, Denys Neymon, age 56
CEO, Jean-Louis Chaussade, age 65

SEVP International Activity, Marie-Ange Debon, age 51
SEVP Finance, Jean-Marc Boursier, age 49
EVP; Director Sustainable Development and Communications, Frederique Raoult, age 50
SEVP Water Activity Europe, Angel Simon, age 59
CEO Australia, Mark Venhoek
CEO Water and Treatment Solutions, David Lamy
CEO SUEZ environnement South-East Asia, Roch Cheroux
CEO SUEZ environnement North America, Eric Gernath
Chairman, Gerard Mestrallet, age 67

LOCATIONS

HQ: SUEZ SA
Tour CB21 - 16, place de l' Iris, Paris La Defense, Cedex 92040
Phone: (33) 1 58 81 20 00   **Fax:** (33) 1 58 81 25 00
Web: www.suez-environnement.com

2013 Sales

	% of total
Europe	69
Oceania	8
North America	6
South America	6
Africa & Middle East	6
Asia	5
Total	**100**

PRODUCTS/OPERATIONS

Selected Subsidiaries
Chine
Degrémont
Lyonnaise des Eaux
Ondeo IS
Ondeo Systems
Safege
SITA France
SITA Trashco
SITA UK
United Water

COMPETITORS

Biffa	Smurfit Kappa
Bouygues	Seche Environnement
Safety-Kleen	United Utilities
Severn Trent	Veolia Environnement
Shanks	

HISTORICAL FINANCIALS
Company Type: Public

Income Statement   FYE: December 31

	REVENUE ($ mil.)	NET INCOME ($ mil.)	NET PROFIT MARGIN	EMPLOYEES
12/15	16,484	443	2.7%	82,536
12/14	17,411	507	2.9%	80,990
12/13	20,160	484	2.4%	79,219
12/12	19,904	331	1.7%	79,549
12/11	19,181	417	2.2%	80,410
Annual Growth	**(3.7%)**	**1.5%**	**—**	**0.7%**

2015 Year-End Financials
Debt ratio: 40.8%	No. of shares (mil.): 540
Return on equity: 7.4%	Dividends
Cash ($ mil.): 2,264	Yield: 3.8%
Current ratio: 0.87	Payout: 95.5%
Long-term debt ($ mil.): 9,259	Market value ($ mil.): 5,109

Sumitomo Chemical Co., Ltd.

Auditors: KPMG AZSA LLC

LOCATIONS

HQ: Sumitomo Chemical Co., Ltd.
2-27-1 Shinkawa, Chuo-ku, Tokyo 104-8260
Phone: (81) 3 5543 5160   **Fax:** (81) 3 5543 5901
Web: www.sumitomo-chem.co.jp

HISTORICAL FINANCIALS
Company Type: Public

Income Statement   FYE: March 31

	REVENUE ($ mil.)	NET INCOME ($ mil.)	NET PROFIT MARGIN	EMPLOYEES
03/16	18,716	725	3.9%	34,139
03/15	19,809	435	2.2%	34,061
03/14	21,738	358	1.6%	30,745
03/13	20,750	(542)	—	30,396
03/12	23,745	68	0.3%	29,839
Annual Growth	**(5.8%)**	**80.6%**	**—**	**3.4%**

2016 Year-End Financials
Debt ratio: 0.2%	No. of shares (mil.): 1,634
Return on equity: 10.4%	Dividends
Cash ($ mil.): 1,216	Yield: 1.9%
Current ratio: 1.50	Payout: 108.6%
Long-term debt ($ mil.): 5,381	Market value ($ mil.): 37,096

	STOCK PRICE ($) FY Close	P/E High/Low		PER SHARE ($) Earnings	Dividends	Book Value
03/16	22.70	1	0	0.44	0.44	4.18
03/15	25.75	1	0	0.27	0.38	4.04
03/14	18.14	—	—	0.22	0.00	5.54
03/13	15.73	—	—	(0.33)	0.00	4.86
03/12	21.18	—	—	0.04	0.00	5.38
Annual Growth	**1.7%**	—	—	**80.6%**	**—**	**(6.1%)**

Sumitomo Corp. (Japan)

Auditors: KPMG AZSA LLC

LOCATIONS

HQ: Sumitomo Corp. (Japan)
1-8-11 Harumi, Chuo-ku, Tokyo 104-8610
Phone: (81) 3 5166 5000   **Fax:** (81) 3 5166 6203
Web: www.sumitomocorp.co.jp

HISTORICAL FINANCIALS
Company Type: Public

Income Statement   FYE: March 31

	REVENUE ($ mil.)	NET INCOME ($ mil.)	NET PROFIT MARGIN	EMPLOYEES
03/16	35,716	663	1.9%	87,173
03/15	31,357	(609)	—	96,795
03/14	32,139	2,161	6.7%	95,557
03/13	32,056	2,470	7.7%	97,451
03/12	39,753	3,055	7.7%	99,075
Annual Growth	**(2.6%)**	**(31.7%)**		**(3.1%)**

2016 Year-End Financials
Debt ratio: 0.4%	No. of shares (mil.): 1,248
Return on equity: 3.1%	Dividends
Cash ($ mil.): 7,736	Yield: 4.0%
Current ratio: 1.60	Payout: 83.2%
Long-term debt ($ mil.): 25,944	Market value ($ mil.): 12,356

	STOCK PRICE ($) FY Close	P/E High/Low		PER SHARE ($) Earnings	Dividends	Book Value
03/16	9.90	0	0	0.53	0.40	16.06
03/15	10.71	—	—	(0.49)	0.44	16.58
03/14	12.80	0	0	1.73	0.44	18.67
03/13	12.61	0	0	1.97	0.54	17.45
03/12	14.52	0	0	2.44	0.54	16.47
Annual Growth	**(9.1%)**	—	—	**(31.7%)**	**(6.8%)**	**(0.6%)**

Sumitomo Electric Industries, Ltd. (Japan)

You might say that Sumitomo Electric Industries (SEI) produces the wide world of wire. The company which has more than 320 subsidiaries and affiliates around the globe is Japan's largest producer of wire and cable. SEI's automotive segment about half of sales makes automotive wiring harnesses wires wheel speed sensors and dash boards. Next in sales is the electric wire and cable division which makes power and industrial cables as well as magnetic and hybrid products. Other units produce optical fiber cables fiber-optic components industrial cables printed circuits ultrafine wire and semiconductors. SEI was formed in 1897 as Sumitomo Copper Rolling Works.

With nearly half the company's sales coming from the automotive segment SEI's 2009 books took a hit when the global recession eroded demand for autos and all the wiring and other components that go into them. A similar drop in demand for cell phones and other consumer electronics compounded the problem. The company also paid high prices for raw copper in 2008 and then saw the price for finished copper products plummet in 2009. Add a strong yen taking a bite out of export profits and it really got ugly. All told net income for fiscal 2009 dropped 84%.

SEI responded by cutting bonuses and other costs and reducing its Japanese workforce. It also acquired Fujitsu's 50% equity stake in Eudyna Devices making Eudyna a wholly owned subsidiary. The company's moves along with a gradual rebound in auto sales increased smart phone sales and growth across all sectors in China lead to improved results for 2010 and 2011 (a 11% sales growth). The improvements were tempered by weakened domestic demand due to The Great East

Japan Earthquake and tsunami that hit the country in early 2011 as well as a higher yen that lead to decreased exports. SEI redoubled its overseas expansion (four new Asian plants) and cost cutting efforts to double operating income and improve net income by 250%.

Because of the number of SEI's customers moving to China the company is expanding its presence in that region. In mid-2010 it formed a joint venture with Chinese partner Nanjing Putian Telecommunications to manufacture fiber-optic equipment to connect Chinese consumers to fiber-optic networks. SEI is investing ¥530 million ($5.72 million) in the venture.

HISTORY

Sumitomo Electric Industries as a part of the Sumitomo group business began nearly 400 years ago with the paired talents of spiritual founder Masatomo Sumitomo (who had received training as a Buddhist priest) and his disciple and brother-in-law Riemon Soga. Sumitomo wrote treatises on the conduct of commercial activity and Soga applied his technological skill in extracting silver from copper ore improving upon traditional Western methods and opened a copper business in Kyoto in 1590 that soon transformed the copper refining industry in Japan.

Soga's prosperous copper business became the founding company of the Sumitomo group. After Soga died in 1636 his son Tomomochi married Masatomo's daughter (entering into the Sumitomo family) and became the company's leader.

By the late 1600s the family was one of Japan's top copper producers. The house of Sumitomo entered several other businesses by the mid-1800s in order to insulate itself from waning copper production. The family established the Sumitomo Copper Rolling Works in 1897 to produce bare copper wire.

In 1909 production of cable for Japan's telecommunications industry began and in 1920 the family took their company public renaming it Sumitomo Electric Wire & Cable Works. The next year the company added high-carbon steel wire manufacturing. Its name changed to Sumitomo Electric Industries (SEI) in 1939.

The company began making rubber products for use in aircraft fuel tanks in 1943. The decade drew to a close with the addition of overhead transmission cable engineering operations.

SEI continued to move into new businesses in the 1960s. In 1960 SEI took a 25% stake in Sumitomo 3M a three-way joint venture with NEC (25%) and 3M (50%) to produce industrial cable in Japan. To capitalize on the boom in Japan's automobile and industrial equipment industries SEI introduced disc brakes to its lineup in 1963. Also SEI formally entered into management participation in Japan's Dunlop Tire Company which was then renamed Sumitomo Rubber Industries. (It had initially invested in the tire maker in 1960.)

SEI hit pay dirt with its automotive businesses producing brakes for manufacturers of passenger cars commercial vehicles motorcycles construction and industrial equipment and railcars. In the late 1960s SEI added traffic control systems.

With the introduction of compound semiconductors (used in wireless transmitters and electronic control devices) and cable television systems the 1970s brought SEI into the arena of value-added high-tech products. SEI began producing optical-fiber cable in 1974.

SEI expanded further into fiber optics when it introduced its first LAN in 1981 and set up its US-based Sumitomo Electric Lightwave unit in 1983.

In 1987 the company began producing antilock brakes (ABS) and invested $45 million in an evenly split ABS manufacturing US joint venture (Lucas

Sumitomo) with a unit of Lucas Varity. Lucas Varity was later bought by TRW and Sumitomo eventually acquired its remaining 50%. SEI closed out the 1980s by adding satellite navigation systems to its growing automobile product offerings.

The 1990s saw wider global expansion through more alliances and acquisitions. In 1990 SEI teamed up again with Lucas Varity to establish a joint venture in the UK to make automobile wiring harnesses. (SEI together with one of its own affiliates bought Lucas' half share in the company in 1999.) That year SEI through its Sumitomo Electric Wiring Systems unit formed AutoNeural Systems a joint venture with Ford-affiliated Visteon for automobile wiring harnesses.

In 2000 SEI set up ExceLight Communications (spun off from Sumitomo Electric Lightwave) to make optical components and subsystems for telecommunications cable TV and broadband equipment industries. The company restructured its electric power cable operations in early 2001 forming a manufacturing joint venture with Hitachi Cable and shutting one of its plants in Japan. Early the following year SEI acquired the Japan-based Calsonic Kansei Corporation's wiring harness business. SEI closed its electric furnaces in Japan and spun off its Sumitomo Steel Wire Corp. in late 2002. In early 2003 the company joined efforts with Hitachi Cable and Tatsuta Electric Wire & Cable to form Sumiden Hitachi Cable Ltd. a company that specialized in the manufacture of low-voltage power cables.

In 2006 the company acquired the former Volkswagen Bordnetze (now called Sumitomo Electric Bordnetze) a Germany-based manufacturer of wire harnesses from its previous joint owners Volkswagen and VDO Automotive.

Continuing to strengthen its European operations the company along with subsidiary Sumitomo Electric Sintered Alloy acquired Germany-based Cloyes Europe a sintered parts maker in 2007. SEI will use this acquisition to supply Japanese auto parts makers that have manufacturing facilities in Europe.

Also in 2007 as part of a group realignment SEI increased its ownership in Nissin Electric to more than 50% and it acquired affiliate Toyokuni Electric Cable. The acquisitions are part of the company's efforts to position itself as a global player.

EXECUTIVES

President and CEO, Masayoshi Matsumoto
EVP, Fumikiyo Uchioke
Managing Director, Atsushi Yano
Managing Executive Officer, Masamichi Yokogawa
Executive Officer, Makoto Tani
Senior Managing Director, Mitsuo Nishida
Senior Managing Director, Fumiyoshi Kawai
Managing Director, Nozomi Ushijima
Managing Director, Junji Itoh
Managing Director, Yoshitomo Kasui
Managing Director, Takahiro Nakano
Managing Executive Officer, Hiroyasu Torii
Managing Executive Officer, Yasuhiro Miyata
Managing Executive Officer, Masaki Shirayama
Managing Executive Officer, Toshiaki Kakii
Managing Executive Officer, Tetsuya Hayashi
Managing Executive Officer, Shigeru Nakajima
Managing Executive Officer, Hideo Hato
Managing Executive Officer, Yoshihiro Matsushita
Managing Executive Officer, Takafumi Uemiya
Auditors: KPMG AZSA LLC

LOCATIONS

HQ: Sumitomo Electric Industries, Ltd. (Japan)
Sumitomo Bldg., 4-5-33 Kitahama, Chuo-ku, Osaka 541-0041
Phone: (81) 6 6220 4141
Web: www.sei.co.jp

2016 sales

	% of total
Asia	
Japan	40
China	18
Others	12
U.S	13
Others	5
Europe & other regions	12
Total	**100**

PRODUCTS/OPERATIONS

2016 sales

	% of total
Automotive	51
Environment and Energy	22
Industrial materials & other	11
Electronics	10
Information & communications	6
Total	**100**

Products
Automotive
Information and Communication
System
Electronics / Consumer Electronics
Semiconduc
Energy
Environment
Infrastructure
Industrial
Bankruptcy
Wiring harnesses
Vibration-proof rubber
Automotive hoses
Car electrical equipment
Electronic wire products
Compound semiconductors
Metallic material for electronic parts
Electric-beam irradiation products
Flexible printed circuits
Fluorine resin products
Electric conductors
Power transmission wires/ cables/equipment
Magnet wires
Air cushions for railroad vehicles
Power systems
Equipment such as substation equipment/control systems
Charged beam equipment and processing
Electrical/power supply work and engineering porous metals

COMPETITORS

Alcatel-Lucent	General Cable
American Superconductor	Hitachi Cable
	LEONI
Amphenol	Lear Corp
Asia Pacific Wire & Cable	Magna International
	Mitsubishi Electric
Belden	Nexans
CommScope	OFS BrightWave
Corning	Robert Bosch
DENSO	SWCC SHOWA
Delphi Automotive Systems	Southwire
	Superior Essex
Finisar	Tatung
Fujikura Ltd.	Tokyo Rope Mfg.
Furukawa Electric	Valeo

HISTORICAL FINANCIALS

Company Type: Public

Income Statement

FYE: March 31

	REVENUE ($ mil.)	NET INCOME ($ mil.)	NET PROFIT MARGIN	EMPLOYEES
03/16	26,119	810	3.1%	279,989
03/15	23,527	998	4.2%	275,351
03/14	24,886	646	2.6%	225,484
03/13	22,955	403	1.8%	206,323
03/12	25,104	717	2.9%	194,734
Annual Growth	1.0%	3.1%	—	9.5%

2016 Year-End Financials

Debt ratio: 0.1%
Return on equity: 6.5%
Cash ($ mil.): 1,555
Current ratio: 1.76
Long-term debt ($ mil.): 2,504

No. of shares (mil.): 793
Dividends
  Yield: 0.0%
  Payout: —
Market value ($ mil.): 9,543

	STOCK PRICE ($) FY Close	P/E High/Low		PER SHARE ($) Earnings	Dividends	Book Value
03/16	12.03	0	0	1.02	0.31	15.27
03/15	13.15	1	0	1.26	0.20	15.04
03/14	148.70	—	—	0.82	0.00	16.86
03/13	118.25	—	—	0.51	0.00	16.68
03/12	138.50	—	—	0.90	0.00	17.51
Annual Growth	(45.7%)	—	—	3.1%	—	(3.4%)

Sumitomo Life Insurance Co. (Japan)

Sumitomo Life is one of Japan's biggest mutual life insurers (along with Nippon Life). The firm sells individual group life and specialized health policies through more than 70 branch offices and about 1500 district offices. Along with its sales force Sumitomo Life sells its products through a network of financial institutions and affiliates. It also administers pension and employee benefit plans and offers brokerage and consulting. The company has a total of some 7 million policyholders. Sumitomo Life which has operations in other Asian and North American countries is part of the Sumitomo Mitsui keiretsu –a group of firms linked by cross-ownership.

Operations

Sumitomo Life has more than $903 billion in individual life insurance in-force and another $309 billion in group insurance plus $103 billion and $26 billion in individual and group annuities respectively.

Geographic Reach

In addition to Japan Sumitomo Life has operations in China and the US. The company has representative offices in New York London Beijing and Hanoi.

In the US it has offices in Atlanta Chicago Kentucky Los Angeles New York and South Carolina. Sumitomo Life is one of the largest Japanese brokers of employee benefits plans in the country.

Sales and Marketing

The company's principal selling channels are its sales force of about 31000 representatives banks and a third party distribution channel formed through sales agreements with Japan Post Group. It also has some online and retail sales operations.

Financial Performance

Sumitomo Life's revenue decreased 17% to ¥3.5 trillion in 2014 due to a decline in premiums and investment gains. However net income rose 14% to ¥1.2 trillion due to factors including a decline in provisions for policy reserves. Cash flow from operations fell 62% to ¥447.6 billion as the company lost money on tangible fixed assets and reported changed in non-investing liabilities.

Strategy

The company's medium-term strategy (through 2016) focuses on improving customer value by enhancing services and improving quality across operations. It is investing in growth areas including expanding its representative sales force its branch network and its international operations (with a focus on Asia).

As part of the company's push into Southeast Asia Sumitomo Life bought a 40% stake in PT BNI Life Insurance the life insurance unit of Bank Negara Indonesia in 2014. The move valued at more than 4 trillion rupiah ($351 million) made Sumitomo Life the second-largest shareholder in BNI Life.

Pursuing further growth in the expanding US market Sumitomo Life acquired Symetra Financial Corporation for $3.7 billion in early 2016. That deal was one of several that Japanese insurers have made in the US to take advantage of that nation's growing population.

EXECUTIVES

Managing Director and Board Member, Yoshio Sato
Senior Managing Executive Officer, Koichi Suzaki
Senior Managing Executive Officer, Haruo Urata
Senior Managing Executive Officer, Masahiro Hashimoto
President CEO and Board Member, Shinichi Yokoyama
Auditors: KPMG AZSA LLC

LOCATIONS

HQ: Sumitomo Life Insurance Co. (Japan)
  1-4-35 Shiromi, Chuo-ku, Osaka 540-8512
Phone: (81) 6 6937 1435   **Fax:** 212 750-7930
Web: www.sumitomolife.co.jp

COMPETITORS

AXA Life Insurance	Gibraltar Life
American Life Insurance	Insurance
Asahi Mutual Life	Meiji Yasuda Life
Dai-ichi Life	Mitsui Life
Daido Life	Nippon Life Insurance
Fukoku Mutual	T&D Holdings
	Taiyo Life

HISTORICAL FINANCIALS

Company Type: Public

Income Statement

FYE: March 31

	ASSETS ($ mil.)	NET INCOME ($ mil.)	INCOME AS % OF ASSETS	EMPLOYEES
03/15	229,128	1,044	0.5%	42,115
03/14	257,612	1,188	0.5%	42,109
03/13	282,347	1,146	0.4%	42,098
03/12	292,984	1,316	0.4%	42,953
03/11	286,871	1,315	0.5%	42,366
Annual Growth	(5.5%)	(5.6%)	—	(0.1%)

2015 Year-End Financials

Return on assets: 0.4%
Return on equity: 7.7%
Long-term debt ($ mil.): —
No. of shares (mil.): —
Sales ($ mil) 29,902

Dividends
  Yield: —
  Payout: —
Market value ($ mil.): —

Sumitomo Mitsui Financial Group Inc
Tokyo

Sumitomo Mitsui Financial Group (SMFG) is the holding company for Sumitomo Mitsui Banking which boasts some 440 domestic branches (mostly in the Tokyo and Osaka regions of Japan) and another nearly 40 locations abroad. As one of Japan's largest banks SMFG provides retail corporate and investment banking; asset management; securities trading; and lending. Other units of SMFG include credit card firm Sumitomo Mitsui Card brokerage SMBC Friend Securities management consulting firm Japan Research Institute and Sumitomo Mitsui Finance and Leasing. SMFG also operates the California-based Manufacturers Bank. SMFG bought Citigroup's Japanese consumer-banking business in late 2014.

OperationsSMFG operates four main business segments. SMFG's Commercial Banking segment made up 65% of the group's entire gross profit (net of the segment's expenses) in FY2015 (ended March 31 2015) and mostly includes the operations of Sumitomo Mitsui Banking as well as other domestic bank subsidiaries including KUBC The Minato Bank and SMBC Trust Bank. It also counts SMFG's foreign bank subsidiaries SMBC Europe SMBC (China) and Manufacturers Bank. Nearly one-third (33%) of the segment's gross profit comes from the Wholesale Banking Unit while more than half (56%) of the segment's gross profit is split fairly evenly between the Retail Banking unit the International Banking unit and the Treasury Unit. The group's Consumer Finance segment (20% of gross profit in FY2015) operates through its Sumitomo Mitsui Card Cedyna and SMBC Consumer Finance subsidiaries. The Securities segment (around 10% of gross profit) operates through SMBC Nikko Securities and SMBC Friend Securities. The group's Leasing segment (5% of gross profit) operates through Sumitomo Mitsui Financial Leasing subsidiary.About 30% of the group's domestic loan portfolio consisted of consumer loans (mostly housing loans) while another 27% was tied to loans made to customers in the real estate/goods rental and leasing and the manufacturing sectors. Loans to the transportation/communications/public enterprises wholesale and retail and services sectors split another 30% of the domestic loan portfolio. Broadly speaking about 51% of SMFG's gross profit came from net interest income in FY2015 while 49% came from net non-interest income mostly stemming from fee and commission revenue through its credit card business investment trust sales commissions fees obtained through securities-related business remittance and transfer fees and loan transaction fees. Geographic Reach-About 76% of SMFG's operating income (and 70% of its loan assets) came from its domestic business in Japan in fiscal 2015 (ended March 31 2015) while the rest came from customers in the Europe and Middle East region (11% of operating income) the Asia and Oceania region (8%) and the Americas (5%).

Financial Performance

Note: Growth rates may differ after conversion to US dollars. This analysis uses financials from the company's annual report.

While somewhat volatile SMFG's revenues and profits (in domestic currency terms) have been trending higher since 2011 thanks to a combination of fee and commission-income based growth slowly growing loan business higher investment income gains and a substantial decline in impairment charges on its financial assets as the economy tied to those assets has strengthened. The group's total operating income (net revenue excluding impairment charges) rose 3% to ¥3.33 trillion ($27.8 billion) in fiscal 2015 (ended March 31 2015) mostly thanks to higher net investment income from an increase in net gains from bond sales and higher "other income" sources mostly from operating leases and income related to leased-asset sales. Interest income rose by 4% with growth in loan and advances balances. Fee and commission income dipped slightly on lower investment trust sales commissions and securities-related income partially offset by a rise in credit card business fees.

Despite higher operating income SMFG's net profit fell 19% to ¥723 billion (over $6 billion) in FY2015 mostly due to a combination of: a 6% rise in general and administrative expenses with increased costs related to overseas business development and increased overseas hiring; and an 18% rise in "other expenses" mostly related to operating lease costs and costs related to leased-asset sales. SMFG's operating cash levels climbed double digits to ¥7.8 trillion ($65.2 billion) for FY2015 despite decreased earnings primarily tied to an increase in deposits.

Mergers and Acquisitions

In December 2015 Sumitomo Mitsui Financial Group won its bidding war for General Electric's leasing business in Japan and was expected to enter an acquisition deal worth ¥570 billion ($4.63 billion) for the unit. The deal would add some ¥500 billion in assets and 1000 new employees to SMFG subsidiary Sumitomo Mitsui Finance and Leasing boosting the subsidiary's assets by more than 10% and making it Japan's second-largest leasing company ahead of Mitsubishi UFJ Lease & Finance upon the deal's closing.

In late 2014 the SMFG purchased Citigroup's Japanese consumer-banking business for ¥40 billion ($330 million) in a private deal. SMFG completed its integration of Citi's Japanese retail banking operations in late 2015.

EXECUTIVES

Director; President Sumitomo Mitsui Banking, Takeshi Kunibe
President, Koichi Miyata
Director, Ken Kubo
Director, Yujiro Ito
Managing Director, Jun Ohta
Managing Director, Yasuyuki Kawasaki
Managing Director, Fumiaki Kurahara
Chairman, Masayuki Oku, age 72
Auditors: KPMG AZSA LLC

LOCATIONS

HQ: Sumitomo Mitsui Financial Group Inc Tokyo
1-2, Marunouchi 1-chome, Chiyoda-ku, Tokyo 100-0005
Phone: (81) 3 3282 8111
Web: www.smfg.co.jp

PRODUCTS/OPERATIONS

2013 Sales

	% of total
Interest	
Loans & advances	43
Investment securities	2
Other	1
Noninterest	
Fees & commissions	27
Investment income	9
Trading profits	4
Other	14
Total	**100**

COMPETITORS

Bank of Yokohama
Credit Saison
Mitsubishi UFJ
  Financial Group
Mizuho Financial

Norinchukin Bank
Resona
Shinsei Bank
Sumitomo Mitsui Trust
  Holdings

HISTORICAL FINANCIALS

Company Type: Public

Income Statement

FYE: March 31

	ASSETS ($ mil.)	NET INCOME ($ mil.)	INCOME AS % OF ASSETS	EMPLOYEES
03/16	1,604,432	7,515	0.5%	90,000
03/15	1,493,436	5,118	0.3%	85,000
03/14	0	7,424	—	82,800
03/13	1,580,333	8,439	0.5%	64,635
03/12	1,743,755	6,321	0.4%	64,225
Annual Growth	**(2.1%)**	**4.4%**	**—**	**8.8%**

2016 Year-End Financials

Return on assets: 0.4%
Return on equity: 8.9%
Long-term debt ($ mil.): —
No. of shares (mil.): 1,367
Sales ($ mil): 38,128

Dividends
  Yield: 4.1%
  Payout: 4.9%
Market value ($ mil.): 8,217

	STOCK PRICE ($) FY Close	P/E High/Low		Earnings	PER SHARE ($) Dividends	Book Value
03/16	6.01	0	0	5.49	0.25	61.90
03/15	7.74	0	0	3.74	0.23	56.93
03/14	8.65	0	0	5.43	0.25	(0.00)
03/13	8.16	—	—	6.23	0.00	66.28
03/12	6.64	—	—	4.56	0.00	65.46
Annual Growth	**(2.5%)**			**4.8%**	**—**	**(1.4%)**

Sumitomo Mitsui Trust Holdings Inc

Auditors: KPMG AZSA LLC

LOCATIONS

HQ: Sumitomo Mitsui Trust Holdings Inc
1-4-1 Marunouchi, Chiyoda-ku, Tokyo 100-6611
Phone: (81) 3 6256 6000
Web: www.smth.jp

HISTORICAL FINANCIALS

Company Type: Public

Income Statement

FYE: March 31

	ASSETS ($ mil.)	NET INCOME ($ mil.)	INCOME AS % OF ASSETS	EMPLOYEES
03/16	518,535	1,486	0.3%	24,546
03/15	385,366	1,330	0.3%	23,617
03/14	405,828	1,333	0.3%	20,890
03/13	400,714	1,421	0.4%	20,189
03/12	419,068	2,007	0.5%	20,305
Annual Growth	**5.5%**	**(7.2%)**	**—**	**4.9%**

2016 Year-End Financials

Return on assets: 0.3%
Return on equity: 6.9%
Long-term debt ($ mil.): —
No. of shares (mil.): —
Sales ($ mil): 10,700

Dividends
  Yield: 3.5%
  Payout: 29.5%
Market value ($ mil.): —

	STOCK PRICE ($) FY Close	P/E High/Low		Earnings	PER SHARE ($) Dividends	Book Value
03/16	2.94	0	0	0.39	0.11	5.51
03/15	4.18	0	0	0.34	0.10	5.16
03/14	4.50	—	—	0.33	0.10	6.06
03/13	4.67	—	—	0.33	0.00	6.72
03/12	3.14	—	—	0.47	0.00	6.86
Annual Growth	**(1.6%)**	**—**	**—**	**(4.8%)**	**—**	**(5.4%)**

Sun Life Financial Inc

Sun Life tries to stay on the sunny side of life and life insurance. The company offers insurance and wealth management products to individuals and business entities primarily in Canada and the US. It also has operations in Asia Europe and the UK. Sun Life's products include individual and group life and health insurance individual annuities group pensions mutual funds and asset management services. The US subsidiaries include Massachusetts Financial Services (or MFS Investment Management). Sun Life's products and services are distributed through direct and independent sales agents as well as banks and consultants.

Geographic Reach

In its home market Sun Life is a key player in individual life insurance employee benefits products as well as mutual funds. Its Asian operations are focused on the growing middle class customers in China India Indonesia and the Philippines.

Strategy

In the wake of the global financial crisis Sun Life has steadily adjusted its goals and worked to "de-risk" its products. It made an effort to build up its sales to individual customers in Canada tightened up its distribution system and expanded direct sales channels in Asia including China and its joint venture in India. To perk up its branding the company purchased the naming rights to the sports stadium in Miami and rolled out fresh ad campaigns in key markets.

Mergers and Acquisitions

In mid-2015 the company bought Washington-based Prime Advisors to broaden its asset management operations. The purchase followed the acquisition of Ryan Labs Asset Management and the planned acquisition of Bentall Kennedy. Together these deals will boost Sun Life Asset Management's third-party assets under management to some C$50 million.

In a move to grow its US group benefits operations Sun Life bought Assurant Employee Benefits from Assurant; the deal was valued at some $975 million. Post-acquisition Sun Life provides coverage through about 64000 employers in the US.

Sun Life now plans to buy the 51% of Indonesian unit PT CIMB Sun Life; it will integrate that firm into another holding PT Sun Life Financial Indonesia (which itself has been expanding) in order to align with that nation's single presence policy.

Company Background

Sun Life demutualized in 2000 and the money it raised as a publicly traded company helped finance growth. During the first 10 years of its public status it grew through a steady pace of acquisitions beginning with its buy of Clarica Life in 2002. Clarica's products were later rebranded with the Sun Life name. International acquisitions have included Genworth's US employee benefits group (2007) and insurance and pension operations in Hong Kong from Commonwealth Bank of Australia (2005).

EXECUTIVES

CEO Sun Life Vietnam, Larry R. Madge
CEO Bentall Kennedy, Gary Whitelaw
Chief Investment Officer Sun Life Financial,
Randolph B. (Randy) Brown
President Sun Life Financial Canada, Kevin P.
Dougherty, $500,000 total compensation
**Chairman and CEO MFS Investment
Management,** Robert J. (Rob) Manning
EVP and CFO, Colm J. Freyne, $334,346 total
compensation
EVP and Chief Risk Officer, Claude A. Accum
President Sun Life Investment Management,
Stephen C. Peacher, $118,592 total compensation
President and CEO, Dean A. Connor, $538,462 total
compensation
President Sun Life Financial U.S., Daniel R.
Fishbein
President Sun Life Investment Management Inc.,
Carl S. Bang
President Sun Life Financial Asia, Kevin D. Strain
**President and CEO Sun Life Canada (Philippines)
Inc.,** Rizalina G. Mantaring
EVP and CIO, Mark S. Saunders
SVP Enterprise Infrastructure and CTO, Stevan
Lewis
Executive Chair Sun Life Financial Quebec,
Isabelle Hudon
CEO Sun Life Financial U.K., Katherine Garner
**VP and Country Head India Sun Life Financial
Asia,** Sandeep Asthana
**EVP and Chief Human Resources and
Communications Officer,** Carrie Blair
EVP and Chief Legal Officer and Public Affairs,
Melissa J. Kennedy
CEO Sun Life Malaysia, Ooi Say Teng
**President and CEO MFS Investment
Management,** Michael W. Roberge
**CEO MFS Investment Management Canada
Limited,** Peter Kotsopoulos
SVP and Chief Marketing Officer, Lisa Ritchie
President Director Sun Life Financial Indonesia,
Elin Waty
President and CEO Prime Advisors Inc., Don
McDonald
President Ryan Labs Asset Management Inc.,
Sean F. McShea
Chairman, William D. (Bill) Anderson, age 67
Chairman, James H. (Jim) Sutcliffe, age 59
Auditors: Deloitte LLP

LOCATIONS

HQ: Sun Life Financial Inc
150 King Street West, Toronto, Ontario M5H 1J9
Phone: 416 979-9966   **Fax:** 416 979-3209
Web: www.sunlife.com

COMPETITORS

AGF Management
AIA Group
Aviva
Canada Life
China Life Insurance
Fairfax Financial Holdings
Great-West Life Assurance
Great-West Lifeco
Industrial Alliance Insurance and Financial Servic
Manulife Financial
MetLife
Prudential
Standard Life
The Hartford

HISTORICAL FINANCIALS

Company Type: Public

Income Statement

FYE: December 31

	ASSETS ($ mil.)	NET INCOME ($ mil.)	INCOME AS % OF ASSETS	EMPLOYEES
12/15	177,731	1,645	0.9%	18,330
12/14	192,880	1,617	0.8%	16,275
12/13	187,646	1,705	0.9%	0
12/12	227,013	1,502	0.7%	14,880
12/11	213,730	(196)	—	15,000
Annual Growth	(4.5%)	—		5.1%

2015 Year-End Financials

Return on assets: 0.9%
Return on equity: 11.3%
Long-term debt ($ mil.): —
No. of shares (mil.): 612
Sales ($ mil): 13,877

Dividends
Yield: 4.8%
Payout: 57.8%
Market value ($ mil.): 19,104

	STOCK PRICE ($) FY Close	P/E High/Low	PER SHARE ($) Earnings	Dividends	Book Value
12/15	31.20	9 7	2.56	1.18	25.18
12/14	36.06	13 11	2.47	1.30	26.59
12/13	35.33	23 16	1.46	1.38	26.80
12/12	26.53	11 7	2.60	1.44	28.65
12/11	18.52	— —	(0.51)	1.41	26.23
Annual Growth	13.9%	— —	—	(4.5%)	(1.0%)

Suncor Energy Inc.

Suncor Energy takes a shine to the cold of Canada. That country's largest energy firm explores for processes and markets oil and natural gas. In 2015 it reported gross proved and probable reserves of 7.6 billion barrels of oil equivalent. Suncor Energy was first company to produce commercial crude oil from Canada's Athabasca oil sands. Its Sunoco unit refines crude oil and processes and distributes fuels petrochemicals and heating oils invests in renewable energy and operates a network of gas stations. In 2016 Suncor Energy acquired rival Canadian Oil Sands. Already a stakeholder that year it also agreed to buy a majority stake in Canada's primary oil sands project Syncrude.

Geographic Reach

The company has operations in Canada Germany Libya the Netherlands Norway Syria the UK and the US. In 2012 Canada accounted for 79% of Suncor Energy's revenues.

Operations

Suncor Energy is one of Canada's largest oil sands producers. It oil sands assets include a 36% interest in the Joslyn North mine 41% in the Fort Hills mine and 51% of the Voyageur upgrader project as well as a 12% stake in the Syncrude oil sands mining venture.

The company also has conventional natural gas assets as well as international and offshore oil exploration and production holdings. In addition to its production refining and marketing operations across Canada (and in Colorado) the company has exploration assets in Libya Norway Syria and the UK.

The company has four refineries (in Alberta Ontario Quebec and Colorado —460000 barrels of combined capacity per day) and a network of 1460 Petro-Canada retail gas stations.

Its Renewable Energy interests include seven wind facilities across Canada including Adelaide which is the most recent addition to the portfolio and the St. Clair ethanol plant in Ontario. An eighth wind farm Cedar Point is planned to commence commercial operations later in 2015. Suncor's Energy Trading activities primarily involve the marketing supply and trading of crude oil natural gas power and byproducts and the use of midstream infrastructure and financial derivatives to optimize related trading strategies.

Sales and Marketing

The company's primary markets for synthetic oil and bitumen production from Suncor's Oil Sands segment which is sold to and subsequently marketed by Suncor's Energy Trading business include refining operations in Alberta Ontario the US Midwest and the U.S. Rocky Mountain regions and markets in the US Gulf Coast. Diesel production from upgrading operations is sold primarily in Western Canada marketed by Suncor's Refining and Marketing business.

Oil and gas production from East Coast Canada the North Sea and from North America Onshore is either marketed by the company's Energy Trading business acting as a marketing agent or sold to its Energy Trading business which then markets the products to customers under direct sales arrangements. Suncor's retail service station network operates nationally in Canada primarily under the Petro-Canada brand. This network consists of 1465 outlets across Canada excluding Pioneer retail locations. In addition refined products are marketed through independent dealers and joint arrangements. Suncor's Canadian retail network had annual sales of gasoline motor fuels averaging approximately 4.8 million liters per site in 2014 and holds a 17.3% share (2013 - 17.7%) of the national retail urban market.

Financial Performance

In 2014 the company's revenue increased by 1% due to increase revenue from the oil sands business. Oil Sands operations increased production by 8% in 2014 compared to 2013 driven primarily by increased Firebag production. Suncor's net income decreased by 31% in 2014 due to higher operating expenses as a result of higher depreciation and exploration costs.

The company's operating cash inflow decreased by 12% in 2014 primarily due to a decline in net income and a change in working capital items.

Strategy

Oil sands which hold deposits of heavy bitumen make up nearly a third of Suncor's oil production and Suncor's long term business focus is developing synthetic oil from its oil sands holdings in Alberta. Suncor plans to produce 1 million barrels per day of oil equivalent from its oil sands holdings by 2020.

To raise cash in 2017 Suncor sold its Petro-Canada Lubricants business to HollyFrontier for about C$1.1 billion.

In 2014 Suncor signed a farm-in agreement with Shell Canada to acquire a 20% interest in a deepwater exploration opportunity in the Shelburne Basin offshore Nova Scotia. In December 2014 Suncor acquired a 30% interest in an exploration licence in the Flemish Pass off the coast of Newfoundland and Labrador and a 50% interest in another exploration licence in the Carson Basin near the Flemish Pass. On the product shipment front that year the rail offloading facilities at Tracy Quebec were used to move crude to new and existing markets. Suncor also started transporting heavy crude on TransCanada's Gulf Coast Pipeline which provided increased access to global-based pricing.

In 2014 the Libya National Oil Company declared force majeure on oil exports from two terminals resulting in the shut in of substantially all

of the Suncor's production in that country. Consequently Suncor also declared force majeure for all exploration commitments in Libya. In 2014 the company agreed to sell the assets of Pioneer Energy to Parkland Fuel Corporation for $378 million. It also agreed to sell its Wilson Creek assets located near Rimbey Alberta to Tamarack Acquisition Corp for $168.5 million. Mergers and Acquisitions In 2015 the company agreed to purchase an additional 10% working interest in the Fort Hills oil sands project from Total E&P Canada Ltd. for $310 million. As part of the transaction Suncor acquires a further proportionate interest in Fort Hills related logistics including pipelines storage terminals and third-party pipeline capacity agreements. The acquisition of the additional working interest also presents an opportunity for Suncor to lower its capital cost per barrel and enhance its projected return on the Fort Hills project
Company Background

To focus on its growth markets and to pay down debt in 2013 the company agreed to sell its conventional natural gas business in Western Canada to a Centrica and Qatar Petroleum partnership for $1 billion.

To further develop its oil sands assets in 2010 the company formed a strategic alliance with TOTAL. As part of the deal France-based TOTAL paid Suncor Energy about $1.7 billion to acquire 19% of Suncor Energy's 60% interest in the Fort Hills mining project and a 49% stake in the Voyageur Upgrader project near Fort McMurray. Suncor Energy acquired about 37% of TOTAL's stake in the Joslyn project.

Boosting its profile as an integrated energy company in 2009 the company acquired Petro-Canada in a $15 billion deal. The acquisition created an energy behemoth with extensive holdings in oil sands solid conventional exploration and production assets and a major refining and retailing network. Following the Petro-Canada deal the company divested about $1.5 billion of non-core assets in Western Canada the US Trinidad and Tobago and the North Sea. In 2010 Suncor Energy sold its North Sea exploration assets (of Petro Canada Netherlands) to Dana Petroleum for $393 million. Later that year it sold a pair of natural gas properties in Alberta to a subsidiary of Abu Dhabi National Energy Company for $285 million. It also sold its Wildcat Hills assets which produce some 80 million cu. ft. of natural gas per day to Direct Energy for about $360 million.

EXECUTIVES

Chairman, James W. (Jim) Simpson, age 72
Auditors: PricewaterhouseCoopers LLP

LOCATIONS

HQ: Suncor Energy Inc.
150 - 6th Avenue S.W., Calgary, Alberta T2P 3E3
Phone: 403 296-6616   **Fax:** 403 724-3627
Web: www.suncor.com

COMPETITORS

Anadarko Petroleum	Husky Energy
BP NGL	Imperial Oil
Canadian Natural	Murphy Oil
Devon Energy	Nordex
Dominion Resources	Repsol Oil & Gas
Encana	Shell Canada

HISTORICAL FINANCIALS
Company Type: Public

Income Statement
FYE: December 31

	REVENUE ($ mil.)	NET INCOME ($ mil.)	NET PROFIT MARGIN	EMPLOYEES
12/15	21,369	(1,436)	—	0
12/14	34,965	2,330	6.7%	13,980
12/13	37,896	3,678	9.7%	13,946
12/12	38,826	2,798	7.2%	13,932
12/11	39,005	4,219	10.8%	13,026
Annual Growth	(14.0%)	—	—	—

2015 Year-End Financials

Debt ratio: 14.2%	No. of shares (mil.): 1,446
Return on equity: (-4.9%)	Dividends
Cash ($ mil.): 2,915	Yield: 4.4%
Current ratio: 1.46	Payout: —
Long-term debt ($ mil.): 10,429	Market value ($ mil.): 37,307

	STOCK PRICE ($) FY Close	P/E High/Low	PER SHARE ($) Earnings	Dividends	Book Value
12/15	25.80	— —	(0.99)	0.88	19.44
12/14	31.78	22 15	1.59	0.92	24.88
12/13	35.05	14 10	2.45	0.70	26.20
12/12	32.98	21 15	1.80	0.50	25.89
12/11	28.83	17 9	2.62	0.42	24.28
Annual Growth	(2.7%)	— —	—	20.3%	(5.4%)

Suncorp Group Ltd.

Suncorp-Metway (aka Suncorp Group) wants to be a rising star in Australia's insurance and banking sectors. The group owns Suncorp Insurance which operates one of the country's largest general insurance companies as well as a small but growing life insurance and wealth management business. The general insurance business sells personal and commercial property/casualty insurance under its Suncorp AAMI GIO Vero and Shannons brands. In addition to its insurance business Suncorp also runs Suncorp Bank an operator of some 200 branches in eastern Australia. Among other products the bank offers personal and commercial banking accounts financial planning and loans to consumers and small to midsized businesses.

EXECUTIVES

Managing Director and Group CEO, Michael A. Cameron
CEO Suncorp Bank, John Nesbitt
Chief Risk Officer, Clayton Herbert
CFO, Steve Johnston
CEO Commercial Insurance, Anthony Day
CEO Vero New Zealand, Gary Dransfield
CEO Suncorp Business Services, Matt Pancino
Acting CEO Suncorp Life, Jeremy Robson
CEO Vero New Zealand, Paul Smeaton
Chairman, Zygmunt Switkowski
Auditors: KPMG

LOCATIONS

HQ: Suncorp Group Ltd.
Level 28, 266 George Street, Brisbane, Queensland 4000
Phone: (61) 7 3362 1222   **Fax:** (61) 7 3135 2940
Web: www.suncorpgroup.com.au

PRODUCTS/OPERATIONS

2013 Sales

	% of total
General Insurance	
Personal	35
Commercial	23
Banking	19
Life and Wealth Management	13
New Zealand General Insurance	10
Total	**100**

Selected Subsidiaries

Asteron Group Ltd. (life insurance)
GIO General Ltd (general insurance products)
Suncorp Life & Superannuation Limited life (insurance products)
Suncorp Metway Insurance Ltd (general insurance products)
Suncorp Metway Investment Management Limited (investment schemes and provides investment management services)
Vero Insurance Ltd. (New Zealand general insurance)

COMPETITORS

AMP Limited	Insurance Australia
AXA Asia Pacific	Macquarie Group
Australia and New Zealand Banking	National Australia Bank
Commonwealth Bank of Australia	Westpac Banking

HISTORICAL FINANCIALS
Company Type: Public

Income Statement
FYE: June 30

	ASSETS ($ mil.)	NET INCOME ($ mil.)	INCOME AS % OF ASSETS	EMPLOYEES
06/16	71,238	772	1.1%	0
06/15	73,504	870	1.2%	0
06/14	88,728	685	0.8%	0
06/13	88,481	452	0.5%	0
06/12	97,829	737	0.8%	0
Annual Growth	(7.6%)	1.2%	—	—

2016 Year-End Financials

Return on assets: 1.0%	Dividends
Return on equity: 7.6%	Yield: 0.0%
Long-term debt ($ mil.): —	Payout: 96.7%
No. of shares (mil.): 1,286	Market value ($ mil.): 11,476
Sales ($ mil): 11,522	

	STOCK PRICE ($) FY Close	P/E High/Low	PER SHARE ($) Earnings	Dividends	Book Value
06/16	8.92	13 10	0.59	0.57	7.84
06/15	10.43	13 11	0.67	0.75	8.05
06/14	12.79	22 19	0.54	0.30	10.06
Annual Growth	(16.5%)	— —	2.6%	17.3%	(6.0%)

Suning Appliance Co., Ltd.

EXECUTIVES

Legal Representative, Yang Bo
Auditors: PricewaterhouseCoopers

LOCATIONS

HQ: Suning Appliance Co., Ltd.
No. 68, Huaihai Road, Nanjing, Jiangsu Province
210005
Phone: (86) 25 84418888   **Fax:** (86) 25 84467008
Web: www.cnsuning.com

HISTORICAL FINANCIALS
Company Type: Public

Income Statement
FYE: December 31

	REVENUE ($ mil.)	NET INCOME ($ mil.)	NET PROFIT MARGIN	EMPLOYEES
12/15	20,871	134	0.6%	0
12/14	17,550	139	0.8%	0
12/13	17,392	61	0.4%	0
12/12	15,776	429	2.7%	0
12/11	14,916	765	5.1%	0
Annual Growth	8.8%	(35.3%)	—	—

2015 Year-End Financials

Debt ratio: 2.0%
Return on equity: 2.9%
Cash ($ mil.): 4,175
Current ratio: 1.21
Long-term debt ($ mil.): 1,283

No. of shares (mil.): —
Dividends
  Yield: —
  Payout: —
Market value ($ mil.): —

Suntory Holdings Ltd

Japan-based Suntory Holdings is a 100-year-old company best known for producing Japan's first whiskey under the Kakubin brand name. Today the company comprises approximately 270 group subsidiaries located worldwide that do everything from distill whiskey to grow and sell flowers. Suntory Holdings has three main areas of operation: producing alcoholic beverages (including MIDORI melon-flavored liqueur); producing health food and supplement and non-alcoholic beverages; and running restaurant fitness and floral operations. It is the Japanese distributor of Häagen-Dazs ice cream and runs a number of Pepsi bottling businesses in both Japan and Vietnam.

Operations

Suntory Beverage & Food which includes the soft drink brands is the largest operating company in the Suntory Group accounting for more than 50% of sales. Beyond its Beverage & Foods and Beer & Spirits (35% of sales) businesses Suntory owns: Tipness a chain of fitness clubs in Japan; Suntory Flowers Ltd. and ice cream distributor Häagen-Dazs Japan. Suntory Wellness Ltd. is a health-related business.

Geographic Reach

Japan is Suntory's largest market accounting for nearly 65% of sales. The rest of Asia and Oceania accounts for about 14% and Europe supplies 13%. The beverage and food company has operations throughout Asia the Pacific Rim the Americas and Europe (Morrison Bowmore Distillers in Scotland for example). Suntory is a big producer of beer in China.

Financial Performance

Suntory's sales jumped 20% in 2014 compared with 2012 to ¥2.44 trillion primarily due to increased beer and spirit sales. Net income decreased over the same period due to an increase in selling and administrative expenses. The Americas and Europe fueled sales growth in 2014 rising 192% and 84% respectively. The company also posted sales gains in its other markets.

Strategy

In late 2013 Suntory announced the formation of a new company to manage its business in Europe which accounts for approximately 10% of the Japan-based company's sales. The new company will be called Suntory Beverage & Food Ltd. and will be based in London.

Suntory bought US spirits company Beam (now called Beam Suntory for $13.6 billion building on an existing distribution partnership in Asia.

In 2015 Beam Suntory sold its Jerez-based brandy and sherry business to Emperador Inc. The agreement includes the Fundador Harveys Terry and Tres Cepas brands as well as production operations in Jerez and Tomelloso Spain.

EXECUTIVES

EVP and COO, Nobuhiro Torii
President and CEO, Takeshi Niinami
President and CEO Beam Suntory, Matthew J. (Matt) Shattock, age 53
Executive Officer; President and CEO Suntory Global Innovation Center, Takayuki Hirashima
Managing Executive Officer; President Suntory Wellness, Masuo Kawasaki
EVP, Yasunori Aiba
EVP, Shunichi Naito
Executive Officer; President Beam Suntory (Asia), Atsushi (Windy) Koizumi
Senior Managing Director, Koji Kojima
Executive Officer; President Suntory Beer, Tetsu Mizutani
Senior Managing Director; President and CEO Suntory Business Expert, Hideo Tsujimura
Senior Managing Director; Chairman Suntory (China) Holding, Shinichiro Hizuka
Managing Executive Officer; President and CEO Suntory Wine International, Yuji Yamazaki
Managing Executive Officer; President and CEO Suntory Liquors, Takashi Kojima
Executive Officer; President and CEO Suntory Spirits, Sho Semba
Vice Chairman, Shingo Torii
Chairman, Nobutada Saji, age 70
Auditors: Deloitte Touche Tohmatsu LLC

LOCATIONS

HQ: Suntory Holdings Ltd
2-1-40 Dojimahama, Kita-ku, Osaka, Osaka 530-8203
Phone: (81) 6 6346 1682
Web: www.suntory.co.jp

2014 Sales

	% of total
Japan	64
Europe	13
Americas	9
Asia Oceania and Other	14
Total	**100**

PRODUCTS/OPERATIONS

2014 Sales

	% of total
Beverages & foods	51
Alcoholic Beverage	36
Other	13
Total	**100**

Selected Operations

Suntory Beverage & Food Ltd.
  Suntory Foods Ltd.
  Suntory Products Ltd.
  Orangina Schweppes Group
  Frucor Group
  Suntory Beverage & Food Asia Pte. Ltd.
  Cerebos Pacific Ltd.
  Pepsi Bottling Ventures LLC
Suntory (China) Holding Co. Ltd.
Suntory Liquors Ltd.
  Suntory Beer & Spirits Ltd.

Suntory Wine International Ltd.
Suntory Wellness Ltd.
Restaurants Processed Foods Fitness Flowers & Other Services
  Dynac Corp.
  Häagen-Dazs Japan Inc.
  Tipness Ltd.
  Suntory Flowers Ltd.

COMPETITORS

Anheuser-Busch InBev	Makita
Asahi Breweries	McDonald's Japan
Asia Pacific Breweries	Mercian
Body Shop	Morinaga
Burger King	Nestle Waters
Coca-Cola	PepsiCo
Danone Water	Pernod Ricard
Diageo	SABMiller
Energy Brands	Sakata Seed
Ezaki Glico	Sapporo
Kikkoman	Seven & i
Kirin Holdings Company	Skylark
Kokubu	Takara
Konami	Tsingtao
LOTTE	

HISTORICAL FINANCIALS
Company Type: Public

Income Statement
FYE: December 31

	REVENUE ($ mil.)	NET INCOME ($ mil.)	NET PROFIT MARGIN	EMPLOYEES
12/15	22,319	375	1.7%	42,081
12/14	20,578	321	1.6%	37,613
12/13	19,435	1,863	9.6%	34,129
12/12	21,497	425	2.0%	28,767
12/11	23,295	809	3.5%	28,532
Annual Growth	(1.1%)	(17.4%)	—	10.2%

2015 Year-End Financials

Debt ratio: 0.3%
Return on equity: 5.2%
Cash ($ mil.): 2,148
Current ratio: 1.29
Long-term debt ($ mil.): 15,365

No. of shares (mil.): 683
Dividends
  Yield: —
  Payout: —
Market value ($ mil.): —

Suzuken Co Ltd

Auditors: Deloitte Touche Tohmatsu LLC

LOCATIONS

HQ: Suzuken Co Ltd
8 Higashi-Katahamachi, Higashi-ku, Nagoya, Aichi 461-8701
Phone: (81) 52 961 2331   **Fax:** (81) 52 961 4071
Web: www.suzuken.co.jp

HISTORICAL FINANCIALS
Company Type: Public

Income Statement
FYE: March 31

	REVENUE ($ mil.)	NET INCOME ($ mil.)	NET PROFIT MARGIN	EMPLOYEES
03/16	19,847	257	1.3%	19,833
03/15	16,421	157	1.0%	19,305
03/14	19,262	207	1.1%	15,287
03/13	20,135	152	0.8%	14,842
03/12	22,673	98	0.4%	15,155
Annual Growth	(3.3%)	27.3%	—	7.0%

2016 Year-End Financials

Debt ratio: 0.0%	No. of shares (mil.): 99
Return on equity: 7.5%	Dividends
Cash ($ mil.): 965	Yield: —
Current ratio: 1.18	Payout: —
Long-term debt ($ mil.): 0	Market value ($ mil.): —

Suzuki Motor Corp. (Japan)

Suzuki Motor Corporation is a leading Japanese carmaker and a global motorcycle manufacturer competing head-to-head with rivals Honda and Yamaha. Suzuki's passenger car models include the Alto Grand Vitara Swift Splash and SX4. Its motorcycle products include cruiser motocross offroad scooter street and touring models as well as ATVs. Suzuki Motor's non-vehicle products include outboard motors for boats and motorized wheelchairs. It builds its lineup on its own and through numerous subsidiaries and joint ventures overseas. Japan accounts for nearly 45% of sales. Suzuki entered the US car market in 1985 with the Samurai the country' first compact SUV.

Geographic Reach

The company has man production facilities in 22 countries and serves more than 200 countries. Outside of Japan (around 45% of its total sales) Asian consumers represent nearly 35% of its sales whereas North American and European purchases combined account for nearly 15%. Suzuki subsidiary Maruti Suzuki India is India's largest passenger car company.

Operations

Suzuki divides its operations into four reportable segments. The Automobile segment generated 88% of the company's total sales for 2012 while its motorcycle operations accounted for 10%. The other segments —marine and power products; and financial services —accounted for the remaining 2%.

Financial Performance

Suzuki's balance sheet has been up and down over the years. After posting increases in both revenue and net income in 2011 the company saw its revenues decrease by 4% in 2012. The lower revenue was attributed to a 1% decrease in its motorcycle segment and a 4% dip in its automobile segment. The company however did recognize a 19% increase in its net income for 2012 due to lower expenses related to sales marketing and promotions.

Strategy

Suzuki is expanding its vehicle lineup in China through Suzuki China which imports and sells Japanese-made cars. The company imports and exports Suzuki-brand vehicles through Suzuki Automobile (Thailand) a joint venture with Siam International Corp. Demand in Vietnam the Philippines and Malaysia has continued to grow modestly too.

In 2012 Suzuki began construction of a new motorcycle plant in Rohtak Haryana of India and a second plant through Chongqing Changan Suzuki Automobile Co. Ltd. (Changan Suzuki) an automobile manufacturing and sales joint venture company in China. The Indian motorcycle market in 2011 exceeded 13 million units and Suzuki expects continuous growth in the region. To capitalize on the expanding Chinese automobile market and to establish an annual capacity of 500000 units Suzuki has decided to construct its second plant in the area next to its current plant.

HISTORY

In 1909 Michio Suzuki started Suzuki Loom Works in Hamamatsu Japan. The company went public in 1920 and continued producing weaving equipment until the onset of WWII when it began to make war-related products.

Suzuki began developing inexpensive motor vehicles in 1947 and in 1952 it introduced a 36cc engine to motorize bicycles. The company changed its name to Suzuki Motor and launched its first motorcycle in 1954. Suzuki's entry into the minicar market came in 1955 with the Suzulight followed by the Suzumoped (1958) a delivery van (1959) and the Suzulight Carry FB small truck (1961).

Suzuki's triumph in the 1962 50cc-class Isle of Man TT motorcycle race started a string of racing successes that brought international prominence to the Suzuki name. The company established its first overseas plant in Thailand in 1967.

In the 1970s Suzuki met market demand for motorcycles with large engines. Meanwhile a mid-1970s recession and falling demand for low-powered cars in Japan led the minicar industry there to produce two-thirds fewer minicars in 1974 than in 1970. Suzuki responded by pushing overseas beginning auto exports and expanding foreign distribution. In 1975 it started producing motorcycles in Taiwan Thailand and Indonesia.

Suzuki boosted capacity internationally throughout the 1980s through joint ventures. Motorcycle sales in Japan peaked in 1982 then tapered off but enjoyed a modest rebound in the late 1980s. In 1988 the company agreed to handle distribution of Peugeot cars in Japan.

Suzuki and General Motors began their longstanding relationship in 1981 when GM bought a small stake in Suzuki. The company began producing Swift subcompacts in 1983 and sold them through GM as the Chevy Sprint and later the Geo Metro. In 1986 Suzuki and GM of Canada jointly formed CAMI Automotive to produce vehicles including Sprints Metros and Geo Trackers (Suzuki Sidekicks) in Ontario; production began in 1989.

Although sales via GM increased through 1990 US efforts with the Suzuki nameplate faltered shortly after Suzuki formed its US subsidiary in Brea California in 1986. A 1988 Consumer Reports claim that the company's Samurai SUV was prone to rolling over devastated US sales. The next year Suzuki's top US executives quit apparently questioning the company's commitment to the US market.

Suzuki established Magyar Suzuki a joint venture with Hungarian automaker Autokonszern Rt. C. Itoh & Co. and International Finance Corporation in 1991 to begin producing the Swift sedan in Hungary. The company expanded a licensing agreement with a Chinese government partner in 1993 becoming the first Japanese company to take an equity stake in a Chinese carmaking venture. The next year Suzuki introduced the Alto van Japan's cheapest car at just over $5000 and the Wagon R miniwagon which quickly became one of Japan's top-selling vehicles.

In a case that was later overturned a woman was awarded $90 million from Suzuki after being paralyzed in a Samurai rollover in 1990. The company sued Consumers Union publisher of Consumer Reports in 1996 charging it had intended to fix the results in the 1988 Samurai testing.

GM raised its 3% stake in Suzuki to 10% in 1998. The company teamed up with GM and Fuji Heavy Industries (Subaru) in 2000 to develop compact cars for the European market. It was also announced that GM would spend about $600 million to double its stake in Suzuki to 20%. In 2001 Suzuki announced that it had agreed to cooperate with Kawasaki in the development of new motorcycles scooters and ATVs.

The following year Suzuki agreed to take control of Maruti Udyog Ltd. the state-owned India-based car manufacturer in an $80 million rights issue deal.

GM sold almost all of its 20% stake in Suzuki in early 2006 to raise cash for its own beleaguered operations. GM divested the remaining 3% stake in late 2008 for about $230 million as it endured a dire cash crisis.

EXECUTIVES

EVP, Toshihiro Suzuki
Senior Technical Executive, Osamu Honda
Executive General Manager Global Business Administration and Planning, Takashi Iwatsuki
Executive Genaral Manager Manufacturing Engineering, Hiroaki Matsuura
Executive General Manager Corporate Planning, Masahiko Nagao
Chairman and CEO, Osamu Suzuki
Vice Chairman, Yasuhito Harayama
Auditors: Seimei Audit Corp.

LOCATIONS

HQ: Suzuki Motor Corp. (Japan)
  300 Takatsuka-cho, Hamamatsu, Shizuoka 432-8611
Phone: (81) 53 440 2030
Web: www.suzuki.co.jp

2016 Sales

	% of total
Asia	44
Japan	41
Europe	10
Other regions	5
Total	**100**

PRODUCTS/OPERATIONS

2016 Salles

	% of total
Automobiles	91
Motorcycles	7
Marine and power products	2
Total	**100**

List of Items
Automobiles
  Alto/CELERIO
  APV
  Grand Vitara SUV
  Jimny
  Kizashi sport sedan
  Splash
  Swift
  SX4 Crossover Sport SportBack
Motorcycles/ATV
  Cruiser
  Dual purpose
  Motocross
  Offroad
  Scooter
  Sport Enduro Tourer
  Street
  Supersport
Outboard motors
  Carburetor
  Electronic
  Kerosene 0

COMPETITORS

BMW	Mahindra
Bajaj Auto	Mazda
Brunswick Corp.	Nissan
Daimler	Piaggio & Co.
Ducati	Polaris Industries
FCA US	Renault
Ford Motor	Tata Motors

General Motors
Harley-Davidson
Honda
Hyundai Motor
Kawasaki Heavy
 Industries

Toyota
Triumph Motorcycles
Volkswagen
Yamaha Motor

HISTORICAL FINANCIALS

Company Type: Public

Income Statement

FYE: March 31

	REVENUE ($ mil.)	NET INCOME ($ mil.)	NET PROFIT MARGIN	EMPLOYEES
03/16	28,323	1,038	3.7%	81,895
03/15	25,133	807	3.2%	74,775
03/14	28,466	1,041	3.7%	57,749
03/13	27,402	854	3.1%	55,948
03/12	30,625	656	2.1%	54,484
Annual Growth	(1.9%)	12.1%	—	10.7%

2016 Year-End Financials

Debt ratio: 0.1%
Return on equity: 9.5%
Cash ($ mil.): 4,427
Current ratio: 1.42
Long-term debt ($ mil.): 2,340

No. of shares (mil.): 441
Dividends
 Yield: 0.0%
 Payout: 25.1%
Market value ($ mil.): 45,619

	STOCK PRICE ($) FY Close	P/E High/Low		PER SHARE ($) Earnings	Dividends	Book Value
03/16	103.42	1	0	2.09	0.53	19.34
03/15	125.00	1	1	1.44	0.80	22.03
03/14	109.45	—	—	1.86	0.00	25.81
03/13	90.52	—	—	1.40	0.00	24.61
03/12	96.10	—	—	1.08	0.00	24.16
Annual Growth	1.9%	—	—	18.1%	—	(5.4%)

Svenska Handelsbanken

Svenska Handelsbanken is Swedish for universal banking. The group provides corporate and individual clients with deposit products loans credit cards and other banking services. Subsidiaries operate in several related areas including life insurance mortgages pensions fund management and Internet banking. The bank boasts more than 830 branches in 25 countries with most in Sweden the UK Denmark Finland Norway and the Netherlands. Subsidiaries include corporate financing unit Handelsbanken Finans Handelsbanken Asset Management and Handelsbanken Liv. Founded in 1871 the bank's assets now exceed $360 billion.

OperationsThe bank operates in seven business segments mostly based on geography. These include branch operation segments in Sweden the UK Denmark Finland Norway and the Netherlands as well as a Capital Markets segment.

The bank made more than 80% of its total revenue in 2014 from interest income mostly from corporate loans and mortgage loans but also from consumer loans. The majority of the remaining revenues came from fee and commission income from its investment banking and other corporate finance services with a small portion (3% of revenues) coming from its insurance and pensions operations.

Geographic Reach

Svenska Handelsbanken generates more than 60% of its revenue in Sweden while its operations in Norway and the UK each bring in 10% of total revenue. The banks other top markets include Denmark Finland and the Netherlands. It also has a presence in countries including Austria China Hong Kong Russia and the US. Financial PerformanceThe bank's net revenues and profits have been on the rise in recent years thanks to a combination of low borrowing rates on deposits growing investment banking and loan business from aggressive branch expansion rising investment gains and strong controls on staffing costs.Svenska's revenue dipped by 5% to SK$63.5 billion ($8.14 billion) in 2014 despite higher loan volumes mostly as interest margins on loans and securities shrank amidst the low-interest environment. Despite lower revenues the bank's net income rose by 6% to SK$15 billion ($1.9 billion) thanks to a decline in interest expenses on deposits and a slower rise in staff costs.

The bank's operating cash fell by more than 50% to SK$52.8 billion ($6.76 billion) despite higher earnings in 2014 mostly as it used more cash toward loans to the public and other credit institutions.

Strategy

With its focus on being as local to its customer as possible Svenska Handelsbanken continues to grow its digital banking and its physical branch network in new markets around the world. During 2014 the bank opened 24 new branches across several countries including 17 in the UK two in each Norway and the Netherlands and one branch in each of Denmark and Finland.

HISTORY

Company BackgroundSvenska Handelsbanken (roughly translated as The Swedish Commercial Bank) was founded as Stockholms Handelsbank in 1871 by former directors of Stockholms Enskilda Bank who lost an internal power struggle. Industrialization in the latter stages of the 19th century saw Stockholms Handelsbank expand nationwide with the bank pursuing an aggressive lending policy. Larger companies required larger financing resulting in smaller local banks running into trouble and forcing them to merge with bigger ones. Through a series of mergers of this kind Stockholms Handelsbank exploded in size and branches increased from seven (all Stockholm-based) to 250 nationwide by 1919. To reflect this growth the company changed its name to Svenska Handelsbanken the same year.

Sweden remained neutral during WWI allowing business to prosper but the depression hit hard. The bank had to write off millions in bad loans and additions to its reserves. During the 1930s Handelsbanken regained stability largely thanks to its geographical diversity; operations in areas with high economic activity made up for struggling regions.

Sweden once again remained neutral during WWII but political uncertainty kept deposits high and it became difficult to maintain profitable loan volumes. In the 1940s Svenska Handelsbanken divested many of its industrial holdings and began to rededicate itself to small- and medium-scale lending.

Through a string of purchases in the 1950s and 1960s the bank became the largest bank in Scandinavia and began looking to expand internationally. Joint ventures and acquisitions saw the company move into other parts of Europe and the US in the 1970s. Nordic American Banking a US subsidiary was set up to handle import and export financing for North and South American clients doing business with Scandinavian countries. The 1980s saw the company establish a merchant-

banking subsidiary in London and enter the Asian market forming Svenska Handelsbanken Asia (based in Singapore).

The bank remained acquisitive during the first half of the 1990s including a purchase of life insurance company RKA (later renamed Handelsbanken Liv) and parts of the Finnish Skopbank. In 1996 Handelsbanken acquired Swedish mortgage company Stadshypotek.

During the latter half of the 1990s it ventured into e-business and increased its presence in the Nordic countries and the UK. In 1999 the company acquired the Norwegian Bergensbanken after having been beaten by MeritaNordbanken in the chase for Christiania Bank (which was Norway's second-largest at the time). The next year Handelsbanken acquired Spartacus a Danish consumer finance company. In 2001 it made another Danish purchase Midtbank making it one of Denmark's largest bankers. That year it also acquired Swedish life insurance company SPP.

In 2004 Handelsbanken bought Swedish fund manager XACT Fonder from OMHEX (now OMX).

The company bought Lokallbanken in Denmark in 2008. The deal added about 15 branches to Handelsbanken's network.

EXECUTIVES

President and Group Chief Executive, Anders Bouvin, age 59

EVP and Head Capital Markets, Per Beckman, age 55

CEO Handelsbanken Norway, Dag Tjernsmo

Chairman Stadshypotek Bank, Yonnie Bergqvist, age 55

Deputy Group CEO Group Management and Head Handelsbanken Stockholm, Carina .kerstr ƒn

Chief Risk Officer Group Risk Control, Maria Hedin

CEO Handelsbanken Finland, Nina Arkilahti

Head Markets and Asset Management, Per Elcar

Head Handelsbanken Northern Sweden, Magnus Ericson

Head Handelsbanken Southern UK, John Hodson

Head Handelsbanken Western Sweden, Katarina Ljungqvist

Head Handelsbanken Yorkshire and North East UK, Simon Lodge

Head Handelsbanken Central UK, Nick Lowe

CEO Handelsbanken Denmark, Lars Moesgaard

Chairman Swedish Subsidiary Boards and International Regional Bank Boards, Stefan Nilsson

Head Handelsbanken Northern UK, John Parker

Head Handelsbanken South East Sweden, G ƒan Stille

CEO Stadshypotek, Ulrika Stolt Kirkegaard

Head Handelsbanken Central Sweden, Pontus .hlund

CEO Handelsbanken UK, Mikael S .rensen

CEO Handelsbanken The Netherlands, Jens Wiklund

Acting CEO Handelsbanken UK, Andrew Copsey

CEO Handelsbanken Liv Pension and Life, Louise Sander

Head Handelsbanken South West UK, Chris Teasdale

CIO Group IT, Agneta Lilja

Acting CFO, Rolf Marquardt

Vice Chairman, Fredrik Lundberg, age 66

Chairman, P ☐r Boman

Auditors: KPMG AB

LOCATIONS

HQ: Svenska Handelsbanken
 Kungstradgardsgatan 2, Stockholm SE-106 70
Phone: (46) 8 701 10 00
Web: www.handelsbanken.se

2014 Sales

	% of total
Sweden	63
Norway	10
UK	10
Denmark	6
Finland	6
Netherlands	4
Other countries	1
Total	**100**

PRODUCTS/OPERATIONS

2014 Sales by Segment

	% of total
Branch operations	
Sweden	52
Other countries	33
Capital markets	15
Total	**100**

COMPETITORS

BNP Paribas	Deutsche Bank
Citigroup	Nordea Bank
Credit Agricole	SEB AB
Danske Bank	Societe Generale

HISTORICAL FINANCIALS

Company Type: Public

Income Statement				FYE: December 31
	ASSETS ($ mil.)	NET INCOME ($ mil.)	INCOME AS % OF ASSETS	EMPLOYEES
12/15	299,169	1,938	0.6%	11,819
12/14	364,372	1,964	0.5%	11,692
12/13	388,352	2,229	0.6%	11,503
12/12	366,543	2,233	0.6%	11,192
12/11	355,859	1,786	0.5%	11,184
Annual Growth	(4.2%)	2.1%	—	1.4%

2015 Year-End Financials

Return on assets: 0.6%
Return on equity: 12.8%
Long-term debt ($ mil.): —
No. of shares (mil.): 1,907
Sales ($ mil): 6,797

Dividends
  Yield: 5.1%
  Payout: 34.0%
Market value ($ mil.): 12,588

	STOCK PRICE ($) FY Close	P/E High/Low		PER SHARE ($) Earnings	Dividends	Book Value
12/15	6.60	3	1	1.00	0.34	7.98
12/14	23.40	3	2	1.01	0.42	8.60
12/13	24.68	3	2	1.16	0.27	9.11
12/12	18.03	3	2	1.16	0.24	8.64
12/11	13.43	2	2	0.94	0.22	7.32
Annual Growth	(16.3%)	—	—	1.5%	11.6%	2.2%

Sveriges Riksbank (Sweden)

EXECUTIVES

Controller, Pether Burvall
Auditors: Swedish National Audit Office

LOCATIONS

HQ: Sveriges Riksbank (Sweden)
  Brunkebergstorg 11, Stockholm SE-103 37
Phone: (46) 8 787 00 00   **Fax:** (46) 8 21 05 31
Web: www.riksbank.se

HISTORICAL FINANCIALS

Company Type: Public

Income Statement				FYE: December 31
	ASSETS ($ mil.)	NET INCOME ($ mil.)	INCOME AS % OF ASSETS	EMPLOYEES
12/15	78,688	231	0.3%	341
12/14	64,991	422	0.7%	330
12/13	67,323	(313)	—	341
12/12	53,071	296	0.6%	351
12/11	50,444	569	1.1%	332
Annual Growth	11.8%	(20.1%)	—	0.7%

Swedbank A B

Auditors: Deloitte AB

LOCATIONS

HQ: Swedbank A B
  Landsvagen 40, Stockholm SE-105 34
Phone: (46) 8 585 900 00   **Fax:** (46) 8 796 80 92
Web: www.swedbank.com

HISTORICAL FINANCIALS

Company Type: Public

Income Statement				FYE: December 31
	ASSETS ($ mil.)	NET INCOME ($ mil.)	INCOME AS % OF ASSETS	EMPLOYEES
12/15	254,892	1,865	0.7%	13,893
12/14	274,416	2,127	0.8%	14,624
12/13	284,004	2,012	0.7%	14,265
12/12	283,511	2,216	0.8%	16,088
12/11	269,256	1,702	0.6%	18,716
Annual Growth	(1.4%)	2.3%	—	(7.2%)

2015 Year-End Financials

Return on assets: 0.7%
Return on equity: 13.0%
Long-term debt ($ mil.): —
No. of shares (mil.): 1,105
Sales ($ mil): 6,677

Dividends
  Yield: 5.9%
  Payout: 78.8%
Market value ($ mil.): 24,313

	STOCK PRICE ($) FY Close	P/E High/Low		PER SHARE ($) Earnings	Dividends	Book Value
12/15	22.00	2	1	1.68	1.31	13.22
12/14	24.91	2	1	1.92	1.56	13.76
12/13	28.31	3	2	1.58	1.52	15.57
12/12	19.80	2	1	1.87	0.78	17.75
12/11	12.85	2	1	1.38	0.31	15.66
Annual Growth	14.4%	—	—	5.0%	43.4%	(4.1%)

Swiss Life (UK) plc (United Kingdom)

Auditors: PricewaterhouseCoopers AG

LOCATIONS

HQ: Swiss Life (UK) plc (United Kingdom)
  General-Guisan-Quai 40, P.O. Box 2831, Zurich CH-8022
Phone: (41) 43 284 33 11
Web: www.swisslife.com

HISTORICAL FINANCIALS

Company Type: Public

Income Statement				FYE: December 31
	ASSETS ($ mil.)	NET INCOME ($ mil.)	INCOME AS % OF ASSETS	EMPLOYEES
12/15	190,566	878	0.5%	7,595
12/14	194,962	822	0.4%	7,492
12/13	191,380	876	0.5%	6,992
12/12*	179,406	106	0.1%	7,046
01/12	161,771	0	—	0
Annual Growth	4.2%	—	—	—

*Fiscal year change

2015 Year-End Financials

Return on assets: 0.4%
Return on equity: 7.0%
Long-term debt ($ mil.): —
No. of shares (mil.): 31
Sales ($ mill): 15,347

Dividends
  Yield: —
  Payout: —
Market value ($ mil.): —

Swiss Life Holding AG

Auditors: PricewaterhouseCoopers AG

LOCATIONS

HQ: Swiss Life Holding AG
  General-Guisan-Quai 40, P.O. Box 2831, Zurich CH-8022
Phone: (41) 43 284 33 11   **Fax:** (41) 43 284 63 11
Web: www.swisslife.com; www.swisslife.com

HISTORICAL FINANCIALS

Company Type: Public

Income Statement				FYE: December 31
	REVENUE ($ mil.)	NET INCOME ($ mil.)	NET PROFIT MARGIN	EMPLOYEES
12/15	20,697	878	4.2%	7,595
12/14	20,697	822	4.0%	7,492
12/13	21,841	876	4.0%	6,992
12/12	20,808	100	0.5%	7,046
12/11	18,379	643	3.5%	7,168
Annual Growth	3.0%	8.1%	—	1.5%

2015 Year-End Financials

Debt ratio: —
Return on equity: 7.0%
Cash ($ mil.): 5,332
Current ratio: —
Long-term debt ($ mil.): —

No. of shares (mil.): 31
Dividends
  Yield: 0.0%
  Payout: 1.1%
Market value ($ mil.): 431

	STOCK PRICE ($) FY Close	P/E High/Low		PER SHARE ($) Earnings	Dividends	Book Value
12/15	13.53	0	0	26.03	0.29	385.26
12/14	11.80	0	0	24.37	0.28	404.36
12/13	10.45	0	0	27.18	0.23	314.77
12/12	5.80	—	—	3.12	0.22	350.28
12/11	5.80	0	0	20.06	0.22	304.53
Annual Growth	23.6%	—	—	6.7%	8.1%	6.1%

Swiss Life Insurance & Pension Co. (Switzerland)

Auditors: PricewaterhouseCoopers AG

LOCATIONS

HQ: Swiss Life Insurance & Pension Co. (Switzerland)
General Guisan-Quai 40, P.O. Box 2831, Zurich CH-8022
Phone: (41) 43 284 33 11
Web: www.swisslife.com

HISTORICAL FINANCIALS

Company Type: Public

Income Statement

FYE: December 31

	REVENUE ($ mil.)	NET INCOME ($ mil.)	NET PROFIT MARGIN	EMPLOYEES
12/15	20,697	878	4.2%	7,595
12/14	20,697	822	4.0%	7,492
12/13	21,841	876	4.0%	6,992
12/12	20,808	100	0.5%	7,046
12/11	18,379	643	3.5%	7,168
Annual Growth	3.0%	8.1%	—	1.5%

2015 Year-End Financials

Debt ratio: —	No. of shares (mil.): 31
Return on equity: 7.0%	Dividends
Cash ($ mil.): 5,332	Yield: —
Current ratio: —	Payout: —
Long-term debt ($ mil.): —	Market value ($ mil.): —

Swiss Re Ltd.

Auditors: PricewaterhouseCoopers Ltd.

LOCATIONS

HQ: Swiss Re Ltd.
Mythenquai 50/60, PO Box, Zurich 8022
Phone: (41) 43 285 2121   **Fax:** (41) 43 285 2999
Web: www.swissre.com

HISTORICAL FINANCIALS

Company Type: Public

Income Statement

FYE: December 31

	ASSETS ($ mil.)	NET INCOME ($ mil.)	INCOME AS % OF ASSETS	EMPLOYEES
12/15	196,135	4,665	2.4%	12,767
12/14	204,461	3,569	1.7%	12,224
12/13	213,520	4,511	2.1%	11,574
12/12	215,785	4,257	2.0%	11,193
12/11	225,899	2,626	1.2%	10,788
Annual Growth	(3.5%)	15.4%	—	4.3%

2015 Year-End Financials

Return on assets: 2.3%	Dividends
Return on equity: 13.4%	Yield: 30.9%
Long-term debt ($ mil.): —	Payout: 15.4%
No. of shares (mil.): 337	Market value ($ mil.): 8,280
Sales ($ mil): 35,714	

	STOCK PRICE ($) FY Close	P/E High/Low		PER SHARE ($) Earnings	Dividends	Book Value
12/15	24.52	7	2	12.28	7.59	99.24
12/14	84.57	9	7	9.39	9.00	105.00
12/13	92.38	7	6	11.89	8.03	96.30
12/12	72.30	6	4	11.06	3.29	99.08
12/11	50.55	8	5	7.49	0.00	86.33
Annual Growth (16.5%)		—	—	13.2%	—	3.5%

T&D Holdings Inc

No mystery in a name here: T&D Holdings serves as the holding company for Japanese insurance companies Taiyo Life and Daido Life. Combined the companies constitute one of Japan's top life insurers. Taiyo Life gears its products to individuals while Daido Life's products are targeted toward small businesses. Another subsidiary T&D Financial Life sells whole life policies through financial institutions the likes of banks securities firms and insurance shop agents. Other businesses under the T&D umbrella include T&D Asset Management T&D Customer Services (administrative services) and Pet & Family (pet insurance) and T&D Information Systems (computer processing).

Operations

T&D Holdings' Taiyo Life division which accounts for 40% of the holding company's annual revenues serves households with comprehensive life products including death benefits and medical or nursing care coverage. Meanwhile the Daido Life unit (another 40% of sales) focuses on the sale of term life insurance and illness policies through business accounts. The third-largest business unit T&D Financial Life sells whole life policies.

Geographic Reach

The company operates in Japan.

Sales and Marketing

The operating units of T&D Holdings use targeted sales techniques. With a focus on selling to housewives and middle-aged women Taiyo Life employs a sales force made up of some 8600 women (similar in age to their target market base) who visit homes to present tailor-made coverage options. Daido Life gears its marketing efforts towards small and midsized businesses by partnering with enterprise associations (such as the National Federation of Corporate Taxpayers Association); it has some 3800 in-house sales representatives. The company's T&D Financial Life unit markets through a network of some 120 agencies including financial institutions.

Financial Performance

In fiscal 2014 (ended March) revenue decreased 14% to ¥2085 billion as new policy sales in the Taiyo Life and Daido Life units declined. The decline in new policies primarily reflected the impact of an increase in insurance premiums in 2013. It was partially offset by an increase in revenue from T&D Financial Life.

Net income rose 24% to ¥78.9 billion in fiscal 2014 as provisions for policy and other reserves declined and operating expenses decreased. Cash flow from operations fell 75% to ¥159 billion.

Strategy

T&D Holdings is seeking to grow by branching out beyond its traditional market segments. Its Taiyo Life unit is working to expand policy sales by marketing policies geared at men and children. Daido Life is adding products for business owners

such as living protection coverage while T&D Financial Life is introducing new products for bereaved families and retirees. The group is also seeking to expand its international operations.

T&D Holdings is also growing its operations into the provision of short-term small-amount policies for pet shops. The company seeks to expand in new and existing business fields through alliances and acquisitions as well.

In 2014 Daido Life launched a new whole life product Life Gift which meets the growing demand for inheritance planning as Japan's population ages.

Company Background

T&D Holdings was formed through the merger of Taiyo Life and Daido Life in 2004. The companies first began working together through an alliance formed in 1999.

EXECUTIVES

Managing Director; Head of General Affairs; Managing Director Taiyo Life Insurance; and Board Member, Kenji Nakagome, age 63
Senior Executive Officer and Director Finance and Accounting Department, Tamiji Matsumoto, age 62
EVP and Representative Director Group Planning Department, Sonosuke Usui
Senior Executive Officer and Director, Terunori Yokoyama, age 63
Senior Managing Executive Officer and Director Daido Life, Masahiro Ueda
Managing Executive Officer and Director Taiyo Life, Kouichi Seike
Auditors: Ernst & Young ShinNihon LLC

LOCATIONS

HQ: T&D Holdings Inc
2-7-1 Nihonbashi, Chuo-ku, Tokyo 103-6031
Phone: (81) 3 3272 6104   **Fax:** (81) 3 3272 6552
Web: www.td-holdings.co.jp

PRODUCTS/OPERATIONS

2014 Sales

	% of total
Daido Life	40
Taiyo Life	37
T&D Financial Life	20
Other	3
Total	**100**

Selected Subsidiaries and Affiliates

AIC Private Equity Fund General Partner Ltd
Alternative Investment Capital Ltd.
Daido Life Insurance Company
Daido Management Service Co. Ltd.
Nihon System Shuno Inc.
Pet & Family Small-amount Short-term Insurance Company
T&D Asset Management Cayman Inc.
T&D Asset Management Co. Ltd.
T&D Confirm Ltd.
T&D Customer Services Co. Ltd.
T&D Financial Life Insurance Company
T&D Information System Ltd.
T&D Lease Co. Ltd.
Taiyo Credit Guarantee Co. Ltd.
Taiyo Life Insurance Company
Toyo Insurance Agency Co. Ltd.
Zenkoku Business Center Co. Ltd.

COMPETITORS

Aflac	Gibraltar Life
American Life	Insurance
Insurance	Meiji Yasuda Life
Asahi Mutual Life	Mitsui Life
Dai-ichi Life	Nippon Life Insurance
Fukoku Mutual	Sumitomo Life

HISTORICAL FINANCIALS
Company Type: Public

Income Statement
FYE: March 31

	ASSETS ($ mil.)	NET INCOME ($ mil.)	INCOME AS % OF ASSETS	EMPLOYEES
03/16	130,673	646	0.5%	21,121
03/15	122,226	785	0.6%	21,033
03/14	133,736	765	0.6%	19,868
03/13	145,269	677	0.5%	20,497
03/12	156,784	326	0.2%	20,982
Annual Growth	(4.5%)	18.6%	—	0.2%

2016 Year-End Financials

Return on assets: 0.4%	Dividends
Return on equity: 5.6%	Yield: 2.1%
Long-term debt ($ mil.): —	Payout: 11.4%
No. of shares (mil.): 648	Market value ($ mil.): 3,010
Sales ($ mil): 17,396	

	STOCK PRICE ($) FY Close	P/E High/Low		PER SHARE ($) Earnings	Dividends	Book Value
03/16	4.64	0	0	0.97	0.10	16.63
03/15	6.95	0	0	1.18	0.12	16.83
03/14	6.21	—	—	1.14	0.00	14.70
03/13	5.90	—	—	1.00	0.00	14.50
03/12	4.85	—	—	0.48	0.00	12.39
Annual Growth	(1.1%)	—	—	19.3%	—	7.6%

Taiwan Cooperative Bank

Taiwan Cooperative Bank is Taking Care of Business. Known as TCB for short the bank was founded in 1946 during the Japanese occupation of Taiwan to foster the country's burgeoning cooperative system. Today the bank still provides financing for economic development particularly for cooperative enterprises and small and middle-market businesses with a focus on the fishing and farming sectors. It also provides standard banking services such as deposits and financial management to businesses and consumers. TCB has more than 300 branches in its home country plus six offices in the US China Belgium and Philippines. The Taiwanese government owns nearly 40% of the bank.

In late 2009 TCB formed a life insurance joint venture with BNP Paribas. The program strengthened the bank's foothold in the insurance market by taking advantage of its branch network. The deal expanded TCB's offerings to include savings-linked insurance products and mortgage insurance. Shortly afterwards TCB and BNP announced plans for another joint venture –this time focused on asset management services. TCB's stake in both ventures is 51% to BNP's 49%.

EXECUTIVES

President, Tsan Chang Liao
Auditors: Deloitte & Touche

LOCATIONS

HQ: Taiwan Cooperative Bank
No. 77, Guan Qian Road, Jhongjheng District, Taipei 100
Phone: (886) 2 2311 8811   **Fax:** (886) 2 2375 2954
Web: www.tcb-bank.com.tw

COMPETITORS

Chang Hwa Bank	SinoPac Holdings
Fubon Financial	Taiwan Business Bank
Hua Nan Financial	

HISTORICAL FINANCIALS
Company Type: Public

Income Statement
FYE: December 31

	ASSETS ($ mil.)	NET INCOME ($ mil.)	INCOME AS % OF ASSETS	EMPLOYEES
12/15	92,751	369	0.4%	8,195
12/14	91,920	319	0.3%	8,437
12/13	97,967	269	0.3%	8,476
12/12*	98,462	254	0.3%	8,563
01/12	90,991	0		0
Annual Growth	0.5%	—	—	—

*Fiscal year change

2015 Year-End Financials

Return on assets: 0.4%	Dividends
Return on equity: 7.2%	Yield: —
Long-term debt ($ mil.): —	Payout: —
No. of shares (mil.): —	Market value ($ mil.): —
Sales ($ mil): 1,842	

Taiwan Power Co.

Taiwan Power (Taipower) is looking to get by with a little help from its friends. With a generating capacity of more than 40790 MW the state-owned utility serves 13.4 million industrial commercial and residential customers. Thermal sources (coal oil and liquefied natural gas) fuel most of Taipower's plants; nuclear energy and hydroelectric sources make up the balance. Unable to meet Taiwan's power needs on its own the utility has opened its market to independent power producers allowing companies to build power plants and sell to Taipower. Taipower has resumed construction on the nation's fourth nuclear plant. The Taiwan government has announced plans to privatize Taipower.

Geographic Reach The company serves customers in the Penghu Kinmen and Matsu areas of Taiwan.

Operations

Taipower's main energy sources are thermal and nuclear fuel combined with hydro and other forms of renewable energy. At the end of 2014 in terms of transmission and distribution the company had 603 transmission (sub) stations along 17286 km of transmission lines and 356428 km of distribution lines. Sales and Marketing The company serves 13.4 million industrial commercial and residential customers.

Financial Performance

Taipower's net revenues hace been increasing since 2010. In 2015 the company's net revenues increased by 8%/It posted a net income of TWD 13.98 billion (compared to net loss of TWD 7.26 billion in fiscal 2014) mainly due to an increase in operating expenses as a result of higher marketing expense and research and development. Strat-

egy In 2014 the company's five-pronged overall business strategy consisted of creating value reducing costs fulfilling social responsibility improving customer service and reengineering the company.

To reduce carbon emissions Taipower is mulling the benefits of wind. The company is planning wind-generated electricity projects that could cost TWD 120 billion. Taipower already operates wind turbines and is planning to build more in mainland Taiwan and on the island of Penghu in the Taiwan Strait.

It is also experimenting with the commercial use of solar power systems and hydrogen fuel cells.

EXECUTIVES

President, Wen Cheng Chu
Auditors: KPMG

LOCATIONS

HQ: Taiwan Power Co.
242 Roosevelt Road, Section 3, Taipei 100
Phone: (886) 2 2365 1234   **Fax:** (886) 2 2365 0037
Web: www.taipower.com.tw

HISTORICAL FINANCIALS
Company Type: Public

Income Statement
FYE: December 31

	REVENUE ($ mil.)	NET INCOME ($ mil.)	NET PROFIT MARGIN	EMPLOYEES
12/15	18,793	1,951	10.4%	26,659
12/14	20,298	441	2.2%	26,533
12/13	19,878	(571)	—	26,629
12/12	18,855	(2,761)	—	27,082
12/11	17,270	(1,430)	—	27,261
Annual Growth	2.1%	—	—	(0.6%)

2015 Year-End Financials

Debt ratio: 1.7%	No. of shares (mil.): —
Return on equity: 28.6%	Dividends
Cash ($ mil.): 59	Yield: —
Current ratio: 0.19	Payout: —
Long-term debt ($ mil.): 22,691	Market value ($ mil.): —

Taiwan Semiconductor Manufacturing Co., Ltd.

If you're absolutely fabless this company is for you. Taiwan Semiconductor Manufacturing Company (TSMC) is the first and largest dedicated silicon foundry (contract semiconductor manufacturer) in the world with nine plants in Asia and one in the US. Logic semiconductors make up about 75% of sales while mixed-signal products are most of the rest. Largely a wafer fabricator TSMC makes chips for semiconductor and systems companies who don't have their own manufacturing facilities (accounting for about 85% of sales). Those companies include AMD Broadcom NVIDIA and QUALCOMM. Remaining sales come from integrated device manufacturers including STMicroelectronics and Texas Instruments. The company gets about 69% of its sales from customers in the US.

Operations

While wafer manufacturing makes up about 90% of sales TSMC's remaining sales come mainly from fabricating masks –a kind of silkscreen used to expose silicon wafers to a certain light pattern –and it also provides services such as design probing and testing and assembly. Constituting its largest-selling product logic semiconductors are standard logic devices such as microprocessors microcontrollers digital signal processors graphic chips and chip sets. The bulk of its remaining business mixed-signal semiconductors is used in systems for data storage and program instructions such as SRAM DRAM and flash memory.

Financial Performance

The company's revenue and net income enjoyed robust year-over-year growth. Revenue increased more than 20% in 2014 from 2013 on increased demand for computer and memory devices from customers –wafer shipments were 18% higher. Its net income jumped more than 30% bolstered by the revenue increase. Cash flow from operations also had a healthy gain up 21% in 2014 from 2013.

Strategy

TSMC continues to increase the capacity and improve the efficiency of its wafer fabrication processes but it is also seeking long-term growth opportunities outside the traditional foundry business model.

But as semiconductor fabrication plants (factories) become more expensive to build more chip companies are concentrating on design and contracting manufacturing to TSMC and rivals like United Microelectronics Corp. Intel still makes its own chips and companies such as NXP make most of their own. But as a leading contractor TSMC must keep pace with the changing technologies for making chips.

In 2014 about 9% of revenue came from the company's newer 20-nanometer wafers which are more complex and carry a higher price. The older more established 28-nanometer wafer were 33% of revenue in 2014 up from 30% in 2013. The company is working on smaller sizes including a 7-nanometer wafer. In 2015 TSMC development for the 7-nanometer technology is to focus on selection of transistor architecture baseline manufacturing process setup for both transistors and interconnects and reliability evaluations.

TSMC hit the off switch on its LED lighting business in early 2015 when it sold TSMC Solid State Lighting to Epistar the largest manufacturer of LED epitaxial wafers and dies. The deal was structured so that no employee of TSMC SSL will lose employment.

HISTORY

Early History

The big foundries –including TSMC's Taiwanese archrival United Microelectronics Corporation (UMC) –played a major role in the growth of the worldwide fabless semiconductor industry in the 21st century. Foundries aim to save clients the costs and time associated with building expensive wafer fabrication plants (fabs) of their own. Their services are especially vital for fabless companies whose entire business model is predicated on outsourcing all manufacturing.

Morris Chang learned early to adapt to rapid change. The future founder and chairman of Taiwan Semiconductor Manufacturing Company (TSMC) lived in six cities before age 18 as his family fled the ravages of the Sino-Japanese War and WWII in China. Chang immigrated to the US to attend MIT and Stanford where he ultimately earned a Ph.

D. in electrical engineering.

In 25 years at Texas Instruments (TI) Chang worked his way up from the ranks of technical management into the executive suite. In 1983 he resigned from TI to become CEO of General Instrument but in 1985 the Taiwanese government recruited him to head its Industrial Technology Research Institute (ITRI). He remained chairman of ITRI from 1988 to 1994.

Working from his position at ITRI Chang became chairman of contract electronics manufacturer United Microelectronics Corporation (UMC) in 1987. Also that year he founded TSMC as the world's first dedicated contract semiconductor manufacturer –the first silicon foundry. Chang's pioneering role in the foundry industry has earned him many accolades including the first-ever Robert N. Noyce Medal of the Institute of Electrical and Electronics Engineers and the first-ever Exemplary Leadership award (subsequently named in his honor) of the Fabless Semiconductor Association (now the Global Semiconductor Alliance). Known for his analytical mind Chang was once ranked among the top 1000 players of contract bridge in the world.

TSMC became profitable within 15 months of its founding. Throughout the 1990s it continued to be among industry leaders both in production capacity and in deployment of cutting-edge technology.

EXECUTIVES

President TSMC Japan, Makoto Onodera
President and Co-CEO, Mark Liu
SVP and CIO, Stephen T. (Steve) Tso
SVP and CFO, Lora Ho
President TSMC Europe, Maria Marced
President TSMC China, L.C. Tu
SVP and President TSMC North America, Rick Cassidy, age 65
VP Research and Development; CTO, Jack Sun
President and Co-CEO, C.C. Wei
VP Operations Mainstream Fabs, J.K. Lin
VP Operations 300mm Fabs, J.K. Wang
Vice Chairman, F. C. Tseng
Chairman, Morris Chang, age 85
Auditors: Deloitte & Touche

LOCATIONS

HQ: Taiwan Semiconductor Manufacturing Co., Ltd.
No. 8, Li-Hsin Road 6, Hsinchu Science Park, Hsinchu 300
Phone: (886) 3 563 6688   **Fax:** (886) 3 563 7000
Web: www.tsmc.com

PRODUCTS/OPERATIONS

Selected Services

Semiconductor photomasks (circuit pattern guides)
  Design
  Manufacturing
Semiconductor wafers (integrated circuits and other semiconductor devices)
  Computer-aided design
  Manufacturing
  Packaging

2014 Sales

	% of Total
Fabless semiconductor companies/Systems companies	85
Integrated Device	15
Others	0
Total	**100**

2014 Sales

	% of Total
North America	69
Asia Pacific	13
China	7
EMEA	6
Japan	5
Total	**100**

2014 Sales

	% of Total
Logic	75
Mixed-Signal	24
Others	1
Total	**100**

Fabless semiconductor companies
  Advanced Micro Devices
  Altera
  Broadcom
  Marvell
  MediaTek
  NVIDIA
  QUALCOMM
Integrated device manufacturers
  LSI Corp.
  STMicroelectronics
  Texas Instruments

COMPETITORS

Advanced Semiconductor Engineering	SK Hynix
	SMIC
Advanced Semiconductor Manufacturing	Samsung Electronics
	Shanghai Hua Hong NEC
ChipMOS	Silterra
Dai Nippon Printing	Toppan Photomasks
Dongbu HiTek	Tower Semiconductor
GLOBALFOUNDRIES	UMC
Grace Semiconductor	Winbond Electronics
MagnaChip	X-FAB Silicon
Photronics	Foundries

HISTORICAL FINANCIALS

Company Type: Public

Income Statement

FYE: December 31

	REVENUE ($ mil.)	NET INCOME ($ mil.)	NET PROFIT MARGIN	EMPLOYEES
12/15	25,669	9,216	35.9%	40,483
12/14	24,091	8,031	33.3%	43,591
12/13	20,019	6,169	30.8%	40,483
12/12	17,442	5,725	32.8%	39,267
12/11	14,087	4,427	31.4%	35,457
Annual Growth	**16.2%**	**20.1%**	**—**	**3.4%**

2015 Year-End Financials

Debt ratio: 0.4%
Return on equity: 27.3%
Cash ($ mil.): 17,123
Current ratio: 3.11
Long-term debt ($ mil.): 5,842

No. of shares (mil.): —
Dividends
  Yield: 2.5%
  Payout: 153.2%
Market value ($ mil.): —

	STOCK PRICE ($) FY Close	P/E High/Low		PER SHARE ($) Earnings	Dividends	Book Value
12/15	22.75	2	2	0.36	0.58	1.40
12/14	22.38	2	2	0.31	0.40	1.25
12/13	17.44	3	2	0.24	0.40	1.08
12/12	17.16	3	2	0.22	0.40	0.96
12/11	12.91	3	2	0.17	0.40	0.80
Annual Growth	**15.2%**	**—**	**—**	**20.1%**	**10.0%**	**15.0%**

Takeda Pharmaceutical Co Ltd

The work of Takeda Pharmaceutical Company started way back in 1781 when its predecessor began selling traditional Japanese and Chinese remedies. These days Takeda is one of Asia's largest pharmaceutical companies making branded prescription drugs that it sells in some 100 countries worldwide. Top-selling products include blood pressure treatment Blopress diabetes drug Actos and ulcer medication Prevacid. The company is also a leading maker of over-the-counter medications such as cold remedies and vitamins within its home country. Takeda markets many of its products in the US through subsidiary Takeda Pharmaceuticals North America.

Operations

The Japanese drug giant operates through about 60 primarily wholly owned subsidiaries throughout the Americas Europe and Asia. Its three reportable segments are Ethical Drugs (representing 90% of total revenues) Consumer Healthcare (OTC drugs and quasi-drugs) and Other (reagents clinical diagnostics chemical products and other lines of business). The company's R&D functions are aligned into four therapeutic areas: Gastroenterology (GI) Oncology Central Nervous System (CNS) and Cardiovascular/Metabolic (CVM).

Geographic Reach

Takeda is Japan's largest pharmaceutical company with a vast global reach. Japan its largest market accounts for nearly half of total sales. The US is the pharmaceutical maker's largest foreign market contributing nearly a quarter of sales. Europe other regions in Asia and beyond represent another quarter. Non-Asian growth markets include India Russia and Brazil.

The company's network spans more than 70 countries and regions around the world in the Asia/Pacific region the Americas Europe the Middle East and Africa. Takeda has R&D sites in Japan the US Brazil the UK Germany China and Singapore.

Financial Performance

Takeda's sales increased 5% in fiscal 2015 (ended March) largely due to growth in sales of antihypertensive agent AZILVA and hyperlipidemia treatment LOTRIGA in Japan. US sales of VELCADE (for patients with multiple myeloma) and ENTYVIO (for ulcerative colitis and Crohn's disease launched in 2014) have been highly successful while in Europe sales of ADCETRIS (for malignant lymphona) have also grown.

The company reported a net loss of ¥143 billion in fiscal 2015 versus net income in 2014 as a result of lower finance income and a huge income tax provision that year. Cash flow from operations rose 23% to ¥182 billion.

Strategy

Takeda's growth strategy includes advancing its market position in North America by cultivating sales of its existing products (Actos and Prevacid) as well as through sales of newer products including Uloric a drug to help manage uric acid levels in patients with gout and heartburn treatment Dexilant (formerly known as Kapidex). As sales in the US and other regions have grown the company's domestic sales have languished in part due to price reductions imposed by Japan's National Health Insurance agency and other market factors.

Takeda is looking to expand in markets like India Russia and Brazil especially in research and development. It also is pursuing growth in Europe where it acquired Swiss drug maker Nycomed. Like many of its rivals Takeda is facing the end of patent protection for some of its drugs while the sales of some of its top products such as Prevacid have peaked. Also like its rivals it is trying to replace those aging products with new blockbuster drugs particularly in its core areas of lifestyle-related illnesses (high blood pressure and diabetes for instance); cancer; central nervous system (CNS) disorders; and gastroenterology. Lifestyle-related disorders have long been Takeda's strongest area but with that market maturing the company has been forced to expand into other therapeutic areas. In 2016 it established a generic drugs joint venture with Teva Pharmaceuticals in order to better focus on the development of new drugs while also benefiting from Japan's growing demand for generics.

The company often enters collaborations with other pharmaceuticals to develop and/or commercialize new products. For example in 2015 it entered an agreement with Chemo-Sero-Therapeutic Research Institute for the distribution of that firm's seasonal influenza vaccine in Japan. Takeda also distributes the Influenza HA Vaccine manufactured by Denka Seiken. In 2015 Takeda and Sumitomo Dainippon Pharma terminated their agreement to develop antipsychotic Latuda in Europe; in another move Takeda and AMAG Pharmaceuticals terminated their licensing development and commercialization agreement for Ferumoxytol outside of the US.

In fiscal 2014 the company launched three new products obtained two successful approvals and completed one new drug application. The FDA approved its Contrave tablets for chronic weight management that year.

Takeda established a new regional hub in Singapore in early 2015; it includes Asia/Pacific commercial operations vaccine operations and the Takeda Development Center Asia.

Mergers and Acquisitions

In early 2017 Takeda acquired US-based cancer drug developer Ariad Pharmaceuticals for $5.2 billion. That deal helped the company expand in oncology a priority therapeutic area.

EXECUTIVES

President Global Oncology, Christophe M. Bianchi, age 53
President Europe and Canada, Marc Princen
President Global Vaccine, Rajeev Venkayya
President Takeda Pharmaceuticals International, Shinji Honda
President Japan Pharma, Masato Iwasaki
President and CEO, Christophe Weber
CFO, James Kehoe, age 54
President US, Ramona Sequeira
Chief Medical and Scientific Officer, Andrew S. Plump
President Emerging Markets, Giles Platford
Chairman, Yasuchika Hasegawa
Auditors: KPMG AZSA LLC

LOCATIONS

HQ: Takeda Pharmaceutical Co Ltd
2-12-10 Nihonbashi, Chuo-ku, Tokyo 103-8668
Phone: (81) 3 3278 2111 **Fax:** (81) 3 3278 2000
Web: www.takeda.co.jp

2015 Sales

	% of total
Japan	40
US	24
Europe & Canada	18
Asia (excluding Japan) & other	6
Latin America	5
Russia/CIS	5
Other	2
Total	**100**

PRODUCTS/OPERATIONS

2015 Sales

	% of total
Ethical drug	91
Consumer healthcare	4
Other	5
Total	**100**

Selected products

Prescription drugs
 Actos (type 2 diabetes)
 Adecut (high blood pressure)
 Amasulin (anti-infective)
 Blopress (high blood pressure)
 Bronica (asthma)
 Ceuleuk (angiosarcoma)
 Dexilant (acid reflux)
 Eurodin (central nervous system)
 Lupron Depot (prostate cancer endometriosis)
 Osten (osteoporosis)
 Pansporin (anti-infective)
 Prevacid (peptic ulcers)
 Rozerem (insomnia)
 Takesulin (anti-infective)
 Uloric (gout)
 Velcade (multiple myeloma)
Consumer health care
 Alinamin (vitamins)
 Benza (cold remedy)
 Scorba (athlete' s foot)

Selected Subsidiaries

Amato Pharmaceutical Products Ltd. (30%)
Millennium Pharmaceuticals Inc. (US)
Nihon Pharmaceutical Co. Ltd. (88%)
Laboratoires Takeda (France)
Takeda America Holdings Inc. (US)
Takeda Europe Holdings B.V. (Netherlands)
Takeda Cambridge Limited (UK)
Takeda Healthcare Products Co. Ltd.
Takeda Italia Farmaceutici S.p.A. (77%)
Takeda Pharma AG (Switzerland)
Takeda Pharma GmbH (Germany)
Takeda Pharma Ireland Limited
Takeda Pharmaceuticals Europe Limited (UK)
Takeda Pharmaceuticals North America Inc. (US)
Takeda Research Investment Inc. (US)
Takeda San Diego Inc. (US)
Takeda San Francisco Inc. (US)
Takeda Singapore Pte Limited
Takeda (Thailand) Ltd. (48%)
Tianjin Takeda Pharmaceuticals Co. Ltd. (75% China)

COMPETITORS

Abbott Labs	Mylan
Allergan plc	Neurocrine Biosciences
Astellas	Novartis
AstraZeneca	Novo Nordisk
Bayer HealthCare	Ono Pharmaceutical
Pharmaceuticals	Pfizer
Boehringer Ingelheim	ROHTO Pharmaceutical
Bristol-Myers Squibb	Roche Holding
Daiichi Sankyo	Sanofi
Eisai	Shionogi & Co.
Eli Lilly	Sumitomo Dainippon
GlaxoSmithKline	Pharma
Johnson & Johnson	Sunovion
Merck	Suzuken
Mitsubishi Tanabe	Taisho Pharmaceutical
Pharma	Teva

HISTORICAL FINANCIALS

Company Type: Public

Income Statement

FYE: March 31

	REVENUE ($ mil.)	NET INCOME ($ mil.)	NET PROFIT MARGIN	EMPLOYEES
03/16	16,094	713	4.4%	31,168
03/15	14,817	(1,215)	—	31,328
03/14	16,389	1,033	6.3%	31,225
03/13	16,547	1,579	9.5%	30,481
03/12	18,394	1,513	8.2%	30,305
Annual Growth	**(3.3%)**	**(17.1%)**	**—**	**0.7%**

2016 Year-End Financials

Debt ratio: 0.1%	No. of shares (mil.): 789
Return on equity: 3.9%	Dividends
Cash ($ mil.): 3,899	Yield: 3.2%
Current ratio: 1.63	Payout: 87.2%
Long-term debt ($ mil.): 4,806	Market value ($ mil.): 18,025

	STOCK PRICE ($) FY Close	P/E High/Low		PER SHARE ($) Earnings	Dividends	Book Value
03/16	22.82	0	0	0.91	0.73	21.97
03/15	25.04	—	—	(1.55)	0.82	22.56
03/14	23.70	0	0	1.31	0.89	30.33
03/13	27.25	0	0	2.00	0.96	30.62
03/12	22.00	—	—	1.92	0.00	32.00
Annual Growth	**0.9%**	—	—	**(17.1%)**	**—**	**(9.0%)**

Talanx AG

Talanx Group offers its customers an army of protection. The Germany-based insurance group is the third-largest in the country. Talanx operates in property/casualty insurance life insurance and financial services as well as reinsurance in both the property/casualty and life categories. Brands include HDI and HDI Direkt which provides insurance policies to both private and industrial customers; Aspecta a provider of individual insurance and investment products; Hannover Re one of the world's largest reinsurers; and fund guarantor and asset manager AmpegaGirling among others. Talanx has operations in 150 countries worldwide. Talanx is part of HDI Haftpflichtverband der Deutschen Industrie.

Operations

The company reports its business in five segments: industrial lines retail Germany retail international non-life reinsurance and life/health reinsurance. Non-life reinsurance leads the pack with 28% of revenue; retail Germany (24% of sales) and life/health reinsurance (22% of sales) follow.

The non-life reinsurance division is primarily handled by subsidiary Hannover Re. Retail Germany (Talanx Deutschland) concentrates on serving the retail and commercial sectors with property/casualty life and bancassurance while retail international does the same in 14 countries abroad (and has more than 8 million clients). The industrial lines division is led by HDI-Gerling Industrie Versicherung which offers individual customer support services from about a dozen locations across the nation.

The group also provides asset management services.

Geographic Reach

Europe accounts for about 65% of premiums written with Germany holding the majority across the board. The US is the company's largest non-European region.

Major operations outside of Germany are located in Austria Hungary Italy Spain Poland Russia and Turkey. The company also has operations in the Americas Africa and the Asia/Pacific region. Talanx prefers to operate semi-independent businesses in local markets and expands by acquiring or opening divisions in new territories. It operates in 150 countries.

Japanese insurer Meiji Yasuda Life Insurance has been expanding into Europe using Talanx as a springboard; it took a 7% stake in Talanx during the company's 2012 IPO. The two companies use a joint venture with a Talanx subsidiary as the framework to grow in Central and Eastern European markets.

Sales and Marketing

Talanx uses both its own sales agents and offices and brokers and independent agents as well as specialized cooperatives in its various markets. Its primary insurance units also advertise via television ads sponsorships and through other channels.

Financial Performance

Revenue grew 3% to euro 23.8 billion in 2014 as most segments reported increased earnings (with the exception of corporate operations). Leading the growth was industrial lines which rose 12% and retail international which rose 6% on the success of Italian subsidiary HDI Assicurazioni.

Net income rose 5% to euro 769 million due to the higher revenue and investment income which improved partly as a result of the sale of the remaining shares in Swiss Life.

Strategy

Growth is the name of the game at Talanx and the company plans to accomplish by organic and acquisitive means. The company has a goal of generating half of its primary insurance premiums from outside of Germany by 2018. Key target areas include Central and Eastern Europe (CEE) and Latin America. In 2015 it acquired Chilean insurer Inversiones Magallenes and in 2014 its industrial lines division added a new unit in Brazil. Streamlining its Eastern European retail operations Talanx sold subsidiaries in Bulgaria and Ukraine in early 2015.

The company also focuses on improving profitability and customer relations especially in its retail divisions.

In the financial services arena Talanx entered into a joint venture with NORD/LB Norddeutsche Landesbank and Bankhaus Lampe in 2015; Talanx holds a 45% stake in the venture which is named Caplantic Alternative Assets.

Mergers and Acquisitions

In 2014 the company acquired Inversiones Magallenes in Chile for approximately euro 180 million.

Background

The company traces its roots back over a century but began operating as a holding company under the name HDI Beteilgung AG in 1996. In 1998 it was renamed Talanx which is a blend of the words "talent" and "phalanx" (a Greek word referring to a battle formation).

In 2012 the company completed its IPO and began trading on Germany's Frankfurt Stock Exchange. The company raised about euro 817 million which it used to grow its business. Post-IPO HDI Haftpflichtverband der Deutschen Industrie maintained a 79% stake in Talanx.

EXECUTIVES

Chairman Management Board, Herbert K. Haas, age 62
Member Management Board, Immo Querner
Member Management Board Reinsurance, Ulrich Wallin, age 55
Member Management Board, Thomas Noth
Member Management Group Retail Germany, Heinz-Peter Ro
Chairman Supervisory Board, Wolf-Dieter Baumgartl, age 73
Deputy Chairman Supervisory Board, Eckhard Rohkamm
Deputy Chairman Supervisory Board, Ralf Rieger
Auditors: KPMG AG Wirtschaftsprufungsgesellschaft

LOCATIONS

HQ: Talanx AG
Riethorst 2, Hannover 30659
Phone: (49) 511 3747 0   **Fax:** (49) 511 3747 2525
Web: www.talanx.com

2014 Sales

	% of total
Europe	
Germany	32
UK	9
Central and Eastern Europe including Turkey	8
Rest of Europe	15
North America	
US	12
Rest of North America	3
Asia & Australia	12
Latin America	7
Africa	2
Total	**100**

PRODUCTS/OPERATIONS

2014 Sales

	% of total
Non-life reinsurance	28
Life/health reinsurance	22
Retail Germany	24
Retail international	16
Industrial lines	10
Total	**100**

COMPETITORS

AEGON	Generali
AXA	ING
Allianz	Munich Re Group
ERGO	Swiss Re
General Re	Zurich Insurance Group

HISTORICAL FINANCIALS

Company Type: Public

Income Statement

FYE: December 31

	REVENUE ($ mil.)	NET INCOME ($ mil.)	NET PROFIT MARGIN	EMPLOYEES
12/15	34,739	799	2.3%	21,965
12/14	36,000	934	2.6%	21,371
12/13	38,938	1,049	2.7%	21,529
12/12	35,397	830	2.3%	20,887
12/11	31,411	672	2.1%	17,061
Annual Growth	**2.5%**	**4.4%**	**—**	**6.5%**

2015 Year-End Financials

Debt ratio: —	No. of shares (mil.): 252
Return on equity: 9.0%	Dividends
Cash ($ mil.): 2,443	Yield: —
Current ratio: —	Payout: —
Long-term debt ($ mil.): —	Market value ($ mil.): —

Tata Consultancy Services Ltd

LOCATIONS

HQ: Tata Consultancy Services Ltd
9th Floor, Nirmal Building, Nariman Point, Mumbai 400 021
Phone: (91) 22 6778 9595   **Fax:** (91) 22 6778 9660
Web: www.tcs.com

HISTORICAL FINANCIALS

Company Type: Public

Income Statement

FYE: March 31

	REVENUE ($ mil.)	NET INCOME ($ mil.)	NET PROFIT MARGIN	EMPLOYEES
03/16	16,890	3,673	21.7%	0
03/15	15,649	3,174	20.3%	0
03/14	13,897	3,191	23.0%	0
03/13	11,820	2,563	21.7%	0
03/12	9,694	2,046	21.1%	0
Annual Growth	**14.9%**	**15.7%**	**—**	**—**

2016 Year-End Financials

Debt ratio: 0.0%	No. of shares (mil.): —
Return on equity: 41.7%	Dividends
Cash ($ mil.): 1,025	Yield: —
Current ratio: 2.87	Payout: —
Long-term debt ($ mil.): 12	Market value ($ mil.): —

Tata Motors Ltd

Tata Motors enjoys giant-sized growth thanks to its Nano cars. The company —India's largest automobile maker by sales —makes buses trucks tractor-trailers passenger cars (Indica Indigo Jaguar Land Rover Safari Sumo and the popular micro car Nano) light commercial vehicles and utility vehicles. It also makes construction equipment and provides IT services. Tata Motors sells through more than 1000 dealers in India as well as exports vehicles to countries in Africa Asia Europe the Middle East and South America. In addition the company distributes Fiat-brand cars in India through its Tata-Fiat dealer network.

Geographic Reach

Through subsidiaries and affiliated companies Tata Motors has operations in India the UK South Korea Thailand Spain and South Africa. China is its largest market representing 28% of its total sales. India the UK and the US follow with 16% 12% and 11% of total sales respectively. Other European countries account for 13% of total sales while the rest of the world contributes roughly 20%.

Operations

Tata Motors' business segments are primarily its automotive operations which develop design manufacture assemble and sell vehicles and provide financing. The automotive segment is divided into Tata and other brand vehicles as well as Jaguar Land Rover. Other operations include information technology or IT services and machine tools and factory automation products and services.

Tata Motors also has franchisee and joint venture assembly operations in Bangladesh Ukraine and Senegal.

Sales and Marketing

Tata Motors' vehicles are sold through a network of authorized dealers and service centers across the Indian market and a network of distributors and local dealers in international markets.

Financial Performance

Tata Motors has seen significant growth over the last five years with 2014 representing its best year to date. From 2013 to 2014 its total revenues in rupees increased by 24% (or 13% when converted into US dollar) and its net income surged by 46% (34% in US dollar).

The historic growth for 2014 was fueled by a spike in sales from its Range Rover and Jaguar vehicles. The increase was also attributable to an indirect tax incentive by Jaguar Land Rover.

Strategy

Tata Motors is a leader in the only growth area for the automotive market in recent years —India —which gives it a slight edge over competitors in the region. It is also extending its commercial vehicles penetration into countries like Bangladesh Nepal Sri Lanka and Bhutan.

In 2015 Tata Motors launched four new next-generation PRIMA heavy commercial vehicles for the very first time in Bangladesh with partner Nitol Motors Limited. The next-generation Tata PRIMA is a combination of power fuel efficiency superior technology and safety. Also in 2015 Tata Motors launched the GenX Nano range its new compact hatch. The new GenX Nano comes with advanced technological features which strengthens its value as a city car.

Company Background

In 2008 Tata Motors bought the Jaguar and Land Rover brands from Ford for about $2.3 billion. It took over the two struggling businesses in an effort to diversify its customer base by expanding its product portfolio from commercial and small passenger vehicles to premium cars.

EXECUTIVES

CEO and Managing Director Jaguar Land Rover, Ralf Speth, age 61

President and Head Engineering Research Centre, Tim Leverton

President and CFO, C. Ramakrishnan, $14,178,000 total compensation

Executive Director and Head Commercial Vehicles Business Unit, Ravindra Pisharody, $8,085,002 total compensation

Executive Director and Head Quality, Satish B. Borwankar

President and Head Passenger Vehicles Business Unit, Ranjit Yadav

SVP and Head Purchasing and Supply Chain, Venkatram Mamillapalle

SVP and Head Commercial Passenger Vehicle Business Unit, Ankush Arora

President Passenger Vehicle Business Unit, Mayank Pareek

CEO and Managing Director, Guenter Butschek, age 56

Chairman, Cyrus P. Mistry, age 48

Auditors: Deloitte Haskins & Sells LLP

LOCATIONS

HQ: Tata Motors Ltd
Bombay House, 24, Homi Mody Street, Mumbai, Maharashtra 400 001
Phone: (91) 22 6665 7219   **Fax:** (91) 22 6665 7260
Web: www.tatamotors.com

2015 Sales

	% of total
China	29
India	14
Europe	
UK	13
Other countries	12
US	12
Other regions	20
Total	**100**

Selected Subsidiaries

Concorde Motors (India) Limited
Jaguar Land Rover PLC-UK
PT Tata Indonesia
Sheba Properties Ltd-India
TAL Manufacturing Solutions Ltd-India
Tata Daewoo Commercial Vehicle Co Ltd- South Korea
Tata Hispano Motors Carrocera SA- Spain
Tata Marcopolo Motors Ltd-India.
Tata Motors (SA) Proprietary Ltd -South Africa.
Tata Motors European Technical center PLC -UK
Tata Motors Finance Ltd -India
Tata Motors Insurance Broking and Advisory Services Ltd-India
Tata Motors(Thailand) Ltd
Tata Precision Industries Pts Ltd-Singapore
Tata Technologies Ltd-India
TML Distribution Company Ltd-India
TML Drivelines Ltd-India
TML Holdings Pte Ltd- Singapore

PRODUCTS/OPERATIONS

2015 Sales

	% of total
Jaguar Land Rover	82
Tata and other brand vehicles including financing	17
Others	1
Total	**100**

Selected Products and Services

Light commercial vehicles
  Ace
  Magic
  Winger
Medium and heavy commercial vehicles
  Paradiso
  Prima
Passenger cars
  Indica
  Indica Vista

Indigo eCS
Indigo Manza
Jaguar
Nano
Utility vehicles
  Aria
  Land Rover
  Range Rover
  Sumo
  Safari
  Venture
  Xenon XT

COMPETITORS

BMW	Isuzu
Bajaj Auto	Kia Motors
Caterpillar	Komatsu
Daimler	Mahindra
FCA US	Mazda
Fiat Chrysler	Nissan
Ford Motor	Renault
Fuji Heavy Industries	Suzuki Motor
General Motors	Toyota
Hindustan Motors	Volkswagen
Honda	Volvo
Hyundai Motor	

HISTORICAL FINANCIALS

Company Type: Public

Income Statement

FYE: March 31

	REVENUE ($ mil.)	NET INCOME ($ mil.)	NET PROFIT MARGIN	EMPLOYEES
03/16	40,789	1,449	3.6%	76,598
03/15	41,974	2,051	4.9%	73,485
03/14	39,000	2,176	5.6%	68,889
03/13	34,813	1,633	4.7%	62,716
03/12	32,724	2,273	6.9%	58,618
Annual Growth	**5.7%**	**(10.6%)**	**—**	**6.9%**

2016 Year-End Financials

Debt ratio: 0.4%	No. of shares (mil.): 3
Return on equity: 14.7%	Dividends
Cash ($ mil.): 4,526	Yield: —
Current ratio: 1.03	Payout: —
Long-term debt ($ mil.): 7,628	Market value ($ mil.): 99

	STOCK PRICE ($) FY Close	P/E High/Low		Earnings	Dividends	Book Value
03/16 3,400.42	29.05	2	1	0.43	0.00	
03/15 2,657.32	45.06	1	1	0.63	0.14	
03/14 3,246.71	35.41	1	1	0.68	0.13	
03/13 2,138.09	24.41	1	1	0.51	0.34	
03/12 2,034.09	26.97	1	0	0.71	0.37	
Annual Growth	**1.9%**	**—**	**—(11.7%)**	**—**	**13.7%**	

Tata Steel Ltd.

Tata Steel is India's largest private sector steel company. The company's steel-making and finishing facilities have the capacity to produce nearly 30 million tons of crude steel a year. Tata Steel's products include hot and cold rolled coils and sheets galvanized sheets tubes wire rods rings and bearings. Its domestic facilities are located in Jamshedpur in eastern India and Tata Steel's international operations include UK-based subsidiary

Tata Steel Europe Singapore's NatSteel and Tata Steel Thailand. The company also owns interests in coal and iron projects that supply the steel maker with raw materials.

Geographic Reach

Tata Steel has operations in 26 countries and a commercial presence in more than 50. About 32% of its net sales come from India. Other markets include Europe (52%) Asia (11%) and other regions (5%).

Operations

Tata Steel is one of the largest steel makers in the world. Products include hot and cold rolled coils and sheets galvanized sheets tubes wire rods rings and bearings. Steel sales primarily in India account for the bulk of the company's business although it also owns interests in coal and iron projects.

Financial Performance

Total Steel's revenues from 2014 to 2015 decreased due to fewer sales from China Europe and Thailand. Throughout 2015 the company's bottom line was negatively affected by slow growth in China low global steel prices and higher pension payments at Tata Steel UK.

Strategy

To combat stagnant growth in Europe and China Tata Steel is entering new segment markets restructuring its operations and cutting costs and introducing new products to diversified markets.

In 2016 the company announced a massive consolidation and debt reduction drive to bring debt down by 10 to 15% by the end of the year. It plans to sell its long products business in Europe and is looking to identify and sell other non-performing assets (including possibly its UK business in Port Talbot). That year it agreed to sell its UK specialty steels business to Liberty House for £100 million.

Its Indian operations in 2015 were adversely impacted by the regulatory uncertainties in the mining sector. For the first time in its history Tata Steel closed several of its critical mines for varying periods. This led to supply and production disruptions that significantly impacted its cost structure.

Company Background

Tat Steel was founded in 1907 as Asia's first private sector integrated steel company.

EXECUTIVES

Group CFO, Koushik Chatterjee, age 49
Managing Director Tata Steel India and South East Asia, T. V. Narendran, age 51
Chairman, Natarajan (Chandra) Chandrasekaran, age 53
Auditors: Messrs Deloitte Haskins & Sells

LOCATIONS

HQ: Tata Steel Ltd.
Bombay House, 24 Homi Mody Street, Mumbai 400 001
Phone: (91) 22 6665 8282   **Fax:** (91) 22 6665 7724
Web: www.tatasteel.com

2016 Sales

	% of total
Outside India	68
Within India	32
Total	**100**

PRODUCTS/OPERATIONS

2016 Sales

	% of total
Steel	91
Others	9
Total	**100**

Selected Operations

Steel
Ferroalloys & Minerals (chrome mines & manufacturing ferro chrome & ferro manganese)
Bearings (ball bearings clutch release bearings & double row self-aligning bearings)
Tubes
Wire

COMPETITORS

ArcelorMittal
Baosteel
Essar Group
JFE Holdings
Kobe Steel
Mitsubishi Materials
Nippon Steel & Sumitomo Metal Corporation
POSCO
Steel Authority of India
United States Steel

HISTORICAL FINANCIALS

Company Type: Public

Income Statement

FYE: March 31

	REVENUE ($ mil.)	NET INCOME ($ mil.)	NET PROFIT MARGIN	EMPLOYEES
03/15	22,432	(627)	—	79,647
03/14	24,836	598	2.4%	80,391
03/13	24,903	(1,300)	—	80,534
03/12	26,431	1,059	4.0%	81,622
03/11	26,787	2,014	7.5%	81,251
Annual Growth	**(4.3%)**	—	—	**(0.5%)**

2015 Year-End Financials

Debt ratio: 0.7%
Return on equity: (-10.2%)
Cash ($ mil.): 1,399
Current ratio: 1.17
Long-term debt ($ mil.): 10,500
No. of shares (mil.): 971
Dividends
Yield: —
Payout: —
Market value ($ mil.): —

Telecom Italia SPA

Telecom Italia's wireline unit is Italy's #1 telephone operator with some 4.1 million fixed access lines. It serves Italian customers through millions of broadband and wireless connections. While Telecom Italia does most of its business in Italy Latin America is a key international market. The company provides wholesale network access in South America as well as Italy. Its TIM Brasil subsidiary is a leader in the Brazilian wireless market with more than 64.1 million subscribers; its Argentina subsidiaries cater to 1.6 million broadband subscribers and 18.2 million mobile subscribers.

Geographic Reach

Telecom Italia has a presence in Italy Latin America North America Europe Africa and Asia. It generates about 64% of its revenue from its domestic market (Italy) and the remaining 36% derive from Brazil and Argentina.

Operations

The operating segments of Telecom Italia are organized according to the relative geographical location for the telecommunications business and relative to the specific businesses for the other segments. The market of its main business unit is focused mainly in serving customers in Europe Asia and South America.

In addition subsidiary Telecom Italia Media produces and distributes TV and Web content and

Olivetti provides office equipment such as ink-jet printer heads mostly for the banking industry.

Financial Performance

Thanks to growth in foreign markets the company's revenues increased by 9% from 2010 to 2011. Revenues from Brazil were up by 18% as a result of a 26% increase in the market share of mobile lines. Revenue from Argentina increased by 27% in 2011 due to the growth of customers in the fixed and broadband businesses as well as mobile businesses.

Despite this growth Telecom Italia recorded a net loss for 2011 due to the acquisition of goods and services and net impairment losses on non-current assets.

Strategy

Over the last few years the company has been selling off interests not related to its businesses in Italy or Brazil. These deals were also part of Telecom Italia's ongoing effort to sell non-core businesses in order to reduce debt.

Outside Italy the company is focused on bolstering its operations only in Brazil an emerging market that now accounts for almost 20% of revenue. In 2011 it bought AES Atimus a Brazilian subsidiary of US power company AES. AES Atimus operates a 3400-mile fiber optic network in Rio de Janeiro and Sao Paulo. The deal euro 700 million ($1 billion) was Telecom Italia's largest acquisition in a decade.

In another 2011 acquisition that boosted its Latin American holdings Telecom Italia paid about $145 million to raise its ownership stake in Sofora Telecomunicaciones the holding company which owns Telecom Argentina from 58% to 68%. Closer to home Telecom Italia bought 71% of Italian mobile phone retailer 4G Holding from GIR Srl a company controlled by 4G's CEO 2011. The deal boosted the company's domestic retail presence by 200 shops as it works to get its brand out in front of more wireless customers in a saturated market. GIR retained 29% of 4G Holding.

Ownership

The former state-owned monopoly has one major institutional shareholder. An investment group made up primarily of Italian financial backers known as Telco SpA owns a 22% stake. Telco is made up of Telefonica (46%) Italian insurance giant Generali (31%) investment bank Mediobanca (12%) and commercial bank Intesa Sanpaolo (11%).

HISTORY

After gaining political power in Italy Benito Mussolini began a program of nationalization focusing first on three major banks and their equity portfolios. Included were three local phone companies that became the core of Società Finanziaria Telefonica (STET) created in 1933 to handle Italy's phone services under the state's industrial holding company Istituto per La Ricostruzione Industriale (IRI).

Germany and Italy grew closer in the years leading up to WWII and Italian equipment makers entered a venture with Siemens to make phone equipment. STET came through the war with most of its infrastructure intact and a monopoly on phone service in Italy. Siemens' properties along with those of other equipment makers were taken over by another company TETI which was nationalized and put under STET's control in 1958. This expanded STET's monopoly to include equipment manufacturing.

Italy's industries were increasingly nationalized under IRI. Companies within the IRI family forged alliances with each other and with independent companies which frequently were absorbed into STET.

STET's scope expanded during the 1960s and 1970s to include satellite and data communications but its monopoly was undermined by new technologies such as faxes PCs and teleconferencing. In the technology race among equipment makers STET fell behind. And in a satellite communications era STET's status as a necessary long-distance carrier was threatened. Despite these pressures change did not come easily to STET. State monopolies maintained popular support not only on nationalistic grounds but also because of labor's strong anticompetitive stance.

Anticipating privatization however IRI reorganized STET in 1994 and poured new capital into the company. STET's five telecom companies —SIP (domestic phone operator) Italcable (intercontinental) Telespazio (satellite) SIRM (maritime) and Iritel (domestic long distance) —were merged into one Telecom Italia. Its mobile phone business was spun off as Telecom Italia Mobile (TIM) in 1995.

To end political feuding the government abruptly replaced the heads of STET and Telecom Italia in 1997. Telecom Italia was merged with STET which took the Telecom Italia name and was privatized that year. Berardino Libonati became chairman and Franco Bernabe formerly CEO of oil company ENI took the helm as CEO. The company began taking stakes in foreign telecom companies including mobilkom austria Spanish broadcaster Retevision and —as European Union competition began in 1998 —Telekom Austria.

Erstwhile rival Olivetti launched a hostile takeover bid for Telecom Italia in 1999. Though Telecom Italia tried to fend off the smaller firm with various maneuvers including a proposed merger with Deutsche Telekom Olivetti gained 55% of Telecom Italia. Olivetti CEO Roberto Colaninno took over as chairman and CEO.

That year Telecom Italia sold 50% of Stream its pay TV unit to an investor group led by News Corp. The company also announced plans to spin off and sell a stake in its ISP Tin.it. In 2000 however Telecom Italia instead combined Tin.it with SEAT Pagine Gialle a yellow pages directory publisher and Internet portal operator (spun off from the parent company and sold in 2003). Also that year the company sold off 81% of its telecom equipment unit Italtel and its 49% stake in installations firm Sirti.

In 2001 Colaninno and several other Telecom Italia officials were named as suspects in an investigation of whether the company had violated accounting conflict of interest and share manipulation laws. Colaninno was replaced when tire maker Pirelli and Edizione Holding the parent company of the Benetton Group acquired a 23% stake in Olivetti.

Telecom Italia teamed up with News Corp. to develop the Stream pay TV joint venture renamed Sky Italia. The venture gained a kick-start when the two companies teamed to buy Italian pay-TV business Telepiu from Vivendi Universal in a cash and debt assumption deal that was valued at $871 million. The deal included agreements to drop disputes between Telepiu and Stream. Telecom Italia then sold a 30% stake in the venture to News Corp. It retained a 20% share with News Corp. controlling 80%.

In 2003 the company abandoned plans to acquire phone directories group Pagine Utili from Fininvest in a deal that would have been worth more than $130 million because of protests by Italian regulators who claimed the deal would breach competition laws. It also spun off its international services division starting in 2003 into a separate company Telecom Italia Sparkle which concentrated on services to other fixed-line operators ISPs and international corporations and sold its nearly 62% stake in SEAT Pagine Gialle to an investor group for $3.55 billion.

Once the subsidiary Telecom Italia became the parent company after the 2003 merger with former parent Olivetti. The reorganization simplified a corporate structure that was at best confusing: Olivetti through its Tecnost unit had acquired a controlling 55% stake in Telecom Italia in 1999. Two years later tire maker Pirelli and the Benetton family teamed up to take control of Olivetti. Olivetti's largest shareholder was Olimpia a company owned by Pirelli and the Benetton Group among others.

Because Telecom Italia accounted for more than 95% of the revenues of Olivetti the reorganization also kept the focus on the core business. The merger was met with favor among market watchers and some shareholders although a group of international investors opposed the restructuring.

Reorganization continued at the company and it began selling some international fixed-line assets and putting some wireless operations outside Italy on the market. Disposals included Digitel the Venezuelan wireless carrier to Oswaldo Cisneros' Telvenco in a deal valued at about $425 million. It also sold its 81% stake in Greek wireless carrier Hellas Telecommunications to US-based private equity firms Texas Pacific Group and Apax Partners in a deal valued at $1.4 billion; stakes in Spanish joint venture Auna and satellite unit Telespazio (to Leonardo - Finmeccanica); and in 2005 it sold its holdings in IT services and consulting company Finsiel to Italian outsourcing firm Gruppo COS.

After spurning an offer from AT&T to buy the company Telecom Italia named Pasquale Pistorio chairman in 2007 replacing Guido Rossi who had held the position for only seven months. Telefonica subsequently won control of the company. Later that year Pistorio was replaced by Gabriele Galateri as chairman; Galateri was nominated by another top shareholder Mediobanca.

In 2010 the company began selling off interests not related to its businesses in Italy or Brazil. It sold its 70% stake in Elettra which specialized in laying submarine cables to France Telecom (later renamed Orange) for euro 20 million ($27 million); its Netherlands fixed-line provider BBNed to Tele2 for euro 50 million ($64 million); and its German broadband unit HanseNet to Telefonica for the tidy sum of euro 900 million ($1.2 billion) in cash. The following year Telecom Italia sold its 27% stake in the state-run Cuban phone company ETECSA for $706 million to Rafin SA a financial services firm in that country. Also in 2011 the company sold subsidiary Loquendo to US-based Nuance Communications. The sales were part of Telecom Italia's ongoing effort to sell non-core businesses in order to reduce debt.

EXECUTIVES

Chairman and Interim CEO, Giuseppe Recchi, age 52

Head of Technology, Giuseppe R. Opilio, age 58

CFO, Piergiorgio Peluso, age 48

CEO TIM Participa § µes S.A., Rodrigo Modesto Abreu

Auditors: PricewaterhouseCoopers S.p.A.

LOCATIONS

HQ: Telecom Italia SPA
Corso d' Italia, 41, Rome 00198
Phone: (39) 06 36 88 1
Web: www.telecomitalia.com

2015 Sales

	% of total
Italy	75
Other regions	25
Total	**100**

PRODUCTS/OPERATIONS

2015 Sales

	% of total
Services	93
Equipment sales	7
Total	**100**

COMPETITORS

America Mvil	Orange
BT	Ricoh Company
Cable & Wireless	Swisscom
Canon	Tele2
Deutsche Telekom	Telefnica
FastWeb	Tiscali
HP	Vivo Participa§µes
IBM	Vodafone Omnitel
KPN	Wind Telecomunicazioni
Millicom	Xerox

HISTORICAL FINANCIALS

Company Type: Public

Income Statement

FYE: December 31

	REVENUE ($ mil.)	NET INCOME ($ mil.)	NET PROFIT MARGIN	EMPLOYEES
12/15	22,504	(78)	—	65,867
12/14	27,424	1,640	6.0%	66,025
12/13	33,418	(927)	—	65,623
12/12	40,044	(2,144)	—	83,184
12/11	39,870	(6,112)	—	84,154
Annual Growth (13.3%)		—	—	(5.9%)

2015 Year-End Financials

Debt ratio: 56.1%	No. of shares (mil.): —
Return on equity: (-0.4%)	Dividends
Cash ($ mil.): 3,876	Yield: —
Current ratio: 0.93	Payout: —
Long-term debt ($ mil.): 33,240	Market value ($ mil.): —

	STOCK PRICE ($) FY Close	P/E High/Low	PER SHARE ($) Earnings	Dividends	Book Value
12/15	12.65	— —	(0.00)	0.00	1.44
12/14	10.54	172121	0.09	0.00	1.66
12/13	9.96	— —	(0.04)	0.64	1.77
12/12	9.05	— —	(0.11)	0.43	1.93
12/11	10.65	— —	(0.31)	0.56	2.22
Annual Growth 4.4% (10.3%)		— —	—	—	—

Telefonaktiebolaget LM Ericsson (Sweden)

Ericsson opens all lines of communication. The world's leading maker of mobile broadband infrastructure gear provides the equipment that telecom carriers use to build and expand their networks. The company also provides wireline broadband metro area Ethernet LTE modems and optical transport equipment. Its services unit handles operations ranging from systems integration to network deployment and management. Ericsson's multimedia arm provides content-related products including Internet television systems. The company traces its roots back to 1876 when Lars Magnus Ericsson opened up a telegraph repair shop in Stockholm.

Operations

Ericsson's core business comprises three segments: networks global services and support solutions. The networks segment which accounts for just more than half of the company's sales develops and deploys the latest generation of mobile broadband networks (LTE) and maintains and refines older networks (GSM WCDMA etc.) for its network operator customers. The segment also provides equipment for Internet protocol (IP) microwave transport and core networks including IP routers core routers and switches cables and interconnect products microwave radio links optical transport components radio base stations and wireline network access equipment.

Serving network operators Ericsson's professional services segment supports its customers network operations through its consulting customer support network design and integration and training services. The segment also offers managed services like application hosting and network operations. The growing professional services unit is supported by four global service centers in India China Mexico and Romania. The services segment accounts for about 43% of the company's net sales.

The company's multimedia support solutions segment offers software for consumer-facing applications including mobile and Internet television messaging and music as well as billing support systems for telecommunications network operators. About 6% of sales come through solutions.

Financial Performance

For 2014 Ericsson's revenue was flat and profit dropped 8% from 2013 levels. Sales growth in China the Middle East and India was offset by lower sales in North America (the company's biggest market) and Japan where several larger mobile broadband coverage projects were completed. Reported sales for segments Networks and Global Services were flat compared with 2013 while Support Solutions reported sales grew by 3%. Net income fell as operating costs and finance expenses rose.

Strategy

Ericsson has focused on building its broadband network equipment and services businesses and expanding geographically. The company strengthened its operations in India in a deal with Tata Sky the leading direct-to-the-home (DTH) telecom in India. Ericsson's AVP 4000 System Encoder will deliver Sky Tata content to homes through its video compression platform. Tata Sky will be able to increase the number of channels it offers and the viewing quality. In Africa Ericsson will manage Smile Communications' LTE operations in Nigeria Tanzania Uganda and the Democratic Republic of Congo (DRC). Ericsson will provide localization and customization of Volvo ITS4Mobility intelligent transportation system in Latin America.

In 2013 semiconductor manufacturer STMicroelectronics (ST) sold its stake in ST-Ericsson a now-dissolved joint venture with Ericsson. The two companies split the joint venture's assets with Ericsson taking over the development and sales of the newer LTE multimedia thin modems (which complement its mobile broadband business) and ST taking a portion of the existing ST-Ericsson modem product line. Other assets including a global navigation satellite system were sold to third parties.

As the top company in its industry Ericsson is the target of its competitors. The proposed union of Lucent-Alcatel and Nokia could strengthen their operations. Huawei based in China is another formidable competitor.

In 4Q 2015 Ericsson entered into a strategic partnership with Cisco Systems the leading maker of networking equipment. The companies intend to cooperate to develop products and services in areas such as 5G cloud computing Internet proto-

col and the Internet of Things. Their goal is to add $1 billion in revenue for each company by 2018. The companies will cooperate on developing networks through reference architectures and joint development systems-based management and control a broad reseller agreement and collaboration in key emerging market segments. Cisco's networking capabilities and increasing development of networking software should complement Ericsson's telecom strengths. It should also strengthen Ericsson in its competition with Lucent-Alcatel-Nokia and Huawei.

Mergers and Acquisitions

Ericsson has been making acquisitions to shore up some areas of its technology offerings and to expand further into areas where it already has strength.

In 2014 Ericsson bought a majority stake in Apcera the US-based developer of the Continuum platform as-a-service (PaaS) product. The acquisition was designed to strengthen Ericsson in the cloud market by extending the company's network approach into operator and enterprise cloud.

With the acquisition of another US company Azuki Systems a provider of TV Anywhere delivery platforms Ericsson adds to its TV and media portfolio. The acquisition should help Ericsson add functions and quality to its video-related services.

Fabrix Systems a provider of cloud storage computing and network delivery for video applications that Ericsson acquired in 2014 adds a cloud-based and computing platform to optimize media storage processing and delivery applications such as cloud DVR and video-on-demand expansion.

The acquisition of MetraTech Corp. a provider of metadata-based billing commerce and settlement software builds on Ericsson's expertise in billing and expands its presence in the US.

HISTORY

Lars Magnus Ericsson opened a telegraph repair shop in Stockholm in 1876 the same year Alexander Graham Bell applied for a US patent on the telephone. Within two years Ericsson was making telephones. His company grew rapidly supplying equipment first to Swedish phone companies and later to other European companies. In 1885 Ericsson crafted a combination receiver-speaker in one handset.

In 1911 Ericsson and SAT the Stockholm telephone company merged under the Ericsson banner. The company adopted its present name in 1926. In 1930 international financier Ivar "The Match King" Kreuger owner of the Swedish Match Co. won control of Ericsson. His triumph was short-lived. Krueger committed suicide in 1932 and one of his creditors Sosthenes Behn's ITT took over.

ITT in 1960 sold its interest in Ericsson to the top Swedish industrialist family the Wallenbergs. In 1975 Ericsson introduced its computer-controlled exchange called AXE. Buoyed by AXE's success the company unveiled the "office of the future" in the early 1980s diversifying into computers and office furniture.

However Ericsson's timing was off: The demand for office automation never materialized and profits plunged. Electrolux chairman Hans Werthen was recruited to split his time between the two companies and rescue Ericsson. The company sold its computer business to Nokia in 1988 and refocused on telephone equipment. It dusted off its aging AXE system for the burgeoning cellular market and quickly won key contracts.

The company and aircraft maker Saab merged their military aviation electronics operations as Ericsson Saab Avionics in 1996. (It was dissolved in 1998.) In 1998 manager Sven-Christer Nilsson

was appointed CEO. He reorganized the company and laid off 14000 workers.

After Ericsson fought bitterly with rival QUALCOMM over wireless standards and patents the companies settled in 1999 agreeing to push for the standardization of third-generation technology based on QUALCOMM's code-division multiple access (CDMA) technology. As a part of the deal Ericsson purchased QUALCOMM's infrastructure business. To expand its Internet offerings Ericsson bought Internet router maker Torrent and Internet telephony company Touchwave.

By 1999 Nilsson was pushed out for moving too slowly on restructuring plans and was replaced as CEO by chairman Lars Ramqvist who put many of the duties on president Kurt Hellström. Hellström immediately set out to simplify the company's managerial and accounting structure trim its workforce and slow-growth businesses and push new phone models to market.

The next year Ericsson sold noncore businesses including its private radio systems power supply and equipment shelter operations. The company also agreed to develop a standard for secure wireless transactions with Nokia and Motorola and formed a joint venture with Web router maker Juniper Networks to sell routers for mobile Internet applications.

Fierce competition an industrywide slowdown in handset sales and manufacturing glitches led Ericsson to outsource the manufacture of its phones to Flextronics and form a joint venture (Sony Ericsson Mobile Communications) with Sony to link the development and marketing of their handsets in 2001. Ericsson also sold its direct enterprise sales and service unit outsourced IT operations in Europe to Electronic Data Systems (which later became HP Enterprise Services) and cut more than 20000 jobs that year. Hellström became CEO in 2001.

Chairman Ramqvist became honorary chairman in 2002; Electrolux CEO Michael Treschow was named as the acting chairman. Ericsson announced 20000 more layoffs in 2002. That year the company sold its semiconductor unit to Infineon for about $380 million.

Ericsson sold its optoelectronic components business in 2003. Hellström retired later that year and Carl-Henric Svanberg former CEO of Assa Abloy was appointed as company president and CEO. In 2005 Ericsson acquired certain telecom hardware assets from troubled Marconi (later renamed telent) for about $2.1 billion.

The company acquired seven companies in 2007 the largest of which were Redback Networks ($1.9 billion) and TANDBERG Television ($1.4 billion). The Redback buy gained Ericsson broadband IP routers while the TANDBERG Television purchase brought software and services for the cable television market. It also picked up fiber-access technology company Entrisphere in an effort to expand its broadband access offerings in North America.

Looking to broaden its multimedia offerings the company purchased Mobeon a Swedish provider of IP-based voice and video mail. Other 2007 acquisitions included German customer care software provider LHS Swedish mobile service deliver platform developer Drutt and Spanish IPTV specialist HyC. In an effort to refocus its multimedia operations on key areas such as service delivery and provisioning Ericsson sold its enterprise PBX products business to Aastra Technologies for about $100 million in 2008.

To expand its North American business Ericsson bought bankrupt Nortel Network's CDMA and LTE-based wireless business there in 2009 for $1.1 billion. The deal significantly boosted its profile as a provider of mobile networking gear to wireless carriers on the continent. The company's other acquisitions that year complemented its manufacturing and services activities. These purchases included the manufacturing operations of Estonian electronics maker Elcoteq as well as Turkish systems integrator Bizitek.

In 2010 EVP/CFO Hans Vestberg took over as president and CEO of Ericsson succeeding Carl-Henric Svanberg who resigned to become chairman of BP.

EXECUTIVES

EVP, Magnus Mandersson, age 54
SVP; Head Business Unit Information Technology and Cloud Products, Anders Lindblad, age 49
EVP, Jan Frykhammar, age 51
SVP and Chief Innovation Officer; Head Business Unit Media, Per G. Borgklint, age 45
President and CEO, B fje E. Ekholm, age 53
SVP; Head Business Unit Network Products, Arun Bansal, age 49
SVP Chief Strategy Officer and CTO, Ulf Ewaldsson, age 52
SVP and Chief Marketing and Communications Officer, Helena Norrman, age 47
Acting CFO, Carl Mellander, age 52
SVP; Head Business Unit Network Services, Fredrik Jejdling, age 48
SVP; Head Customer Group Industry and Society, Charlotta Sund, age 54
SVP and Chief Sustainability Officer, Elaine Weidman-Grunewald, age 50
Chairman, Leif Johansson, age 65
Deputy Chairman, Jacob Wallenberg, age 60
Deputy Chairman, Helena Stjernholm, age 47
Auditors: PricewaterhouseCoopers AB

LOCATIONS

HQ: Telefonaktiebolaget LM Ericsson (Sweden)
Torshamnsgatan 23, Stockholm SE-164 83
Phone: (46) 10 719 0000
Web: www.ericsson.com

2014 Sales

	% of total
North America	24
China & North East Asia	12
Mediterranean	10
Latin America	10
Western & Central Europe	9
Middle East	9
South East Asia & Pacific	7
Northern Europe & Central Asia	6
Sub-Saharan Africa	4
India	3
Other	6
Total	**100**

PRODUCTS/OPERATIONS

2014 Sales

	% of total
Networks	51
Services	43
Support	6
Total	**100**

COMPETITORS

Accenture	Motorola Mobility
Alcatel-Lucent	NSN
Amdocs	Oracle
Cisco Systems	QUALCOMM
HP Enterprise Services	Samsung Electronics
HTC Corporation	Sharp Corp.
Harmonic	Tata Consultancy
Huawei Technologies	Tech Mahindra
IBM	Technicolor
Juniper Networks	ZTE
LG Electronics	

HISTORICAL FINANCIALS

Company Type: Public

Income Statement

FYE: December 31

	REVENUE ($ mil.)	NET INCOME ($ mil.)	NET PROFIT MARGIN	EMPLOYEES
12/15	29,289	1,607	5.5%	116,281
12/14	29,492	1,496	5.1%	118,055
12/13	35,465	1,872	5.3%	114,340
12/12	34,964	886	2.5%	110,255
12/11	32,901	1,768	5.4%	104,525
Annual Growth	(2.9%)	(2.4%)	—	2.7%

2015 Year-End Financials

Debt ratio: 1.0%
Return on equity: 9.3%
Cash ($ mil.): 4,771
Current ratio: 2.18
Long-term debt ($ mil.): 2,697

No. of shares (mil.): —
Dividends
Yield: —
Payout: —
Market value ($ mil.): —

Telefonica SA

Auditors: Ernst & Young, S.L.

LOCATIONS

HQ: Telefonica SA
Distrito Telefonica, Ronda de la Comunicacion, s/n, Madrid 28050
Phone: (34) 91 482 8700   **Fax:** (34) 91 482 8600
Web: www.telefonica.com

HISTORICAL FINANCIALS

Company Type: Public

Income Statement

FYE: December 31

	REVENUE ($ mil.)	NET INCOME ($ mil.)	NET PROFIT MARGIN	EMPLOYEES
12/15	51,431	2,989	5.8%	129,890
12/14	61,233	3,647	6.0%	123,700
12/13	78,557	6,323	8.0%	291,027
12/12	82,188	5,177	6.3%	133,186
12/11	81,276	6,988	8.6%	291,027
Annual Growth	(10.8%)	(19.1%)	—	(18.3%)

2015 Year-End Financials

Debt ratio: 53.2%
Return on equity: 14.0%
Cash ($ mil.): 2,830
Current ratio: 0.91
Long-term debt ($ mil.): 51,320

No. of shares (mil.): —
Dividends
Yield: 8.8%
Payout: 175.2%
Market value ($ mil.): —

	STOCK PRICE ($) FY Close	P/E High/Low		PER SHARE ($) Earnings	Dividends	Book Value
12/15	11.06	30	22	0.56	0.98	3.92
12/14	14.21	26	22	0.74	0.96	5.51
12/13	16.34	18	13	1.39	0.47	6.45
12/12	13.49	21	13	1.15	2.08	5.99
12/11	17.19	59	14	1.53	1.93	6.25
Annual Growth (11.0%)	(10.4%)			—	(22.3%)	(15.5%)

Telstra Corp., Ltd.

As Australia's #1 telecommunications carrier Telstra serves more than 16.7 million mobile phone customers and provides fixed-line services to about 11 million access lines. It is also a leading ISP with more than 7.3 million fixed line broadband subscribers. Telstra's largest market is consumer and residential customers and its business and government segment follows. The company also provides wholesale network services to other communications companies. Telstra owns half of pay-television operator FOXTEL while News Corp. and Consolidated Media Holdings each own 25% of the joint venture. The company is expanding Asian operations in ventures with companies in the Philippines (San Miguel) and Indonesia (Telkom Indonesia).

Operations

Mobile accounts for 40% of Telstra's revenue with the fixed line business supplying 26%. There's a bit of a drop from those segments to Data and IP and Network Applications and Services (NAS) generating 11% and 9% of revenue respectively. Telstra owns 62% of Autohome a car-buying website in China.

Geographic Reach

Telstra's networks cover about 99% of Australia's population. Australia accounts for 95% of Telstra's revenue. The rest comes from international operations mainly its operations in China.

Sales and Marketing

Telstra has many ways to reach its customers and prospective customers. It operates 362 branded retail stores 90 Telstra Business Centers and it has 127 business and enterprise partners. Its products are available in more 15000 partner retail locations. A company initiative is to improve and expedite customer service. About 52% of its customer service interactions are handled online and 2.3 million customers use Telstra's smartphone app.

Financial Performance

In 2015 (ended June) Telstra's revenue ticked down 1% to $26.6 billion from $26.8 billion in 2014. Revenue in its fixed line business fell 2% from 2014 to 2015 and data and IP revenue was off 3%. Revenue grew 10% in its mobile operations and 23% in the NAS segment.

Net income decreased by 1% to $4.3 billion in 2015 mainly due to the lower revenue and an increase in labor expenses. Telstra added stafff through organic growth and acquisitions including the Pacnet deal.

Cash flow from operation fell 4% to $8.3 billion in 2015.

Strategy

Telstra aims to extend its market leadership in Australia as it expands its businesses to Asia.

The company has increased its capital spending by $5 billion through 2014 to expand and enhance its wireless network in Australia. It is maneuvering to stay ahead of rivals such as Singtel-Optus and Vodafone. Telstra launched its Telstra Health unit in October 2014 to offer integrated ehealth services. The company also is putting $100 million toward a public Wi-Fi access network that is to provide 2 million hot spots in Australia (and access to 13 million worldwide) in five years.

Telstra wants to increase the 5% of revenue its collects from overseas customers. It holds 62% of Autohome.com a Chinese car-buying website. It has signed an agreement with brewing company San Miguel Corp. to develop a mobile phone venture in the Philippines. Telstra also is working with Telkom Indonesia on a joint venture to provide network applications and services primarily in Indonesia. The company also has a growing amount of international revenue from its Network Applications and Services unit and its Global Enterprise and Services unit.

Mergers and Acquisitions

The company acquired Pacnet Ltd. which operates undersea cables through Asia and from North America to Asia across the Pacific Ocean. The $697 million transaction brings Telstra an expanded data center network more submarine cables and major customers across the region. The move boosts Telstra's engagement with corporate customers.

HISTORY

Early History

When Australia gained independence in 1901 telecommunications were assigned to the new state-owned Postmaster-General's Department (PMG). Engineer H. P. Brown who had managed the UK's telegraph and telephone system became head of PMG in 1923. He set up research labs that year oversaw the first overseas call to London in 1930 and streamlined operations until his reign ended in 1939.

During WWII Australia quickly expanded its communications infrastructure to assist the Allied Front in the South Pacific. Following the war the government formed the Overseas Telecommunications Commission (OTC) in 1946 to handle international operations independent of PMG.

Even as new technology connected the continent and boosted the productivity of PMG its postal operations steadily recorded losses in the postwar era. In 1974 a Royal Commission recommended that postal and telecom services be split. Australian Telecommunications Commission (Telecom Australia) was launched in 1975 (OTC retained overseas services); it turned a profit in its first year.

Looking to connect residents in the outback the firm signed Japan's Nippon Electric (now NEC) in 1981 to set up a digital radio transmission system; by the next decade it connected some 50000 outback users. Also in 1981 Telecom Australia took a 25% stake in government-owned satellite operator AUSSAT and launched nationwide paging and mobile phone service in Melbourne and Sydney.

Renamed Australian Telecommunications in 1989 the carrier got its first whiff of competition as others were allowed to provide phone equipment. Two years later Optus Communications began competing with Telecom Australia; for the privilege it was forced to buy the unsuccessful AUSSAT. Long-distance competition began in 1991 and mobile phone competition began in 1992. In response Telecom Australia merged with OTC to become Australian and Overseas Telecommunications Corporation (AOTC).

AOTC became Telstra Corporation in 1993 and launched a digital wireless GSM-based network. It joined with Rupert Murdoch's News Corp. to form pay TV operator FOXTEL in 1995.

EXECUTIVES

CTO, Hkan Eriksson
Auditors: Ernst & Young

LOCATIONS

HQ: Telstra Corp., Ltd.
  Level 41, 242 Exhibition Street, Melbourne, Victoria 3000
Phone: (61) 8 8308 1721   **Fax:** (61) 3 9632 3215
Web: www.telstra.com.au

2015 Sales

	% of total
Australia	95
Other countries	5
Total	**100**

PRODUCTS/OPERATIONS

2015 Sales

	% of total
Fixed	26
Mobile	40
Data & IP	11
Network applications & services	9
Media	3
Global connectivity	3
Other	8
Total	**100**

2015 Sales

	% of total
Retail	64
Global enterprises & services	21
Operations	2
Wholesale	10
Other	3
Total	**100**

Selected Services

Advertising and directory services
Audio video and Internet conferencing
Broadband ISP
Cable TV
Data transmission
E-mail
Enhanced fax products and services
Freecall (toll-free 1-800 phone service)
Information technology (IT) services
Internet access
Mobile phone service
Prepaid telephony
Satellite transmission

COMPETITORS

Hutchison Telecommunications Australia
Optus
PowerTel
Spark New Zealand
Vodafone

HISTORICAL FINANCIALS

Company Type: Public

Income Statement

FYE: June 30

	REVENUE ($ mil.)	NET INCOME ($ mil.)	NET PROFIT MARGIN	EMPLOYEES
06/16	19,278	4,300	22.3%	0
06/15	19,997	3,251	16.3%	36,000
06/14	23,791	4,016	16.9%	0
06/13	23,684	3,517	14.8%	37,000
06/12	25,834	3,467	13.4%	39,972
Annual Growth	**(7.1%)**	**5.5%**	**—**	**—**

2016 Year-End Financials

Debt ratio: 29.7%
Return on equity: 38.4%
Cash ($ mil.): 2,641
Current ratio: 1.02
Long-term debt ($ mil.): 10,897

No. of shares (mil.): —
Dividends
  Yield: 5.2%
  Payout: 323.0%
Market value ($ mil.): —

	STOCK PRICE ($) FY Close	P/E High/Low		PER SHARE ($) Earnings	Dividends	Book Value
06/16	20.80	51	40	0.35	1.09	0.97
06/15	23.58	76	58	0.27	1.20	0.89
06/14	24.60	74	64	0.32	1.29	1.04
06/13	21.84	78	55	0.28	1.25	0.93
06/12	18.85	69	50	0.28	1.31	0.94
Annual Growth	**2.5%**		**—**	**6.0%**	**(4.5%)**	**0.7%**

Tencent Holdings Ltd.

Auditors: PricewaterhouseCoopers

LOCATIONS

HQ: Tencent Holdings Ltd.
  Tencent Building, Kejizhongyi Avenue, Hi-tech Park, Nanshan District, Shenzhen, Guangdong Province 518057
Phone: (86) 755 86013388   **Fax:** (86) 755 86013399
Web: www.tencent.com

HISTORICAL FINANCIALS

Company Type: Public

Income Statement

FYE: December 31

	REVENUE ($ mil.)	NET INCOME ($ mil.)	NET PROFIT MARGIN	EMPLOYEES
12/15	15,838	4,435	28.0%	30,641
12/14	12,717	3,836	30.2%	27,690
12/13	9,983	2,560	25.6%	27,492
12/12	7,040	2,042	29.0%	24,160
12/11	4,527	1,620	35.8%	17,446
Annual Growth	**36.8%**	**28.6%**	**—**	**15.1%**

2015 Year-End Financials

Debt ratio: 3.2%
Return on equity: 28.8%
Cash ($ mil.): 6,688
Current ratio: 1.25
Long-term debt ($ mil.): 7,700

No. of shares (mil.): —
Dividends
  Yield: 0.2%
  Payout: 8.3%
Market value ($ mil.): —

	STOCK PRICE ($) FY Close	P/E High/Low		PER SHARE ($) Earnings	Dividends	Book Value
12/15	19.62	7	4	0.47	0.04	1.97
12/14	14.51	32	5	0.41	0.03	1.38
12/13	64.42	38	18	0.27	0.02	1.03
12/12	32.65	26	14	0.22	0.02	0.72
12/11	20.14	27	17	0.17	0.01	0.50
Annual Growth	**(0.7%)**		**—**	**28.1%**	**34.4%**	**41.1%**

Tesco PLC (United Kingdom)

Auditors: Deloitte LLP

LOCATIONS

HQ: Tesco PLC (United Kingdom)
  Tesco House, Shire Park, Kestrel Way, Welwyn Garden City, Hertfordshire AL7 1GA
Phone: (44) 1992 632222   **Fax:** (44) 1992 630794
Web: www.tescoplc.com

HISTORICAL FINANCIALS

Company Type: Public

Income Statement

FYE: February 27

	REVENUE ($ mil.)	NET INCOME ($ mil.)	NET PROFIT MARGIN	EMPLOYEES
02/16	75,950	192	0.3%	482,152
02/15	96,065	(8,854)	—	506,984
02/14	105,931	1,623	1.5%	510,444
02/13	98,950	189	0.2%	537,784
02/12	101,973	4,433	4.3%	519,671
Annual Growth	**(7.1%)**	**(54.3%)**	**—**	**(1.9%)**

2016 Year-End Financials

Debt ratio: 43.0%
Return on equity: 1.7%
Cash ($ mil.): 4,300
Current ratio: 0.75
Long-term debt ($ mil.): 14,945

No. of shares (mil.): —
Dividends
Yield: —
Payout: —
Market value ($ mil.): —

	STOCK PRICE ($) FY Close	P/E High/Low	PER SHARE ($) Earnings	Dividends	Book Value
02/16	7.72	617344	0.02	0.00	1.48
02/15	11.38	— —	(1.09)	0.50	1.34
02/14	16.76	162131	0.20	0.68	3.03
02/13	17.14	1121884	0.02	0.62	3.21
02/12	15.24	57 43	0.55	0.64	3.51
Annual Growth	(15.6%) (19.4%)	— —	(54.5%)	—	

Teva Pharmaceutical Industries Ltd

Teva Pharmaceutical Industries is the biggest name in the no-name world of generic pharmaceuticals. The company makes hundreds of generic versions of brand-name antibiotics heart drugs heartburn medications and more. Headquartered in Israel Teva is the world's largest generic medicines maker using its portfolio of more than 1000 molecules to produce generics in nearly every therapeutic area. In specialty medicines Teva is a leader in making innovative treatments for disorders of the central nervous system (CNS) as well as respiratory products. The company operates in two segments: generics (which accounts for about half of sales) and specialty medicines.

Operations

Generic medicines produced by Teva include chemical and therapeutic versions of a tablets capsules injectables inhalants liquids ointments and creams. Specialty medicines include Copaxone Azilect Nuvigil ProAir HFA and QVAR. In addition to focusing on CNR and respiratory therapies Teva also provides specialty medicines in the areas of oncology women's health and others.

Teva also participates in a joint venture with Procter & Gamble. It owns 49% of the venture named PGT Healthcare which makes over-the-counter drugs. P&G brought big consumer health brand names to the venture (including Pepto Bismol and Vicks) while Teva brought international manufacturing and regulatory expertise. The company also has a collaboration with Takeda Pharmaceutical through which Takeda can commercialize Teva's treatments for Parkinson's disease (Copaxone) and multiple sclerosis (Azilect) in Japan.

The company also supplies active pharmaceutical ingredients (APIs) the essential raw materials used in drug manufacturing.

Teva holds a portfolio of more than 1000 molecules; it produces some 64 billion tablets and capsules annually at its 66 manufacturing facilities. Its pipeline includes about 20 products in phase II or III.

Geographic Reach

While Teva has research and manufacturing operations in more than 60 countries in the Americas Europe Asia and the Middle East more than half of the company's sales come from its US operations.

In 2014 the US accounted for 45% of Teva's generic revenues while Europe accounted for 32%.

Sales and Marketing

Teva's finished product are sold directly to retailers and medical providers as well as through wholesale distribution firms.

Advertising expenses for 2014 totaled $302 million down from $321 million in 2013 and $337 million in 2012.

Financial Performance

Teva's revenue has been relatively flat at around $20.3 billion since fiscal 2012. In 2014 revenue decreased by less than one percent to $20.3 billion as declines in generics occurred. In Europe regulatory measures such as price reductions impacted earnings. However US operations saw growth due to the release of new generics.

Net income had been on a decline until 2014 when it more than doubled to $3.1 billion thanks to income from legal settlements (related to the settlement of pantoprazole patent litigation) as well as a reduction in selling and marketing expenses. Cash flow from operations rose 58% to $5.1 billion due to lower payments for legal settlements and Israeli tax settlements among other factors.

Strategy

Continuing growth strategies include expansion efforts in emerging markets and increasing its portfolio in over-the-counter medicines. Teva continues with its historical strategy of filing patent challenges on branded products thus attempting to gain a "first-to-market" advantage with its generic equivalents; however in recent years these patent challenges have grown more expensive and less exclusive which has eroded their usefulness.

Lingering impacts from acquisition expenses as well as the patent expiration of top-selling branded drug Copaxone prompted Teva to launch a cost control program in 2013 to cut $2 billion in annual expenses by 2017. The program includes a 10% workforce reduction; the first such downsizing program in the company's history. In 2015 it agreed to sell its facility in Sellersville Pennsylvania to G&W Laboratories to cut excess manufacturing capacity and cut costs.

Perhaps in response to losing exclusivity of its Copaxone Teva made an unsolicited $40 billion bid for generics rival Mylan in mid-2015. Mylan had just made its own unsolicited offer to purchase Perrigo for some $29 billion; either deal would be among the largest of the year. However Teva subsequently dropped its plans to buy Mylan; instead it bought the generics business of Allergan for some $40.5 billion in mid-2016. In another deal to build its portfolio Teva agreed to form a joint venture with top Japanese firm Takeda Pharmaceutical. Takeda will gradually transfer its generics business to the venture (which will be 51%-owned by Teva) as it focuses more heavily on developing new drugs. That venture allows Teva to expand in Japan a nation it has targeted for years.

After regulatory compliance expenses pinched the company's animal health business in 2011 Teva sold off those operations to Bayer HealthCare in early 2013 in a deal worth up to $145 million. The business included dermatology and food products for companion animals.

In 2015 Teva plans to launch inhalation powder ProAir RespiClick in the US. It did launch a generic version of Exforge tablets which treat high blood pressure as well as Lovenox both in the US. In 2014 the company introduced psychiatric drug Adasuve.

Mergers and Acquisitions

Acquisitions around the globe have helped the company enter new markets and secure market dominance in others. In 2014 Teva acquired biotech company Labrys Biologics which is focused on migraine treatments for $207 million.

The company now plans to buy California-based Auspex Pharmaceuticals which is developing drugs for central nervous system disorders including Huntington's disease and Tourette's syndrome for some $3.2 billion. It is also buying US-based private software firm Gecko Health Innovations which makes products that alert respiratory patients when it's time to take their medicine.

And in yet another deal aimed at growing its emerging market operations Teva acquired Mexico-based drugmaker Representaciones e Investigaciones Medicas SA (more simply known as Rimsa) for $2.3 billion in 2016. That purchase makes Teva one of Mexico's top pharmaceutical firms.

Shortly after buying Allergan's generics business in 2016 Teva bought that firm's Anda distribution business for $500 million. Anda distributes branded generic OTC and specialty products from more than 300 manufacturers in the US. The deal included three distribution centers and fits in well with Teva's strategy to build up its supply chain network.

HISTORY

Company Background

Teva traces its origins to Salomon Levin and Elstein Ltd. a drug distribution firm based in Jerusalem which at the time was a Jewish section of British-controlled Palestine.

Ironically in the 1930s the company benefited from the emigration of Jewish people many of whom were scientists seeking to escape the Nazi regime in Germany which at the time was the global leader in drug development. The company went public in 1951.

In 1968 Eli Hurvitz was appointed to Teva's board of directors and scripted much of the company's growth. In 1970 Teva merged with Assia Chemical Laboratories (Hurvitz's old employer) and another company to form Teva Pharmaceutical Industries.

Ten years later Teva sold a 20% stake of itself to Koor Industries in exchange for Koor subsidiary Ikapharm Teva's closest competitor. (Koor later launched a takeover bid but the Founders Group Teva's controlling shareholders foiled the attempt.)

In 1985 Teva moved into the US. It formed a joint venture with W. R. Grace called TAG Pharmaceuticals (Teva bought out W. R. Grace's portion in 1991). In 1985 TAG bought Lemmon Co. famous — or infamous — for its tranquilizer Quaalude which had gained notoriety as the recreational drug of choice for many young people. Lemmon which ceased production of Quaalude prior to Teva's purchase became the acquirer's generic manufacturing division.

Teva bought Abic Israel's #2 drugmaker in a complex 1988 transaction that gave Canadian investor and Seagram's heir Charles Bronfman a stake in the company. British publisher Robert Maxwell also bought a substantial stake in Teva. (Following Maxwell's mysterious death in 1993 his estate sold his stake.)

In the 1990s Teva turned its attention to Europe buying companies in France Hungary Italy and the UK. In 1996 the company bought US firm Biocraft Laboratories merging it with Lemmon and forming Teva Pharmaceuticals USA.

In 1998 the company reorganized after officials realized that it had to evolve from being a collection of disparate operating entities to a more centralized operation. It also divested several operations –including its Russian joint venture its yeast and alcohol fermentation business and some of its German operations —in order to concentrate on pharmaceuticals.

EXECUTIVES

EVP and CFO, Eyal Desheh, age 63
EVP Business Development Strategy and Commercial Innovation, Timothy R. Wright, age 59
President and CEO Global Operations, Carlo de Notaristefani, age 58
President and CEO Global Generic Medicines Group, Sigurdur O. (Siggi) Olafsson, age 47
President of Global R&D and Chief Scientific Officer, Michael Hayden
President and CEO Teva Europe, Robert Koremans
Group EVP Corporate Marketing and Communications, Iris Beck-Codner
EVP Human Resources, Mark Sabag
Chairman and Interim Chief Executive, Yitzhak Peterburg
General Manager UK and Ireland, Kim Innes
EVP and Chief Internal Auditor, Nir Baron
Auditors: Kesselman & Kesselman

LOCATIONS

HQ: Teva Pharmaceutical Industries Ltd
5 Basel Street, P.O. Box 3190, Petach Tikva 4951033
Phone: (972) 3 926 7267
Web: www.tevapharm.com

2014 Sales

	% of total
US	52
Europe	29
Rest of the world	19
Total	**100**

PRODUCTS/OPERATIONS

2014 Sales

	$ mil.	% of total
Generic products	9,814	48
Specialty products		
Central nervous system	5,575	28
Oncology	1,180	6
Respiratory	957	5
Women's health	504	2
Other	344	2
Other revenues	1,898	9
Total	**20,272**	**100**

Selected Products

Branded products
  Central nervous system
  Azilect (Parkinson' s)
  Copaxone (multiple sclerosis)
  Provigil (narcolepsy)
  Specialty respiratory
  ProAir (bronchial spasms)
  Qvar (chronic asthma)
  Women' s health
  Seasonique
Biosimilar products
  Eporatio (erythropoietin treatment for chemotherapy-induced anemia)
  Granulocyte Colony Stimulating Factor (anti-infective for oncology patients)
  Tev-Tropin (human growth hormone)
Generic products
  Amoxicillin (Amoxil)
  Atorvastatin (Lipitor)
  Bromatapp (Dimetapp)
  Candesartan (Atacand)
  Cimetidine (Tagamet)
  Ciprofloxacin (Cipro)
  Clemastine fumarate (Tavist)
  Clotrimazole (Lotrimin)
  Diclofenac extended release (Voltaren XR)
  Diltiazem HCl (Cardizem)
  Donepezil (Aricept)
  Fluconazole Injection (Diflucan)
  Fluoxetine (Prozac)
  Galantamine (Reminyl)
  Ketoconazole cream (Nizoral Cream)
  Lamivudine (Epivir)
  Lovastatin (Mevacor)
  Metronidazole (Flagyl)
  Quetiapine (Seroquel)

Sotalol hydrochloride (Betapace)
Sulfamethoxazole and Trimethoprim (Bactrim)
Tizanidine (Zanaflex)
Tramadol hydrochloride (Ultram/Ultracet)

Selected Acquisitions

COMPETITORS

Abbott Labs	Johnson & Johnson
Allergan plc	Merck
AstraZeneca	Mylan
Bayer HealthCare	Novartis
Pharmaceuticals Inc.	Perrigo
Bio-Rad Labs	Pfizer
Biogen	Sandoz International
Boehringer Ingelheim	GmbH
Bristol-Myers Squibb	Sanofi
Dr. Reddy' s	Taro
GlaxoSmithKline	Wockhardt

HISTORICAL FINANCIALS

Company Type: Public

Income Statement

FYE: December 31

	REVENUE ($ mil.)	NET INCOME ($ mil.)	NET PROFIT MARGIN	EMPLOYEES
12/16	21,903	329	1.5%	56,960
12/15	19,652	1,588	8.1%	42,888
12/14	20,272	3,055	15.1%	43,009
12/13	20,314	1,269	6.2%	44,945
12/12	20,317	1,963	9.7%	45,948
Annual Growth	**1.9%**	**(36.0%)**	**—**	**5.5%**

2016 Year-End Financials

Debt ratio: 38.5%
Return on equity: 1.0%
Cash ($ mil.): 988
Current ratio: 0.92
Long-term debt ($ mil.): 32,524

No. of shares (mil.): 1,015
Dividends
  Yield: 0.0%
  Payout: 1,651.4%
Market value ($ mil.): 36,794

	STOCK PRICE ($) FY Close	P/E High/Low	Earnings	Dividends	Book Value
12/16	36.25	941500	0.07	1.16	32.84
12/15	65.64	39 30	1.82	1.16	32.80
12/14	57.51	16 11	3.56	1.15	27.36
12/13	40.08	28 25	1.49	1.09	26.61
12/12	37.34	20 16	2.25	0.80	26.57
Annual Growth	**(0.7%)**	**—**	**—(58.0%)**	**9.5%**	**5.4%**

THALES

Best known for its work in weapons manufacture Thales makes electrical systems defence aerospace and transportation. The Defence & Security segment Thales' largest works primarily with governments and provides security products and systems across all defensible spheres: land air water space and digital. The Aerospace segments makes systems and products for the commercial aviation industry including things in-flight entertainment as well as flight simulators for planes and helicopters. Transport which predominantly supports non-government markets designs and develops rail signaling and ticketing systems. The French government owns about 26% of Thales while UK-based Dassault holds about 25%.

Operations

Defence & Security which pulls in around half of revenue is divided into three business units: Secure Communications and Information Systems Land and Air Systems and Defence Mission Systems. Between the three Thales can equip militaries with communications and radar systems for use in the field a range of missile and weapons systems for short- and medium-range land-based engagements including the RAPID line and combat systems for air and naval warfare. Thales also owns 50% of Thales Raytheon Systems which makes air defence radars and is the main contractor for NATO's Command and Control System.

Thales is active in the US defense market via relationships with US companies on everything from missiles to radars to sonar. It makes components for Raytheon's missiles and the company's combat management system is at the core of Northrop Grumman's Integrated Combat Management system (which is a fixture on General Dynamics' Littoral Combat Ship).

Aerospace is divided into Avionics which manufactures in-flight entertainment and connectivity equipment and Space a joint venture with Italy's Finmeccanica and which primarily serves the telecommunications market for instance geostationary satellites.

Geographic Reach

Thales organizes its divisions across three geographical areas: France holds its own division while the rest of the world is included in the other two divisions. The UK is Thales' second-biggest customer.

The company manufactures its products in one of 13 sites located throughout Europe in France the Netherlands Spain and the UK as well as in Australia. The company extends its global presence through acquisitions joint ventures and partnerships.

Financial Performance

Note: Growth rates may differ after conversion to US Dollars.

An increase in geopolitical unrest particularly in the Middle East is driving an increase in government spending. Consequently Thales saw sales grow 8.4% in 2015 to euro 14.1 billion representing a return to organic growth in mature markets and 16% growth in emerging markets. Indeed sales in emerging markets as a whole now exceed France Thales' #1 individual market at 24% of total revenue. In terms of order growth (as a distinct metric to sales) the Middle East region saw growth of 93% while order intake from the UK increased 68%. In 2015 the company added 24 contracts worth more than euro 100 million as well as five euro +500 million contracts which include signaling on the London Underground and 1000 Hawkei light protected vehicles for the Australian military.

The London Underground contract helped the Transport segment return to growth follow a couple of difficult years.

Growth in net income to euro 800 million tracked organic growth and an increase in cash from operating activities to euro 1.7 billion reflected an increase in sales volume.

Strategy

As with most companies that operate in the aerospace and defence sectors fortunes are dependent on government spending. To mitigate against fluctuations in military spending Thales makes efforts to keep its defence and civil operations evenly weighted. To this end it signed contracts with US airline JetBlue to equip its A320 fleet with latest-generation in-seat screens and with the European Space Agency for Sentinel 1C/1D observation and exploration satellites.

Satellites and security (both digital and transport) also play into this state/private dynamic. For example Thales Alenia Space the joint venture between Thales (67% stake) and Italian aerospace group Leonardo-Finmeccanica (33%) seeks to snare a growing share of the global market for large commercial-communications satellites that are launched by commercial rockets.

Further in the civil space the ongoing rapid expansion of cities across the globe is driving the need for expanded and more efficient underground train lines for which Thales is well positioned. In 2015 the company signed contracts in the London New York Sydney and Doha as well as four Chinese cities (Qingdao Nanchang Wuhan and Shijiazhuang).

Thales' involvement in the Middle East market is growing - as well as the fastest sales growth the region also saw the fastest increase in employee numbers. Thales' AVANT entertainment system was equipped in Qatar Air planes and Thales was also contracted to supply signaling and ticketing systems for a new metro in Doha.

HISTORY

Compagnie Française Thomson-Houston (CFTH) began as a subsidiary for US-based tramway-equipment maker Thomson-Houston Electric Corporation in 1893. French investors bought the subsidiary when Thomson-Houston and Edison General Electric merged to become General Electric (GE). The fledgling company kept its founder's name and maintained a licensing agreement with GE. Early interests included power stations and the electrification of tramways. Diversification in the 1920s included the acquisition of Societe des Usines du Pied-Selle (kitchen and heating equipment 1920) and the formation of a finance company Financiere ?lectricite (1925).

Alsthom was created in 1928 when Thomson and Societe Alsacienne de Constructions Mecaniques joined to make industrial electrical equipment. Radio and TV receivers were added in 1929 when Thomson acquired ?tablissements Ducretet.

The 1930s brought the acquisition of ?tablissement Kraemer (radio equipment 1936). During WWII however operations not used by the German military sat idle.

Postwar political conflict between France and the US plus Thomson's involvement in defense and nuclear technology caused it to end association with GE in 1953. A 1959 agreement with Pathe-Marconi began radio and TV production.

A 1966 merger with Hotchkiss-Brandt resulted in a new name Thomson-Brandt. In 1968 another merger and another name change Thomson-CSF occurred when Compagnie Generale de TSF joined Thomson. In 1981 the French nationalized Thomson-Brandt and in 1982 created holding company Thomson S.A. to manage it. Opposition to the government's nationalization in 1987 forced Thomson's return to the private sector and the company formed semiconductor unit SGS-Thomson Microelectronics. In 1989 the company acquired defense electronics businesses MBLE (Belgium) and Signaal (Denmark) from Philips.

Arms sales declined in 1991 and the company began to produce consumer goods such as satellite TV dishes. A 1992 agreement introduced IBM technology to Thomson defense and space products. UK-based GEC and Thomson began making sonar and antisubmarine systems after a 1995 agreement.

Thomson sold its interests in Credit Lyonnais Securities to the French government in 1996. The company sold its semiconductor unit in 1997. Thomson strengthened its defense business by taking a majority interest in Siemens Forvarssystemer (military communications Norway) in 1998 and striking a $500 million deal with Raytheon to make control systems for NATO in 1999. That year Thomson also purchased a 42% stake in Singapore-based optronics company Avimo Group.

Late in 1999 Shorts Missile Systems Ltd. (SMS) —Thomson's joint venture with Canada-based Bombardier —won a long-term $319 million contract to make short-range Starstreak anti-aircraft missiles for the UK. In 2000 Thomson-CSF acquired UK-based Racal Electronics a defense electronics firm for $2.17 billion and bought out Bombardier's share in the SMS venture. Also in 2000 the company announced plans to sell Crouzet-Automatismes (its electro-mechanical components division) to Schneider Electric. In December Thomson-CSF changed its name to Thales and agreed to form a joint air-defense venture (Thales-Raytheon Systems) with Raytheon.

In 2001 the company acquired majority control over optronics company Avimo. The same year Thales sold its 48.8% stake in Alcatel Space to joint venture partner Alcatel for about $700 million. (That deal and another sale of Thales' stock late in the year reduced Alcatel's stake to about 16%.) Thales also agreed to buy Orbital Science's GPS businesses Magellan Corporation and Navigation Solutions LLC (NavSol) a joint venture with Hertz for about $70 million. In November the company sold Thales Instruments (the former instruments business of Racal) to an investment firm consortium for about $120 million.

Thales agreed to sell its computer services arm Thales IS to French IT company GFI Informatique in 2002. However GFI abandoned the deal which would have been worth more than $300 million soon after it was announced.

In 2004 Thales gained ground when BAE lost prime contractor status in building the Royal Navy's new carriers; but the two companies would ultimately work together with US-based KBR coordinating things. The following year Thales inked a euro 236 million deal to supply 18 facilities with Tiger combat helicopter simulators.

In 2006 Thales and Germany's Diehl Stiftung & Co. merged their aerospace activities specifically cockpit avionics systems and flight and engine control to create a new joint venture company Diehl Aerospace GmbH. The two companies teamed up again to form Junghans Microtec GmbH a combination of the two companies' ammunition fuse and safety device operations.

In exchange for a near 21% stake in Thales plus cash Thales acquired the satellite-building and homeland security businesses of telecom-equipment maker Alcatel-Lucent in 2006. The deal included Alcatel-Lucent's transport systems division which makes signaling systems for railways and subway systems. As part of the acquisition the French government's stake in Thales decreased.

Thales acquired a 25% slice of shipyard concern Direction des Constructions Navales (DCN) in 2007 with an option to increase its stake to as much as 35%. In return Thales handed over its Naval France business to DCN and a stake in three of Thales's concerns. The tie-up pushes Thales's system capabilities to the front of the European naval market. Also that same year ITT Gilfillan and Thales inked a deal that would enable ITT radar systems to have the exclusive right to market and produce the Smart SMK II radar system for the US market. Thales also has a manufacturing facility in Maryland where it works on the Joint Tactical Radio System.

The company sold its Thales Computers unit to Kontron Modular Computers in 2008 for euro 11 million (over $14 million). It also divested its electronic payment business that same year; American Group Hypercom purchased it for over euro 93 million (almost $125 million).

To expand its information and communications systems security business the company pocketed nCipher in 2008 a supplier of encryption products for government financial institutions and enterprises that need to protect sensitive data. Also in

2008 Thales joined Emirates Advanced Investments subsidiary C4 Advanced Solutions (C4AS) to step up military communication systems and equipment in the Middle East and Northern Africa. Holding a 49% stake in the Abu Dhabi-based joint venture (Thales Advanced Solutions) Thales supplies tactical radio maintenance in-service support for products and systems and software for communications systems to UAE armed forces. The joint venture extended Thales's regional influence; the company already won a deal to integrate communications at Abu Dhabi International Airport's air traffic control center tower. India is a customer too and operates combat aircraft built by Dassault and Thales.

Thales purchased Israel-based medical imaging company CMT Medical Technologies in 2009 for about euro 20 million (more than $28 million). While its medical imaging business took a giant hit during the recession its joint venture with Philips and Siemens (Thales holds 51%) to make digital X-ray detectors offset the impact. The acquisition of CMT satisfies all the needs of OEM requirements.

EXECUTIVES

SEVP Human Resources, David Tournadre, age 47
EVP Avionics, Michel Mathieu, age 65
EVP International Development, Pascale Sourisse
CEO, Victor Chavez
EVP Secure Communications and Information Systems, Marc Darmon, age 50
EVP Defence Mission Systems, Pierre-Eric Pommellet, age 51
EVP Air Operations; EVP Land Defence, Alex Cresswell, age 51
EVP Strategy Research and Technology, Herve Multon
EVP Space, Jean-Lo c Galle, age 56
EVP Transportation Systems, Jean-Pierre Forestier, age 68
SEVP; CFO, Pascal Bouchiat
Chairman and CEO, Patrice Caine
CEO Germany, Christoph Hoppe
Auditors: Mazars

LOCATIONS

HQ: THALES
Tour Carpe Diem, 31, Place des Corolles Esplanade Nord, Courbevoie 92400
Phone: (33) 1 57 77 80 00
Web: www.thalesgroup.com

2015 Sales

	% of total
Europe (minus France)	32
Emerging Markets	28
France	24
North America	11
Australia & New Zealand	5
Total	**100**

PRODUCTS/OPERATIONS

2015 Sales

	% of total
Defense & Security	51
Aerospace	38
Transport	11
Other	0
Total	**100**

Selected Divisions

Air operations
Avionics
Defense & security C4I systems
Defense mission systems
Land defense
Space
Transportation systems

HISTORICAL FINANCIALS

Company Type: Public

Income Statement

FYE: December 31

	REVENUE ($ mil.)	NET INCOME ($ mil.)	NET PROFIT MARGIN	EMPLOYEES
12/15	15,317	833	5.4%	61,848
12/14	15,769	868	5.5%	60,781
12/13	19,541	789	4.0%	66,447
12/12	18,661	706	3.8%	65,992
12/11	16,851	661	3.9%	68,325
Annual Growth	(2.4%)	5.9%	—	(2.5%)

2015 Year-End Financials

Debt ratio: 7.7%	No. of shares (mil.): 210
Return on equity: 18.1%	Dividends
Cash ($ mil.): 3,758	Yield: 0.0%
Current ratio: 0.99	Payout: 31.1%
Long-term debt ($ mil.): 912	Market value ($ mil.): 15,654

	STOCK PRICE ($) FY Close	P/E High/Low	PER SHARE ($) Earnings	Dividends	Book Value
12/15	74.50	21 13	3.95	1.23	24.08
12/14	54.43	17 13	4.22	1.58	22.26
12/13	59.55	21 13	3.91	1.24	26.49
12/12	32.98	14 11	3.55	1.03	30.23
12/11	30.20	15 11	3.36	0.97	26.81
Annual Growth	25.3%	— —	4.1%	6.1%	(2.6%)

ThyssenKrupp AG

How do you say "giant engineering and steel company" in German? Try ThyssenKrupp and pronounce it "TISS-in kroop." The company is one of the world's largest steel producers and operates worldwide in two business areas: Materials and Technologies. The first comprises the company's steel (carbon and stainless steel) and materials services businesses. ThyssenKrupp's Technologies group consists of its elevators unit marine systems components technology (for the auto and engineering markets) and plant technology (construction and environmental services) segments. Although its combined interests range from elevators to shipbuilding the company has historically relied upon the steel market.

Geographic Reach

Led by regional headquarters ThyssenKrupp serves customers in North and South America China India and the Asia-Pacific region. It has operations in 78 countries and has 546 subsidiaries.

Operations

The company's business operations are organized into two divisions and seven operating business areas. The Materials division consists of the Steel Europe Steel Americas and Materials Services units. The Technologies division comprises the company's Elevator Technology Plant Technology Components Technology and Marine Systems units.

Financial Performance

In fiscal 2014 (ended September) ThyssenKrupp's revenues grew by 7% due to strong growth in its capital goods business and sales from the recent acquisitions of Acciai Speciali Terni (AST) and VDM.

That year the company posted net income of euro 195 million (compared to net loss of euro 1.58 billion in 2013) thanks to higher revenues and lower operating expenses.

ThyssenKrupp's operating cash inflow increased to euro 887 million in 2014 (up from euro 786 million in the previous year) as the result of improved net income and a change in working capital.

Strategy

In 2014 ThyssenKrupp Metallurgical Products expanded its operations in South America opening its first location in Bolivia extending its global network of sales offices. As well as marketing non-ferrous metal tin ThyssenKrupp Metallurgical Products will focus on trading copper and tungsten from that country. That year it also began construction of a new automotive supply plant in Brazil.

To raise cash to reinvest in core operations in 2014 ThyssenKrupp sold ThyssenKrupp Steel USA's rolling and coating plant in Calvert Alabama to a consortium of ArcelorMittal and Nippon Steel & Sumitomo Metal for $1.55 billion. (The deal is expected to deliver $60 million in annual savings). That year the company also arranged for a long-term slab supply contract with the ThyssenKrupp CSA steel mill in Brazil. The consortium will purchase 2 million tons of slabs per year from ThyssenKrupp CSA up to 2019.

In 2014 ThyssenKrupp Metallurgical Products expanded its product portfolio signing an 10-year offtake agreement with NioCorp Developments for ferroniobium a rare heavy metal. This offtake agreement makes the ThyssenKrupp Metallurgical Products the exclusive European distribution partner to NioCorp which is developing the only primary niobium deposits in the US at its Elk Creek project in Nebraska.

Mergers and Acquisitions

As part of the 2014 acquisitions of the AST and VDM service centers from Outokumpu ThyssenKrupp sold its 29.9% holdings in that company. (The deal stems from the sale of ThyssenKrupp's stainless steel company Inoxumto to Outokumpu in 2012).

In 2013 ThyssenKrupp Aerospace acquired UK-based The Waterjet Group. With its equipment ThyssenKrupp is able to process a wide range of materials and sizes for its European and international customer base.

HISTORY

Company Background

Formed separately in the 1800s both Thyssen and Krupp flourished in their early years under family control. Friedrich Krupp opened his steel factory in 1811. He died in 1826 and left the nearly bankrupt factory in the hands of his 14-year-old son Alfred who turned the business around. At the first World's Fair in 1851 Alfred unveiled a steel cannon far superior to earlier bronze models.

Twenty years later August Thyssen founded a puddling and rolling mill near Mulheim. He bought small factories and mines and by WWI he ran Germany's largest iron and steel company. During the world wars the resources of both companies were turned toward military efforts.

Post-WWII years were tough for both companies. Thyssen was split up by the Allies and when it began production again in 1953 it consisted of one steel plant. In the Krupp camp Alfred's great-grandson Alfried was convicted in 1948 of using slave labor during WWII. Released from prison in 1951 Alfried rebuilt Krupp. After near ruin following WWII both companies emerged and enjoyed a resurgence along with the German economy in which they prospered and expanded during the 1950s.

By the 1980s Thyssen's businesses included ships locomotives offshore oil rigs specialty steel and metals trading and distribution. Krupp continued to grow and in 1992 it took over engineering and steelmaking concern Hoesch AG. (Eberhard Hoesch had begun making railroad tracks in the 1820s. The company grew and expanded into infrastructure and building products.)

The new Fried. Krupp AG Hoesch-Krupp bought Italian specialty steelmaker Acciai Speciali Terni chemical-plant builder Uhde and South African shipper J.

H. Bachmann. Its automotive division formed a joint venture in Brazil and added production sites in China Mexico Romania and the US.

In 1997 Thyssen expanded in North America with its $675 million acquisition of Giddings & Lewis (machine tools US) and the purchase of Copper & Brass Sales (metals processing and distributing).

Krupp attempted a hostile takeover of Thyssen in 1997. The takeover failed but the companies soon agreed to merge their steel operations to form Thyssen Krupp Stahl. Bigger plans were in the works and in 1998 the two companies agreed to merge. That year Thyssen sold its Plusnet fixed-line phone business to Esprit Telecom Group.

In 1999 Krupp's automotive division (Krupp Hoesch Automotive) bought Cummins' Atlas Crankshaft subsidiary. Thyssen also bought US-based Dover's elevator business for $1.1 billion. Krupp and Thyssen completed their merger in 1999. The company planned to spin off its steel operations but held off due to its success in 2000. ThyssenKrupp did however sell its Krupp Kunststofftechnik unit (plastic molding machines) for about $183 million. To speed corporate decision-making the company made plans to scrap its dual-management structure in 2001.

Early in 2001 ThyssenKrupp agreed to buy 51% of Fiat unit Magneti Marelli's suspension-systems and shock-absorbers business. It also had the option of buying the remainder after 2004. In 2002 the company formed alliances with NKK and Kawasaki Steel to share its steel sheet making technologies while expanding its business with Japanese automotive makers in Europe. ThyssenKrupp's joint venture with Chinese steelmaker ANSC Angang New Steel known as TAGAL began producing galvanized coil of which about 80% will be used in China's burgeoning automotive industry.

In 2004 ThyssenKrupp sold its residential real estate unit for around $2.8 billion to a consortium of real estate funds operated by Morgan Stanley and Corpus-Immobiliengruppe. It divested the automotive segment of the capital goods unit in 2006 selling it off in pieces.

ThyssenKrupp opened three major new steel facilities in the Americas in 2010. A new integrated steel mill in Santa Cruz Brazil started production in mid-year. The $7 billion plant the company's biggest project ever is a partnership with South American giant Vale SA which owns a 25% stake in the venture. The company also began production at two plants in Calvert Alabama: a $3.6 billion carbon steel plant and a $1.4 billion stainless steel rolling plant. The company also constructed —and consolidated its corporate staff in —a new headquarters building in Essen Germany in 2010.

EXECUTIVES

Chairman Executive Board, Heinrich Hiesinger, age 56
CEO ThyssenKrupp Materials Services, Joachim Limberg, age 62
CEO Components Technology Business, Karsten Kroos, age 57
CEO ThyssenKrupp Steel Europe, Andreas J. Goss, age 52
CEO ThyssenKrupp Elevator, Andreas Schierenbeck
CFO, Guido Kerkhoff, age 49
CEO ThyssenKrupp North America, Patrick Bass
CIO, Martin Hoelz
CEO Industrial Solutions, Stefan Gesing, age 38
Chairman Supervisory Board, Ulrich Lehner, age 70
Auditors: PricewaterhouseCoopers AG Wirtschaftspruefungsgesellschaft

LOCATIONS

HQ: ThyssenKrupp AG
ThyssenKrupp Allee 1, Essen D-45143
Phone: (49) 201 844 0   **Fax:** (49) 201 844 53600
Web: www.thyssenkrupp.com

COMPETITORS

Acerinox
ArcelorMittal
Bechtel
Descours & Cabaud
GEA Group
ITOCHU
Ingersoll-Rand
JFE Holdings
Kobe Steel
MAN
Magna International
Marubeni
Nippon Steel & Sumitomo Metal Corporation
POSCO
Qingdao Iron and Steel
Schindler Holding
Tata Europe
United States Steel
United Technologies

HISTORICAL FINANCIALS
Company Type: Public

Income Statement
FYE: September 30

	REVENUE ($ mil.)	NET INCOME ($ mil.)	NET PROFIT MARGIN	EMPLOYEES
09/16	43,829	330	0.8%	156,487
09/15	47,960	346	0.7%	154,906
09/14	51,996	264	0.5%	160,745
09/13	52,044	(1,884)	—	156,856
09/12	51,880	(6,035)	—	167,961
Annual Growth	(4.1%)			(1.8%)

2016 Year-End Financials

Debt ratio: 24.2%
Return on equity: 11.1%
Cash ($ mil.): 4,582
Current ratio: 1.13
Long-term debt ($ mil.): 6,873

No. of shares (mil.): 565
Dividends
  Yield: 0.0%
  Payout: 28.8%
Market value ($ mil.): 13,300

	STOCK PRICE ($) FY Close	P/E High/Low	PER SHARE ($) Earnings	Dividends	Book Value
09/16	23.50	47 28	0.58	0.17	4.15
09/15	17.25	53 31	0.62	0.12	6.30
09/14	27.67	75 55	0.48	0.00	6.63
09/13	23.94	— —	(3.66)	0.00	5.88
09/12	21.50	— —	(11.73)	0.00	8.94
Annual Growth (17.5%)	2.2%	— —	—	—	—

Toho Bank, Ltd. (The)

The Toho Bank is a regional bank serving the Fukushima Prefecture in Japan. Armed with more than 115 branches and ATMs installed at more than 230 locations the bank offers local customers businesses and public institutions the traditional array of banking services including savings lending real estate venture firm support and financing and foreign and domestic exchange products. Toho Bank was established in 1941 and owns subsidiaries and affiliated companies such as The Toho Real Estate Service Co. The Toho Card Co. and The Toho Staff Service Co.

EXECUTIVES

President, SEISHI KITAMURA
Auditors: Ernst & Young ShinNihon LLC

LOCATIONS

HQ: Toho Bank, Ltd. (The)
3-25 Ohmachi, Fukushima 960-8633
Phone: (81) 24 523 3131   **Fax:** (81) 24 524 1583
Web: www.tohobank.co.jp

COMPETITORS

Aozora Bank
Iyo Bank
Mitsubishi UFJ
  Financial Group
Miyazaki Bank
Shizuoka Bank
Towa Bank

HISTORICAL FINANCIALS
Company Type: Public

Income Statement
FYE: March 31

	ASSETS ($ mil.)	NET INCOME ($ mil.)	INCOME AS % OF ASSETS	EMPLOYEES
03/16	52,224	162	0.3%	2,866
03/15	48,952	82	0.2%	2,600
03/14	52,170	88	0.2%	1,923
03/13	49,604	67	0.1%	1,925
03/12	51,716	57	0.1%	1,934
Annual Growth	0.2%	29.6%	—	10.3%

2016 Year-End Financials

Return on assets: 0.3%
Return on equity: 9.4%
Long-term debt ($ mil.): —
No. of shares (mil.): 252
Sales ($ mil): 734

Dividends
  Yield: —
  Payout: —
Market value ($ mil.): —

Tohoku Electric Power Co., Inc. (Japan)

The people of Tohoku the northern part of Japan's main island rely on Tohoku Electric Power for their electricity needs. Founded in 1951 the company produces power primarily through its thermal hydroelectric and nuclear power plants although it is also developing solar and power plants to cut carbon emissions. Overall it has a generating capacity of almost 17000 MW. Tohoku Electric Power one if Japan's top electric utilities delivers electricity to some 7.7 million residential and business customers. Deregulation measures in Japan have led the company to enter new markets including wholesale gas marketing and LNG supply. The company also has construction telecommunications and other operations.

EXECUTIVES

President, Hiroya Harada, age 60
EVP, Mitsuhiro Sakamoto
EVP, Takao Watanabe
EVP, Shinichi Okanobu
EVP, Toshiro Sasagawa
Chairman, Makoto Kaiwa, age 66
Auditors: Ernst & Young ShinNihon LLC

LOCATIONS

HQ: Tohoku Electric Power Co., Inc. (Japan)
1-7-1 Honcho, Aoba-ku, Sendai, Miyagi 980-8550
Phone: (81) 22 225 2111
Web: www.tohoku-epco.co.jp

Tohoku Electric Power distributes electricity in the seven prefectures of the Tohoku region of Japan.2015 Sales

	% of total
Electric Power Business	78
Construction Business	12
Others	10
Total	**100**

COMPETITORS

Chubu Electric Power
Chugoku Electric Power
Hokkaido Electric
  Power
Hokuriku Electric
  Power
KEPCO
Kyushu Electric Power
Osaka Gas
Shikoku Electric
Tokyo Electric

HISTORICAL FINANCIALS
Company Type: Public

Income Statement
FYE: March 31

	REVENUE ($ mil.)	NET INCOME ($ mil.)	NET PROFIT MARGIN	EMPLOYEES
03/16	18,661	866	4.6%	24,285
03/15	18,187	637	3.5%	24,536
03/14	19,752	332	1.7%	24,667
03/13	19,052	(1,102)	—	24,726
03/12	20,540	(2,827)	—	24,567
Annual Growth	(2.4%)	—		(0.3%)

2016 Year-End Financials

Debt ratio: 0.5%
Return on equity: 15.7%
Cash ($ mil.): 1,942
Current ratio: 0.75
Long-term debt ($ mil.): 18,848

No. of shares (mil.): 499
Dividends
  Yield: 0.0%
  Payout: 13.0%
Market value ($ mil.): —

STOCK PRICE ($)		P/E		PER SHARE ($)		
	FY Close	High/Low		Earnings	Dividends	Book Value
03/16	0.00	0	0	1.70	0.22	11.25
03/15	11.31	0	0	1.28	0.13	10.07
03/14	10.20	—	—	0.67	0.00	11.16
03/13	7.23	—	—	(2.21)	0.00	11.14
Annual Growth	—	—	—	—	—	0.2%

Tokio Marine Holdings Inc

Tokio Marine Holdings might have old roots but it still knows how to learn new tricks. Japan's oldest property/casualty insurance company the firm has one of the largest insurance sales networks in Japan and has expanded its insurance operations to about 40 additional countries in Asia Oceania Europe Africa the Middle East and the Americas. Through Tokio Marine & Nichido Fire (TMNF) Nisshin Fire Philadelphia Insurance Companies Kiln HCC Insurance and other subsidiaries Tokio Marine Holdings provides marine property/casualty personal accident fire auto and life insurance as well as reinsurance. It also offers asset management pension plans and other services.

Operations

Tokio Marine operates in four segments: domestic property/casualty insurance domestic life insurance overseas insurance and finance and others (investment advisory staffing business etc.). Domestic property/casualty insurance accounts for some 60% of sales.

Geographic Reach

The firm has insurance operations in about 40 countries throughout Asia and Oceania Europe the Middle East and the Americas. The majority of Tokio Marine's revenue comes from Japan (about 70% in fiscal 2014).

Sales and Marketing

Tokio Marine markets its products through a network of agents. Property/casualty subsidiary Tokio Marine & Nichido Life sells its products through banks property/casualty insurance agencies and an in-house sales staff.

Financial Performance

Tokio Marine's revenue has been trending upward during recent fiscal years. In fiscal 2014 (ended March) revenue increased 8% to ¥4166 billion largely due to an increase in overseas business. Domestic sales of automobile and fire policies also boosted earnings. Net income rose 42% to ¥184 billion in fiscal 2014 as fewer claims were paid and impairment losses on securities declined. Meanwhile operating cash flow increased 26% to ¥424 billion.

Strategy

The company is looking to expand both by offering new products and through acquisitions. It has increasingly built up its international operations lowering its dependence on the saturated Japanese market. In 2015 it opened its fifth branch in China. Tokio Marine Management opened a branch in Dallas that year as well.

In early 2014 Tokio Marine & Nichido Life launched a new medical insurance product —Medical Kit Love R —which is easier for customers with pre-existing medical conditions to purchase.

Mergers and Acquisitions

In 2015 Tokio Marine bought US-based HCC Insurance Holdings in a $7.5 billion transaction. The purchase significantly expands the company's presence in the US particularly in the specialty property/casualty market and will boost its international earnings. HCC sells coverage including directors' and officers' liability medical stop-loss insurance and policies for the marine aviation and energy industries.

Other countries targeted for growth efforts include China and India.

HISTORY

Company Background

After the US forced Japan to open to trade in 1854 Western marine insurers began operating there. In 1878 Japan's government organized backers for a Japanese marine insurance firm. Tokio Marine and Fire Insurance was founded the next year.

Tokio grew quickly insuring trading companies like Mitsubishi and Mitsui; it soon had offices in London Paris and New York. Increased competition in the 1890s forced it to curtail its foreign operations and begin using brokers in most other countries.

Victory in the Russo-Japanese War of 1904-05 buoyed the country but the economy slowed as it demobilized. Businesses responded by forming cooperative groups known as zaibatsu. Tokio Marine and Fire was allied with the Mitsubishi group.

Before WWI Tokio expanded by adding fire personal accident theft and auto insurance and it continued to buy foreign sales brokers. Japan's insurance industry consolidated in the 1920s and the company bought up smaller competitors. The 1923 Tokyo earthquake hit the industry hard but Tokio's new fire insurance operations had little exposure.

Most of Tokio's foreign operations were seized during WWII. In 1944 Tokio merged with Mitsubishi Marine Insurance and Meiji Fire Insurance. Business grew in WWII but wartime destruction left Tokio with nothing to insure and no money to pay claims.

After the war Tokio slowly recovered and resumed overseas operations. Although the US had dismantled the zaibatsu during occupation Tokio allied once again with Mitsubishi when Japan's government rebuilt most of the old groups as keiretsu.

During the 1950s and 1960s the company grew its personal lines adding homeowners coverage. Domestic business slowed during the 1970s and 1980s and Tokio boosted operations overseas. It added commercial property/casualty insurer Houston General Insurance (a US company sold in 1997) Tokio Reinsurance and interests in insurance and investment management firms.

In the 1980s the firm invested heavily in real estate through jusen (mortgage companies). Japan's overheated real estate market collapsed in the early 1990s dumping masses of nonperforming assets on jusen and their investors (the country's major banks and insurers including Tokio).

Deregulation began in 1996 and economic recession soon followed. In 1998 Tokio joined other members of the Mitsubishi group including Bank of Tokyo-Mitsubishi and Meiji Life Insurance to form investment banking pension and trust joint ventures. The firm also formed its own investment trust and allied with such foreign financial companies as BANK ONE and United Asset Management to develop new investment products. Brokerage firm Charles Schwab Tokio Marine Securities a joint venture was launched in 1999. That year Tokio consolidated its foreign reinsurance operations into Tokio Marine Global Re in Dublin Ireland and kicked off a business push that included

reorganizing its agent force and planning for on-line sales.

Millea Holdings was created in 2002 as the holding company for the merger between Tokio Marine and Fire and Nichido Fire and Marine. The two were combined and renamed Tokio Marine & Nichido Fire Insurance a subsidiary of Millea Holdings.

The company's 2005 acquisition of Real Seguros allowed the company to bring its life insurance products to Brazil (renamed Tokio Marine Seguradora). In 2006 Millea acquired Nisshin Fire and Marine Insurance Company as a separately operated subsidiary. In 2007 the firm purchased Asia General Holdings and its life insurance subsidiaries which operated in Singapore and Malaysia. It also purchased Japanese fire insurance provider Nihon Kousei Kyousaikai.

In 2008 Millea Holdings changed its name to Tokio Marine Holdings to reflect the positive brand recognition associated with the Tokio Marine name.

EXECUTIVES

EVP, Takaaki Tamai, age 66
President and CEO, Tsuyoshi Nagano
Managing Executive Officer, Masashi Oba
President Tokio Marine & Nichido Life, Toshifumi Kitazawa
EVP, Kazuo Kouduki
Chairman, Shuzo Sumi
Auditors: PricewaterhouseCoopers Aarata

LOCATIONS

HQ: Tokio Marine Holdings Inc
1-2-1 Marunouchi, Chiyoda-ku, Tokyo 100-0005
Phone: (81) 3 6212 3333
Web: www.tokiomarinehd.com/en/

2014 Sales

	% of total
Japan	71
US	16
Other regions	13
Total	**100**

PRODUCTS/OPERATIONS

2014 Sales

	% of total
Domestic property/casualty insurance	58
Overseas insurance	27
Domestic life & insurance	13
Finance & others	2
Total	**100**

Selected Mergers and Acquisitions

FY2012
Delphi Financial Group ($2.7 billion; Wilmington DE; specialty life insurer)

COMPETITORS

AIG	ING
Allianz	MS&AD Holdings
Aviva	Markel
Brit Insurance	Nippon Life Insurance
Dai-ichi Life	Prudential plc
Daido Life	Sompo Holdings
Equity Insurance	Sumitomo Life
Fuji Fire and Marine	Travelers Companies
HCC Insurance	Zurich Insurance Group
Hiscox	

HISTORICAL FINANCIALS

Company Type: Public

Income Statement

FYE: March 31

	ASSETS ($ mil.)	NET INCOME ($ mil.)	INCOME AS % OF ASSETS	EMPLOYEES
03/16	194,621	2,266	1.2%	36,902
03/15	174,110	2,062	1.2%	33,829
03/14	183,570	1,783	1.0%	33,310
03/13	191,614	1,377	0.7%	33,006
03/12	199,176	73	0.0%	30,831
Annual Growth	(0.6%)	135.9%	—	4.6%

2016 Year-End Financials

Return on assets: 1.1%	Dividends
Return on equity: 7.1%	Yield: 2.5%
Long-term debt ($ mil.): —	Payout: 31.6%
No. of shares (mil.): 754	Market value ($ mil.): 25,576
Sales ($ mil): 39,800	

	STOCK PRICE ($) FY Close	P/E High/Low		PER SHARE ($) Earnings	Dividends	Book Value
03/16	33.89	0	0	3.00	0.87	41.15
03/15	37.78	0	0	2.70	0.73	39.55
03/14	30.16	—	—	2.32	0.96	34.59
03/13	28.72	—	—	1.79	0.00	32.74
03/12	27.66	—	—	0.10	0.00	29.53
Annual Growth	5.2%	—	—136.9%	—		8.7%

Tokyo Electric Power Company Holdings Inc

Japan Inc. would grind to a halt without Tokyo Electric Power Company (TEPCO) which supplies power to 29 million customers in Tokyo Yokohama and the rest of the Kanto region. As one of the world's largest electric utilities TEPCO's 190 power plants have the generating capacity of approximately 66023 MW primarily produced by thermal nuclear and hydroelectric power sources. In 2011 the company was plunged into a major crisis when its Fukushima Dai-ichi nuclear plant complex experienced a partial meltdown at three reactors and radioactive material was released in the wake of a major earthquake and tsunami.

Geographic Reach The company has offices in Tokyo Washington DC and London.

Operations

The company operates through four reportable segments: Fuel & Power Power Grid Customer Service and Corporate. Fuel & Power includes the sales of electricity generated by thermal power stations procurement of fuel development of thermal power stations. and investment in fuel businesses. Power Grid includes sales of electricity via transmission lines substations and distribution lines sales of electricity generated by hydro power stations the construction and maintenance of transmission/distribution lines and telecommunication equipment research and the acquisition and maintenance of land and buildings for facilities. Customer Service (95% of revenues in 2015) covers TEPCO's customer service activities and infrastructure. Corporate covers supporting management services common to all TEPCO's companies and nuclear power generation.

Through affiliates TEPCO also offers cable TV and Internet services international consulting and investing in non-Japan-based independent power producers. Other businesses include construction real estate and transportation companies.

Sales and Marketing The company supplies power to 29 million customers.

Financial Performance

TEPCO's net revenues has been increasing in last three years (2013-2015). In fiscal 2015 the company's net revenues increased 3% due to an increase in Customer Service revenues. After experiencing net losses (2011-2013) largely related to the Fukushima plant disaster the company posted a net income in 2014 and 2015. In fiscal 2015 the company's net income increased by 3% due to higher net revenues and the absence of loss on decommissioning of Units 5 and 6 of the Fukushima nuclear plant.

The company's operating cash inflow increased by 37% in 2015.

Strategy

TEPCO is selling assets to pay off its massive debt.

In 2015 the company and Chubu Electric Power agreed to form a comprehensive alliance encompassing the entire supply chain from upstream investment and fuel procurement through power generation. A new joint venture company JERA Co. will collectively handle companies' fuel-related business as well as thermal power generation facility development and replacement in Japan and overseas.

HISTORY

Company Background

The Tokyo Electric Power Company (TEPCO) descended from Tokyo Electric Light which was formed in 1883. In 1887 the company switched on Japan's first power plant a 25-KW fossil fuel generator. Fossil fuels were the main source of electricity in Japan until 1912 when long-distance transmission techniques became more efficient making hydroelectric power cheaper.

In 1938 Japan nationalized electric utilities despite strong objections from Yasuzaemon Matsunaga a leader in Japan's utility industry and former president of the Japan Electric Association. After WWII Matsunaga championed public ownership of Japan's power companies which helped in 1951 to establish the current system of 10 regional companies each with a service monopoly. Tokyo Electric Power was the largest. That year it was listed on the Tokyo Stock Exchange and was regulated by the Ministry of International Trade and Industry. (The ministry has regulated electric utilities since 1965.)

Fossil fuel plants made a comeback in Japan in the postwar era because they could be built more economically than hydroelectric plants. When the OPEC oil embargo of the 1970s demonstrated Japan's dependence on foreign oil TEPCO increased its use of liquefied natural gas (LNG) and nuclear energy sources. (It brought its first nuke online in 1971.) In 1977 it formed the Energy Conservation Center to promote conservation and related legislation.

To further reduce its oil dependence TEPCO joined other US and Japanese firms in building a coal gasification plant in California's Mojave Desert in 1982. Two years later TEPCO announced it would begin building its first coal-burning generator since the oil crisis. It established Tokyo Telecommunication Network (TTNet) a partnership to provide telecommunications services in 1986 and TEPCO Cable TV in 1989.

As part of its interest in alternative energy systems TEPCO established a global environment department in 1990 to conduct R&D on energy and the environment. Its environmental program has included reforestation and fuel cell research.

Liberalization in 1995 allowed Japan's electric utilities to buy power from independent power producers; TEPCO quickly lined up 10 suppliers. The company proceeded with energy experimentation in 1996 trying a 6000-KW sodium-sulfur battery at a Yokohama transformer station. The next year the company announced that it would become the first electric utility to sell liquefied natural gas as part of its energy mix and finished building the world's largest nuclear plant.

To gain experience in deregulating markets TEPCO invested in US power generating company Orion Power in 1999. (It agreed to sell its 5% stake to Reliant Energy in 2001.) At home the firm joined Microsoft and SOFTBANK to form SpeedNet which provides Internet access over TTNet's network. In 2000 TEPCO got its first taste of deregulation when large customers (accounting for about a third of the market) began choosing their electricity suppliers. Also in 2000 TEPCO joined a group of nine Japanese electric companies to create POWEREDCOM. (In 2005 TEPCO sold its stake in POWEREDCOM to KDDI in order to focus on its core power business).

In 2001 TEPCO joined up with Sumitomo and Electricite de France to build Vietnam's first independent power plant.

To raise cash in 2006 Mirant (now GenOn Energy) sold its power plants in the Philippines to TEPCO and Marubeni for $3.4 billion.

Public confidence was shaken by a rash of accidents within Japan's nuclear industry. The company had struggled to restore its credibility after the Japanese government shut down TEPCO's 17 nuclear reactors due to safety concerns prompted by the company's admittance of falsifying safety data to cover up faults at several of its nuclear facilities in 2002. In 2009 it reopened the Kashiwazaki-Kariwa Nuclear Power Station which was closed in 2007 due to a major earthquake in the region.

Through affiliates TEPCO also offers cable TV and Internet services international consulting and investing in non-Japan-based independent power producers. Other businesses include construction real estate and transportation companies.

The company is developing new green energy sources such as wind and solar in order to meet carbon emission reduction targets. In 2009 the company agreed to build a major solar project in Kawasaki Kanagawa to serve about 5900 households. In 2010 it teamed up with Toyota Tsusho to fund wind power company Eurus Energy Holdings which acquired solar power company Jindosun Park in 2011. Jindosun oversees the generation of 2974 KW of electricity mostly in South Korea and activated a 45000 KW plant in the US in mid-2011.

Broadening its international power assets in 2011 the company agreed to buy 12% of Thailand-based independent power producer Electricity Generating PCL for about $274 million. However the daunting financial impact of the Fukushima disaster has cast a pall over the company's international expansion plans.

In 2012 it agreed to sell its 67.5% stake in Australian power station Loy Yang A to the plant's minority owner AGL Resources for $1.6 billion.

EXECUTIVES

EVP, Hiroshi Yamaguchi
EVP, Zengo Aizawa
President, Naomi Hirose
EVP, Yoshiyuki Ishizaki
Chairman, Kazuhiko Shimokobe
Auditors: Ernst & Young ShinNihon LLC

LOCATIONS

HQ: Tokyo Electric Power Company Holdings Inc
1-1-3 Uchisaiwai-cho, Chiyoda-Ku, Tokyo 100-8560
Phone: (81) 3 6373 1111
Web: www.tepco.co.jp

PRODUCTS/OPERATIONS

Selected Subsidiaries

TEPCO CABLE TELEVISION Inc. (85% cable television)
TEPCO SYSTEMS CORPORATION (information software
  and services)
Toden Kogyo Co. Ltd. (facilities construction and
  maintenance)
Toden Real Estate Co. Inc. (property management)
Tokyo Densetsu Service Co. Ltd. (facilities construction
  and maintenance)
Tokyo Electric Power Environmental Engineering
  Company Incorporated (facilities construction and
  maintenance)
Tokyo Electric Power Services Company Limited
  (facilities construction and maintenance)

COMPETITORS

Chubu Electric Power	KDDI
Chugoku Electric Power	KEPCO
Hokkaido Electric	Korea Electric Power
Power	Kyushu Electric Power
Hokuriku Electric	NTT
Power	Osaka Gas
Internet Initiative	Shikoku Electric
Japan	Tohoku Electric Power
Jinpan International	Tokyo Gas

HISTORICAL FINANCIALS

Company Type: Public

Income Statement

FYE: March 31

	REVENUE ($ mil.)	NET INCOME ($ mil.)	NET PROFIT MARGIN	EMPLOYEES
03/16	54,052	1,253	2.3%	45,710
03/15	56,696	3,763	6.6%	46,045
03/14	64,245	4,249	6.6%	45,744
03/13	63,514	(7,283)	—	48,757
03/12	65,213	(9,528)	—	52,046
Annual Growth	(4.6%)	—	—	(3.2%)

2016 Year-End Financials

Debt ratio: 0.4%
Return on equity: 6.5%
Cash ($ mil.): 12,677
Current ratio: 0.83
Long-term debt ($ mil.): 42,910

No. of shares (mil.): 1,603
Dividends
  Yield: —
  Payout: —
Market value ($ mil.): 8,693

	STOCK PRICE ($) FY Close	P/E High/Low		PER SHARE ($) Earnings	Dividends	Book Value
03/16	5.42	0	0	0.23	0.00	12.19
03/15	4.00	0	0	0.76	0.00	10.80
03/14	4.12	—	—	0.86	0.00	9.55
03/13	2.01	—	—	(4.54)	0.00	7.56
03/12	2.40	—	—	(5.95)	0.00	6.19
Annual Growth	22.6%	—	—	—	—	18.5%

Tokyo Gas Co., Ltd.

Auditors: KPMG AZSA LLC

LOCATIONS

HQ: Tokyo Gas Co., Ltd.
1-5-20 Kaigan, Minato-ku, Tokyo 105-8527
Phone: (81) 3 5400 7736   **Fax:** 646 865-0592
Web: www.tokyo-gas.co.jp

HISTORICAL FINANCIALS

Company Type: Public

Income Statement

FYE: March 31

	REVENUE ($ mil.)	NET INCOME ($ mil.)	NET PROFIT MARGIN	EMPLOYEES
03/16	16,782	996	5.9%	16,998
03/15	19,107	798	4.2%	16,835
03/14	20,462	1,050	5.1%	17,076
03/13	20,359	1,080	5.3%	16,832
03/12	21,385	561	2.6%	16,528
Annual Growth	(5.9%)	15.4%	—	0.7%

2016 Year-End Financials

Debt ratio: 0.2%
Return on equity: 10.2%
Cash ($ mil.): 1,516
Current ratio: 1.55
Long-term debt ($ mil.): 5,773

No. of shares (mil.): —
Dividends
  Yield: 1.7%
  Payout: —
Market value ($ mil.): —

	STOCK PRICE ($) FY Close	P/E High/Low		PER SHARE ($) Earnings	Dividends	Book Value
03/16	18.63	1	0	0.42	0.33	4.10
03/15	25.22	1	0	0.33	0.37	3.65
03/14	20.48	—	—	0.42	0.42	3.97
03/13	21.73	—	—	0.42	0.00	3.91
03/12	47.59	—	—	0.22	0.00	4.03
Annual Growth	(20.9%)	—	—	17.8%	—	0.4%

TonenGeneral Sekiyu K.K.

TonenGeneral Sekiyu is a leading Japanese refiner that came into being in 2000 as the result of the merger of Japanese refiners Tonen and General Sekiyu both affiliates of global oil and gas behemoth Exxon Mobil. TonenGeneral Sekiyu (50.02%-owned by Exxon Mobil) combines Tonen's 505000 barrels a day of refining capacity in Kawasaki and Wakayama with General Sekiyu's 156000 barrels a day of capacity at Sakai. It also operates a 100000 barrels-a-day refinery at Nishihara (in Okinawa) through its 87.5%-owned Nansei Sekiyu subsidiary. TonenGeneral Sekiyu operates gas stations across Japan under the Esso General and Mobil brands. In 2015 JX Holdings agreed to merge with TonenGeneral Sekiyu.

The company is trying to diversify its sources of crude oil supply (about 70% comes from the Middle East) and upgrade its refineries in order to reduce costs.

EXECUTIVES

President, Jun Mutoh
VP, Takashi Hirose
Senior Managing Director, Tomohide Miyata
Senior Managing Director, Yasushi Onoda
Auditors: PricewaterhouseCoopers Aarata

LOCATIONS

HQ: TonenGeneral Sekiyu K.K.
1-8-15 Kohnan, Minato-ku, Tokyo 108-8005
Phone: (81) 3 6713 4400
Web: www.tonengeneral.co.jp

PRODUCTS/OPERATIONS

2015 Sales

	% of total
Oil	90
Chemical	10
Total	**100**

2015 Sales

	% of total
Japan	80
Other	20
Total	**100**

COMPETITORS

Idemitsu Kosan	JX Nippon Oil & Energy
JX Nippon Mining &	Showa Shell Sekiyu
Metals	

HISTORICAL FINANCIALS

Company Type: Public

Income Statement

FYE: December 31

	REVENUE ($ mil.)	NET INCOME ($ mil.)	NET PROFIT MARGIN	EMPLOYEES
12/15	21,829	0	0.0%	3,383
12/14	28,924	(117)	—	3,512
12/13	30,876	218	0.7%	2,921
12/12	32,566	635	2.0%	2,805
12/11	34,594	1,715	5.0%	2,171
Annual Growth	(10.9%)	(87.5%)	—	11.7%

2015 Year-End Financials

Debt ratio: 0.2%
Return on equity: 0.0%
Cash ($ mil.): 832
Current ratio: 0.83
Long-term debt ($ mil.): 1,794

No. of shares (mil.): 364
Dividends
  Yield: —
  Payout: —
Market value ($ mil.): —

Toray Industries, Inc.

Auditors: Ernst & Young ShinNihon LLC

LOCATIONS

HQ: Toray Industries, Inc.
Nihonbashi Mitsui Tower, 2-1-1 Nihonbashi-
Muromachi, Chuo-ku, Tokyo 103-8666
Phone: (81) 3 3245 5201   **Fax:** (81) 3 3245 5054
Web: www.toray.co.jp

HISTORICAL FINANCIALS

Company Type: Public

Income Statement

FYE: March 31

	REVENUE ($ mil.)	NET INCOME ($ mil.)	NET PROFIT MARGIN	EMPLOYEES
03/16	18,739	802	4.3%	45,839
03/15	16,759	591	3.5%	45,789
03/14	17,804	577	3.2%	45,881
03/13	16,922	515	3.0%	42,584
03/12	19,366	782	4.0%	40,227
Annual Growth	(0.8%)	0.6%	—	3.3%

Debt ratio: 0.2% No. of shares (mil.): 1,599
Return on equity: 9.3% Dividends
Cash ($ mil.): 1,070 Yield: 1.1%
Current ratio: 1.77 Payout: 41.9%
Long-term debt ($ mil.): 4,544 Market value ($ mil.): 27,078

	STOCK PRICE ($) FY Close	P/E High/Low		PER SHARE ($) Earnings	Dividends	Book Value
03/16	16.93	2	0	0.50	0.19	5.27
03/15	84.01	2	1	0.37	0.18	5.14
03/14	66.53	—	—	0.07	0.20	1.12
03/13	68.08	—	—	0.06	0.00	1.02
03/12	74.36	—	—	0.09	0.00	1.01
Annual Growth	(30.9%)	—	—	53.1%	—	51.2%

Toronto Dominion Bank

The Toronto-Dominion Bank wants to score financial TDs at home and abroad. Also known as TD Bank or TD Financial the company ranks among the world's top online financial services firms and is one of the largest banks in Canada where it operates more than 1100 branches under the TD Trust banner. US subsidiary TD Bank N.A. has another 1300 branches in about 15 eastern states. TD also offers commercial financial and advisory services. Other units include TD Insurance TD Asset Management (mutual funds) and TD Securities (investment banking equities and foreign exchange). Its TD Waterhouse is the largest online brokerage in the UK and Canada; TD Bank also owns 45% of US discount brokerage TD Ameritrade.

OperationsTD Bank operates three main business segments: Canadian Retail U.S. Retail and Wholesale Banking.

Canadian Retail which generates nearly 65% of the bank's revenue provides a full range of traditional banking products and other financial services to customers in the Canadian personal and commercial banking businesses including wealth and insurance services. Within this segment under its TD Canada Trust brand the bank offers personal and small business banking products and services to nearly 15 million customers through its network of 1165 branches.

U.S. Retail which brings in another roughly 25% of revenue operates under the brand TD Bank and comprises the bank's US-based retail commercial and wealth management services. Retail provides a full suite of financial products and services through its network of 1300-plus branches located along the east coast of the US.

Wholesale Banking which contributes just under 10% of bank revenue provides a variety of capital market investment banking and corporate banking products and services. Operating under the TD Securities brand this segment also provides services including underwriting and distribution of new debt and equity issues offering advice on strategic acquisitions and divestitures and meeting the investment brokerage needs of clients. Geographic ReachTD Bank mainly operates through its more than 1165 branches spread across Canada. Its US subsidiary TD Bank N.A. operates another 1300 branches in 15 eastern states from Maine to Florida.

Sales and Marketing

Under the TD Securities brand the bank targets highly-rated companies governments and institutions in key financial markets around the world.

Interested in building its brand across the US the bank boosted its marketing and business development spending by 9% to C$750 million in fiscal 2014. By comparison in 2012 the bank spent C$668 million or 12% less than in fiscal 2014. Financial PerformanceNote: Growth rates may differ after conversion to US dollars.TD Bank enjoyed its seventh straight year of revenue growth in fiscal 2014 (ended October) thanks to an improving economy domestically and in the US. Revenue jumped by 8% to C$36.65 billion ($32.7 billion) thanks to higher interest income from strong loan and deposit volume growth from the US Retail and Canadian Retail and from higher trading-related interest income from the Wholesale Banking segment. The bank also reported higher non-interest income mostly as its Canadian Retail segment collected more trading and management fees from wealth asset growth. The bank's net income also spiked by 20% to C$7.63 billion ($6.82 billion) in 2014 mostly thanks to higher revenues a decline in loan loss provisions and because the bank paid less interest on its deposits.

Operations provided C$25.97 billion ($23.2 billion) or 6% less cash than in 2013 mostly as the bank paid back more of its securitization liabilities as their terms expired.

Strategy

To expand its consumer base TD has made its services more convenient to customers through a series of actions. In 2015 it launched its new SMS-based customer service for mobile phones in Canada via "TDHELP" making it the first major bank in Canada to offer such a service. In 2014 it opened a new branch in the fast-growing town of Milton in Ontario Canada. It's also been growing its credit accounts through smart acquisitions in recent years. In late 2015 the company along with brokerage arm TD Ameritrade agreed to buy US online brokerage and banking rival Scottrade in a two-step $4 billion transaction. Scottrade subsidiary Scottrade Bank will merge into TD Bank N.A. while the rest of Scottrade will merge into TD Ameritrade greatly expanding that company's branch network.

In 2013 the bank acquired a controlling stake of Aimia's Aeroplan credit card portfolio gaining new business from non-TD customers and new revenue streams from their lines of credit. Similarly in late 2012 TD Bank and Target Corporation inked a deal for the purchase of the retailer's existing US Visa and private label credit card portfolio (with a gross outstanding balance of $5.9 billion). As part of an associated seven-year program agreement TD was granted exclusive rights as the issuer of the Target-branded Visa and private label credit cards to Target's US customers. Both deals have been paying off as the bank reported its eighth year of revenue growth in fiscal 2014 largely thanks to these relatively new revenue sources. To raise capital and better focus on its core operations TD Bank has also divested some of its businesses in recent years. In 2013 for example bank subsidiary TD Waterhouse Canada sold its TD Waterhouse Institutional Services business to a subsidiary of National Bank of Canada for $250 million in cash.

Mergers and Acquisitions

In 2014 TD Bank acquired the remaining stake in NatWest Stockbrokers Limited from National Westminster Bank (NatWest). UK-subsidiary TD Direct Investing Limited had been partnering with NatWest for the past dozen years to provide stock-broking services to NatWest and Royal Bank of Scotland (RBS) customers under the NatWest Stockbrokers and RBS Direct Trader brands.

HISTORY

The Bank of Toronto was established in 1855 by flour traders who wanted their own banking facilities. Its growth encouraged another group of businessmen to found the Dominion Bank in 1869. Dominion emphasized commercial banking and invested heavily in railways and construction.

As the new nation expanded westward both banks established branch networks. They helped fund Canada's primary industries –dairy mining oil pulp and textiles. True to its pioneering spirit a Bank of Toronto official claimed to be the first to have set up a branch office with the help of aviation (in Manitoba in the 1920s).

The demand for agricultural products and commodities dropped after WWI but production continued full throttle creating a world grain glut that helped trigger the stock market crash of 1929. Both the Bank of Toronto and Dominion Bank contracted during the 1930s. After growing during and subsequent to WWII The Bank of Toronto and Dominion Bank decided to increase their capital base merging into a 450-branch bank in 1955.

In the 1970s TD Bank opened offices in Bangkok Beirut and Frankfurt among other cities abroad. During the 1980s it was active in making loans to less-developed countries. After the deregulation of the Canadian securities industry in 1987 then-CEO Richard Thomson reduced international lending and began focusing on brokerage activities. The strategy paid off when several Latin American countries fell behind on their loans in the late 1980s.

As the North American economy slowed in the early 1990s TD Bank's nonperforming loans increased and with it its loan loss reserves. The bank still made acquisitions including Central Guaranty Trust (1993) and Lancaster Financial Holdings (1995 investment banking). It worked to build its financial services expanding its range of service offerings and geographic coverage and buying New York-based Waterhouse Investor Services (1996); 97% of Australia-based Pont Securities (1997); and California-based Kennedy Cabot & Co. (1997). In 1998 the bank sold its payroll services to Ceridian and its Waterhouse Securities unit bought US discount brokerage Jack White & Co.

That year the government nixed TD Bank's merger with Canadian Imperial on the same day it voided the Royal Bank of Canada/Bank of Montreal deal. The banks believed the consolidation was necessary to stave off foreign banks' encroachment into Canada but the government had domestic antitrust concerns: Though Canada has one-tenth the population of the US its five top banks all ranked in the top 15 in North America.

In 1999 TD Bank bought Trimark Financial's retail trust banking business and spun off part of Waterhouse Investor Services which would become part of TD Waterhouse Group. That year the bank ramped up its focus on Internet banking.

Not giving up on acquisition-fueled growth in 2000 the company bought CT Financial Services (now TD Canada Trust) from British American Tobacco. As a condition for government approval TD Bank had to sell its MasterCard credit portfolio (sold to Citibank Canada) and a dozen southern Ontario branches (to Bank of Montreal).

The company's plans to hitch a ride on the Wal-Mart gravy train derailed in 2001. Arrangements to open bank branches in some US-based Wal-Mart stores were squelched by regulators enforcing the banking and commerce barrier. TD Bank later closed all of its existing branches (more than 100 in all) inside Canadian Wal-Marts as part of a broader restructuring.

TD Bank suffered its first-ever annual loss during fiscal year 2002. Write-downs on loans to telecommunications technology and energy firms contributed mightily to the dismal results.

Frustrated by limited growth opportunities at home in 2005 TD Bank ventured south of the border with its purchase of a stake in Banknorth. TD Bank paid about $4.8 billion in cash and stock for its original 51% stake (it bought the rest in 2007). Additionally in 2006 the company assumed about a 40% ownership in TD AMERITRADE as part of the sale of TD Waterhouse.

In 2008 the company acquired New Jersey-based Commerce Bancorp. The $8.5 billion acquisition deal added some 450 branches along the eastern seaboard to TD Bank's US network and exemplified the company's plans to expand abroad. TD merged Commerce with its TD Banknorth unit to create TD Bank.

EXECUTIVES

Group Head US Banking; President and CEO TD Bank, Mike Pedersen
SVP Corporate Development, Riaz E. Ahmed
Group Head Wholesale Banking and Chairman President and CEO TD Securities, Robert E. (Bob) Dorrance, age 60, $500,000 total compensation
EVP Insurance and President and CEO TD Insurance, Kenn W. Lalonde
President and CEO, Bharat B. Masrani, age 60, $584,650 total compensation
Group Head Risk Management and Chief Risk Officer, Mark R. Chauvin
EVP Canadian Business Banking, Paul C. Douglas
Group Head Direct Channels Technology Marketing and Corporate & Public Affairs, Colleen M. Johnston, $490,274 total compensation
Group Head Canadian Personal Banking, Theresa L. (Teri) Currie
Group Head Legal Compliance and Anti-Money Laundering Financial Crimes and Fraud Management Enterprise Projects and General Counsel, Norie C. Campbell
COO TD Bank USA, Greg Braca
EVP Human Resources, Sue Cummings
Chairman, Brian M. Levitt, age 69
Deputy Chair, Frank J. McKenna, age 68
Auditors: Ernst & Young LLP

LOCATIONS

HQ: Toronto Dominion Bank
Toronto-Dominion Centre, King Street West & Bay Street, Toronto, Ontario M5K 1A2
Phone: 416 944-6367   **Fax:** 416 982-6166
Web: www.td.com

PRODUCTS/OPERATIONS

2013 Sales

	% of total
Interest	
Loans	55
Securities	11
Noninterest	
Insurance revenue	11
Investments & securities services	9
Serice charges	6
Others	8
Total	**100**

Selected Canadian Subsidiaries

CT Financial Assurance Company (99.9%)
Meloche Monnex Inc.
  Security National Insurance Company
  Primmum Insurance Company
  TD Direct Insurance Inc.
  TD General Insurance Company
  TD Home and Auto Insurance Company
TD Asset Finance Corp.
TD Asset Management Inc.
  TD Waterhouse Private Investment Counsel Inc.
TD Investment Services Inc.
TD Life Insurance Company

TD Mortgage Corporation
  The Canada Trust Company
  TD Pacific Mortgage Corporation
TD Mortgage Investment Corporation
TD Nordique Investments Limited
TD Parellel Private Equity Investors Ltd.
TD Securities Inc.
TD Timberlane Investments Limited
  TD McMurray Investments Limited
  TD Redpath Investments Limited
  TD Riverside Investments Limited
TD Vermillion Holdings ULC
  TD Financial International Ltd. (Bermuda)
  Canada Trustco International Limited (Barbados)
  TD Reinsurance (Barbados) Inc.
  Toronto Dominion International Inc. (Barbados)
TD Waterhouse Canada Inc.
  thinkorswim Canada
Truscan Property Corporation

Selected US Subsidiaries

TDAM USA Inc.
Toronto Dominion Holdings (U.S.A.) Inc.
  TD Holdings II Inc.
  TD Securities (USA) LLC
  Toronto Dominion (Texas) LLC
  Toronto Dominion Capital (U.S.A.) Inc.
  Toronto Dominion Investments Inc.

Selected Other International Subsidiaries

Internaxx Bank S.A. (Luxembourg)
NatWest Personal Financial Management Limited (50% UK)
  NatWest Stockbrokers Limited
TD Ireland
  TD Global Finance
TD Waterhouse Bank N.V. (The Netherlands)
TD Waterhouse Investor Services (UK) Limited
  TD Waterhouse Investor Services (Europe) Limited (UK)
Toronto Dominion (South East Asia) Limited (Singapore)

COMPETITORS

BMO Financial Group	Edward Jones
Bank of America	FMR
Berkshire Hills	KeyCorp
Bancorp	Laurentian Bank
CI Financial	Morgan Stanley
CIBC	National Bank of
Caisses centrale	Canada
Desjardins	RBC Financial Group
Charles Schwab	Scotiabank
E*TRADE Financial	Sovereign Bank

HISTORICAL FINANCIALS

Company Type: Public

Income Statement

FYE: October 31

	ASSETS ($ mil.)	NET INCOME ($ mil.)	INCOME AS % OF ASSETS	EMPLOYEES
10/16	879,748	6,488	0.7%	81,233
10/15	839,261	5,937	0.7%	81,483
10/14	844,306	6,821	0.8%	81,137
10/13	824,651	6,092	0.7%	78,748
10/12	813,315	6,187	0.8%	78,397
Annual Growth	**2.0%**	**1.2%**	**—**	**0.9%**

2016 Year-End Financials

Return on assets: 0.7%
Return on equity: 12.5%
Long-term debt ($ mil.): —
No. of shares (mil.): 1,857
Sales ($ mil): 30,934
Dividends
Yield: 4.7%
Payout: 70.8%
Market value ($ mil.): 84,280

	STOCK PRICE ($) FY Close	P/E High/Low		Earnings	PER SHARE ($) Dividends	Book Value
10/16	45.38	10	8	3.49	1.62	29.20
10/15	41.02	10	9	3.20	1.52	26.80
10/14	49.26	22	10	3.70	1.69	26.49
10/13	91.72	26	22	3.30	1.59	26.29
10/12	81.34	25	20	3.39	1.44	26.01
Annual Growth	**(13.6%)**	**—**	**—**	**0.7%**	**2.9%**	**2.9%**

Toshiba Corp

Auditors: Ernst & Young ShinNihon LLC

LOCATIONS

HQ: Toshiba Corp
1-1-1 Shibaura, Minato-ku, Tokyo 105-8001
Phone: (81) 3 3457 4511   **Fax:** (81) 3 3456 1631
Web: www.toshiba.co.jp

HISTORICAL FINANCIALS

Company Type: Public

Income Statement

FYE: March 31

	REVENUE ($ mil.)	NET INCOME ($ mil.)	NET PROFIT MARGIN	EMPLOYEES
03/16	52,569	(4,096)	—	187,809
03/15	56,723	(315)	—	198,741
03/14	63,811	492	0.8%	200,260
03/13	63,079	824	1.3%	206,087
03/12	75,639	898	1.2%	209,784
Annual Growth	**(8.7%)**	**—**	**—**	**(2.7%)**

2016 Year-End Financials

Debt ratio: 0.2%
Return on equity: (-64.9%)
Cash ($ mil.): 8,635
Current ratio: 1.13
Long-term debt ($ mil.): 7,402
No. of shares (mil.): —
Dividends
Yield: —
Payout: —
Market value ($ mil.): —

	STOCK PRICE ($) FY Close	P/E High/Low		Earnings	PER SHARE ($) Dividends	Book Value
03/16	11.65	—	—	(0.97)	0.00	0.69
03/15	25.17	—	—	(0.07)	0.44	2.13
03/14	25.41	3	2	0.12	0.47	2.81
03/13	30.40	2	1	0.19	0.52	2.60
03/12	26.57	2	1	0.21	0.51	2.50
Annual Growth	**(18.6%)**	**—**	**—**	**—**	**—**	**—**
(27.4%)						

Total SA

With operations in more than 130 countries TOTAL engages in all aspects of the petroleum industry including Upstream operations (oil and gas exploration development and production LNG) and Marketing and Services operations (refining marketing and the trading and shipping of crude oil and petroleum products). The company also produces base chemicals (petrochemicals and fertilizers) and specialty chemicals for the industrial and consumer markets (rubber processing adhesives resins and electroplating). In addition TOTAL has interests in power generation.

Geographic Reach

TOTAL has operations in 130 countries. France accounts for nearly a quarter of sales with the rest of Europe generating about 48%.

Operations

The company's business is divided into three main segments: Upstream Marketing and Services and Refining and Chemicals.

TOTAL has a refining capacity of 2.2 million barrels a day and explores for and produces oil and gas in 50 countries and had reserves of 11.5 billion barrels of oil equivalent (50% of which were proved developed reserves) in 2014. Liquids (crude oil condensates natural gas liquids and bitumen) represented 46% of these reserves; natural gas the remaining 54%. With more than 60 years of experience in the field its expertise covers natural gas as well as liquid natural gas (LNG) and liquefied petroleum gas (LPG).

The company's Marketing and Services segment has more than 15500 service stations.

TOTAL is also one of the world's largest integrated chemical producers and a leader in each of its markets —Petrochemicals and Fertilizers and Specialties.

Financial Performance

In 2014 the company's net revenues decreased by 10% due to an 11% drop in Upstream sales 7% in Refining & Chemicals and 4% in Marketing & Services .

TOTAL's net income dropped by 62% in 2014 due to lower revenues the impact of purchases and an increase in depreciation depletion and amortization of tangible assets and mineral interests.

In 2014 the company's cash flow decreased by 10% due to a drop in net income and changes in working capital as a result of higher inventories and accounts receivable.

Strategy

In 2014 TOTAL teamed up with Denmark's DONG Energy to develop the Edradour gas field in the West of Shetland area and to acquire a 60% stake in the neighboring Glenlivet discovery. The fields are expected to yield more than 65 million barrels of oil equivalent of reserves. That year it also signed an LNG (liquefied natural gas) Cooperation Agreement strengthening the partnership between TOTAL and CNOOC. Under the terms of an existing 15-year contract TOTAL has been supplying China with up to 1 million tons per year of LNG since 2010. The new deal sets a framework for an additional supply of 1 million tons per year of LNG as well as further cooperation throughout the LNG value chainTo raise cash and to focus on its core businesses in 2015 Total agreed to sell its gas station network and commercial sales supply and logistics assets in Turkey to Demirören for euro 325 million (around $356 million). It also agreed to sell all of its interests in the FUKA and SIRGE gas pipelines and the St. Fergus Gas Terminal to North Sea Midstream Partners for £585 million ($905 million).

In 2014 TOTAL sold Total Coal South Africa its coal-producing affiliate to Exxaro Resources for $472 million. The deal is part of the company's 2012-14 asset sale program designed to help it more actively manage its portfolio. In 2014 the company also entered into a definitive agreement for the acquisition by Temasek of TOTAL's entire remaining 10.4% stake in GTT (Gaztransport & Technigaz). To raise cash in 2014 affiliate Total E&P USA signed an agreement to sell its 25% interest in Cardinal Gas Services LLC a midstream company in Ohio's Utica shale play to E1 Corporation and a consortium led by Samchully both from Korea for about $450 million.

Over the long term the company is committed to building its leading position in all three segments of its business through acquisitions divesti-

tures and investments. It is investing heavily in refinery expansion in Jubail Saudi Arabia and in Port Arthur Texas. Other long-term growth initiatives include teaming up with Gazprom and Statoil to develop the vast Shtokman gas field in the Barents Sea.

In 2014 the company signed an agreement with Pavilion Gas a subsidiary of Pavilion Energy for the supply of 0.7 million tonnes per year of liquefied natural gas to Asia including Singapore starting in 2018.

In 2013 the Upstream segment launched major projects in Canada Congo Nigeria and Russia and acquired 20% of the high-potential Libra field in Brazil. TOTAL continued to extend its oil and gas acreage that year by obtaining licenses in promising exploration areas particularly in Bolivia Brazil Iraq and South Africa. It made large discoveries in Iraq and Argentina in 2013.

Mergers and Acquisitions

To boost its access to gas assets in Papua New Guinea in 2016 TOTAL made a bid to acquire InterOil but was outbid by Exxon Mobil.

To boost its energy storage portfolio in 2016 TOTAL purchased battery maker SAFT (Societe des Accumulateurs Fixes et de Traction) for $1.1 billion. The deal complemented TOTAL's strategy to achieve future growth in the renewable energy sector.

As part of its strategy of developing higher-value-added polymers and differentiating itself in markets away from commodity plastics in 2015 the company acquired 68% of Germany's Polyblend which makes polymer plastics intended primarily for the automotive industry.

HISTORY

Company Background

A French consortium formed the Compagnie Française des Petroles (CFP) in 1924 to develop an oil industry for the country. Lacking reserves within its borders France had a 24% stake in the Turkish Petroleum Company (TPC) acquired from Germany in 1920 as part of the spoils from WWI. When oil was discovered in Iraq in 1927 the TPC partners (CFP; Anglo-Persian Oil later BP; Royal Dutch Shell; and a consortium of five US oil companies) became major players in the oil game.

After WWII CFP diversified its sources for crude opening a supply in 1947 from the Venezuelan company Pantepec and making several major discoveries in colonial Algeria in 1956. It also began supplying crude to Japan South Korea and Taiwan in the 1950s. To market its products in North Africa and France and other European areas it introduced the brand name TOTAL in 1954. It began making petrochemicals in 1956. Decades later in 1985 the company adopted its brand name as part of its new name TOTAL Compagnie Française des Petroles shortened in 1991 to TOTAL.

EXECUTIVES

SVP Human Resources and Corporate Communications, Jean-Jacques Guilbaud, age 64

President Exploration and Production, Yves-Louis Darricarrere, age 65

President Marketing and Services and New Energies, Philippe Boisseau, age 54

President Exploration and Production, Arnaud Breuillac

CEO Total E&P Nigeria, Elisabeth Proust

CFO, Patrick de La Chevardiˉre

Chairman and CEO, Patrick Pouyanne, age 53

CEO Total E&P Canada, Laurent Maurel

President Refining and Chemicals, Philippe Sauquet

CIO, Patrick Hereng

President Gas Division, Laurent Vivier

President of the Executive Committee, Patrick Pouyann

Auditors: KPMG Audit

LOCATIONS

HQ: Total SA
2, place Jean Millier, La Defense 6, Courbevoie, La Defense 92400
Phone: (33) 1 47 44 45 46   **Fax:** (33) 1 47 44 49 44
Web: www.total.com

2014 Sales

	% of total
Europe	
France	22
Other countries	48
Africa	10
North America	10
Other regions	10
Total	**100**

PRODUCTS/OPERATIONS

2014 Sales

	% of total
Refining & Chemicals	45
Marketing & Services	45
Upstream	10
Total	**100**

COMPETITORS

Akzo Nobel	MOL
Ashland Inc.	Norsk Hydro ASA
BASF SE	Occidental Petroleum
BHP Billiton	PEMEX
BP	PETROBRAS
Chevron	Pakistan State Oil
ConocoPhillips	Petrłeos de
DuPont	Venezuela
Eni	Royal Dutch Shell
Exxon Mobil	Statoil
Imperial Oil	ZaZa Energy

HISTORICAL FINANCIALS

Company Type: Public

Income Statement

FYE: December 31

	REVENUE ($ mil.)	NET INCOME ($ mil.)	NET PROFIT MARGIN	EMPLOYEES
12/15	143,421	5,087	3.5%	96,019
12/14	212,018	4,244	2.0%	100,307
12/13	236,323	11,619	4.9%	98,799
12/12	240,279	14,095	5.9%	97,126
12/11	215,424	15,878	7.4%	96,104
Annual Growth	(9.7%)	(24.8%)	—	(0.0%)

2015 Year-End Financials

Debt ratio: 25.3%	No. of shares (mil.): —
Return on equity: 5.5%	Dividends
Cash ($ mil.): 23,269	Yield: 6.0%
Current ratio: 1.38	Payout: —
Long-term debt ($ mil.): 44,464	Market value ($ mil.): —

	STOCK PRICE ($) FY Close	P/E High/Low	PER SHARE ($) Earnings	Dividends	Book Value
12/15	44.95	26 20	2.16	2.70	39.76
12/14	51.20	40 26	1.86	3.16	39.69
12/13	61.27	17 13	5.12	3.11	44.08
12/12	52.01	12 9	6.22	2.86	42.57
12/11	51.11	11 7	7.04	0.00	39.04
Annual Growth	(3.2%)	— —	(25.6%)	—	0.5%

Toyota Industries Corporation (Japan)

If you're in the market for a forklift call Toyota Industries. Those on the hunt for a Corolla should call Toyota Motor. Toyota Industries builds forklifts and other lift trucks automotive parts (engines air-conditioning compressors and electronics) looms (which established the company in 1926) and chip package substrates. It also offers logistics services. The company does make three Toyota-brand passenger vehicles –the Vitz (or Yaris in the US) the RAV4 and the Mark X ZiO (only sold in Asia). Toyota Industries has more than 20 production plants in Asia Europe and North America. Its largest shareholders are Toyota Motor which owns nearly 25% of the company and DENSO which has a 9% stake.

Operations

Toyota Industries operates through five segments —automotive materials handling logistics textile machinery and other (chip package substrates). Automotive and materials handling together make up the bulk of sales (almost 90% in fiscal 2015). The automotive division which accounts for around half of the group's overall sales manufactures vehicles diesel and gasoline engines car air-conditioning compressors and electronics components. The materials handling division which accounts for 40% of sales makes industrial vehicles under four brand names —Aichi BT Raymond and Toyota.

Logistics which accounts for 5% of sales in 2015 is made up of four subsidiaries in Japan —Advanced Logistics Solutions Asahi Security Taikoh Transportation and Wanbishi Archives. These logistics companies offer freight trucking operate distribution centers store documents and provide cash management and security services. Textile machinery (loom manufacturing) and other (chip package substrates) combined account for 3% of sales.

Financial Performance

From 2014 to 2015 Toyota Industries' revenues increased by 8% due to growth across all segments except for textile machinery. Its net income increased 26% from 2014 to 2015 due to the increased sales along with cost reduction efforts rise in dividends income and interest income.

Materials handling equipment sales spiked 16% in 2015 resulting from the launch of new products worldwide; growth in the North America European and Chinese markets; and increased sales of lift trucks. In addition its logistics segment increased by 7% resulting from a rise in the sales of its commissioned logistics operations. Its automobile business also jumped by 5% due to growth in the North American and Chinese markets.

Strategy

Pursuing business expansion is the cornerstone of Toyota Industries' strategy for promoting its portfolio of products and services. Hybrid and electric powered technologies which are lighter weight and more energy efficient than the industries' current offerings figure prominently on the company's workbench.

Toyota Industries is integrating a slew of such green technologies into its automotive and materials handling products specifically in hopes of appealing to customers in North America and China. Simultaneously Toyota Industries is taking every opportunity to target developing economies such as Eastern Europe China India and Latin America that promise strong demand by expanding its sales network.

Mergers and Acquisitions

In 2013 Toyota Industries made a move to strengthen its forklift portfolio when it acquired Cascade Corporation for $759 million. Cascade makes a variety of forklift attachments handling forks cylinders and other related parts to dealers and manufacturers of lift trucks in North America Europe China and the Asia/Pacific region. It now operates as a wholly owned subsidiary of Toyota Industries.

EXECUTIVES

EVP, Chiaki Yamaguchi, age 65
EVP, Kazue Sasaki
President, Akira Onishi, age 58
EVP, Hirotaka Morishita
Chairman, Tetsuro Toyoda
Vice Chairman, Kazunori Yoshida
Auditors: PricewaterhouseCoopers Aarata

LOCATIONS

HQ: Toyota Industries Corporation (Japan)
2-1 Toyoda-cho, Kariya, Aichi 448-8671
Phone: (81) 566 22 2511   **Fax:** (81) 566 27 5650
Web: www.toyota-shokki.co.jp

PRODUCTS/OPERATIONS

Selected Products
Automobile
   Car air-conditioning compressors
   Diesel and gasoline engines
   Electronics components
   Foundry parts
   Passenger vehicles
Materials Handling Equipment
   Aerial work platforms
   Automated storage and retrieval systems
   Automatic guided vehicles
   Counterbalanced lift trucks
   Warehouse trucks
Logistics
   Collection and delivery of cash and management of sales proceeds
   Logistics planning
   Management collection and delivery of corporate documents
   Operation of distribution centers
   Secure storage
   Transportation services
Textile Machinery
   Air-jet looms
   High-speed ring spinning frames
   High-speed roving frames
Other
   Semiconductor package substrates

COMPETITORS

Aisin Seiki	Linde Lift Truck
Atlas Copco	NACCO Materials
CLARK Material	Handling
Handling	Picanol
Cummins	Rieter Holding
Daifuku	Shiloh Industries
Detroit Diesel	Standard Motor
Hino Motors	Products
Jungheinrich	UniCarriers Americas
Komatsu	Valeo

HISTORICAL FINANCIALS
Company Type: Public

Income Statement
FYE: March 31

	REVENUE ($ mil.)	NET INCOME ($ mil.)	NET PROFIT MARGIN	EMPLOYEES
03/16	19,848	1,629	8.2%	9,871
03/15	18,058	960	5.3%	12,095
03/14	19,452	888	4.6%	49,333
03/13	17,166	564	3.3%	47,412
03/12	18,814	714	3.8%	43,516
Annual Growth	1.3%	22.9%	—	(31.0%)

2016 Year-End Financials

Debt ratio: 0.2%
Return on equity: 8.3%
Cash ($ mil.): 3,137
Current ratio: 1.55
Long-term debt ($ mil.): 7,114
No. of shares (mil.): 314
Dividends
   Yield: 0.0%
   Payout: 20.4%
Market value ($ mil.): 14,272

	STOCK PRICE ($) FY Close	P/E High/Low		PER SHARE ($) Earnings	Dividends	Book Value
03/16	45.42	0	0	5.19	1.06	57.72
03/15	59.25	0	0	3.06	0.83	62.51
03/14	45.45	—	—	2.83	0.00	56.49
03/13	36.93	—	—	1.81	0.00	51.91
03/12	30.80	—	—	2.29	0.00	46.85
Annual Growth	10.2%	—	—	22.7%	—	5.4%

Toyota Motor Corp

Toyota Motor among the world's largest automotive manufacturers by revenue designs and manufactures a diverse product line-up that ranges from subcompacts to luxury and sports vehicles to SUVs trucks minivans and buses. Its vehicles are produced either with combustion or hybrid engines as with the Prius. Toyota's subsidiaries also manufacture vehicles: Daihatsu Motor produces mini-vehicles while Hino Motors produces trucks and buses. Additionally Toyota makes automotive parts for its own use and for sale to others. Popular models include the Camry Corolla Land Cruiser and luxury Lexus line as well as the Tundra truck.

Operations

Major Toyota subsidiaries include Toyota Auto Body Co. Ltd. Toyota Motor Sales U.S.A. Toyota Motor North America Toyota Motor Engineering & Manufacturing North America Toyota Financial Services Corporation and Toyota Motor Credit Corporation.

Toyota divides its operations into the three segments of automotive (90% of total sales) financial services (5%) and other (5%). Automotive is obviously Toyota's bread and butter; the segment makes passenger and commercial vehicles minivans trucks and related parts. Its less known financial services segment provides financing to dealers and their customers for the lease or purchase of Toyota vehicles.

Geographic Reach

Toyota maintains a vast geographical reach selling to almost 190 countries and regions through 550 consolidated subsidiaries and some 200 affiliated companies. Almost 55% of its sales come from Asia (Japan counts for more than 40%) while North America generates around 30% of total sales. Countries in Europe Africa the Middle East Oceania and Latin America account for the remainder.

Sales and Marketers

Toyota sells its products mainly through dealers distributors and sales channels.

Financial Performance

Toyota's revenues jumped 4% from 2015 to 2016 due to a 14% spike in financial services revenue and a 4% bump in automotive revenue. The company also experienced a 14% increase in North American revenue due primarily to an increase of 124000 vehicle unit sales compared with the prior fiscal year. This was fueled by favorable market conditions coupled with strong sales of the RAV4 NX and other car models. Despite the overall growth Toyota sold 8.7 million units in 2016 down from the almost 9 million units it sold in 2015.

Strategy

Toyota's growth strategy is centered around global market penetration. To fulfill this goal Toyota ensures that it offers products for every market segment. For example the company makes and offers sedans trucks SUVs luxury vehicles and other product lines for every type of customer.

Toyota is also focused on producing electric vehicles amid the strengthening of regulations around increasing the use of zero emission vehicles. It has created an in-house company dedicated solely to this product line and plans to start mass production of its new electric vehicles by 2020.

Like its competitors Toyota is also beefing up its Chinese operations by joining forces with local automotive players. With its partner China FAW Group Corporation Toyota builds nine models including Land Cruisers and Corollas in the country.

In 2016 Toyota acquired the remaining stake of 49% of Japanese carmaker Daihatsu. The company plans for the deal to help strengthen cooperation by integrating development and production technologies in the categories of subcompact cars and eco-friendly vehicles.

HISTORY

Company Background
In 1926 Sakichi Toyoda founded Toyoda Automatic Loom Works. In 1930 he sold the rights to the loom he invented and gave the proceeds to his son Kiichiro Toyoda to begin an automotive business. Kiichiro opened an auto shop within the loom works in 1933. When protectionist legislation (1936) improved prospects for Japanese automakers Kiichiro split off the car department took it public (1937) and changed its name to Toyota.

During WWII the company made military trucks but financial problems after the war caused Toyota to reorganize in 1950. Its postwar commitment to R&D paid off with the launch of the four-wheel-drive Land Cruiser (1951); full-sized Crown (1955); and the small Corona (1957).

Toyota Motor Sales U.S.A. debuted the Toyopet Crown in the US in 1957 but it proved underpowered for the US market. Toyota had better luck with the Corona in 1965 and with the Corolla (which became the best-selling car of all time) in 1968. By 1970 Toyota was the world's fourth largest carmaker.

Toyota expanded rapidly in the US. During the 1970s the oil crisis caused demand for fuel-efficient cars and Toyota was there to grab market share from US makers. In 1975 Toyota displaced Volkswagen as the US's #1 auto importer. Toyota began auto production in the US in 1984 through NUMMI its joint venture with General Motors. The Lexus line was launched in the US in 1989.

Because of European restrictions on Japanese auto imports until 2000 Toyota's European expansion slowed. Toyota responded in 1992 by agreeing to distribute cars in Japan for Volkswagen and also by establishing an engine plant (later moved to full auto production) in the UK.

The SUV mania of the 1990s spurred Toyota's introduction of luxury minivans and light trucks. Hiroshi Okuda a 40-year veteran with Toyota and the first person from outside the Toyoda family to run the firm succeeded Tatsuro Toyoda as president in 1995. The next year Toyota consolidated its North American production units into Cincinnati-based Toyota Motor Manufacturing North America.

In 1997 Toyota introduced the Prius a hybrid electric- and gas-powered car. The next year Toyota boosted its stake in affiliate Daihatsu Motor (mini-vehicles) to about 51% and started Toyota Mapmaster (51% owned) to make map databases for car navigation systems. Okuda became chairman in 1999 replacing Shoichiro Toyoda and Fujio

Cho became president (later chairman). Also that year Toyota agreed to form a joint venture with Isuzu Motors to manufacture buses.

In 2000 Toyota launched the WiLL Vi a sedan aimed at young people. It announced that it was building an online replacement parts marketplace with i2 Technologies and formed a financial services company (Toyota Financial Service) and a brokerage firm (Toyota Financial Services Securities Corp.). Toyota also bought a 5% stake in Yamaha Motor (the world's #2 motorcycle maker) and raised its stake in truck maker Hino Motors from about 20% to around 34%.

International developments included Toyota's agreement with the Chinese government to produce passenger cars for sale in China built by Tianjin Toyota Motor Corp. a joint venture between Chinese carmaker Tianjin Automobile Xiali and Toyota. In 2001 Toyota opened a plant in France. Later that year Toyota also increased its stake in Hino Motors to 50%. With partners Toyoda Gosei and Horie Metal Co. Ltd. Toyota formed a joint venture in 2002 to manufacture resin fuel tank systems. In 2004 Toyota forged a joint venture agreement with Guangzhou Automobile Group to build engines in China. The following year Toyota established 14 Lexus dealerships in China. The company began joint car production in Europe with Peugeot S.A. in 2005. Also in 2005 Toyota bought just under 9% of Fuji Heavy Industries –the Japanese maker of Subaru passenger vehicles. The two companies began production of Toyota Camrys at Fuji Heavy Industries' underutilized Subaru of Indiana plant in 2007.

After suffering through the Great Recession from 2008 to 2010 Toyota faced another unforeseen crisis. In March 2011 its business suffered unexpectedly from the Great East Japan Earthquake which triggered a deadly tsunami and subsequent nuclear crisis that forced Tokyo Electric Power (Tepco) to shut down reactors at two nuclear power plants and five other conventional power plants. The events forced manufacturers to reduce their output or move production to other regions. Toyota along with its rivals (Nissan Honda and Mazda) were forced to close their factories days after the devastation.

EXECUTIVES

President and Board Member, Akio Toyoda, age 60
EVP Secretary General Strategic Top Executive Meeting Office Chief Officer Global Audit Department Chief Officer Corporate Strategy Division Chief Officer Research Division and Director, Shigeki Terashi, age 61
Senior Managing Officer, Mitsuhisa Kato, age 63
EVP CFO and Director, Takahiko Ijichi, age 64
EVP President Business Unit Toyota No. 1 Chief Competitive Officer Chairman Toyota Motor Europe NV/SA and Director, Didier Leroy, age 59
President Toyota Venezuela, Rafael Chang
President Vietnam, Toru Kinoshita
Chairman, Takeshi Uchiyamada, age 70
Auditors: PricewaterhouseCoopers Aarata

LOCATIONS

HQ: Toyota Motor Corp
1 Toyota-cho, Toyota, Aichi 471-8571
Phone: (81) 565 28 2121   **Fax:** (81) 565 23 5800
Web: www.toyota.co.jp

2016 Sales

	% of total
Japan	41
North America	31
Asia	14
Europe	8
Other	6
Total	**100**

PRODUCTS/OPERATIONS

2016 Sales

	% of total
Automotive	89
Financial services	7
Other	4
Total	**100**

2016 Sales

	% of total
Sales of products	93
Financing operations	7
Total	**100**

Selected Products

Vehicles
  4Runner
  Allion (sold in Japan)
  Alphard (minivan sold in Japan)
  Aurus (hybrid)
  Avalon
  Camry (also hybrid)
  Corolla
  Corolla Rumion
  Crown
  FJ Cruiser
  Highlander (also hybrid)
  Land Cruiser
  Lexus
  GX
  LS600h (hybrid)
  LX (SUV)
  RX
  SC
  Mark X (sold in Japan)
  Matrix
  Premio (sold in Japan)
  Prius (hybrid)
  RAV4
  Scion
  Sequoia
  Sienna (minivan)
  Tacoma (truck)
  Tundra (truck)
  Vanguard
  Vellfire (minivan)
  Venza
  Wish (minivan sold in Japan)
  Yaris (marketed in Japan as the Vitz)
Other products
  Factory automation equipment
  Forklifts and other industrial vehicles
  Housing products

COMPETITORS

BMW	Isuzu
Brilliance China	Kia Motors
Caterpillar	Komatsu
Chery Automobile	Kubota
Daimler	Land Rover
Deere	Mazda
FCA US	Mitsubishi Motors
Fiat Chrysler	Nissan
Ford Motor	Peugeot
Fuji Heavy Industries	Renault
General Motors	Shanghai Automotive
Global Diversified	Suzuki Motor
Industries	Tata Motors
Honda	Volkswagen
Hyundai Motor	Volvo

HISTORICAL FINANCIALS
Company Type: Public

Income Statement
FYE: March 31

	REVENUE ($ mil.)	NET INCOME ($ mil.)	NET PROFIT MARGIN	EMPLOYEES
03/16	252,928	20,594	8.1%	348,877
03/15	226,993	18,114	8.0%	344,109
03/14	248,905	17,662	7.1%	338,875
03/13	234,495	10,225	4.4%	333,498
03/12	226,546	3,456	1.5%	325,905
Annual Growth	2.8%	56.2%	—	1.7%

2016 Year-End Financials

Debt ratio: 0.3%
Return on equity: 13.5%
Cash ($ mil.): 48,824
Current ratio: 1.13
Long-term debt ($ mil.): 87,019

No. of shares (mil.): —
Dividends
  Yield: 3.4%
  Payout: 59.9%
Market value ($ mil.): —

	STOCK PRICE ($) FY Close	P/E High/Low		PER SHARE ($) Earnings	Dividends	Book Value
03/16	106.32	0	0	6.55	3.64	50.50
03/15	139.89	0	0	5.73	3.22	44.47
03/14	112.90	0	0	5.57	2.54	44.22
03/13	102.64	0	0	3.23	1.28	40.76
03/12	86.82	1	1	1.10	1.22	40.61
Annual Growth	5.2%	—	—	56.2%	31.5%	5.6%

Toyota Tsusho Corp

Auditors: PricewaterhouseCoopers Aarata

LOCATIONS

HQ: Toyota Tsusho Corp
  Century Toyota Bldg., 4-9-8 Meieki, Nakamura-ku, Nagoya, Aichi 450-8575
Phone: (81) 52 584 5482   **Fax:** (81) 52 584 5659
Web: www.toyota-tsusho.com

HISTORICAL FINANCIALS
Company Type: Public

Income Statement
FYE: March 31

	REVENUE ($ mil.)	NET INCOME ($ mil.)	NET PROFIT MARGIN	EMPLOYEES
03/16	72,755	(389)		61,707
03/15	72,207	563	0.8%	56,643
03/14	75,017	707	0.9%	50,423
03/13	67,001	716	1.1%	48,336
03/12	72,129	807	1.1%	33,845
Annual Growth	0.2%			16.2%

2016 Year-End Financials

Debt ratio: 0.3%
Return on equity: (-4.3%)
Cash ($ mil.): 3,635
Current ratio: 1.40
Long-term debt ($ mil.): 8,643

No. of shares (mil.): 352
Dividends
  Yield: —
  Payout: —
Market value ($ mil.): —

	STOCK PRICE ($) FY Close	P/E High/Low		PER SHARE ($) Earnings	Dividends	Book Value
03/16	0.00	—	—	(1.11)	0.00	22.48
03/15	26.10	0	0	1.60	0.00	26.68
03/14	22.74	—	—	2.01	0.00	31.87
03/13	23.04	—	—	2.05	0.00	27.88
Annual Growth	—			—	—	(5.2%)

TSB Banking Group Plc

Auditors: PricewaterhouseCoopers LLP

LOCATIONS

HQ: TSB Banking Group Plc
  20 Gresham Street, London EC2V 7JE
Phone: (44) 20 7003 9000
Web: www.tsb.co.uk

HISTORICAL FINANCIALS
Company Type: Public

Income Statement
FYE: December 31

	ASSETS ($ mil.)	NET INCOME ($ mil.)	INCOME AS % OF ASSETS	EMPLOYEES
12/16	45,755	157	0.3%	8,296
12/15	46,856	131	0.3%	8,620
12/14	42,415	209	0.5%	8,427
12/13	41,239	305	0.7%	4,721
Annual Growth	3.5%	(19.9%)	—	20.7%

2016 Year-End Financials

Return on assets: 0.3%
Return on equity: 7.0%
Long-term debt ($ mil.): —
No. of shares (mil.): 500
Sales ($ mil): 1,654

Dividends
  Yield: —
  Payout: —
Market value ($ mil.): —

	STOCK PRICE ($) FY Close	P/E High/Low		PER SHARE ($) Earnings	Dividends	Book Value
12/16	0.00	—	—	(0.00)	0.00	4.59
12/15	0.00	—	—	(0.00)	0.00	5.18
Annual Growth	—			—	—	(3.9%)

TUI AG

TUI has the European travel business cornered. The world's largest integrated tourism company TUI sells end-to-end leisure travel packages and provides other travel services under some 200 brands in around 20 countries. Its hotel portfolio numbers some 300 sites (brands include Riu TUI Blue and Dorfhotel) it owns 140 aircraft and its cruise segment includes subsidiary Hapag-Lloyd Cruises and TUI Cruises. The travel company also owns a stake in container ship operator Hapag-Lloyd AG. In 2014 the company merged with TUI Travel to create the world's leading tourism business.

Operations

TUI's end-to-end holiday offering comprises tour operators some 1800 travel agencies five airlines over 300 hotels with 210000 beds and 13 cruise liners.

Its businesses segments are made up of three regional segments (Northern Central and Western for a combined 78% of revenue) and Hotels & Resorts Cruises Other Tourism Specialist Group and Hotelbeds Group. Northern the largest segment by revenue at around 35% works in the UK Ireland and Nordic countries. Germany Austria Poland and Switzerland make up the Central operation (around 28% of revenue) while Western comprises Belgium the Netherlands and France.

Of the 310 hotels run under the Hotels & Resorts segment 272 are four- and five-star and around 75% are on the Mediterranean coastline (which includes North Africa). The Cruises segment includes Hapag-Lloyd Cruises a leading provider of discovery and luxury cruises to the German market and own-brand expedition cruises TUI Cruises (Thomson Cruises in the UK).

The company owns more than 140 aircraft operated by five airlines which serve around 13 million customers a year.

Geographic Reach

TUI takes European tourists to 180 countries with a focus on sunnier climes particularly in the Mediterranean Egypt the Caribbean and the Americas. Outside of its focus on mature markets in Europe TUI also runs a strategic Canada venture Sunwing and has a joint venture that works in Russia TUI Russia.

Sales and Marketing

TUI sells to 20 million customers annually and it serves the 3rd (Germany) 4th (UK) and 6th (France) biggest source markets in the world. Online sales are growing as a proportion of revenue and account for some 40% of sales.

Financial Performance

Note: Growth rates may differ after conversion to US Dollars.

Total revenue grew 8% to euro 20 billion in 2015 (year ended September 2015) with gains mostly found in growth in the Northern Region particularly in the UK which saw customer numbers grow 5%. Specialist and Hotelbeds also posted positive results with growth in Hotelbeds driven by its bedbank business which saw 18% growth in roomnights.

Net income jumped euro 250 million to euro 340 million as a consequence of lower income taxes following the 2014 merger with TUI Travel.

Cash from operating activities fell by 26% to euro 790 million due to an increase in receivables and other assets.

Strategy

TUI AG merged with TUI Travel in 2014 creating the world's largest tourism company. The merger allowed a coming together of TUI AG's leisure and cruise brands and TUI Travel's marketing capabilities airline fleet and holiday concepts to create an end-to-end holiday offering. TUI is now in a position to offer tailored holidays that its smaller-scale competitors will struggle to match and additionally the merger will also allow for a more competitive pricing strategy. There was also a tax benefit and expected cost savings of euro 50 million a year to the merger.

The company's approach to customer acquisition involves launching new destinations the reassurance of end-to-end packages and a full online offering.

TUI is considering divesting its Hotelbeds business.

Mergers and Acquisitions

The company merged with British company TUI Travel for £5.6 billion in December 2014. The merger makes TUI the world's largest leisure travel company and allows the company to exploit its scale for cost savings and offer a full travel package.

HISTORY

What became TUI was founded in Berlin in 1923 as Preussische Bergwerks-und Hutten-Aktiengesellschaft (Prussian Mine and Foundry Company) to operate former state-owned mining companies saltworks and smelters. Despite outmoded equipment and a war-shattered economy the company prospered. So in 1929 the Prussian parliament combined Preussag with Hibernia and Preussischen Elektrizitats to form the state-run VEBA group hoping to stimulate foreign investment.

Operating as part of VEBA didn't work out as well as Preussag had hoped and WWII left the company a shell of its former self. In 1952 as restrictions on steel production were lifted and industry rebounded Preussag relocated to Hanover. After taking steps to reestablish itself Preussag made a public offering in 1959; VEBA kept about 22%.

A worldwide steel glut that lasted through the 1960s forced Preussag to diversify. Acquisitions included railroad tank car and transport agent VTG and shipbuilding and chemical companies. The company also formed oil exploration unit Preussag Energie in 1968. In 1969 VEBA sold its remaining stake in Preussag to Westdeusche Landesbank (WestLB).

When the 1970s oil crisis drove up steel costs Preussag began international ventures to counter falling revenues at home. But the 1980s brought PR disasters. The European Commission fined Preussag and five other zinc producers for antitrust violations in 1984.

In 1989 Preussag reorganized into a holding company with four independent units: coal oil natural gas and plant construction. But it was about to take a sharp business turn. Michael Frenzel who had managed WestLB's industry holdings became CEO in 1994 in the midst of another steel recession. Frenzel was determined to shift Preussag away from its rusting past and toward services and technology. In 1997 it acquired container shipping and travel firm Hapag-Lloyd which had a 30% stake in Touristik Union International (TUI). By the end of 1998 the acquisitions of the rest of TUI First Reisebuero Management and a 25% stake in the UK's Thomas Cook (raised to 50.1% in 1999) had made Preussag Europe's top tourism group.

As part of its restructuring Preussag traded its plant engineering units and half of its shipbuilding unit (HDW) to Babcock Borsig for a 33% stake in that company in 1999. Preussag then made plans to transfer another 25% of HDW to Sweden's Celsius in a deal (along with Babcock Borsig) to merge Celsius' Kockums submarine shipyards with HDW. That year Hapag-Lloyd and TUI were merged into Hapag Touristik Union (renamed TUI Group in 2000); VTG merged with Lehnkering a 126-year-old freight forwarding group becoming VTG-Lehnkering.

Preussag also acquired a stake in French package tour leader Nouvelles Frontières and sold a metals trading unit W. & O. Bergmann to Enron. By 2002 the company had sold off most of its non-tourism operations changed its name to TUI and restructured its business to concentrate on travel-related businesses.

In 2004 TUI sold a division of its VTG-Lehnkering logistics operation to investors for an undisclosed amount. Also that year TUI Travel Solutions GmbH sold 50% of its stake in TQ3 Travel Solutions to Navigant International. (It sold the rest of TQ3 to Navigant two years later.)

WestLB surrendered its majority shareholding of TUI in 2004 freeing up 90% of the company's shares for free float.

In 2005 the company purchased Canada-based CP Ships for almost $2 billion making Hapag-Lloyd one of the world's largest container carriers.

Two years later TUI expanded its travel business by buying First Choice Holidays and combining the UK-based company with its existing tourism operations to form TUI Travel a publicly traded company in which TUI held a controlling stake. Around the same time the company decided to shed its container shipping operations and focus solely on its tourism and travel services businesses. To this end in March 2009 TUI sold Hapag-Lloyd to a German consortium but retained a 43% stake in the company. (TUI's stake in Hapag-Lloyd increased to about 50% as loans to the company were converted to equity.)

EXECUTIVES

Chief HR and Legal Affairs, Peter Engelen, age 60
Chief Tourism; CEO First Choice Holidays and TUI Travel, Peter Long, age 64
CFO, Mikhail Noskov
Chairman, Michael Frenzel, age 69
Deputy Chairman, Petra Gerstenkorn, age 62
Auditors: PricewaterhouseCoopers Aktiengesellschaft

LOCATIONS

HQ: TUI AG
Karl-Wiechert-Allee 4, Hanover D-30625
Phone: (49) 511 566 00   **Fax:** (49) 511 56 1901
Web: www.tui-group.com

PRODUCTS/OPERATIONS

2015 Sales

	% of total
Tourism	
Northern Region	35
Central Region	28
Western Region	15
Hotels & Resorts	3
Cruise	1
Other Tourism	2
Specialist Group	9
Hotelbeds Group	6
All other segments	1
Total	**100**

COMPETITORS

Accor	REWE
American Express	Royal Caribbean
Carlson Wagonlit	Cruises
Carnival Corporation	Thomas Cook
Club Med	Travelport
Kuoni Travel	

HISTORICAL FINANCIALS

Company Type: Public

Income Statement

FYE: September 30

	REVENUE ($ mil.)	NET INCOME ($ mil.)	NET PROFIT MARGIN	EMPLOYEES
09/15	22,436	381	1.7%	76,036
09/14	23,559	131	0.6%	77,309
09/13	24,939	5	0.0%	74,445
09/12	23,701	(19)	—	73,812
09/11	23,582	32	0.1%	73,707
Annual Growth	**(1.2%)**	**85.5%**	**—**	**0.8%**

2015 Year-End Financials

Debt ratio: 15.0%
Return on equity: 15.7%
Cash ($ mil.): 1,875
Current ratio: 0.58
Long-term debt ($ mil.): 1,853

No. of shares (mil.): 586
Dividends
  Yield: 1.3%
  Payout: 16.7%
Market value ($ mil.): 5,338

	STOCK PRICE ($) FY Close	P/E High/Low		PER SHARE ($) Earnings	Dividends	Book Value
09/15	9.10	15	12	0.71	0.12	3.66
09/14	6.97	28	21	0.39	0.00	10.57
09/13	6.05	—	—	(0.11)	0.00	10.96
09/12	6.04	—	—	(0.21)	0.00	10.67
09/11	6.04	—	—	(0.01)	0.00	13.24
Annual Growth	**10.8%**	—	—	—	—	**(27.5%)**

Turkiye Garanti Bankasi A.S.

Türkiye Garanti Bankasi (Garanti Bank Turkey) provides banking services from about 1000 domestic branches and more than 4000 ATMs across Turkey though subsidiaries and branches can also be found in China Cyprus Germany Luxembourg Malta Russia and the UK. In addition to traditional deposit products Garanti Bank provides brokerage factoring insurance leasing personal pension plans portfolio management and other services. As Turkey's second-largest private bank Garanti serves more than 13 million customers and boasts assets of more than $100 billion. The bank is jointly owned by Dogus Holding Co. and Spain's second-largest lender Banco Bilbao Vizcaya Argentaria which owns a 39% stake.

OperationsBroadly speaking Garanti Bank Turkey generates more than 80% of its revenue in the form of interest income (mostly from retail and corporate loans) while the remainder of its revenue comes from fee and commission income. Its three main segments include Retail Banking (which generates 30% of revenue); Corporate Banking (which brings in more than 30% of revenue) and Investment Banking (making up nearly 15% of revenue). The bank's subsidiaries include Garantibank International N.V. Garantibank Moscow and Garanti Romania.

Geographic Reach
In addition to its nearly 1000 domestic branches across Turkey Garanti has six foreign branches in Cyprus and one branch in Luxembourg and Malta each. It also has three representative offices in London Dusseldorf and Shanghai.

Sales and Marketing
Garanti's 19000 employees provide banking services to more than 13 million customers through its branch network and call center as well as through digital banking platforms (social banking mobile and internet).

Financial Performance
Note: Growth rates may differ after conversion to US dollars.Garanti's revenue has hovered between $8 billion and $10 billion over the past few years. Revenue in 2014 jumped by double digits to T$17.89 billion ($9.43 billion) mostly thanks to 12% growth in net fees and commissions income but also thanks to a 20% jump in interest income (loan business grew by 16%) as interest rates remained high while the country's central bank battled 9.5% inflation.

Higher revenue in 2014 drove the bank's net income up by double digits to T$3.68 billion. Cash levels also improved along with the higher cash earnings.

Strategy
To achieve its long-term sustainable growth strategy Garanti Bank Turkey has been focusing on growing its domestic loan business with an eye toward making safer loans with strong risk-adjusted returns. Indeed to its credit the bank's non-performing loans made up just 3% of its total loan portfolio in 2014. For 2015 the bank's CEO remained fairly certain that its domestic loan business would be driven by new business loans and grow by 15% to 20% for the year right in line with industry-wide forecasts in the country. The bank also provides a "one-stop-shop" experience for its clients with its wide array of other financial products and services giving the bank cross-selling leverage to grow existing business relationships with its more than 13 million customers. In 2014

the bank was the market leader in consumer loans mortgages and auto loans in Turkey and the second largest market player in the assets loans and customer deposits categories.

EXECUTIVES

President CEO and Director, Ergun –zen
Executive Vice President Financial Institutions and Corporate Banking, Ali Fuat Erbil
Executive Vice President Technology Operational Services and Central Marketing, H sn Erel
Executive Vice President Domestic & Overseas Subsidiaries Coordination, Turgay G hensin
Executive Vice President Support Services, Adnan Memis
Executive Vice President Strategic and Financial Planning, Murat Mergin
EVP Human Resources Training Treasury & Investment Banking, G khan Er n
Executive Vice President - Loans, Erhan Adali
Executive Vice President Delivery Channels Social Platforms Management Customer Satisfaction, Didem Din r Baser
Executive Vice President General Accounting & Financial Reporting, brahim Aydinli
Executive Vice President Commercial Banking, Recep Bastug
Executive Vice President Legal Services and Retail Risk Monitoring, Aydin D ren
Executive Vice President Project and Acquisition Finance Sustainability, Ebru Dildar Edin
EVP Retail and Private Banking Call Center Garanti Payment Systems CEO, Onur Gen §
Executive Vice President SME Banking Corporate Brand Management and Marketing Communication, Nafiz Karadere
Executive Vice President Purchasing & Tax Management, Aydin Senel
Executive Vice President Delivery Channels, Didem Bas
Chairman, Ferit Faik Sahenk
Vice Chairman, S leyman S zen
Auditors: Deloitte-DRT Bagimsiz Denetim ve Serbest Muhasebeci Mali Musavirlik AS

LOCATIONS

HQ: Turkiye Garanti Bankasi A.S.
Levent, Nispetiye Mahallesi, Aytar Caddesi, No. 2, Besiktas, Istanbul, Istanbul Province 34340
Phone: (90) 212 318 18 18   **Fax:** (90) 212 318 18 88
Web: www.garantibank.com

PRODUCTS/OPERATIONS

2014 Sales

	% of total
Interest income	80
Net fee and commission income	15
Other operting income	5
Total	**100**

2014 Sales

	% of total
Corporate Banking	33
Retail Banking	31
Investment Banking	13
Others	23
Total	**100**

COMPETITORS

Akbank	Sabanci
Finansbank	Sekerbank
Isbank	Trk Ekonomi Bankasi
Ko§	Yapi Kredi

HISTORICAL FINANCIALS

Company Type: Public

Income Statement

FYE: December 31

	ASSETS ($ mil.)	NET INCOME ($ mil.)	INCOME AS % OF ASSETS	EMPLOYEES
12/15	94,086	1,291	1.4%	23,191
12/14	104,782	1,638	1.6%	19,036
12/13	101,791	1,669	1.6%	21,853
12/12	99,102	1,878	1.9%	20,287
12/11	85,900	1,789	2.1%	16,775
Annual Growth	**2.3%**	**(7.8%)**	**—**	**8.4%**

2015 Year-End Financials

Return on assets: 1.4%	Dividends
Return on equity: 12.8%	Yield: 1.5%
Long-term debt ($ mil.): —	Payout: 11.4%
No. of shares (mil.): —	Market value ($ mil.): —
Sales ($ mil): 8,344	

	STOCK PRICE ($) FY Close	P/E High/Low		PER SHARE ($) Earnings	Dividends	Book Value
12/15	2.38	4	2	0.31	0.04	0.03
12/14	3.97	5	3	0.39	0.09	0.03
12/13	3.21	6	4	0.40	0.06	0.03
12/12	5.20	7	4	0.45	0.06	0.03
12/11	3.11	5	4	0.43	0.05	0.02
Annual Growth	**(6.5%)**	**—**	**—**	**(7.8%)**	**(7.8%)**	**3.3%**

Turkiye Is Bankasi AS

Türkiye İş Bankası or Isbank is banking in Turkey. Serving some 15 million customers the institution known as Isbank is the country's largest publicly-traded bank and provides corporate banking commercial lending treasury banking private banking and traditional retail banking products and services through more than 1300 branches and 6300-plus ATMs across Turkey. It also boasts insurance investment advisory and real estate investment businesses. Founded in 1924 by mandate of the Turkish Republic's founding father Mustafa Kemal Atatürk employees now own a roughly 40% stake in the bank while the Republican People's Party owns a 28% stake in the name of the founder.

OperationsThe bank operates through five main banking businesses. Its Commercial Banking and Corporate Banking businesses which made up 36% and 18% of the bank's total revenue in 2014 respectively provides large corporations SMEs and other trading companies with project financing traditional account and card products operating and investment loans foreign trade transactions and financing letters of guarantee and credit and other corporate banking services.

Isbank's Retail Banking (20% of revenue) provides traditional banking services to individuals while its Treasury Banking business (20% of revenue) provides medium and long-term funding tools including securities and foreign currency trading money market transactions swaps futures and other complex financial transactions. The bank's small Private Banking business (less than 1% of revenue) serves high-net worth individuals with cash management and wealth management services.

Its non-banking operations (5% of revenue) include: insurance; 'investment and finance' which provides leasing factoring brokerage corporate finance investment advisory private portfolio management and real estate investments; and the 'manufacturing and trading' business which involves glass production and complementary industrial and commercial operations and food production. In 2015 the bank also had equity investments in 25 companies operating mainly in the industry and financial sector.

The bank generated more than 80% of its total revenue in 2014 from interest income (mostly from loans) while about 12% came from fee and commission based income. The rest of revenue mostly came from non-banking business (mostly manufacturing and insurance) and securities trading income. Geographic ReachIsbank boasts more than 1330 branches across Turkey (it's home country) but also has foreign branches in London The Turkish Republic of Northern Cyprus Baghdad Batumi Tbilisi Pristine and Prizren. It also has banking subsidiaries in Germany and Russia.

Financial Performance
Note: Growth rates may differ after conversion to US dollars.

Isbank has struggled to consistently grow its revenue profit in recent years though its financials have been relatively stable in the years following the financial crisis. Isbank enjoyed a breakout year in 2014 however with revenue growing by double digits to 33.37 billion Turkish Lira (about $14.4 billion) as the bank grew its loan business across its Corporate Commercial and Retail Banking businesses. Commercial banking led most of the growth with its revenue spiking by more than 50% during the year while income from Commercial and Retail banking swelled by 31% and 23% respectively. The bank also saw 30%-plus growth in its Investment and Finance and Manufacturing and Trading divisions during the year as well.

Higher revenue in 2014 drove Isbank's net income up by 4% to TL$4.57 billion (roughly $1.96 billion) while the bank's operations used more cash than in the prior year as it took in fewer deposits and used more cash toward repurchase agreements.

Strategy
Isbank stated in 2015 that its top three objectives were to: provide fast and efficient services that meet its customers needs; consistently enhance its shareholder value; and motivate its employees to maximize their performance.

The bank has been expanding its branch and ATM network in recent years to grow its loan business focusing mostly on growing relationships with large corporate as well as small-to-midsize enterprise (SME) customers. In 2014 alone the bank added 44 new branches to its network and more than 600 new ATMs growing its total network by more than 3%.

Ownership
The Isbank Pension Fund representing active and retired bank employees owned about 40% of Isbank through the Private Pension Fund of Employees in early 2015. Some 28% of the bank was owned in the name of Atatürk by the Republican People's Party.

EXECUTIVES

CEO and Director, Adnan Bali, age 55
Auditors: Akis Bagimsiz Denetim ve Serbest Muhasebeci Mali Musavirlik A.S. (a member of KPMG)

LOCATIONS

HQ: Turkiye Is Bankasi AS
Is Kuleleri, Istanbul, Levent 34330
Phone: (90) 212 316 00 00   **Fax:** (90) 212 316 09 00
Web: www.isbank.com.tr

2014 Sales

	% of total
Interest income	52
Non-interest income	
Income from manufacturing operations	21
Income from insurance operations	11
Fee and commission income	7
Securities trading income	3
Income from other operations	2
Foreign exchange gains	2
Others	2
Total	**100**

2014 Sales

	% of total
Banking business	
Commercial	35
Retail	20
Treasury investment	19
Corporate	18
others	2
Non-banking business	
Investment and finance	3
Insurance	2
Manufacturingtrading and service	1
Total	**100**

COMPETITORS

Akbank	GarantiBank
Bank of Cyprus	Sekerbank
Development Bank of Turkey	Trk Ekonomi Bankasi
Finansbank	Yapi Kredi

HISTORICAL FINANCIALS

Company Type: Public

Income Statement

FYE: December 31

	ASSETS ($ mil.)	NET INCOME ($ mil.)	INCOME AS % OF ASSETS	EMPLOYEES
12/15	110,824	1,597	1.4%	25,157
12/14	116,528	1,615	1.4%	24,308
12/13	112,508	1,724	1.5%	24,129
12/12	111,088	2,330	2.1%	24,411
12/11	96,960	1,303	1.3%	24,887
Annual Growth	**3.4%**	**5.2%**	**—**	**0.3%**

2015 Year-End Financials

Return on assets: 1.5%	Dividends
Return on equity: 15.0%	Yield: —
Long-term debt ($ mil.): —	Payout: 289.3%
No. of shares (mil.): —	Market value ($ mil.): —
Sales ($ mil) 12,850	

	STOCK PRICE ($) FY Close	P/E High/Low		PER SHARE ($) Earnings	Dividends	Book Value
12/15	0.00	—	—	0.01	0.04	(0.00)
12/14	0.00	—	—	0.01	0.04	(0.00)
12/13	2.02	59	43	0.02	0.05	(0.00)
Annual Growth	**—**		**—**	**(1.9%)**	**(5.8%)**	

UBS Group AG

Auditors: Ernst & Young Ltd.

LOCATIONS

HQ: UBS Group AG
Bahnhofstrasse 45, Zurich CH-8001
Phone: (41) 44 234 11 11
Web: www.ubs.com

HISTORICAL FINANCIALS

Company Type: Public

Income Statement

FYE: December 31

	REVENUE ($ mil.)	NET INCOME ($ mil.)	NET PROFIT MARGIN	EMPLOYEES
12/15	37,424	6,246	16.7%	60,099
12/14	35,123	3,503	10.0%	60,155
12/13	39,429	3,559	9.0%	60,205
12/12	38,759	(2,705)	—	62,628
Annual Growth	**(1.2%)**	**—**	**—**	**(1.4%)**

2015 Year-End Financials

Debt ratio: —	No. of shares (mil.): —
Return on equity: 11.7%	Dividends
Cash ($ mil.): 91,940	Yield: 3.8%
Current ratio: —	Payout: 91.4%
Long-term debt ($ mil.): —	Market value ($ mil.): —

	STOCK PRICE ($) FY Close	P/E High/Low		PER SHARE ($) Earnings	Dividends	Book Value
12/15	19.37	13	9	1.65	0.80	14.85
12/14	17.05	24	18	0.92	0.00	14.10
12/13	0.00	—	—	0.93	0.00	14.86
Annual Growth	**—**		**—**	**21.0%**	**—**	**(0.0%)**

Ultrapar Participacoes SA

Ultrapar's strategy goes well beyond breaking even in Brazil. Holding company Ultrapar Participações' subsidiaries distribute liquefied petroleum gas (LPG) through subsidiary Ultragaz refine and market petroleum products (through Companhia Brasileira de Petroleo Ipiranga) produce chemicals and petrochemicals and provide storage- and transportation-related products. Its Oxiteno unit oversees chemical and petrochemical activities while Ultracargo handles transportation and storage. Ultrapar also operates a petroleum refining business through its investment in Refinaria de Petroleo Riograndense S.A. Ultra S.A holds a 66% stake in Ultrapar.

Operations

The company operates five main business segments: gas distribution fuel distribution chemicals storage and drugstores. The gas distribution segment (Ultragaz) distributes LPG to residential commercial and industrial consumers especially in the South Southeast and Northeast regions of Brazil. The fuel distribution segment (Ipiranga) operates the distribution and marketing of gasoline ethanol diesel fuel oil kerosene natural gas for vehicles and lubricants and related activities throughout all the Brazilian territory. Ipiranga contributed 86% of the company's total revenues in 2014. The chemicals segment (Oxiteno) produces ethylene oxide and its main derivatives and fatty alcohols which are raw materials used in the home and personal care agrochemical paints varnishes and other industries. The storage segment (Ultracargo) operates liquid bulk terminals especially in the Southeast and Northeast regions of Brazil. The drugstores segment (Extrafarma) trades pharmaceutical hygiene and beauty products through its own drugstore chain in the states of Para Amapa Maranhão Piaui Ceara and Rio Grande do Norte. Ultragaz (the LPG distribution subsidiary

of Ultrapar and one of the largest distributors in Brazil) introduced LPG for home cooking in that country and helped pioneer the development of the petrochemical industry there. It delivers LPG to 11 million households and to 48000 customers in the bulk segment. The company also manufactures 1500 products used in various industrial sectors such as cosmetics detergents crop protection chemicals packaging textiles and coatings.

Geographic Reach

Ultragaz operates in all regions of Brazil through a distribution network comprised of 17 filling plants. Ipiranga has presence in Brazilian territory. Extrafarma operates in six states in the North and Northeast regions of Brazil and distribution centers one in Belem and another one in Aquiraz. Oxiteno has eleven industrial units in Brazil Mexico the US Uruguay and Venezuela and commercial offices in Argentina Belgium China and Colombia. Ultrapar through Oxiteno operates three plants in Mexico. Oxiteno's six international plants produce specialty chemicals. It also has commercial offices in the US Argentina Belgium China and Colombia.

Sales and Marketing

Ultragaz distributes LPG to residential commercial and industrial market segments. Ipiranga distributes gasoline ethanol diesel NGV fuel oil kerosene and lubricants through a network of 7056 service stations and directly to large customers. Extrafarma has distribution centers and has 223 drugstores. It has a vehicle fleet and a network of 4900 independent retailers in the bottled segment.

Financial Performance

In 2014 Ultrapar's net revenues from sales and services increased 11% (in local currency) mainly as a result of the increased sales volumes in all businesses. Ultrapar's net revenues from sales and services includes revenues from fuel and gas sales by Ultragaz and Ipiranga respectively pharmaceutical products sales by Extrafarma specialty chemicals sales by Oxiteno and liquid bulk storage services provided by Ultracargo reduced by sales taxes such as ICMS PIS and Cofins and by discounts and sales returns.

Ipiranga's net revenues from sales and services increased by 10% due to higher sales volume and diesel refinery prices and an increase in gasoline refinery prices coupled with an increase in ethanol costs and an improved sales mix resulting from investments in the expansion of the service station network. Sales volume of gasoline ethanol and natural gas for vehicles increased mainly as a result of growth in the light vehicles fleet and strong investments made in new service stations and in the conversion of unbranded service stations. Diesel volumes remained stable with an increase in the reseller segment (the result of investments for the expansion of the network) offset by the weak performance of the economy.

Ultragaz Oxiteno Ultracargo and Extrafarma also reported higher revenues.

Ultrapar's net income increased by 2% (in local currency) thanks to higher net sales.

In 2014 Ultrapar's cash from operating activities grew by 25%.

Strategy

Ultrapar's strategy is to grow via organic expansion and investment in research and development and innovation. The company is focusing in on the Midwest Northeast and North regions of Brazil to open new service stations geographically. Ultragaz aims at expanding the use of LPG for localized heating such as pre-heating of industrial furnaces especially in steel and metallurgical plants and in new applications in agribusiness such as drying grains and plague control with greater operational and economic efficiency. Ultrapar's focus on R&D has resulted in the introduction of 57 new products. The company's strategy based on the growth and improvement of its reseller network on differentiating its services with the support of innovation and also on creating new marketing channels. The Ultragaz Connect application was created in 2014 to allow the purchase of LPG bottles through smartphones and to generate greater speed and safety for the consumer as well as cost reduction for resellers.

Mergers and Acquisitions

Moving into the retail pharmacy business in 2014 Ultrapar acquired Extrafarma one of Brazil's top ten drugstore chains. This acquisition allows Ultrapar to accelerate Extrafarma's expansion plans through drugstore openings in the company's Ipiranga service stations and Ultragaz resellers. The deal is valued at $419 million.

Company Background

In 2008 Ultrapar acquired Chevron's Texaco-branded fuel distribution business (2000 gas stations) in Brazil for $720 million.

In 2010 it bought fuel distributor Distribuidora Nacional de Petroleo (DNP) for about $50 million. DNP has a network of 110 gas stations in the northern Brazilian states of Acre Amazonas Mato Grosso Para Rondonia and Roraima.

EXECUTIVES

CEO, Thilo Mannhardt, age 61

CEO Ultragaz, Pedro Jorge Filho, age 63

CEO Oxiteno, Jo o Benjamin Parolin, age 57

CEO Extrafarma, Andre Covre, age 45

CEO Ipiranga, Leocadio Antunes de Almeida Filho, age 65

CEO Ultracargo, Ricardo Isaac Catran, age 61

Chief Financial and Investor Relations Officer, Andre Pires de Oliveira Dias, age 49

Vice Chairman, Lucio de Castro Andrade Filho, age 72

Chairman, Paulo Guliherme Aguiar Cunha, age 77

Auditors: Deloitte Touche Tohmatsu Auditores Independentes

LOCATIONS

HQ: Ultrapar Participacoes SA
Av. Brigadeiro Luis Antonio 1343, 9 Andar, Sao Paulo 01317-910
Phone: (55) 11 3177 6695   **Fax:** (55) 11 3177 6107
Web: www.ultra.com.br

PRODUCTS/OPERATIONS

2013 Sales

	% of total
Fuels/lubricants	88
Gas	6
Chemicals	5
Logistics	1
Total	**100**

Selected Subsidiaries

Ipiranga (fuels & lubricants)
Oxiteno (petrochemicals)
Ultracargo (transportation logistics)
Ultragaz (LPG distribution)

HISTORICAL FINANCIALS

Company Type: Public

Income Statement

FYE: December 31

	REVENUE ($ mil.)	NET INCOME ($ mil.)	NET PROFIT MARGIN	EMPLOYEES
12/15	19,101	379	2.0%	14,597
12/14	25,490	467	1.8%	13,973
12/13	25,798	518	2.0%	9,235
12/12	26,372	494	1.9%	9,282
12/11	26,091	455	1.7%	9,055
Annual Growth	**(7.5%)**	**(4.4%)**	**—**	**12.7%**

2015 Year-End Financials

Debt ratio: 10.7%
Return on equity: 19.2%
Cash ($ mil.): 682
Current ratio: 2.59
Long-term debt ($ mil.): 1,970

No. of shares (mil.): 556
Dividends
  Yield: 2.9%
  Payout: 52.5%
Market value ($ mil.): 8,485

	STOCK PRICE ($) FY Close	P/E High/Low		PER SHARE ($) Earnings	Dividends	Book Value
12/15	15.25	7	4	0.69	0.45	3.61
12/14	19.07	10	8	0.85	0.61	5.21
12/13	23.65	11	8	0.97	0.61	5.07
12/12	22.28	13	8	0.92	0.55	5.38
12/11	17.20	37	8	0.85	0.50	5.47
Annual Growth	**(3.0%)**	**—**	**—**	**(4.9%)**	**(2.7%)**	**(9.9%)**

UniCredit Bank AG

UniCredit Bank AG which does business as HypoVereinsbank (HVB Group) is one of Germany's top five largest banks by assets. Boasting nearly $400 billion in assets and some 730 branches across the country HVB Group offers commercial and private banking services for retail and affluent customers as well as capital market investment banking and related consulting services for corporations and institutions. The bank mainly serves customers in the Automobile Logistics Engineering Construction Health Pharmaceuticals and Chemicals sectors. HVB Group operates as the German arm of European financial giant UniCredit SPA.

OperationsThe bank operates three business segments. The Commercial Banking segment serves 2.5 million customers under the HypoVereinsbank brand in Germany and consists of the company's Private Clients Bank and Unternehmer (entrepreneur) Bank business units which offer retail banking private banking and wealth management services. Its Corporate & Investment Banking segment offers investment banking capital market and financial advisory services to corporations institutions and select multinational corporations. The Other/Consolidation segment consists of the Global Banking Services unit and the Group Corporate Centre. The Global Banking Services business unit acts as a central internal service provider for customers and employees providing purchasing organization corporate security logistics and facility management cost management and production functions for credit accounts foreign exchange money market and derivatives and in-house consulting services. About 66% of HVB Group's operating income came in the form of net interest income in 2014 while net fees and commissions made up another 26%. The rest came from net gains on the held-for-trading portfolio (3%) and other net operating income (5%). The company had a staff of 17600 employees at the end of 2014.

Geographic Reach

HVB boasts nearly 730 branches or offices in Germany. Most of its German locations are concentrated in the Bavaria and greater Hamburg area. Its parent UniCredit SPA operates in 17 European countries in some 50 markets. Sales and MarketingAs a universal bank HVB Group caters to retail banking private banking and high net worth clients businesses corporations and institutional clients.

Financial Performance

Note: Growth rates may differ after conversion to US dollars.

HVB Group has struggled to grow its revenues in recent years due to shrinking interest margins in the low-rate environment and declining fee and commission income from challenging financial markets. The bank's revenue fell 8% to euro 4.4 billion ($5.3 billion) during 2014 mostly as its Corporate & Investment Banking segment shrank with a difficult market environment and a large drop in German net trading income also impacted by credit value adjustments. Its Commercial Banking segment declined as well mostly due to shrinking interest margins as the central bank continued to cut rates.

Revenue declines in 2014 caused HVB Group's net income to drop 17% to euro 627 million ($762 million) for the year. Its operating cash levels fell further during the year with operations using euro 3.8 billion ($4.6 million) due to unfavorable changes in working capital mostly related to larger outflows from customer deposits and debt securities in issue.

Strategy

With its operational expenses eating at its profits parent-company UniCredit has been looking to restructure HVB Group to make it more efficient and profitable. Indeed UniCredit's chief executive in September 2015 said the HVB had a cost-income ratio of 75% compared to UniCredit's 60% which prompted a later announcement of job cuts of more than 1500 in Germany.Additionally HVB Group has been moving toward digital banking channels that are quickly taking the industry by storm allowing the bank to slow expensive branch-expansion plans and cut operating costs significantly while giving customers faster access to banking services. Indeed thanks partially to these measures the bank reported that it had shrunk its branch office count by 14% to 796 in 2014 from 934 in 2011. It had also shrunk its staff by nearly double digits to 17980 from 19442 in 2011.

HISTORY

Company BackgroundKing Ludwig I formed Bayerische Hypotheken- und Wechsel-Bank (BHWB) in 1835 as Bavaria's national bank to provide real estate loans offer insurance and issue currency (until German unification in 1871). The bank had become Germany's largest mortgage lender by 1908.

Bayerische Vereinsbank was created by Bavarian investors in 1869 with the permission of Ludwig's more eccentric grandson Ludwig II. Formed as a commercial bank to stimulate the Bavarian economy it began writing mortgage loans within two years.

By the end of WWI both Vereinsbank and BHWB had formed agreements with other regional lenders to guard against larger banks. Due partly to these agreements Vereinsbank slipped through the Great Depression relatively unscathed. As paper currency value sank daily the bank began issuing gold-backed loans in 1924.

Germany's defeat in WWII was crucial to Vereinsbank and BHWB's ascent: As punishment for having financed Nazi rampages national banks were broken up and regionals filled the void. By 1946 Vereinsbank and BHWB had emerged as each other's main competitors; they considered but nixed a merger.

Both banks expanded throughout West Germany and overseas in the 1950s. In 1958 however the national banks regrouped and within 10 years Germany's former Big Three (Deutsche Bank Dresdner Bank and Commerzbank) were back on top. Vereinsbank and BHWB again flirted with merging in 1969 but Bavaria intervened insisting on the inclusion of state bank Bayerische Staatsbank in any merger. Ultimately Vereinsbank bought only Staatsbank in 1971.

Over the next decade both banks expanded. As the Soviet Union faltered in 1989 Vereinsbank formed the Bank of Moscow through a joint venture with Credit Lyonnais and other European banks. After reunification BHWB made the most real estate loans in the former East (and was thus the most exposed to failed loans).

In 1994 BHWB formed Direkt Anlage Bank Germany's first discount brokerage. In 1996 Vereinsbank formed online bank Advance Bank (sold to Dresdner after the HypoVereinsbank merger when Direkt Anlage became the merged bank's online unit).

Throughout the 1990s the Big Three overran the regional markets vital to BHWB and Vereinsbank; to stay alive the banks finally merged in 1998 creating Europe's largest mortgage lender and Germany's first US-style superregional bank. HypoVereinsbank stayed regionally focused as Deutsche and Dresdner carved up foreign markets.

In 1999 HypoVereinsbank began talks with competitors about merging retail units; the bank decided to take its Direkt Anlage (now operating under the name DAB Bank AG) unit public that year. The following year the bank made plans to acquire Bank Austria to strengthen its presence in Eastern Europe and Austria (the deal was completed in 2001). Its Activest fund management unit began selling third-party funds which made the business of UK asset manager subsidiary Foreign & Colonial redundant. Accordingly HypoVereinsbank sold Foreign & Colonial to Eureko B.V. the pan-European insurance consortium.

In an effort to bolster flagging profits in mortgage lending HypoVereinsbank announced plans to roll its real estate financing businesses together into a new bank by 2002. In 2001 the bank announced about 8000 layoffs and the closure of up to 15% of its branches. The move underscores HypoVereinsbank's hopes to corral more customers into using its online and telephone banking services.

HypoVereinsbank also sold a 50% stake in mortgage-lender Westfälische Hypothekenbank to Düsseldorf-based WGZ Bank. HypoVereinsbank's remaining 25% share was sold to German insurer Signal Iduna. In a bid to become more universally recognized the bank took on the name HVB Group.

A loss of nearly $1 billion in 2002 caused in part by investment losses and Germany's languid economy compelled the company to cancel its dividend for the first time since WWII. HVB overhauled its management and pared more than 10000 positions mainly in Germany and in its Polish subsidiaries such as BPH-PBK Bank.

The company spun off its commercial real estate financing business as Hypo Real Estate Holding in 2003.

In one of the largest cross-border banking deals Europe had seen HypoVereinsbank was acquired by Italian banking giant UniCredit in 2008 three years after UniCredit took its initial majority stake.

A year after UniCredit took over HypoVereinsbank reorganized from four divisions into three merging the corporate and investment banking divisions together to make it the bank's largest segment.

UniCredit sold the majority of HVB's Poland-based Bank BPH to GE Money Bank in 2008. Other dispositions include International Moscow Bank and the former HVB Bank Latvia and HVB branches in Estonia and Lithuania.

EXECUTIVES

CEO and Divisions Retail and Wealth Management, Wolfgang Sprissler, age 71
First Executive Group IT, Matthias Sohler, age 48
Managing Director Wealth Management (Private Clients Family Office), Andreas W ffer, age 55
First Executive Corporates, Ronald Seilheimer, age 58
First Executive and Board Spokesman Vereins-und Westbank, Stefan Schmittmann, age 60
CFO and Member Management Board, Rolf Friedhofen, age 58
CEO HVB Banque Luxembourg, Ernst-Dieter Wiesner
Head Corporate Banking Division, Lutz Diederichs
Chairman, Alessandro Profumo, age 59
Deputy Chairman, Lothar Meyer, age 74
Deputy Chairman, Peter K hig

LOCATIONS

HQ: UniCredit Bank AG
Kardinal-Faulhaber-Strasse 1, Munich D-80333
Phone: (49) 89 378 0   **Fax:** (49) 89 378 2 40 83
Web: www.unicredit.de

PRODUCTS/OPERATIONS

2014 Sales

	% of total
Net interest income	66
Net fee and commissions	26
Net incom from the held for trading portfolio	3
Others	5
Total	**100**

2014 Sales

	% of total
Commercial Banking	49
Corporte and investment banking	15
Others	36
Total	**100**

COMPETITORS

Aareal Bank	IKB
BayernLB	KfW
Commerzbank	Landesbank
DEPFA BANK	Baden-Wrttemberg
DVB Bank	Landesbank Berlin
DZ BANK	Oberbank AG
Deutsche Bank	Sparkasse Dachau
Deutsche Postbank	WGZ BANK
Eurohypo	WestLB

HISTORICAL FINANCIALS

Company Type: Public

Income Statement

FYE: December 31

	ASSETS ($ mil.)	NET INCOME ($ mil.)	INCOME AS % OF ASSETS	EMPLOYEES
12/15	268,074	474	0.2%	14,485
12/14	281,957	797	0.3%	14,890
12/13	325,538	1,066	0.3%	19,842
12/12	459,076	1,642	0.4%	20,153
12/11	498,643	1,204	0.2%	20,585
Annual Growth	**(14.4%)**	**(20.8%)**	**—**	**(8.4%)**

2015 Year-End Financials

Return on assets: 0.1%
Return on equity: 2.3%
Long-term debt ($ mil.): —
No. of shares (mil.): 802
Sales ($ mil): 7,249

Dividends
Yield: —
Payout: —
Market value ($ mil.): —

Unicredito SpA

Let's give credit where credit is due: UniCredit (formerly UniCredito Italiano) is a giant in Europe and is Italy's largest bank. The financial services group and its units operate in nearly 20 European countries with more than 8500 branches in about 50 markets. UniCredit is also the largest foreign bank in Central and Eastern Europe (CEE) with 4295 branches and units. It is organized into several divisions including retail banking (targeting families and small- to mid-sized businesses) corporate and investment banking private banking and CEE. UniCredit's retail banking operations are led by its bank of the same name in Italy UniCredit Bank in Germany UniCredit Bank Austria and Bank Pekao in Poland.

OperationsUniCredit operates eight main business segments. Its Commercial Banking Italy segment makes up more than 35% of the bank's overall revenue while the Central and Eastern Europe (CEE) division and the Corporate & Investment Banking segments each make up more than 15% of revenue. The Commercial Banking Germany (10%) Poland (8%) and Commercial Banking Austria (7%) segments each make up the next largest segments while Asset Management and Asset Gathering make up the remainder of revenue.

Geographic Reach

The bank operates through more than 8500 branches across 17 European countries and 50 markets. Nearly 50% of its revenue is generated in Italy while another 20% of revenue is generated in Germany. The company's other largest markets include the Central and Eastern Europe region (roughly 15% of revenue) Austria (nearly 10%) and Poland (more than 5%). Financial PerformanceNote: Growth rates may differ after conversion to US dollars.

UniCredit has struggled with declining revenue and profit in recent years as its relatively risky loan portfolio has been plagued with goodwill impairment charges and loan loss provisions. Revenue in 2014 fell by 4% to euro 22.51 billion ($27.36 billion) mostly as net trading income fell by nearly 38% as it collected less in gains on its financial assets and liabilities held for trading. Dividend and other income from equity investments also fell by 18% during the year hurting the top line further. The bank did see 4% growth however in its fee and commission income thanks to more investment service fees as its assets under management grew by euro 29.2 billion ($35.49 billion) over the year. Profit on the other hand rebounded sharply to euro 2.01 billion ($2.44 billion) in 2014 (compared to a euro 13.97 billion loss in 2013) mostly as the bank paid 68% less toward its loan loss provision expenses as it continued to de-risk its loan portfolio.

Cash levels declined considerably in 2014 with operations using euro 5.57 billion ($6.77 billion) mostly as the bank used more of its cash toward financial assets held for trading.

Strategy

Struggling with an unfavorable loan portfolio UniCredit has been following its 2013-2018 Strategic Plan targets with the goal of increasing its loan coverage levels and decrease its impairment charges and risk. Meanwhile it's been collecting more of its revenue from non-interest income sources and fee income; indeed in 2014 fee and commission income (which made up 34% of total revenue) was the bright spot for growth during the year adding euro 211 million ($256.47 million) to the company's top line.

With the goal of establishing itself as the premier bank in Europe for quality of service UniCredit strives to differentiate itself from competitors by looking at and participating in digital upgrades such as mobile-banking mobile payment and other customer-oriented banking channels that are quickly taking the industry by storm. A digital channel focus will allow the bank to decrease its branch network and cut operating costs significantly while giving customers faster access to banking services at the same time over digital devices.

HISTORY

Company BackgroundUniCredito Italiano's ancestor Banca di Genova was formed in 1870 just after Italy unified. Within a year the bank was in a South American banking venture Banco de Italia y Rio de la Plata. A banking crisis beginning in the late 1880s threatened the company which was saved and reorganized with the aid of German banking interests. The changes gave the bank — which was renamed Credito Italiano –an advantage over home-grown rivals and pointed it in the direction of German-style universal banking including making direct investments in Italy's late-blooming industrial sector.

In the early 20th century Credito Italiano joined other banks in foreign ventures in Albania Brazil and China and opened offices in London and New York.

After the 1929 crash Credito Italiano acquired several failed banks. But Credito Italiano itself was none too healthy: Government attempts in the 1920s to peg the lira to the pound led to industrial stagnation leaving the bank holding highly illiquid industrial investments and by the early 1930s it was essentially an industrial holding company.

Credito Italiano's existence was threatened when the Depression hit in earnest. To save the bank and its peers Mussolini established the Istituto per la Ricostruzione Industriale (IRI) in 1933 as a "temporary" Resolution Trust-style holding company (IRI was finally liquidated in 2000) to take over the industrial assets of Credito Italiano and several other banks. IRI was instantly a major shareholder in Credito Italiano. IRI-held banks were designated "banks of national interest" three years later and were allowed to provide only short-term commercial banking services a limit that remained in effect for more than 50 years.

In 1946 to fill the need for long-term industrial credit to rebuild war-torn Italy Credito Italiano joined with Banca Commerciale Italiana (now part of IntesaBci) and Banco di Roma to form Mediobanca.

Credito Italiano went public in 1969 (IRI sold its interest in the bank in 1993). As a bank of national interest Credito Italiano was called upon to help bail out several of the country's industrial groups in 1979 (it did so reluctantly).

Changing laws allowed the company to expand its branch network in 1980 and in 1982 IRI allowed Credito Italiano to raise capital (although it was still obliged to prop up struggling state industries). But the 1987 US stock market crash caused Credito Italiano's earnings to plunge 33%. Two years later it bought a stake in Banca Nazionale dell'Agricoltura then Italy's largest private bank.

In 1995 the company joined forces with Rolo Banca 1473 (named for the year its progenitor was founded) to form Credito Italiano Group. Two years later Alessandro Profumo became CEO. He would usher in more than a decade of rapid and agressive expansion.

Credito Italiano merged in 1998 with UniCredito a collection of several northern Italian banks. One Cassa di Risparmio di Verona Vicenza Belluno e Ancona (Cariverona) began in 1501 as a pawn-shop operated by monks.

Foreshadowing the bank's shift to an Internet growth strategy (announced after talks with Spain's Banco Bilbao Vizcaya Argentaria fell through) UniCredito in 1999 announced plans for an electronic stock market to include after-hours trading. It also continued to boost holdings in Eastern European banks. In 2000 the company entered into securities brokerage and mutual fund administration with its purchase of US-based Pioneer Investment Management.

In 2001 UniCredito bought 10% of the Pirelli/Benetton-owned holding company formed to control Italian telecommunications company Olivetti. The following year the company partnered with Koç Holding to take a majority stake in Yapi Kredi.

The bank acquired HVB and Bank Austria in 2005 in an $18 billion cross-border deal one of the largest such deals ever seen in Europe. The bank strengthened its hold at home in 2007 with the nearly $30 billion purchase of Italian bank Capitalia. Antitrust authorities ordered UniCredit to sell its stake in Assicurazioni Generali following the Capitalia transaction.

EXECUTIVES

CEO, Jean-Pierre Mustier, age 55
Deputy General Manager and COO, Paolo Fiorentino, age 61
Deputy General Manager and Head of Strategy and Finance, Marina Natale, age 54
Country Chairman Italy, Gabriele Piccini, age 60
Country Chairman Austria, Robert Zadrazil
Country Chairman Germany, Theodor Weimer, age 57
Country Chairman Poland, Luigi Lovaglio, age 61
Deputy General Manager and Head CIB Division, Gianni Franco Papa, age 60
Head Asset Gathering and CEO and General Manager FinecoBank, Alessandro Foti, age 56
Head Central and Eastern Europe Division, Carlo Vivaldi, age 51
Chief Risk Officer, Massimiliano Fossati, age 49
Vice Chairman, Fabrizio Palenzona, age 63
Chairman, Giuseppe Vita, age 81
Deputy Vice Chairman, Vincenzo Calandra Buonaura, age 70
Vice Chairman, Luca Cordero di Montezemolo, age 69
Auditors: Deloitte & Touche S.p.A.

LOCATIONS

HQ: Unicredito SpA
Piazza Gae Aulenti 3 - Tower A, Milano 20154
Phone: (39) 2 88 621   **Fax:** (39) 2 8862 3463
Web: www.unicreditgroup.eu

2014 Sales

	% of total
Italy	48
Germany	20
Austria	9
Poland	7
Other countries	16
Total	**100**

PRODUCTS/OPERATIONS

2014 Sales

	% of total
Commercial banking Italy	36
Corporate & investment banking	16
Central & Eastern Europe	16
Commercial Banking Germany	11
Poland	8
Commercial Banking Austria	7
Asset management	4
Asset gathering	2
Total	**100**

COMPETITORS

ABN AMRO Group	Banco Popolare
Antonveneta	Credit Suisse
BNL bc	Deutsche Bank
BNP Paribas	Intesa Sanpaolo
Banca Popolare di Milano	UBS

HISTORICAL FINANCIALS

Company Type: Public

Income Statement

FYE: December 31

	ASSETS ($ mil.)	NET INCOME ($ mil.)	INCOME AS % OF ASSETS	EMPLOYEES
12/15	937,193	1,845	0.2%	139,469
12/14	1,026,150	2,440	0.2%	143,520
12/13	1,164,495	(19,225)	—	153,449
12/12	1,221,604	1,139	0.1%	162,864
12/11	1,198,730	(11,908)	—	167,014
Annual Growth	**(6.0%)**	**—**	**—**	**(4.4%)**

2015 Year-End Financials

Return on assets: 0.2%	Dividends
Return on equity: 3.4%	Yield: 0.0%
Long-term debt ($ mil.): —	Payout: 44.4%
No. of shares (mil.): —	Market value ($ mil.): —
Sales ($ mil): 35,448	

	STOCK PRICE ($) FY Close	P/E High/Low	PER SHARE ($) Earnings	Dividends	Book Value
12/15	5.47	27 20	0.29	0.13	9.14
12/14	6.50	24 18	0.42	0.10	10.24
12/13	7.46	— —	(3.39)	0.12	11.14
12/12	4.89	56 20	0.20	0.00	14.30
12/11	8.35	— —	(6.61)	0.04	34.55
Annual Growth	**(10.0%)**		**—**	**—**	**35.5%**
(28.3%)					

Unilever N.V.

From Dove soap to Ben & Jerry's ice cream Unilever N.V. manufactures more than 400 different food and wellness product brands that are used by two billion people worldwide every day. Along with its UK-based counterpart Unilever PLC the Netherlands-based Unilever N.V. operates jointly as the Unilever Group which has a single board of directors and one set of financial statements. Unilever is one of the top manufacturers of dressings savory and spreads with brand names Hellmann's Knorr and Ragu. Its other top products include ice cream (Breyers Ben & Jerry's) tea (Lipton) and soaps (Dove Lux). Unilever traces its roots back to 1872.

Operations

The company boasts a vast products portfolio consisting of 400 health and wellness brands which include: Knorr Hellmann's Lipton Becel/Flora (Healthy Heart) Rama/Blue Band (Family Goodness) Wall's/Algida (Heartbrand) Omo Dove Lux Rexona (including Sure and Degree) and Axe/Lynx among others.

Unilever group is organized based on its four main product groups. Roughly 35% of its revenue is generated by personal care products which include skin and hair care products deodorants and oral care products. Another nearly 30% comes from the food product segment which consist of snacks soups bouillons sauces margarines mayonnaise salad dressings and spreads. Refreshment products bring in nearly 20% of sales and include ice cream tea beverages weight-management products and nutritionally enhanced staples for sale in developing markets. The home care product division brings in the remainder of revenue and consists of a variety of cleaning products powders liquids and capsules and soap bars.

Financial Performance

Following five years of sales growth Unilever Group's revenue in 2014 fell by 14% to $58.9 billion with sales declines from all product segments. Two-thirds of the drop was driven by a 7% decline food product sales mostly from lagging spread sales in the European and North American markets. The group's refreshment product sales also fell by 4% further hurting the top line. The company's Personal Care segment fell the least as its Dove brand remained strong.

Declining revenue caused the group's net income to drop by 6% to $6.29 billion after two years of profit growth in 2012 and 2013. Operations provided $6.74 billion or 22% less cash than in 2013 partly from lower earnings but mostly due to a combination of negative cash flows from working capital and from an elimination of profits from discontinued brand operations.

Strategy

To free up resources and focus them on growing divisions and product lines Unilever Group has made a series of brand divestitures in recent years. In In 2013 as part of its strategy of making Foods fit for growth the company sold off its flailing Wish-Bone Skippy and Unipro brands. Between 2011 and 2013 the company made a series of brand acquisitions to strategically expand its product portfolio buying Alberto Culver Sara Lee Kalina and Toni & Guy.

Mergers and Acquisitions

In 2016 Unilever acquired start-up razor manufacturer Dollar Shave Club for $1 billion in cash. Founded in 2011 Dollar Shave Club built its business selling inexpensive men's razors exclusively through digital commerce sites. The acquisition bolsters Unilever's presence in the online sales space; the company traditionally sells its products through brick-and-mortar retailers where profit margins can be smaller.

EXECUTIVES

CEO, Paul Polman, age 59, $1,033,000 total compensation
CEO Unilever Indonesia, Hemant Bakshi
President Personal Care, Alan Jope
President Foods, Antoine de Saint Affrique
President Europe, Jan Zijderveld
CFO, Jean Marc Hu ‹t
President Refreshment, Kevin Havelock
President Home Care, Nitin Paranjpe
President Russia Ukraine and Belarus, J.V. Raman
Chairman, Michael Treschow, age 73
Auditors: PricewaterhouseCoopers Accountants N.V.

LOCATIONS

HQ: Unilever N.V.
  Weena 455, Rotterdam 3013 AL
Phone: (31) 10 217 4000   **Fax:** (31) 10 217 4798
Web: www.unilever.com

2014 Sales

	% of total
United States	14
Netherlands/ United Kingdom	8
Others	78
Total	**100**

PRODUCTS/OPERATIONS

2014 Sales

	% of total
Personal Care	37
Foods	25
Refreshment	19
Home Care	19
Total	**100**

Selected Brands

Axe
Becel
Bertolli
Biotex
Blue Band
Cif
Conimex
Domestos
Dove
Duke
Hellmann' s
Knorr
Lipton
Neutral
OLA
OMO
Prodent
Unox
Zendium
zwitsal　

COMPETITORS

Alticor	Johnson & Johnson
Atkins Nutritionals	Kao
Avon	L' Oreal
Beiersdorf	LVMH
Big Heart Pet Brands	Mars Incorporated
Boulder Brands	McBride plc
Campbell Soup	Meda Pharmaceuticals
Church & Dwight	Mondelez International
Clorox	Nestle
Coca-Cola	Procter & Gamble
Colgate-Palmolive	R.C. Bigelow
ConAgra	Reckitt Benckiser
Dairy Farmers of	Republic of Tea
America	Revlon
Danone	S.C. Johnson
Estee Lauder	Shiseido
General Mills	Tata Global Beverages
Henkel	The Dial Corporation

HISTORICAL FINANCIALS

Company Type: Public

Income Statement

FYE: December 31

	REVENUE ($ mil.)	NET INCOME ($ mil.)	NET PROFIT MARGIN	EMPLOYEES
12/15	58,024	5,346	9.2%	171,000
12/14	58,874	6,285	10.7%	173,000
12/13	68,557	6,666	9.7%	174,000
12/12	67,647	5,904	8.7%	172,000
12/11	60,102	5,499	9.2%	169,000
Annual Growth	**(0.9%)**	**(0.7%)**	**—**	**0.3%**

2015 Year-End Financials

Debt ratio: 30.5%	No. of shares (mil.): 1,573	
Return on equity: 33.7%	Dividends	
Cash ($ mil.): 2,507	Yield: 3.0%	
Current ratio: 0.63	Payout: 69.6%	
Long-term debt ($ mil.): 10,733	Market value ($ mil.): 68,150	

	STOCK PRICE ($) FY Close	P/E High/Low		PER SHARE ($) Earnings	Dividends	Book Value
12/15	43.32	27	20	1.87	1.32	10.69
12/14	39.04	22	18	2.18	1.51	10.55
12/13	40.23	27	22	2.29	1.40	12.55
12/12	38.30	25	20	2.03	1.23	11.71
12/11	34.37	23	18	1.89	1.14	10.78
Annual Growth	**6.0%**			**(0.2%)**	**3.7%**	**(0.2%)**

Unilever Plc (United Kingdom)

It takes two parents –one Dutch and one British –to make one Unilever. Unilever N.V. and Unilever PLC together with their group companies constitute a global food personal care and household products powerhouse. The group's vast portfolio of consumer products includes a dozen global brands including Hellmann's (mayonnaise) Knorr (soups) Lipton (tea) and Dove and Lux (soaps) that each ring up more than euro 1 billion ($1.4 billion) in sales. Unilever's consumer goods are sold in more than 190 countries. The company was the world's #1 consumer products maker until Procter & Gamble purchased Gillette in 2005. Based in England Unilever PLC trades on the London and New York stock exchanges.

Geographic Reach

Unilever's business is organized across three geographic areas: the Americas; Europe; and Other markets (Asia Australasia Africa the Middle East Turkey Russia Ukraine and Belarus).

Operations

The company operates in four segments: Personal Care (36% of Unilever's 2014 revenues); Foods 27%; Refreshment 19%; and Home Care 18%.

Sales and Marketing

Unilever's products are generally sold through its own sales force as well as through independent brokers agents and distributors to chain wholesale co-operative and independent grocery accounts food service distributors and institutions. Products are physically distributed through a network of distribution centers satellite warehouses company-operated and public storage facilities depots and other facilities.

E-commerceis an increasingly significant distribution channel. In the retail market e-commerce sales account for 1.2% of total sales and it is expected to double to 2.4% by 2020 due to growth in emerging markets where mobile phones one of the most effective ways of delivering advertising to individuals.

Global digital advertising is estimated at $137.5 billion or about 25% of Unilever's total advertising spend.

Financial Performance

In 2014 the company's revenues decreased by 14% due the following factors:Revenues from personal care dropped as the result of lower volume growth driven by a slowdown in global markets and strong competition;

Food sales declined due to exchange rate movements and business disposals (including the Ragu and Bertolli pasta sauces business) while savory and dressings both grew (but spreads declined due to lower consumer demand for margarine in Europe and North America);Refreshment revenues dropped due to exchange rate movements and business disposals (primarily SlimŸFast) offset by acquisitions (Talenti Gelato & Sorbetto); Revenues from Home Care showed strong growth supported by the impact of the Qinyuan acquisition partially offset by exchange rate movements. Unilever's net income declined by 5.7% in 2014 due to lower revenues.

In 2014 cash from operating activities increased by 12% due to the net inflow of acquisitions and disposals.

Strategy

Unilever aims to double its business with innovative brands backed by marketing and a best-in-class supply chain. The strategic choices across four categories (personal care home care foods refreshment emerging markets) focus on growing brands in emerging markets which retain good long-term growth prospects.

Unilever points to several countries for steady growth. These include Africa the Americas (including Brazil and Mexico) China Europe India and Russia. China Russia and Brazil are three of the company's biggest hair care markets in the world.

In 2015 Unilever launched a crowdsourcing initiative to drive sustainable growth by serving as a hub to centrally organize all crowdsourcing briefs.

To raise cash to pay down debt a reinvest in growth areas in 2014 company sold its global Ragu and Bertolli pasta sauce business to Mizkan Group for $2.15 billion and its SlimŸFast brand to Kainos Capital for an undisclosed amount. Ot also sold its global Skippy business to Hormel Foods for $700 million.

Other 2014 disposals included its Royal pasta brand in the Philippines to RFM Corporation for $48 million and the sale of its meat snacks business including the Bifi and Peperami brands to Jack Link's for an undisclosed amount.

Mergers and Acquisitions

In 2016 Unilever acquired plant-based household products maker Seventh Generation for $700 million. The acquisition brings to Unilever's Home Care business a well-established line of eco-friendly detergents and household cleaners. The addition also complements the company's sustainable living public relations initiative which is rooted in "purpose-driven" products like Ben & Jerry's Dove and Seventh Generation.

Growing its portfolio in emerging markets in 2014 Unilever acquired 55% of the Qinyuan Group a leading Chinese water purification business for an undisclosed amount. It also acquired US-based Talenti Gelato & Sorbetto for an undisclosed amount.

Company Background

Unilever acquired salon hair care products maker TIGI in 2009. The more than $410 million purchase which includes the firm's hair styling academies adds the Bed Head Catwalk and S-factor brands among others to Unilever's hair care products offering. TIGI remains headquartered in Dallas and operates as a stand-alone global business unit within Unilever.

CEO Patrick Cescau retired at the end of 2008 and was replaced by Paul Polman an executive at Nestle USA who has some 25 years of experience at P&G.

EXECUTIVES

CFO, Graeme Pitkethly
President Refreshment, Kevin Havelock, age 59
CEO, Paul Polman, age 59
Chief Research and Development Officer, David Blanchard
President Home Care, Nitin Paranjpe, age 52
President Foods, Amanda Sourry
President Personal Care, Alan Jope
President Europe, Jan Zijderveld
President North America, Kees Kruythoff
Chief Supply Chain Officer, Marc Engel
Chairman, Marijn Dekkers
Auditors: KPMG LLP

LOCATIONS

HQ: Unilever Plc (United Kingdom)
Unilever House, Blackfriars, 100 Victoria Embankment, London EC4Y 0DY
Phone: (44) 20 7822 5252 **Fax:** (44) 20 7822 6108
Web: www.unilever.com

PRODUCTS/OPERATIONS

Selected Global Brands
Axe/Lynx (male grooming)
Blue Band (margarine)
Dove (personal care)
Heartbrand ice creams
Hellmann's (mayonnaise)
Knorr (soup)
Lipton (tea)
Lux (soap)
Omo (detergent)
Rexona (deodorant)
Sunsilk (hair care)

2014 Sales

	% in total
Personal	36
Foods	27
Refreshment	19
Home Care	18
Total	**100**

COMPETITORS

Church & Dwight Canada	Premier Foods
Henkel	Procter & Gamble
Mondelez International	R&R Ice Cream
Nestle	Reckitt Benckiser

HISTORICAL FINANCIALS
Company Type: Public

Income Statement
FYE: December 31

	REVENUE ($ mil.)	NET INCOME ($ mil.)	NET PROFIT MARGIN	EMPLOYEES
12/15	58,024	5,346	9.2%	168,921
12/14	58,874	6,285	10.7%	173,000
12/13	68,557	6,666	9.7%	174,000
12/12	67,647	5,904	8.7%	172,000
12/11	60,102	5,499	9.2%	169,000
Annual Growth	(0.9%)	(0.7%)	—	(0.0%)

2015 Year-End Financials

Debt ratio: 30.5%	No. of shares (mil.): 1,283
Return on equity: 33.7%	Dividends
Cash ($ mil.): 2,507	Yield: 3.0%
Current ratio: 0.63	Payout: 68.5%
Long-term debt ($ mil.): 10,733	Market value ($ mil.): 55,343

	STOCK PRICE ($) FY Close	P/E High/Low	PER SHARE ($) Earnings	Dividends	Book Value
12/15	43.12	27 21	1.87	1.30	13.10
12/14	40.48	23 19	2.18	1.49	12.93
12/13	41.20	27 22	2.29	1.40	15.39
12/12	38.72	25 20	2.03	1.23	15.57
12/11	33.52	22 18	1.89	1.14	14.11
Annual Growth	6.5%	— —	(0.2%)	3.3%	(1.8%)

Union Bank Of India

LOCATIONS

HQ: Union Bank Of India
Union Bank Bhavan,, 239, Vidhan Bhavan Marg,, Nariman Point, Mumbai 400 021
Phone: 800 22 22 44
Web: www.unionbankofindia.com

HISTORICAL FINANCIALS
Company Type: Public

Income Statement
FYE: March 31

	ASSETS ($ mil.)	NET INCOME ($ mil.)	INCOME AS % OF ASSETS	EMPLOYEES
03/15	61,327	281	0.5%	0
03/14	59,124	279	0.5%	0
03/13	57,641	397	0.7%	0
03/12	51,700	348	0.7%	0
03/11	53,058	495	0.9%	0
Annual Growth	3.7%	(13.2%)	—	—

2015 Year-End Financials

Return on assets: 0.4%	Dividends
Return on equity: 9.1%	Yield: —
Long-term debt ($ mil.): —	Payout: —
No. of shares (mil.): —	Market value ($ mil.): —
Sales ($ mil): 5,777	

Unione Di Banche Italiane SpA

Unione di Banche Italiane known as UBI Banca serves individuals and businesses through nine subsidiary banks with some 1560 branches in Italy (concentrated in the Lombardy region). It also operates offices in about a dozen other countries across Europe Asia and South America and boasts some 3.6 million customers worldwide. Beyond standard retail banking deposit and checking accounts the banking group also provides asset management leasing operations private banking insurance corporate banking mortgages and other types of loans. The group was formed in 2007 when Banche Popolari Unite acquired rival Banca Lombarda e Piemontese and changed its name to UBI Banca.

OperationsBroadly speaking about 53% of UBI Banca's operating income (net of expenses) came from net interest income (mostly from loans) in 2014. Another 36% of its operating income came from net fee and commission income with half of that coming from management trading and advisory services (mostly portfolio management services) and another one-third of that coming from collection and payment services and management of multilateral trading systems. Nearly 61% of UBI Banca's loan portfolio was split fairly evenly between mortgage loans and other medium to long-term financing in 2014. An additional 12% of the loan portfolio was made up of current account overdrafts while 8% was from finance leases. The rest of the portfolio was split among credit card debt personal loans and salary-backed loans (4% of the portfolio) factoring (2%) reverse repurchase agreements (1%) and other debt instruments (less than 1%). By sector about 14% of its loan portfolio was tied to funds lent to various types of manufacturing companies. Another 27% of the portfolio was tied to loans to the real estate construction and wholesale/retail/auto repair sectors.

Geographic Reach

The banking group boasted 1560 branches in Italy; six international branches in France Germany and Spain; and eight offices in Poland Luxembourg Shanghai Sao Paolo Moscow Mumbai and Hong Kong in 2014. About half of UBI Banca's branches and (68% of its loan portfolio assets) were located in the Lombardy region of Italy.

About 82% of the group's loans were held by branches in the North West region of Italy while about 10% were held by branches in Central Italy.

Sales and Marketing

UBI Banca served some 3.3 million private individuals and families 270 thousand businesses (mostly small businesses and small-to-midsize enterprises or SMEs) and 29 thousand authorities and associations in 2014.

Strategy

UBI Banca has been moving toward digital banking channels that are quickly taking the industry by storm allowing the bank to slow expensive branch-expansion plans and cut operating costs significantly while giving customers faster access to banking services. During 2014 the company's mobile banking customer base grew by 51% while its internet banking customer base increased nearly 15% to 1.12 million users. All told the group's "multi-channel" customers grew 11% to 1.35 million during 2014 an amount equal to one-third of the bank's total customer base. The banking group has taken a number of cost-cutting and growth initiative measures in recent years to boost profits amidst an increasingly regulated industry. From April 2007 through the January 2015 the banking group reduced its branch count by more than 20% (from 1970 branches to 1560) while reducing its staff count by 16% over the same time period. As a result the group has slashed its total operating costs by a staggering 19% since 2007. Additionally the group reduced its cost-to-income ratio (a measure of efficiency) from a high of 70% in 2010 to 61.8% at the end of 2014.

UBI Banca is better capitalized than many of its Italian peers. In a late 2014 stress test among European banks nine out of 15 failing banks were Italian but UBI Banca reported that it passed with capital levels "well above the minimum thresholds required." Strong financial capitalization could help quell risk-averse customer concerns and could keep its financial condition more stable than peers' in market downturns and recessions.

EXECUTIVES

Vice Presidente, MARIO CERA
Vice Presidente, PIETRO GUSSALLI BERETTA
Vice Presidente, ARMANDO SANTUS
Vice Presidente, FLAVIO PIZZINI
Auditors: Deloitte & Touche S.p.A.

LOCATIONS

HQ: Unione Di Banche Italiane SpA
Piazza Vittorio Veneto 8, Bergamo 24122
Phone: (39) 035 392111
Web: www.ubibanca.it

PRODUCTS/OPERATIONS

2013 Branch Offices
Total

Banca Popolare di Bergamo Spa	357
Banco di Brescia spa	322
Banca Regionale Europea Spa	256
Banca Carime Spa	255
Banca Popolare di Ancona Spa	219
Banca Popolare Commerceio e industria Spa	219
Banca di valle Camonica Spa	66
UBI Banca Private Investment Spa	25
IW Bank Spa	2
UBI Banca Scpa	4
Total	**0**	**1,725**

2013 Sales

	% of total
Retail	
Private	37
Small Business	31
Corporate	26
Private	6
Total	**100**

Selected Subsidiaries

Aviva Assicurazioni Vita Spa (49.9%)
Banco di San Giorgio Spa (93%)
Banca Populare Commercio e Industria Spa (84%)
Banca Populare di Bergamo Spa
Banca Regionale Europea Spa (60%)
Capitalgest Alternative Investments SGR Spa
Centrobanca Spa (98%)
FinanzAttiva Servizi Srl
IW Bank Spa (80%)
Mercato Impresa Spa (99%)
Prestitalia Spa (23%)
S.B.I.M. Spa
UBI Assicurazioni Spa
UBI Banca Private Investment Spa
UBI Gestioni Fiduciarie Sim Spa
UBI Leasing Spa (99%)
UBI Pramerica SGR Spa (65%)

COMPETITORS

Antonveneta	Banco Popolare
BNL bc	HSBC
BPER-Emilia Romagna	Intesa Sanpaolo
Banca Carige	Monte dei Paschi di
Banca Popolare di	Siena
Milano	UniCredit

HISTORICAL FINANCIALS

Company Type: Public

Income Statement
FYE: December 31

	ASSETS ($ mil.)	NET INCOME ($ mil.)	INCOME AS % OF ASSETS	EMPLOYEES
12/15	127,656	127	0.1%	17,718
12/14	148,032	(882)	—	18,132
12/13	171,048	345	0.2%	18,337
12/12	174,554	109	0.1%	19,114
12/11	167,894	(2,381)	—	19,405
Annual Growth	(6.6%)	—		(2.2%)

2015 Year-End Financials

Return on assets: 0.1%
Return on equity: 1.1%
Long-term debt ($ mil.): —
No. of shares (mil.): 900
Sales ($ mil): 4,721

Dividends
Yield: —
Payout: —
Market value ($ mil.): 5,789

	STOCK PRICE ($) FY Close	P/E High/Low		Earnings	Dividends	Book Value
12/15	6.43	59	51	0.14	0.00	12.08
12/14	7.56	—	—	(0.98)	0.00	13.24
12/13	3.05	—	—	0.37	0.00	15.82
12/12	3.05	34	29	0.12	0.00	14.25
12/11	3.80	—	—	(3.06)	0.00	12.84
Annual Growth	14.1%	—	—	—	—	(1.5%)

Unipol Gruppo Finanziaro SPA Bologna

Unipol Gruppo Finanziario (better known simply as Unipol) serves the insurance and banking sectors and other markets such as supplementary pensions and health. It operates primarily through its subsidiary UnipolSai Assicurazioni SpA established in 2014 when three companies merged. While its main focus is on offering life auto property/casualty health and other general insurance Unipol provides merchant banking and consumer banking services. The firm has euro 5 billion in as-

sets under management. Its Unipol Banca boasts about 300 branches. The acquisitive company targets insurance firms and banks. Holding company Holmo SpA controls Unipol through its Finanziaria dell'Economia Sociale (Finsoe) unit.

EXECUTIVES

General Manager; CEO UGF Assicurazioni, Carlo Cimbri, age 51
Director, Pierluigi Stefanini, age 63
Vice Chairman, Giovanni Antonelli
Auditors: PricewaterhouseCoopers SpA

LOCATIONS

HQ: Unipol Gruppo Finanziaro SPA Bologna
Via Stalingrado, 45, Bologna 40128
Phone: (39) 051 507 61 11   Fax: (39) 051 507 66 66
Web: www.unipol.it

COMPETITORS

Allianz S.p.A.	Milano Assicurazioni
BNL bc	Monte dei Paschi di
Banco Popolare	Siena
Cattolica	UniCredit
Assicurazioni	UnipolSai
ERGO Previdenza	Vittoria Assicurazioni
Generali	alleanza toro
Intesa Sanpaolo	

HISTORICAL FINANCIALS

Company Type: Public

Income Statement
FYE: December 31

	REVENUE ($ mil.)	NET INCOME ($ mil.)	NET PROFIT MARGIN	EMPLOYEES
12/15	20,241	296	1.5%	13,864
12/14	25,862	233	0.9%	14,223
12/13	27,056	(108)	—	15,230
12/12	18,905	393	2.1%	15,212
12/11	12,895	(140)	—	7,638
Annual Growth	11.9%	—		16.1%

2015 Year-End Financials

Debt ratio: —
Return on equity: 4.8%
Cash ($ mil.): 952
Current ratio: —
Long-term debt ($ mil.): —

No. of shares (mil.): 711
Dividends
Yield: 0.0%
Payout: 14.3%
Market value ($ mil.): 2,845

	STOCK PRICE ($) FY Close	P/E High/Low		Earnings	Dividends	Book Value
12/15	4.00	10	9	0.41	0.06	8.46
12/14	3.34	11	11	0.32	0.07	15.81
12/13	0.11	—	—	(0.15)	0.07	17.05
12/12	10.77	10	0	1.67	1.21	16.59
12/11	0.08	—	—	(0.04)	0.00	1.88
Annual Growth	165.9%	—	—	—	—	45.6%

UnipolSai Assicurazioni SpA

Auditors: PricewaterhouseCoopers S.p.A.

LOCATIONS

HQ: UnipolSai Assicurazioni SpA
Via Stalingrado 45, Bologna 40128
Phone: (39) 051 5077111   Fax: (39) 051 375349
Web: www.unipolsai.com

HISTORICAL FINANCIALS

Company Type: Public

Income Statement

FYE: December 31

	REVENUE ($ mil.)	NET INCOME ($ mil.)	NET PROFIT MARGIN	EMPLOYEES
12/15	17,243	774	4.5%	9,951
12/14	23,185	898	3.9%	7,376
12/13	15,660	454	2.9%	7,389
12/12	14,992	(988)	—	7,377
12/11	15,178	(1,102)	—	7,591
Annual Growth	3.2%	—	—	7.0%

2015 Year-End Financials

Debt ratio: —
Return on equity: 11.3%
Cash ($ mil.): 1,042
Current ratio: —
Long-term debt ($ mil.): —

No. of shares (mil.): —
Dividends
Yield: —
Payout: —
Market value ($ mil.): —

United Arab Emirates (United Arab Emirates)

Auditors: PricewaterhouseCoopers

LOCATIONS

HQ: United Arab Emirates (United Arab Emirates)
  PO Box 686, P.O. Box 686, Dubai
Phone:
Web: www.emirates.com

HISTORICAL FINANCIALS

Company Type: Public

Income Statement

FYE: March 31

	REVENUE ($ mil.)	NET INCOME ($ mil.)	NET PROFIT MARGIN	EMPLOYEES
03/16	22,733	1,939	8.5%	95,322
03/15	23,613	1,240	5.3%	84,153
03/14	21,976	885	4.0%	75,496
03/13	19,373	621	3.2%	69,707
Annual Growth	5.5%	46.1%	—	11.0%

2016 Year-End Financials

Debt ratio: 11.4%
Return on equity: 23.7%
Cash ($ mil.): 5,441
Current ratio: 0.82
Long-term debt ($ mil.): 11,120

No. of shares (mil.): —
Dividends
Yield: —
Payout: —
Market value ($ mil.): —

	STOCK PRICE ($) FY Close	P/E High/Low	PER SHARE ($) Earnings	Dividends	Book Value
03/16	0.00	— —	(0.00)	0.00	(0.00)
Annual Growth					

United Overseas Bank Ltd. (Singapore)

One of Singapore's top financial institutions United Overseas Bank (UOB) provides a range of commercial banking and personal financial services. Offerings include checking and savings accounts private banking loans investment banking commodities trading and asset management. It is also one of the largest issuers of credit cards in the Asia-Pacific region. Altogether the bank has about 500 branches and 1300 ATMs across Asia (its largest markets are in Singapore Thailand and Indonesia) and a handful of representative offices in Europe and North America.

Operations

UOB is organized into three businesses - Retail Wholesale and Global Markets and Investment Management. Its retail business covers personal accounts private banking and small businesses. It accounts for about 35% of revenue. The wholesale division serves large corporations and financial institutions; it also accounts for about 35% of revenue. Global markets and investment management which provides asset management foreign exchange money market funds derivatives and other capital market activities accounts for 20% of revenue.

Geographic Reach

Altogether the bank has operations in about 15 Asian countries. While it's headquartered in Singapore it only has about 75 branches in that country of 5 million people. The more populated countries of Indonesia (246 million people) has some 215 branches while Thailand with 67 million people has more than 160 branches. Outside Asia UOB has branches in London Los Angeles New York City Paris and Vancouver.

Company Background

UOB was founded in 1935 as the United Chinese Bank and catered mainly to the Fujian community in Singapore. The bank changed its name to United Overseas Bank in 1965.

EXECUTIVES

SEVP International, Francis C. Y. Lee
Head Global Markets and Investment Management, Terence S. E. Ong
Chief Risk Officer, Chan Seong
CFO, Lee Wai Fai
Deputy Chairman and CEO, Wee Ee Cheong, age 62
Head Group Wholesale Banking, Frederick V. F. Chin
Head Group Technology and Operations, Susan W. C. Hwee
President and Director PT Bank UOB Indonesia, Armand B. Arief
President and CEO United Overseas Bank (Thai) Public Company Limited, Peter M. T. Foo
President and CEO United Overseas Bank (China) Limited, Eric V. F. Lian
CEO United Overseas Bank (Malaysia) Bhd, Wong Kim Choong
Chairman, Hsieh Fu Hua, age 64
Auditors: Ernst & Young LLP

LOCATIONS

HQ: United Overseas Bank Ltd. (Singapore)
  80 Raffles Place, UOB Plaza, 048624
Phone: (65) 6533 9898   **Fax:** (65) 6534 2334
Web: www.uobgroup.com

2012 Sales

	% of sales
Singapore	58
Malaysia	15
Thailand	8
Indonesia	7
China	6
Other	6
Total	**100**

Selected Subsidiaries

Far Eastern Bank Limited (Singapore)
PT Bank UOB Indonesia
United Overseas Bank (China)
United Overseas Bank (Malaysia)
United Overseas Bank (Philippines)
United Overseas Bank (Thailand)
United Overseas Insurance Limited Singapore
UOB Australia Limited
UOB Capital Investments Pte Ltd Singapore
UOB Capital Management Pte Ltd Singapore
UOB Holdings Private Limited Singapore
UOB Insurance (H.K.) Limited Hong Kong
UOB International Investment Private Limited

PRODUCTS/OPERATIONS

2012 Sales

	% of total
Interest income	61
Fees & commission	23
Other non-interest income	16
Total	**100**

2012 Sales

	% of total
Retail	36
Wholesale	36
Global markets & investment mgmt.	19
Other	9
Total	**100**

COMPETITORS

Astra International	Edaran Otomobil
Bangkok Bank	HSBC
Bank Central Asia	Hang Seng Bank
Bank Danamon Indonesia	Hong Leong Finance
Bank Mandiri	Maybank
Bank Rakyat	OCBC Bank
Bank of China	Standard Chartered
DBS Group Holdings	

HISTORICAL FINANCIALS

Company Type: Public

Income Statement

FYE: December 31

	ASSETS ($ mil.)	NET INCOME ($ mil.)	INCOME AS % OF ASSETS	EMPLOYEES
12/15	223,570	2,270	1.0%	0
12/14	232,170	2,459	1.1%	0
12/13	224,984	2,380	1.1%	0
12/12	206,769	2,291	1.1%	0
12/11	182,320	1,790	1.0%	0
Annual Growth	5.2%	6.1%	—	—

2015 Year-End Financials

Return on assets: 1.0%
Return on equity: 10.6%
Long-term debt ($ mil.): —
No. of shares (mil.): 1,602
Sales ($ mil): 7,808

Dividends
Yield: 5.8%
Payout: 113.2%
Market value ($ mil.): 44,142

	STOCK PRICE ($)	P/E	PER SHARE ($)		
	FY Close	High/Low	Earnings	Dividends	Book Value
12/15	27.55	18 13	1.37	1.61	13.59
12/14	36.97	19 15	1.49	1.20	13.96
12/13	33.62	19 16	1.46	1.11	13.25
12/12	32.85	19 14	1.40	0.95	13.02
12/11	23.56	22 16	1.09	1.06	11.23
Annual Growth	4.0%	— —	5.7%	10.9%	4.9%

Vale SA

Vale has more than just one iron in the fire. Iron ore and pellets account for more than two-thirds of Vale's sales and the company accounts for a third of the world's ocean-shipped iron ore. Vale also mines for bauxite nickel kaolin and potash. Other products include steel copper and aluminum. It has holdings in hydroelectric power generation and in the rail and shipping businesses mainly to support its mining activities in Brazil. The company is the world's second-largest iron ore miner having grown dramatically with the 2006 acquisition of Vale Limited (formerly Vale Inco). To raise cash in late 2016 Vale agreed to sell its fertilizer business to Mosaic for $2.5 billion.

To keep all of its materials coming out of the ground Vale maintains its exploration efforts in 24 countries around the world.

Vale's revenues almost doubled in 2010 growing more than 94% as a result of increased production and higher prices for its major products particularly metals including iron ore nickel and copper. Net income grew 223% for the year on the strength of higher sales volumes and profit on the sale of assets.

In early 2012 the company declared force majeure on a number of its iron ore sales contract after high rainfall in three Brazilian states curtailed Vale's operations. The company estimated a loss of 2 million metric tons in iron ore shipments.

In 2011 Vale agreed to buy out minority shareholders of its Vale Fertilizantes SA subsidiary in a $1.4 billion move to consolidate its fertilizer business. Vale sought to buy the 16% of Fertilizantes it did not already own. The subsidiary is a small part of Vale's overall fertilizer business which the company had planned to spin off in 2011 but canceled those plans when it proved to be more profitable than Vale had projected.

Vale spent much of 2010 acquiring fertilizer companies and forming ventures. Mitsui teamed up with US fertilizer company Mosaic in 2010 for a joint venture investing in a Vale phosphorus ore development project in Peru. Mitsui spent $275 million to acquire a 25% stake and voting rights in a Vale subsidiary while Mosaic holds a 24% stake. The project is located in northwestern Peru's Piura province. Vale also completed a $4.7 billion deal for Brazil's Fosfertil and US-based agribusiness Bunge Co. to create Vale Fertilizantes.

Also in 2011 Vale announced plans to acquire South Africa-based copper and cobalt miner Metorex Ltd. for about $1.1 billion. However prior to the deal's close China's Jinchuan Group countered Vale's bid for Metorex with a $1.34 billion offer. Vale subsequently dropped its offer refusing to engage in a bidding war.

In 2010 Vale sold its Brazilian aluminum operations to Norwegian aluminum producer Norsk Hydro for $5.7 billion. Norsk Hydro paid Vale a combination of cash and a 22% stake in Norsk Hydro. Vale said it divested Paragominas one of the world's largest bauxite mines because it did not see enough growth potential in the operation.

Remaining active in the mining sector Vale is developing a copper mine in Zambia in a $400 million joint venture with African Rainbow Minerals. The Konkola North project is expected to begin production in 2013. In 2010 Vale acquired a 51% stake in Guinea iron-ore mining firm BSG Resources for $2.5 billion. The acquisition expands Vale's presence in Africa where it is also developing the Moatize coal deposit in Mozambique in a $6 billion joint venture with South Korean steelmaker POSCO.

In 2011 Vale resumed work on a $6.2 billion steelworks operation in Espirito Santo in southeast Brazil. The project part of a network of five mills planned around the country was dropped in 2009 after local authorities refused to issue an environmental permit. Now with permit in hand Vale is going forward with the redesigned project which is expected to produce about 5 million tons of slab steel a year beginning in 2014. Vale which had originally partnered with China's Baosteel Group is seeking another partner for the project.

To complement its rail port and shipping facilities Vale created a new logistics company for cargo transport in 2011. Vale Logistics Integrada will handle the company's general cargo assets including its operations for moving iron ore and other minerals from its mines to its customers. The company received $1.5 billion in sales from logistics services in 2010 primarily from the shipping of agricultural and steel products fuel and construction materials.

Murilo Pinto de Oliveira Ferreira was named president and CEO of Vale in 2011. He succeeds Roger Agnelli who completed his 10-year term in the position. Ferreira was previously the CEO of Vale Canada and Executive Director of Vale's Nickel and Base Metals Sales.

Investment group Valepar controls a third of Vale. The Brazilian government holds limited veto power on any permanent company changes.

HISTORY

During the 1890s as land reforms opened the way for foreign investments in Brazil the mineral-rich state of Minas Gerais caught the attention of mining companies from Europe and the US. British engineers founded the Itabira Iron Ore Company and took over the Doce River Valley's Vitoria-Minas Railroad. After Brazil's revolution (1930) Itabira was split up. One of the new companies Itabira Mineração began shipping iron ore in 1940.

A 1942 agreement prompted by the outbreak of WWII established iron export regulations from Brazil to the US and the UK. Later that year the Companhia Vale do Rio Doce (CVRD) was formed with the Brazilian government owning 80%. The new company received the assets of Itabira including Brazil's "iron mountain" Caue Peak. By the end of the 1940s 80% of Brazil's iron ore exports were mined by CVRD. During the 1950s CVRD invested in land holdings and shipping operations. The company set up a shipping and logistics subsidiary in 1962.

CVRD teamed up with US Steel in 1970 to mine iron ore at Carajas in Amazonian Brazil; two years later the site was found to hold the world's largest iron ore reserves (18 billion tons). By 1975 CVRD had become the world's largest iron ore exporter. A year later the company finished doubling the tracks of the Vitoria-Minas Railroad. It also set up a manganese mining company (Urucum Mineração) and an alumina production facility (Alumina do Norte do Brasil or Alunorte).

To support its Carajas mining operations CVRD added the Estrada de Ferro de Carajas railway (finished 1985) and a hydroelectric project. In all the giant Carajas project involved investments from the US Japan France the European Economic Community and the World Bank. (The Carajas area like many mining sites in Brazil has been the site of intense controversy because it attracts subsistence miners including children who work under dangerous circumstances.) By the late 1980s the company had become a major supplier of pelletized iron used as feed for steel mill blast furnaces.

In 1992 CVRD expanded into the production of chemicals (Rio Capim Quimica now Para Pigmentos SA). The company acquired stakes in two steel mills — Siderurgica de Tubarão and Aço Minas Gerais SA —in 1993. In 1996 it invested in gold finds in Para state. CVRD was privatized in 1997 and the next year set the sales record for a private Brazilian company.

The company listed ADR shares on the NYSE in 2000. Acquisitions that year included Brazilian iron ore companies SOCOIMEX and SAMITRI (73%). CVRD sold its 50% stake in pulp and paper group Bahia Sul to Suzano for $320 million in 2001. It also sold its 51% share of pulp maker Cenibra and its share of steelmaker Companhia Siderurgica Nacional (CSN).

In 2002 the Brazilian Treasury and the National Social and Economic Bank (BNDES) sold 33% of CVRD's shares further privatizing the company. CVRD disposed of its last gold mine (Fazenda Brasileiro) in 2003. It also exited the dry bulk-shipping business that year.

Under pressure from increasing globalization Vale had been forced to trim some of its operations (including its stake in CSN) to focus on mining and bulk transport. Those asset sales helped fund Vale's win over Australian mining giant BHP Billiton the world's #2 iron ore producer in a battle for Brazil's iron miner Caemi Mineração e Metalurgia #4 worldwide. (From 2001 through 2006 the company picked up stakes in Caemi until it owned it fully.) The deal for Inco trumped offers from Canadian miner Teck and US copper producer Phelps Dodge.

Toward the end of 2007 the company —then called Companhia Vale do Rio Doce —decided that it wanted a new brand identity and so ditched its longtime nickname CVRD in favor of Vale. Two years later it changed its name legally dropping the more formal Companhia Vale do Rio Doce.

EXECUTIVES

Executive Director Capital Projects, Galib Chaim
Executive Director Fertilizers and Coal, Roger Downey
CFO, Luciano Siani
Executive Director Logistics and Mineral Research, Humberto Freitas
Executive Director Ferrous Minerals, Peter Poppinga
Executive Director Base Metals; CEO Vale Canada, Jennifer Maki
Vice Chairman, M˜rio da Silveira Teixeira, age 71
Chairman, Dan Conrado
Auditors: KPMG Auditores Independentes

LOCATIONS

HQ: Vale SA
Avenida das Americas 700, Bloco 8-Loja 318, Rio de Janeiro 22640-100
Phone: (55) 21 3814 4477   Fax: (55) 21 3814 9935
Web: www.vale.com

2013 Sales

	$ mil.	% of total
China	18,921	40

Europe	8,763	19
Brazil	6,190	13
Japan	4,035	9
Asia except Japan and China	3,600	8
America except United States	1,848	4
Middle East/ Africa/Oceania	2,098	4
United States of America	1,312	3
Total	**46,767**	**100**

PRODUCTS/OPERATIONS

2013 Sales chart

	$ mil.	% of total
Bulk Materials	35,802	76
Basic Metals	7,286	16
Fertilizers	2,814	6
Others	865	2
Total	**46,767**	**100**

COMPETITORS

AHMSA	Exxaro
Anglo American	Freeport-McMoRan
Arconic	Kumba Iron Ore
BHP Billiton	Norilsk Nickel
BHP Billiton Plc	Rio Tinto Limited
Cliffs Natural	Rio Tinto plc
Resources	Teck

HISTORICAL FINANCIALS

Company Type: Public

Income Statement   FYE: December 31

	REVENUE ($ mil.)	NET INCOME ($ mil.)	NET PROFIT MARGIN	EMPLOYEES
12/15	25,609	(12,129)	—	74,098
12/14	37,539	657	1.8%	76,531
12/13	46,767	584	1.2%	83,286
12/12	47,694	5,511	11.6%	70,785
12/11	58,990	22,885	38.8%	79,646
Annual Growth	**(18.8%)**	**—**	**—**	**(1.8%)**

2015 Year-End Financials

Debt ratio: 32.9%
Return on equity: (-27.3%)
Cash ($ mil.): 3,591
Current ratio: 1.08
Long-term debt ($ mil.): 26,689

No. of shares (mil.): —
Dividends
  Yield: 7.4%
  Payout: —
Market value ($ mil.): —

	STOCK PRICE ($) FY Close	P/E High/Low	Earnings	PER SHARE ($) Dividends	Book Value
12/15	3.29	—	(2.35)	0.25	10.54
12/14	8.18	117 53	0.13	0.67	17.30
12/13	15.25	195 115	0.11	0.72	19.88
12/12	20.96	25 15	1.07	0.99	14.41
12/11	21.45	9 5	4.33	1.56	15.25
Annual Growth	**(37.4%)**	**— —**		**(37.0%)**	**(8.8%)**

Valeo SA

Auditors: ERNST & YOUNG et Autres

LOCATIONS

HQ: Valeo SA
43, rue Bayen, Paris, Cedex 17 75848
Phone: (33) 1 40 55 20 20 **Fax:** (33) 1 40 55 21 71
Web: www.valeo.com

HISTORICAL FINANCIALS

Company Type: Public

Income Statement   FYE: December 31

	REVENUE ($ mil.)	NET INCOME ($ mil.)	NET PROFIT MARGIN	EMPLOYEES
12/15	15,841	794	5.0%	82,800
12/14	15,467	683	4.4%	78,495
12/13	16,672	604	3.6%	74,770
12/12	15,498	500	3.2%	72,600
12/11	14,057	552	3.9%	68,000
Annual Growth	**3.0%**	**9.5%**	**—**	**5.0%**

2015 Year-End Financials

Debt ratio: 16.6%
Return on equity: 23.4%
Cash ($ mil.): 1,878
Current ratio: 0.99
Long-term debt ($ mil.): 1,247

No. of shares (mil.): 235
Dividends
  Yield: 4.6%
  Payout: 35.2%
Market value ($ mil.): 18,221

	STOCK PRICE ($) FY Close	P/E High/Low	Earnings	PER SHARE ($) Dividends	Book Value
12/15	77.42	27 18	3.32	1.20	16.07
12/14	61.93	27 20	2.93	2.13	14.28
12/13	55.61	29 14	2.62	0.98	14.07
12/12	25.70	17 12	2.21	0.88	11.85
12/11	19.78	17 10	2.44	0.79	11.13
Annual Growth	**40.7%**	**— —**	**8.0%**	**11.0%**	**9.6%**

Veolia Environnement

Auditors: ERNST & YOUNG et Autres

LOCATIONS

HQ: Veolia Environnement
36/38, avenue Kleber, Paris, Cedex 75116
Phone: (33) 1 71 75 00 00
Web: www.veolia.com

HISTORICAL FINANCIALS

Company Type: Public

Income Statement   FYE: December 31

	REVENUE ($ mil.)	NET INCOME ($ mil.)	NET PROFIT MARGIN	EMPLOYEES
12/15	27,191	490	1.8%	173,959
12/14	29,025	299	1.0%	179,508
12/13	30,721	(186)	—	202,800
12/12	38,801	519	1.3%	318,376
12/11	38,347	(633)	—	331,266
Annual Growth	**(8.2%)**	**—**	**—**	**(14.9%)**

2015 Year-End Financials

Debt ratio: 37.4%
Return on equity: 5.4%
Cash ($ mil.): 4,548
Current ratio: 0.95
Long-term debt ($ mil.): 8,737

No. of shares (mil.): 549
Dividends
  Yield: 3.3%
  Payout: 102.4%
Market value ($ mil.): 12,964

	STOCK PRICE ($) FY Close	P/E High/Low	Earnings	PER SHARE ($) Dividends	Book Value
12/15	23.59	36 22	0.75	0.79	16.53
12/14	17.58	55 42	0.40	0.95	18.38
12/13	16.36	— —	(0.40)	0.93	21.13
12/12	12.24	22 12	1.03	0.89	18.56
12/11	11.05	— —	(1.28)	1.58	18.09
Annual Growth	**20.9%**	**— —**		**(16.0%)**	**(2.2%)**

Vinci SA

Veni vidi vici ...VINCI. Through its VINCI Construction division this company conquers the world as one of the largest building civil engineering and maintenance contractors. VINCI operates in two divisions: concessions and contracting. Its concessions business which builds and operates motorways parking garages rail infrastructure stadiums and airports includes motorway operator VINCI Autoroutes and airport manager VINCI Airports. Under the contracting umbrella VINCI provides electrical engineering maintenance and facilities management. Roadworks and transportation infrastructure is handled by Eurovia. VINCI is active in some 100 countries with France accounting for more than 60% of its sales.

Operations

VINCI divides its business into two segments: Contracting and Concessions.

The Contracting segment which generated 84% of the company's total revenue in 2014 consists of VINCI Construction (39% of revenue); VINCI Energies (24% of revenues); and its Eurovia subsidiary (21% of revenues) which builds roads motorways airports rail and light rail infrastructure and operates a network of more than 400 quarries that produce 82 million tons of aggregates per year. Concessions which accounted for 15% of total revenue in 2014 consists of VINCI Autoroutes VINCI Airports VINCI Railways and VINCI Park. VINCI Park (and subsidiaries such as LAZ Parking in the US) which the firm sold the bulk of its stakes in 2014 managed more than a million on-street and off-street parking spaces in Europe North America and Asia. VINCI Immobilier the group's real estate unit accounted for about 1% of sales in 2014.

Geographic Reach

VINCI is Europe's biggest construction and concessions company. France is the company's largest market accounting for more than 60% of its annual revenue. Other important markets for the firm include Germany and the UK. Beyond Europe the group is active in Asia Africa the Americas and the Middle East.

Financial Performance

VINCI's revenues and profits have been growing at a steady pace over the past few years thanks to a strengthening global construction market and growth across its various Concessions businesses.

The firm's revenue reversed course in 2014 however falling by 4% to euro 38.7 billion ($47.04 billion) mostly as its main contracting business shrank by 5% as construction demand declined in the telecom manufacturing and infrastructure sectors in France. The VINCI Construction business in France shrank by nearly 5% due to a combination of reduced share holdings on the Belgian group CFE (from 47% to 12% at the end of 2013) the advancement of the LGV Tours-Brodeaux project and lower market demand in the building and public infrastructure sectors. The Eurovia subsidiary's revenue also declined after a slowdown in public sector orders after budget cuts followed the local elections in France. The company's concessions businesses however grew by nearly 4% thanks to growth in VINCI Autoroutes and double-digit growth at VINCI Airports.

Despite revenue declines in 2014 VINCI's net income jumped by 27% to euro 2.5 billion ($3.04 billion) thanks to several non-recurring income items mostly stemming from the sale of the company's investment securities and the capital gain on the sale of the bulk of its investment stake in VINCI Park. Not counting these non-recurring items profits inched up by less than 1% thanks to tight controls on operating costs. The firm's operating cash remained mostly flat at euro 3.6 billion ($4.38 billion) in 2014.

Strategy

VINCI continued to pursue its global expansion and diversification strategy in 2015 seeking to grow organically and through acquisitions. It also looked to bolster the expertise of its international specialized civil engineering networks especially in Latin America and continued developing major projects in emerging markets in central and eastern Europe the Middle East and India. In 2014 to free up cash for more international expansion in the Americas and Asia VINCI sold the bulk of its parking lot business to Ardian and Credit Agricole Assurances.

The company also sees opportunities in North America where aging infrastructure needs to be replaced. Indeed VINCI in 2014 won major contracts to expand or upgrade roads and transportation infrastructure in California Indiana and Georgia.VINCI has an ongoing strategy to acquire specialty companies that have a global reach. Specific target areas include ground technologies oil and gas infrastructure and nuclear engineering. VINCI is aligning its growth areas with marketplace trends such as urban development mobility needs and growing demand for new energy infrastructure.

Mergers and Acquisitions

In 2015 to extend its reach into Asia's oil and gas industry and diversify its revenue VINCI purchased Indonesia-based PT Istana Karang Laut which had expertise in onshore and offshore activities. The deal opened up markets in Central and South-East Asia where energy demand remained strong and where resources had not yet been exploited.Also in 2015 to strengthen its position in the Brazilian market the company acquired Orteng Engenharia e Sistemas S.A. which is based in Belo Horizonte Minas Gerais and designs builds and maintains electrical equipment PLCs and turnkey solutions in the energy manufacturing and infrastructure sectors.

In 2014 the company added to its holdings in Confiroute taking 100% ownership. The deal was priced in the range of euro 780 million to euro 800 million. It also acquired Imtech ICT the information and communication technologies division of Imtech as well as the Electrix company from McConnell Dowell a subsidiary of South African group Aveng.

In 2013 the company acquired ANA the company holding the 50-year concession for Portugal's 10 airports in a transaction valued at about euro 3.1 billion ($4.3 billion). The purchase furthered VINCI's strategy of making VINCI Airports a leading international players in airport concessions. With the addition of ANA'S airports VINCI now manages concessions at 23 airports in Portugal France and Cambodia. The French firm in July 2013 acquired an additional 5% stake in Aerports de Paris in July for euro 365 million ($504.5 million) bringing its holding to 8%. Also in 2013 VINCI purchased London-based Mentor IMC Group Ltd. a global oil and gas project resource specialist thereby broadening the customer base of its Energies' oil and gas business.

Company Background

In 2009 in Qatar the French firm partnered with Qatari Diar which holds shares in VINCI to design and build a new motorway on the outskirts of Doha. The project was an outgrowth of an effort by VINCI to establish local roots in Qatar through the formation of subsidiary QDVC which had positioned itself in seven years as a major player in the Qatari construction market. Previously VINCI and Quatri Diar announced plans for a parking lot joint venture which would run lots in Qatar. The two entities also worked together on a euro 2.2 billion ($3 billion) bridge linking Qatar and Bahrain.

HISTORY

Company BackgroundVINCI's origins lie with French conglomerate Vivendi (now Vivendi Universal) which was founded in 1853 as Compagnie Generale des Eaux. Its mission was to irrigate French farmland and supply water to towns. The company won contracts to serve Lyons (1853) Nantes (1854) Paris (1860) and Venice (1880). Generale des Eaux moved into construction in 1972 building an office tower (and later hotels and houses) in Paris. The company also entered communications in the 1980s.

In 1988 Generale des Eaux acquired control of construction and civil engineering giant Societe Generale d'Entreprises. SGE subsidiaries included Campenon Bernard SGE (part of Generale des Eaux since 1981) Sogea Freyssinet Cochery Bourdin Chausse Saunier Duval Tunzini Lefort Francheteau and Wanner. SGE traces its construction roots to 1910. It became a subsidiary of Generale d'Electricite in 1966. Glassmaker Saint-Gobain acquired control of SGE in 1984. Under Generale des Eaux SGE enhanced its European profile through acquisitions including British builder Norwest Holst (1989) German road builder VBU (1991) and German pipe and duct maker MLTU (1992).

Generale des Eaux acquired publisher Havas in 1998 and took the name Vivendi –representing vivacity and mobility. Its purchase of USFilter in 1999 made Vivendi the world's largest water company. Vivendi's SGE unit (renamed VINCI) agreed to acquire the construction arm of rival conglomerate Suez's GTM unit in 2000.

Groupe GTM traces its roots to Societe Lyonnaise des Eaux et de L'Eclairage a leading French water utility. Formed in 1880 Lyonnaise des Eaux built up its French and international operations to include water distribution as well as gas and electricity production and distribution. A century later the company had diversified into such businesses as heating (Cofreth) waste management (Sita) and communications acquiring a stake in Lyonnaise Communications (now Lyonnaise Câble) in 1986.

In 1990 Lyonnaise des Eaux acquired construction firm Dumez whose subsidiary GTM-Entrepose was France's largest car park manager. Four years later Dumez-GTM was formed to consolidate the construction and civil engineering businesses of Dumez and GTM-Entrepose. In 1997 Lyonnaise des Eaux and Compagnie de Suez merged to create a leading provider of private infrastructure services Suez Lyonnaise des Eaux (which shortened its name to SUEZ in 2001). Compagnie Universal du Canal Maritime de Suez the builder of the Suez Canal was founded in 1858 and became Financière de Suez in 1958. In 1967 Financière de Suez acquired control of Lyonnaise des Eaux.

SGE changed its name to VINCI in 2000. That year as part of their strategy to rationalize operations and focus on core businesses Vivendi and SUEZ agreed to a friendly takeover of GTM by VINCI. SUEZ emerged as the combined company's largest shareholder but by the following year both SUEZ and Vivendi Universal had exited most of VINCI's capital leaving no core stockholder.

To better control its car park management operations the company in 2001 created VINCI Park to operate as an umbrella of its VINCI Concessions unit. It expanded its concessions holdings even more in 2002 by hooking up with construction group Eiffage to grab a 17% stake in Europe's second-largest toll road operator ASF which was floated that year by the French government.

In 2003 the group won the contract to manage the restoration of the historic Hall of Mirrors. It also won the concession contract to operate along with joint venture partner Keolis the International Airport of Grenoble.

VINCI completed its acquisition of ASF in 2005. The deal was part of a government program to privatize motorway companies.

The company has had volatile internal struggles. There was unrest in the board room during 2006 as chairman Antoine Zacharias reportedly wanted to oust CEO Xavier Vuillard in favor of Nexity CEO Alain Dinin. Zacharias was the one who ended up resigning and at the end of 2006 Dinin resigned from VINCI's board.

In 2007 VINCI's top French construction businesses Sogea Construction and GTM Construction merged to create VINCI Construction France its domestic construction giant.

The company strengthened its position in the UK in 2008 when it bought British construction and facilities management firm Taylor Woodrow from Taylor Wimpey. The deal consolidated VINCI's position in UK facilities management and public-private partnership projects such as rail airports and energy infrastructure. In 2009 VINCI Construction acquired the troubled UK builder Haymills Group as that company teetered on the brink of collapse.

In 2008 Eurovia branched out from the road to the rails when it acquired rail infrastructure firm Vossloh Infrastructure Services (now ETF-Eurovia Travaux Ferrovaires) from Vossloh. The division specializes in rail track maintenance and installation.

EXECUTIVES

COO Energy Business Line, Yves Meignie, age 60
VP Corporate Communications Human Resources and Synergies, Pierre Coppey, age 53
Executive Vice-President and Chief Financial Officer, Christian Labeyrie, age 60
Chairman and Chief Executive Officer, Xavier Huillard, age 62
Chairman VINCI Construction, Jean Rossi, age 67
Executive Vice-President Contracting, Richard Francioli, age 57
Chairman and Chief Executive Officer Eurovia, Jacques Tavernier, age 66
CEO VINCI Concessions, Louis-Roch Burgard, age 48
Auditors: Deloitte & Associés

LOCATIONS

HQ: Vinci SA
1, cours Ferdinand-de-Lesseps, Rueil-Malmaison, Cedex 92851
Phone: (33) 1 47 16 35 00   **Fax:** (33) 1 47 51 91 02
Web: www.vinci.com

2014 Sales

	% of total
France	62
United Kingdom	7
Germany	6
Central and Eastern Europe	5
Benelux	2
Rest of Europe	4
Americas	5
Asia Middle East and other	5
Africa	4
Total	**100**

PRODUCTS/OPERATIONS

2014 Sales

	% of total
Contracting	84
Concessions	15
VINCI immobilier	1
Total	**100**

Selected Subsidiaries

VINCI Construction
 CFE (12.11%; Benelux)
 VINCI Construction France
 VINCI PLC (UK)
 VINCI Construction Filiales Internationales (Germany Central Europe overseas France Africa)
 VINCI Construction Grands Projets
 Freyssinet (specialized civil engineering)
VINCI Concessions
VINCI Park
Eurovia
VINCI Energies
 Actemium (industry solutions)
 Axians (voice-data-image communication)
 Citéos (urban lighting)
 Graniou (telecommunications infrastructure)
 Omexom (high-voltage power transmission)
 Opteor (maintenance)

COMPETITORS

Atlantia	HOCHTIEF
Bechtel	Louis Berger
Bilfinger	Parsons Corporation
Bouygues	Schneider Electric
EIFFAGE	Skanska
FCC Barcelona	WS Atkins

HISTORICAL FINANCIALS

Company Type: Public

Income Statement

FYE: December 31

	REVENUE ($ mil.)	NET INCOME ($ mil.)	NET PROFIT MARGIN	EMPLOYEES
12/15	42,925	2,228	5.2%	185,452
12/14	47,720	3,021	6.3%	185,293
12/13	56,568	2,701	4.8%	190,704
12/12	52,062	2,526	4.9%	192,701
12/11	49,023	2,463	5.0%	183,320
Annual Growth	(3.3%)	(2.5%)	—	0.3%

2015 Year-End Financials

Debt ratio: 33.2%
Return on equity: 13.7%
Cash ($ mil.): 6,134
Current ratio: 0.83
Long-term debt ($ mil.): 16,339

No. of shares (mil.): 554
Dividends
 Yield: 3.0%
 Payout: 12.2%
Market value ($ mil.): 8,893

	STOCK PRICE ($) FY Close	P/E High/Low		PER SHARE ($) Earnings	Dividends	Book Value
12/15	16.05	5	3	4.02	0.49	29.71
12/14	13.55	4	3	5.38	0.73	32.32
12/13	16.46	5	3	4.87	0.58	34.96
12/12	12.00	4	3	4.67	0.73	32.77
12/11	10.86	4	3	4.50	0.55	30.86
Annual Growth	10.2%	—	—	(2.8%)	(2.8%)	(0.9%)

Virgin Money Holdings (UK) PLC

Auditors: KPMG LLP

LOCATIONS

HQ: Virgin Money Holdings (UK) PLC
 Jubilee House, Gosforth, Newcastle-Upon-Tyne NE3 4PL
Phone:
Web: www.virginmoney.com

HISTORICAL FINANCIALS

Company Type: Public

Income Statement

FYE: December 31

	ASSETS ($ mil.)	NET INCOME ($ mil.)	INCOME AS % OF ASSETS	EMPLOYEES
12/15	44,797	164	0.4%	3,058
12/14	41,424	13	0.0%	2,904
12/13	40,595	295	0.7%	2,718
Annual Growth	5.0%	(25.4%)		6.1%

2015 Year-End Financials

Return on assets: 0.3%
Return on equity: 8.6%
Long-term debt ($ mil.): —
No. of shares (mil.): 443
Sales ($ mil): 1,345

Dividends
 Yield: —
 Payout: —
Market value ($ mil.): —

	STOCK PRICE ($) FY Close	P/E High/Low		PER SHARE ($) Earnings	Dividends	Book Value
12/15	0.00	—	—	0.34	0.00	4.48
12/14	0.00	—	—	(0.01)	0.00	4.39
Annual Growth	—	—	—	—	—	0.9%

Vodafone Group Plc

Customers have voted with their phones to make Vodafone one of the world's top wireless phone carriers. The company's phone book is stuffed with more than 470 million customers in nearly 30 countries and it has partnerships with other mobile networks in another 50. In terms of subscribers Vodafone trails only China Mobile. As well as telephony it has 14 million fixed broadband customers and 9.8 million TV customers. The company does around 70% of its business in Europe where it is a leader in the wireless markets in the UK and Germany. Vodafone increasingly serves callers in Africa the Middle East and Asia through subsidiaries and joint ventures.

Geographic Reach

Vodafone is remarkably geographically well balanced. Its strength is in Europe which provides some 70% of sales but it also has a significant presence in India the Asia/Pacific region and Africa. Germany the company's largest individual market accounts for less than 20% of sales while the smallest the Vodacom operator in Sub-Saharan Africa accounts for 9%. The remaining geographies fall within that range.

Altogether Vodafone has direct operations in 26 countries: Albania Australia Congo the Czech Republic Egypt Germany Ghana Greece Hungary India Ireland Italy Kenya Lesotho Malta Mozambique the Netherlands New Zealand Portugal Qatar Romania South Africa Spain Tanzania Turkey and the UK.

The company has retail stores in all of its markets as well as offshore operations in finance administration IT customer service and human resources across Egypt India and Europe.

Sales and Marketing

More than 90% of its mobile customers are individuals or households with the rest being enterprise customers ranging from large multinational firms to small and mid-sized businesses and public sector departments. Vodafone's broadband service is the fourth-largest in Western Europe.

Vodafone markets its products through branded stores distribution partners third-party retailers and online services. It reaches these customers via direct sales teams indirect partners and telesales channels.

Financial Performance

Note: Growth rates may differ after conversion to US Dollars.

In fiscal 2016 revenue fell 3% (£1.25 billion) to £41.0 billion. Unfavorable exchange rate movements to the tune of £802 million impacted the top line. Vodafone made a substantial loss in 2016 posting a net loss of £3.8 billion. This came after a 2015 net income of £5.9 billion. The difference was due in part to a large investment and finance expense of £726 million versus a credit of £276 million the year before as well as exchange rate effects.

Revenue for 2015 (ended March) increased 10% fueled by acquisitions. The company's organic growth slowed nearly 5% in Europe in the face of intense competition. Net income plummeted 90% lower in 2015 on rising costs. Capital spending in 2015 reduced cash flow from operations.

Strategy

Vodafone's top priority is staying abreast of the shift from texts and calls to internet data. It invests heavily in capital expenditure spectrum licenses and acquisitions —in excess of £47 billion since 2013 —in order to drive internet and data penetration. In 2016 it added 26 million 4G customers during the year taking the total to 47 million and added one million fixed broadband customers for a total of 13.4 million. Internet of Things connections are up 37%.

In order to strengthen its presence in the Indian home broadband market Vodafone India acquired Mumbai-based ISP You Broadband and You System Integration for £35 million in 2016.

Mergers and Acquisitions

In fiscal 2016 Vodafone completed a number of small acquisitions including two ISPs in India — You Broadband and You System Integration.

In February 2016 Vodafone merged with Liberty Global Europe Holding in the Netherlands to form a 50:50 joint venture. This will create a national unified communications provider in the Netherlands with complementary strengths across video broadband mobile and B2B services. Vodafone paid euro 1 billion.

HISTORY

Early History

Vodafone was formed in 1983 as a joint venture between Racal Electronics (a UK electronics firm) and Millicom (a US telecom company) and was granted one of two mobile phone licenses in the UK. It launched service in 1985 as a Racal subsidiary. Vodafone and Cellnet the other licensee were swamped with demand. In 1988 Racal offered 20% of Vodafone to the public; three years later the rest of the firm was spun off to become Vodafone Group.

Vodafone moved beyond the UK in the 1990s. By 1993 it had interests in mobile phone networks in Australia Greece Hong Kong Malta and Scandinavia.

EXECUTIVES

CEO, Vittorio A. Colao, age 53, $1,110,000 total compensation
CEO India, Marten Pieters, age 63
CFO, Nicholas J. (Nick) Read, age 50
Group Chief Commercial and Operations Officer, Paolo Bertoluzzo, age 50
CEO UK Business, Jeroen Hoencamp
CEO Ghana, Haris Broumidis
CEO Australia, I ±aki Berroeta
CEO New Zealand, Russell Stanners

CEO Egypt, Hatem Dowidar
CEO Africa Middle East and Asia-Pacific, Vivek
   Badrinath, age 46
CEO Germany, Jens Schulte-Bockum
Regional CEO Europe, Philipp Humm, age 57
EVP Managed Network and Services, Nick Lambert
CEO Vodafone Fiji, Pradeep Lal
CEO Vodafone Uganda, John Ndego
Chairman, Gerard J. Kleisterlee, age 68
Auditors: PricewaterhouseCoopers LLP

LOCATIONS

HQ: Vodafone Group Plc
   Vodafone House, The Connection, Newbury, Berkshire
   RG14 2FN
Phone: (44) 1635 33251   Fax: (44) 1635 238080
Web: www.vodafone.com

2016 Sales

	% of total
Europe	
Germany	19
UK	15
Italy	11
Spain	9
Other Europe	12
Africa Middle East and Asia Pacific (AMAP)	
India	11
Vodacom	9
Other AMAP	12
Common Functions	2
Total	**100**

PRODUCTS/OPERATIONS

2016 Sales

	% of total
Service revenue	91
Other revenue	9
Total	**100**

Countries of Operation (controlled interests)
Africa/the Middle East/Asia-Pacific
Australia
Democratic Republic of Congo
Egypt
Ghana
India
Lesotho
Mozambique
New Zealand
Qatar
South Africa
Tanzania
Europe
Albania
Czech Republic
Germany
Greece
Hungary
Ireland
Italy
Malta
Portugal
Romania
Spain
The Netherlands
Turkey
UK

COMPETITORS

AT&T Mobility	Orange
BT	Proximus
China Mobile	Swisscom
Deutsche Telekom	Telefnica Europe
KPN	Telekom Austria
M1	Telstra
NTT DoCoMo	Virgin Mobile Telecoms

HISTORICAL FINANCIALS

Company Type: Public

Income Statement

FYE: March 31

	REVENUE ($ mil.)	NET INCOME ($ mil.)	NET PROFIT MARGIN	EMPLOYEES
03/16	58,977	(5,792)	—	111,684
03/15	62,408	8,514	13.6%	105,300
03/14	63,838	98,646	154.5%	89,146
03/13	67,539	651	1.0%	91,272
03/12	74,379	11,148	15.0%	86,373
Annual Growth	**(5.6%)**	**—**		**6.6%**

2016 Year-End Financials

Debt ratio: 48.8%   No. of shares (mil.): —
Return on equity: (-6.0%)   Dividends
Cash ($ mil.): 14,708   Yield: 5.2%
Current ratio: 0.84   Payout: —
Long-term debt ($ mil.): 42,214   Market value ($ mil.): —

	STOCK PRICE ($) FY Close	P/E High/Low		PER SHARE ($) Earnings	Dividends	Book Value
03/16	32.05	—	—	(0.22)	1.68	3.57
03/15	32.68	163 126		0.32	1.78	3.69
03/14	36.81	19 13		3.70	0.00	4.46
03/13	28.40	1837 1479		0.02	0.00	4.07
03/12	27.67	116 98		0.40	0.00	4.55
Annual Growth	**3.7%**	**—**	**—**	**—**	**—**	**(5.9%)**

Volkswagen A.G. (Germany, Fed. Rep.)

With its cars named after an assortment of climate patterns insects and small mammals Volkswagen (VW) is Europe's leading carmaker and second in the world by vehicle sales after Toyota. Along with the world-renowned Beetle and the Gulf-Steam referencing Golf VW's garage of cars trucks and vans includes models such as Passat (named after a trade wind) Jetta (jet stream) and Fox. VW owns a garage full of luxury carmakers which it grants significant autonomy: AUDI Lamborghini Porsche Bentley and Bugatti. Other owned brands include Spanish automaker SEAT Czech automaker Škoda and commercial vehicle makers Scania and Man. The company made headlines in 2015 when the Environmental Protection Agency publicly announced that 11 million of its diesel cars contained software used to cheat emission tests.

Operations

VW makes more than 10 million cars trucks and vans annually. VW AG is the holding company for VW Group which alongside its suite of automakers includes a Financial Services division which provides customer financing leasing banking insurance and fleet management.

VW manufactures 12 brands (Volkswagen Passenger Cars Audi SEAT ŠKODA Bentley Bugatti Lamborghini Porsche Ducati Volkswagen Commercial Vehicles Scania and MAN encompassing almost 335 models) in 120 production plants.

For its commercial vehicles segment VW holds 99.6% of the voting rights in Swedish truck maker Scania. It holds more than 30% of MAN which is considered a majority stake.

Geographic Reach

VW sells its cars worldwide with operations in 153 countries across Europe North America South America Africa and Asia. The company holds a global market share of more than 11%. Sales outside of Germany account for almost 81% of the company's revenue although the rest of Europe accounted for more than 40% of revenue in 2014.

Financial Performance

Note: Growth rates may differ after conversion to US Dollars.

The effects of the 2015 emissions scandal are being felt in a number of ways. Total units sold dropped 2% on 2014 to a touch over 10 million and the euro 16.1 billion allocated to the various efforts to mitigate the impact of the scandal - recalls modifications legal costs customer outreach etc. - dragged net income down to euro -4.1 billion. Despite all this Volkswagen nevertheless grew total sales by 5.4% in 2016 to euro 213.3 billion with the most impressive growth rate realized in North America which saw unit sales as well as revenue grow.

Cash flow from operating activities grew euro 2.9 billion in 2015 in line with the sales increase.

Strategy

Volkswagen is on the defensive. The company's primary concern is containing the fallout of the 2015 emissions testing scandal - in autumn 2015 the Environmental Protection Agency publicly announced that the company has been using software to cheat emissions tests. 11 million Volkswagen cars were equipped with software that altered emission control systems when under testing conditions; in normal conditions the vehicles released around 40 times more nitrogen oxide into the air than is allowed by EPA regulations. Volkswagen has earmarked euro 16.2 billion to cover the service corrections and win back public support with its customers. In addition VW could pay up to $18 billion in fines in the US alone and VW executives could face criminal charges. Total cost estimates faced by Volkswagen from the scandal range from under $20 billion to some $40 billion.

The company is also predicting that the rise of ride-sharing services like Uber will reduce the need for car ownership and eat into car sales in the long term. In spring 2016 Volkswagen acquired a controlling stake in Uber-rival Gett an Israeli firm that has a strong presence in the UK. The move follows a $500 million investment by General Motors in Lyft a similar service.

HISTORY

Company Background

Since the early 1920s auto engineer Ferdinand Porsche (whose son later founded the Porsche car company) had wanted to make a small car for the masses. He found no backers until he met Adolf Hitler in 1934. Hitler formed the Gesellschaft zur Vorbereitung des deutschen Volkswagen (Company for the Development of the German People's Car) in 1937 and built a factory in Wolfsburg Germany. No cars were delivered during WWII as the company produced military vehicles using the slave labor of Jews and Russian prisoners of war.

Following WWII British occupation forces oversaw the rebuilding of the bomb-damaged plant and initial production of the odd-looking "people's car" (1945). The British appointed Heinz Nordhoff to manage Volkswagen (1948) and then turned the company over to the German government (1949).

In the 1950s VW launched the Microbus and built foreign plants. Although US sales began slowly by the end of the decade acceptance of the little car had increased. Advertising that coined the name "Beetle" helped carve VW's niche in the US.

VW sold stock to the German public in 1960. In 1966 it purchased Auto Union (AUDI) from Daimler-Benz. The Beetle became a counterculture symbol in the 1960s and US sales took off. By the time of Nordhoff's death in 1968 the Beetle had become the best-selling car in history.

EXECUTIVES

Member Management Board China, Jochem Heizmann, age 65
Member Management Board and Chairman Board of Management Audi AG, Rupert Stadler, age 53
Member Management Board Finance and Contrilling, Frank Witter, age 57
Member Board of Management Commercial Vehicles, Andreas Renschler, age 58
Chairman, Hans D. P ¶sch, age 65
Member Management Board Procurement, Francisco J. Garc a Sanz, age 60
Chairman Volkswagen Passenger Cars, Herbert Diess, age 58
CEO, Matthias M ller, age 63
CEO Moia, Ole Harms
Auditors: PricewaterhouseCoopers Aktiengesellschaft

LOCATIONS

HQ: Volkswagen A.G. (Germany, Fed. Rep.)
Letterbox 1848-2, Wolfsburg D-38436
Phone: (49) 5361 9 0   **Fax:** (49) 5361 928282
Web: www.volkswagen.com

PRODUCTS/OPERATIONS

Selected Brands
Audi
Bentley
Bugatti
Lamborghini
Scania
SEAT
Škoda
Volkswagen
Volkswagen Commercial Vehicles

Selected Makes and Models
AUDI
A1
A3
A3 Cabriolet
A3 Sportback
A4
A4 allroad quattro
A4 Avant
A5 Cabriolet
A5 Coupé
A5 Sportback
A6
A6 allroad quattro
A6 Avant
A7 Sportback
A8
A8L
A8L W12
Q5
Q7
Q7 V12 TDI
R8
R8 Spyder
R8 Spyder FSI quattro
RS5 Coupé
RS6
S3
S3 Sportback
S4
S4 Avant
S5 Cabriolet
S5 Coupé
S5 Sportback
TT Coupé
TT Roadster
TT RS Coupé
TT RS Roadster
TTS Coupé
TTS Roadster

Bentley
Continental Flying Spur
Continental Flying Spur Speed
Continental GT
Continental GTC
Continental GTC Speed
Continental SuperSports
Continental SuperSports Convertible
Mulsanne
Bugatti
Veyron
Veyron Grand Sport
Veyron Super Sport
Lamborghini
Gallardo LP
Gallardo LP Spyder
Gallardo LP Spyder Performante
Gallardo LP Superleggera
Murciélago LP Coupé
Murciélago LP Roadster
Scania
Buses
Engines
Trucks
SEAT
Alhambra
Alhambra ECOMOTIVE
Altea
Altea ECOMOTIVE
Altea Freetrack
Altea XL
Altea XL ECOMOTIVE
Cordoba
Exeo
Exeo ST
Ibiza
Ibiza Cupra
Ibiza ECOMOTIVE
Ibiza FR
Ibiza SC
Ibiza SC Bocanegra
Ibiza ST
León
León Cupra
León ECOMOTIVE
León FR
Škoda
Fabia
Fabia Combi
Fabia Combi GreenLine
Fabia Combi RS
Fabia Combi Scout
Fabia GreenLine
Fabia RS
Fabia Scout
Octavia
Octavia Combi
Octavia Combi GreenLine
Octavia Combi GreenLine
Octavia Combi LPG
Octavia GreenLine
Octavia LPG
Octavia RS
Octavia Scout
Octavia Tour
Octavia Tour Combi
Roomster
Roomster GreenLine
Roomster Scout
Praktik
Superb
Superb Combi
Superb Combi GreenLine
Superb GreenLine
Yeti
Yeti GreenLine
Volkswagen Commercial Vehicles
Caddy
California
Caravelle
Crafter
Multivan
Saveiro
Transporter shuttle
Volkswagen Passenger Vehicles
CrossPolo
CrossTouran
Eos
Fox
Golf
Golf Estate

New Beetle
New Beetle Cabriolet
Jetta
Passat
Phaeton
Polo
Routan
Scirocco
Sharan
Tiguan
Touareg
Touran
Voyage

COMPETITORS

BMW	Isuzu
Daimler	Mazda
FCA US	Nissan
Ford Motor	Peugeot
Fuji Heavy Industries	Renault
General Motors	Suzuki Motor
Honda	Toyota

HISTORICAL FINANCIALS

Company Type: Public

Income Statement

FYE: December 31

	REVENUE ($ mil.)	NET INCOME ($ mil.)	NET PROFIT MARGIN	EMPLOYEES
12/15	232,319	(1,723)	—	610,076
12/14	246,088	13,184	5.4%	592,586
12/13	271,226	12,481	4.6%	578,171
12/12	253,956	28,624	11.3%	549,763
12/11	206,094	19,930	9.7%	501,956
Annual Growth	3.0%	—	—	5.0%

2015 Year-End Financials

Debt ratio: 41.5%
Return on equity: (-1.7%)
Cash ($ mil.): 22,732
Current ratio: 0.98
Long-term debt ($ mil.): 79,830

No. of shares (mil.): 295
Dividends
Yield: 2.5%
Payout: —
Market value ($ mil.): 9,140

	STOCK PRICE ($) FY Close	P/E High/Low		PER SHARE ($) Earnings	Dividends	Book Value
12/15	30.98	—	—	(3.49)	0.80	325.04
12/14	43.06	2	2	26.55	0.81	370.68
12/13	54.70	3	2	25.65	0.67	409.31
12/12	43.47	1	1	61.18	0.58	346.23
12/11	26.69	1	1	42.81	0.42	252.20
Annual Growth	3.8%	—	—	—	17.6%	6.5%

Volvo AB

Despite the fact that the name "Volvo" still conjures up visions of soccer moms Volvo should really only inspire images of burly truck drivers. The company is one of the world's largest makers of trucks buses and construction equipment. In North America the company makes big rigs through its Volvo Trucks North America unit; Volvo also owns controlling interests in the well-known Mack Trucks brand in North America and Renault Trucks in Europe. Other products include marine (Volvo Penta) and industrial engines. Overall Volvo has production facilities in nearly 20 countries.

Geographic Reach

Volvo's main business segments (Trucks Construction Equipment Buses Financial Services and Penta) sell their products and services in 190 markets worldwide. It has production facilities in nearly 20 countries. Europe accounts for 37% of sales. Other major markets include North America (27%) Asia (18%) South America (10%) and other markets (8%).

Strategy

Part of the company's response to continued economic uncertainty is building smaller less expensive trucks particularly under its Renault label. It positions them for developing markets but lower price appeals to all. Volvo is also working to meet strict EU environmental requirements for trucks buses construction equipment and its Penta vehicles.

Speaking of developing markets Volvo positioned itself to take part in the world's largest economy when in 2013 it signed an agreement with China's Dongfeng Motor Group to produce heavy-duty trucks. The Swedish company in 2015 obtained a 45% stake in Dongfeng Commercial Vehicles a subsidiary of the Chinese firm that will make big trucks for China and other countries.

Company Background

Swedish ball bearing maker SKF formed Volvo (Latin for "I roll") as a subsidiary in 1915. Volvo began building cars in 1926 trucks in 1928 and bus chassis in 1932 in Gothenburg. Sweden's winters and icy roads made the company keenly attentive to engineering and safety. Volvo bought an engine maker in 1931. In 1935 Volvo became an independent company led by Assar Gabrielsson and Gustaf Larson.

Sweden's neutrality during WWII allowed Volvo to grow and move into component manufacturing and tractor production. Output in 1949 exceeded 100000 units 80% of which were sold in Sweden. The purchase of Bolinder-Munktell (farm machinery diesel engines; Sweden; 1950) enhanced Volvo's position in the Swedish tractor market. Volvo introduced turbocharged diesel truck engines and windshield defrosters and washers in the 1950s. By 1956 car production had outstripped truck and bus output.

EXECUTIVES

CFO, Jan Gurander, age 55

EVP Corporate Strategy, Karin Falk, age 51

EVP Group Trucks Technology and Volvo Group; CTO, Torbj§rn Holmstr§m, age 61

President Volvo Trucks North America, Peter Karlsten, age 59

EVP Group Trucks Sales and Marketing Americas, Dennis R. (Denny) Slagle, age 63

EVP Corporate Communications, M rten Wikforss, age 52

EVP Business Areas, H kan Karlsson, age 55

President and CEO, Olof Persson, age 51

EVP Group Trucks Operations, Mikael Bratt, age 49

EVP Corporate Human Resources, Kerstin Renard, age 56

EVP Corporate Process IT and CIO, Magnus Carlander, age 62

EVP Group Truck Sales and Marketing and JVs APAC, Joachim Rosenberg, age 46

EVP Volvo Construction Equipment, Martin Weissburg, age 54

EVP Corporate Legal and Compliance and General Counsel, Sofia Fr¤ndberg, age 52

EVP Corporate Sustainability and Public Affairs, Niklas Gustavsson, age 45

EVP Volvo Financial Services, Scott Rafkin, age 47

Chairman, Carl-Henric Svanberg, age 64

Auditors: PricewaterhouseCoopers AB

LOCATIONS

HQ: Volvo AB
Volvo Bergegaards v., Goeteborg SE-405 08
Phone: (46) 31 66 00 00   **Fax:** (46) 31 53 72 96
Web: www.volvogroup.com

2014 Sales

	% of total
Europe	37
North America	27
Asia	18
South America	10
Other regions	8
Total	**100**

PRODUCTS/OPERATIONS

2014 Sales

	% of total
Trucks	66
Construction equipment	18
Buses	6
Customer finance	4
Volvo Penta	3
Corporate functions Group functions and Other	3
Total	**100**

Selected Products & Brand Names

Buses
  Chassis
  City & intercity buses
  Coaches
Construction equipment
  Articulated haulers
  Asphalt milling machines
  Backhoe loaders
  Compaction equipment
  Crawler excavators
  Motor graders
  Pavers
  Skid steer loaders
  Wheel loaders
  Wheeled excavators
Financial services
  Customer & dealer financing
Trucks
  Mack
  Renault
  UD Trucks
  VE Commercial Vehicles (46% India)
  Volvo
Volvo Penta
  Industrial engines & drive systems (gensets & materials handling)
  Marine engines & drive systems (leisure & commercial boats)

COMPETITORS

Cummins Westport	Mitsubishi Motors
Daimler	Navistar
Daimler Trucks North America	Navistar International
Deere	Nissan
Fiat Chrysler	Oshkosh Truck
Fuji Heavy Industries	PACCAR
General Motors	Penske
Hino Motors	Scania
Honda	Suzuki Motor
Isuzu	Terex
MAN	Toyota

HISTORICAL FINANCIALS

Company Type: Public

Income Statement

FYE: December 31

	REVENUE ($ mil.)	NET INCOME ($ mil.)	NET PROFIT MARGIN	EMPLOYEES
12/15	37,069	1,786	4.8%	99,501
12/14	36,602	271	0.7%	92,822
12/13	42,522	558	1.3%	95,533
12/12	46,610	1,694	3.6%	102,082
12/11	45,000	2,573	5.7%	102,248
Annual Growth	**(4.7%)**	**(8.7%)**	**—**	**(0.7%)**

2015 Year-End Financials

Debt ratio: 4.2%
Return on equity: 18.5%
Cash ($ mil.): 2,496
Current ratio: 1.10
Long-term debt ($ mil.): 8,929

No. of shares (mil.): 2,030
Dividends
  Yield: —
  Payout: —
Market value ($ mil.): —

Volvo Car Corp. (Sweden)

LOCATIONS

HQ: Volvo Car Corp. (Sweden)
50400 - HA2S, Gothenburg SE-405 31
Phone:
Web: www.volvocars.com/corporate

HISTORICAL FINANCIALS

Company Type: Public

Income Statement

FYE: December 31

	REVENUE ($ mil.)	NET INCOME ($ mil.)	NET PROFIT MARGIN	EMPLOYEES
12/15	19,458	371	1.9%	28,119
12/14	16,811	107	0.6%	24,124
12/13	19,067	149	0.8%	23,242
12/12	19,118	(90)	—	22,881
Annual Growth	**0.6%**	**—**	**—**	**7.1%**

2015 Year-End Financials

Debt ratio: 1.9%
Return on equity: 9.5%
Cash ($ mil.): 3,039
Current ratio: 0.95
Long-term debt ($ mil.): 1,799

No. of shares (mil.): —
Dividends
  Yield: —
  Payout: —
Market value ($ mil.): —

	STOCK PRICE ($) FY Close	P/E High/Low	PER SHARE ($) Earnings	Dividends	Book Value
12/15	0.00	— —	(0.00)	0.00	0.04
Annual Growth	**—**	**— —**	**—**	**—**	**—**

Wal-Mart de Mexico S.A.B. de C.V.

Wal-Mart de Mexico y Centroamerica is the numero uno retailer in Mexico Costa Rica El Salvador Guatemala Honduras and Nicaragua with about 3070 stores. These include Bodega food and general merchandise stores and Superama supermarkets as well about 10 Medimart Farmacia de Walmart. It also runs Wal-Mart Supercenters SAM'S CLUB and ClubCo warehouse stores. Its stores are located in 555 cities throughout the region. Wal-Mart Stores formed a joint venture with Mexico's Cifra in 1991 and in 2000 acquired it and renamed it Wal-Mart de Mexico. Wal-Mex then added Wal-Mart's operations in Central America and became Wal-Mart de Mexico y Centroamerica.

Geographic Reach Wal-Mart de Mexico y Centroamerica owns and operates self-service retail stores in Mexico and Central America.

It operates in Costa Rica (230 stores) El Salvador (88) Guatemala (217) Honduras (82) Mexico (2363) and Nicaragua (92).

Operations In Mexico alone the company has 1719 Bodega Aurrera discount stores 256 Walmart hypermarkets 160 Sam's Club membership self-service wholesale stores 95 Superama supermarkets 10 Medimart pharmacies and 114 Suburbia apparel and accessories stores in Mexico. In addition it imports and sells goods; develops properties; and manages real estate companies.

In Costa Rica Guatemala Honduras Nicaragua and El Salvador Wal-Mart de Mexico y Centroamerica operates through 484 discount stores 99 supermarkets 102 discount warehouse stores 24 Walmart hypermarkets and 1 ClubCo membership self-service wholesale store.

Financial Performance

Wal-Mart de Mexico y Centroamerica reported 485.8 billion pesos in sales for the the 12 months ended June 2015 (up from 432.9 billion pesos in fiscal 2014).

Strategy

The company is focusing on growth it of its core assets by selling of some of its businesses. It has refocused on its stores after selling restaurants and a bank.

That year it planned to invest 14.7 billion pesos ($822.6 million) in 2016. Some 39% of the total would be earmarked to opening new stores 31% to remodeling and maintaining existing ones 24% to technology and e-commerce and the remaining 6% to logistical improvements.

In 2016 Wal-Mart de Mexico y Centroamerica agreed to sell its Suburbia clothing chain to El Puerto de Liverpool SAB Mexico's biggest department store chain operator in a deal valued at 19 billion pesos ($1.03 billion).

Walmex discontinued its Vips restaurant business in early 2014 with an agreement to sell the 360 restaurants to Alsea S.A.

B. de C.V. for about $625 million.

Banco Wal-Mart (launched in 2007) operates more than 260 branches located inside Bodega Aurrera Wal-Mart and SAM'S CLUB stores in some 30 cities and cater to a clientele that for the most part is new to banking. The bank has been losing money for its parent though. To cut its losses in late 2014 Wal-Mart de Mexico y Centroamerica sold the banking unit to a group of buyers that includes Grupo Financiero Inbursa the financial services operations of billionaire Carlos Slim Helu. The deal was valued at MXN 3.6 billion ($247 million).

HISTORY

Company Background

Spanish-born Jeronimo Arango Arias studied art and literature at several American universities without graduating. In his twenties he wandered around Spain Mexico and the US. He struck upon an idea after seeing a crowd waiting in line at the E. J. Korvette discount department store in New York City. Jeronimo called his two brothers Placido and Manuel and convinced them to join him in a new business venture.

Borrowing about $250000 from their father a Spanish immigrant to Mexico successful in textiles the three brothers opened their first Aurrera Bolivar discount store in downtown Mexico City in 1958. Offering goods and clothing well below manufacturers' list prices the store was an immediate hit with consumers but encountered hostility from competing Mexico City retailers. When local retailers threatened to boycott the Arangos' suppliers the company turned to suppliers in Guadalajara and Monterrey.

In 1965 the Arango brothers formed a joint venture with Jewel Cos. of Chicago to open new Aurrera stores. Jewel bought a 49% interest in the business a year later. Placido and Manuel left the business with their portion of the money but Jeronimo stayed as head of the company taking it public in 1976.

By 1981 almost a third of Jewel's earnings came from its operations in Mexico. But the next year the peso crashed obliterating its earnings there. American Stores took over Jewel in 1984 and Jeronimo bought back Jewel's stake in the company (which was renamed Cifra that year).

With the Mexican economy staggering from the peso devaluation weak oil markets and a huge debt crisis Jeronimo was taking a major risk. Although no new stores were opened none were closed. Employees were expected to work longer and those who left were not replaced. With Mexico's middle class hit hard Jeronimo emphasized the Bodega Aurrera no-frills warehouses which discounted all kinds of nonperishable merchandise from canned chili to VCRs.

Cifra and Wal-Mart Stores formed a joint venture in 1991 to open Club Aurrera membership clubs similar to Sam's Club outlets. The two companies expanded the venture the next year to include the development of Sam's Club and Wal-Mart Supercenters in Mexico.

Remodeling began on Cifra's stores in 1992. The work was completed two years later and the company was poised to take advantage of Mexico's much-improved economy.

However devaluation struck again late in 1994. The resulting contraction of credit and rise in prices hit Mexican consumers hard and Cifra's 1995 sales declined 15%. But again it kept on as many employees as possible transferring them to new stores that had been in development. Despite the hard times Cifra opened 27 new stores (including 15 restaurants). The company was able to withstand the difficulties in part because it stayed debt-free.

Wal-Mart consolidated its joint venture into Cifra in 1997 in exchange for about 34% of that company; Wal-Mart later raised its stake to 51%. The cost-conscious companies combined the joint venture stores and Cifra's separate stores under one umbrella. Cifra opened 11 stores and eight restaurants that year.

Cifra opened nine stores and 17 restaurants in 1998; the next year it opened about 20 stores and nearly 25 restaurants. In early 2000 Cifra was renamed Wal-Mart de Mexico. Shortly thereafter Wal-Mart upped its stake in Wal-Mart de Mexico to about 61%.

In 2001 all the Aurrera stores were converted to either Wal-Mart Supercenters or Bodega stores.

Eduardo Castro-Wright was promoted in 2002 from COO to CEO of Wal-Mart de Mexico succeeding Cesareo Fernandez who retained the chairman's title. The retailer opened 50 new outlets that year.

In March 2003 Mexico's Federal Competition Commission closed an investigation of Wal-Mex's purchasing practices citing a lack of evidence that the retailer violated competition laws. Overall that year Wal-Mex entered nine new cities in Mexico and added 46 new outlets. In 2004 Mexico's

largest retailer grew bigger adding 17 restaurants 23 Aurrera stores eight SAM'S CLUBS six supercenters and four Superama stores.

In January 2005 Fernandez stepped down as chairman and was succeeded by Ernesto Vega. A month later Castro-Wright left Wal-Mex to become EVP and COO of the Wal-Mart Stores Division in the US. He was succeeded by Eduardo Solorzano formerly COO of Wal-Mex. Also that year Wal-Mex acquired the Mexican assets of French retailer Carrefour. Carrefour which operated 29 hypermarkets in Mexico restructured its operations and left the Mexican market.

In November 2006 Wal-Mex received a license from Mexico's Finance Ministry to organize and operate a bank there. Overall in 2006 the retailer opened 120 new locations including stores in Monterrey the country's most affluent city and throughout northern Mexico where its Texas rival H. E. Butt Grocery is well established. In November 2007 Wal-Mart Bank began operations with 16 branches in five Mexican states.

Wal-Mex inked a deal with Tobacco One in August 2008 to distribute the tobacco firm's Rojo cigarette line in about 140 supercenters and some 60 Superarma stores throughout Mexico.

In December 2009 Wal-Mex announced the acquisition of Walmart's operations in Central America from Walmart Stores and two minority partners. The transaction was completed in early 2010 and Wal-Mex became Walmart Mexico and Central America.

EXECUTIVES

CFO, Pedro Farah
CEO, Guilherme Loureiro
COO, Todd Harbaugh
Chairman, Enrique Ostale
Auditors: Mancera, S.C. (member of Ernst & Young Global)

LOCATIONS

HQ: Wal-Mart de Mexico S.A.B. de C.V.
    Blvd. Manuel Avila Camacho # 647, Delegacion Miguel Hidalgo, Mexico City, Distrito Federal 11220
Phone: (52) 55 5283 0100   **Fax:** (52) 55 5328 3557
Web: www.walmartmexico.com.mx

2015 Stores

	No.
Mexico	2,363
Costa Rica	230
Guatemala	217
El Salvador	88
Nicaragua	92
Honduras	82
Total	**3,072**

PRODUCTS/OPERATIONS

2015 Mexico Stores

	% of total
Bodega Aurrera Express	924
Bodega Aurrera	475
Mi Bodega Aurrera	324
Walmart Supercenter	256
Sam's Club	160
Suburbia	114
Superama	95
Medimart Farmacia de Walmart	10
Zona Suburbia	5
Total	**2,363**

Selected Operations

Bodegas & discount stores
    Bodega Aurrera
    Dispensa Familiar
    MAXI Bodega
    PALI
Hypermarkets
    Hiper Paiz

Hiper Mas
Walmart
Warehouse clubs
  Sam's Club
  ClubCo
Supermarkets
  La Union
  Mas por Menos
  Paiz
  Superama
Apparel Stores
  Suburbia
Restaurants
  El Porton
  VIPS

COMPETITORS

Comerci   H-E-B
Costco Wholesale   Safeway
El Puerto de Liverpool Sanborns
Gigante   Soriana
Grupo Carso

HISTORICAL FINANCIALS

Company Type: Public

Income Statement

FYE: December 31

	REVENUE ($ mil.)	NET INCOME ($ mil.)	NET PROFIT MARGIN	EMPLOYEES
12/15	28,169	1,518	5.4%	231,996
12/14	30,003	2,070	6.9%	228,063
12/13	32,467	1,734	5.3%	226,289
12/12	32,172	1,791	5.6%	248,246
12/11	27,120	1,580	5.8%	238,128
Annual Growth	1.0%	(1.0%)	—	(0.7%)

2015 Year-End Financials

Debt ratio: 1.2%   No. of shares (mil.): —
Return on equity: 17.4%   Dividends
Cash ($ mil.): 1,427   Yield: 4.5%
Current ratio: 1.10   Payout: 1,209.4%
Long-term debt ($ mil.): —   Market value ($ mil.): —

	STOCK PRICE ($) FY Close	P/E High/Low	Earnings	PER SHARE ($) Dividends	Book Value
12/15	25.15	18 11	0.09	1.14	0.50
12/14	21.44	14 11	0.12	0.95	0.58
12/13	26.12	25 19	0.10	0.75	0.62
12/12	32.78	26 20	0.10	0.40	0.61
12/11	27.39	22 16	0.09	0.40	0.52
Annual Growth	(2.1%)	— —	(0.6%)	30.3%	(0.9%)

Wesfarmers Ltd.

Auditors: Ernst & Young

LOCATIONS

HQ: Wesfarmers Ltd.
  Level 11, Wesfarmers House, 40 The Esplanade, Perth,
  Western Australia 6000
Phone: (61) 8 9327 4211   **Fax:** (61) 8 9327 4216
Web: www.wesfarmers.com.au

HISTORICAL FINANCIALS

Company Type: Public

Income Statement

FYE: June 30

	REVENUE ($ mil.)	NET INCOME ($ mil.)	NET PROFIT MARGIN	EMPLOYEES
06/16	49,091	302	0.6%	220,000
06/15	47,988	1,875	3.9%	205,000
06/14	56,547	2,526	4.5%	99,000
06/13	55,187	2,085	3.8%	200,000
06/12	59,148	2,165	3.7%	0
Annual Growth	(4.6%)	(38.8%)	—	—

2016 Year-End Financials

Debt ratio: 13.3%   No. of shares (mil.): 1,126
Return on equity: 1.7%   Dividends
Cash ($ mil.): 454   Yield: 4.2%
Current ratio: 0.93   Payout: 245.5%
Long-term debt ($ mil.): 4,219 Market value ($ mil.): 16,869

	STOCK PRICE ($) FY Close	P/E High/Low	Earnings	PER SHARE ($) Dividends	Book Value
06/16	14.98	46 38	0.27	0.64	15.16
06/15	14.97	8 0	1.66	0.23	16.95
06/14	19.69	10 8	2.20	178.53	21.36
06/13	18.16	10 7	1.80	0.00	20.74
06/12	15.30	9 7	1.87	0.00	22.56
Annual Growth	(0.5%)	—	— (38.4%)	—	(9.5%)

Weston (George) Limited

George Weston Limited fuels Canadians through those long winters. About 95% of the company's sales come from its 63%-owned Loblaw Companies Limited Canada's largest supermarket operator (with more than 1000 stores under some 20 banners including Loblaws Extra Foods T&T and Zehrs Markets) and the country's largest wholesale food distributor. The rest comes from Weston Foods with operations in Canada and the US that focus on freshly baked goods frozen dough biscuits and other bakery products. (Its Interbake Foods division is a major supplier of Girl Scout cookies in the US.) Chairman Galen Weston owns about 63% of the company which was founded by his grandfather in 1882.

Both Loblaw and Weston Foods are facing challenges resulting from changing consumer preferences concerning what to eat and where to shop. In response George Weston has been restructuring both businesses to better match changing tastes. The weak economy on both sides of the US and Canadian border have put a damper on sales. Total sales rose less than 1% in 2010 vs. 2009 and were slightly below 2008 levels. The Loblaw segment outperformed Weston Foods with sales up about 1% vs. a nearly 4% decline for Weston Foods. Loblaw's 2010 sales got a boost from the acquisition of T&T Supermarket in late 2009. (T&T is Canada's largest retailer of Asian foods.)

Looking to position itself on a more profitable path to growth George Weston purged a couple of its businesses. In early 2009 the company sold its US-based fresh baked and baked goods business Dunedin Holdings to Mexico's Grupo Bimbo for about $2.5 billion. The sale included the Arnold Brownberry Entenmann's Freihofer Stroehmann and Thomas' brand names. (The company's Interbake Foods and Maplehurst Bakeries businesses in the US were not included in the transaction.) Previously George Weston had sold its Neilson Dairy business to Saputo.

Cash from the divestitures was used to introduce new higher-margin products that customers want to eat and to fund acquisitions. To this end George Weston acquired Keystone Bakery Holdings a US provider of frozen cupcakes doughnuts and cookies for in-store bakeries and foodservice firms. The $185-million deal expanded the frozen baked goods division of its Maplehurst Bakeries unit. Aside from sweet treats George Weston is looking to shift its product mix to include more whole grains as an increased focus on healthier breads has hurt sales of white-flour-based products. In late 2010 the company acquired artisan and European-style bread manufacturer ACE Bakery for C$110 million (US$108 million). Based in Toronto ACE was made a subsidiary of Weston Foods (Canada). Its breads are distributed in Canada and the US.

Loblaw which is in the last year of a five-year restructuring plan is facing increased competition from non-traditional rivals such as Wal-Mart Canada and Costco Wholesale Canada which are claiming a growing share of the retail grocery market. In response the company is cutting prices and sprucing up its retail stores. It's also aggressively expanding its low-price Real Canadian Superstore format which numbers more than 100 stores and its No Frill chain of discount supermarkets to better compete with foreign superstore operators. In recent years Loblaw has been shuttering struggling Provigo stores.

HISTORY

A baker's apprentice George Weston began delivering bread in Toronto with a single horse in 1882. He added the Model Bakery in 1896 and began making cookies and biscuits in 1908.

Upon George's death in 1924 his son Garfield gained control of the company and took it public as George Weston Limited in 1928. Having popularized the premium English biscuit in Canada Garfield acquired bakeries in the UK to make cheap biscuits (uncommon at the time). He grouped the bakeries as a separate public company called Allied Bakeries in 1935 (it later became Associated British Foods and is still controlled by the Weston family).

Expansion-minded Garfield led the company into the US with the purchase of Associated Biscuit in 1939. By the late 1930s George Weston was making cakes breads and almost 500 kinds of candy and biscuits.

During the 1940s the company made a number of acquisitions including papermaker E.

B. Eddy (1943; sold 1998 to papermaker Domtar giving it a 20% stake in Domtar) Southern Biscuit (1944) Western Grocers (1944 its first distribution company) and William Neilson (1948 chocolate and dairy products).

In 1953 it acquired a controlling interest in Loblaw Groceterias Canada's largest grocery chain. George Weston continued its acquisitions during the 1950s and 1960s adding grocer National Tea and diversifying into packaging (Somerville Industries 1957) and fisheries (British Columbia Packers 1962; Conners Bros. 1967).

By 1970 when Garfield's son Galen became president the company's holdings were in disarray. Galen brought in new managers consolidated the food distribution and sales operations under Loblaw Companies Limited and cut back on National Tea (which shrank from over 900 stores in 1972 to 82 in 1993). When Garfield died in 1978 Galen became chairman.

Ever since Galen a polo-playing chum of Prince Charles was the target of a failed kidnapping attempt by the Irish Republican Army in 1983 the family has kept a low public profile.

George Weston became the #1 chocolate maker in Canada with its purchase of Cadbury Schweppes' Canadian assets in 1987. The 1980s concluded with a five-year price war in St. Louis among its National Tea stores Kroger and a local grocer. This ultimately proved fruitless and Loblaw sold its US supermarkets in 1995 ending its US retail presence. As part of its divestiture of under-achieving subsidiaries the company sold its Neilson confectionery business back to Cadbury Schweppes in 1996 and sold its chocolate products company in 1998.

In early 1998 Loblaw set its sights on Quebec buying Montreal-based Provigo. Other George Weston acquisitions in the late 1990s included Oshawa Foods' 80-store Agora Foods franchise supermarket unit in eastern Canada and its Fieldfresh Farms dairy business the frozen-bagel business of Quaker Oats Pennsylvania-based Maier's Bakery and Bunge International's Australian meat processor Don Smallgoods. It also sold its British Columbia Packers fisheries unit.

Early in 2001 George Weston surprised analysts when it won Unilever's Bestfoods Baking Company (Entenmann's Oroweat) with a bid of $1.8 billion. The company reduced its stake in Loblaw by 2% and sold its Connors canned seafood business to fund the purchase which was completed in July 2001. To help pay down debt in early 2002 the company sold its Orowheat business in the western US to Mexican bread giant Grupo Bimbo for $610 million.

In 2003 Weston's food distribution business introduced about 1500 private label products. It sold its fisheries operations in Chile at a loss in 2004 for about $20 million. That September the company purchased Quebec-based Boulangerie Gadoua Ltee a family-owned baking business.

In 2005 the company sold its Heritage Salmon subsidiary thus exiting the unprofitable fisheries business entirely. The company also restructured its US biscuit operations and opened a new fresh bakery plant in Orlando Florida in 2005 as part of its push to increase its business in the southeastern US. A new bakery in the midwestern US began production of bread and English muffins in late 2006.

In early 2007 Weston's Loblaw subsidiary announced it was writing down its operations in Quebec to the tune of $768 million tied to its struggling Provigo grocery stores.

In December 2008 the company sold the Neilson dairy division of Weston Foods Canada to Saputo for some C$465 million in cash (about $373 million). It will use the money to pay down debt. In January 2009 it completed the sale of its fresh bread and baked goods business in the US. Later in the year Loblaw acquired T&T Supermarket Canada's largest retailer of Asian food.

In September 2010 George Weston through its Maplehurst Bakeries subsidiary acquired Keystone Bakery Holdings for approximately $185 million. Keystone is comprised of three operating companies: Freed's Bakery of Manchester New Hampshire a leading supplier of frozen thaw and sell iced cupcakes; Granny's Kitchens of Frankfort New York a leading supplier of both frozen pre-fried and frozen thaw and sell donuts; and Heartland Baking of DuQuoin Illinois a specialty supplier of frozen thaw and sell cookies. In November Weston Foods acquired artisan and European-style bread manufacturer ACE Bakery for C$110 million (US$108 million). Based in Toronto ACE was made a subsidiary of Weston Foods (Canada). Its breads are distributed in Canada and the US.

Chairman and president Galen Weston stepped down as the company's president in late 2011 but remained chairman.

EXECUTIVES

Chairman and CEO George Weston Limited and Loblaw Companies Ltd., Galen G. Weston, age 43
EVP and CFO, Richard Dufresne
President Weston Foods, Luc Mongeau
EVP and Chief Legal Officer, Gordon A.M. Currie
Chief Administrative Officer Loblaw Companies Ltd., Sarah R. Davis
EVP and Chief Talent Officer, Rashid Wasti
Deputy Chairman, Alannah Weston
Auditors: KPMG LLP

LOCATIONS

HQ: Weston (George) Limited
22 St. Clair Avenue East, Toronto, Ontario M4T 2S7
Phone: 416 922-2500   **Fax:** 416 922-8508
Web: www.weston.ca

2015 Sales

	% of total
Canada	98
US	2
Total	**100**

PRODUCTS/OPERATIONS

2015 Sales

	% of total
Loblaw	95
Weston Foods	5
Total	**100**

Selected Operating Divisions

Food Distribution (selected Loblaw banners)
  Atlantic SaveEasy
  Dominion
  Extra Foods
  Fortinos
  Loblaws
  Maxi
  Maxi & Co.
  No frills
  The Real Canadian Superstore
  The Real Canadian Wholesale Club
  SuperValu
  T&T Supermarkets
  Your Independent Grocer
  Zehrs Markets
Food Processing (selected units)
  ACE Bakery (artisan breads)
  Interbake Foods Inc. (cookies and crackers US)
  Maplehurst Bakeries Inc. (frozen bakery products US)
  Weston Bakeries Limited (fresh baked goods)

COMPETITORS

7-Eleven	Jim Pattison Group
Bridgford Foods	Katz Group
Campbell Canada	Kellogg U.S. Snacks
Canadian Tire	METRO
Costco Wholesale	Maple Leaf Foods
Canada	Otis Spunkmeyer
Couche-Tard	Shoppers Drug Mart
Flowers Foods	Sobeys
Grupo Bimbo	Urban Outfitters
H and M Construction	Wal-Mart Canada
IGA	Zara
Jean Coutu	

HISTORICAL FINANCIALS

Company Type: Public

Income Statement

FYE: December 31

	REVENUE ($ mil.)	NET INCOME ($ mil.)	NET PROFIT MARGIN	EMPLOYEES
12/15	33,763	379	1.1%	0
12/14	37,925	108	0.3%	0
12/13	31,581	852	2.7%	138,000
12/12	32,920	488	1.5%	140,000
12/11	31,738	622	2.0%	142,000
Annual Growth	**1.6%**	**(11.6%)**	**—**	**—**

2015 Year-End Financials

Debt ratio: 25.7%   No. of shares (mil.): 127
Return on equity: 7.0%   Dividends
Cash ($ mil.): 1,017   Yield: 0.0%
Current ratio: 1.39   Payout: 45.3%
Long-term debt ($ mil.): 7,868   Market value ($ mil.): 9,853

	STOCK PRICE ($) FY Close	P/E High/Low	PER SHARE ($) Earnings	Dividends	Book Value
12/15	77.03	22 18	2.69	1.22	43.34
12/14	86.18	139 101	0.55	1.45	49.21
12/13	73.07	17 13	4.62	1.53	46.51
12/12	71.20	21 17	3.40	1.47	44.63
12/11	65.49	18 14	4.46	9.01	41.75
Annual Growth	**4.1%**	**— —**	**(11.9%)**	**(39.3%)**	**0.9%**

Westpac Banking Corp

Westpac Banking keeps its pact to serve customers in Australia New Zealand and the neighboring Pacific Islands. The company serves some 12 million customers through more than 1500 branches and is one of the largest banks in Australia. Retail banking division Australian Financial Services (AFS) group includes Westpac St. George Bank of Melbourne and BankSA branded banking locations. AFS also offers wealth management insurance and consulting through BT Financial Group. Meanwhile Westpac Institutional Bank offers corporate financial services and Westpac New Zealand provides retail wealth and institutional services.

Operations

Between its six operating divisions Westpac has a total of some $770 billion in assets. The company's Australian Financial Services (AFS) division is the largest segment generating 40% of the bank's revenue. It includes the Westpac Retail and Business Banking unit (consumer and small to midsized banking customers) the St. George Banking group and the BT Financial Group as well as the banking products and risk management segments. The Westpac Retail & Business Banking (RBB) segment is the next largest making up more than 20% of the bank's revenue and provides sales and services for consumers small-to-medium enterprises (SME) commercial and agribusiness customers in Australia.

The remaining segments split the remaining revenue and include: St. George Banking Group Westpac Institutional Bank BT Financial Group and Westpac New Zealand. St. George Banking Group offers similar services to the RBB segment but operates under the St. George BankSA Bank of Melbourne and RAMS brands in Australia. Westpac Institutional Bank serves corporations institutions and government entities across Australia and New

Zealand as well as overseas. BT Financial operates under brands including Ascalon Asgard Advance Asset Management Magnitude and Securitor. Westpac New Zealand which makes up just over 5% of revenue primarily serves small to midsized businesses and consumers in New Zealand.

Geographic Reach

Australia accounts for 85% of Westpac's annual revenues while New Zealand accounts for another 12%. In addition to branches and subsidiaries located across Australia New Zealand and neighboring islands Westpac's institutional division has offices in London New York City Hong Kong and Singapore.

Sales and Marketing

Westpac's retail services are promoted through its retail banking locations as well as through relationship managers wealth specialists business banking centers customer service channels and online. The institutional segment conducts sales through dedicated industry relationship and specialist product teams. The bank spent roughly A$159 million (about $138.7 million) on advertising in fiscal 2014 about 3% less than in 2013 but 8% more than it spent in 2012.

Financial Performance

(Note: Growth rates may differ after conversion to US dollars.)Westpac's revenue fell for a second year to A$38.6 billion (In US dollars a 6% revenue decline to $33.75 billion) in fiscal 2014 as it collected less interest income from treasury investments and as net interest margins were squeezed. The bank's non-interest income however grew by 11% thanks to growth in wealth management insurance and banking fees.

Despite falling revenue the bank was able to boost net income by 12% to A$7.6 million (In US dollars a 4% revenue increase to $6.6 billion) as it collected more from fee-based income and incurred less interest expense in paying lower rates on customer deposits. Operations provided A$25.6 million (about $24.8 billion) in fiscal 2014 or 11% more cash than it did in 2013 as the bank collected more from deposits and other financial liabilities at fair value.

Broadly speaking the bank's assets have been consistently growing for the past several years. From fiscal 2013 to fiscal 2014 total assets grew by 10% to A$770.8 billion (about $672.5 billion) with loan assets growing by 8% to A$580.3 billion (about $506.3 billion) and deposits growing by 9% to A$460.8 billion (about $402.1 billion).

Strategy

Westpac's primary operating vision is to become the largest financial services firm in Australia. The company also aims to build strong customer relationships and provide superior shareholder returns. Though it occasionally makes acquisitions Westpac is currently focused on organic growth measures to increase customer numbers. To those ends Westpac is beginning to expand its operations and relations in Asia. In 2014 the bank opened its first sub-branch in the Shanghai Free Trade Zone (FTZ) which it intends to use as a testing ground for a number of economic reforms and to be a strategic zone for the bank's customers to increase their presence in China. The bank hopes to take advantage of future opportunities in the region as China continues to liberate its economic and financial markets. Also in 2014 in a move designed to increase its brand awareness and please business travelers and tourists from China the bank also announced that it would accept China UnionPay cards —one of the fastest growing card networks in the world —at its more than 150000 ATMs branches and other acceptance points in Australia and New Zealand.

In addition the firm is working to increase products-per-customer numbers through deposit wealth and insurance cross-selling programs. In late 2013 it acquired motor vehicle finance business Capital Finance Australia Ltd. and BOS International Australia Ltd. to add a new customer base that it can cross-sell all of its other banking products to. The acquisition also effectively broadened the bank's geographic reach and product line and added $7.9 billion more in motor vehicle finance equipment finance and corporate loans to Westpac's portfolio.

Mergers and Acquisitions

In late 2013 Westpac acquired Lloyds Banking Group's Australian asset finance business Capital Finance Australia Limited and its corporate loan portfolio BOS International (Australia) Ltd. for $1.45 billion which was funded from internal resources.

HISTORY

Westpac proudly calls itself Australia's "First Bank." But when predecessor Bank of New South Wales was founded in 1817 some 90% of the eponymous colony's inhabitants were convicts or their relatives. (The penal colony was established just 30 years before the bank.) The British challenged the bank's charter forcing it to become a joint-stock company.

New South Wales' parliament rechartered the company as a bank in 1850 amidst the country's first gold rushes. (Some bank branches consisted of tents in mining camps.) Heavy British investment and an influx of colonists kept the country growing. The bank's future partner Commercial Bank of Australia was founded in 1866 in Melbourne in the neighboring colony of Victoria. More than half of the country's banks disappeared in a panic at the end of the century when land speculation and a collapse in wool prices caused a depression.

Australia became a country with the onset of the 20th century and its government formed Commonwealth Bank a central bank. The Bank of New South Wales now known as "The Wales" helped finance Australia's WWI efforts. Along with the rest of the world the country and the bank rode up the Roaring '20s and down the Great Depression.

About 65% of the bank's male staff enlisted during WWII. Its New Guinea branches closed; others were hit by air raids. In 1947 the government moved to nationalize the prospering country's banks within the Commonwealth Bank but the courts helped the banks fend off the attack on their independence.

The Bank of New South Wales moved into the newly opened savings banking market in 1956. The next year it bought into Australian Guarantee Corporation (it bought the rest in 1988).

The bank expanded abroad and diversified operations in the 1970s. Battered by a lagging protectionist economy Australia moved to deregulate banking in the 1980s. As foreign banks hustled in Bank of New South Wales and Commercial Bank of Australia in 1982 made what was then the largest merger in Australia's history.

The new bank known as Westpac (for its Western Pacific market area) began building its non-teller-based banking networks in the early 1980s. The company developed an extensive ATM network and established telephone and computerized banking. Later that decade it bought a stake in London gold dealer Johnson Matthey (1986) and all of William E. Pollock Government Securities (1987).

In 1992 Australia's wealthiest man Kerry Packer took a 10% share in troubled Westpac gaining board seats for himself and friend "Chainsaw" Al Dunlap. Packer's power grab failed and he sold the stake in 1993.

After buying itself into the equities market in the mid-1980s Westpac sold its Ord Minnett brokerage division in 1993. The bank withdrew from Asia and expanded closer to home in the mid 1990s buying Western Australia's Challenge Bank in 1995 Trust Bank of New Zealand in 1996 and Victoria's Bank of Melbourne in 1997.

In 1998 the bank agreed to merge its back-office operations with those of ANZ Banking Group providing economies of scale while avoiding antitrust issues. The next year Westpac announced 3000 job cuts mainly through attrition to ready itself for increased competition from changes in Australian law. Pacific operations caused waves in 2000: Westpac said it would pull out of Kiribati in response to government action and a coup in Fiji prompted the bank to reduce employees' hours (a move that was criticized by the Fiji government). The next year however Westpac was strengthening ties to the Pacific market. It doubled its holdings in the Bank of Tonga (on the island of Tonga) and its share of Pacific Commercial Bank (on the island of Samoa).

In 2007 subsidiary Westpac Essential Services Trust formed a joint venture with another Australian firm to operate the Airport Link Company a rail-to-airport passenger service in Sydney. The trust was established so investors could invest in public-private partnership (PPP) assets.

Westpac's acquisition of St.George Bank in 2008 catapulted Westpac from fourth to second among Australia's leading banks. The combination set Westpac and its St.George subsidiary behind only the National Australia Bank in terms of assets.

EXECUTIVES

CEO, Brian C. Hartzer, age 49
COO, John Arthur
Deputy CEO, Philip (Phil) Coffey, age 57, $752,226 total compensation
CEO St.George Banking Group, George Frazis, age 52
Group Executive Westpac Institutional Bank, Rob Whitfield, age 49, $439,250 total compensation
CEO BT Financial Group, Brad Cooper, age 53, $403,670 total compensation
Group Executive Westpac Retail and Business Banking, Jason Yetton
CIO, David Curran
Chief Risk Officer, Alexandra Holcomb
CFO, Peter King
Acting CEO Westpac New Zealand Limited, David McLean
Chairman, Lindsay P. Maxsted
Auditors: PricewaterhouseCoopers

LOCATIONS

HQ: Westpac Banking Corp
 275 Kent Street, Sydney, New South Wales 2000
Phone: (61) 2 9374 7113   **Fax:** (61) 2 8253 4128
Web: www.westpac.com.au

2014 Sales

	% of total
Australia	85
New Zealand	12
Other countries	3
Total	**100**

PRODUCTS/OPERATIONS

2014 Sales by Segment

	% of total
Australian Financial Services	41
Westpac Retail and Business Banking	22
St.George Bank	12
Westpac Institutional Bank	9
BT Financial Group (Australia)	8
Westpac New Zealand	6
Other	2
Total	**100**

COMPETITORS

Australia and New Zealand Banking	HSBC
Barclays	Hang Seng Bank
Commonwealth Bank of Australia	Macquarie Group
HBOS Australia	National Australia Bank

HISTORICAL FINANCIALS
Company Type: Public

Income Statement
FYE: September 30

	ASSETS ($ mil.)	NET INCOME ($ mil.)	INCOME AS % OF ASSETS	EMPLOYEES
09/16	639,350	5,672	0.9%	35,280
09/15	570,798	5,630	1.0%	35,241
09/14	671,697	6,588	1.0%	36,373
09/13	648,927	6,349	1.0%	35,597
09/12	704,404	6,230	0.9%	35,675
Annual Growth	(2.4%)	(2.3%)	—	(0.3%)

2016 Year-End Financials

Return on assets: 0.9%	Dividends
Return on equity: 13.3%	Yield: 6.5%
Long-term debt ($ mil.): —	Payout: 95.0%
No. of shares (mil.): —	Market value ($ mil.): —
Sales ($ mil): 28,690	

	STOCK PRICE ($) FY Close	P/E High/Low		PER SHARE ($) Earnings	Dividends	Book Value
09/16	22.74	11	9	1.66	1.50	13.25
09/15	21.06	11	8	1.75	1.44	11.76
09/14	28.11	13	11	2.08	1.71	13.63
09/13	30.67	72	13	2.01	8.75	14.03
09/12	128.33	67	51	1.99	1.69	15.06
Annual Growth	(35.1%)	—	—	(4.4%)	(2.9%)	(3.2%)

Wilmar International Ltd

Founded in 1991 Wilmar International is among Asia's largest agribusiness groups. The company grows refines and sells palm soy and other edible oils and grains. It is divided into three units: plantations for growing palm and rubber trees; processing plants for refining the oil and grains; and a consumer division which sells the oils in China India and Indonesia. Wilmar International also makes and sells fertilizer and palm-based biodiesel sold in Europe and the US. The company has operations in 15-plus countries on four continents and owns more than 450 processing plants across Southeast Asia. It sells its products in 50-plus countries worldwide. Beyond agribusiness it is acquiring property in China.

EXECUTIVES

Chairman and CEO, Kuok Khoon Hong, age 65
Country Head Indonesia, Hendri Saksti
Country Head Malaysia, Yee Chek Toong
Head Technical Division, Matthew J. Morgenroth
Head Plantations Division, Goh Ing Sing
Vice Chairman China, Mu Yankui
Chief Scientific Advisor, Chua Nam-Hai
Head Oleochemicals and Biofuels, Rahul Kale
Head Sugar Division, Bohbot Jean-Luc
Head Shipping Division, Kenny B. H. Chwee

CFO, Ho Kiam Kong
COO, Pua Seck Guan
Executive Deputy Chairman, Martua Sitorus, age 55
Auditors: Ernst & Young LLP

LOCATIONS

HQ: Wilmar International Ltd
56 Neil Road, 088830
Phone: (65) 6216 0244   **Fax:** (65) 6536 2192
Web: www.wilmar-international.com

2013 Sales

	% of total
China	37
Southeast Asia	23
Australia/New Zealand	9
Europe	7
India	5
Africa	3
Others	16
Total	**100**

PRODUCTS/OPERATIONS

2013 Sales

	% of total
Palm & laurics	49
Oilseeds & grains	25
Consumer products	7
Plantation & palm oil mills	1
Sugar	12
Others	6
Total	**100**

Selected Operations

Palm oil cultivation
Oilseed crushing
Edible oil refining
Sugar milling & refining
Grain processing
Fertilizer manufacturing

COMPETITORS

Amsteel	IOI Corporation
Anglo-Eastern Plantations	Inch Kenneth Kajang Rubber
Asia Food & Properties	Kuala Lumpur Kepong
Bunge Limited	Narborough Plantations
Genting Malaysia	New Britain Palm
Golden Agri-Resources	Sime Darby
Hong Leong Malaysia	

HISTORICAL FINANCIALS
Company Type: Public

Income Statement
FYE: December 31

	REVENUE ($ mil.)	NET INCOME ($ mil.)	NET PROFIT MARGIN	EMPLOYEES
12/15	38,776	1,056	2.7%	92,000
12/14	43,084	1,156	2.7%	92,000
12/13	44,085	1,318	3.0%	90,000
12/12	45,463	1,255	2.8%	93,000
12/11	44,710	1,600	3.6%	90,000
Annual Growth	(3.5%)	(9.9%)	—	0.6%

2015 Year-End Financials

Debt ratio: 45.9%	No. of shares (mil.): —
Return on equity: 6.9%	Dividends
Cash ($ mil.): 1,296	Yield: 2.5%
Current ratio: 1.28	Payout: 314.1%
Long-term debt ($ mil.): 6,347	Market value ($ mil.): —

	STOCK PRICE ($) FY Close	P/E High/Low		PER SHARE ($) Earnings	Dividends	Book Value
12/15	20.50	15	3106	0.17	0.52	2.39
12/14	24.41	15	6129	0.18	0.54	2.42
12/13	26.84	15	2116	0.21	0.40	2.34
12/12	27.35	22	3126	0.20	0.37	2.24
12/11	38.48	19	7138	0.25	0.38	2.09
Annual Growth	(14.6%)	—	—	(9.7%)	8.0%	3.5%

Wistron Corp

Wistron has manufactured by design since its founding in 1976. The company is a contract manufacturer of computer and consumer electronics products including notebook computers desktop PCs servers LCD TVs and set-top boxes. It is organized into four business groups: digital consumer enterprise mobile and services. Wistron also offers design services prototyping compliance and reliability testing and supply chain management. The company focuses on providing services to large computer firms such as Dell Hewlett-Packard and Microsoft. Wistron is one of the world's largest producers of notebook computers. The company gets more than one-third of its sales from outside of Taiwan.

EXECUTIVES

President and CEO, Robert P. T. Hwang, age 59
CFO, Henry Lin, age 60
CTO; President Enterprise Business Group, Donald Hwang, age 58
President Consumer and Smart Product Business Group and Smart Devices Business Group, David Shen, age 49
Chairman, Simon H. M. Lin, age 63
Auditors: KPMG

LOCATIONS

HQ: Wistron Corp
158, Singahan Road, Neihu, Taipei 11469
Phone: (886) 2 6616 9999   **Fax:** (886) 2 6612 5188
Web: www.wistron.com

2013 Sales

	% of total
Asia/Pacific	
Taiwan	65
Other countries	17
Other regions	18
Total	**100**

PRODUCTS/OPERATIONS

Selected Products

Application PC
Desktop computers
Information appliance
Interface cards
LCD TVs
Mobile television
Monitors
Motherboards
Netbook computers
Network storage system
Notebook computers
Portable navigation devices
Printed circuit boards (PCBs)
Rugged mobile computers
Set-top boxes
Servers
Smartphone

Spare parts
Storage products
Tablet PC
Voice over Internet Protocol (VoIP) phones
Wireless data products
Workstations

Selected Services

Design and product development
Logistics
Outsourcing management
Prototyping
Repair
Safety and compliance testing
Supply chain management
Usability and reliability testing

COMPETITORS

ASUSTeK	MiTAC
Compal Electronics	Orient Semiconductor
First International	Pegatron
Computer	Quanta Computer
Flextronics	SYNNEX
Hon Hai	Sanmina
Inventec	Super Micro Computer
Lenovo	Universal Scientific

HISTORICAL FINANCIALS

Company Type: Public

Income Statement

FYE: December 31

	REVENUE ($ mil.)	NET INCOME ($ mil.)	NET PROFIT MARGIN	EMPLOYEES
12/15	18,967	40	0.2%	0
12/14	18,706	113	0.6%	0
12/13	20,925	192	0.9%	6,660
12/12	22,667	250	1.1%	58,738
12/11	0	0	—	61,518
Annual Growth	—	—	—	—

2015 Year-End Financials

Debt ratio: 0.9%   No. of shares (mil.): —
Return on equity: 1.9%   Dividends
Cash ($ mil.): 1,782   Yield: —
Current ratio: 1.16   Payout: 225.1%
Long-term debt ($ mil.): 428   Market value ($ mil.): —

Wolseley Plc Jersey

In its 100-year history Wolseley's gone from shearing sheep in Australia to becoming the world's largest distributor of heating and plumbing supplies to professional contractors. The company distributes heating and cooling equipment plumbing supplies pipes valves safety equipment and fire protection products as well as building materials in about 23 countries throughout North America and Europe. Key customers include building contractors plumbing and heating engineers and industrial and mechanical contractors. Outside the UK Wolseley subsidiaries include Ferguson Enterprises in the US Reseau Pro in France and Wasco in the Netherlands.

Wolseley offers a broad range of products. Its largest product segment plumbing heating and air conditioning equipment generated roughly 40% of revenues in fiscal 2011. Its building materials segment and its civil/waterworks commercial and industrial segment each accounted for about 30% of revenues while the remaining 2% came from the sale of electrical cables wiring and lighting as well as installation maintenance and customer inventory management services.

This product mix serves customers in the residential commercial and industrial sectors —both new construction and repair and maintenance. Customers range from individual plumbers and builders to national contractor chains and home builders. Professional contractors are Wolseley's main customer base; within that category building contractors and plumbing and heating engineers together generate about 50% of Wolseley's total revenues.

In fiscal 2011 as markets stabilized Wolseley reported revenues of £13.6 billion (about $22.3 billion) up a modest 3% from £13.2 billion (about $20.7 billion) in 2010. These results were driven mainly by improving new residential construction and the repair and maintenance market.

Wolseley's business is divided into six geographic regions. In the US and Canada —which together generate about half of the company's total sales —the group is bringing the business activities of Wolseley Canada under the management of Ferguson the US's largest wholesale distributor of plumbing supplies pipes valves and fittings and a major distributor of heating ventilation and air conditioning (HVAC) equipment. Ferguson operates in all 50 states and has 10 distribution centers across the US.

Its UK Nordic region and France units generated 18% 16% and 14% of revenue in 2011 respectively. The UK business is driven by its Plumb Center and Parts Center branches which are market leaders in the UK plumbing and heating distribution market. The Nordic region business comprises Denmark Finland Norway and Sweden and is represented by such brands as Beijer Neumann Silvan Stark and Starkki. Wolseley France's key brands include Reseau Pro (building materials) and Silverwood (timber). In mid-2011 Wolseley sold Brossette its French plumbing and heating supplier and Build Center its building materials dealer in the UK to France's Compagnie de Saint-Gobain for a total of £310 million (about $487 million).

Wolseley's smallest geographic segment Central Europe accounts for about 6% of sales and covers Austria Luxembourg Netherlands and Switzerland. Its primary businesses are OAG an Austrian supplier of heating and plumbing supplies Tobler a Swiss distributor of heating and sanitation plumbing supplies and Wasco a Dutch distributor of central heating equipment.

HISTORY

In the late 1800s Irishman Frederick Wolseley immigrated to Australia where he developed the world's first mechanical sheep shearer. In 1889 he formed Wolseley Sheep Shearing Machine Company. Herbert Austin a young engineer who perfected Wolseley's machine moved back to England and became manager of the company's Birmingham factory when the company relocated there in 1893.

In 1895 Austin amazed by an automobile exhibition he attended in Paris obtained an advance from the company to develop an automobile; it went into production in 1901. The car manufacturing operations were separated from the company's other machinery operations and soon were bought by Vickers. (Austin went out on his own in 1905 and began producing cars under his own name —the venerable Austin line.)

By the middle of the century Wolseley Sheep Shearing had grown to include central heating and plumbing products distribution. In 1958 it joined with Geo. H. Hughes to form Wolseley-Hughes. At the time the company was a small manufacturer with 11 distribution depots.

The company's watershed transition began in 1976 when Jeremy Lancaster took over the chairmanship from his father. (In the 20 years that Lancaster was chairman profits rose from about $6 million in 1976 to more than $350 million in 1996.) In the late 1970s the company began expanding rapidly through acquisitions. In 1982 it went public and acquired Ferguson Enterprises a leading distributor of plumbing supplies on the US's East Coast. The acquisition marked the company's first substantial US purchase. Three years later the company formed Wolseley Centers which distributed building products under the names Plumb Center Controls Center and Pipeline Center. In 1986 the company changed its name to Wolseley plc. Acquisitions that year included Carolina Builders Corporation and M.P. Harris & Co. Late 1980s acquisitions included Familian (1987) the largest plumbing supplier on the US's West Coast and Familian Northwest (1988).

Wolseley then looked across the English Channel. In 1992 it bought Brossette France's largest specialist distributor of plumbing supplies. The company moved further eastward in 1994 acquiring ÖAG Group (now Wolseley Austria) Austria's largest wholesale plumbing supply business. In addition to 40 Austrian branches ÖAG also had five branches in both Hungary and Germany and four in the Czech Republic. The ÖAG deal solidified Wolseley's position as the world's #1 plumbing and heating merchant.

Wolseley turned its attention back to the US in the mid-1990s buying a half-dozen companies including Building Material Supply. John Young became CEO that year when Jeremy Lancaster retired from the company.

In 1998 the company began integrating California-based Familian and Virginia-based Ferguson Enterprises —together responsible for more than half of Wolseley's US distribution revenues —under Ferguson's management. The company continued making acquisitions that year and the next including its first Italian company (Manzardo plumbing and heating supplies); it also grew by opening new outlets. Wolseley sold some of its burner and boiler manufacturing operations in 1999.

Chairman Richard Ireland became acting chief executive in June 2000 with the retirement of Young for health reasons. That year the company sold most of its manufacturing businesses. It sold its remaining boiler and burner manufacturing businesses in early 2001. In May 2001 Ferguson Enterprises CEO Charles Banks was named group chief executive.

Also in 2001 Wolseley bought the heating and plumbing operations of Westburne Group (from France-based Rexel a distributor of electrical equipment) for $356 million to further expand in the US. In 2002 Wolseley bought Clayton Acquisition a Florida-based wholesale distributor of waterworks for $110 million. Additionally in 2002 the company bought Wasco a Dutch heating-equipment supplier for $58 million to expand in Europe. In December of that year Ireland was replaced as chairman by deputy chairman John Whybrow.

In July 2003 Wolseley bought Pinault Bois & Materiaux (now PB & M) which distributes lumber and building supplies in France from Pinault-Printemps-Redoute. Wolseley acquired three North American businesses JM Lumber Liberty Equipment & Supply and Nuroc Plumbing and Heating Supplies in September 2003.

The company acquired Tobler Management [now Wolseley (Schweiz)] a Swiss HVAC wholesaler from CapVis in December 2003. PB & M acquired Groupe Simoni a French building materials distributor in January 2004. Wolseley expanded its Irish business through the August 2004 acquisition of Brooks Group an Irish building supply company from UPM-Kymmene. Capping an acquisitive year Wolseley also acquired Parnell-Martin Management and Record Supply Company in the US and TAPS Wholesale Bath Centre in Canada in December 2004.

Overall in the fiscal year ended July 2005 the company spent £431 million on 26 acquisitions.

In April 2006 Wolseley acquired Brandon Hire for £72 million. The acquisition of DT Group in September brought Wolseley into new markets in Denmark Finland Norway and Sweden. In October the company purchased Woodcote - stavebni materialy a.s. a general builders merchant with operations in the Czech Republic Croatia Hungary Poland Romania and Slovakia. Overall in fiscal 2006 the company added 279 new locations.

In August 2007 Wolseley purchased Davidson Pipe Company in the US thereby gaining access to the New York metropolitan market.

In 2008 the company acquired Gama Myjava in Slovakia.

In May 2009 Wolseley sold a 51% stake in BMC Stock to The Gores Group LLC a US private equity firm. In June Ian Meakins joined Wolseley as CEO. He succeeded Claude "Chip" Hornsby who resigned from the position after three years.

In July 2011 the company sold its Electric Center business to Edmundson Electrical. In November Wolseley sold its remaining 49% stake in Stock Building Supply to Gores Group.

EXECUTIVES

Chief Executive Officer, Frank Roach
Chief Executive Officer, Ian Meakins
Chairman, Gareth Davis
Auditors: Deloitte LLP

LOCATIONS

HQ: Wolseley Plc Jersey
26 New Street, St Helier, Jersey JE2 3RA
Phone: (44) 118 929 8700   **Fax:** (44) 118 929 8701
Web: www.wolseley.com

2011 Sales

	% of total
North America	
US	40
Canada	6
UK	18
Nordic region	16
France	14
Central Europe	6
Total	**100**

PRODUCTS/OPERATIONS

2011 Sales by Market

	% of total
Residential repair maintenance & improvement	36
Non-residential repair maintenance & improvement	21
Residential new construction	20
Non-residential new construction	16
Civil infrastructure	7
Total	**100**

2011 Sales by Product

	% of total
Plumbing heating & air conditioning	40
Building materials	30
Civil/waterworks commercial & industrial	28
Other	2
Total	**100**

Selected Products

Building materials
  Beams and trusses
  Bricks blocks and aggregates
  Cement
  Doors and frames
  Glass

Insulation
Plaster and plasterboard
Roofing materials
Tiles and flooring
Timber products
Civil/waterworks industrial and commercial
  Carbon and stainless steel pipes valves and fittings
  Drainage pipes
  Underground pressure pipes
Plumbing heating and air conditioning
  Air conditioning equipment
  Baths and showers
  Boilers and burners
  Brassware
  Control equipment
  Copper tubing
  Heat pumps
  Hot water cylinders
  Plastic pipes and fittings
  Radiators and valves
  Sanitaryware
  Solar equipment
  Ventilation equipment
Other
  Electrical cables
  Lighting
  Wiring
  Services
  Customer inventory management
  Installation
  Maintenance

Selected Subsidiaries

CFM
  Heating appliances Luxembourg
DT Group
  Building materials Denmark
Ferguson Enterprises Inc.
  Wholesale distribution of plumbing heating and piping products US
Manzardo SpA
  Heating and plumbing equipment Italy
OAG AG
  Heating and plumbing products Austria
PB&M
  Building materials and wood distribution France
Tobler
  Heating and plumbing products Switzerland
Wasco Holding BV
  Heating equipment The Netherlands
Wolseley Canada
  Wholesale distribution of plumbing heating and ventilation products Canada
Wolseley France
  Building materials plumbing and heating products France
Wolseley UK Limited
  Construction products UK
Woodcote Group
  Construction materials Czech Republic

COMPETITORS

84 Lumber	MPS Builders and
B&Q	Merchants
Castorama Dubois	MSC Industrial Direct
Emco Corporation	Noland
Grafton Group	SIG plc
HD Supply	Saint-Gobain Building
HSS Hire	Distribution
Hewden Stuart	Speedy Hire
Interline Brands	Thermador Groupe
Jewson	Travis Perkins
Kingfisher	Waxman
Lowe's	

HISTORICAL FINANCIALS

Company Type: Public

Income Statement

FYE: July 31

	REVENUE ($ mil.)	NET INCOME ($ mil.)	NET PROFIT MARGIN	EMPLOYEES
07/16	19,017	868	4.6%	39,717
07/15	20,761	331	1.6%	40,375
07/14	22,162	850	3.8%	39,454
07/13	20,003	463	2.3%	39,995
07/12	21,038	89	0.4%	43,170
Annual Growth	(2.5%)	76.6%	—	(2.1%)

2016 Year-End Financials

Debt ratio: 30.8%
Return on equity: 23.8%
Cash ($ mil.): 1,238
Current ratio: 1.46
Long-term debt ($ mil.): 1,584
No. of shares (mil.): 252
Dividends
  Yield: 0.0%
  Payout: 1.9%
Market value ($ mil.): 1,408

	STOCK PRICE ($) FY Close	P/E High/Low		PER SHARE ($) Earnings	Dividends	Book Value
07/16	5.58	2	2	3.36	0.07	15.16
07/15	6.71	8	6	1.28	0.12	15.60
07/14	5.20	3	3	3.19	0.04	18.28
07/13	4.81	5	3	1.67	0.00	16.92
07/12	3.58	19	10	0.32	0.00	17.73
Annual Growth	11.7%	—	—	79.7%	—	(3.8%)

Woolworths Ltd.

Chow Down Under with Australia's #1 food retailer (ahead of Coles) — Woolworths (aka "Woolies"). The diversified retailer operates about 3200 stores in Australia and New Zealand including more than 1000 supermarkets under the Woolworths Foodtown Countdown and Thomas Dux banners. It also operates BWS and Dan Murphy's liquor stores. In addition Woolworths sells gasoline and leverages its distribution network to provide wholesale merchandise for third-party supermarkets. Woolworths' 165-odd general merchandise discount stores operate under the Big W name. It also runs about 395 consumer electronics shops under the Dick Smith and Tandy brand names. Woolworths also operates nearly 300 hotels.

Woolworths' total fiscal 2011 (ends June) sales rose nearly 5% vs. the previous year. The retailer's supermarket Australian supermarkets outperformed their counterparts in New Zealand. Indeed sales at the New Zealand markets declined slightly in 2011 vs. 2010 while the Australian markets rose more than 4%. Sales at the company's Big W general merchandise stores dipped while the consumer electronics category rose 4%. Online sales increased 63% with Woolworths onlne now available to 85% of Australia's population.

Woolworths along with other Australian retailers has been hit by weak consumer demand and competition from online retailers. Looking to streamline its operations the company in early 2012 announced plans to sell its Dick Smith consumer electronics business but will continue to participate in the category through its Big W stores and an expanded online offering. Stung by competition from Internet retailers the company is focused on expanding its online operations. (The company's pending exit from the Dick Smith business will not impact the its partnership with India's

Tata Group for a chain of consumer electronics stores in India. Woolworths is supplying Tata's chain of 50 Croma stores there.)

The decision to sell Dick Smith followed the purchase by the firm's Australian Leisure and Hospitality Group (ALH) of about 30 hotels in New South Wales in late 2011. ALH operates sports bars and pubs restaurants retail liquor stores gaming outlets and nightclubs and hotels across Australia. To stock its liquor cabinet Woolworths in 2011 acquired The Cellarmasters Group from Archer Capital for A$340 million ($346 million). Cellarmasters is a leading direct-to-home wine retailer with operations in Australia and New Zealand. It also has a winemaking operation. The purchase complemented the company's existing liquor brands which include Dan Murphy's BWS Woolworth's Liquor and Langton's.

On the home front Woolworths is taking on the big-box home improvement market in partnership with the #2 home improvement chain in the US — Lowe's Companies. The Danks joint venture which is two-thirds owned by Woolworths has begun opening Lowe's-style home improvement stores in Australia under the Danks and Masters banners. Plans are for more than 150 such sites over the next five years. The stores will compete with market leader Bunnings owned by rival Wesfarmers which also owns Coles.

HISTORY

Harold Percival Christmas first tried a mail-order dress business before opening the popular Frock Salon retail store. Christmas and his partners opened a branch store in the Imperial Arcade in Sydney in 1924 renaming it "Woolworths Stupendous Bargain Basement" and luring customers with advertisements calling it "a handy place where good things are cheap ... you'll want to live at Woolworths." The company borrowed the name from Frank Woolworth's successful US chain after determining that chain had no plans to open stores in Australia. Woolworths was listed on the Australian stock exchange in 1924.

Food sales came more than 30 years later. Woolworths opened its first freestanding full-line supermarket in 1960 then diversified into specialty retail buying the Rockmans women's clothing store chain the next year (sold in 2000). It expanded into discounting with the Big W chain in 1976 and further diversified when it bought 60% of the Dick Smith Electronics store chain in 1981 (buying the remainder in 1983).

The purchase of the Safeway grocery chain (the Australian operations of the US-based chain) put Woolworths on the top of the supermarket heap in 1985. But the company was hurting (it lost $13 million in 1985-86) because of a restructuring in the early 1980s that had weakened management by bulking up the front offices and dividing responsibilities. Woolworths got a shot in the arm from Paul Simons who returned to the company in 1987 after running competitor Franklins. Simons cleaned house in the front offices closed unprofitable stores and began the successful "Fresh Food People" marketing strategy.

Industrial Equity Limited (IEL) bought the company in 1989; IEL then became part of the Adelaide Steamship group which spun off Woolworths as a public company in 1993. Career Woolworths manager Reg Clairs took over as CEO the following year following the untimely death (on a golf course) in 1993 of Harry Watts who was being groomed for the job. As a result the company has an unwritten rule of avoiding CEOs older than 60.

Clairs took the company in a variety of new directions. Woolworths began supplying fresh food to neighbor Asia in 1995. The company added Plus Petrol outlets adjacent to Woolworths Super-

markets in 1996. It also started a superstore concept for its Dick Smith Electronics chain (Power House) that year. In 1997 the company launched its Woolworths Metro store chain which targets commuters and other on-the-run shoppers in urban areas and it aggressively jumped into wholesaling to independent grocers.

Clairs (who was turning 60 in 1999) stepped down in late 1998 and Roger Corbett took over as CEO. Woolworths also began offering banking services to its customers and bought Dan Murphy a Victoria-based liquor chain in 1998. It divested its Chisholm Manufacturing meat plants in 2000.

In 2001 Woolworths acquired two liquor store chains (Liberty Liquor Booze Bros) more than 200 Tandy Electronics stores and 72 Franklins supermarkets from Hong Kong-based Dairy Farm International Holdings (most of which were later converted to the Woolworths and Food for Less banners). It sold its Crazy Prices general merchandise stores and began restructuring its liquor operations into four distinctive formats.

Woolworths exited the New Zealand market in 2002 when it sold its supermarkets group there to Foodland Associated for $690 million.

Supermarket division chief Bill Wavish resigned in May 2003 and was replaced by former chief general manager of supermarket operations Tom Flood. Wavish was considered one of the top candidates to replace CEO Corbett. Also in 2003 the company discontinued its Australian Independent Wholesalers (AIW) operations. Flood who like Wavish was considered a likely successor to Corbett resigned abruptly in August 2004.

The company acquired Australia's biggest pub owner Australian Leisure & Hospitality (ALH) in 2005. Woolworths operates ALH's retailing activities leaving the pubs and gaming operations to its partner in the purchase The Bruce Mathieson Group. (Previously the duo had acquired a 16% stake in ALH.) In mid-2005 the company acquired the New Zealand supermarkets of Foodland Associated and 22 Action stores in Western Australia Queensland and New South Wales for about $1.8 billion.

In September 2006 the company announced it had purchased a 10% stake in New Zealand's The Warehouse retail chain. Corbett retired as CEO in October. He was succeeded by Michael Luscombe the company's long-serving director of supermarkets.

Woolworths offered about $1.7 billion in 2008 to buy all of New Zealand's leading general merchandise retailer Warehouse Group. The purchase however which would have allowed Woolworths to expand from food into general merchandise in New Zealand was blocked by that country's competition regulator in mid-2008. An attempt to take over Australia's JB Hi-Fi an independent chain of home entertainment products also failed.

In February 2011 Woolworths acquired The Cellarmasters Group from Archer Capital for A$340 million ($346 million). In October Grant O'Brien was named CEO of the company.

EXECUTIVES

Managing Director CEO and Managing Director Food Group, Bradford (Brad) Banducci
CFO, David Marr
CEO BIG W, Sally Macdonald
Managing Director Woolworths Liquor Group, Martin Smith
Chairman, Gordon M. Cairns, age 59
Auditors: Deloitte Touche Tohmatsu

LOCATIONS

HQ: Woolworths Ltd.
1 Woolworths Way, Bella Vista, Sydney, New South Wales 2153
Phone: (61) 2 8885 0000
Web: www.woolworthslimited.com.au

2016 Sales

	% of total
Australia	90
New Zealand	10
Total	**0**

PRODUCTS/OPERATIONS

2016 Sales

	% of total
Australian Food and Petrol	68
New Zealand Supermarkets	10
Endeavour Drinks Group	13
BIGW	6
Hotels	2
Unallocated	1
Total	**100**

COMPETITORS

ALDI	Metcash
BP	Royal Dutch Shell
Harvey Norman Holdings	Wesfarmers

HISTORICAL FINANCIALS

Company Type: Public

Income Statement

FYE: June 30

	REVENUE ($ mil.)	NET INCOME ($ mil.)	NET PROFIT MARGIN	EMPLOYEES
06/16	43,358	(918)	—	205,000
06/15	46,775	1,649	3.5%	190,000
06/14	57,272	2,303	4.0%	198,000
06/13	54,119	2,084	3.9%	197,637
06/12	55,514	1,824	3.3%	190,000
Annual Growth	**(6.0%)**	**—**	**—**	**1.9%**

2016 Year-End Financials

Debt ratio: 13.8%	No. of shares (mil.): 1,278
Return on equity: (-12.7%)	Dividends
Cash ($ mil.): 705	Yield: 0.1%
Current ratio: 0.83	Payout: —
Long-term debt ($ mil.): 2,880	Market value ($ mil.): 19,859

	STOCK PRICE ($) FY Close	P/E High/Low		PER SHARE ($) Earnings	Dividends	Book Value
06/16	15.53	—	—	(0.73)	2.59	4.93
06/15	20.50	17	12	1.31	3.20	6.57
06/14	33.40	18	15	1.84	3.83	7.65
06/13	30.65	19	13	1.68	3.57	6.66
06/12	27.05	19	16	1.49	3.74	6.68
Annual Growth	**(13.0%)**	**—**	**—**	**—**	**(8.8%)**	**(7.3%)**

WPG Holding Co Ltd

WPG provides logistics and supply chain management services to clients in Asia's semiconductor industry. The company supplies semiconductors interconnect and passive components and computer and peripheral products. With warehouses in Taiwan Hong Kong and Singapore WPG distributes more than 100 product lines from such chip makers as Hynix Infineon Intel Micron Technology NXP ON Semiconductor and Texas Instruments and offers online order management and inventory management services to its customers. Electronic component distributors World Peace Industrial and Silicon Applications Corp. jointly established WPG; the company listed on the Taiwan exchange in 2005.

In 2010 WPG acquired key Taiwanese rival Yosun Industrial in a stock-swap transaction. The company was attracted to Yosun's experienced management team and its complementary product lines among other attributes. The deal gave WPG a boost in market share in the Asia Pacific region.

In 2009 subsidiary WPG Americas acquired certain assets of the Jaco Electronics electronic components distribution business. The purchase greatly expanded WPG's operations in North America.

EXECUTIVES

Chairman and President, Simon Huang
VP Marketing Management Unit, Scott Lin
VP Corporate Finance and Accounting, Cliff Yuan
Auditors: PricewaterhouseCoopers Taiwan

LOCATIONS

HQ: WPG Holding Co Ltd
8F, No. 489, Section 2, Tiding Boulevard, Neihu District, Taipei
Phone: (886) 2 8797 8860
Web: www.wpgholdings.com

2015 sales

	% of total
Taiwan	18
Mainland China	69
Others	13
Total	**100**

PRODUCTS/OPERATIONS

Services
One Stop-Shopping
Built-to-Order
Integrated Solution
On-line Service
Warehouse Logistic and Cross-Border Support
Virtual Managed Inventory system
Financial Support

COMPETITORS

Arrow Electronics   Future Electronics
Avnet   Premier Farnell

HISTORICAL FINANCIALS

Company Type: Public

Income Statement

FYE: December 31

	REVENUE ($ mil.)	NET INCOME ($ mil.)	NET PROFIT MARGIN	EMPLOYEES
12/15	15,688	164	1.1%	5,518
12/14	14,289	183	1.3%	5,595
12/13	13,623	159	1.2%	5,971
12/12	12,425	156	1.3%	6,227
12/11	10,964	167	1.5%	6,120
Annual Growth	**9.4%**	**(0.4%)**	—	**(2.6%)**

2015 Year-End Financials

Debt ratio: 1.3%
Return on equity: 11.6%
Cash ($ mil.): 287
Current ratio: 1.48
Long-term debt ($ mil.): 547
No. of shares (mil.): 1,655
Dividends
  Yield: —
  Payout: —
Market value ($ mil.): —

WPP Plc (New)

Once upon a time WPP sold wiring and plastics products but now it's the world's largest marketing and advertising agency. The company operates through more than 3000 offices in upwards of 112 countries and works with some 350 of the Fortune 500 Global Companies among others. Its advertising agency networks including Grey Worldwide JWT Ogilvy & Mather and Young & Rubicam offer creative campaign development and brand management services. WPP's holdings also include public relations firms media buying and planning agencies and many specialized marketing and communications units. In addition its Kantar Group division is one of the world's leading market research organizations.

Operations

WPP operates four business segments: Advertising and Media Investment Management (45% of total revenue); Data Investment Management (20%); Public Relations & Public Affairs (8%); and Branding Identity Healthcare and Specialist Communications (27%).

The Advertising segment produces advertising content across essentially all sectors such as television internet radio magazines and newspapers. The segment also includes GroupM which is WPP's media investment management operation and is the largest global player in its field; GroupM boasts that it serves one in three adverts globally.

WWP's Data Investment Management segment is organized under the Kantar Group umbrella which comprises 12 specialized operating brands that together aim to offer a complete view of consumers. Public Relations offers advice to clients looking to communicate to customers governmental bodies and other businesses. Lastly the Branding & Identity segment offers branding and design services; marketing solutions for healthcare firms; and a range of specialist and customer services including for sports youth and entertainment marketing.

The company's nine "billion-dollar brands" include Ogilvy J. Walter Thompson Mindshare MEC MediaCom Y&R MillwardBrown TNS and Wunderman.

Geographical Reach

WPP has a worldwide reach and operates out of upwards of 3000 offices in 112 countries. North America (mostly the US) is the company's most valuable region by revenue at around 37% of total; the UK and Western Continental Europe pull in approximately 34%. The Asia-Pacific region Latin America the Middle East and North Africa and Eastern Europe make up the rest.

The company generated revenue of more than $1 billion in five markets: the US the UK Germany Australia/New Zealand and Greater China.

Financial Performance

Note: Growth rates may differ after conversion to US Dollars.

Total revenue in 2015 was up on prior year by 6% to £12.2 billion after taking into account headwinds from foreign currency movements - the strength of the pound against the euro detracted from revenue by 1.4%. This was the fifth consecutive year of record sales. The strongest growth was in the Advertising and Media Investment Management segment which grew by £400 million. The second-largest segment Branding & Identity brought in £3.3 billion. Factors behind the year's strong results include an industry-leading performance in winning new business and customer retention as well as greater focus on emerging markets.

By region North America generated sales of £4.5 billion - representing growth of around 15%. Western Continental Europe was the only region to see sales fall in 2015 down nearly 6% on prior year to £2.4 billion - this was due to a poor macroeconomic climate and unfavorable currency movements.

Net income was up to £1245 for the year. Factors in this include exceptional gains of £296 million in 2015 which came from the sale of Kantar's internet measurement business and WPP's stakes in e-Rewards and Chime Communications. On the other hand WPP incurred £106 million in restructuring costs almost half of which was severance-related from the Data Investment Management business in Western Continental Europe.

The company's cash flow from operating activities fell from £1703 million in 2014 to a still-considerable £1360 million.

Strategy

WPP strategy comprises four key tenets: 'horizontality' which means closer links between the various WPP businesses via global client leaders and regional sub-regional and country managers (there are 45 cross-group client teams today up from 10 in 2010); a concerted effort to increase emerging market revenue to 40-45% of total sales (currently at 19% up a point since 2010); a focus on expanding new media to 40-45% of revenue (currently at 38% up 9 points since 2010); and hold firm in the more measurable marketing services such as Data Investment Management at 50% of revenue.

WPP aims to increase flexibility in cost structure particularly in staffing costs in order to mitigate against WWP's vulnerability and overreliance on large clients (the company's 10 largest customers account for 16% of revenue in 2015) which can scale back marketing budgets at short notice.

Acquisitions are a big part of WPP strategy particularly as a means to access new markets. Of the 52 new acquisitions in 2015 18 were in new markets and 37 in quantitative and digital. This was in line with the company's drive to expand the share of revenue in the Asia-Pacific region Latin America Eastern Europe and the Middle East and Africa to 40-45% and in new media to 40-45% also.

Mergers and Acquisitions

WPP has long been exceptionally active on the acquisition front and 2015 was no exception - indeed it was among the industry's most prolific acquirer for the year. The group made 40 acquisitions to a sum of £693.1 million up 40% on 2014's £495 million (although down in number from 52). The most notable acquisition includes GroupM's purchase of a majority stake of Essence the world's largest independent buyer of digital media alongside a number of bolt-ons such as ABS Creative (euro 2.8 million revenue in 2015) Webling Interactive (A$4.4 million) and WANDA Digital ($3.4 million). Emerging market acquisitions include nudeJEH in Thailand and Ideal Group and Jüssi Intention Marketing in Brazil.

HISTORY

Company Background

WPP Group began as Wire and Plastic Products a maker of grocery baskets and other goods founded in 1958 by Gordon Sampson (who retired from the company in 2000). Investors led by former Saatchi & Saatchi advertising executive (and current WPP CEO) Martin Sorrell bought the company in 1985 and began acquiring marketing firms under the shortened name of WPP. In 1987 Sorrell used revenue from these businesses (and a sizable loan) to buy US advertising warhorse J. Walter Thompson (now JWT).

JWT was founded by William James Carlton as the Carlton & Smith agency in 1864. The New York City-based firm was bought by James Walter Thompson in 1877 and was later responsible for Prudential Insurance's Rock of Gibraltar symbol (1896). It began working for Ford (which is still a client) in 1943. JWT went public in 1969.

Following its acquisition of JWT WPP formed European agency Conquest in 1988. The company (and its debt) grew the next year when it bought the Ogilvy Group (founded by David Ogilvy in 1948) for $860 million making WPP the world's largest advertising company. But its acquisition frenzy also positioned the company for a fall in 1991 when depressed economies in the US and the UK slowed advertising spending. Saddled with debt WPP nearly went into receivership before recovering the next year.

WPP began a period of controlled growth with no major acquisitions in 1993. It expanded internationally in 1994 opening new offices in South America Europe the Middle East and Asia. Winning IBM's $500 million international advertising contract that year also aided WPP's financial recovery. However this led to the loss of business from IBM's rivals including AT&T Compaq's European division (Compaq was purchased by Hewlett-Packard in 2002) and Microsoft.

By 1997 the company was again ready to flex its acquisition muscle. The firm bought 21 companies that year including a stake in IBOPE (a market research firm in Latin America) and a share of Batey Holdings (the majority owner of Batey Ads a prominent ad agency in the Asia/Pacific region). That year WPP also created its media planning unit Mindshare.

More acquisitions followed in 1998 including a 20% stake in Asatsu (the #3 advertising agency in Japan). The next year the company bought Texas-based market research firm IntelliQuest Information Group which was merged with WPP's Millward Brown unit. Along with its acquisitions WPP snagged some significant new accounts in 1998 and 1999 lining up business with Kimberly-Clark Merrill Lynch and the embattled International Olympic Committee.

In 2000 the company bought US-based rival Young & Rubicam for about $4.7 billion —one of the largest advertising mergers ever. The move catapulted WPP to the top spot among the world's advertising firms. As if that wasn't enough its Mindshare unit later snagged the $700 million media planning account of consumer products giant Unilever. WPP also took a 49% stake in Uni-World Group the largest African-American-owned ad agency in the US.

Hamish Maxwell chairman since 1996 retired in 2001 and was replaced by Philip Lader the former US ambassador to the UK. That year however WPP's top ranking was stolen away by Interpublic Group following its acquisition of True North Communications. It later sparked a bidding war with Havas Advertising when it offered $630 million to buy UK media services firm Tempus Group. WPP grudgingly completed its acquisition of Tempus in 2002. The following year the company acquired Cordiant Communications.

WPP positioned itself for both short- and long-term growth in 2005 when it completed a $1.75 billion acquisition of US-based rival Grey Group beating out bids from private equity players (including Kohlberg Kravis Roberts & Co.) and rival advertising firm Havas.

WPP in 2007 expanded its digital marketing and advertising services by acquiring 24/7 Real Media. The company snatched up Blast Radius an interactive marketing agency a few months later and aligned Blast Radius with Wunderman a marketing communications unit of WPP's Young & Rubicam Brands division.

During the same year WPP signed a lucrative $4.5 billion three-year deal for providing advertising and marketing services to Dell. In an unconventional move WPP created a new agency Enfatico to cater to the computer giant during the three-year contract.

Throughout 2008 market research rival TNS rejected several unsolicited takeover bids from WPP (including a $2.1 billion offer in July). However TNS eventually acquiesced to the proposal when more than 60% of its shareholders accepted WPP's offer in October. The deal greatly enhanced WPP's Kantar operations and created a global market research juggernaut. In late 2008 WPP also shortened its legal name from WPP Group plc to WPP plc.

The next year WPP worked to streamline its operating structure when it integrated TNS Custom with its Research International subsidiary to create the world's largest custom research group. Throughout 2010 WPP focused on acquisitions and investments in the digital arena deriving from China Brazil Singapore the UK and the US.

EXECUTIVES

Chief Executive Officer, Martin Sorrell
Chairman, Philip Lader
Auditors: Deloitte LLP

LOCATIONS

HQ: WPP Plc (New)
27 Farm Street, London W1J 5RJ
Phone: (44) 20 7408 2204   **Fax:** (44) 20 7493 6819
Web: www.wpp.com

22015 Sales

	% of total
North America	37
Asia-Pacific Latin America Africa & Middle East and Central & Eastern Europe	29
Western Continental Europe	20
United Kingdom	14
Total	**100**

PRODUCTS/OPERATIONS

2015 Sales

% total		
Advertising and Media Investment Management		45
Branding Identity Healthcare and Specialist Communications		27
Data Investment Management		20
Public Relations & Public Affairs		8
Total	**0**	**100**

Selected Operations

Advertising
  Asatsu-DK (21% Japan)
  Bates Asia (China)
  Diamond Ogilvy
  Direct.com (US)
  Gallagher Group (US)
  Grey Worldwide (US)
  JWT (US)
  Kinetic Worldwide
  Malone Advertising (US)
  Ogilvy & Mather Worldwide (US)
  Red Cell (US)
  Soho Square (US)
  Studio.com (US)
  Tarantula
  The Weinstein Company (US)
  The Voluntarily United Group of Creative Agencies
  Y&R (US)
  Rainey Kelly Campbell Roalfe / Y&R (UK)
  SicolaMartin (US)
Media services
  GroupM
  MAXUS
  MediaCom Worldwide (US)
  Mediaedge:cia
  The Digital Edge
  Outrider
  Wunderman Media (US)
  Mindshare

Performance
Portland Outdoor
Research information and consulting
  The Kantar Group (US)
  Added Value Group
  Cheskin Added Value
  ASI/Kantar Research
  BPRI
  Cannondale Associates (US)
  Center Partners (US)
  Everystone
  Fusion 5 (US)
  The Futures Company
  Glendinning Management Consultants
  IMRB International (India)
  KMR
  AGBNielsen Media Research (50%)
  BMRB International
  Mediafax (Puerto Rico)
  Lightspeed Research (US)
  MVI
  Mattson Jack Group (US)
  Millward Brown (US)
  Research International
  RMS Instore
  TNS
  Ziment (US)
  ohal
Public relations and public affairs
  ABC Public Relations (Denmark)
  BKSH (US)
  Blanc & Otus
  Buchanan Communications
  Bulletin International
  Burson-Marsteller (US)
  Chime Communications (21%)
  Clarion Communications
  Cohn & Wolfe (US)
  Federalist Group (US)
  Finsbury
  Hill & Knowlton (US)
  Blanc & Otus (US)
  Wexler & Walker Public Policy Associates (US)
  Impact Employee Communications (Australia)
  IPR Asia Holdings (China)
  Ogilvy Public Relations Worldwide (US)
  Penn Schoen & Berland (US)
  Quinn Gillespie (US)
  Robinson Lerer & Montgomery (US)
  Timmons & Company (US)
  Wexler & Walker Public Policy Associates
Branding and corporate identity services
  Addison Corporate Marketing
  BDGMcColl
  BDGworkfutures
  The Brand Union
  Coley Porter Bell
  Dovetail
  Fitch (US)
  G2 Worldwide
  Lambie-Nairn
  Landor Associates (US)
  The Partners
  MJM Creative Services (US)
  WalkerGroup (US)
  Warwicks
Direct marketing promotions and relationship marketing
  A. Eicoff & Company (US)
  Bridge Worldwide
  Dialog Marketing
  Einson Freeman (US)
  EWA
  Good Technology
  G2
  G2 Branding & Design (US)
  G2 Direct & Digital (US)
  G2 Interactive (US)
  G2 Promotional Marketing (US)
  Headcount Worldwide Field Marketing
  High Co. (34% France)
  Imaginet (US)
  Mando Brand Assurance
  Maxx Marketing (China)
  OgilvyAction (formerly 141 Worldwide)
  OgilvyOne Worldwide (US)
  rmg:connect
  RTC Relationship Marketing (US)
  VML (US)
  Wunderman
  KBM Group (US)

Health care communications
Grey Healthcare Group (US)
Feinstein Kean Healthcare (US)
Geoff Howe Marketing Communications (US)
Ogilvy CommonHealth Worldwide (US)
Sudler & Hennessey (US)
Specialized communications
Alliance Agency (US)
Banner Corporation
The Bravo Group (US)
The Farm Group
The Food Group (US)
Forward
G WHIZ (US)
The Geppetto Group (US)
Global Sportnet (Germany)
JWT Specialized Communications (US)
Kang & Lee (US)
MosaicaMD (US)
Metro Group
Ogilvy Primary Contact
PACE (US)
PCI Fitch
Première Group
PRISM Group
Spafax
UniWorld Group (49% US)
WING Latino (US)

COMPETITORS

Dentsu	Ipsos
Dentsu Aegis	Nielsen
GfK	Nielsen Audio
GfK NOP	Omnicom
Havas	Publicis Groupe
Interpublic Group	

HISTORICAL FINANCIALS

Company Type: Public

Income Statement

FYE: December 31

	REVENUE ($ mil.)	NET INCOME ($ mil.)	NET PROFIT MARGIN	EMPLOYEES
12/15	18,131	1,719	9.5%	128,123
12/14	17,996	1,681	9.3%	123,621
12/13	18,210	1,547	8.5%	119,116
12/12	16,720	1,326	7.9%	115,711
12/11	15,482	1,297	8.4%	109,971
Annual Growth	4.0%	7.3%	—	3.9%

2015 Year-End Financials

Debt ratio: 28.8%
Return on equity: 15.3%
Cash ($ mil.): 3,530
Current ratio: 0.94
Long-term debt ($ mil.): 6,907
No. of shares (mil.): 1,294
Dividends
  Yield: 2.8%
  Payout: 242.7%
Market value ($ mil.): 148,559

	STOCK PRICE ($) FY Close	P/E High/Low		Earnings	PER SHARE ($) Dividends	Book Value
12/15	114.74	133	107	1.31	3.28	8.74
12/14	104.10	132	106	1.26	2.91	8.88
12/13	114.86	158	103	1.15	2.30	9.31
12/12	72.90	109	82	1.01	2.02	8.68
12/11	52.23	97	66	1.00	1.47	8.13
Annual Growth	21.7%	—	—	7.1%	22.2%	1.8%

Xiamen C & D Inc

You name it —Xiamen C&D trades it. Abbreviated as C&D which stands for construction and development the company primarily imports and exports sundry light industry merchandise including apparel and accessories automobiles ceramics chemicals consumer electronics edible oils luggage medical equipment metals paper products plastics textiles and wine. It also provides real estate development and property leasing through subsidiary Lianfa Group. Among its prestigious projects it operates the Xiamen International Conference & Exhibition Center a property that provides exhibit conference and hotel facilities. Xiamen C&D was founded in 1998 and is owned by Xiamen C&D Corp.

Xiamen C&D also has 40% interest in Sichuan Yongfeng Paper Industry a state-owned mill; a 20% interest in Xiamen Shipbuilding Industry (XSI) whose industrial ships are exported to Europe the US and Southeast Asia; and a 20% interest in Ziamen Zijin Tongguan Mining Investment Development Company which owns Monterrico Metals.

In 2008 Xiamen C&D announced a joint venture with Taiwan's fourth-largest life insurance company Taiwan Life Insurance Co. Ltd.

EXECUTIVES

General Manager and Director, Wen Zhou Huang
Auditors: Ascenda Certified Public Accountants Co., Ltd.

LOCATIONS

HQ: Xiamen C & D Inc
7/F., Seaside Building, No. 52, Lujiang Road, Xiamen, Fujian Province 361001
Phone: (86) 592 2132319   **Fax:** (86) 592 2112185
Web: www.chinacnd.com

COMPETITORS

Anhui Technology	Sinochem
COFCO	Sinotrans
COSCO Group	

HISTORICAL FINANCIALS

Company Type: Public

Income Statement

FYE: December 31

	REVENUE ($ mil.)	NET INCOME ($ mil.)	NET PROFIT MARGIN	EMPLOYEES
12/15	19,722	406	2.1%	0
12/14	19,483	403	2.1%	0
12/13	16,859	444	2.6%	0
12/12	14,623	345	2.4%	0
12/11	12,750	357	2.8%	0
Annual Growth	11.5%	3.3%	—	—

2015 Year-End Financials

Debt ratio: 3.5%
Return on equity: 14.6%
Cash ($ mil.): 1,505
Current ratio: 1.59
Long-term debt ($ mil.): 2,696
No. of shares (mil.): —
Dividends
  Yield: —
  Payout: —
Market value ($ mil.): —

XL Group Ltd

Auditors: PricewaterhouseCoopers LLP

LOCATIONS

HQ: XL Group Ltd
O' Hara House, One Bermudiana Road, Hamilton HM 08
Phone: (441) 292 8515
Web: www.xlgroup.com

HISTORICAL FINANCIALS

Company Type: Public

Income Statement

FYE: December 31

	ASSETS ($ mil.)	NET INCOME ($ mil.)	INCOME AS % OF ASSETS	EMPLOYEES
12/15	58,682	1,207	2.1%	7,200
12/14	45,046	188	0.4%	4,663
12/13	45,652	1,059	2.3%	4,291
12/12	45,387	651	1.4%	4,007
12/11	44,626	(403)	—	3,818
Annual Growth	7.1%	—	—	17.2%

2015 Year-End Financials

Return on assets: 2.3%
Return on equity: 11.1%
Long-term debt ($ mil.): —
No. of shares (mil.): 294
Sales ($ mil): 9,308
Dividends
  Yield: —
  Payout: 16.1%
Market value ($ mil.): 11,548

	STOCK PRICE ($) FY Close	P/E High/Low		Earnings	PER SHARE ($) Dividends	Book Value
12/15	39.18	10	8	4.15	0.00	39.62
12/14	34.37	51	39	0.69	0.00	39.32
12/13	31.84	9	7	3.63	0.00	35.93
12/12	25.06	12	9	2.10	0.00	35.19
12/11	19.77	—	—	(1.52)	0.00	29.86
Annual Growth	18.6%	—	—	—	—	7.3%

Yapi Ve Kredi Bankasi A.S.

Yapi ve Kredi Bankasi (Yapi Kredi for short) boasts over $80 billion in assets making it Turkey's fourth-largest private bank. Yapi Kredi provides financial services —including retail corporate and private banking services –in Turkey through more than 1000 branches and about 4025 ATMs. It also operates in Bahrain and has subsidiary banks in Azerbaijan Germany the Netherlands and Russia. Yapi Kredi which launched Turkey's first credit card in 1988 now has 6 million cardholders. The bank also provides leasing factoring mutual funds insurance investment banking and brokerage services. Koç Financial Services (KFS) jointly owned by UniCredit and Koç Holding owns 82% of Yapi Kredi.

OperationsYapi Kredi's operates three major business segments. Its Retail Banking segment serves individuals and small- to medium- enterprises (SMEs) with consumer loans (auto mortgage and general purpose) and commercial installment loans respectively. About 59% of its loans were corporate and commercial loans in 2014 while retail loans and credit card receivables made up 27% and 14% of its total portfolio. The Retail Banking segment also provides card payment systems investment accounts insurance products and payroll services. Its Corporate & Commercial Banking segment has three subgroups: Corporate Banking for large-scale companies Commercial Banking for medium-sized companies and Multinational Companies Banking. Yapi Kredi's Private Banking and Wealth Management segment provides investment products to high net worth customers. About 80% of Yapi Kredi's total revenue came from interest income (mostly from loans) in 2014 while another 14% came from fees and commissions income. The rest of its revenue came from trading gains (2%) and other miscellaneous income sources (4%). Geographic ReachBeyond its 1000 branches in Turkey Yapi Kredi has subsidiary-owned branches in Amsterdam Moscow Baku (in Azerbaijan) and an offshore branch in Bahrain.

Sales and Marketing

Yapi Kredi's retail banking arm serves individuals with up to T$500000 (roughly $170000) in financial assets and SMEs with annual turnovers of less than $10 million. Its commercial banking customers typically have annual turnover of more than $10 million while its corporate banking customers are businesses with turnover of more than $100 million. The bank served more than 10 million customers in 2014.

Financial Performance

Note: Growth rates may differ after conversion to US dollars. This analysis uses financials from the company's annual report.Yapi Kredi's revenue jumped 21% to T$15.9 billion ($6.8 billion) in 2014 mostly from higher interest income as its loan assets swelled by 26% (compared to sector growth of 18%) with growth in TL company general purpose and SME loans during the year. Its fee and commission income grew by 10% despite new regulations while deposits rose by 22%.

Even with revenue growth the bank's net income fell 44% to T$2.06 billion ($887 million) mostly as its discontinued operations had generated some T$1.6 billion in 2013 but also because the bank incurred higher provisions for loan and other receivable impairments. Yapi Kredi's operating cash levels jumped 72% with operations using T$1.13 billion ($486 million) –compared to T$3.97 billion ($1.86 billion) in 2013 –mostly thanks to favorable working capital changes and higher cash earnings.

Strategy

Yapi Kredi has been moving toward digital banking channels that are quickly taking the industry by storm allowing the bank to slow expensive branch-expansion plans and cut operating costs significantly while giving customers faster access to banking services. To this end the bank in 2015 planned to continue boosting its mobile and internet banking customer base (which reached 1.2 million and 4.2 million users at the end of 2014 respectively). It also would continue to expand its ATM network and self-service banking corners implement video channel for digital banking customers increase IVR self service usage for its call center and divert more of its calls away from branches into a central location. Though its brick-and-mortar expansion plans have slowed compared to prior years Yapi Kredi still added 54 physical branches to its network in 2014 to grow its business. Yapi Kredi's aggressive expansion over the years has been effective at growing its customer base and overall business. Indeed during 2014 the bank added 600000 new customers to its business growing its base about 2.7 times faster than in previous years and bringing its total customer count to 10.6 million.

The bank has been the market leader in credit card market share since 1988 and controlled nearly a 22% market share of the outstanding volume nearly 20% of the issuing volume and an 18% market share on the number of credit cards outstanding during 2014. Yapi Kredi was also the market leader in leasing and factoring and was number two in mutual funds and brokerage categories. Company BackgroundYapi Kredi was previously controlled by Çukurova one of Turkey's largest business congomerates. Çukurova fell to near-collapse in the aftermath of Turkey's economic crisis in 2001 and the group sold Yapi Kredi to Koçbank owner Koçbank owner Koç Financial Services (KFS) in 2005. The

following year KFS merged Yapi Kredi and Koçbank in what was the largest bank merger Turkey had seen. The combined group took the Yapi Kredi name.

Koç Financial Services (KFS) which is jointly owned by UniCredit and Koç Holding owns 82% of Yapi Kredi which was founded in 1944.

EXECUTIVES

Chairman, Yildirim Ali Koc
Auditors: Guney Bagimsiz Denetim ve Serbest Muhasebeci Mali Musavirlik Anonim Sirketi

LOCATIONS

HQ: Yapi Ve Kredi Bankasi A.S.
 Yapi Kredi Plaza D Blok, Istanbul, Levent 34330
Phone: (90) 212 339 70 00   **Fax:** (90) 212 339 60 00
Web: www.yapikredi.com.tr

COMPETITORS

Akbank	GarantiBank
Citigroup	HSBC
Deutsche Bank	Isbank
Finansbank	Trk Ekonomi Bankasi

HISTORICAL FINANCIALS

Company Type: Public

Income Statement

FYE: December 31

	ASSETS ($ mil.)	NET INCOME ($ mil.)	INCOME AS % OF ASSETS	EMPLOYEES
12/15	80,540	653	0.8%	19,345
12/14	83,754	883	1.1%	18,534
12/13	74,944	1,710	2.3%	16,680
12/12	73,418	1,165	1.6%	17,459
12/11	62,224	1,210	1.9%	17,306
Annual Growth	6.7%	(14.3%)	—	2.8%

2015 Year-End Financials

Return on assets: 0.8%
Return on equity: 8.8%
Long-term debt ($ mil.): —
No. of shares (mil.): —
Sales ($ mil): 6,877

Dividends
 Yield: 0.0%
 Payout: 1,538.8%
Market value ($ mil.): —

	STOCK PRICE ($) FY Close	P/E High/Low	PER SHARE ($) Earnings	Dividends	Book Value
12/15	1.35	285285	0.00	0.02	0.02
12/14	2.10	409301	0.00	0.03	0.02
12/13	3.50	— —	0.00	0.02	0.02
12/12	3.50	— —	0.00	0.00	0.02
12/11	3.50	— —	0.00	0.00	0.02
Annual Growth	(21.2%)	— —	(14.4%)	—	4.4%

Yorkshire Building Society

Yorkshire Building Society (YBS) provides mortgages savings personal loans and brokerage services. One of the UK's largest mutually owned financial institutions the group also offers insurance coverage including mortgage-payment policies and home and auto insurance. YBS's brands include the Chelsea Building Society the Norwich & Peterborough Building Society YBS Share Plans

and other subsidiaries including Accord Mortgages. All together YBS operates more than 200 branches and agency offices in the UK and Northern Ireland. It has 3.1 million members and assets of more than £39 billion.

OperationsYBS is one of the largest building societies in the UK and as a mutual organization is owned by and run for the benefit of members. It has no external shareholders. Its YBS Share Plans unit has been administering share plans for more than 30 years.

Geographic Reach

YBS is based in Bradford in the North of England.

Financial Performance

Note: Growth rates may differ after conversion to US Dollars.

In fiscal 2015 interest income fell 4% to £1.3 billion. A few factors were behind the fall: a reduction in mortgage rates due to high industry competition and the continued availability of low-cost retail funding. Net interest income (interest income less interest payable) was also down by 3% to £534 million. Similarly profit was down 6% to £144.6 million.

Strategy

YBS decided in 2015 to reduce its target lending volumes to avoid competing in over-heated parts of the market.

In 2016 the company re-jigged its brand portfolio retiring its Barnsley Building Society brand in 2016 and making Chelsea Building Society online and telephone only. Branches under the two brands were rebranded as Yorkshire Building Society. The change will allow customers of both brands access the wider YBS network of more than 250 branches and agencies across the UK. YBS also enacted a consolidation process whereby if it operated two or more brands in any given area the number of branches would be reduced to one.

Company Background

The society merged with Chelsea Building Society in 2010 and with Norwich & Peterborough Building Society the following year; the two institutions continue to operate under their own brands.

The company was established in 1864 as the Huddersfield Equitable Permanent Benefit Building Society.

EXECUTIVES

Finance Director, Robin Churchouse, age 50
COO, Stephen White, age 44
Chief Executive, Mike Regnier
Vice Chairman, Mark A. Pain, age 55
Chairman, John Heaps
Auditors: Deloitte LLP

LOCATIONS

HQ: Yorkshire Building Society
 Yorkshire House, Yorkshire Drive, Bradford BD5 8LJ
Phone:
Web: www.ybs.co.uk

PRODUCTS/OPERATIONS

2015 Sales

	% of total
Interest receivable and similar income	96
Fees and commissions receivable	3
Other operating income	1
Total	**100**

COMPETITORS

The Newcastle	West Bromwich Building
The Principality	Society

HISTORICAL FINANCIALS

Company Type: Public

Income Statement

FYE: December 31

	ASSETS ($ mil.)	NET INCOME ($ mil.)	INCOME AS % OF ASSETS	EMPLOYEES
12/15	56,637	205	0.4%	4,576
12/14	58,650	230	0.4%	4,516
12/13	56,936	244	0.4%	4,218
12/12	53,992	198	0.4%	4,088
12/11	50,434	164	0.3%	3,266
Annual Growth	2.9%	5.8%		8.8%

2015 Year-End Financials

Return on assets: 0.3%
Return on equity: 0.4%
Long-term debt ($ mil.): —
No. of shares (mil.): —
Sales ($ mil): 1,920

Dividends
Yield: —
Payout: —
Market value ($ mil.): —

Yuken Kogyo Co., Ltd. (Japan)

EXECUTIVES

President, Osamu Tanaka
Auditors: Royal Audit Corp.

LOCATIONS

HQ: Yuken Kogyo Co., Ltd. (Japan)
4-4-34 Kamitsuchidana-Naka, Ayase, Kanagawa 252-1113
Phone: (81) 467 77 2111 **Fax:** (81) 467 77 3330
Web: www.yuken.co.jp

HISTORICAL FINANCIALS

Company Type: Public

Income Statement

FYE: March 31

	REVENUE ($ mil.)	NET INCOME ($ mil.)	NET PROFIT MARGIN	EMPLOYEES
03/16	27,701	1,078	3.9%	1,702
03/15	250	8	3.5%	1,693
03/14	271	8	3.1%	1,246
03/13	275	5	2.0%	1,177
03/12	328	4	1.3%	1,208
Annual Growth	202.9%	298.2%		8.9%

2016 Year-End Financials

Debt ratio: 24.9%
Return on equity: 7.0%
Cash ($ mil.): 4,508
Current ratio: 2.15
Long-term debt ($ mil.): 4,450

No. of shares (mil.): 42
Dividends
Yield: —
Payout: —
Market value ($ mil.): —

ZF Friedrichshafen AG (Germany)

ZF Friedrichshafen (ZF) shifts easily from land to air to sea. The company makes automatic and manual transmissions for commercial vehicles cars aircraft and marine vessels. ZF also makes rail transmissions and industrial drives such as servo gearboxes. Its off-road division makes transmissions for construction equipment and farm machinery. ZF's chassis unit makes automotive rear-axle systems and suspension modules. ZF was founded in 1915 by Ferdinand von Zeppelin (the Zeppelin inventor). The Zeppelin Stiftung Foundation which is largely controlled by the town of Friedrichshafen owns more than 90% of the company.

Geographic Reach

ZF has 230 locations in 40 countries and almost 115 production companies. Europe is ZF's largest geographic segment and typically represents around 55% of its net sales.

Operations

ZF operates through five divisions: Car Powertrain Technology Car Chassis Technology Commercial Vehicle Technology and Industrial Technology. A new division called Active & Passive Safety Technology was added after its acquisition of TRW Automotive.

Financial Performance

Note: Growth rates may differ after conversion to the US dollar.

ZF achieved extraordinary growth in 2015 with revenues peaking at a record-setting $31.9 billion and profits reaching more than $1 billion in 2015 another company milestone. The historic growth was attributed to additional revenue generated from its TRW Automotive acquisition.

Mergers and Acquisitions

In 2015 ZW made its largest acquisition to date with the $12.4 billion purchase of TRW Automotive a global maker of vehicle systems components and modules. TRW was incorporated into ZF as a new division called Active & Passive Safety Technology.

HISTORY

Company Background

After the 1908 fiery demonstration of an early airship Count Ferdinand Graf von Zeppelin thought he was ruined. However despite its unfortunate fate the airship's brief flight managed to captivate the interest of the citizens of Friedrichshafen Germany. The townspeople donated funds to Count Zeppelin raising more than 6 million German marks. He used the money to found Luftschiffbau Zeppelin GmbH in 1908. The company was controlled by the Zeppelin Stiftung (founded by the count) for the town of Friedrichshafen.

In 1915 Zahnradfabrik Friedrichshafen GmbH (ZF) was created by Luftschiffbau Zeppelin for the development and manufacture of special gears for airships and other aircraft. Count Zeppelin died two years later.

ZF was converted from a private firm to a stock corporation in 1921. To reflect the change the company's name was changed to Zahnradfabrik Friedrichshafen AG. ZF AG developed the first helical-gear transmission in 1929. The company began producing automotive steering systems in 1932.

Like much of Germany's industrial production capacity Zahnradfabrik Friedrichshafen's operations were out of commission by the end of WWII. Reconstruction of the company's factories was completed in 1946 when production resumed with 1000 workers.

In accordance with the count's will complete ownership of the Zeppelin Stiftung foundation was transferred to the city of Friedrichshafen in 1947. Three years later most of ZF's ownership (90%) was assigned to the Zeppelin Stiftung.

EXECUTIVES

EVP ZF Group, Michael Paul, age 65

CEO, Stefan Sommer, age 54

EVP and Member Management Board, Reinhard Buhl, age 64

EVP and Member Management Board, Peter Ottenbruch, age 59

Member Management Board, Rolf Lutz, age 64

EVP and Member Management Board, Gerhard Wagner, age 63

EVP and Financial Director, Konstantin Sauer, age 57

President Asia/Pacific, Rudi von Meister

EVP and Member Management Board, Jürgen Holeksa, age 51

EVP and Member Board Management, Wilhelm Rehm

CEO ZF Marine Propulsion Systems, Daniel Hörter

Chairman Supervisory Board, Dr. Giorgio Behr, age 69

Auditors: Ernst & Young GmbH Wirtschaftsprufungsgesellschaft

LOCATIONS

HQ: ZF Friedrichshafen AG (Germany)
Graf-von-Soden-Platz 1, Friedrichshafen D-88046
Phone: (49) 7541 77 0 **Fax:** (49) 7541 77 90 80 00
Web: www.zf.com

PRODUCTS/OPERATIONS

Selected Divisions and Products
Aftermarket
 Spare parts
Aviation technology
 Aircraft transmissions
Car chassis technology
 Airbag housings
 Axle systems
 Gearshift systems
 Rubber-metal components
 Suspension joints
 Tie rods
 Wheel suspension modules
Car driveline technology
 Automatic transmissions
 Continuously variable transmissions
 Manual transmissions
Commercial vehicle and special driveline technology
 Automatic transmissions
 Electromagnetic clutches
 Hydrodynamic retarders
 Manual transmissions
 Torque converter units
 Transfer gearboxes
Marine propulsion systems
 Marine transmissions
Off-road driveline technology and axle systems
 Agricultural machinery axles
 Agricultural machinery transmissions
 Axles for fork-lift trucks
 Axle systems for commercial vehicles
 Construction machinery axles
 Construction machinery transmissions
 Transmissions for elevators
 Transmissions for fork-lift trucks
 Transmissions for mobile mixers
Powertrain and suspension components
 Axle modules
 Cab dampers
 Clutch systems
 Electric propulsion systems
 Powertrain automation
 Ride-height control systems
 Shock absorbers
 Torque converters
Rubber-metal technology
 Bumper impact dampers
 Chassis suspension
 Plastic components
 Powertrain suspension
 Vibration and noise control products
Steering technology
 Ball and nut power steerings for cars and commercial vehicles

Electro-hydraulic steering systems
Limited-slip differentials
Rack and pinion power steerings
Rear axle steering systems for commercial vehicles
Steer by wire systems (electric steerings)
Steering accessories
Steering columns
Steering pumps
Steering shafts
Steering valves

COMPETITORS

Aisin Seiki	GKN
American Axle &	Magna International
Manufacturing	Meritor
Carraro	Metaldyne
Continental AG	Robert Bosch LLC
DENSO	Visteon
Dana	
Delphi Automotive	
Systems	

HISTORICAL FINANCIALS

Company Type: Public

Income Statement

	REVENUE ($ mil.)	NET INCOME ($ mil.)	NET PROFIT MARGIN	EMPLOYEES
				FYE: December 31
12/15	31,754	1,060	3.3%	138,269
12/14	22,383	787	3.5%	71,402
12/13	23,180	601	2.6%	72,643
12/12	22,889	402	1.8%	74,775
12/11	20,060	649	3.2%	71,488
Annual Growth	12.2%	13.1%	—	17.9%

2015 Year-End Financials

Debt ratio: 35.5%
Return on equity: 19.6%
Cash ($ mil.): 1,628
Current ratio: 1.23
Long-term debt ($ mil.): 10,315

No. of shares (mil.): 500
Dividends
  Yield: —
  Payout: —
Market value ($ mil.): —

Zhejiang Material Industrial Zhongda Yuantong Group Co., Ltd.

EXECUTIVES

Chairman, Jida Chen
Auditors: Pan-China Certified Public Accountants Co., Ltd.

LOCATIONS

HQ: Zhejiang Material Industrial Zhongda Yuantong Group Co., Ltd.
  Tower A, Zhongda Plaza, Hangzhou, Zhejiang Province 310003
Phone: (86) 571 85777029   **Fax:** (86) 571 85778008
Web: www.zhongda.com

HISTORICAL FINANCIALS

Company Type: Public

Income Statement

	REVENUE ($ mil.)	NET INCOME ($ mil.)	NET PROFIT MARGIN	EMPLOYEES
				FYE: December 31
12/15	28,111	213	0.8%	0
12/14	6,148	57	0.9%	0
12/13	6,688	83	1.3%	0
12/12	6,382	68	1.1%	0
12/11	5,865	83	1.4%	0
Annual Growth	48.0%	26.3%	—	—

2015 Year-End Financials

Debt ratio: 3.6%
Return on equity: 11.2%
Cash ($ mil.): 2,114
Current ratio: 1.13
Long-term debt ($ mil.): 381

No. of shares (mil.): —
Dividends
  Yield: —
  Payout: —
Market value ($ mil.): —

Zte Corp.

ZTE Corporation is one of China's largest telecommunications manufacturers. The company offers a variety of telecom hardware including base stations phones and systems for switching optical transport videoconferencing power supply and monitoring. The company is a leading holder of intellectual property (patents) and one of the largest telecommunications equipment exporters in China. ZTE sells to more than 500 telecom carriers worldwide with customers that include AT&T China Mobile China Unicom and China Telecom. ZTE was founded in 1985 as Zhongxing Semiconductor Co. Ltd.

Operations
ZTE gets 57% of its revenue from carriers and another 32% from its consumer business. Sales to government and corporate customers accounts for the remainder. About 19% of revenue comes from one customer and ZTE's five biggest customers account for 43% of the company's revenue.

The company does its own manufacturing from major production facilities in Brazil China Sweden France Japan Canada and the US.

Geographic Reach
ZTE has been focusing on globalization introducing more of its products and services to international markets. Some 47%of sales come from customers outside of China. ZTE offers its products and services in 160 countries with customers in every region including Asia/Pacific South Asia Europe North America Latin America and Africa.

Financial Performance
ZTE rang up higher sales profit and cash flow in 2015 from 2014.

Revenue rose 16.6% to $15.5 billion in 2015 from 2014. It posted gains in all business and geographic segments emphasized by higher increases in its biggest business and market.

Profit followed revenue rising 11.5% in 2015 to $494 million from $428 million.

Cash poured in to the tune of $869 million in 2015 compared to $179 million in 2014.

Strategy
ZTE sees an opportunity for growth in the construction of mobile and wireline broadband networks where growth is being spurred by the mobile Internet and cloud computing. The company is looking to shift its focus from supply of products to integrated product offerings for the government enterprise and service market segments while con-

tinuing to offer more in-depth products to the traditional carrier segment.

Ownership
A Chinese state-owned manufacturer of telecom cabinets and related products Shenzhen Zhongxingxin Telecommunications Equipment Company owns a 31% stake in ZTE and is the company's controlling shareholder.

EXECUTIVES

Executive Director, Yin Yimin, age 54
EVP, Tian Wenguo, age 48
EVP and CFO, Wei Zaisheng, age 55
Executive Director, He Shiyou, age 50
EVP Logistics and Administration Affairs, Qiu Weizhao, age 54
Chairman and President, Zhao Xianming, age 51
EVP, Fan Qingfeng, age 48
EVP Terminals Division, Zeng Xuezhong, age 44
CEO India, Liu Peng
Vice Chairman, Xie Weiliang, age 61
Vice Chairman, Zhang Jianheng, age 56
Auditors: Ernst & Young Hua Ming LLP

LOCATIONS

HQ: Zte Corp.
  ZTE Plaza, Keji Road South, Hi-Tech Industrial Park, Nanshan District, Shenzhen, Guangdong Province 518057
Phone: (86) 755 26770282   **Fax:** (86) 755 26770286
Web: www.zte.com.cn

PRODUCTS/OPERATIONS

2015 Sales

	% of total
Carriers' networks	57
Consumer business	32
Government and corporate business	11
Total	**100**

2015 Sales

	% of total
Asia	
PRC (People's Republic of China)	53
Other countries	15
Europe the Americas and Oceania	25
Africa	7
Total	**100**

COMPETITORS

Alcatel-Lucent	Motorola Mobility
CHINA PUTIAN	NEC
Cisco Systems	Nokia
Datang Telecom	Qiao Xing
Technology	Samsung Electronics
Ericsson	UTStarcom
Huawei Technologies	

HISTORICAL FINANCIALS

Company Type: Public

Income Statement

	REVENUE ($ mil.)	NET INCOME ($ mil.)	NET PROFIT MARGIN	EMPLOYEES
				FYE: December 31
12/15	15,426	493	3.2%	84,622
12/14	13,127	424	3.2%	75,609
12/13	12,427	224	1.8%	69,093
12/12	13,509	(455)	—	78,402
12/11	13,703	327	2.4%	89,786
Annual Growth	3.0%	10.8%	—	(1.5%)

2015 Year-End Financials

Debt ratio: 2.7%
Return on equity: 10.0%
Cash ($ mil.): 4,098
Current ratio: 1.39
Long-term debt ($ mil.): 926

No. of shares (mil.): —
Dividends
  Yield: 0.0%
  Payout: 21.9%
Market value ($ mil.): —

	STOCK PRICE ($) FY Close	P/E High/Low		PER SHARE ($) Earnings	Dividends	Book Value
12/15	2.23	5	2	0.12	0.03	1.45
12/14	2.02	4	3	0.10	0.01	0.97
12/13	2.10	7	4	0.05	0.00	0.90
12/12	1.63	—	—	(0.11)	0.04	0.84
12/11	3.07	10	4	0.08	0.04	0.93
Annual Growth	(7.7%)	—	—	10.1%	(10.1%)	11.6%

Zuercher Kantonalbank (Switzerland)

LOCATIONS

HQ: Zuercher Kantonalbank (Switzerland)
Bahnhofstrasse 3, Zurich CH-8001
Phone: (41) 844 843 823
Web: www.zkb.ch

HISTORICAL FINANCIALS

Company Type: Public

Income Statement

FYE: December 31

	ASSETS ($ mil.)	NET INCOME ($ mil.)	INCOME AS % OF ASSETS	EMPLOYEES
12/15	155,482	727	0.5%	5,179
12/14	160	0	0.4%	4,844
12/13	168	0	0.5%	4,818
12/12	164	0	0.4%	0
12/11	0	0	—	0
Annual Growth	—	446.1%	—	—

2015 Year-End Financials

Return on assets: 0.9%
Return on equity: 13.8%
Long-term debt ($ mil.): —
No. of shares (mil.): —
Sales ($ mil): 2,720

Dividends
Yield: —
Payout: —
Market value ($ mil.): —

Zurich Insurance Group Ltd

The operations of Zurich Insurance Group have crossed over the Alps and spread around the globe. Serving approximately 170 countries worldwide the company is a major global provider of property/casualty and life insurance. Focused on markets in Europe and North America the company's general insurance segment offers commercial and personal property/casualty and specialty coverage while its global life segment offers life insurance annuities and other investment policies. Zurich's Farmers Group division offers personal property/casualty insurance policies in the US. The company was founded in 1872.

Operations

Zurich's general insurance segment which accounts for about half of the company's annual premiums and fees provides property/casualty and specialty insurance to a variety of clients. Its global corporate unit focuses on risk management for large international and domestic clients while the Europe general insurance division provides property/casualty and specialty lines for businesses and individuals. In the US Zurich provides commercial and specialty property/casualty policies for small to midsized business customers through its North America commercial unit which includes Zurich American Insurance Company and its subsidiaries.

Zurich's global life segment (40% of premiums and fees) offers life investment pension and savings plans for individuals and groups. Global life operates through regional subsidiaries to provide localized services to its clients. Its businesses include Farmers New World Life in the US Openwork in the UK and other subsidiaries and partnerships in Europe. The division is growing in emerging markets as well.

The company's third major division Farmers Group provides personal auto and homeowners' coverage in the US as well as small business life and specialty insurance policies. Its operating divisions include 21st Century Insurance and Bristol West Holdings.

Geographic Reach

With operations spread around the globe Zurich's general insurance division's core markets include Germany Italy Spain Switzerland the UK and the US in addition to the domestic Swiss market. Other international business units are focused in Latin America the Asia/Pacific region South Africa and other emerging markets.

In 2015 Zurich established a new Global Life Europe Middle East and Africa region which included its existing Global Life operations in Europe and the Middle East its International Life business on the Isle of Man and the EuroLife Luxembourg business.

Marketing and Sales

All of the Zurich operating segments use a mixture of distribution channels to promote their products. The company has affiliated agents and it also uses independent brokers employee benefits consultants financial advisors and bank representatives to promote its policies. Zurich markets its products to individual commercial and corporate customers.

Financial Performance

Zurich reported a revenue increase of just under 1% to $72.5 billion in 2014 due to growth in net premiums driven by sales of individual savings products in the markets of Spain and Germany; investment gains also contributed to the rise. Net income decreased 3% that year to $3.9 billion due to higher insurance benefits and losses gross of reinsurance.

Cash flow from operations spiked 194% to $5.8 billion in 2014 due to a change in reserves for insurance contracts and movements in receivables and payables.

Strategy

The company's strategy for growth includes targeting corporate mid-market commercial and select retail markets increasing operational efficiency cutting costs and investing for improved returns. At the same time as it is focused on tightening its organization and improving returns in existing markets Zurich is also looking to expand in high-growth emerging markets such as Brazil China Russia Spain Turkey and Taiwan. Zurich has also benefited from its efforts to expand into markets deemed "under-represented." One strategy is to provide niche product offerings to reach targeted customer segments such as expatriates and minority groups. In the US market the Farmers division is working to expand its operations in the eastern states.

While investing in promising markets the group also intends to turn underperforming units around or exit those markets completely. For example in 2014 Zurich sold its general insurance retail business in Russia to OLMA Group for some $23 million. Two years later the company agreed to sell its South Africa and Botswana operations to Canadian firm Fairfax Financial.

Mergers and Acquisitions

Zurich agreed to buy Australian travel insurer Cover-More Group for some $554 million in late 2016.

In 2014 the company acquired a 50% stake in Mediterraneo Seguros Diversos in Spain boosting its general insurance operations even further. It also acquired the rest of Deutscher Herold it didn't already own.

HISTORY

Company Background

The roots of Zurich Financial Services stretch back to the 1872 founding of a reinsurer for Switzerland Transport Insurance. The company soon branched out into accident travel and workers' compensation insurance and in 1875 it changed its name to Transport and Accident Insurance plc Zurich to reflect the changes. It then expanded into Berlin (the jumping-off point for its expansion into Scandinavia and Russia) and Stuttgart Germany. The company exited marine lines in 1880; it later left the reinsurance business and expanded into liability insurance; in 1894 it changed its name to Zurich General Accident and Liability Insurance.

In 1912 Zurich crossed the Atlantic expanding operations into the US. It agreed in 1925 to provide insurance for Ford cars at favorable terms. Zurich's business was hard hit during the war years of the late 1930s and 1940s. In 1955 the company changed its name to Zurich Insurance.

Starting in the 1960s Zurich began buying other insurers including Alpina (1965 Switzerland) Agrippina (1969 Germany) and Maryland Casualty Group (1989 US). It also bought the property liability operations of American General.

The company shifted its strategy in the early 1990s expanding into what it deemed underrepresented markets in the UK and the US. Being big wasn't enough; Zurich needed to find a focus. It also jettisoned such marginal or unprofitable business lines as commercial fire insurance in Germany.

In 1995 Zurich bought struggling Chicago-based asset manager Kemper and in 1997 bought lackluster mutual fund manager Scudder Stevens & Clark forming Scudder Kemper. That year it also bought failed Hong Kong investment bank Peregrine Investment Holdings.

Zurich merged in 1998 with the financial services businesses of B.A.T Industries formerly known as the British-American Tobacco Co. created in 1902 as a joint venture between UK-based Imperial Tobacco and American Tobacco. As public disapproval of smoking grew in the 1970s British-American Tobacco began diversifying; it changed its name to B.A.T Industries in 1976 and moved into insurance. In 1984 it rescued UK insurer Eagle Star from a hostile offer by German insurance giant Allianz. The next year it bought Hambro Life Assurance renaming it Allied Dunbar. Moving into the large US market in 1988 B.A.T bought Farmers Insurance Group.

While B.A.T battled the antismoking army of the 1990s the insurance industry struggled with stagnant growth. In 1997 Europe's largest insurance firms were named as defendants in class action lawsuits that sought recovery for unpaid claims on Holocaust-era insurance policies. In 1998 Zurich became a founding member of the International Commission on Holocaust Era Insurance Claims (ICHEIC).

Also in 1998 Zurich and B.A.T's insurance units merged to create Zurich Financial Services. The firm reshuffled some of its holdings and sold Eagle Star Reinsurance. In 1999 Zurich spun off its real estate holdings into PSP Swiss Property and at the turn of the century it focused on expansion buying the new business of insurer Abbey Life which it merged into Allied Dunbar. In 2000 the holding companies formed to own Zurich (Zurich Allied and Allied Zurich) were merged into the firm.

EXECUTIVES

Group CEO, Mario Greco, age 57
COO and CTO, Robert Dickie, age 56
CEO Farmer's Group, Jeffrey J. (Jeff) Dailey, age 59
CEO North American Commercial; Regional Chairman North America, Mike Foley, age 55
CEO General Insurance, Kristof Terryn, age 50
CFO, George Quinn
Chief Risk Officer and Regional Chairman Asia Pacific, Cecilia Reyes, age 58
Chief Investment Officer, Urban Angehrn, age 52
CEO UK, Tulsi R. Naidu
Chief Human Resources Officer; Regional Chairman Latin America, Isabelle Welton, age 53
CEO UK Life and Interim CEO Global Life Europe the Middle East and Asia (EMEA), Gary Shaughnessy, age 50
Chairman, Tom de Swaan, age 71
Vice Chairman, Fred Kindle, age 57
Auditors: PricewaterhouseCoopers AG

LOCATIONS

HQ: Zurich Insurance Group Ltd
  Mythenquai 2, Zurich 8002
Phone: (41) 0 625 25 25   **Fax:** (41) 0 625 35 55
Web: www.zurich.com

PRODUCTS/OPERATIONS

2014 Premiums and Fees

	% of total
General Insurance	45
Global Life	42
Farmers	9
Other operations	4
Total	**100**

Selected Subsidiaries

Farmers Group Inc. (property/casualty US)
  21st Century Insurance Company (property/casualty US)
  Farmers New World Life Insurance Company (life insurance US)
  Foremost Insurance Company (specialty insurance US)
  Bristol West Holdings Inc. (specialty insurance US)
  Zurich American Insurance Company (general insurance US)
Zurich Insurance plc (general insurance UK)
Zurich International Life Limited (life insurance UK)

Selected Acquisitions

COMPETITORS

AEGON	MetLife
AIG	Mitsui Sumitomo
AXA	Insurance
Allianz	Prudential
Aviva	Prudential plc
CNA Financial	State Farm
GEICO	The Hartford
Generali	Travelers Companies
ING	

HISTORICAL FINANCIALS

Company Type: Public

Income Statement

FYE: December 31

	ASSETS ($ mil.)	NET INCOME ($ mil.)	INCOME AS % OF ASSETS	EMPLOYEES
12/15	381,972	1,842	0.5%	54,335
12/14	406,529	3,895	1.0%	54,551
12/13	415,053	4,028	1.0%	55,102
12/12	409,267	3,878	0.9%	52,722
12/11	385,869	3,766	1.0%	52,648
Annual Growth	(0.3%)	(16.4%)	—	0.8%

2015 Year-End Financials

Return on assets: 0.4%
Return on equity: 5.5%
Long-term debt ($ mil.): —
No. of shares (mil.): 149
Sales ($ mil): 60,568

Dividends
  Yield: 6.7%
  Payout: 13.9%
Market value ($ mil.): 3,822

	STOCK PRICE ($) FY Close	P/E High/Low		PER SHARE ($) Earnings	Dividends	Book Value
12/15	25.63	3	2	12.33	1.72	209.02
12/14	31.20	1	1	26.08	1.90	234.14
12/13	29.17	1	1	27.22	1.80	220.24
12/12	26.80	1	1	26.31	1.82	234.73
12/11	22.68	1	1	25.61	1.83	216.67
Annual Growth	3.1%	—	—	(16.7%)	(1.6%)	(0.9%)

Hoover's Handbook of

World
Business

Executive index

Index of Executives